GUIDE TO THE ANTIQUE SHOPS OF BRITAIN

2002/2003

compiled by

Carol Adams

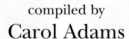

© Copyright 2002 Antique Collectors' Club Ltd.
World Copyright reserved ISBN 1 85149 414 6

British Library CIP Data Guide to the Antique Shops of Britain. - 2002 (June 2002- May 2003)
1. Great Britain. Antiques trades: Directories - Serials I. Antique Collectors' Club 380. 1' 457451'02541

FRONT COVER: Mahogany Irish plate bucket, c.1800. Mahogany cabriolet stool, c.1850. Satinwood inlaid
mahogany triple swing mirror, c.1880. Bohemian glass overlay lamp, c.1850. Scottish open-twist mahogany
candlesticks, c.1820. Walnut serpentine-front chest of drawers, c.1800. Perpetual calendar, c.1880.

Printed in England by The Antique Collectors' Club Ltd., Woodbridge, Suffolk IP12 1DS
Sandy Lane, Old Martlesham,
Woodbridge, Suffolk IP12 4SD, UK.
Tel: 01394 389950 Fax: 01394 389999
Email: carol.adams@antique-acc.com Website: www.antique-acc.com

U.S. OFFICE
Market Street Industrial Park, Wappingers' Falls, NY 12590, USA.
Tel: (845) 297 0003 Fax: (845) 297 0068 Orders: (800) 252 5231 Email: info@antiquecc.com
Website: www.antiquecc.com

**The Tetbury Antique Dealers Association
aims to promote and encourage trade
in the Tetbury area and to assist all visiting
antique dealers and collectors.**

Over twenty shops with over fifty dealers

COTSWOLD ANTIQUE DEALERS' ASSOCIATION

A wealth of Antiques and Fine Art in the heart of England

Please write to the Secretary
for a free brochure.

FOR ASSISTANCE WITH BUYING, SHIPPING, ACCOMMODATION DURING YOUR VISIT, WRITE TO:

Secretary, CADA, Broadwell House, Sheep Street,
Stow-on-the-Wold, Gloucestershire GL54 1JS
Tel: 01451 830053 Fax: 01451 870028
www.cotswolds-antiques-art.com

10

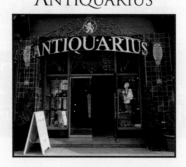

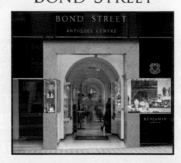

12

LONDON ~ NEW YORK ~ PARIS

UNITED KINGDOM

Gander & White Shipping Ltd.
21 Lillie Road, London SW6 1UE
Tel: 00 44 20 7381 0571
Fax: 00 44 20 7381 5428

Newpound, Wisborough Green, Billingshurst,
West Sussex RH14 0AY
Tel: 00 44 1403 70 00 44
Fax: 00 44 1403 70 08 14

FRANCE

Gander & White Shipping Ltd.
8, rue de Duras, 75008 Paris
Tél: 01 43 12 31 32
Fax: 01 43 12 31 33

USA

Gander & White Shipping Inc.
21-44, 44th Road, Long Island City
New York 11101
Tel: 00 1 718 784 8444
Fax: 00 1 718 784 9337

14

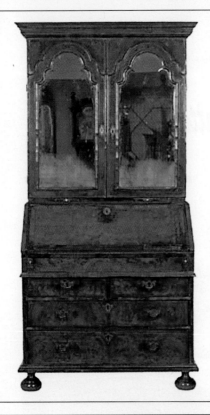

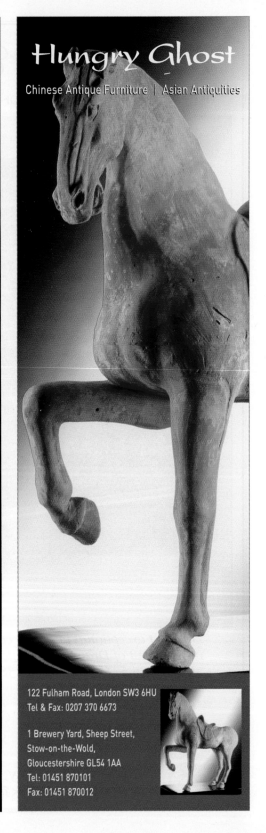

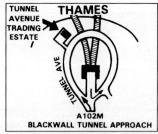

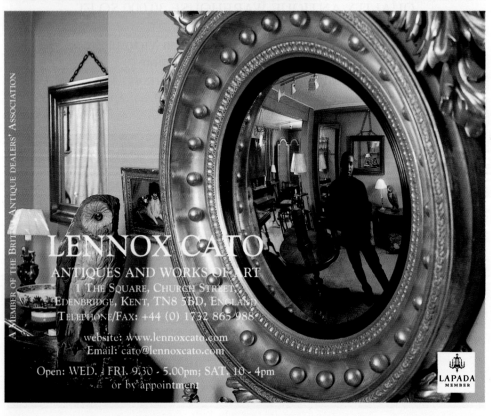

Witney Antiques, LSA, CJ Jarrett & RR Scott
96-100 Corn Street, Witney, Oxon OX28 6BU.

Tel: 01993 703902.   Fax: 01993 779852.

E-mail: witneyantiques@community.co.uk   Website: www.witneyantiques.com

Fine Antique Furniture, Clocks, Samplers and Early Needlework.

UK's top aged stone statuary manufacturer
Family business, founded 1970
Friendly, helpful service
400 different designs
3 Unique finishes
Mythical Creatures
Classical Statuary
Contemporary Statuary
Heads, Hands, Feet & Torsos
Fruit, Finials, Obelisks & Stones
Pedestals, Urns, Vases & Troughs
Sundials, Seats, Birdbaths, Fountains

LUCAS STONE

LUCAS GARDEN STATUARY Firstland Park Estate, Albourne, West Sussex BN6 9JJ
Tel: +44 (0) 1273 494931 Fax: +44 (0) 1273 495125
www.lucasstone.co.uk   Email: trade@lucasstone.co.uk

CONTENTS

INTRODUCTION

This is the 31st edition of the **Guide to the Antique Shops of Britain** which is now universally accepted as *the* guide for anybody who wishes to buy antiques in Britain.

Nearly 6,000 establishments are listed in this latest edition and, as usual, every one has been confirmed before reprinting. We appreciate, however, that quantity without quality is meaningless and therefore the range of information we provide is more detailed and up-to-date than in any other publication. We state the obvious facts - name of proprietor, address, telephone number, opening hours and stock and also size of showroom and price range (where supplied). Additional information gives details of major trade association members, the date the business was established, the location and also the parking situation. Whilst none of these points are decisive in themselves, we feel they build up to a useful picture of the sort of establishment likely to be found and may well influence a prospective buyer's decision whether or not to visit a particular shop.

We start preparing the next edition in early 2003. Please let us know of any changes in your area - openings and closures. We do not print information about other dealers without first contacting them, but obviously the more shops in a particular town or village, the more attractive it is to prospective buyers on trips around the country. We would also be grateful for your comments on the Guide and, if you find any information given in the Guide to be incorrect, please let us know. We have occasionally had prospective customers telephoning to say that the stock listed is not what they found when visiting a particular establishment but then refuse to tell us the name of the shop - which means we can do nothing about the complaint. Constructive criticism is welcomed and we look forward to your comments.

ACKNOWLEDGEMENTS

Our main sources of information are still the trade magazines but we would like to thank those dealers who provide information about new shops and closures in their area. Without their assistance our job would be far more difficult.

We would also like to thank those dealers who supported us with advertising - without this revenue each copy would cost £30, instead of £14.95. Each year we include a form at the end of the Guide which dealers can use to up-date details about their own business. In anticipation of next year's Guide, we are grateful to those dealers who make use of this form.

Editorial **Carol Adams and Diana Dutson**
Advertising Sales **Jean Johnson**

HOW TO USE THIS GUIDE

The Guide is set out under six main headings; London, Counties, Channel Islands, Northern Ireland, Scotland and Wales. Counties are listed alphabetically, within counties the towns are listed alphabetically and within towns the shops are listed, again alphabetically. London is divided into postal districts.

To make route planning easier there is a map at the beginning of each county, and a list showing the number of shops in any one town or village. The roads indicated on the map are only a broad intimation of the routes available and it is advisable to use an up-to-date map showing the latest improvements in the road system.

Apart from the six main headings above, there are further helpful lists - an alphabetical list of towns, showing the counties in which they will be found for those not familiar with the location of towns within counties, e.g. Woodbridge is shown in the county of Suffolk. One therefore turns to the Suffolk section to look up Woodbridge. This listing is a valuable aid to the overseas visitor. The second is particularly important to British dealers and collectors - giving an alphabetical list of the name of every shop, proprietor and company director known to be connected with a shop or gallery. Thus, if A. Bloggs and B. Brown own an antique shop called Castle Antiques, there will be entries under Bloggs, A., Brown, B., and Castle Antiques. Listings of specialist dealers, auctioneers, shippers and packers, services, and fairs organisers are also included.

We strongly suggest making prior telephone call to confirm opening hours before setting off on a long journey. In the main, dealers are factual and accurate in describing their stock to us but there are probably a few who list what they would like to stock rather than as it is! We would appreciate you letting us know of any such anomalies. Please telephone (01394) 385501 or drop us a postcard and help us to ensure that the Guide remains Britain's premier listing of antique shops and galleries

ABBREVIATIONS IN ENTRIES

BADA:	British Antique Dealers Association.
LAPADA:	The Association of Art and Antique Dealers
BABAADA:	Bath and Bradford on Avon Antique Dealers Association.
EADA:	Essex Antique Dealers Association.
HADA:	Highlands Antique Dealers Association.
TADA:	Tetbury Antique Dealers Association.
TVADA:	Thames Valley Antique Dealers Association.
CADA:	Cotswold Antique Dealers Association.
CL:	When the business is normally closed in addition to Sunday.
SIZE:	Showroom size. Small - under 60 sq. metres; medium - between 60 and 150 sq. metres; large over150 sq.metres.
LOC:	Location of shop.
SER:	Additional services which the dealer offers.

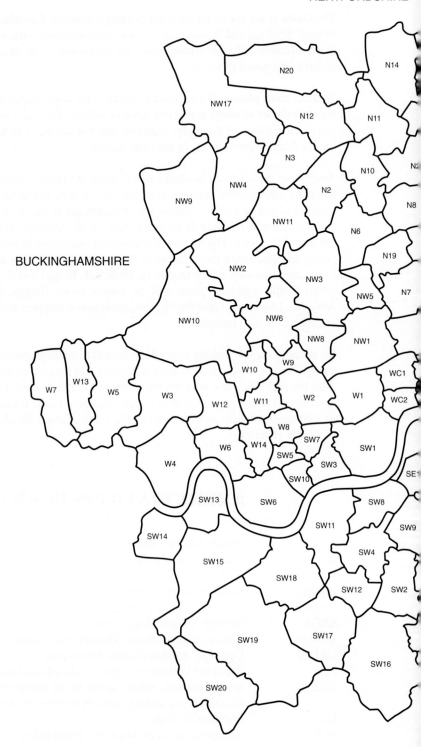

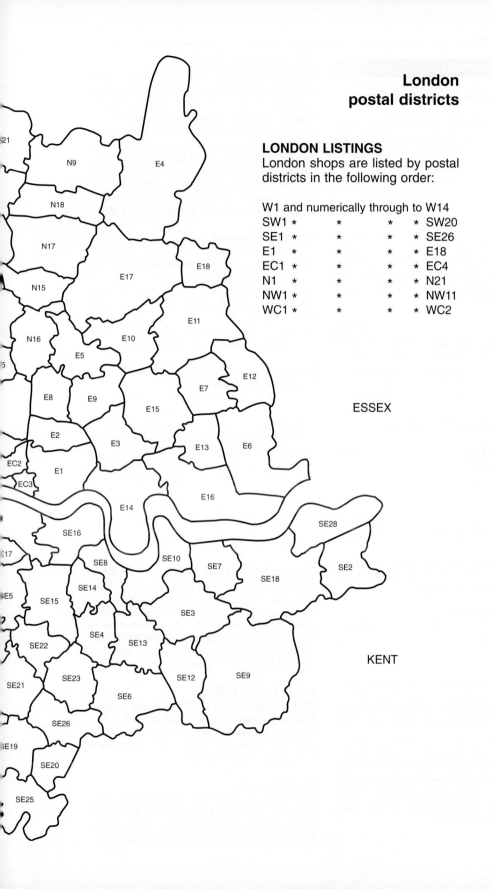

London
postal districts

LONDON LISTINGS
London shops are listed by postal districts in the following order:

W1 and numerically through to W14
SW1 *	*	*	* SW20
SE1 *	*	*	* SE26
E1 *	*	*	* E18
EC1 *	*	*	* EC4
N1 *	*	*	* N21
NW1 *	*	*	* NW11
WC1 *	*	*	* WC2

ESSEX

KENT

W1

David Aaron Ancient Arts & Rare Carpets

22 Berkeley Sq., Mayfair. W1X 7DD. Est. 1910. Open 9.30-6, Sat. by appointment. SIZE: Large. *STOCK: Islamic and ancient art; antique carpets.* PARK: Easy. TEL: 020 7491 9588; fax - 020 7491 9522. SER: Valuations; restorations (trade); buys at auction (as stock). VAT: Stan/Spec.

Aaron Gallery

125 Mount St. W1K 3NS. Open 10-6, Sat. by appointment. *STOCK: Ancient art; Greek, Roman, Egyptian, Near Eastern and Islamic antiquities.* TEL: 020 7499 9434; fax - 020 7499 0072; website - www.aarongallery.com; e-mail - simon@aarongallery.com.

Agnew's   BADA

43 Old Bond St. W1S 4BA. SLAD. Est. 1817. Open 9.30-5.30, Sat.11-4. SIZE: Large. *STOCK: Paintings, drawings, watercolours, engravings of all schools; contemporary art.* **TEL: 020 7290 9250; fax - 020 7629 4359; e-mail - agnews@agnewsgallery.co.uk; website - www.agnewsgallery.co.uk. VAT: Spec.**

Adrian Alan Ltd   BADA

66/67 South Audley St. W1K 2QX. LAPADA. Est. 1963. Open 10-6. CL: Sat. SIZE: Large. *STOCK: English and Continental furniture, especially fine 19th C; sculpture and works of art.* **TEL: 020 7495 2324; fax - 020 7495 0204; e-mail - enquiries@adrianalan.com; website - www.adrianalan.com. SER: Restorations; transport, storage and shipping; insurance and finance. FAIRS: Olympia (June); Palm Beach; Texas. VAT: Stan/Spec.**

Altea Maps & Books

Third Floor, 91 Regent St. W1B 4EL. (Massimo De Martini). PBFA, ABA, ILAB, IMCOS. Est. 1993. Open Mon.-Fri. 10-6 or by appointment. SIZE: Medium. *STOCK: Antiquarian maps, 15th-19th C, £50-£5,000; travel books, atlases, 16th-19th C, £200-£20,000; globes, 17th-20th C, £200-£20,000.* LOC: 150 yards from Piccadilly Circus. PARK: NCP nearby. TEL: 020 7494 9060; fax - 020 7287 7938, e-mail - altea@antique-maps.co.uk; website - www.antique-maps.co.uk. SER: Valuations; restorations (paper, cleaning, colouring and book binding); buys at auction (maps, books and globes). FAIRS: IMCOS (June); ABA Chelsea (Nov); ABA Olympia (June). VAT: Stan.

Argyll Etkin Gallery

Ramillies Buildings, 1-9 Hills Place, Oxford Circus. W1R 1AG. (Argyll Etkin Ltd). Est. 1954. Open 9-5.30. CL: Sat. SIZE: Medium. *STOCK: Classic postage stamps, postal history and covers, Royal autographs, signed photographs, historical documents and antique letters, 1400-1950, £50-£25,000; stamp boxes and associated writing equipment, 1700-1930, £50-£500.* TEL: 020 7437 7800 (6 lines); fax - 020 7434 1060. SER: Valuations; collections purchased. FAIRS: Major stamp exhibitions worldwide. VAT: Stan.

Armour-Winston Ltd

43 Burlington Arcade. W1J 0QQ. Est. 1952. Open 9-5. Sat. 9.30-2. SIZE: Small. *STOCK: Jewellery, especially Victorian; gentlemen's cufflinks, classic watches.* LOC: Off Piccadilly. Between Green Park and Piccadilly tube stations. PARK: Savile Row. TEL: 020 7493 8937; website - www.armourwinston.co.uk. SER: Valuations; restorations. VAT: Stan/Spec.

Victor Arwas Gallery - Editions Graphiques Gallery Ltd

3 Clifford St. W1. (V. Arwas). Est. 1966. Open 10-6, Sat. 10-2. SIZE: Large. *STOCK: Art Nouveau and Art Deco, glass, ceramics, bronzes, sculpture, furniture, jewellery, silver, pewter, books and posters 1880-1940, £25-£50,000; paintings, watercolours and drawings, 1880 to date, £100-£20,000; original graphics, lithographs, etchings, woodcuts, 1890 to date, £5-£10,000.* LOC: Between New Bond St. and Savile Row. PARK: 50yds. TEL: 020 7734 3944; fax - 020 7437 1859. SER: Valuations; buys at auction. VAT: Stan/Spec.

Asprey & Garrard Ltd   BADA

167 New Bond St. W1Y 0AR. Est. 1781. Open 10-6, Sat. 10-5. SIZE: Large. *STOCK: Furniture, works of art, clocks, silver, jewellery, glass.* **PARK: Albemarle St., entrance No.22. TEL: 020 7493 6767; fax - 020 7491 0384. SER: Valuations; restorations (furniture, jewellery, clocks, silver). VAT: Stan/Spec.**

J & A Beare Ltd   BADA

30 Queen Anne St. W1G 8HX. (J. and A. Beare Ltd). Est. 1892. Open 10-12.30 and 1.30-5. *STOCK: Violins, violas, cellos and bows.* **TEL: 020 7307 9666; fax - 020 7307 9651. SER: Valuations. VAT: Stan/Spec.**

Paul Bennett

48A George St. W1H 5RF. (M.J. Dubiner). Open 9.30-6. CL: Sat. SIZE: Large. *STOCK: Silver, 1740-1963, £10-£10,000; Sheffield plate.* PARK: Meters. TEL: 020 7935 1555/7486 8836. VAT: Stan/Spec.

BOND STREET
ANTIQUES CENTRE
124 New Bond Street, London W1

"The most prestigious antiques centre
in London"

Antique Monthly

Enquiries: Mike Spooner/Neil Jackson
Tel: 020-7969 1500 Fax: 020-7969 1639

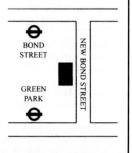

Bentley & Skinner Ltd
8 New Bond St. W1S 3SL. (Mark Evans).
LAPADA. Open 10-5.30. *STOCK: Jewellery,
Fabergé, objets d'art, silver.* PARK: Meters.
TEL: 020 7629 0651. SER: Valuations; repairs;
tiara and jewellery hire. VAT: Stan/Spec.

Daniel Bexfield Antiques
26 Burlington Arcade, Mayfair. W1J 0PU.
LAPADA. CINOA. Open 9-6. SIZE: Small.
*STOCK: Silver and objets de vertu, 17th-20th C,
£400-£25,000.* PARK: Nearby. TEL: 020 7491
1720; fax - 020 7491 1730; e-mail - antiques@
bexfield.co.uk; website - www.bexfield.co.uk.
SER: Valuations; restorations (repairs and repolishing silver, blue glass liners); buys at
auction. FAIRS: LAPADA. VAT: Spec.

Peter Biddulph
34 St George St., Hanover Sq. W1R 0ND. Open
10-6. CL: Sat. *STOCK: Violins, violas, cellos and
bows.* TEL: 020 7491 8621; fax - 020 7495 1428.

H. Blairman and Sons Ltd.   BADA
119 Mount St. W1K 3NL. (M.P., P.A. and W.Y.
Levy and L.G. Hannen). Est. 1884. Open daily.
CL: Sat. SIZE: Medium. *STOCK: English and
Continental furniture and works of art, 1800-
1900.* TEL: 020 7493 0444; fax - 020 7495
0766; e-mail - blairman@atlas.co.uk. FAIRS:
Grosvenor House; Fine Art & Antique Dealers,
New York. VAT: Spec.

Blunderbuss Antiques
29 Thayer St. W1U 2QW. (T. Greenaway). Open
9.30-4.30. *STOCK: Arms and armour, militaria.*
TEL: 020 7486 2444; fax - 020 7935 1645; e-mail
- mail@blunderbuss-antiques.co.uk; website -
www.blunderbuss-antiques.co.uk.

Bond Street Antiques Centre
124 New Bond St. W1. (Atlantic Antique Centres
Ltd). Est. 1970. Open 10-5.30, Sat. 11-5.30.

SIZE: Large - 27 dealers. *STOCK: Wide range of
general antiques especially jewellery.* LOC: Bond
St., Oxford St. or Green Park tube stations. TEL:
Enquiries - 020 7969 1500; fax - 020 7969 1639;
e-mail - antique@dial.pipex.com. Below are listed
some of the dealers at this market.

Emmy Abe
Stand 33. *Jewellery and silver.* TEL: 020 7629
1826.

Accurate Trading Co
Stand 1D. (E. Fahimian). *Jewellery.* TEL: 020 7629
0277.

Cohen
Stand 12. TEL: Mobile - 07946 523843. SER:
Restoration and manufacture (jewellery).

Philip Cyrlin
Stand 17. *Watches.* TEL: 020 7629 0133.

Adele de Havilland
Stand 18. *Oriental porcelain, netsuke, jade.* TEL:
020 7499 7127.

David Duggan
Stands 1A, 1B, 22. LAPADA. *Vintage watches.*
TEL: 020 7491 1362; fax - 020 7408 1727.

Elisabeth's Antiques
Stands 42/43. (Mrs E. Hage). LAPADA. *Jewellery.*
TEL: 020 7491 1723; mobile - 07860 550300.

Matthew Foster
Stand 4-6. *Jewellery.* TEL: 020 7629 4977.

R. Gender
Stand 25. *Oil paintings.* TEL: 020 7493 6272.

Anthony Green Antiques
Stand 39. *Watches and objects.* TEL: 020 7409
2854; fax - 020 7408 0010; website - www.anthony
green. co.uk.

Jan Havlik
Stand 21. Jewellery. Mobile - 07775 708198.

Massada Antiques
Stand 2. (C.B. and C. Yacobi). Est. 1970. LAPADA. Open Mon.-Fri. 10-5.30. *Jewellery and silver.* TEL: 020 7493 4792/7629 3402.

Nonesuch Antiques
Stand 3. (E. Michelson). LAPADA. *Jewellery and objects.* TEL: 020 7629 6783.

Sergio Tencati
Stand 16. *Jewellery and silver.* TEL: 020 7493 6272.

Trianon Antiques
Stands 1C, 10/11. (Mrs. Horton). LAPADA. *Jewellery.* TEL: 020 7629 6678.

Matsuko Yamamoto
Stand 14/15. *Jewellery and porcelain.* TEL: 020 7491 0983.

Bond Street Silver Galleries
111-112 New Bond St. W1Y 0BQ. Open 9-5.30. CL: Sat. PARK: Meters. TEL: 020 7493 6180; fax - 020 7495 3493. Below are listed the dealers at these galleries.

Barnes Jewellers
Fine jewellery. TEL: 020 7495 7554; fax - 020 7495 7556.

Brian Beet
Silver and works of art. TEL: 020 7437 4975; fax - 020 7495 8635.

A. and B. Bloomstein Ltd   BADA
LAPADA. *Silver, Sheffield plate.* **TEL: 020 7493 6180; fax - 020 7495 3493.** SER: Valuations; restorations.

Bruford and Heming
NAG. LAPADA. *Domestic silver especially flatware, jewellery.* TEL: 020 7499 7644/629 4289; fax - 020 7493 5879. SER: Valuations; restorations. VAT: Stan/Spec.

R. Close Jewellery Restoration
TEL: 020 7495 0287.

O. Frydman
Silver, Sheffield and Victorian plate. TEL: 020 7493 4895. VAT: Stan/Spec.

Michael Gardner Antiques
Jewellery and object d'arts. TEL: 020 7495 7592; mobile - 07831 863852.

Graus Antiques
Objets d'art, jewellery and silver. TEL: 020 7629 6680/6651; fax - 020 7629 3361.

R.S. & S. Necus
Silver and plate. TEL: 020 7499 0770; fax - same.

A. Pash & Son
Silver and old Sheffield plate. TEL: 020 7493 5176; fax - 020 7355 3676.

Rare Jewellery Collections Limited
(Elizabeth Powell). *Fine and collectable jewellery.* TEL: 020 7499 5414; fax - 020 7499 6906; mobile - 07771 788189; e-mail - info@rarejewelcollections.com.

Damian Scott
Fine jewellery. TEL: 020 7495 4975; fax - same.

M. Sedler
Silver and plate. TEL: 020 7839 3131.

Selco Crystal Ltd.
Crystal and glass. TEL: 0870 230 7215; fax - 0870 330 1003; e-mail - info@selcocrystal.com.

Guy Steel
Fine jewels. TEL: 020 7495 7554/7594; fax - 020 7495 7556.

D. P. Stern Jewellery and Silver Restoration
TEL: 020 7629 6292; fax - 020 7355 1427.

E. Swonnell (Silverware) Ltd
Silver, Sheffield plate. TEL: 020 7629 9649; fax - same. VAT: Stan/Spec.

Zebrak - London
Fine jewels. TEL: 020 7495 7554/7594; fax - 020 7495 7556.

Brandt Oriental Art   BADA
First Floor, 29 New Bond St. W1Y 9HD. (R. Brandt). Est. 1981. Open by appointment. *STOCK: Oriental works of art, £500-£10,000.* **TEL: 020 7499 8835; mobile - 07774 989661. VAT: Spec.**

The British Art Gallery
47 Albemarle St. W1S 4JW. (J. Conway). Est. 1870. Open 9.30-5. CL: Sat. *STOCK: English oil paintings, 18th-19th C.* TEL: 020 7493 9196; website - www.british-artgallery.com.

Browse and Darby Ltd
19 Cork St. W1X 2LP. SLAD. Est. 1977. *STOCK: French and British paintings, drawings and sculpture, 19th-20th C.* TEL: 020 7734 7984. VAT: Spec.

John Bull (Antiques) Ltd JB Silverware
139A New Bond St. W1S 2TN. LAPADA. Open 9-5. CL: Sat. *STOCK: Antique silver and reproduction giftware, photo frames, cutlery.* TEL: 020 7629 1251; fax - 020 7495 3001; websites - www.jbsilverware.co.uk; www.sales@ jbsilverware.co.uk; www.antique-silver.co.uk. SER: Valuations; repairs. FAIRS: Antiques For Everyone, NEC. VAT: Global/Margin.

Burlington Paintings Ltd   BADA
10 and 12 Burlington Gardens. W1S 3EY. (A. Lloyd, M. Day, J. Lloyd and A. Hardy). Est. 1981. Open 9.30-5.30, Sat. 10-5. SIZE: Medium. *STOCK: British and European oil paintings, 19th-20th C, from £1,000.* LOC: Between Old Bond St. and Regent St., facing Savile Row. PARK: APCOA, Old Burlington St. TEL: 020 7734 9984; fax - 020 7494 3770; e-mail - pictures@burlington.co.uk; website - www. burlington.co.uk. SER: Valuations; restorations (lining, cleaning, reframing oils and watercolours); buys at auction (pictures). VAT: Stan/Spec.

C. & L. Burman   BADA
5 Vigo St. W1S 3HF. (Charles Truman and Lucy Burniston). Open by appointment. *STOCK: 18th-19th works of art including silver, glass, furniture, ceramics and sculpture.* TEL: 020 7439 6604; fax - 020 7439 6605. SER: Valuations; restorations; buys at auction. FAIRS: BADA (March); Grosvenor House (June); Olympia (Nov). VAT: Spec.

The Button Queen Ltd.
19 Marylebone Lane. W1U 2NF. (I. and M. Frith). Est. 1953. Open 10-5, Thurs. and Fri. 10-6, Sat. 10-4. SIZE: Large. *STOCK: Antique, old and modern buttons.* LOC: Off Wigmore St. TEL: 020 7935 1505. VAT: Stan.

Carrington and Co. Ltd
170 Regent St. W1R 6BQ. Open 10-6. *STOCK: Regimental jewellery and silver, trophies, watches, clocks.* TEL: 020 7734 3727.

Paul Champkins   BADA
41 Dover St. W1X 3RB. Est. 1995. Open by appointment. SIZE: Small. *STOCK: Chinese, Korean and Japanese art, £1,000-£100,000.* LOC: Off Piccadilly. TEL: 020 7495 4600; fax - 01235 751658. SER: Valuations; restorations. FAIRS: Grosvenor House; BADA (March). VAT: Spec.

Antoine Cheneviere Fine Arts   BADA
27 Bruton St. W1. Open 9.30-6. CL: Sat. *STOCK: 18th-19th C furniture and paintings, objets d'art from Russia, Italy, Austria, Sweden and Germany.* TEL: 020 7491 1007.

Andrew Clayton-Payne Ltd
2nd Floor, 14 Old Bond St. W1S 4PP. Open by appointment. SIZE: Small. *STOCK: British paintings and watercolours, 1700-1850, £2,000-£500,000.* PARK: Easy. TEL: 020 7493 6980; fax - 020 7629 9151. SER: Valuations; buys at auction (pictures). VAT: Spec.

Sibyl Colefax & John Fowler
39 Brook St. W1K 4JE. Est. 1933. Open 9.30-5.30. CL: Sat. SIZE: Large. *STOCK: Decorative furniture, pictures, lamps and carpets, 18th-19th C.* PARK: Meters. TEL: 020 7493 2231/7355 4037; e-mail - antiques@sibylcolefax.com; website - www.colefaxantiques.com. FAIRS: Olympia (June). VAT: Spec.

P. and D. Colnaghi & Co Ltd   BADA
15 Old Bond St. W1X 4JL. SLAD. Est. 1760. Open 9.30-6. SIZE: Large. *STOCK: Master paintings and drawings, 14th-19th C; English paintings.* TEL: 020 7491 7408. SER: Experts and appraisers. VAT: Spec.

Connaught Brown plc
2 Albemarle St. W1X 3HF. (A. Brown). SLAD. Est. 1985. Open 10-6, Sat. 10-12.30. SIZE: Medium. *STOCK: Post Impressionist, Scandinavian and modern works, from £5,000+; contemporary, from £500+.* LOC: Off Piccadilly and parallel to Bond St. PARK: Berkeley Sq. TEL: 020 7408 0362. SER: Valuations; restorations (paintings, drawings, watercolours and sculpture). FAIRS: Olympia. VAT: Stan/Spec.

Sandra Cronan Ltd   BADA
18 Burlington Arcade. W1J 0PN. LAPADA. Est. 1975. Open 10-5. *STOCK: Fine and unusual jewels, 18th to early 20th C, £500-£150,000.* TEL: 020 7491 4851; fax - 020 7493 2758. SER: Valuations; design commissions. FAIRS: Fine Art & Antiques; BADA (March): 20th Century, New York (Nov): Grosvenor House (June). VAT: Stan/Spec.

Barry Davies Oriental Art   BADA
1 Davies St. W1K 3DB. Open 10-6. CL: Sat. *STOCK: Japanese works of art, netsuke, lacquer and bronzes.* TEL: 020 7408 0207.

A. B. Davis Ltd
18 Brook St., (Corner of New Bond St). W1Y 1AA. Est. 1920. Open 10-5. CL: Sat. *STOCK: Antique and secondhand jewellery, small silver items and objets d'art.* TEL: 020 7629 1053; 020 7242 7357 (ansaphone).; fax and ansaphone - 020 7499 6454. SER: Valuations; repairs (jewellery and silver). VAT: Stan/Spec.

Richard Day Ltd
173 New Bond St. W1Y 9PB. Open 10-5. CL: Sat. *STOCK: Old Master drawings.* TEL: 020 7629 2991; fax - 020 7493 7569. VAT: Stan.

Dover Street Gallery
13 Dover St. W1S 4LN. (Edmondo di Robilant and Richard Nagy). SLAD, CINOA. Est. 1978. Open

Mon.-Fri. 10-6 by appointment. SIZE: Large. *STOCK: Austrian and German Expressionists, including Gustav Klimt, Egon Schiele, 1910-30, from £20,000; Italian and French Old Master paintings, 15th-19th C.* LOC: Parallel to Albemarle St., opposite The Ritz. TEL: 020 7409 1540; fax - 020 7409 1565; e-mail - info@ doverstreetgallery.com; website - www.artnet. com/dover.html. SER: Valuations; buys at auction. FAIRS: New York Fine Art; Tefaf, Maastricht; Milan; Florence. VAT: Spec.

Charles Ede Ltd   BADA
20 Brook St. W1K 5DE. Est. 1970. Open 12.30-4.30 or by appointment. CL: Mon and Sat. *STOCK: Greek, Roman and Egyptian antiquities, £50-£50,000.* PARK: Meters. TEL: 020 7493 4944; fax - 020 7491 2548; e-mail - charlesede @attglobal.net; website - www.charlesede. com. SER: Valuations; buys at auction. VAT: Spec.

Andrew Edmunds
44 Lexington St. W1R 3LH. Open 10-6. CL: Sat. *STOCK: 18th to early 19th C caricature and decorative prints and drawings.* TEL: 020 7437 8594; fax - 020 7439 2551. VAT: Stan/Spec.

Elwes and Hanham Ltd
14 Old Bond St. W1S 4PP. (Ben Elwes and William Hanham). Est. 1993. SIZE: Medium. *STOCK: Old Master and British paintings, 1500-1830.* LOC: 150 yards from Piccadilly. TEL: 020 7491 4966; fax - 020 7491 4976; e-mail - info@ eandh.co.uk; website - www.eandh.co.uk. SER: Valuations. FAIRS: Olympia. VAT: Stan/Spec.

Emanouel Corporation (UK) Ltd
64 & 64a South Audley St. W1K 2QT. (E. Naghi). LAPADA. Est. 1974. Open 10-6, Sat. by appointment only. *STOCK: Important antiques and fine works of art, 18th-19th C; Islamic works of art.* TEL: 020 7493 4350/7499 0996; mobile - 07831 241899; fax - 020 7629 3125; e-mail - emanouelnaghi@aol.com; website - www. emanouel.net. VAT: Stan/Spec.

Eskenazi Ltd   BADA
10 Clifford St. W1S 2LJ. (J.E. Eskenazi, P.S. Constantinidi and D.M. Eskenazi). Est. 1960. Open 9.30-6, Sat. by appointment. SIZE: Large. *STOCK: Early Chinese ceramics; bronzes, sculpture, works of art; Japanese porcelain and screens.* TEL: 020 7493 5464; fax - 020 7499 3136. VAT: Spec.

John Eskenazi Ltd   BADA
15 Old Bond St. W1S 4AX. Open 9-6, Sat. by appointment. SIZE: Medium. *STOCK: Oriental art, rugs and textiles; Indian, Himalayan and

South East Asian art. **PARK: Meters. TEL: 020 7409 3001; fax - 020 7629 2146; e-mail - john.eskenazi@john-eskenazi.com. SER: Rug conservation. FAIRS: International Asian Art, New York (March); Asian Art, London (Nov). VAT: Spec.**

Essie Carpets
62 Piccadilly. W1V 9HL. (E. Sakhai). Est. 1766. Open 9.30-6.30, Sun. 10.30-6.30. CL: Sat. SIZE: Large. *STOCK: Persian and Oriental carpets and rugs.* LOC: Opposite St. James St. and Ritz Hotel. PARK: Easy. TEL: 020 7493 7766; home - 020 7586 3388. SER: Valuations; restorations; commissions undertaken; exchange. VAT: Stan/Spec.

The Fine Art Society plc
148 New Bond St. W1S 2JT. SLAD. Est. 1876. Open 9.30-5.30, Sat. 10-1. SIZE: Large. *STOCK: British fine and decorative arts, 19th-20th C.* PARK: 300yds. TEL: 020 7629 5116. SER: Buys at auction. VAT: Stan/Spec.

Sam Fogg   BADA
15d Clifford St. W1S 4JZ. ABA. Est. 1971. Open Mon.-Fri. 9.30-5.30 or by appointment. *STOCK: Manuscripts - Western medieval, Islamic and Oriental and works of art; Indian paintings.* LOC: Off New Bond St. PARK: NCP Burlington Gardens. TEL: 020 7534 2100; fax - 020 7534 2122; e-mail - info@ samfogg.com; website - www.samfogg. com. SER: Valuations; buys at auction. FAIRS: International Asian Art, New York; Paris. VAT: Margin.

H. Fritz-Denneville Fine Arts Ltd
31 New Bond St. W1S 2RW. SLAD. *STOCK: Paintings, drawings and prints, especially German Romantics, Nazarenes and Expressionists.* TEL: 020 7629 2466; fax - 020 7408 0604. SER: Valuations; restorations; buys at auction.

Deborah Gage (Works of Art) Ltd
38 Old Bond St. W1S 4QW. Est. 1982. Open 9.30-5.30. CL: Sat. *STOCK: European decorative arts, British and European paintings, Renaissance to 1940, from £5,000.* TEL: 020 7493 3249; fax - 020 7495 1352; e-mail - art@deborahgage. com. SER: Valuations; cataloguing; buys at auction. VAT: Stan/Spec.

Thomas Goode and Co (London) Ltd
19 South Audley St. W1. Est. 1827. Open 10-6. SIZE: Large. *STOCK: China, glass, silver, tableware, ornamental, lamps, mirrors and furniture.* TEL: 020 7499 2823; fax - 020 7629 4230. SER: Restorations. VAT: Spec.

The Graham Gallery
60 South Audley St., Mayfair. W1K 2QW. LAPADA. Est. 1973. Open 10.30-6. SIZE: Large. *STOCK: Library furniture, works of art, oil and sculptures.* PARK: Easy. TEL: 020 7495 3151. VAT: Stan.

Grays Antique Markets
58 Davies St. and 1-7 Davies Mews. W1K 5LP. Est. 1970. Open 10-6. CL: Sat. TEL: 020 7629 7034; fax - 020 7629 3279. SER: Engraving and jewellery repair. Below are listed the dealers at this market.

A & T
Stand 104. *Jewellery.* TEL: 020 7495 7068.

Abacus
Stand 313-315. Jewellery. TEL: 020 7629 9681.

Adams Antiques
Stand C24/25. *Islamic antiquities.* TEL: 020 7409 3285.

Maria Alcazar
Stand 323. *Jewellery.* TEL: 020 7629 7034.

Anthea Antiques
Stand 153-5. (Anthea Geshua) LAPADA. *Jewellery.* TEL: 020 7493 7564.

S. Arbab
Stand C21. *Islamic and antiquities.* TEL: 020 7629 7034.

Arca
Stand 351-3. (R. & E. Innocentini). *Objets d'art and miniatures.* TEL: 020 7629 2729.

Elias Assad
Stand J28-31/K13. *Islamic and antiquities.* TEL: 020 7499 4778.

Aurum Antiques
Stand 310/11*Jewellery.* TEL: 020 7409 0215.

Osman Aytac
Stand 331/2. *Watches and clocks.* TEL: 020 7629 7380.

Colin Baddiel
Stand B24/25/C12/13. *Toys.* TEL: 020 7408 1239.

David Baker
Stand M10/11. *Asian.* TEL: 020 8346 1387.

Don Bayney
Stand C22/23. *Militaria.* TEL: 020 7491 7200.

Bennett & Co.
Stand 109. *Engraving.* TEL: 020 7408 1880.

Barbara Berg
Stand 333/4. *Jewellery.* TEL: 020 7499 0560.

Beverley R
Stand 342/3/4. *Jewellery.* TEL: 020 7408 1129.

Biblion
Books. TEL: 020 7629 1374.

Bijoux Signes
Stand 384. *Clocks and watches.* TEL: 020 7495 6814

Britannia
Stand 101-2, 159-60. *Ceramics.* TEL: 020 7629 6772.

S. Brown
Stand M12. *Jewellery.* TEL: 020 7491 4287.

Christopher Cavey
Stand 178. *Gems and minerals.* TEL: 020 7495 1743.

Cekay
Stand 172. *Small antiques.* 0777 641 2058.

D. & J. Church
Stand 163. *Jewellery.* TEL: 020 7499 7935.

George Cichy
Stand 359. *Watches and silver.* TEL: 020 7629 7034.

Collection Antiques
Stand 329/30. *Jewellery.* TEL: 020 7493 2654.

Continium
Stand 124. (F. and E. Joy). *Oriental.* TEL: 020 7493 4909.

Cyjer Jewellery Ltd
Stand 143/4. *Jewellery.* TEL: 020 7629 3206.

Dadajan
Stand A28/29. *Islamic and antiquities.* TEL: 020 7629 7034.

Daisycrest Ltd
Stand 385. *Jewellery.* TEL: 020 7493 6044.

Deacon Antiques
Stand L17. *Silver.* TEL: 020 7499 0911.

Douch & Nicolov
Stand G10/11. *Jewellery.* TEL: 020 7493 9413.

Rosemary Erbrich
Stand C26. *Small antiques.* TEL: 020 7629 7034.

Evonne Antiques
Stand 301. *Silver.* TEL: 020 7491 0143.

Finishing Touch
Stand 176. *Jewellery.* TEL: 020 7495 0592.

Forever Young
Stand 371. *Jewellery.* TEL: 07970 832026.

Gallery Diem
Stand171. *Jewellery.* TEL: 020 7493 0224.

Peter Gaunt
Stand 120. *Silver.* TEL: 020 7629 1072.

Gilded Lily
Stand 133/4 & 145/6. (Korin Harvey). LAPADA.
Jewellery. TEL: 020 7499 6260.

Jasper Glen Antiquities
Stand 152, 16½. *Jewellery.* TEL: 020 7629 5511.

Gordons Medals Ltd
Stand G14/15/17. *Militaria.* TEL: 020 7495 0900.

R.G. Grahame
Stand 129/30. *Prints and paintings.* TEL: 020 7629 7034.

Sarah Groombridge
Stand 335-7. LAPADA. *Jewellery.* TEL: 020 7629 0225.

Guest & Gray
Stand H25-28 & J10/11. *Asian.* TEL: 020 7408 1252.

Alice Guillesarian
Stand K33. *Jewellery.* TEL: 020 7629 7034.

Linda Gumb
Stand 123. *Textiles.* TEL: 020 7629 2544.

Abdul Hadi
Stand A30. *Islamic and antiquities.* TEL: 020 7629 2813.

Diane Harby
Stand 148. *Textiles.* TEL: 020 7629 5130.

Satoe Hatrell
Stand 156/166. *Jewellery and jet.* TEL: 020 7629 4296.

Lynn and Brian Holmes
Stand 304-6. LAPADA. *Jewellery.* TEL: 020 7629 7327.

J.L.A.
Stand 364-6. (Alan Jacobs, Stephen Lack). LAPADA. *Jewellery.* TEL: 020 7499 1681.

Jacobs Gallery
Stand E18-20. *Islamic and antiquities.* TEL: 020 7499 9966.

Baba Jethwa
Stand 136. *Clocks and watches.* TEL: 020 7495 7327.

J. Joseph
Stand 345-7. *Jewellery.* TEL: 020 7629 1140.

Judson
Stand 321. *Jewellery.* TEL: 020 7499 4001.

JUS Watches
Stand 108. *Clocks and watches.* TEL: 020 7495 7404.

K & M Antiques
Stand 369/70. (Martin Harris). *Ceramics.* TEL: 020 7491 4310.

K. & Y. Oriental Antiques
Stand K24-27. *Asian.* TEL: 020 7491 0264.

Minoo & Andre Kaae
Stand G22/23. *Jewellery.* TEL: 020 7629 1200.

Kikuchi Trading Co Ltd
Stand 357/8 & 368. LAPADA. *Jewellery and watches.* TEL: 020 7629 6808.

Lazarell
Stand 325/6. *Jewellery.* TEL: 020 7408 0154.

Lennox Gallery
Stand K10-12 & K36-8. *Coins and medals.* TEL: 020 7491 0091.

Licht & Morrison
Stand 158 & 168-70. *Jewellery.* TEL: 020 7493 7497.

Linda B
Stand L18-21. *Jewellery.* TEL: 020 7629 5921.

Michael Marks
Stand 324. *Jewellery.* TEL: 020 7491 0332.

Andree Mart
Stand L26/27. *Objets d'art and miniatures.* TEL: 020 7629 7034.

Pete McAskie
Stand A12/13. *Toys.* TEL: 020 7629 2813.

Michael's Boxes
Stand L14/15. *Objets d'art and miniatures.* TEL: 020 7629 5716.

A. Atighi Moghadam
Stand E14/15. *Islamic and antiquities.* TEL: 020 7629 7034.

Clive Morley
Stand 121. *Harps.* TEL: 020 7495 4495.

Mozafarian
Stand 103. *Jewellery.* TEL: 020 7491 3795.

Marsha Myers
Stand 386. *Silver.* TEL: 020 7493 0768.

Myra Antiques
Stand 327. *Jewellery.* TEL: 020 7629 3596.

Stephen Naegel
Stand B23 & C14. *Toys.* TEL: 020 7491 3066.

M. Namdar
Stand B18/19. *Islamic and antiquities.* TEL: 020 7629 1183.

Neville & Carpenter
Stand 127/177. *Prints and paintings.* TEL: 020 7491 7621/7623.

Nabi Ozbek
Stand C20. *Islamic and antiquities.* TEL: 020 7629 7034.

M. Payne
Stand 312. *Jewellery.* TEL: 020 7629 6219. SER: Bead stringing.

The Pearl Gallery
Stand 328 & 340. *Jewellery.* TEL: 020 7409 2743.

Peter's Clocks
Stand K32. *Watches and clocks.* TEL: 07968 253327.

Pieces of Time BADA
Stand M17-19. (Johnny Wachsman). LAPADA.
Watches and clocks. **TEL: 020 7629 3272.**

Jack Podlewski
Stand 320. *Silver.* TEL: 020 7409 1468.

Rasoul Gallery
Stand K34/35. *Islamic and antiquities.* TEL: 020 7495 7422.

RBR Grp
Stand 175. (Olivia Gerrish). *Jewellery.* TEL: 020 7629 4769.

Regal Watches
Stand 128-140. *Clocks and watches.* TEL: 020 7491 7722.

Ian Roper
Stand L12/13. *Coins and medals.* TEL: 020 7491 0091.

Sabor Safi
Stand C27. *Jewellery.* TEL: 020 7434 0575.

Samiramis
Stand M14-16. (Hamid Ismail). LAPADA. *Islamic and antiquities.* TEL: 020 7629 1161.

Satrapel
Stand M20/21. *Coins and medals.* TEL: Mobile - 07956 597075.

Charlotte Sayers
Stand 360/1. *Jewellery.* TEL: 020 7499 5478.

Second Time Around Ltd/Jadefare
Stand 105 & 316-318. *Clocks and watches.* TEL: 020 7499 7442.

Chris Seidler
Stand G12/13. *Militaria.* TEL: 020 7629 2815.

Shadad Antiques
Stand A16/17. (Farah Hakemi). *Islamic and antiquities.* TEL: 020 7499 0572.

Shapiro & Co
Stand 380. LAPADA. *Jewellery.* TEL: 020 7491 2720.

Mousa Shavolian
Stand B13 & B19-22. *Glass and perfume bottles.* TEL: 020 7499 8273.

Shiraz Antiques
Stand H10/11. (R.P. Kiadah). *Islamic and antiquities.* TEL: 020 7495 0635.

Peter Sloane
Stand E12/13 & MBO29. *Asian.* TEL: 020 7408 1043.

Margaret Soane-Sands
Stand 322. *Objets d'art.* TEL: 020 7491 1718.

Solemani
Stand A20/21.(Helen Zokee). *Islamic and antiquities.* TEL: 020 7491 2562.

Solveig & Gray
Stand 307-9. LAPADA. *Asian.* TEL: 020 7408 1638.

Boris Sosna
Stand 374/5. *Jewellery.* TEL: 020 7629 2371.

Spectrum
Stand 372/3. (Sylvia Bedwell). *Jewellery.* TEL: 020 7629 3501.

Star Signings Ltd
Stand E16/17. *Sporting memorabilia.* TEL: 020 7491 1010.

Jane Stewart
Stand L25. *Pewter, early 17th C-19th C, £50-£1,000; oak, £500-£1,000; writing slopes, 19th C, £80-£150; medieval.* TEL: 020 7355 3333. SER: Valuations; restorations (pewter, oak). VAT: Spec.

Sultani Antiques
Stand K28-31. *Islamic and antiquities.* TEL: 020 7629 7034.

Tagore Ltd
Stand 302/3. (Ronald Falloon). *Gentlemen's gifts, drinking and smoking paraphernalia.* TEL: 020 7499 0158.

Tantra Art
Stand L10/11. *Asian.* TEL: 020 7629 7034.

A. Tendler
Stand 362/3. *Jewellery.* TEL: 020 7499 1087. SER: Jewellery repairs

Timespec
Stand 366. *Watches and clocks.* TEL: 020 7499 9814.

By appointment to Her Majesty The Queen Suppliers of Objects of Art — By appointment to H.R.H. The Duke of Edinburgh Suppliers of Objects of Art — By appointment to H.M. Queen Elizabeth The Queen Mother Suppliers of Objects of Art — By appointment to H.R.H. The Prince of Wales Suppliers of Objects of Art

HALCYON DAYS

18th-century English enamels, fans, objects of vertu, tortoiseshell, papier mâché and treen

14 Brook Street, London W1S 1BD
4 Royal Exchange, London EC3V 3LL

Tel: 020 7629 8811
Fax: 020 7409 0280
http://www.halcyondays.co.uk

Tingri Ltd.
Stand A14/15. *Asian.* TEL: 020 7493 5100.

Tradwinds
Stand 149. *Glass and perfume bottles.* TEL: 020 7629 5130.

Trianon Ltd.
Stand 378/9. *Objets d'art.* TEL: 020 7491 2764.

Trio
Stand L24. (Teresa Clayton). *Glass and perfume bottles.* TEL: 020 7492 2736.

Michael Ventura-Pauly
Stand 354-357. *Jewellery.* TEL: 020 7495 6868.

Mary Akin Wellard
Stand 164/5. *Small antiques.* TEL: 020 7629 7034.

Westleigh Antiques
Stand 339 & 350. (Pat Sneath). *Jewellery.* TEL: 020 7493 0123.

Westminster Group
Stand 138/39 & 150. (Paulette Bates and Richard Harrison). LAPADA. *Jewellery.* TEL: 020 7493 8672.

David Wheatley
Stand 106. LAPADA. *Asian.* TEL: 020 7629 1352.

Wheels of Steel
Stand B10/11. (Jeff Williams). *Toys.* TEL: 020 7629 2813.

Wimpole Antiques
Stand 338 & 348/9. LAPADA. *Jewellery.* TEL: 020 7499 2889.

ZMS Antiques
Stand 125. *Silver.* TEL: 020 7491 1144.

Richard Green　　　　　　　BADA
147 New Bond St., 33 New Bond St. and 39 Dover St. W1S 2TS. SLAD. Open 9.30-6, Sat. 10-12.30. *STOCK: Paintings - Old Master and British; French impressionist and modern*

British; Victorian sporting and British marine. **PARK: Meters. TEL: 020 7493 3939; fax - 020 7629 2609; e-mail - paintings@richard-green.com; website - www.richard-green.com. VAT: Stan/Spec.**

Simon Griffin Antiques Ltd
3 Royal Arcade, 28 Old Bond St. W1. (S.J. Griffin). Est. 1979. Open 10-5, Sat. 10-5.30. *STOCK: Silver, old Sheffield plate.* TEL: 020 7491 7367; fax - same. VAT: Stan/Spec.

Hadji Baba Ancient Art
34a Davies St. W1Y 1LG. (Hadji Soleimani). Est. 1939. Open 9.30-6, Sat. and Sun. by appointment. SIZE: Medium. *STOCK: Antiquities and Islamic art.* LOC: Next to Claridges Hotel. PARK: Meters. TEL: 020 7499 9363/9384; fax - 020 7493 5504. SER: Valuations.

Halcyon Days　　　　　　　　　BADA
14 Brook St. W1S 1BD. (P. Norman). Est. 1950. Open 9.30-6. *STOCK: 18th to early 19th C enamels, fans, treen, papier mâché, tôle, objects of vertu, Georgian and Victorian scent bottles.* **LOC: Hanover Sq. end of Brook St. PARK: Meters and in Hanover Sq. TEL: 020 7629 8811; fax - 020 7409 0280; e-mail - info@ halcyondays.co.uk; website - www.halcyondays. co.uk. FAIRS: Grosvenor House. VAT: Stan/Spec.**

Robert Hall　　　　　　　　　　BADA
15c Clifford St. W1X 1RF. Est. 1976. *STOCK: Chinese snuff bottles, Ching dynasty; Oriental works of art, 17th-19th C; all £300-£20,000.* **TEL: 020 7734 4008; fax - 020 7734 4408. SER: Buys at auction. VAT: Stan/Spec.**

Hancocks and Co　　　　　　　BADA
52 & 53 Burlington Arcade. W1J 0HH. Est. 1849. Open 9.30-5.30. SIZE: Medium. *STOCK: Fine estate jewellery and silver.* **TEL: 020 7493 8904; fax - 020 7493 8905; e-mail - info@**

hancocks-london.com; website - www. hancocks-london.com. SER: Valuations; re-modelling. FAIRS: Grosvenor House. VAT: Stan/Spec.

Harcourt Antiques
5 Harcourt St. W1 1DS. (J. Christophe). Est. 1961. Open by appointment only. SIZE: Medium. *STOCK: English, Continental and Oriental porcelain, pre-1830.* PARK: Easy. TEL: 020 7727 6936. VAT: Stan. *Trade Only.*

Brian Haughton Antiques
3B Burlington Gardens, Old Bond St. W1S 3EP. Est. 1965. Open 10-5.30. SIZE: Large. *STOCK: British and European ceramics, porcelain and pottery, 18th-19th C, £100-£50,000.* PARK: Nearby, Savile Row N.C.P. TEL: 020 7734 5491; fax - 020 7494 4604; e-mail - info@haughton.com; website - www.haughton.com. SER: Buys at auction (porcelain and pottery). FAIRS: Organiser - International Ceramics Fair & Seminar, Park Lane Hotel; International Fine Art & Antique Dealers Show, International Fine Art and International Asian Art, New York; International Art & Design. VAT: Spec.

Gerard Hawthorn Ltd　　BADA
104 Mount St., Mayfair. W1K 2TL. Open 10-6, Sat. by appointment. *STOCK: Oriental art - Chinese ceramics, porcelain and pottery; cloisonné and painted enamels, jade, hardstones, lacquer, bronzes, metalwork, paintings, textiles, ivory, works of art including Korean, Tibetan and Japanese, 2000BC to 1960.* **LOC: Opposite Connaught Hotel. PARK: Easy. TEL: 020 7409 2888; fax - 020 7409 2777. SER: Valuations; restorations; buys at auction; exhibitions twice yearly (illustrated catalogues). FAIRS: New York; Olympia (June).**

G. Heywood Hill Ltd
10 Curzon St. W1J 5HH. Open 9-5.30, Sat. 9-12.30. *STOCK: Books, new and old, architecture, literature, children's, natural history and illustrated.* TEL: 020 7629 0647; fax - 020 7408 0286; e-mail - books@gheywoodhill.com; website - www.gheywoodhill.com.

Holland & Holland
31-33 Bruton St. W1X 8JS. Est. 1835. Open 9.30-5.30, Sat. 10-4. SIZE: Medium. *STOCK: Modern and antique guns, rifles, associated items; sporting prints, pictures and antiquarian books; antique sporting objects.* PARK: Meters in Bruton St. TEL: 020 7499 4411; fax - 020 7499 4544.

Holmes Ltd　　BADA
24 Burlington Arcade. W1V 9AD. (A.N., B.J. and I.J. Neale). Open 9.30-5. *STOCK: Jewels and silver.* **TEL: 020 7629 8380. SER: Valuations; restorations. VAT: Stan.**

Howard Antiques
8 Davies St., Berkeley Sq. W1Y 1LJ. Est. 1955. Open 10-6, Sat. by appointment. SIZE: Medium. *STOCK: English and Continental furniture, objects.* PARK: NCP nearby. TEL: 020 7629 2628. SER: Valuations; advice; commissions.

Patrick Jefferson
94 Mount St., Mayfair. W1K 2SZ. Est. 1978. Open 9.30-5. SIZE: Large. *STOCK: Unusual furniture, works of art, sculpture and paintings, 1700-1930.* LOC: Between Berkeley Square and Park Lane, opposite Scotts. PARK: Easy. TEL: 020 7491 4931; fax - 020 7491 4932. SER: Buys at auction.

C. John (Rare Rugs) Ltd　　BADA
70 South Audley St., Mayfair. W1Y 5FE. Est. 1947. Open 9-5. CL: Sat. *STOCK: Rugs, carpets, tapestries, textiles and embroideries, 16th - 19th C.* **TEL: 020 7493 5288; fax - 020 7409 7030; e-mail - cjohn@dircon.co.uk. SER: Restorations, cleaning. FAIRS: Grosvenor House. VAT: Stan/Spec.**

Johnson Walker & Tolhurst Ltd　BADA
64 Burlington Arcade. W1J 0QT. (Miss R. Gill). Est. 1849. Open 9.30-5.30. *STOCK: Antique and secondhand jewellery, objets d'art, silver.* **TEL: 020 7629 2615. SER: Restorations (jewellery, pearl-stringing). VAT: Stan/Spec.**

Roger Keverne　　BADA
2nd Floor, 16 Clifford St. W1S 3RG. Est. 1996. Open Mon.-Fri. 9.30-5.30. SIZE: Large. *STOCK: Oriental art - Chinese jade, lacquer, pottery and porcelain, bronzes, ivories and enamels; all Chinese art from 2500 BC to 1916.* **PARK: Meters. TEL: 020 7434 9100; fax - 020 7434 9101. SER: Valuations; restorations; buys at auction. FAIRS: New York (Winter and March Oriental). VAT: Stan/Spec.**

D.S. Lavender (Antiques) Ltd　　BADA
26 Conduit St. W1R 9TA. Est. 1945. Open 9.30-5. CL: Sat. *STOCK: Jewels, miniatures, works of art.* **PARK: Meters. TEL: 020 7629 1782; fax - 020 7629 3106. SER: Valuations. VAT: Stan/Spec.**

Leuchars and Jefferson
94 Mount St., Mayfair. W1K 2SZ. (Patrick Jefferson and Hugh Leuchars). Est. 1978. Open 9.30-6. SIZE: Large. *STOCK: English 18th C furniture and works of art.* LOC: Between

Berkeley Square and Park Lane, opposite Scotts. PARK: Easy. TEL: 020 7491 4931; fax - 020 7491 4932. VAT: Spec.

Liberty

Regent St. W1R 6AH. Est. 1875. Open 10-6.30, Thurs. 10-8, Fri. and Sat. 10-7. SIZE: Large. *STOCK: British furniture, ceramics, glass and metalware, 1860-1930, Gothic Revival, Aesthetic Movement and Arts & Crafts.* LOC: Regent St. joins Piccadilly and Oxford Circus. PARK: Meters and underground in Cavendish Sq. TEL: 020 7734 1234. VAT: Stan.

Maas Gallery

15a Clifford St. W1S 4JZ. (R.N. Maas). SLAD. Est. 1960. Open Mon.-Fri. 10-5.30. SIZE: Medium. *STOCK: Victorian and Pre-Raphaelite paintings, drawings, watercolours and illustrations.* LOC: Between New Bond St. and Cork St. PARK: Easy. TEL: 020 7734 2302; fax - 020 7287 4836; e-mail - mail@maasgallery.co.uk; website - www.maasgallery.com. SER: Valuations; buys at auction. VAT: Spec.

Maggs Bros Ltd   BADA

50 Berkeley Sq. W1J 5BA. (J.F., B.D. and E.F. Maggs, P. Harcourt, R. Harding, H. Bett and J. Collins). ABA. Est. 1853. Open 9.30-5. CL: Sat. SIZE: Large. *STOCK: Rare books, manuscripts, autograph letters and medieval miniatures.* PARK: Meters. TEL: 020 7493 7160 (6 lines); fax - 020 7499 2007; e-mail - ed@maggs.com; website - www.maggs.com. VAT: Stan/Spec.

Mahboubian Gallery

65 Grosvenor St. W1X 9DB. (H. Mahboubian). Open 10-6. CL: Sat. TEL: 020 7493 9112.

Mallett and Son (Antiques) Ltd BADA

141 New Bond St. W1S 2BS. Est. 1865. Open 9.15-6, Sat. 10-4. SIZE: Large. *STOCK: English furniture, 1690-1835; clocks, 17th-18th C; china, needlework, paintings and watercolours, objects and glass.* PARK: Meters in Berkeley Sq. TEL: 020 7499 7411; fax - 020 7495 3179; e-mail - antiques@mallett.co.uk. FAIRS: Grosvenor House; Maastricht; IAADF New York.

Mallett at Bourdon House Ltd

2 Davies St., Berkeley Sq. W1Y 1LJ. Open 9-6. SIZE: Large. *STOCK: Continental furniture, clocks, objets d'art; garden statuary and ornaments.* PARK: Meters, Berkeley Sq. TEL: 020 7629 2444; fax - 020 7499 2670; e-mail - antiques@mallett.co.uk; website - www.mallett. co.uk. VAT: Stan/Spec.

Mallett Gallery   BADA

141 New Bond St. W1S 2BS. SLAD. Open 9.30-6, Sat. 11-4. *STOCK: 18th to early 20th C paintings, watercolours and drawings.* TEL: 020 7499 7411; fax - 020 7495 3179. VAT: Spec.

Mansour Gallery   BADA

46-48 Davies St. W1K 5JB. (M. Mokhtarzadeh). Open 9.30-5.30, Sat. by appointment. *STOCK: Islamic works of art, miniatures; ancient glass and glazed wares; Greek, Roman and Egyptian antiquities.* TEL: 020 7491 7444/7499 0510. VAT: Stan.

Map World

25 Burlington Arcade, Piccadilly. W1J 0PT. (J. T. Sharpe). LAPADA, IMCOS. Est. 1980. Open 10-5.30. SIZE: Small. *STOCK: Maps, worldwide, 1500-1850, £50-£85,000.* TEL: 020 7495 5377; fax - same; e-mail - info@map-world.com; website - www.map-world.com. SER: Valuations; buys at auction.

Marks Antiques   BADA

49 Curzon St. W1. (Anthony Marks). LAPADA. Est. 1945. Open 9.30-6 including Bank Holidays. SIZE: Large. *STOCK: Fine silver and Faberge.* LOC: Green Park tube, opposite Washington Hotel. PARK: Meters. TEL: 020 7499 1788; fax - 020 7409 3183. SER: Valuations; buys at auction. FAIRS: Grosvenor House, BADA, Olympia, Hong Kong, Palm Beach, Dallas. VAT: Stan/Spec.

Marlborough Fine Art (London) Ltd

6 Albemarle St. W1S 4BY. SLAD. Est. 1946. Open 10-5.30, Sat. 10-12.30. *STOCK: Graphic works; exhibitions by leading contemporary artists and sculptures.* PARK: Meters or near Cork St. TEL: 020 7629 5161; fax - 020 7629 6338; e-mail - mfa@marlboroughfineart.com; website - www.marlboroughfineart.com. FAIRS: Madrid; Maastricht; Geneva; Basel; Paris; Cologne.

Marlborough Rare Books Ltd

144-146 New Bond St. W1S 2TR. (Jonathan Gestetner). ABA. Est. 1946. Open 9.30-5.30. CL: Sat. SIZE: Medium. *STOCK: Illustrated books of all periods; rare books on fine and applied arts and architecture; English literature.* PARK: Meters. TEL: 020 7493 6993; e-mail - sales@ mrb-books.co.uk. SER: Buys at auction; valuations; catalogues available. FAIRS: Olympia; Chelsea; Los Angeles; New York.

Mayfair Carpet Gallery Ltd

10a Berkeley St. W1X 5AD. *STOCK: Persian, Oriental rugs and carpets.* TEL: 020 7493 0126.

Mayfair Gallery
39 South Audley St. W1Y 5DH. (M. Sinai). Open 9.30-6, Sat. by appointment. *STOCK: 19th C antiques and decorative Continental furniture, clocks, chandeliers, Meissen, ivories and objets d'art.* TEL: 020 7491 3435/6; fax - 020 7491 3437; e-mail - mayfair.gallery@dial.pipex.com; website - www.artnet.com/mayfairgallery.htm.

Melton's
27 Bruton Place. W1J 6NQ. (Cecilia Neal). IDDA, IIDA. Est. 1990. Open Mon.-Fri. 9.30-5.30. *STOCK: Small antiques and decorative accessories: lamps, prints, porcelain, textiles, English and Continental.* LOC: Mayfair, near Bond St. PARK: Meters Berkeley Sq. TEL: 020 7629 3612; fax - 020 7495 3196; e-mail - meltons.uk@virgin.net; website - www. meltons. co.uk. SER: Interior design and decoration.

Messums (Contemporary)   BADA
8 Cork St. W1X 1PB. LAPADA, SLAD. Open 10-6, Sat. 10-4, other times by appointment. *STOCK: British Impressionist and contemporary paintings and sculpture.* TEL: 020 7437 5545; fax - 020 7734 7018. SER: Valuations; restorations; framing. VAT: Stan/Spec.

John Mitchell and Son   BADA
1st Floor, 160 New Bond St. W1S 2UE. SLAD. Est. 1931. Open 9.30-5, Sat. by appointment. SIZE: Small. *STOCK: Old Master paintings, drawings and watercolours, especially flower paintings, 17th C Dutch, 18th C English and 19th C French.* LOC: Nearest tube Green Park. PARK: Meters. TEL: 020 7493 7567. SER: Valuations; restorations (pictures); buys at auction.

Paul Mitchell Ltd   BADA
99 New Bond St. W1Y 9LF. Open 9.30-5.30. CL: Sat. SIZE: Large. *STOCK: Picture frames.* PARK: Meters. TEL: 020 7493 8732/0860. VAT: Stan.

Bashir Mohamed Ltd
8 Broadbent St. W1X 9HH. Open 10-5 by appointment only. CL: Sat. *STOCK: Islamic art, Moghul and south east Asian manuscripts and objects.* TEL: 020 7723 1844. VAT: Spec.

Moira
11 New Bond St. W1. Open 9-6. *STOCK: Fine antique and Art Deco jewellery.* TEL: 020 7629 0160. SER: Valuations; repairs.

Sydney L. Moss Ltd   BADA
51 Brook St. W1K 4HP. (P.G. Moss). Est. 1910. Open Mon.-Fri. 10-5.30. SIZE: Large.

STOCK: Chinese and Japanese paintings and works of art; Japanese netsuke and lacquer, 17th-20th C; reference books (as stock). LOC: From Grosvenor Sq., up Brook St. to Claridges. PARK: Meters. TEL: 020 7629 4670/7493 7374; fax - 020 7491 9278. SER: Valuations and advice; buys at auction. FAIRS: Asian Art, New York (March). VAT: Spec.

The O'Shea Gallery   BADA
120a Mount St., Mayfair. W1K 3NN. ABA. Open 9.30-6, Sat. by appointment only. *STOCK: Maps, topographical, decorative, natural history, sporting and marine prints; rare atlases, illustrated books, 15th-19th C, £5-£25,000.* LOC: Near Berkeley Sq. TEL: 020 7629 1122; fax - 020 7629 1116; e-mail - prints@osheagallery.com; website - www.osheagallery.com. SER: Decorative framing; restorations. VAT: Stan/Spec.

Richard Ogden Ltd   BADA
28 and 29 Burlington Arcade, Piccadilly. W1J 0NX. Est. 1948. Open 9.30-5.15, Sat. 9.30-5. SIZE: Medium. *STOCK: Antique jewellery.* LOC: Near Old Bond St. PARK: Meters and NCP. TEL: 020 7493 9136; e-mail - post@richardogden.com. SER: Valuations; repairs. VAT: Spec.

Paralos Ltd
4th Floor, 23/24 Margaret St. W1W 8RU. (Panagiotis Chantziaras, Louise Bryan and Tim Bryars). ABA, ILAB, PBFA, IMCOS. Est. 1997. Open by appointment. SIZE: Large. *STOCK: Antiquarian books, prints (including decorative and natural history), maps and atlases, printed before 1800; early printing, classics, plate books, voyages and travels, £10-£20,000.* LOC: From Oxford Circus, north up Regent St., second road on right. PARK: Cavendish Sq. TEL: 020 7637 0796; fax - 020 7637 0819; e-mail - paralos@paralos.co.uk; website - www.paralos.co.uk. FAIRS: Map & Print (2nd Sun. monthly), Bonnington Hotel. VAT: Stan. *Trade Only.*

Partridge Fine Arts plc   BADA
144-146 New Bond St. W1S 2PF. (John & Frank Partridge and Michael Pick). SLAD, CINOA. Est. 1905. Open Mon - Fri. 9-1 and 2-5.30, other times by appointment. SIZE: Large. *STOCK: 18th-19th C English and French furniture; silver, clocks, porcelain, objets d'art, chandeliers, lighting, carpets, needlework; English, French and Italian paintings.* LOC: North of Bruton St., opposite Sotheby's. PARK: Meters and NCP nearby. TEL: 020 7629 0834; fax - 020 7495 6266; e-

mail - enquiries@partridgeplc.com; website - www.partridgeplc.com. SER: Buys at auction; restorations including upholstery; carving and gilding; exhibitions held. VAT: Spec.

W.H. Patterson Fine Arts Ltd   BADA
19 Albemarle St. W1X 3LA. (W.H. and Mrs. P.M. Patterson and J. Kayll). SLAD. Open 9.30-6. SIZE: Large. *STOCK: 19th C and regular exhibitions for contemporary artists, the New English Art Club, Paul Brown, Andrew Coates, Willem Dolphyn and Peter Kuhfeld. LOC: Near Green Park tube station. PARK: Meters. TEL: 020 7629 4119; fax - 020 7499 0119. SER: Valuations; restorations. VAT: Spec.*

Pelham Galleries Ltd   BADA
24/25 Mount St., Mayfair. W1K 2RR. (A. and L.J. Rubin). Est. 1928. *STOCK: Furniture, English and Continental; tapestries, decorative works of art and musical instruments. TEL: 020 7629 0905; fax - 020 7495 4511. FAIRS: Palm Beach; Maastricht; Grosvenor House; Biennale Paris. VAT: Spec.*

Pendulum of Mayfair Ltd
King House, 51 Maddox St. W1. (K. R. Clements and Dr H. Specht). Open 10-6, Sat. 10-5. *STOCK:*

Clocks, mainly longcase, also bracket, mantel and wall; Georgian mahogany furniture. TEL: 020 7629 6606; fax - 020 7629 6616. SER: Valuations. FAIRS: Buxton. VAT: Spec.

Ronald Phillips Ltd   BADA
26 Bruton St. W1J 6LQ. Est. 1952. *STOCK: English 18th C furniture, objets d'art, glass, clocks and barometers.* TEL: 020 7493 2341; fax - 020 7495 0843. FAIRS: Grosvenor House. VAT: Mainly Spec.

S.J. Phillips Ltd   BADA
139 New Bond St. W1A 3DL. (M.S., N.E.L., J.P. and F.E. Norton). Est. 1869. Open 10-5. CL: Sat. SIZE: Large. *STOCK: Silver, jewellery, gold boxes, miniatures.* LOC: Near Bond St. tube station. PARK: Meters. TEL: 020 7629 6261; fax - 020 7495 6180; website - www.sjphillips.com. SER: Restorations; buys at auction. FAIRS: Grosvenor House; Maastricht. VAT: Stan/Spec.

Piccadilly Gallery
43 Dover St. W1S 4NU. SLAD. Est. 1953. Open 10-5.30. *STOCK: Symbolist and Art Nouveau works, 20th C; drawings and watercolours.* PARK: Meters. TEL: 020 7629 2875; fax - 020 7499 0431; e-mail - art@piccadillygall. demon.co.uk; website - www.piccadillygall. demon.co.uk. VAT: Spec.

Pickering and Chatto
1st Floor, 36 St George St. W1R 9FA. Est. 1820. Open Mon.-Fri. 9.30-5.30 or by appointment. SIZE: Medium. *STOCK: Literature, economics, politics, philosophy, science, medicine, general antiquarian.* PARK: Meters. TEL: 020 7491 2656; fax - 020 7491 9161; e-mail - rarebooks@ pickering-chatto.com.

Nicholas S. Pitcher Oriental Art
1st Floor, 29 New Bond St. W1Y 9HD. Est. 1990. Open 10.30-5 by appointment. CL: Sat. except by appointment. SIZE: Medium. *STOCK: Chinese ceramics and works of art, early pottery, to 18th C, £200-£10,000.* LOC: Four doors from Sotheby's, above Gordon Scott shoe shop. PARK: Nearby. TEL: 020 7499 6621; home - 020 7731 5672; mobile - 07831 391574; e-mail - nickpitcher@ cs.com. SER: Valuations; buys at auction. FAIRS: Arts of Pacific Asia New York. VAT: Spec.

Portal Gallery
43 Dover St. W1X 3RE. (Lionel Levy and Jess Wilder). Est. 1959. Open 10-5.30, Sat. 10-4. SIZE: Medium. *STOCK: Curios, bygones, artefacts, country pieces and objects of virtue, 19th C, £50-£500; contemporary British idiosyncratic paintings, including Beryl Cook.* TEL: 020 7493 0706; fax - 020 7629 3506.

Jonathan Potter Ltd BADA
125 New Bond St. W1S 1DY. LAPADA, ABA.
Est. 1975. Open 10-6, Sat. by appointment.
STOCK: British and world maps, atlases and
travel books, 16th-19th C, £50-£10,000. PARK:
Meters nearby. TEL: 020 7491 3520; fax - 020
7491 9754; e-mail - jpmaps@attglobal.net;
website - www.jpmaps.co.uk. SER: Valuations;
restorations; colouring, framing; buys at
auction (maps and prints); catalogue available.
VAT: Stan.

Pyms Gallery BADA
9 Mount St., Mayfair. W1K 3NG. (A. and M.
Hobart). SLAD. Est. 1975. Open 9.30-6. CL:
Sat. STOCK: British, Irish and French paintings,
18th-20th C. TEL: 020 7629 2020; fax - 020
7629 2060; e-mail - paintings@pymsgallery.
com; website - www.pymsgallery.com. SER:
Valuations; restorations; buys at auction.
FAIRS: Grosvenor House. VAT: Spec.

Bernard Quaritch Ltd (Booksellers)
BADA
5-8 Lower John St., Golden Sq. W1F 9AU. Est.
1847. Open 9.30-5.30. CL: Sat. SIZE: Large.
STOCK: Rare books and manuscripts. PARK:
Meters, 50yds. TEL: 020 7734 2983; fax - 020
7437 0967; e-mail - rarebooks@quaritch.com;
website - www.quaritch.com. SER: Buys at
auction. VAT: Stan.

Rabi Gallery Ltd
82P Portland Place. W1N 3DH. (R. Soleymani).
Est. 1878. Open 10-6. CL: Sat. STOCK: Ancient
art, antique carpets and works of art. TEL: 020
7580 9064; fax - 020 7436 0772.

Gordon Reece Gallery
16 Clifford St., Mayfair. W1X 1RG. Open 11-
5.30. CL: Mon. SIZE: Large. STOCK: Flat woven
rugs and nomadic carpets, tribal sculpture, jewellery, Chinese, Japanese and Indian furniture,
decorative and non-European folk art, ethnic and
Oriental ceramics. TEL: 020 7439 0007; fax -
020 7437 5715; website - www.gordon.reece.
galleries.com. SER: Restorations.

David Richards and Sons
10 New Cavendish St. W1G 8UL. (M. and E.
Richards). Open 9.30-5.30. CL: Sat. SIZE: Large.
STOCK: Silver and plate. LOC: Off Harley St., at
corner of Marylebone High St. PARK: Nearby.
TEL: 020 7935 3206/0322; fax - 020 7224 4423.
SER: Valuations; restorations. VAT: Stan/Spec.

Michael Rose - Source of the Unusual
3, 15, 44 Burlington Arcade, Piccadilly and 10
New Bond St. W1J 0QY. STOCK: Victorian,

antique and period diamonds, jewellery and
watches. TEL: 020 7493 0714; 020 7493 0590;
website - www.rosejewels.co.uk.

The Royal Arcade Watch Shop
4 Royal Arcade - at 28 Old Bond St. W1S 4SD.
Open 10-5.30. SIZE: Small. STOCK: Modern
and vintage Rolex, Cartier, Patek Phillipe.
PARK: Easy. TEL: 020 7495 4882.

Royal Exchange Art Gallery at Cork St.
24 Cork St. W1S 3NJ. Est. 1974. Open 10-6.
STOCK: Fine marine oils, watercolours and
etchings. TEL: 020 7439 6655; fax - 020 7439
6622; e-mail - enquiries@marinepictures.com;
website - www.marinepictures.com.

Frank T. Sabin Ltd BADA
46 Albemarle St. W1X 3FE. (John Sabin).
Open 9.30-5.30, Sat. by appointment only.
STOCK: English sporting and decorative prints;
English 18th-19th C paintings. TEL: 020 7493
3288; fax - 020 7499 3593.

Alistair Sampson Antiques Ltd BADA
120 Mount St., Mayfair. (Formerly of 156
Brompton Rd). W1K 3NN. Open 9.30-5.30. SIZE:
Large. STOCK: English pottery, oak and country
furniture, metalwork, needlework, primitive
pictures, decorative and interesting items, 17th-18th
C. PARK: Meters. TEL: 020 7409 1799; fax - 020
7409 7717; e-mail - info@alistairsampson.com;
website - www.alistairsampson.com. VAT: Spec.

Robert G. Sawers
PO Box 4QA. W1A 4QA. Open by appointment.
STOCK: Books on the Orient, Japanese prints,
screens, paintings. TEL: 020 7794 9618; fax -
020 7794 9571; website - www.bobsawers.com.

Scarisbrick and Bate Ltd
111 Mount St. W1Y 5HE. (R.A.J. Cotgrove). Est.
1958. Open 9.30-5.30. CL: Sat. SIZE: Medium.
STOCK: Furniture, decorative items, mid-18th C
to early 19th C. Not Stocked: Glass and china.
LOC: By Connaught Hotel (off Park Lane).
PARK: Meters. TEL: 020 7499 2043/4/5; fax -
020 7499 2897. SER: Restorations (furniture);
buys at auction. VAT: Stan.

Seaby Antiquities
14 Old Bond St. W1S 4PP. Est. 1926. Open 10-5.
CL: Sat. SIZE: Medium. STOCK: Antiquities.
LOC: Just off Piccadilly, nearest tube Green Park.
TEL: 020 7495 2590; fax - 020 7491 1595.

Jeremy Seale Antiques/Interiors
15 St. Andrews Mansions, Dorset St. W1U 4EQ.
Est. 1988. By appointment only. SIZE: Small.

STOCK: Furniture, 18th-19th C, £300-£6,000; decorative items, 19th C; pictures and prints, 18th-19th C; both £50-£500. TEL: 020 7935 5131; mobile - 07956 457795. SER: Finder; valuations; interior design consultant; home-finder. VAT: Stan/Spec.

Bernard J. Shapero Rare Books BADA
32 St George St. W1S 2EA. Est. 1979. Open 9.30-6.30, Sat. 11-5. SIZE: Large. *STOCK: Antiquarian books - travel, natural history, modern first edition, colour plate.* LOC: Near Hanover Sq. and Bond St. TEL: 020 7493 0876; fax - 020 7229 7860; e-mail - rarebooks@ shapero.com; website - www.shapero.com. SER: Valuations; restorations (antiquarian books); buys at auction. FAIRS: Book - London, Paris, New York, San Francisco.

W. Sitch and Co. Ltd.
48 Berwick St. W1F 8JD. (R. Sitch). Est. 1776. Open 8-5. SIZE: Large. *STOCK: Edwardian and Victorian lighting fixtures and floor standards.* LOC: Off Oxford St. TEL: 020 7437 3776; fax - 020 7437 5707. SER: Valuations; restorations; repairs. VAT: Stan.

The Sladmore Gallery of Sculpture
BADA
32 Bruton Place, Berkeley Sq. W1J 6NW. (E.F. Horswell). SLAD. Open 10-6. CL: Sat. SIZE: Large. *STOCK: Bronze sculptures, 19th C - Mene, Barye, Fremiet, Bonheur; Impressionist, Bugatti, Troubetzkoy, Pompon; contemporary, Geoffrey Dashwood birds, Mark Coreth African wildlife, Nic Fiddian-Green horse heads; sporting, polo.* TEL: 020 7499 0365; fax - 020 7409 1381; e-mail - sculpture@sladmore.com; website - www.sladmore.com. SER: Valuations; restorations. VAT: Stan/Spec.

Stephen Somerville (W.A.) Ltd
14 Old Bond St. W1S 4PP. SLAD. Est. 1987. By appointment only. SIZE: Small. *STOCK: Old Master prints and drawings; English paintings, watercolours, prints and drawings, 17th-20th C, £50-£50,000.* LOC: Piccadilly end of Old Bond St. TEL: 020 7493 8363. SER: Buys at auction (as stock). VAT: Spec.

Henry Sotheran Ltd
2/5 Sackville St., Piccadilly. W1S 3DP. ABA, PBFA, ILAB. Est. 1761. Open 9.30-6, Sat. 10-4. *STOCK: Antiquarian books and prints.* TEL: 020 7439 6151; fax - 020 7434 2019; e-mail - sotherans@sotherans.co.uk; website - www. sotherans.co.uk. SER: Restorations and binding (books, prints); buys at auction. VAT: Stan.

A & J Speelman Ltd BADA
129 Mount St. W1K 3NX. Est. 1931. Open 9.30-6. SIZE: Large. *STOCK: Rare Chinese, Japanese and Himalayan works of art including Tang pottery and Chinese export ceramics, Buddhist images and ritual objects.* LOC: Mayfair. TEL: 020 7499 5126; fax - 020 7355 3391; e-mail - speelman@enterprise.net; website - www.artnet.com/ajspeelman.html. SER: Valuations. FAIRS: International Asian, New York and Paris. VAT: Spec.

Spink Leger Pictures BADA
13 Old Bond St. W1X 4HU. (L.J. Libson). SLAD. Est. 1892. Open Mon.-Fri. 9-5.30. SIZE: Large. *STOCK: British paintings, drawings and watercolours, 17th-20th C and Old Master drawings.* PARK: Meters. TEL: 020 7629 3538; fax - 020 7493 8681. SER: Valuations; restorations.

Stair and Company Ltd BADA
14 Mount St. W1K 2RF. CINOA. Est. 1911. Open 9.30-5.30, Sat. by appointment. SIZE: Large. *STOCK: 18th-19th C English furniture, works of art, mirrors, chandeliers, barometers, needlework, lamps, clocks, prints.* LOC: Past Connaught Hotel, towards South Audley St. PARK: Meters and Adam's Row. TEL: 020 7499 1784; fax - 020 7629 1050; e-mail - stair-andcompany@talk21.com. SER: Restorations. FAIRS: Grosvenor House. VAT: Spec.

Jacob Stodel BADA
Flat 53 Macready House, 75 Crawford St. W1H 5LP. Est. 1949. By appointment. *STOCK: Continental furniture, objets d'art, ceramics, English furniture.* TEL: 020 7723 3732; fax - 020 7723 9813; e-mail - jacobstodel@aol.com. VAT: Margin/Spec.

Stoppenbach & Delestre Ltd
25 Cork St. W1S 3NB. SLAD. Open 10-5.30, Sat. 10-1. *STOCK: French paintings, drawings and sculpture, 19th-20th C.* TEL: 020 7734 3534.

Tessiers Ltd BADA
26 New Bond St. W1S 2JY. Open 10-5. *STOCK: Jewellery, silver, objets d'art.* TEL: 020 7629 0458; fax - 020 7629 1857. SER: Valuations; restorations. VAT: Spec.

William Thuillier
14 Old Bond St. W1S 4PP. Open by appointment only. *STOCK: Old Master paintings and drawings.* TEL: 020 7499 0106; website - www. thuillart.com; e-mail - thuillart@aol.com. SER: Valuations; research. FAIRS: Olympia (Feb., June, Nov).

Toynbee-Clarke Interiors Ltd

95 Mount St. W1Y 5HG. (G. and D. Toynbee-Clarke). Est. 1953. Open 11-5.30. CL: Sat. SIZE: Medium. *STOCK: Decorative English and Continental furniture and objects, 17th-18th C; Chinese hand painted wallpapers, 18th C; French scenic wallpapers, early 19th C; Chinese and Japanese paintings and screens, 17th-19th C.* LOC: Between north-west corner of Berkeley Sq. and Park Lane. PARK: Meters. TEL: 020 7499 4472; fax - 020 7495 1204. SER: Buys at auction. VAT: Stan/Spec.

M. Turpin Ltd

27 Bruton St. W1J 6QN. LAPADA. Open 10-6 or by appointment. CL: Sat. SIZE: Large. *STOCK: English and some Continental furniture, mirrors, chandeliers and objets d'art, 18th C.* LOC: Between Berkeley Sq. and Bond St. PARK: Limited and meters. TEL: 020 7493 3275; fax - 020 7408 1869; e-mail - mturpin@mturpin.co.uk; website - www.mturpin.co.uk.

Jan van Beers Oriental Art   BADA

34 Davies St. W1Y 1LG. Est. 1978. Open 10-6. CL: Sat. SIZE: Medium. *STOCK: Chinese and Japanese ceramics and works of art, 200BC to 1800AD.* LOC: Between Berkeley Sq. and Oxford St. PARK: Easy. TEL: 020 7408 0434. SER: Valuations. VAT: Spec.

Vigo Carpet Gallery

6a Vigo St. W1S 3HF. LAPADA. Open 10-6, Sat. 11-5. *STOCK: Oriental antique carpets and rugs; re-creations of hand-made carpets and rugs in vegetable dyes and hand-spun wool.* TEL: 020 7439 6971; fax - 020 7439 2353; e-mail - vigo@btinternet.com. SER: Valuations; restorations.

Rupert Wace Ancient Art Ltd   BADA

14 Old Bond St. W1S 4PP. (Rupert Wace and Martin Clist). IADAA, ADA. Est. 1984. Open Mon.-Fri. 10-5 or by appointment. *STOCK: Ancient Egyptian, Classical, near Eastern and Celtic antiquities.* LOC: West End. TEL: 020 7495 1623; fax - 020 7495 8495; e-mail - rupert.wace@btinternet.com; website - www.rupertwace.co.uk. SER: Valuations. FAIRS: Grosvenor House, Basel, New York.

Walpole Gallery

38 Dover St. W1S 4NL. SLAD. Open 9.30-5.30. CL: Sat. except when exhibitions held. *STOCK: Italian Old Master paintings.* TEL: 020 7499 6626.

Wartski Ltd   BADA

14 Grafton St. W1S 4DE. Est. 1865. Open 9.30-5. CL: Sat. SIZE: Medium. *STOCK: Jewellery,*

18th C gold boxes, Fabergé, Russian works of art, silver. **PARK: Meters. TEL: 020 7493 1141. SER: Restorations. FAIRS: IFAAD Show, New York; European Fine Art: TEFAF; Maastricht; IAA, Palm Beach. VAT: Stan/Spec.**

Waterhouse and Dodd   BADA

26 Cork St. W1S 3MQ. (R. Waterhouse and J. Dodd). Est. 1987. Open 9.30-6, Sat. 11-4. SIZE: Medium. *STOCK: British and European oil paintings, watercolours and drawings, 1850-1950, £2,000-£50,000.* **TEL: 020 7734 7800. SER: Valuations; restorations; buys at auction (paintings). FAIRS: Antiques and Fine Art; Olympia. VAT: Spec.**

Captain O.M. Watts

7 Dover St., Piccadilly. W1S 4LD. Open 9-6. SIZE: Small. *STOCK: Nautical antiques and collectables, £30-£2,000.* LOC: Near Green Park. PARK: Meters. TEL: 020 7493 4633; fax - 020 7495 0755. SER: Restorations (scientific instruments); buys at auction (nautical and scientific instruments); hire. VAT: Stan.

The Weiss Gallery

1B Albemarle St. W1. Open 10-6. CL: Sat. *STOCK: Elizabethan, Jacobean and early European portraits.* TEL: 020 7409 0035. SER: Valuations; restorations.

William Weston Gallery

7 Royal Arcade, Albemarle St. W1X 3HD. SLAD. IFPDA. Est. 1964. Open 9.30-5.30, Sat. 11-4. SIZE: Small. *STOCK: Lithographs and etchings, 1850-1990.* LOC: Off Piccadilly. TEL: 020 7493 0722; fax - 020 7491 9240; e-mail - www@williamweston.co.uk; website - www. williamweston.co.uk. FAIRS: Grosvenor House; 20th/21st C British Art; Royal Academy Print: New York. VAT: Spec.

Rollo Whately Ltd

1st Floor, 9 Old Bond St. W1X 3TA. Est. 1995. Open 9-6. CL: Sat. SIZE: Small. *STOCK: Picture frames, 16th-19th C, £500-£2,000.* LOC: Piccadilly end of Old Bond St. TEL: 020 7629 7861; e-mail - frames@rollowhately.demon. co.uk. SER: Valuations; restorations (frames); search; buys at auction. VAT: Stan.

Wilkins and Wilkins

1 Barrett St., St Christophers Pl. W1M 6DN. (M. Wilkins). Est. 1981. Open 10-5. CL: Sat. SIZE: Small. *STOCK: English 17th-18th C portraits and decorative paintings, £700-£20,000.* LOC: Near Selfridges. TEL: 020 7935 9613; fax - 020 7935 4696; e-mail - info@wilkinsandwilkins. com. VAT: Stan/Spec.

Wilkinson plc

1 Grafton St. W1X 3LB. Est. 1947. Open 9.30-5. CL: Sat. *STOCK: Glass, especially chandeliers, 18th C and reproduction; art metal work.* LOC: Nearest underground - Green Park. TEL: 020 7495 2477; fax - 020 7491 1737; e-mail -enquiries@ wilkinson-plc.com; website - www. wilkinson-plc.com. SER: Restorations and repairs (glass and metalwork).

Williams and Son

2 Grafton St. W1X 3LB. (J.R. Williams). Est. 1931. Open 9.30-6. CL: Sat. SIZE: Large. *STOCK: British and European paintings, 19th C.* LOC: Between Bond St. and Berkeley Sq. TEL: 020 7493 4985/5751; fax - 020 7409 7363; e-mail - art@williamsandson.com; website - www. williamsandson.com. VAT: Stan/Spec.

Thomas Williams (Fine Art) Ltd

22 Old Bond St. W1S 4PY. Open 9-6. CL: Sat. *STOCK: Old Master drawings, £300-£1,000,000.* TEL: 020 7491 1485; fax - 020 7408 0197. SER: Valuations; buys at auction (paintings and drawings).

Windsor House Antiques Ltd

28-29 Dover St., Mayfair. W1S 4NA. (D.K. Smith). LAPADA. Est. 1959. Open 10-6, Sat. 10-1. SIZE: Large. *STOCK: English furniture, 18th-19th C; paintings and objects.* TEL: 020 7659 0340; fax - 020 7499 6728; e-mail - sales@ windsorhouseantiques.co.uk; website - www. windsorhouseantiques.co.uk. SER: Shipping arranged. VAT: Stan/Spec.

Linda Wrigglesworth Ltd

34 Brook St. W1K 5DN. LAPADA. Est. 1978. Open 10-6. CL: Sat. *STOCK: Chinese, Korean and Tibetan costume and textiles, 14th-19th C.* LOC: Corner of South Molton Lane. PARK: Grosvenor Square. TEL: 020 7408 0177. SER: Valuations; restorations; mounting, framing; buys on commission (Oriental). FAIRS: Maastricht; Asian Art, London and New York; San Francisco.

A. Zadah

130 Mount St. W1K 3UY. LAPADA. Est. 1976. Open 9.30-6. *STOCK: Oriental and European carpets, rugs, tapestries and textiles.* TEL: 020 7493 2622/2673.

W2

Sean Arnold Sporting Antiques

21-22 Chepstow Corner, off Westbourne Grove. W2 4XE. Open 10-6. *STOCK: Sporting antiques and decorative items; golf clubs, 1840-1915, £30-£6,000; tennis racquets, £10-£3,000; football memorablia, globes and pond yachts; vintage luggage.* LOC: Notting Hill Gate. TEL: 020 7221 2267; fax - 020 7221 5464.

David Black Oriental Carpets
27 Chepstow Corner, Chepstow Place. W2 4XE. Est. 1966. Open 11-6. SIZE: Large. *STOCK: Antique and new Oriental room size decorative carpets; tribal rugs, kilims, dhurries, embroideries, £500-£25,000.* TEL: 020 7727 2566; fax - 020 7229 4599. SER: Valuations; restorations; cleaning underfelt. VAT: Spec.

Connaught Galleries
44 Connaught St. W2 2AA. (M. Hollamby). Est. 1966. Open 10-6, Sat. 10-1. SIZE: Medium. *STOCK: Antique and reproduction sporting, historical, geographical and decorative prints.* LOC: Near Marble Arch. PARK: Meters. TEL: 020 7723 1660. SER: Picture framing. VAT: Spec.

Craven Gallery
30 Craven Terrace. W2. (A. Quaradeghini). Est. 1974. Open 11-6, Sat. 3-7, other times by appointment. SIZE: Large and warehouse. *STOCK: Silver and plate, 19th-20th C; furniture, china and glass, Victorian.* LOC: Off Bayswater Rd. PARK: Easy. TEL: 020 7402 2802; home - 020 8998 0769. VAT: Stan. *Trade Only.*

Manya Igel Fine Arts Ltd
21/22 Peters Court, Porchester Rd. W2 5DR. (M. Igel and B.S. Prydal). LAPADA. Est. 1977. Open 10-5 by appointment only. SIZE: Large. *STOCK: Mainly modern and contemporary British works, £250-£25,000.* LOC: Off Queensway. PARK: Nearby. TEL: 020 7229 1669/8429; fax - 020 7229 6770. FAIRS: 20th/21st. British Art; Olympia (Spring); Chelsea (Spring); Claridges; VAT: Spec.

Ian Lieber
The Shop, 29 Craven Terrace, Lancaster Gate. W2 3EL. Est. 1965. Open by appointment. SIZE: Medium. *STOCK: Furniture, early 19th C and decorative; porcelain, objets d'art, paintings, costume jewellery.* LOC: Near Bayswater Rd. TEL: 020 7262 5505; fax - 020 7402 4445. SER: Buys at auction. FAIRS: Olympia. VAT: Stan/Spec.

The Mark Gallery   BADA
9 Porchester Place, Marble Arch. W2 2BS. (H. Mark). CINOA. Est. 1969. Open 10-1 and 2-6, Sat. 11-1. SIZE: Medium. *STOCK: Russian icons, 16th-19th C; modern graphics - French school.* **LOC: Near Marble Arch. TEL: 020 7262 4906; fax - 020 7224 9416. SER: Valuations; restorations; buys at auction. VAT: Stan/Spec.**

M. McAleer
(M.J. McAleer). Est. 1969. By appointment. *STOCK: Scottish provincial, Irish and small collectable silver.* TEL: 020 7727 7979. SER: Buys at auction (silver).

W3

Remember When
310 Uxbridge Rd., Acton. W3 9QP. Est. 1973. Open 9.30-7 including Sun. *STOCK: Pine furniture.* TEL: 020 8896 2357.

W4

The Chiswick Fireplace Co.
68 Southfield Rd., Chiswick. W4 1BD. (Mrs O'Grady). Open 9.30-5. SIZE: Medium. *STOCK: Original cast iron fireplaces, late Victorian to early 1900's, £200-£1,000; marble, wood and limestone surrounds.* LOC: 8 minutes walk from Turnham Green underground. PARK: Easy. TEL: 020 8995 4011. SER: Restorations. VAT: Stan.

David Edmonds
1-4 Prince of Wales Terrace, Chiswick. W4 2EY. Est. 1985. Open 10.30-6, Sun. 12-4. SIZE: Large. *STOCK: Fine antiques from India and sub-continent, £10-£10,000.* LOC: Off Chiswick High St. PARK: Easy. TEL: 020 8742 1920; fax - 020 8742 3030; mobile - 07831 666436; e-mail - daveindia@aol.com. SER: Valuations; restorations; buys at auction (as stock). VAT: Stan.

J. D. Marshall
38 Chiswick Lane, Chiswick. W4 2JQ. Est. 1985. Open 10-6, Sat. 10-5. SIZE: Medium. *STOCK: Decorative and unusual objects, furniture, bronzes and chandeliers, £100-£50,000; garden statuary and furniture, to £30,000.* LOC: Off A4/M4 at the Hogarth roundabout or Chiswick High Rd. PARK: Easy. TEL: 020 8742 8089; fax - same. SER: Valuations; restorations (oil and water gilding; metal patination and non-ferrous casting). VAT: Spec.

The Old Cinema Antique Department Store
160 Chiswick High Rd. W4 1PR. Est. 1977. Open 10-6, Sun. 12-5. SIZE: Large. *STOCK: General antiques including furniture, gardenalia, decorative and architectural items, 1660-1960, £100-£6,000.* PARK: Easy. TEL: 020 8995 4166; fax - 020 8995 4167; e-mail - theoldcinema @antiques-uk.co.uk; website - www.antiques-uk.co.uk. SER: Restorations; deliveries. VAT: Stan/Spec.

Oriental Furniture and Arts

11a Devonshire Rd., Chiswick. W4 2EU. (Steven Glynn-Williams). Est. 1993. Open 10-5. SIZE: Medium. *STOCK: Oriental furniture, 18th-19th C, to £3,500; Oriental decorative objects, 19th C and modern, £40-£350; tomb figures and neolithic potteries.* LOC: Off Chiswick High Rd. PARK: Easy. TEL: 020 8987 8571; fax - same.

Strand Antiques

46 Devonshire Rd., Chiswick. W4 2HD. Est. 1977. Open 10.30-5.30. SIZE: Medium. *STOCK: English and French Brocante, furniture, glass, lighting, jewellery and silver, garden and kitchenware, books and prints, textiles and collectables, £1-£500.* LOC: Off Chiswick High Rd. 5 mins Turnham Green Tube. PARK: Meters. TEL: 020 8994 1912.

W5

Aberdeen House Antiques

75 St. Mary's Rd. W5 5RH. (N. Schwartz). LAPADA, CINOA. Est. 1971. Open 10-5.30. SIZE: Medium. *STOCK: Furniture and pictures, £150-£4,000; decorative items and textiles, £25-£2,000; china, glass and silver, £25-£1,000; all 18th-20th C.* LOC: On B455 1 mile north of A4. PARK: Easy and at rear. TEL: 020 8567 5194/1223. SER: Valuations. FAIRS: Olympia. VAT: Stan.

Ealing Gallery

78 St. Mary's Rd., Ealing. W5 5EX. (Mrs N. Lane). Est. 1984. Open 10.30-6. CL: Mon. and Wed. *STOCK: Oil paintings, £250-£10,000; watercolours, £100-£5,000; both 18th-20th C; contemporary paintings, £150-£4,000.* LOC: Piccadilly Line underground, South Ealing. PARK: Nearby. TEL: 020 8840 7883; fax - same; e-mail - info@ealinggallery.com; website - www.ealinggallery.com. SER: Valuations; restorations (oils and watercolours); framing. VAT: Spec.

Terrace Antiques

10-12 South Ealing Rd. W5 4QA. (N. Schwartz). Est. 1971. Open 10-5.30. SIZE: Medium. *STOCK: Georgian, Victorian and Edwardian furniture, 1780-1920, £50-£1,000; china, glass and pictures, silver and plate, 1850-1950, £10-£600.* LOC: 1 mile north of A4 on B455. PARK: Easy and opposite. TEL: 020 8567 5194/1223. SER: Valuations. FAIRS: Olympia. VAT: Stan.

W6

Architectural Antiques

351 King St. W6 9NH. (G.P.A. Duc). Est. 1985. Open 9-5. SIZE: Medium. *STOCK: Marble/stone chimney pieces, 18th-19th C, £500-£8,000; gilt/painted overmantles, 19th C, £300-£1,500; antique French doors, £200-£1,000; bathroom fixtures, basins, £200-£800.* PARK: Easy and Black Lion Lane. TEL: 020 8741 7883; fax - 020 8741 1109; mobile - 07831 127541; website - www.AA-fireplaces.co.uk. SER: Valuations. VAT: Stan. *Trade Only.*

Paravent

Flat 10, Ranelagh Gardens, Stamford Brook Ave. W6 0YE. (M. Aldbrook). Est. 1989. Open by appointment only. *STOCK: Screens, 17th-20th C, £500-£10,000.* TEL: 020 8748 6323; fax - 020 8563 2912; e-mail - aldbrook@paravent.free serve.co.uk. SER: Restorations; finder (screens). VAT: Stan/Spec.

Zoom

Arch 65 Cambridge Grove, Hammersmith. W6 0LD. Est. 1973. Open 10-8, Sun. telephone call advisable. *STOCK: 50's, 60's, 70's furniture, lighting and unusual retro objects.* LOC: Off King Street. TEL: 07000 9666 2001; fax - same; mobile - 07958 372975; e-mail - eddiesandham@hot mail.com; website - www.retrozoom.com. SER: Rental for photo shoots, TV and film sets, styling.

W8

AntikWest AB

150-152 Kensington Church St. W8 4BN. (Bjorn Gremner and Jonathan Robinson). CINOA. Est. 1979. Open 10-6, Sat. 10-4. SIZE: Small. *STOCK: Chinese pottery and porcelain, Tang to late 19th C, £200-£35,000; Chinese furniture, £200-£2,000.* LOC: 100 yards south of Notting Hill Gate. PARK: Meters. TEL: 020 7229 4115; website - www.antikwest.com. FAIRS: Olympia (June); Eurantica, Brussels; Stockholm, Alvsjo; Helsingborg, Sweden; Hong Kong International. VAT: Spec.

Valerie Arieta

97b Kensington Church St. W8 7LN. Open 10.30-5 appointment advisable. *STOCK: American Indian and Eskimo art; English and Continental antiques.* TEL: 020 7243 1074/7794 7613.

Garry Atkins

107 Kensington Church St. W8 7LN. (Garry and Julie Atkins). Est. 1986. Open 10-5.30, Sat. am. by appointment. SIZE: Small. *STOCK: English and Continental pottery, to 18th C, £100-£10,000.* LOC: Between Kensington High St. and Notting Hill Gate. PARK: Meters. TEL: 020 7727 8737; fax - 020 7792 9010. SER: Valuations; buys at auction (English and Continental pottery); annual exhibition (March), catalogues available. FAIRS: New York Ceramic. VAT: Spec.

Gregg Baker Asian Art BADA
132 Kensington Church St. W8 4BH.
LAPADA. Est. 1985. Open 10-6, weekends by
appointment. SIZE: Small. *STOCK: Japanese
and Chinese works of art and screens, mainly
18th-19th C, £500-£100,000.* PARK: Meters.
TEL: 020 7221 3533; fax - 020 7221 4410; e-
mail - gbakerart@aol.com; website - www.
greggbaker.com. SER: Valuations. FAIRS:
Olympia (June), NY International Asian Art
(March). VAT: Stan/Spec.

Eddy Bardawil BADA
106 Kensington Church St. W8 4BH. (E.S.
Bardawil). Est. 1979. Open 10-1 and 2-5.30, Sat.
10-1.30. SIZE: Medium. *STOCK: English furniture - mahogany, satinwood, walnut; mirrors,
brassware, tea-caddies, all pre-1830, £500-
£50,000; prints, 18th C.* LOC: Corner premises,
Berkeley Gardens/Church St. PARK: Easy.
TEL: 020 7221 3967; fax - 020 7221 5124. SER:
Valuations; restorations (furniture); polishing.
VAT: Stan/Spec.

Baumkotter Gallery
63a Kensington Church St. W8 4BA. (Mrs L.
Baumkotter). LAPADA. Est. 1968. Open 10-
5.30, Sat. by appointment. SIZE: Large. *STOCK:
17th-19th C oil paintings.* TEL: 020 7937 5171;
fax - 020 7938 2312. VAT: Spec.

Berwald Oriental Art BADA
101 Kensington Church St. W8 7LN. (John R.
Berwald). Est. 1986. Open Mon.-Fri.10-6, other
times by appointment. SIZE: Medium. *STOCK:
Chinese porcelain, 16th to early 18th C; Chinese
pottery, 200BC to 15th C; Oriental works of art;
all £1,000-£100,000.* PARK: Meters and nearby.
TEL: 020 7229 0800; fax - 020 7229 1101;
website - www.berwald-oriental.com; e-mail -
berwald@aapi.co.uk. SER: Valuations; restorations; buys at auction (Oriental). FAIRS:
International Asian Arts, New York; International Ceramics, London. VAT: Spec.

David Brower Antiques
113 Kensington Church St. W8 7LN. Est. 1970.
Open 10-6. CL: Sat. SIZE: Large. *STOCK:
Specialist in Meissen, KPM, European and
Oriental porcelain, French bronzes and Japanese
works of art.* PARK: Meters nearby. TEL: 020
7221 4155; fax - 020 7221 6211; e-mail -
David@davidbrower-antiques.com; website -
www.davidbrower-antiques.com. SER: Buys at
auction. VAT: Stan/Spec.

The Lucy B. Campbell Gallery BADA
123 Kensington Church St. W8 7LP. Est. 1983.
Open 10-6, Sat. 10-4. SIZE: Medium. *STOCK:*

*Antiquarian prints and drawings, contemporary,
naive and botanical paintings.* Not Stocked:
Maps and sporting prints. PARK: Meters.
TEL: 020 7727 2205; fax - 020 7229 4252; e-mail
- lucy@lucybcampbell.co.uk; website - www.
lucybcampbell.com. SER: Framing. VAT: Stan.

Cohen & Cohen BADA
101B Kensington Church St. W8 7LN. Open
10-6, Sat. 11-4. *STOCK: Chinese export
porcelain and works of art.* TEL: 020 7727
7677; fax - 020 7229 9653; e-mail - cohenand
cohen@aol.com. SER: Valuations; buys at
auction. VAT: Stan/Spec.

Garrick D. Coleman
5 Kensington Court. W8 5DL. (G.D. and G.E.
Coleman). Est. 1944. Open strictly by appointment only. SIZE: Medium. *STOCK: Chess sets,
1750-1880, £100-£4,000; decorative items, £50-
£2,000; glass paperweights, £200-£3,000;
conjuring and magic items.* PARK: Easy. TEL: 020
7937 5524; fax - 020 7937 5530; e-mail - coleman-
antiques-london@compuserve.com; website -
www.antiquechess.co.uk/. VAT: Stan/Spec.

Mrs. M.E. Crick Chandeliers
166 Kensington Church St. W8 4BN. (M.T.
Denton). Est. 1897. Open Mon.-Fri. 9.30-5.30.
*STOCK: English and Continental crystal, glass
and ormulu chandeliers, 18th-19th C.* TEL: 020
7229 1338; fax - 020 7792 1073.

Davies Antiques
40 Kensington Church St. W8 4BX. (H.Q.
Davies). LAPADA. Est. 1976. Open 10-5.30, Sat.
10-3. *STOCK: Continental porcelain especially
Meissen, 1710-1930.* TEL: 020 7937 9216; fax -
020 7938 2032.

Denton Antiques
156 Kensington Church St. W8 4BN. (M.T.
Denton). Open Mon.- Fri. 9.30-5.30. *STOCK:
Glass, chandeliers, candelabra, 18th-19th C.*
TEL: 020 7229 5866; fax - 020 7792 1073.

H. and W. Deutsch Antiques
111 Kensington Church St. W8 7LN. LAPADA.
Est. 1897. Open 10-5. CL: Tues., Wed. and Sat.
SIZE: Large. *STOCK: 18th-19th C Continental
and English porcelain and glassware; silver,
plate and enamel ware, miniature portraits;
Oriental porcelain, cloisonné, bronzes, £300-
£5,000.* TEL: 020 7727 5984. VAT: Stan/Spec.

Peter Farlow
34 Kensington Church St. W8 4HA. Est. 1986.
Open 9.30-5, Sat. 11-4. SIZE: Small. *STOCK:
Decorative arts, Gothic Revival furniture, Arts*

and Crafts. PARK: NCP Kensington High St. TEL: 020 7937 3388; fax - 020 7937 5588. VAT: Stan/Spec.

C. Fredericks and Son   BADA
142 Kensington Church St. W8 4BN. (R.F. Fredericks). Est. 1974. Open 9.30-5.30, Sat. by appointment. SIZE: Large. *STOCK: Furniture, 18th C, £500-£15,000.* **LOC: Near Notting Hill Gate underground station. TEL: 020 7727 2240; fax - same; mobile - 07831 336937; e-mail - antiques@cfredericksandson.freeserve.co.uk. SER: Restorations. FAIRS: BADA; Olympia (Winter). VAT: Stan/Spec.**

Michael German Antiques Ltd BADA
38B Kensington Church St. W8 4BX. LAPADA. Est. 1954. Open 10-5, Sat. 10-12.30. *STOCK: European and Oriental arms and armour; walking stick specialist.* **TEL: 020 7937 2771; fax - 020 7937 8566; websites - www. antiquecanes. com and www.antiqueweapons. com.**

Green's Antique Galleries
117 Kensington Church St. W8 7LN. (S. Green). Open 9-5. SIZE: Medium. *STOCK: Jewellery, 18th C to date; pre-1930 clothes and lace; dolls, china, silver, furniture, paintings, masonic, crocodile and leather items.* PARK: Easy. TEL: 020 7229 9618. VAT: Stan/Spec.

Robert Hales Antiques
131 Kensington Church St. W8 7LP. Est. 1967. Open 9.30-5.30. CL: Mon. and Sat. SIZE: Small. *STOCK: Islamic, Oriental and ethnographic arms and armour; oceanic art, 16th-19th C.* PARK: Easy. TEL: 020 7229 3887; e-mail - RHAntique @aol.com. SER: Valuations; buys at auction. FAIRS: Park Lane Arms (Feb). VAT: Spec.

Adrian Harrington
64A Kensington Church St. W8 4DB. ABA, ILAB, PBFA. Est. 1970. Open 10-6. SIZE: Large. *STOCK: Fine and rare antiquarian books, first editions, literature, children's, fore-edge paintings, library sets.* LOC: Half-way up Kensington Church St. PARK: Meters. TEL: 020 7937 1465; fax - 020 7368 0912; e-mail - rare@harringtonbooks.co.uk; websites - www.harringtonbooks.co.uk; www.harrypotter.uk.net; www.modernfirsts.eu.com. SER: Valuations; restorations (bookbinding, prints); framing; buys at auction (antiquarian books). FAIRS: Olympia Book (June); Chelsea Book (Nov). VAT: Stan.

Haslam and Whiteway
105 Kensington Church St. W8 7LN. (T.M. Whiteway). Est. 1972. Open 10-6, Sat. 10-2. SIZE: Small. *STOCK: British furniture, £300-£50,000; British decorative arts, £200-£50,000;*

Continental and American decorative arts, £200-£10,000; all 1850-1930. Not Stocked: Pre-Victorian items. LOC: From Notting Hill Gate tube station, down Kensington Church St. Shop is approx. 300yds. down on right. PARK: Meters. TEL: 020 7229 1145; fax - 020 7221 7065. SER: Valuations; buys at auction. VAT: Stan.

Jeanette Hayhurst Fine Glass   BADA
32A Kensington Church St. W8. Open 10-5, Sat. 12-5. *STOCK: Glass - 18th C English drinking, fine 19th C engraved, table decanters, contemporary art, scent bottles, Roman and Continental.* **TEL: 020 7938 1539.**

D. Holmes
47c Earls Court Rd. (in Abingdon Villas), Kensington. W8 6EE. (Don and Sarah Holmes). Est. 1965. Open Fri. 9-7, Sat. 9-2 or by appointment. *STOCK: Decorative items and furniture, 18th-19th C.* PARK: Meters. TEL: 020 7937 6961 or 01208 880254; mobile - 07790 431895. SER: Restorations (furniture). FAIRS: Olympia (June). VAT: Stan/Spec.

Hope and Glory
(Commemorative Ceramics Specialists) 131a Kensington Church St. W8 7LP. (R.R. Lower). KCSADA. Est. 1982. Open 10-5. *STOCK: Commemorative china.* LOC: Entrance in Peel St. TEL: 020 7727 8424. SER: Mail order (no catalogue).

Jonathan Horne   BADA
66b & 66c Kensington Church St. W8 4BY. Est. 1968. Open 9.30-5.30. CL: Sat. and Sun. except by appointment. SIZE: Medium. *STOCK: Early English pottery, needlework and works of art.* **TEL: 020 7221 5658; fax - 020 7792 3090; e-mail - JH@jonathanhorne.co.uk; website - www.jonathanhorne.co.uk. VAT: Stan/Spec.**

Valerie Howard
4 Campden St., Off Kensington Church St. W8 7EP. LAPADA. Open 10-5.30, Sat. 10-4.30. *STOCK: Mason's and English Ironstone china, 1810-1860, £50-£10,000; French faience especially from Quimper and Rouen regions, 1750-1920, £20-£3,000; mirrors, 19th C, £500-£2,000.* TEL: 020 7792 9702 (ansaphone at night); fax - 020 7221 7008; e-mail - valeriehoward@ quimperpottery.co.uk.; web-sites - www.masons ironstonechina.co.uk. and www.quimperpottery. co.uk. SER: Valuations; buys at auction (as stock). FAIRS: International Ceramics, Park Lane Hotel (June). VAT: Spec.

Iona Antiques   BADA
PO Box 285. W8 6HZ. Est. 1974. Open by appointment only. SIZE: Large. *STOCK: 19th C*

animal paintings, £1,000-£30,000. LOC: 3 minutes walk from Odeon Cinema, Kensington High St. PARK: Nearby. TEL: 020 7602 1193; fax - 020 7371 2843. FAIRS: Grosvenor House, Olympia.

J.A.N. Fine Art

134 Kensington Church St. W8. (Mrs F.K. Shimizu). Est. 1976. Open 10-6, Sat. by appointment. SIZE: Medium. *STOCK: Japanese and Chinese porcelain, 1st to 20th C, from £150; Japanese bronzes and works of art, 15th-20th C, from £150; Japanese paintings and screens, 16th-20th C, from £250; Tibetan thankas and ritual objects, 12th-18th C, from £250.* PARK: Meters. TEL: 020 7792 0736; fax - 020 7221 1380. VAT: Spec.

Japanese Gallery

66d Kensington Church St. W8 4BY. (Mr and Mrs C.D. Wertheim). Est. 1977. Open 10-6. *STOCK: Japanese wood-cut prints; books, porcelain, netsuke.* TEL: 020 7229 2934; fax - same; e-mail - sales@japanesegallery.co.uk; website - www. japanesegallery.co.uk. SER: Free authentification; on-the-spot framing for Japanese prints; sales exhibitions.

Roderick Jellicoe   BADA

3A Campden St., off Kensington Church St. W8 4EP. Est. 1974. Open 10-5.30, Sat. by appointment. SIZE: Medium. *STOCK: English porcelain, 18th-19th C, £50-£20,000.* PARK: Meters. TEL: 020 7727 1571; mobile - 07775 580051; e-mail - Jellicoe@EnglishPorcelain. com; website - www.EnglishPorcelain.com. SER: Valuations; buys at auction (18th C English porcelain). VAT: Spec.

John Jesse

160 Kensington Church St. W8 4BN. Open 10-6, Sat. 11-4. *STOCK: Decorative arts, 1880-1980, especially Art Nouveau and Art Deco silver, glass, bronzes and jewellery.* TEL: 020 7229 0312; fax - 020 7229 4732; e-mail - jj@johnjesse. com; website - www.johnjesse.com.

Howard Jones - The Silver Shop

43 Kensington Church St. W8 4BA. (H. Howard-Jones). Est. 1971. Open 9.30-5.30. SIZE: Small. *STOCK: Silver, antique and modern, £10-£3,000.* Not Stocked: Furniture. PARK: Nearby. TEL: 020 7937 4359; fax - same. VAT: Stan.

Peter Kemp

170 Kensington Church St. W8 4BN. Est. 1975. Open 10-5. CL: Sat. SIZE: Medium. *STOCK:*

Porcelain - 10th-19th C Chinese, 17th-19th C Japanese, 18th C Continental; Oriental works of art and porcelain, 18th-19th C. LOC: 200yds. from Notting Hill tube station. PARK: Meters nearby. TEL: 020 7229 2988. SER: Valuations; restorations (porcelain). VAT: Spec.

Kensington Church Street Antiques Centre

58-60 Kensington Church St. W8 4DB. Open 10-6. Below are listed some of the dealers at this Centre. TEL: 020 7376 0425; fax - 020 7937 3400.

Abstract
LAPADA. *20th C decorative and design.* TEL: 020 7376 2652; fax - same; website - www.abstract-antiques.com.

Nigel Benson
20th C glass, British 1870-1980 including Powell, Monart/Vasart; post-war Scandanavian and Italian. TEL: 020 7938 1137; home - 020 7729 9875; fax - same.

Nicolaus Boston
Majolica, Palissy, Dresser and Aesthetic movement porcelain. TEL: 020 7937 2237; fax - 020 8944 1280. VAT: Stan/Spec.

Didier Antiques
LAPADA. Open by appointment only. *Jewellery and silver, objets d'art, 1860-1960.* TEL: 020 7938 5237; fax - same. VAT: Stan/Spec.

F C R Gallery
20th C fine art and design. TEL: 020 7938 5385.

Freeforms
Mid century decorative arts. TEL: 020 7937 9447.

Graven Image
Victorian engravings and limited edition prints. TEL: 020 7376 0425.

Jag
20th C decorative arts, Liberty pewter and silver, terracotta and watercolours by Archibald Knox. TEL: 020 7938 4404; fax - same.

Colin Monk
Oriental porcelain. TEL: 020 7229 3727; fax - 020 7376 1501.

Robert Peterson Ltd.
19th-20th C decorative arts, all the major movements. TEL: 020 7937 8319; mobile - 07768 951617; e-mail - info@20th.co.uk; website - www.20th.co.uk.

Zeitgeist
Continental Art Nouveau and Art Deco metalware, ceramics and glass. TEL: 020 7938 4817; fax - same; e-mail - zeitgeistantiques@ btopenworld.com; website - www.zeitgeistantiques.com. VAT: Stan/Spec.

The Lacquer Chest

71 and 75 Kensington Church St. W8 4BG. (G. and V. Andersen). Est. 1959. Open 9.30-5.30, Sat. 10.30-3. SIZE: Large. *STOCK: Furniture - painted, oak, mahogany; blue and white, Staffordshire, lamps, candlesticks, samplers, prints, paintings, brass, mirrors, garden furniture, unusual items.* LOC: Half-way up left-hand side from High St. PARK: Meters. TEL: 020 7937 1306; fax - 020 7376 0223. VAT: Stan/Spec.

Lev (Antiques) Ltd

97A & B Kensington Church St. W8 7LN. (Mrs Lev). Est. 1882. Open 10.30-5.30. SIZE: Medium. *STOCK: Jewellery, silver, plate, curios.* PARK: Meters. TEL: 020 7727 9248; fax - same. SER: Restorations (pictures).

Lewis and Lloyd   BADA

65 Kensington Church St. W8 4BA. Est. 1968. Open 10.15-5.00, Sat. 10-2.30. SIZE: Medium. *STOCK: Furniture and works of art, 18th-19th C, £2,000-£100,000.* PARK: Easy. TEL: 020 7938 3323; fax - 020 7361 0086; e-mail - pclewis2000@aol.com. FAIRS: Olympia (Feb., June, Nov). VAT: Spec.

Libra Antiques

131d Kensington Church St. W8. *STOCK: Blue and white pottery, lustre ware.* TEL: 020 7727 2990.

London Antique Gallery

66E Kensington Church St. W8 4BY. (Mr and Mrs C.D. Wertheim). Open 10-6. *STOCK: Porcelain including English, Meissen, Dresden and Sèvres; French and German bisque dolls.* TEL: 020 7229 2934; fax - same. SER: Restorations (prints, porcelain and dolls).

C.H. Major (Antiques) Ltd

154 Kensington Church St. W8 4BN. (Sally Major and Christopher Cowen). Est. 1905. Open 10-5.30, Sat. 10-2. SIZE: Large. *STOCK: English furniture, from 1760, £200-£25,000.* PARK: Easy. TEL: 020 7229 1162; fax - 020 7221 9676; e-mail - majorantiques@ukonline.co.uk. VAT: Stan/Spec.

E. and H. Manners   BADA

66a Kensington Church St. W8 4BY. Est. 1986. Open Mon.-Fri. 10-5.30 appointment advisable. *STOCK: European ceramics, pre-19th C, £100-£20,000.* TEL: 020 7229 5516; fax - same; home - 020 8741 7084; e-mail - manners@european porcelain.com; website - www.europeanporcelain.com. FAIRS: International Ceramic. VAT: Spec.

S. Marchant & Son   BADA

120 Kensington Church St. W8 4BH. (R.P. and S.J. Marchant). Est. 1925. Open 9.30-5.30. CL:

Sat. *STOCK: Chinese and Japanese pottery and porcelain, jades, cloisonné, Chinese furniture and paintings.* PARK: Easy. TEL: 020 7229 5319/ 3770; fax - 020 7792 8979; e-mail - marchant@ dircon.co.uk; website - www.marchantasian art.com. SER: Valuations; restorations (porcelain); buys at auction. FAIRS: Grosvenor House; Asian Art New York and Paris. VAT: Stan/Spec.

R. and G. McPherson Antiques BADA

at Stockspring Antiques, 114 Kensington Church St. W8 4BH. Est. 1985. Open 10-5.30, Sat. 10-1. SIZE: Large. *STOCK: Chinese ceramics, 2500 BC to 1800, £5-£10,000; early wares, 16th-18th C export, Hatcher cargo, Vung Tau, Nanking, Hoi An porcelain.* LOC: Notting Hill Tube Station. PARK: Meters. TEL: 020 7727 7995; e-mail - rmcpherson@oriental ceramics.com; website - www. orientalceramics. com. SER: Valuations (verbal); identification. FAIRS: Olympia (June). VAT: Spec.

Michael Coins

6 Hillgate St., (off Notting Hill Gate). W8 7SR. (M. Gouby). Est. 1966. Open 10-5. CL: Mon. and Sat. SIZE: Small. *STOCK: Coins, English and foreign, 1066 A.D. to date; stamps, banknotes and collectors' items.* LOC: From Marble Arch to Notting Hill Gate, turn left at corner of Coronet Cinema. PARK: Easy. TEL: 020 7727 1518; fax - 020 7727 1518; website - www.michael-coins. co.uk. SER: Valuations; buys at auction. VAT: Stan/Spec.

Arthur Millner

2 Campden St. W8 7EP. Est. 1996. Open Tues.-Fri. 12-6, Sat. 10-3. SIZE: Small. *STOCK: Indian objects, 16th-19th C, £800-£4,000; Indian paintings, 18th-19th C, £200-£1,500; Islamic art, 16th-18th C, £1,000-£5,000.* LOC: Off Kensington Church St. PARK: Meter. TEL: 020 7229 3268; fax - same; e-mail - info@arthurmillner.com; website - www.arthurmillner. com. SER: Valuations; buys at auction (Indian and Islamic art). FAIRS: Olympia; Arts of Pacific Asia, New York, San Francisco. VAT: Spec.

New Century

69 Kensington Church St. W8 4BG. (H.S. Lyons). Est. 1988. *STOCK: Arts and Crafts, aesthetic and Art Nouveau furniture, metal, glass and ceramics, 1860-1910, £20-£10,000.* TEL: 020 7937 2410. SER: Valuations; restorations; buys at auction. VAT: Stan/Spec.

Pawsey and Payne   BADA

PO Box 11830 W8. (Hon. N.V.B. and L.N.J. Wallop). Est. 1910. Open by appointment.

Wearing the uniform of a Guards Officer, King George VI was represented by this doll made by Farnell, c.1938. (Jane Vandell Associates)

From an article entitled "Military Dolls" by Constance King which appeared in the October 2001 issue of **Antique Collecting**. For more details and to subscribe see page 21.

Raffety & Walwyn

79 Kensington Church Street,
London W8 4BG

Tel: 020 7938 1100

THOMAS HARRIS LONDINI FECIT
*A Charles II period walnut and floral marquetry
longcase clock. The 8-day movement with "Royal"
seconds and a quarter pendulum, the base panel hinged
to facilitate regulation. Circa 1695. Height: 80in.*

STOCK: English oils and watercolours, 18th-19th C. TEL: 020 7930 4221; fax - 020 7937 3440; e-mail - nicholas@wallop3.freeserve.co.uk. SER: Valuations; restorations. VAT: Stan/Spec.

Pruskin Gallery

73 Kensington Church St. W8 4BG. *STOCK: Fine Art Nouveau and Art Deco glass, bronzes, silver, furniture, ceramics, paintings, posters and prints.* TEL: 020 7937 1994; evenings - 020 7938 2892.

Raffety & Walwyn   BADA

79 Kensington Church St. W8 4BG. LAPADA, CINOA. Open 10.00-5.30, Sat. 11-2.30. *STOCK: Fine English longcase and bracket clocks, 17th-18th C; barometers and period furniture.* TEL: 020 7938 1100; fax - 020 7938 2519; e-mail - raffety@globalnet.co.uk; website - www.raffetyantiqueclocks.com. SER: Valuations; buys at auction. FAIRS: BADA, Olympia (June). VAT: Stan/Spec.

Paul Reeves

32B Kensington Church St. W8 4HA. Est. 1976. Open 10-6, Sat. 11-4. *STOCK: Architect designed furniture and artifacts, 1860-1960.* TEL: 020 7937 1594.

Reindeer Antiques Ltd   BADA

81 Kensington Church St. W8 4BG. (Adrian Butterworth and Peter Alexander). LAPADA. Open 9.30-6, Sat. 10.30-5.30. *STOCK: Period English and Continental furniture and works of art.* PARK: Meters. TEL: 020 7937 3754; fax - 020 7937 7199. VAT: Stan/Spec.

Roderick Antique Clocks

23 Vicarage Gate, Kensington. W8 4AA. (R. Mee). LAPADA. Est. 1975. Open 10-5.15, Sat. 10-3. *STOCK: Clocks - French decorative and carriage, 19th C, £250-£3,500; English longcase and bracket, 18th-19th C, £2,000-£12,000.* LOC: At junction of Kensington Church St. PARK: Easy. TEL: 020 7937 8517; e-mail - rick@roderickantiqueclocks.com; website - www.roderickantiqueclocks.com. SER: Valuations; restorations (English and French movements and cases). VAT: Spec.

Brian Rolleston Antiques Ltd   BADA

104A Kensington Church St. W8 4BU. Est. 1950. Open 10-1 and 2-5.30. SIZE: Large. *STOCK: English furniture, 18th C.* TEL: 020 7229 5892; fax - same.

Dyala Salam Antiques

174A Kensington Church St. W8 4DP. Est. 1990. Open 11-5.30, Sat. 11.30-3.30. SIZE: Small.

STOCK: Textiles, glass and furniture from the Ottoman Empire, 18th-19th C, from £200. PARK: Nearby. TEL: 020 7229 4045; fax - 020 7229 2433. VAT: Spec.

Patrick Sandberg Antiques   BADA
150-152 Kensington Church St. W8 4BN. (P.C.F.Sandberg). Est. 1983. Open 10-6, Sat. 10-4. SIZE: Large. *STOCK: 18th to early 19th C English furniture and accessories - candlesticks, tea caddies, clocks and prints.* **TEL: 020 7229 0373; fax - 020 7792 3467. FAIRS: Olympia (Feb., June, Nov). VAT: Spec.**

Santos   BADA
21 Old Court House. W8 4PD. CINOA. Open by appointment only. *STOCK: Chinese export porcelain, 17th-18th C.* **TEL: 020 7937 6000; fax - 020 7937 3351; e-mail - companhiaindias @aol.com; website - www.santoslondon.com. VAT: Spec.**

Sinai Antiques Ltd
219-221 Kensington Church St. W8 7LX. (E. Sinai and Sons). KCSADA. Est. 1973. Open 10-6, Sat. and Sun. by appointment. *STOCK: Fine 19th C Continental furniture, clocks, porcelain, chandeliers and objet d'art; Oriental and Islamic decorative arts and antiques.* TEL: 020 7229 6190; fax - 020 7221 0543.

Simon Spero
109 Kensington Church St. W8 7LN. Author of 'The Price Guide to 18th C English Porcelain' and three other standard reference books. Est. 1964. Open 10-5, Sat. by appointment. SIZE: Medium. *STOCK: 18th C English ceramics and enamels.* PARK: Meters. TEL: 020 7727 7413; fax - 020 7727 7414. SER: Valuations; buys at auction; lecturer. VAT: Spec.

Stockspring Antiques   BADA
114 Kensington Church St. W8 4BH. (A. Agnew and F. Marno). LAPADA. Open 10-5.30, Sat. 10-1. *STOCK: English, European and Oriental pottery and porcelain.* **TEL: 020 7727 7995; fax - same; e-mail - stockspring@antiqueporcelain. co.uk. FAIRS: Olympia (June, Nov). VAT: Spec.**

Pamela Teignmouth and Son
108 Kensington Church St. W8 4BH. (Lady Teignmouth and Mr T. Meyer). Est. 1982. Open 10-6, including Sat. in winter only. SIZE: Medium. *STOCK: English and Continental furniture, 18th-19th C, decorative items, £100-£10,000.* TEL: 020 7229 1602; fax - 020 7792 5042. FAIRS: Olympia (June). VAT: Spec.

Through the Looking Glass Ltd
137 Kensington Church St. W8 7LP. (J.J.A. and D.A. Pulton). Est. 1958. Open 10-5.30. SIZE: Large. *STOCK: Mirrors, 19th C, £500-£10,000.* LOC: 200yds. from Notting Hill Gate. PARK: Side roads. TEL: 020 7221 4026. VAT: Spec.

Jorge Welsh Oriental Porcelain & Works of Art   BADA
116 Kensington Church St. W8 4BH. Est. 1987. Open 10-5.30, Sat. 10-2. SIZE: Medium. *STOCK: Chinese export porcelain and Oriental works of art.* **LOC: Off Kensington High St. PARK: NCP Bayswater Rd. TEL: 020 7229 2140; fax - 020 7792 3535; e-mail - uk@jorge welsh.com; website - www. jorgewelsh.com. SER: Valuations; restorations; buys at auction. FAIRS: International Ceramic. VAT: Spec.**

Neil Wibroe and Natasha MacIlwaine
77 Kensington Church St. W8 4BG. Est. 1984. Open 9-6. *STOCK: 18th C English furniture and works of art.* TEL: 020 7937 2461; fax - 020 7938 3286. VAT: Spec.

Mary Wise & Grosvenor Antiques   BADA
27 Holland St., Kensington. W8 4NA. Est. 1959. *STOCK: English porcelain, works of art, bronzes.* **Not Stocked: English pottery, jewellery. TEL: 020 7937 8649; fax - 020 7937 7179; e-mail - info@wiseantiques.com; website - www.wiseantiques.com. SER: Buys at auction (Chinese and English porcelain). FAIRS: BADA; Grosvenor House; Olympia (Nov); San Francisco. VAT: Spec.**

Yang Guifei
140 Kensington Church St. W8 4JD. (Anne Marie Ellis). KCSADA. Est. 1999. Open 10.30-6, Sat. 10.30-4. CL: Mon. SIZE: Small. *STOCK: Chinese Shanxi lacquer cabinets, 18th-19th C, £2,500-£20,000; Oriental furniture, 18th-19th C, £1,500-£5,000; Han Tang pottery, 206BC to 906AD, £1,500-£15,000.* PARK: Meters. TEL: 020 7792 1637; fax - 020 7792 0529; e-mail - annemarie@cix.co.uk. FAIRS: Asian Art: Daily Telegraph House & Garden. VAT: Margin.

W9

Fluss and Charlesworth Ltd
1 Lauderdale Rd. W9 1LT. (E. Fluss and J. Charlesworth). LAPADA. Est. 1970. Open by appointment. *STOCK: 18th to early 19th C furniture and works of art.* TEL: 020 7286 8339; mobile - 07831 830323. SER: Interior decor. FAIRS: Olympia; LAPADA.

Beryl Kendall, The English Watercolour Gallery

2 Warwick Place, Little Venice. W9 2PX. Est. 1953. Open 2-6, Sat. 11-3.30. CL: Mon. *STOCK: English watercolours, 19th C.* PARK: Easy. TEL: 020 7286 9902.

Vale Antiques

245 Elgin Ave., Maida Vale. W9 1NJ. (P. Gooley). *STOCK: General antiques.* TEL: 020 7328 4796.

W10

Crawley and Asquith Ltd   BADA
133 Oxford Gardens. W10 6NE. Open by appointment. *STOCK: 18th-19th C paintings, watercolours, prints, books.* TEL: 020 8969 6161; fax - 020 8960 6494.

W11

Admiral Vernon Antiques Market

141-149 Portobello Rd. W11 2DY. (Angelo Soteriades). PADA. Est. 1995. Open Sat. 5-5. SIZE: 200+ dealers. *STOCK: Wide range of general antiques and collectables.* TEL: 020 7727 5242; mobile - 07956 277077; e-mail - info@portobello-antiques.com; website - www.portobello-antiques.co.uk. SER: Valuations; repairs (pens, jewellery, watches, and lighter).

Alice's

86 Portobello Rd. W11 2QD. (D. Carter). Est. 1960. Open 9-5. SIZE: Large. *STOCK: General antiques and decorative items.* TEL: 020 7229 8187; fax - 020 7792 2456.

Arbras Gallery

292 Westbourne Grove. W11 2PS. Est. 1972. Open Fri. 10-4, Sat. 7-5. SIZE: 2 floors. *STOCK: General antiques - silver, jewellery, glass, porcelain, clocks, scientific instruments, decorative arts and antiquities.* LOC: 50 yards from Portobello Road. TEL: 020 7229 6772; fax - same. VAT: Stan/Spec.

Axia Art Consultants Ltd

121 Ledbury Rd. W11 2AQ. Est. 1974. Open Mon.-Fri. 10-6. *STOCK: Works of art, icons, textiles, metalwork, woodwork and ceramics, Islamic and Byzantine.* TEL: 020 7727 9724; fax - 020 7229 1272.

B. and T. Antiques

79/81 Ledbury Rd. W11 2AG. (Mrs B. Lewis). LAPADA. Open 10-6. *STOCK: Furniture especially mirrored, silver, objets d'art, Art Deco.* TEL: 020 7229 7001; fax - 020 7229 2033; e-mail - bt.antiques@virgin.net.

Sebastiano Barbagallo

15-17 Pembridge Rd., Notting Hill Gate. W11 3HL. Est. 1975. Open 10.30-6 including Sun., Sat. 9-7. SIZE: Medium. *STOCK: Chinese furniture; antiques and handicrafts from India, Tibet, SE Asia and China.* LOC: Just before Portobello Road. TEL: 020 7792 3320; fax - same. VAT: Stan.

Barham Antiques

83 Portobello Rd. W11. Est. 1954. Open 9.30-5, Sat. 7-5. SIZE: Large. *STOCK: Victorian and Georgian writing boxes, tea caddies, inkwells and inkstands, glass epergnes, silver plate, clocks, paintings and Victorian furniture.* TEL: 020 7727 3845; fax - same; e-mail - mchlbarham@aol.com; website - www.barhamantiques.co.uk. SER: Valuations; buys at auction.

Elizabeth Bradwin

Stands 1 & 2, 75 Portobello Rd. W11 2QB. PADA. Est. 1989. Open 10.30-4.30, Sat. 7-5. SIZE: Small. *STOCK: Animal subjects including animalier bronzes, 19th-20th C, £100-£4,000; Vienna bronzes, Staffordshire, carved wood, inkwells, tobacco jars.* PARK: Easy. TEL: 020 7221 1121; home and fax - 020 8947 2629; mobile - 07778 731826; e-mail - elizoo@ukgateway.net; website - www.elizabethbradwin.com. VAT: Spec.

Butchoff Antiques

220 Westbourne Grove. W11 2RH. LAPADA. Est. 1962. Open 10-6, Sat. 10-4. SIZE: Large. *STOCK: Fine 18th-19th C English and Continental furniture, decorative smalls and paintings, £500-£50,000.* TEL: 020 7221 8174; fax - 020 7792 8923. FAIRS: Olympia (June).

Caelt Gallery

182 Westbourne Grove. W11 2RH. Est. 1967. Open 9.30-6, Sun. 10.30-6. SIZE: Large. *STOCK: Oil paintings, 17th-20th C, £200-£10,000 but mainly £300-£900.* PARK: Easy. TEL: 020 7229 9309; fax - 020 7727 8746; e-mail - art@caeltgallery.com; website - www.caeltgallery.com. SER: Re-lining; restorations; framing. VAT: Spec.

Canonbury

174 Westbourne Grove. W11 2RW. (M. Worster). Est. 1965. Open 10-6, Sat. 10-4.30. SIZE: Large. *STOCK: Dutch, English and French furniture; some porcelain.* LOC: Off Portobello Road. PARK: Easy. TEL: 020 7727 4268; fax - 020 7229 5840. SER: Valuations; restorations. VAT: Stan/Spec.

Jack Casimir Ltd   BADA
23 Pembridge Rd. W11 3HG. LAPADA. Est. 1933. Open 10-5.30 and by appointment.

SIZE: Large. *STOCK: 16th - 19th C British and European brass, copper, pewter, paktong.* Not Stocked: Silver, china, jewellery. LOC: 2 mins. walk from Notting Hill Gate station. PARK: 100yds. TEL: 020 7727 8643. SER: Exports. VAT: Stan/Spec.

Central Gallery (Portobello)
125 Portobello Rd. W11 2DY. (C. Hickey). Est. 1991. Open Sat. 6-3. SIZE: 25+ dealers. *STOCK: Jewellery, 18th C to 1960's, including cameos, hardstone, shell, lava, coral, amber, ivory, jet, tortoiseshell, piqué, micro-mosaics, pietra-dura, Art Nouveau, plique é jour, horn pendants, Art Deco, enamels, Austro-Hungarian, cut-steel, Berlin iron, Scottish, Victorian silver and gold, Alberts, Albertines, longuards, curbs, gates, fobs, seals, intaglios, pocket watches, vintage wristwatches, cufflinks, fine diamonds, rare gemstones, signed pieces, pearls, from £50-£5,000+.* LOC: Notting Hill. TEL: 020 7243 8027; fax - same. FAIRS: Olympia; Park Lane Hotel (every Sunday); NEC; Miami Beach. VAT: Stan/Spec/Global.

The Coach House   BADA
Ledbury Mews North, Notting Hill. W11 2AF. (Jay Arenski and Peter Petrou). LAPADA. Open by appointment only. *STOCK: Fine furniture - Regency, Gothic Revival, Arts & Crafts, Aesthetic, Colonial and Campaign, Islamic and Egyptian Revival; oil paintings including maritime, Old Masters and modern, naïve portraits including animal, watercolours and prints; classical and Vienna bronzes, Grand Tour items, ormolu, metalware and treen; decorative glass, silver and plate, pottery including majolica, equestrian objects and tribal art, £200-£200,000.* Not Stocked: Shipping goods and jewellery. PARK: Easy. TEL: 020 7727 8599/7229 9575; fax - 020 7727 7584; e-mail - arenski@netcomuk.co.uk and peter petrou@btinternet.com; websites - www. arenski.com and www.peterpetrou.com. SER: Interior decor; shipping arranged. FAIRS: Olympia (June); BADA (May). VAT: Stan/Spec.

Garrick D. Coleman
75 Portobello Rd. W11 2QB. Est. 1944. Open 10.30-4.30, Sat. 8.30-3.30. *STOCK: Chess sets, 1750-1880, £300-£15,000; works of art £50-£3,000; glass paperweights, £200-£3,000; also conjuring and magic items.* TEL: 020 7937 5524; fax - 020 7937 5530; e-mail - coleman-antiques-london@compuserve.com; website - www. antiquechess.co.uk/. VAT: Stan/Spec.

Sheila Cook
283 Westbourne Grove. W11 2QA. Est. 1970. Open Wed.-Sat. 10-6. SIZE: Medium. *STOCK: Textiles, costume and accessories, 1750-1980, £15-£3,000.* LOC: Corner of Portobello Rd. PARK: Meters. TEL: 020 7792 8001; fax - 020 7229 3855; e-mail - sheilacook@sheilacook. co.uk; website - www.sheilacook.co.uk. SER: Valuations. VAT: Global/Spec.

The Corner Portobello Antiques Supermarket
282-290 Westbourne Grove. W11. (B. Lipka & Son Ltd). Open Fri. 12-4, Sat. 7-5. SIZE: 150 dealers. *STOCK: General miniature antiques, silver and jewellery.* TEL: 020 7727 2027. SER: Valuations; restorations.

Crown Arcade
119 Portobello Rd. W11. (Angelo Soteriades). PADA. Est. 1986. Open Sat. 5.30-5. SIZE: Medium, 25 stalls. *STOCK: 18th-19th C glass, bronzes, sculpture, silver, jewellery, Arts & Crafts, Art Nouveau, Art Deco, treen, boxes, humidors, tortoishell, ivory, Austrian glass, pewter, decorative prints, Italian glass, decanters, decorative objects.* LOC: Near Westbourne Grove. TEL: 020 7436 9416/7792 3619 (Sat. only); mobile - 07956 277077; e-mail - info@portobello-antiques.com; website - www.portobello-collections.co.uk. SER: Valuations.

Curá Antiques
34 Ledbury Rd. W11 2AB. (G. and M. Antichi). Open 11-6, Sat. 10.30-1. *STOCK: Continental furniture, sculptures, majolica and paintings.* TEL: 020 7229 6880.

Daggett Gallery
1st and 2nd Floors, 153 Portobello Rd. W11 2DY. (Caroline Daggett). LAPADA. Est. 1992. Open 10-5 (prior telephone call advisable), Sat. 9-3.30. SIZE: Medium. *STOCK: Frames, 18th-20th C, from £1.* LOC: 200 yards from Westbourne Grove towards Elgin Crescent. PARK: Meters. TEL: 020 7229 2248. SER: Restorations (frames); gilding; picture plaques; framing; special paint effects. VAT: Stan/Spec.

Charles Daggett Gallery
1st and 2nd Floors, 153 Portobello Rd. W11 2DY. (Charles and Caroline Daggett). LAPADA. Est. 1977. Open 10-4 (prior telephone call advisable), Sat. 9-3.30. SIZE: Medium. *STOCK: British pictures, 1740-1840.* LOC: 200 yards from Westbourne Grove, towards Elgin Crescent. PARK: Meters. TEL: 020 7229 2248; fax - 020 7229 0193. SER: Restorations (pictures and frames); framing. VAT: Stan/Spec.

John Dale
87 Portobello Rd. W11 2QB. Est. 1950. Open 11-3, Sat. 7-5. SIZE: Medium. *STOCK: General antiques.* TEL: 020 7727 1304. VAT: Stan.

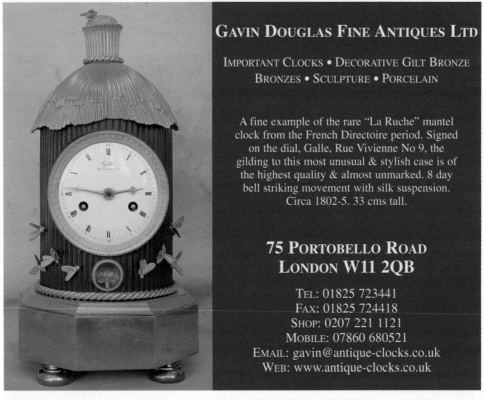

Michael Davidson
54 Ledbury Rd., Westbourne Grove. W11 2AJ.
Est. 1961. Open 9.45-12.45 and 1.15-5. CL: Sat.
pm. in winter. *STOCK: Regency and period
furniture, objets d'art.* TEL: 020 7229 6088.
SER: Valuations. VAT: Stan/Spec.

Delehar
146 Portobello Rd. W11 2DZ. Est. 1919. Open
Sat. 9-4. SIZE: Medium. *STOCK: General
antiques, works of art.* Not Stocked: Furniture.
TEL: 020 7727 9860. VAT: Spec.

Peter Delehar
146 Portobello Rd. W11 2DZ. Est. 1919. Open
Sat. 10-4. SIZE: Medium. *STOCK: Unusual
scientific and medical instruments.* TEL: 020
7727 9860 (Sat.) or 020 8866 8659; fax - same;
website - www.peterdelehar.co.uk. FAIRS: International Scientific and Medical Instrument
(Organiser). VAT: Stan/Spec.

Demetzy Books
113 Portobello Rd. W11. (P. and M. Hutchinson).
ABA, PBFA. Est. 1972. Open Sat. 7.30-3.30.
SIZE: Medium. *STOCK: Antiquarian leather
bound books, 18th-19th C, £5-£1,000; Dickens'
first editions and children's and illustrated books,*

18th-20th C, £5-£200. LOC: 20yds. from junction
with Westbourne Grove, opposite Earl of
Lonsdale public house. PARK: Meters. TEL:
01993 702209. SER: Valuations; buys at auction
(books). FAIRS: ABA Chelsea; PBFA Russell
Hotel, London (monthly); Randolph Hotel,
Oxford; York..

Gavin Douglas Fine Antiques Ltd
75 Portobello Rd. W11 2QB. (G.A. Douglas).
PADA. LAPADA. CINOA. Est. 1993. Open
10.30-4.30, Sat. 7.30-5. SIZE: Medium. *STOCK:
Neo-classical clocks, 18th-19th C, to £100,000;
bronzes, sculpture, porcelain and objects, to
£50,000.* LOC: Notting Hill. PARK: Easy. TEL:
020 7221 1121; 01825 723441; fax - 01825
724418; website - www.antique-clocks.co.uk; e-
mail - gavin@antique-clocks.co.uk. SER: Valuations; restorations; buys at auction. FAIRS:
Olympia (Summer, Winter, Spring); LAPADA;
Harrogate. VAT: Stan/Spec.

The Facade
196 Westbourne Grove. W11 2RH. Est. 1973.
Open Tues.-Sat. 10.30-5. *STOCK: French decorative items and lighting, 1900-1940.* PARK: Easy.
TEL: 020 7727 2159. VAT: Stan.

Fairman Carpets Ltd
218 Westbourne Grove. W11 2RH. (D.R.J. and S.J. Page). Open 10-6. *STOCK: Persian and Oriental carpets and rugs.* TEL: 020 7229 2262; fax - 020 7229 2263; e-mail - fairman-carpets @ukonline.co.uk; websites - www.fairman carpets.com and www.fairman-carpets.com. SER: Valuations; repairs; cleaning. VAT: Stan.

Fleur de Lys Gallery
227a Westbourne Grove. W11 2SE. (H.S. Coronel). Est. 1967. Open 10.30-5.30. SIZE: Medium. *STOCK: Oil paintings, 19th C, £2,000-£6,000.* PARK: Easy, but limited. TEL: 020 7727 8595; fax - same; home - 01372 467934; e-mail - fleurdelysgallery@yahoo.com; website - www. fleur-de-lys.com. VAT: Spec.

Judy Fox
81 Portobello Rd. and 176 Westbourne Grove. W11. LAPADA. Est. 1970. Open 10-5. SIZE: Large. *STOCK: Furniture and decorative items, 18th-20th C; inlaid furniture, mainly 19th C; pottery and porcelain.* TEL: 020 7229 8130; fax - 020 7229 6998.

Graham and Green
4 Elgin Crescent. W11 2JA. (A. Graham and R. Harrison). Est. 1974. Open 10-6, Sun. 11-5. SIZE: Medium. *STOCK: Turkish kelim rugs, Indian and Vietnamese Colonial furniture, re-upholstered Victorian chairs and decorative objects.* LOC: Near Portobello Rd. PARK: Nearby. TEL: 020 7727 4594; fax - 020 7229 9717; e-mail - info@grahamandgreen.co.uk; website - www.grahamandgreen.co.uk. VAT: Stan.

Gavin Graham Gallery
47 Ledbury Rd. W11 2AA. Est. 1973. *STOCK: Oil paintings.* TEL: 020 7229 4848; fax - 020 7792 9697. VAT: Spec.

Henry Gregory
82 Portobello Rd. W11 2QD. (H. and C. Gregory). Est. 1969. Open 10-4, Sat. 8-5. SIZE: Medium. *STOCK: Victorian decorative objects, silver, plate, jewellery, small furniture and sporting items, £2-£2,000.* LOC: Between Westbourne Grove and Chepstow Villas. PARK: Easy. TEL: 020 7792 9221; fax - same. SER: Export packing and shipping. VAT: Stan/Spec.

Hickmet Fine Arts
75 Portobello Rd. W11 2QB. (David Hickmet). LAPADA. CINOA. PADA. Open 10-4, Sat. 8-5. SIZE: Medium. *STOCK: Art Deco sculpture, £500-£5,000; Art Nouveau glass, £200-£2,000; contemporary sculpture, £1,000-£10,000.* PARK: Easy. TEL: Mobile - 07050 123450. SER:

Valuations; buys at auction (bronze and/or ivory sculpture). FAIRS: Olympia, LAPADA, NEC, Harrogate, GMEX, SECC. VAT: Spec.

Hirst Antiques
59 Pembridge Rd. W11 3HG. Est. 1963. Open 10-6. SIZE: Medium. *STOCK: Four poster and half-tester beds; decorative furniture and articles; bronze and marble sculpture.* LOC: End of Portobello Rd., near Notting Hill Gate tube station. TEL: 020 7727 9364. SER: Valuations.

Jones Antique Lighting
194 Westbourne Grove. W11. (Judy Jones). Est. 1978. Open 9.30-6 or by appointment. SIZE: Large. *STOCK: Original decorative lighting, 1860-1960.* Not Stocked: Reproductions. TEL: 020 7229 6866; fax - same. SER: Valuations; repairs; prop hire. VAT: Stan.

Kleanthous Antiques
144 Portobello Rd. W11 2DZ. LAPADA. Open Sat. only 8-4 and by appointment. TEL: 020 7727 3649; fax - 01923 897618; mobile - 07850 375501. Below are listed the dealers at this address.

James Forbes Fine Art
Est. 1982. *Works of art, silver and jewellery, from 1700, £50-£5,000.* TEL: 01886 821216.

Kleanthous Antiques Ltd
Est. 1969. LAPADA. Open Sat. 7.30-4 and by appointment. *Specially selected pieces of jewellery - Georgian, Victorian, Art Nouveau, Art Deco, to 1950; vintage pocket and wrist watches by Rolex, Cartier, Patek Phillipe, Vacheron and Constantin, Jaeger le Coultre, Longines, I.W.C., Universal and Omega; English and Continental silver, 18th-20th C; boudoir, desk, carriage and mantel clocks; objects of vertu; furniture. Full guarantee with all purchases.* TEL: 020 7727 3649; fax - 020 7243 2488; mobile - 07850 375501/375502; e-mail - antiques@kleanthous.com; website - www.kleanthous.com. VAT: Stan/Spec.

S. and G. Antiques
(G. Sirett). *Specialist in miniature porcelain cups and saucers, teasets and vases, £25-£500; English and Continental glass, £25-£1,000; Meissen porcelain and objets d'art, £20-£5,000.* TEL: 020 7229 2178 (Sat.); 020 8907 7140; fax - 020 8909 3277; mobile - 07768 366677; e-mail - gary @sandgantiques.co.uk; website - www.sandg antiques.co.uk. VAT: Stan/Spec.

Lacy Gallery
203 Westbourne Grove. W11 2AB. Est. 1960. Open Tues.-Fri.10-5, Sat. 10-4. SIZE: Large. *STOCK: Period frames, 1700-1940; decorative paintings and art.* LOC: Two roads east of Portobello Rd. PARK: Easy. TEL: 020 7229 6340; fax - 020 7229 9105. VAT: Stan/Spec.

M. and D. Lewis

1 Lonsdale Rd., 172 Westbourne Grove, 83-85 Ledbury Rd. W11. Est. 1960. Open 9.30-5.30, Sat. 9.30-4. *STOCK: Continental and Victorian furniture, porcelain, bronzes.* TEL: 020 7727 3908. VAT: Stan.

M.C.N. Antiques

183 Westbourne Grove. W11 2SB. Est. 1971. Open 9.30-6, Sat. 11-3 or by appointment. *STOCK: Japanese porcelain, cloisonné, Satsuma, bronze, lacquer, ivory.* LOC: Near Portobello Rd. market. PARK: Easy. TEL: 020 7727 3796; fax - 020 7229 8839. VAT: Stan.

Robin Martin Antiques

44 Ledbury Rd. W11 2AB. (Paul Martin). Est. 1972. Open 10-6. SIZE: Medium. *STOCK: English and Continental furniture and works of art, 17th-19th C.* LOC: Westbourne Grove area. TEL: 020 7727 1301; fax - same; mobile - 07831 544055; e-mail - paul.martin11@virgin.net. FAIRS: Olympia (June, Nov). VAT: Spec.

Mayflower Antiques

117 Portobello Rd. W11. (J.W. Odgers). PADA. Est. 1970. Open Sat. 7-5. SIZE: Medium. *STOCK: Clocks, mechanical music, scientific and marine instruments, general antiques.* TEL: Sat. - 020 7727 0381; mobile - 07860 843569; e-mails - mayflower@ukshells.co.uk and mail@ johnodgers. com; website - www.oldjunk.co.uk. FAIRS: Newark. VAT: Stan/Spec.

Mercury Antiques   BADA

1 Ladbroke Rd. W11 3PA. (L. Richards). Est. 1963. Open 10-5.30, Sat. 10-1. SIZE: Medium. STOCK: English porcelain, 1745-1840; English pottery and Delft, 1700-1850; glass, 1780-1850. Not Stocked: Jewellery, silver, plate, Art

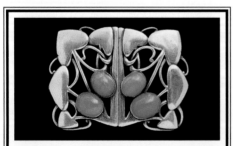

Buckle; silver and chrysoprase, 1900-4. £1,300-£1,800. (Tadema Gallery)

From an article entitled "A Passionate Endeavour – Collecting Archibald Knox" by Stephen A. Martin which appeared in the December 2001/ January 2002 issue of **Antique Collecting**. For more details and to subscribe see page 21.

Nouveau. LOC: Half minute from Notting Hill Gate underground station, turn into Pembridge Rd. and bear left. TEL: 020 7727 5106; fax - 020 7229 3738. VAT: Spec.

Milne and Moller

W11 2BU. (Mr and Mrs C. Moller). LAPADA. Est. 1976. Open by appointment. SIZE: Small. *STOCK: Watercolours, oils, ceramics and sculpture, 19th C to contemporary.* LOC: Near junction of Westbourne Grove and Ledbury Rd. PARK: Easy. TEL: 020 7727 1679; home - same. SER: Portrait commissioning. FAIRS: Olympia; Chelsea Art. VAT: Spec.

Mimi Fifi

27 Pembridge Rd., Notting Hill Gate. W11 3HG. (Mrs Rita Delaforge). Est. 1990. Open 11-6.30, Sat. 10-7, Sun. 11-4. SIZE: Medium. *STOCK: Vintage and collectable toys, especially Snoopy, Smurfs, Betty Boop, Simpsons, and memorabilia, 20th C, £5-£500; perfume miniatures and related collectables, 19th-20th C, £5-£1,000.* LOC: 200 yards from Notting Hill underground. PARK: Nearby. TEL: 020 7243 3154; fax - 020 7938 4222; website - www.mimififi.com.

Terence Morse and Son Ltd

237 Westbourne Grove. W11 2SE. Est. 1947. Open 10-6, Sat. 11-2. SIZE: Large. *STOCK: Furniture, 18th-19th C, £1,000+.* LOC: 200yds. from Portobello Rd. PARK: Easy. TEL: 020 7229 4059; fax - 020 7792 3284. VAT: Stan/Spec.

Myriad Antiques

131 Portland Rd., Holland Park Ave. W11 4LW. (S. Nickerson). Est. 1970. Open 11-6. SIZE: Medium. *STOCK: Decorative and unusual furniture (including garden) and objects, mainly 19th C, £10-£1,500.* LOC: Between Notting Hill Gate and Shepherds Bush roundabout. TEL: 020 7229 1709. VAT: Stan.

The Nanking Porcelain Co. Ltd

Admiral Vernon Arcade, 141-149 Portobello Rd. W11 2DY. (Maurice Hyams and Elizabeth Porter). Open Sat. only 8.30-3.30. SIZE: Small. *STOCK: Chinese export porcelain, Oriental ivories.* TEL: 020 7924 2349; fax - 020 7924 2352; mobile - 07836 594 885; e-mail - nanking porcelain@aol.com. SER: Valuations. FAIRS: Olympia (June).

Old Father Time Clock Centre

Portobello Studios, 1st Floor, 101 Portobello Rd. W11 2QB. (John Denvir). Open Fri. 10-1, Sat. 8-2, other times by appointment. *STOCK: Clocks - all types, especially electric (eg. Eureka), mystery, Atmos, novelty, skeleton, carriage, dial,*

THE NANKING PORCELAIN CO. LTD.

Specialising in 17ᵗʰ, 18ᵗʰ and 19ᵗʰ century Chinese Export and shipwreck porcelain.

Portobello shop open 9:00 to 3:30 Saturdays or by appointment.
L21-25 Admiral Vernon Arcade, 141 Portobello Road,
London W11. Tel: **020 7243-3030**

Office: 202 Broomwood Road,
London SW11 6JY. Tel: **020 7924-2349**
E-mail: **nankingporcelain@aol.com**
Fax: **020 7924-2352**
Mobile: **0783 659 4885**

bracket; barometers. TEL: 020 8546 6299; fax - same; 020 7727 3394; mobile - 07836 712088; website -www.oldfathertime.net; e-mail - clocks @oldfathertime.net.

Neil Phillips Ltd.
99 Portobello Rd. W11 2QB. LAPADA. Est. 1962. Open 10-5. *STOCK: Ecclesiastical antiques and stained glass.* TEL: 020 7229 2113; fax - 020 7229 1963.

Richard Philp   BADA
59 Ledbury Rd. W11 2AA. SLAD. Est. 1961. Open by appointment. STOCK: Old Master drawings, 16th-17th C English portraiture and Old Master paintings, medieval sculpture, early furniture and 20th C drawings, £50-£40,000. PARK: Easy. TEL: 020 7727 7915. VAT: Spec.

Piano Nobile Fine Paintings
129 Portland Rd., Holland Park. W11 4LW. (Dr Robert A. Travers). SLAD. Est. 1986. Open Tues.-Sat. 10.30-5.30. SIZE: Medium. *STOCK: Fine 19th C Impressionist and 20th C Post-Impressionist and Modernist British and Continental oil paintings and sculpture, especially Les Petit Maitres of the Paris Schools, £500-£100,000.* PARK: Easy. TEL: 020 7229 1099; fax - same; e-mail -robert@pianonobile.fsnet.co.uk; website - www.piano-nobile.com. SER: Valuations; restorations (paintings and sculptures); framing; buys at auction (19th-20th C oil paintings). FAIRS: Grosvenor; 20th C British Art; Olympia: BADA; Art London.

Portobello Antique Co
133 Portobello Rd. W11 2DY. (L. Meltzer and A. Goldsmith). PADA. Est. 1950. Open Fri. 11-4.30, Sat. 8-4.30, other times by appointment. SIZE: Small. *STOCK: Porcelain, small furniture, reproduction silver plate and cutlery.* LOC: Off Westbourne Grove. PARK: Easy. TEL: 020 7221 0344; home - 020 8959 8886; fax - 020 8801 1780. SER: Packing and shipping. VAT: Stan/Spec.

Portobello Antique Store
79 Portobello Rd. W11 2QB. (J.F. Ewing). Est. 1971. Open Tues.-Fri. 10-4, Sat. 8.15-4. SIZE: Large. *STOCK: Silver and plate, £2-£3,000.* LOC: Notting Hill end of Portobello Rd. PARK: Easy weekdays. TEL: 020 7221 1994. SER: Export. VAT: Stan.

Quadrille
146 Portobello Rd. W11 2DZ. (Valerie Jackson-Harris). Open Sat. 9-4. *STOCK: Ephemera.* TEL: 01923 829079; fax - 01923 825079.

The Red Lion Antiques Arcade
165/169 Portobello Rd. W11. (Angelo Soteriades). PADA. Est. 1951. Open Sat. 5.30-5.30. SIZE: 80 dealers. *STOCK: General antiques including ethnic antiquities, bronzes, ivory statues, jade, precious metals, dolls, silver and plate, drinking vessels, costumes, Oriental and Western porcelain, furniture, collectables, prints, lace, linen, books, manuscripts, stamps, coins, banknotes, paintings, etchings, sporting memorabilia, Tibetan, East and South East Asian antiquities, decorative arts and designer objects, jewellery - gold, silver, pearls, semi precious stones.* TEL: 020 7436 9416; mobile - 07956 277077; e-mail - info@portobello-antiques.com; website - www.portobello-collections .co.uk. SER: Valuations; shipping.

Rezai Persian Carpets
123 Portobello Rd. W11 2DY. Open 9-5. *STOCK: Oriental carpets, kilims, tribal rugs and silk embroideries.* TEL: 020 7221 5012.

Roger's Antiques Gallery
65 Portobello Rd. W11. (Bath Antiques Market Ltd). Open Sat. 7-4.30. SIZE: 65 dealers. *STOCK: Wide range of general antiques and collectables with specialist dealers in most fields, especially jewellery.* TEL: Enquiries - 020 7351 5353; fax - 020 7351 5350. SER: Valuations.

Justin F. Skrebowski Ground Floor, 177 Portobello Road, London, W11 2DY, UK
Tel/Fax/Answerphone: 020 7792 9742 Mobile: 07774 612474
e-mail: justin@skreb.co.uk website: www.skreb.co.uk

- Folio Stands/Browsers
- Display Easels
- Desk Top Stands
- Solid Mahogany

- Beautiful Antique Finish
- Exported Worldwide
- Used by Galleries & Museums
- Ideal for Studies & Homes

Schredds of Portobello

107 Portobello Rd. W11 2QB. (H.J. and G.R. Schrager). LAPADA, PADA. Est. 1969. Open Sat. 7.30-3. SIZE: Small. *STOCK: Collectors' silver, 17th-19th C, £10-£5,000; Wedgwood, 18th-19th C.* TEL: 020 8348 3314; home - same; fax - 020 8341 5971; website - www.schredds. com/. SER: Valuations; buys at auction. FAIRS: Kensington (Jan. and Aug). VAT: Stan/Spec.

The Silver Fox Gallery (Portobello)

121 Portobello Rd. W11 2DY. (C. Hickey). Est. 1991. Open Sat. only 6-3. SIZE: 25+ dealers. *STOCK: Jewellery - 18th C to 1960's including Victorian, Art Nouveau, Arts & Crafts, Art Deco, rings (diamond and gemset), earrings, brooches, pendants, gold and silver, Alberts, Albertines, chains longuards, bracelets, curbs, gates, fobs, seals, intaglios, pocket watches, vintage wrist-watches, cufflinks, fine diamonds, rare gem-stones, cameos, coral, amber, ivory, jet tortoise-shell, piqué, micro-mosaics, pietra-dura, lava, horn pendants, enamels, pearls, Austro-Hungarian cut steel, Berlin iron, Scottish, niello, £50-£5,000+.* LOC: Notting Hill. PARK: Pay and Display. TEL: 020 7243 8027; fax - same. FAIRS: Olympia; Park Lane Hotel (every Sunday). VAT: Stan/Spec/Global.

Justin F. Skrebowski Prints

Ground Floor, 177 Portobello Rd. W11 2DY. Est. 1985. Open Sat. 9-4, otherwise by appointment. SIZE: Small. *STOCK: Prints, engravings and lithographs, 1700-1850, £50-£500; oil paintings, 1700-1900, £200-£1,500; watercolours, drawings including Old Masters, 1600-1900, £50-£1,000; modern mahogany folio stands and easels; frames - gilt, rosewood, maple, carved, 18th-19th C.* PARK: Meters. TEL: 020 7792 9742; mobile - 07774 612474; e-mail - justin@skreb.co.uk; website - www.skreb.co.uk. SER: Valuations. FAIRS: PBFA; Hotel Russell (Monthly). VAT: Stan/Spec.

Colin Smith and Gerald Robinson Antiques

105 Portobello Rd. W11 2QB. Est. 1979. Open Sat., and Fri. by appointment. SIZE: Large. *STOCK: Tortoiseshell, £100-£2,000; silver, ivory and crocodile items.* TEL: 020 8994 3783/020 7225 1163. FAIRS: Olympia. VAT: Stan.

Staffordshire Pride

Lipka Arcade, 290 Westbourne Grove. W11. (Sharon Racklyeft). Est. 1976. Open Sat. 8.30-2.30. SIZE: Medium. *STOCK: Staffordshire figures, 1800-1870, £50-£300; blue and white china, £10-£50.* LOC: Corner of Portobello Rd. TEL: Mobile - 07958 453295; home - 020 8883 6180. SER: Valuations.

Stern Art Dealers

46 Ledbury Rd. W11 2AB. (David Stern). LAPADA. Est. 1963. Open 10-6. SIZE: Medium. *STOCK: English and European oil paintings, 19th-20th C, especially the Pissarro family.* LOC: Off Westbourne Grove near Portobello. PARK: Easy. TEL: 020 7229 6187; fax - 020 7229 7016; e-mail - pissarro@ukgateway.net; website - www.stern-art.com. SER: Valuations; restorations. VAT: Stan.

June and Tony Stone Fine Antique Boxes

75 Portobello Rd. W11 2QB. LAPADA. Open 10.30-4.30, Sat. 8-5. *STOCK: Fine boxes especially tea caddies, 18th-19th C, £200-£30,000.* TEL: Office - 01273 579333; fax - 01273 588908; Sales - 07092 106600; fax - 07092 106611; e-mail - jts@boxes.co.uk; website - www.boxes.co.uk. FAIRS: Olympia (June, Nov. and Feb); LAPADA (Oct); Claridges (April); Harrogate (April, Sept). VAT: Stan/Spec.

Temple Gallery

6 Clarendon Cross. W11 4AP. (R.C.C. Temple). Est. 1959. Open 10-6, weekends and evenings by appointment. SIZE: Large. *STOCK: Icons,*

Russian and Greek, 12th-16th C, £1,000-£50,000. PARK: Easy. TEL: 020 7727 3809; fax - 020 7727 1546; e-mail - info@templegallery.com; website - www.templegallery.com. SER: Valuations; restorations; buys at auction (icons); illustrated catalogues published. VAT: Spec.

Themes and Variations
231 Westbourne Grove. W11 2SE. (L. Fawcett). Open 10-1 and 2-6, Sat 10-6. *STOCK: Post war and contemporary decorative items, furniture, glass, ceramics, carpets, lamps, jewellery.* TEL: 020 7727 5531; fax - 020 7221 6378.

Tomkinson Stained Glass
87 Portobello Rd. W11 2QB. (S. Tomkinson). Open 10-5, Sat. 7-5. SIZE: Medium. *STOCK: Stained glass windows.* LOC: 5 minutes from Notting Hill Gate underground. PARK: Easy. TEL: 01582 527866; mobile - 07831 861641. SER: Valuations; restorations (as stock). VAT: Stan.

Christina Truscott
Geoffrey Van Arcade, 105-107 Portobello Rd. W11 2QB. PADA. Est. 1967. Open Sat. 6.45-3.30. *STOCK: Chinese export lacquer, papier-mâché, tortoiseshell, fans.* TEL: 01403 730554.

Victoriana Dolls
101 Portobello Rd. W11 2BQ. (Mrs H. Bond). Open Sat. 8-3 or by appointment. *STOCK: Dolls, toys and accessories.* TEL: Home - 01737 249525.

Virginia
98 Portland Rd., Holland Park. W11 4LQ. (V. Bates). Est. 1971. Open 11-6. SIZE: Medium. *STOCK: Clothes and lace, 1880-1940, from £100.* LOC: Holland Park Ave. PARK: Easy. TEL: 020 7727 9908; fax - 020 7229 2198. VAT: Stan.

Visto
41 Pembridge Rd., Notting Hill. W11 3HG. (H. Little and H. Lister). Est. 1997. Open 11-6, Sat. 10-6. SIZE: Small. *STOCK: Ceramics, furniture, glass and lamps, 1950's-1960's, £5-£600.* LOC: Between Notting Hill Gate underground and Portobello Rd. PARK: Nearby. TEL: 020 7243 4392; fax - 020 7243 1374.

Johnny Von Pflugh Antiques
286 Westbourne Grove. W11. Est. 1985. Open Sat. 8-5 at Portobello Market or by appointment. SIZE: Small. *STOCK: European works of art, Italian oil paintings, gouaches, 17th-19th C, £300-£1,500; fine ironware, 17th-18th C, £300-£800; medical and scientific instruments, 18th-*

19th C, £200-£1,000. PARK: Easy. TEL: 020 8740 5306; mobile - 07949 086243. SER: Valuations; buys at auction (keys, caskets, medical instruments, Italian oil paintings and gouaches). FAIRS: Olympia (June); Scientific and Medical (April, Oct). VAT: Spec.

David Wainwright
63 Portobello Rd. W11 3DB and 251 Portobello Rd. W11 1LT. Est. 1989. Open 9-6 (No. 63) and 9.30-6.30, Sun. 11-7 (No. 251). SIZE: Large. *STOCK: Furniture, mainly from the sub-continent and Far East, 15th-20th C including 18th-19th C cupboards, dining tables and architectural pieces, £5-£2000; stonework - urns, mortars, water containers, to 19th C; contemporary wrought iron.* PARK: Easy. TEL: 020 7727 0707 (No. 63) and 020 7792 1988 (No. 251). FAIRS: Olympia. VAT: Stan.

Trude Weaver
71 Portobello Rd. W11 2QB. LAPADA. Est. 1968. Open Wed.-Sat. 9-5. SIZE: Medium. *STOCK: 18th-19th C furniture, associated accessories.* PARK: Easy. TEL: 020 7229 8738; fax - same. SER: Valuations.

Wolseley Fine Arts Ltd
12 Needham Rd. W11 2RP. (Rupert Otten and Hanneke van der Werf). SLAD. TEFAF. Open during exhibitions Wed., Thurs. and Fri. 11-6, Sat. 11-5 or by appointment. *STOCK: British and European 20th C works on paper and sculpture, works by David Jones, Eric Gill, John Buckland Wright, Pierre Bonnard, Edouard Vuillard, Ker Xavier Roussel and Eugeen van Mieghem; contemporary still life paintings, art, sculpture and carved lettering.* TEL: 020 7792 2788; fax - 020 7792 2988; e-mail - info@wolseleyfinearts.com; website - www.wolseleyfinearts.com. SER: Regular catalogues. FAIRS: Works on Paper; New York; TEFAF; Art London, and 20th/21st C British Art.

World Famous Portobello Market
177 Portobello Rd. W11. (Angelo Soteriades). PADA. Est. 1951. Open Sat. 5.30-5.30. SIZE: 60 dealers. *STOCK: Stamps, coins, Art Deco, amber, jewellery, oils, watercolours, engravings, prints, maps, books, photographs, objects, teddy bears, toys, dolls, wood, soapstone, Africana, picture frames, ephemera, auction catalogues.* TEL: 020 7436 9416; mobile - 07956 277077; e-mail - info@portobello-antiques.com; website - www.portobello-collections.co.uk. SER: Valuations; framing.

W13

W.13 Antiques
10 The Avenue, Ealing. W13 8PH. Open Tues., Thurs. and Sat. 10-5 or by appointment. SIZE: Medium. STOCK: Furniture, china and general antiques, 18th-20th C. LOC: Off Uxbridge Rd., West Ealing. PARK: Easy. TEL: 020 8998 0390; mobile - 07778 177102. SER: Valuations. VAT: Stan.

W14

David Alexander Antiques & Kate Thurlow   BADA
The Warehouse, 7a North End Rd. W14 8ST. (Kate Thurlow and Rodney Robertson). LAPADA, CINOA. Est. 1970. Open by appointment or by chance. SIZE: Large. STOCK: European furniture, 15th-17th C, £500-£20,000. LOC: At junction with Hammersmith Rd., opposite Olympia Exhibition Hall. PARK: Limited or meters. TEL: 020 7602 8388; fax - same; mobile - 07836 588776. SER: Valuations; restorations (furniture); buys at auction. FAIRS: Olympia. VAT: Spec.

Marshall Gallery
67 Masbro Rd. W14 0LS. (D. A. and J. Marshall). Resident. Est. 1978. Open 10-6, Sat. 10-5. CL: Mon. SIZE: Medium. STOCK: French and decorative furniture, £500-£20,000; objects and lighting, £200-£12,000; pictures, from £100; all 18th-20th C. LOC: Just behind Olympia, off Hammersmith Rd. PARK: Easy. TEL: 020 7602 3317. SER: Restorations (furniture, re-gilding, re-wiring). VAT: Spec.

D. Parikian
3 Caithness Rd. W14 0JB. Open by appointment. STOCK: Antiquarian books, mythology, iconography, emblemata, Continental books pre-1800. TEL: 020 7603 8375; fax - 020 7602 1178; e-mail - dparikian@aol.com.

J. Roger (Antiques) Ltd   BADA
W14. (C. Bayley). Open by appointment only. STOCK: Late 18th to early 19th C small elegant pieces furniture, mirrors, prints, porcelain and boxes. TEL: 020 7603 7627.

SW1

A.D.C. Heritage Ltd   BADA
(F. Raeymaekers and E. Bellord). Open by appointment only. STOCK: Silver, old Sheffield plate. TEL: 020 7976 5271; fax - 020 7828 7432. SER: Valuations; restorations; buys at auction.

Didier Aaron (London)Ltd   BADA
21 Ryder St., St. James's. SW1Y 6PX. Open 9-5 by appointment. SIZE: Large. STOCK: French furniture, 18th C, £5,000-£500,000; Old Master and 19th C pictures, £5,000-£500,000; objets d'art, £1,000-£50,000. LOC: 20 yds. from Christie's. TEL: 020 7839 4716; e-mail - contact@didieraaronltd.com. FAIRS: Paris Biennale, Maastricht (Tefaf). VAT: Stan/Spec.

Ackermann & Johnson   BADA
27 Lowndes St. SW1X 9HY. (Peter Johnson). Est. 1783. Open 9-5.30, Sat. by appointment. SIZE: Medium. STOCK: British paintings and watercolours, especially sporting, marine and landscapes including the Norwich School, 18th-20th C. PARK: Meters. TEL: 020 7235 6464; fax - 020 7823 1057; e-mail - ackermann johnson@btconnect.com; website - www. artnet.com/ackermann.johnson. SER: Valuations; restorations; framing. VAT: Spec.

ADEC
227 Ebury St. SW1W 8UT. (A. De Cacqueray). Open 10-6, Sat. 11-4. STOCK: French and Continental furniture, objets d'art. TEL: 020 7730 5000; fax - 020 7730 0005.

Verner Åmell Ltd
4 Ryder St., St. James's. SW1Y 6QB. SLAD. Est. 1988. Open 10-5.30. CL: Sat. STOCK: Dutch and Flemish Old Masters, 16th-17th C; 18th C French and 19th C Scandinavian paintings. TEL: 020 7925 2759. FAIRS: Tefaf; Grosvenor House. VAT: Spec.

Albert Amor Ltd
37 Bury St., St. James's. SW1Y 6AU. Est. 1903. Open 9.30-4.30. CL: Sat. SIZE: Small. STOCK: 18th C English ceramics, especially first period Worcester and blue and white porcelain. PARK: Meters. TEL: 020 7930 2444; fax - 020 7930 9067. SER: Valuations. VAT: Spec.

Anno Domini Antiques   BADA
66 Pimlico Rd. SW1W 8LS. (F. Bartman). Est. 1960. Open 10-1 and 2.15-6. CL: Sat. pm. SIZE: Large. STOCK: Furniture, 17th to early 19th C, £500-£20,000; mirrors, 17th-19th C, £300-£3,000; glass, screens, decorative items and tapestries, £15-£10,000. Not Stocked: Silver, jewellery, arms, coins. LOC: From Sloane Sq. go down Lower Sloane St., turn left at traffic lights. PARK: Easy. TEL: 020 7730 5496; home - 020 7352 3084. SER: Buys at auction. VAT: Stan/Spec.

Antiquus
90-92 Pimlico Rd. SW1W 8PL. (E. Amati). Open 9.30-5.30. SIZE: Large. STOCK: Classical, medi-

Anno Domini Antiques

66 Pimlico Road, London S.W.1
020-7730 5496

Fine small Regency rosewood brass inlaid sofa table,
c.1820. 30 in. x 12 in. x 28½in. (high)

eval and Renaissance works of art, paintings, textiles and glass. LOC: Near Sloane Sq. underground station. PARK: Meters in Holbein Place. TEL: 020 7730 8681; fax - 020 7823 6409; e-mail - enquiries@antiquus-london.co.uk; website - www.antiquus-london.co.uk.

Appley Hoare Antiques
30 Pimlico Rd. SW1W 8LJ. (Appley & Zoe Hoare). Est. 1980. Open 10.30-6, Sat. 11-4.30. SIZE: Medium. *STOCK: French 18th-19th C furniture with original paint and patination, and decorative items.* LOC: Corner Pimlico Green. PARK: Easy. TEL: 020 7730 7070; fax - 020 7730 8188; e-mail - appley@appleyhoare.com; website - www.appleyhoare.com. SER: Shipping. VAT: Spec.

The Armoury of St. James's Military Antiquarians
17 Piccadilly Arcade, Piccadilly. SW1Y 6NH. Open 9.30-6. SIZE: Small. *STOCK: British and foreign Orders of Chivalry, 18th C to date, £50-£50,000; militaria, including regimental brooches and drums; toy and hand-painted collectors model soldiers, £4-£4,000.* LOC: Between Piccadilly and Jermyn St. TEL: 020 7493 5082; e-mail - welcome@armoury.co.uk; website - www.armoury.co.uk/home. SER: Valuations. special commissions. VAT: Stan/Spec.

Artemis Fine Arts Limited
15 Duke St., St. James's. SW1Y 6DB. (Timothy Bathurst, Adrian Eeles, Armin Kunz and Francois Borne). SLAD. Open 9.30-5.30. CL: Sat. *STOCK: Old Master, 19th C and modern paintings, drawings and prints; Scandinavian paintings.* TEL: 020 7930 8733; fax - 020 7839 5009; website - www.artemisfinearts.com. FAIRS: Maastricht; London Original Print. VAT: Margin.

Nigel A. Bartlett
25 St Barnabas St. SW1W 8QB. Open 9.30-5.30. CL: Sat. *STOCK: Marble, pine and stone chimney pieces.* TEL: 020 7730 3223; fax - 020 7730 2332.

Hilary Batstone Antiques inc. Rose Uniacke Interiors
8 Holbein Place. SW1W 8NL. LAPADA. Est. 1983. Open 10.30-5.30, Sat. 10.30-3.30. SIZE: Medium. *STOCK: 18th-20th C decorative furniture.* TEL: 020 7730 5335; e-mail - hilary @batstone.com. SER: Interior decorating. FAIRS: Decorative Antiques and Textiles, Chelsea. VAT: Spec.

Chris Beetles Ltd
10 Ryder St., St. James's. SW1Y 6QB. Open 10-5.30. SIZE: Large. *STOCK: English watercolours, paintings and illustrations, 18th-20th C, £500-£50,000.* LOC: 100yds. from Royal Academy. PARK: Meters. TEL: 020 7839 7551. SER: Valuations; framing. VAT: Spec.

Belgrave Carpet Gallery Ltd
91 Knightsbridge. SW1. (A.H. Khawaja). Open 9.30-6.30. *STOCK: Hand knotted Oriental carpets and rugs.* TEL: 020 7235 2541/7245 9749.

Blanchard Ltd
86/88 Pimlico Rd. SW1W 8PL. Est. 1990. Open 10-6, Sat. 10-3. SIZE: Medium. *STOCK: English and Continental furniture, lighting and objets d'art, 1700-1950.* LOC: Near Sloane Sq. underground station. TEL: 020 7823 6310; fax - 020 7823 6303. SER: Valuations; restorations; buys at auction. VAT: Stan/Spec.

N. Bloom & Son (1912) Ltd.
12 Piccadilly Arcade, Piccadilly. SW1Y 6NH. (Ian Harris). CINOA, LAPADA. *STOCK: Jewellery, mainly 1860-1960; small silver, objets d'art and vertu; paintings.* TEL: 020 7629 5060; fax - 020 7493 2528; mobile - 07973 149363; e-mail - nbloom@nbloom.co.uk; website - www.nbloom. co.uk. SER: Valuations; restorations and repairs; buys at auction. VAT: Stan/Spec.

John Bly   BADA
27 Bury St., St. James's. SW1Y 6AL. (J. and V. Bly). CINOA Est. 1891. Open 9.30-5.30, Sat. and Sun. by appointment. *STOCK: Fine English furniture, silver, glass, porcelain and fine paintings, 18th-19th C.* TEL: 020 7930 1292; fax - 020 7839 4775; e -mail - john@john bly.com; website - www.johnbly.com. SER: Restorations; valuations; consultancy. FAIRS: BADA; Grosvenor House; W. Palm Beach.

J.H. Bourdon-Smith Ltd   BADA
24 Mason's Yard, Duke St., St. James's. SW1Y 6BU. CINOA. Est. 1954. Open 9.30-6. CL: Sat. SIZE: Medium. *STOCK: Silver, 1680-1830, £50-£15,000; Victorian and modern silver, 1830 to date, £25-£10,000.* PARK: Meters. TEL: 020 7839 4714/3951; e-mail - julia@bourdonsmith. co.uk. SER: Valuations; restorations (silver); buys at auction. FAIRS: Olympia (Nov); Harrogate; Grosvenor House; BADA; New York; San Francisco. VAT: Stan/Spec.

Robert Bowman   BADA
8 Duke St., St. James's. SW1Y 6BN. Est. 1992. Open Mon.-Fri. 10-6. SIZE: Medium. *STOCK:*

Sculpture in bronze, marble and terracotta, 19th-20th C, £3,000-£200,000. PARK: Metered bays. TEL: 020 7839 3100; fax - 020 7839 3223. SER: Valuations; restorations (bronze, marble and terracotta). FAIRS: Olympia, Maastricht, Palm Beach, New York. VAT: Spec.

Brisigotti Antiques Ltd
44 Duke St., St. James's. SW1Y 6DD. Open 9.30-1 and 2-6. *STOCK: European works of art, Old Master paintings.* TEL: 020 7839 4441; fax - 020 7976 1663.

Camerer Cuss and Co
17 Ryder St., St. James's. SW1Y 6PY. Est. 1788. Open 9.30-5. CL: Sat. SIZE: Medium. *STOCK: Clocks, 1600-1910, £250-£30,000; watches, 1600-1930, £100-£35,000.* TEL: 020 7930 1941; e-mail - camerercuss@17ryderstreet.freeserve. co.uk; website - www.camerercuss.com. SER: Valuations; restorations (clocks and watches); buys at auction. VAT: Stan/Spec.

John Carlton-Smith   BADA
17 Ryder St., St. James's. SW1Y 6PY. Open 9.30-5.30. CL: Sat. *STOCK: Clocks, barometers, chronometers, 17th-19th C.* TEL: 020 7930 6622; fax - same; website - www. fineantique clocks.com. SER: Valuations. VAT: Spec.

Miles Wynn Cato
60 Lower Sloane St. SW1W 8BP. Open Mon.-Fri. 9.30-5.30 and by appointment. SIZE: Medium. *STOCK: English and Welsh pictures and works of art, 1550-1950.* LOC: South of Sloane Sq. TEL: 020 7259 0306; fax - 020 7259 0305; e-mail - wynncato@welshart.co.uk; website - www. welshart.co.uk.

Chaucer Fine Arts Ltd
45 Pimlico Rd. SW1W 8NE. Open Mon.-Fri. 10-6 and by appointment. *STOCK: Old Master paintings, sculpture and works of art; 19th C European paintings, 20th C Russian paintings and drawings.* TEL: 020 7730 2972; fax - 020 7730 5861.

Chelsea Antique Mirrors
72 Pimlico Rd. SW1W 2LS. (A. Koll). Est. 1976. Open 10-6, Sat. 10-2. SIZE: Medium. *STOCK: Antique mirrors, £1,000-£25,000.* PARK: Easy. TEL: 020 7824 8024; fax - 020 7824 8233. SER: Valuations; restorations (gilding).

Ciancimino Ltd
99 Pimlico Rd. SW1W 8PH. Open 10-6, Sat. 11-5. *STOCK: Art Deco furniture, Oriental art and ethnography.* TEL: 020 7730 9950/9959; fax - 020 7730 5365.

Classic Bindings
61 Cambridge St. SW1V 4PS. (Sasha Poklewski-Koziell and Simon Phillips-Williams). Est. 1989. Open Mon. - Fri. 9.30-5.30 and by appointment. *STOCK: English and French literature, history, bound sets, first editions, voyages and travel, illustrated, fine bindings.* LOC: Off Warwick Way, Pimlico. PARK: Easy. TEL: 020 7834 5554; fax - 020 7630 6632; e-mail - info@classic bindings.net; website - www.classic bindings.net. FAIRS: ABA Olympia and Chelsea.

Cobra and Bellamy
149 Sloane St. SW1X 9BZ. (V. Manussis and T. Hunter). Est. 1976. Open 10.30-5.30. SIZE: Medium. *STOCK: Fine art, ceramics and 20th C designer jewellery, £50-£5,000.* TEL: 020 7730 9993; e-mail - cobrabellamy@hotmail.com. VAT: Stan/Margin.

Cornucopia
12 Upper Tachbrook St. SW1V 1SH. Est. 1967. Open 11-6. SIZE: Large. *STOCK: Jewellery, 20th C clothing and accessories.* PARK: Meters. TEL: 020 7828 5752.

Cox and Company
37 Duke St., St. James's. SW1Y 6DF. (Mr and Mrs R. Cox). Est. 1972. Open 10-5.30, Sat. by appointment. SIZE: Small. *STOCK: European paintings, 19th-20th C, £1,000-£20,000; sporting (racing) and wildlife paintings.* LOC: Off Piccadilly. TEL: 020 7930 1987/7839 4539; e-mail - coxco@bellatlantic.net; website - www. coxco.uk.com. SER: Valuations; restorations; buys at auction. VAT: Spec.

Crowther of Syon Lodge Ltd
77/79 Pimlico Rd. SW1W 8PH. Open 10-6, Sat. 11-3. *STOCK: Period panelled rooms in pine and oak; chimney-pieces in marble, stone and wood; classical stone and marble statues; wrought iron entrance gates, garden temples, vases, wellheads, lead cisterns, animal figures, seats, fountains and other features.* LOC: Just off Sloane Sq. TEL: 020 7730 8668; website - www.crowthersyon lodge. com. SER: Bespoke summerhouses; quality reproduction ornaments. VAT: Stan/Spec.

Peter Dale Ltd
12 Royal Opera Arcade, Pall Mall. SW1Y 4UY. LAPADA. Est. 1955. Open 9.30-5. CL: Sat. SIZE: Medium. *STOCK: Firearms, 16th-19th C; edged weapons, armour, 14th-19th C; militaria.* LOC: Arcade behind Her Majesty's Theatre and New Zealand House. PARK: 350yds. Whitcomb St. public garage. TEL: 020 7930 3695; fax - 020 7930 2223. SER: Valuations; buys at auction. FAIRS: Arms, spring and autumn. VAT: Spec.

Kenneth Davis (Works of Art) Ltd
15 King St., St. James's. SW1Y 6QU. Open 9-5. CL: Sat. *STOCK: Antique silver and works of art.* TEL: 020 7930 0313; fax - 020 7976 1306.

Alastair Dickenson Fine Silver Ltd
BADA

90 Jermyn St. SW1Y 6JD. Est. 1996. Open 9.30-5.30. CL: Sat. SIZE: Small. *STOCK: Fine English, Irish and Scottish silver, 16th to early 19th C; unusual collectable silver - vinaigrettes, wine labels, card cases, caddy spoons, snuff boxes; Arts and Crafts silver including Omar Ramsden.* LOC: Off Duke St. PARK: Meters. TEL: 020 7839 2808; fax - 020 7839 2809; mobile - 07976 283530. SER: Valuations; restorations (repairs, gilding, re-plating), replacement cruet and ink bottles; buys at auction. VAT: Spec.

Simon C. Dickinson Ltd
58 Jermyn St. SW1Y 6LX. (Simon Dickinson, David Ker and James Roundell). SLAD. Est. 1993. Open 10-5.30, Fri. 10-4.30. CL: Sat. SIZE: Large. *STOCK: Important Old Master and Modern Master paintings.* LOC: 2 mins. from Piccadilly. TEL: 020 7493 0340; fax - 020 7493 0796; website - www.simondickinson.com. SER: Valuations; restorations; buys at auction. VAT: Spec.

Douwes Fine Art Ltd
38 Duke St., St. James's. SW1Y 6DF. SLAD. Est. 1805. Open 9.30-5.30. CL: Sat. SIZE: Medium. *STOCK: 16th-20th C paintings, drawings and watercolours, Dutch, Flemish, French and Russian schools.* PARK: Meters. TEL: 020 7839 5795. SER: Valuations; restorations. VAT: Spec.

Eaton Gallery
34 Duke St., St. James's and 9 and 12a Princes Arcade, Jermyn St. SW1Y 6DF. (Dr J. D. George). LAPADA. Est. 1976. Open 10-5.30. *STOCK: English and European paintings, 19th-20th C and contemporary.* TEL: 020 7930 5950; fax - 020 7839 8076.

N. and I. Franklin
BADA

11 Bury St., St. James's. SW1Y 6AB. Open 9.30-5.30. CL: Sat. *STOCK: Fine silver and works of art.* TEL: 020 7839 3131; fax - 020 7839 3132.

Victor Franses Gallery
BADA

57 Jermyn St., St. James's. SW1Y 6LX. Est. 1972. Open 10-5, Sat. by appointment. *STOCK: 19th C animalier bronzes, paintings, watercolours and drawings.* TEL: 020 7493 6284/7629 1144; fax - 020 7495 3668. SER: Valuations; restorations. FAIRS: Grosvenor House.

ALASTAIR DICKENSON
FINE SILVER LTD.

90 Jermyn Street, London SW1Y 6JD
Tel: 020 7839 2808 Fax: 020 7839 2809

An important pair of Queen Anne snuffers with stand,
engraved with the arms of Martyn of Woodford, Essex,
both by Joseph Bird, 1709, 8in. high, 15oz.

73

S. Franses Ltd
80 Jermyn St. at Duke St., St. James's. SW1Y 6JD. Est. 1909. Open 9-5. CL: Sat. SIZE: Large. *STOCK: Historic and decorative tapestries, carpets, fabrics and textiles.* TEL: 020 7976 1234; fax - 020 7930 8451; e-mail - gallery@franses.com; website - www.franses.com. SER: Valuations; restorations; cleaning. VAT: Spec.

Charles Frodsham & Co Ltd
32 Bury St., St. James's. SW1Y 6AU. By appointment only. SIZE: Medium. *STOCK: Clocks, watches, marine chronometers and other horological items.* LOC: Between Jermyn St. and St. James's St. PARK: Meters. TEL: 020 7839 1234; fax - 020 7839 2000. VAT: Stan/Spec.

Frost and Reed Ltd (Est. 1808) BADA
2-4 King St., St James's. SW1Y 6QP. SLAD. Open 9-5.30. CL: Sat. *STOCK: Fine 19th C British and Continental paintings, marine and sporting pictures, Post-Impressionist drawings and watercolours; works by Sir Alfred Munnings, Montague Dawson, Marcel Dyf, Peter Smith, and Heather St Clair Davis.* **PARK: Meters. TEL: 020 7839 4645; fax - 020 7839 1166; e-mail - frostandreed@btinternet.com; website - www.frostandreed.co.uk. VAT: Spec.**

Gallery '25
26 Pimlico Rd. SW1W 8LJ. (D. Iglesis). Est. 1969. Open 9.30-5.30, Sat. 10-2. SIZE: Medium. *STOCK: Art glass, £100-£5,000; signed furniture, £1,000-£10,000; decorative fine art, £500-£5,000; all 1900-1960's.* TEL: 020 7730 7516; fax - same. SER: Valuations; buys at auction (as stock). FAIRS: Park Lane; Olympia. VAT: Stan/Spec.

Christopher Gibbs Ltd
3 Dove Walk, Pimlico Rd. SW1W 8PH. LAPADA. Est. 1960. Open Mon.-Fri. 9.30-5.30. SIZE: Large. *STOCK: Unusual and decorative paintings, furniture, works of art and sculpture.* TEL: 020 7730 8200; fax - 020 7730 8420. VAT: Spec.

Nicholas Gifford-Mead BADA
68 Pimlico Rd. SW1W 8LS. LAPADA. Est. 1972. Open 9.30-5.30. CL: Sat. SIZE: Medium. *STOCK: Chimney pieces and sculpture, 18th-19th C, from £1,000.* **LOC: 3 minutes from Sloane Sq. TEL: 020 7730 6233; fax - 020 7730 6239. SER: Valuations. VAT: Stan/Spec.**

Joss Graham
10 Eccleston St. SW1W 9LT. Est. 1980. Open 10-6. SIZE: 2 floors. *STOCK: Textiles including rugs, kelims, embroideries, tribal costume and shawls; jewellery, metalwork, furniture, masks and primitive art - Indian, Middle Eastern, Central Asian and African.* LOC: 5 minutes walk from Victoria station. PARK: NCP, Semley Place. TEL: 020 7730 4370; fax - same; e-mail - joss.graham@btinternet.com. SER: Valuations; restorations; conservation. FAIRS: Hali International, London; Arts of Pacific Asia; Tribal Art Show, San Francisco.

Martyn Gregory Gallery BADA
34 Bury St., St. James's. SW1Y 6AU. SLAD. Open 10-6. CL: Sat. SIZE: Medium. *STOCK: China Trade paintings relating to China and the Far East; early English watercolours, 18th-20th C; British paintings, both £500-£100,000.* **PARK: Meters. TEL: 020 7839 3731; fax - 020 7930 0812; e-mail - mgregory@dircon.co.uk; website - www.martyngregory.com. SER: Valuations. FAIRS: Grosvenor House; Maastricht (Tefaf); New York (Winter); Boston (Ellis Memorial); London (Watercolours & Drawings). VAT: Spec.**

Ross Hamilton Ltd
95 Pimlico Rd. SW1W 8PH. (Mark Boyce and John Underwood). LAPADA. Est. 1971. Open 9.30-6, Sat. 11-1.30. SIZE: Large. *STOCK: English and Continental furniture, 17th-19th C, £1,000-£100,000; porcelain and objects, 18th-19th C, £1,000-£3,000; paintings, 17th-19th C, £1,000-£10,000+.* LOC: 2 minutes walk from Sloane Square. PARK: Side streets. TEL: 020 7730 3015; website - www.lapada.co.uk/ross hamilton/. VAT: Stan/Spec.

Brian Harkins Oriental Art
3 Bury St., St. James's. SW1Y 6AB. Est. 1978. Open 10-6. SIZE: Small. *STOCK: Japanese bronzes, 1868-1989, £2,000-£60,000; Japanese Art Deco, £500-£12,000; Chinese scholar's art and rock from Ming (1368-1643) and Qing dynasties, (1643-1912), £500-£20,000.* LOC: Near Green Park underground. TEL: 020 7839 3338; fax - 0207 839 9339; e-mail - info@brianharkins.co.uk; website - www.brianharkins.co.uk. FAIRS: International Asian Art, New York.

Harris Lindsay BADA
67 Jermyn St. SW1Y 6NY. (Jonathan Harris and Bruce Lindsay). CINOA. Open 9.30-6. CL: Sat. *STOCK: English, Continental and Oriental furniture and works of art.* **TEL: 020 7839 5767; fax - 020 7839 5768. FAIRS: Grosvenor House; New York. VAT: Spec.**

Harrods Ltd
Brompton Rd., Knightsbridge. SW1X 7XL. Open 10-7. SIZE: Large. *STOCK: Fine Victorian, Edwardian and period furniture and clocks.* PARK: Own. TEL: 020 7225 5940.

Julian Hartnoll
3rd. Floor, 14 Mason's Yard, Duke St., St. James's. SW1Y 6BU. Est. 1968. Open by appointment or by chance. *STOCK: 19th-20th C British paintings, drawings and prints especially pre-Raphaelite and works by the kitchen sink artists, including Bratby.* TEL: 020 7839 3842. VAT: Spec.

Harvey and Gore   BADA
41 Duke St., St. James's. SW1Y 6DF. (B.E. Norman). Est. 1723. Open 9.30-5. CL: Sat. SIZE: Small. *STOCK: Jewellery, £150-£50,000; silver, £50-£15,000; old Sheffield plate, £125-£15,000; antique paste.* TEL: 020 7839 4033; fax - 020 7839 3313; e-mail - norman@harveyand gore.co.uk; website - www. harveyandgore.co. uk. SER: Valuations; restorations (jewellery and silver); buys at auction. VAT: Stan/Spec.

Hazlitt, Gooden and Fox Ltd
38 Bury St., St. James's. SW1Y 6BB. SLAD. Open 9.30-5.30. CL: Sat. SIZE: Large. *STOCK: Paintings, drawings and sculpture.* PARK: Meters. TEL: 020 7930 6422; fax - 020 7839 5984. SER: Valuations; restorations. VAT: Spec.

Thomas Heneage Art Books
42 Duke St., St. James's. SW1Y 6DJ. LAPADA. Est. 1975. Open 9.30-6 or by appointment. CL: Sat. *STOCK: Art reference books.* TEL: 020 7930 9223; fax - 020 7839 9223; e-mail - artbooks@ heneage.com.

Hermitage Antiques plc
97 Pimlico Rd. SW1W 8PH. (B. Vieux-Pernon). Est. 1967. Open 10-6, Sat. 10-5, Sun. by appointment. SIZE: Large. *STOCK: Biedermeier, Empire and Russian furniture; oil paintings; decorative arts; chandeliers; bronzes.* Not Stocked: Silver and jewellery. LOC: Off Sloane Square. PARK: Easy. TEL: 020 7730 1973; fax - 020 7730 6586; e-mail - info@hermitage-antiques.co.uk; website - www.hermitage-antiques.co.uk. VAT: Stan/Spec.

Carlton Hobbs   BADA
Est. 1975. Open by appointment only. *STOCK: English and Continental furniture, paintings, chandeliers, works of art, £4,000-£850,000.* LOC: Westminster. TEL: 020 7340 1000; fax - 020 7340 1001; e-mail - chobbs65@aol.com; website - www.interiorinternet.com.

Christopher Hodsoll Ltd inc. Bennison
                                    BADA
89-91 Pimlico Rd. SW1W 8PH. Est. 1991. Open 9-6. *STOCK: Furniture, sculpture, pictures and objects.* PARK: Meters. TEL: 020

7730 3370; fax - 020 7730 1516; website - www. hodsoll.com. SER: Search; interior design. VAT: Stan/Spec.

Hotspur Ltd   BADA
14 Lowndes St. SW1X 9EX. (R.A.B. Kern). Est. 1924. Open 8.30-6, Sat. 9.30-1. SIZE: Large. *STOCK: Fine English furniture, 1680-1800.* LOC: Between Belgrave Sq. and Lowndes Sq. PARK: Underground within 100yds. TEL: 020 7235 1918; fax - 020 7235 4371; e-mail - hotspurltd@msn.com. FAIRS: Grosvenor House. VAT: Spec.

Christopher Howe
93 Pimlico Rd. SW1W 8PH. Est. 1982. Open 9-5.30, Sat. 10.30-4.30. SIZE: Large. *STOCK: English and European furniture, 16th-20th C, £100-£250,000; decorative objects and lighting.* LOC: Near Sloane Square. PARK: Easy. TEL: 020 7730 7987; fax - 020 7730 0157; e-mail - c.howe@easynet.co.uk. SER: Valuations. VAT: Stan/Spec.

Humphrey-Carrasco
43 Pimlico Rd. SW1W 8NE. (David Humphrey and Marylise Carrasco). Est. 1987. Open 10-6, Sat. 10-5. *STOCK: English furniture and lighting, architectural objects, 18th-19th C.* LOC: 10 minute walk from Sloane Sq. PARK: Easy. TEL: 020 7730 9911; fax - 020 7730 9944; e-mail - hc@humphreycarrasco.demon.co.uk. FAIRS: Olympia. VAT: Stan/Spec.

Jeremy Ltd   BADA
29 Lowndes St. SW1X 9HX. (M. and J. Hill). Est. 1946. Open 8.30-6, Sat. 9-1. SIZE: Large. *STOCK: English, French and Russian furniture, objets d'art, glass chandeliers, 18th to early 19th C.* PARK: Easy. TEL: 020 7823 2923; fax - 020 7245 6197; e-mail - jeremy@jeremique.co.uk; website - www. jeremy.ltd.uk. FAIRS: Grosvenor House; New York Armory Show. VAT: Spec.

Derek Johns Ltd
12 Duke St., St. James's. SW1Y 6BN. SLAD. Open 10-6. *STOCK: Old Master paintings.* TEL: 020 7839 7671; fax - 020 7930 0986.

Daniel Katz Ltd
59 Jermyn St. SW1Y 6LX. (Daniel Katz and Stuart Lochhead). SLAD. Est. 1970. Open 9-6. CL: Sat. SIZE: Large. *STOCK: European sculpture, early medieval to 19th C, from £5,000.* LOC: Near Green Park underground. TEL: 020 7493 0688; fax - 020 7499 7493. FAIRS: Paris Biennale. VAT: Spec.

Keshishian
BADA
73 Pimlico Rd. SW1W 8NE. Est. 1978. Open 9.30-6, Sat. 10-5. SIZE: Large. *STOCK: European and Oriental carpets, to late 19th C; Aubussons, mid 19th C; European tapestries, 16th-18th C; Arts and Crafts and Art Deco carpet specialists.* LOC: Off Lower Sloane St. PARK: Easy. TEL: 020 7730 8810; fax - 020 7730 8803. SER: Valuations; restorations. VAT: Stan/Spec.

John King
BADA
74 Pimlico Rd. SW1W 8LS. Est. 1970. Open 10-6, Sat. by appointment. SIZE: Medium. *STOCK: Fine and unusual antiques, £500-£150,000.* TEL: 020 7730 0427; fax - 020 7730 2515. FAIRS: Olympia (June and Nov). VAT: Spec.

Knightsbridge Coins
43 Duke St., St. James's. SW1. Open 10-6. CL: Sat. *STOCK: Coins - British, American and South African; medals.* TEL: 020 7930 7597/7930 8215.

Kojis Antique Jewellery Ltd
Harrods Fine Jewellery Room, Harrods Ltd., Brompton Rd., Knightsbridge. SW1X 7XL. Open 10-7. *STOCK: Antique and contemporary jewellery and objects; jade.* TEL: 020 7730 1234 ext. 4062/4072.

Bob Lawrence Gallery
93 Lower Sloane St. SW1. Est. 1972. Open 10-6. SIZE: Medium. *STOCK: Decorative arts to Art Deco - furniture, paintings, objects and furnishings, £50-£10,000.* LOC: 2 minutes Sloane Sq., adjacent Pimlico Rd. PARK: Easy. TEL: 020 7730 5900; fax - 020 7730 5902. SER: Valuations; restorations; buys at auction. VAT: Stan/Spec.

M. and D. Lewis
84 Pimlico Rd. SW1. Open 9.30-5.30, Sat. 9.30-12, Sun. by appointment. *STOCK: Continental and Victorian furniture, porcelain, bronzes.* TEL: 020 7730 1015; fax - 020 7727 3908 (after 6). VAT: Stan.

Lion, Witch and Lampshade
c/o Muriel Michalos Ltd., 57 Elizabeth St. SW1W 9PP. (Mr and Mrs N. Dixon). Est. 1984. Open by appointment. *STOCK: Unusual decorative objects, 18th to early 20th C, £5-£150; lamps, wall brackets, chandeliers and candlesticks, £50-£1,000.* PARK: Easy. TEL: 020 7730 1774. SER: Restorations (porcelain and glass). VAT: Stan/Spec.

Longmire Ltd (Three Royal Warrants)
12 Bury St., St. James's. SW1Y 6AB. Open 9.30-5.30, Sat. in Nov. and Dec. only. *STOCK: Individual antique jewellery, cufflink and dress sets: antique, signed, platinum, gold, gem set, hardstone, pearl, carved crystal or enamel - four vices, fishing, polo, golfing, shooting, big game, ladybird and pigs.* LOC: Coming from Piccadilly, down Duke St., right into King St. past Christie's, first right into Bury St. PARK: Easy. TEL: 020 7930 8720; fax - 020 7930 1898. SER: Custom hand engraving or enamelling in colour - any corporate logo, initials, crest, coats of arms or tartan, any animal (cat, dog etc.), racing silks, sailing burgees, favourite hobbies or own automobiles.

MacConnal-Mason Gallery
BADA
14 and 17 Duke St., St. James's. SW1Y 6DB. TEFAF. Est. 1893. Open 9-6. SIZE: Large. *STOCK: Pictures, 19th-20th C.* PARK: Meters. TEL: 020 7839 7693; fax - 020 7839 6797; e-mail - macconnal-mason@msn.com; website - www.macconnal-mason-gallery.co.uk. SER: Valuations; restorations. FAIRS: Maastricht; New York; Palm Beach; Dallas; London. VAT: Spec.

The Mall Galleries
The Mall. SW1. Est. 1971. Open 10-5 seven days. *STOCK: Paintings, sculpture, prints and drawings.* LOC: Near Trafalgar Sq. TEL: 020 7930 6844; fax - 020 7839 7830; website - www.mallgalleries.org.uk. SER: Contemporary art exhibitions held; commissioning; gallery hire; workshops.

Paul Mason Gallery
BADA
149 Sloane St. SW1X 9BZ. Est. 1969. Open 9-6, Wed. 9-7, Sat. 12-5. *STOCK: Marine, sporting and decorative paintings and prints, 18th-19th C; period and old frames, portfolio stands, ship models and nautical items.* LOC: Sloane Sq. end of Sloane St. PARK: Easy. TEL: 020 7730 3683; fax - 020 7730 7359; e-mail - paulmasonart@aol.com. SER: Valuations; restorations (prints, paintings); buys at auction. FAIRS: England and Europe. VAT: Stan/Spec.

Jeremy Mason (Sainsbury & Mason)
145 Ebury St. SW1. Est. 1968. Open 10-1. *STOCK: Period Oriental and European works of art, especially Chinese and Japanese, bronzes, lacquer, porcelain, glass and pictures.* TEL: 020 7730 8331; home - 020 8874 4173; fax - 020 7730 8334. VAT: Spec.

Mathaf Gallery Ltd
24 Motcomb St. SW1X 8JU. (Brian and Gina MacDermot). LAPADA, SLAD. Est. 1975. Open

9.30-5.30. CL: Sat. *STOCK: Paintings, Middle East subjects, 19th C.* LOC: Knightsbridge. TEL: 020 7235 0010; e-mail - art@mathafgallery. demon.co.uk; website - www.mathafgallery.com. SER: Valuations. VAT: Spec.

Matthiesen Fine Art Ltd.
7-8 Mason's Yard, Duke St., St. James's. SW1Y 6BU. Est. 1978. Open by appointment only. *STOCK: Fine Italian Old Master paintings, 1300-1800; French and Spanish Old Master paintings.* TEL: 020 7930 2437; fax - 020 7930 1387. SER: Valuations; buys at auction.

McClenaghan
69 Pimlico Rd. SW1W 8NE. (John McClenaghan and Bob Gilhooly). Open 10-6, Sat. 10.30-4. *STOCK: English country house furniture, objects and period lighting.* TEL: 020 7730 4187; fax - same; e-mail - mcclenaghan.mcced@virgin.net. VAT: Stan/Spec/Export.

Thomas Mercer (Chronometers) Ltd
32 Bury St., St. James's. SW1Y 6AU. By appointment only. SIZE: Medium. *STOCK: Marine chronometers.* LOC: Between Jermyn St. and St. James's St. PARK: Meters. TEL: 020 7930 9300; fax - 020 7321 0350. VAT: Stan/Spec.

Messums   BADA
40 Duke St., St James's. SW1Y 6DF. LAPADA. Open Mon.-Fri. 10-6, other times by appointment. SIZE: Medium. *STOCK: Traditional and British Impressionist paintings.* **TEL: 020 7839 5180; fax - 020 7839 5188. SER: Valuations; restorations; framing. VAT: Stan/Spec.**

Duncan R. Miller Fine Arts   BADA
6 Bury St., St. James's. SW1Y 6AB. CINOA. Open 10-6. SIZE: Small. *STOCK: Modern British and European paintings, drawings and sculpture, especially Scottish Colourist paintings.* **TEL: 020 7839 8806. SER: Valuations; conservation and restoration (oils, works on paper and Oriental rugs); buys at auction. FAIRS: Grosvenor House; BADA; Olympia. VAT: Spec.**

Nigel Milne Ltd
38 Jermyn St. SW1Y 6DN. Est. 1979. Open 9.30-5.30. SIZE: Small. *STOCK: Jewellery, silver frames and objects.* TEL: 020 7434 9343. SER: Valuations. VAT: Stan/Spec.

Mrs Monro Ltd
Jubilee House, 70 Cadogan Place. SW1X 9AH. (John Lusk). FBIDA. Est. 1926. Open 9.30-5.30, Fri. 9.30-5. CL: Sat. SIZE: Medium. *STOCK: Small decorative furniture, £500-£1,000+; china,*

£50-£500+; *rugs, prints, pictures and general decorative items, from £50; all 18th-19th C.* LOC: Between Sloane Sq. and Pont St. PARK: Garage nearby. TEL: 020 7235 0326; fax - 020 7259 6305; e-mail - design@mrsmonro.co.uk; website - www.mrsmunro.co.uk. SER: Restorations (furniture and china). VAT: Stan/Spec.

Moreton Street Gallery
40 Moreton St. SW1V 2PB. (W.M. Pearson - Frasco International Ltd). Est. 1972. Open 9-1 and 2-6. CL: Sat. SIZE: Medium. *STOCK: Contemporary oils, watercolours, limited editions, posters; early engravings - Bunbury, Rowlandson, Hogarth, Gilray and Heath.* LOC: Off Belgrave Rd. PARK: Easy. TEL: 020 7834 7773/5; fax - 020 7834 7834. SER: Valuations; restorations; buys at auction (originals and engravings). VAT: Stan.

Guy Morrison
91a Jermyn St. SW1Y 6JB. SLAD. Open 9.30-5.30. CL: Sat. *STOCK: British paintings from 1900.* TEL: 020 7839 1454.

Peter Nahum at The Leicester
Galleries   BADA
5 Ryder St. SW1Y 6PY. Est. 1983. Open 9.30-6. CL: Sat. and Sun. except by appointment. SIZE: Large. *STOCK: British and European paintings, works on paper and bronzes, including the Pre-Raphaelites and Modern British, 19th-20th C, £1,000-£100,000+.* **LOC: 100yds. from Royal Academy. PARK: Meters. TEL: 020 7930 6059; fax - 020 7930 4678; e-mail - peter nahum@leicestergalleries.com; website - www.leicestergalleries.com. SER: Valuations; restorations; framing. FAIRS: Grosvenor House; 20th/21st C British Art; Tefaf, New York (May). VAT: Spec.**

Old Maps and Prints
3rd Floor, Harrods, Knightsbridge. SW1X 7XL. Est. 1976. *STOCK: Maps, 16th C to 1890; engravings (all subjects); watercolours.* TEL: 020 7730 1234, ext. 2124.

Ossowski   BADA
83 Pimlico Rd. SW1W 8PH. Est. 1960. Open 10-6. CL: Sat. pm. SIZE: Medium. *STOCK: Carved gilt, 18th C; mirrors, consoles, wood carvings.* **TEL: 020 7730 3256. SER: Restorations (gilt furniture). FAIRS: New York; Palm Beach. VAT: Stan/Spec.**

Anthony Outred   BADA
46 Pimlico Rd. SW1W 8LP. Open 9-6, Sat. 10-5. SIZE: Large. *STOCK: Exceptional English*

and Continental furniture especially unusual and amusing, £1,000-£100,000. LOC: 2 minutes from Sloane Sq. PARK: Meters. TEL: 020 7730 4782; fax - 020 7730 5643; mobile - 07767 848132; e-mail - antiques@outred.co.uk; website - www.outred.co.uk. SER: Finder. FAIRS: Olympia. VAT: Stan/Spec.

Paisnel Gallery
22 Mason's Yard, Duke St., St James's. SW1Y 6BU. (Stephen and Sylvia Paisnel). SLAD. Est. 1977. Open 10-6. CL: Sat. SIZE: Small. *STOCK: Modern British paintings, especially Newlyn and St. Ives Schools, £5,000-£50,000.* LOC: Duke St. runs between Piccadilly and King St. 1 minute from Christies. PARK: St. James Sq. TEL: 020 7930 9293; fax - 020 7930 7280; e-mail - info @paisnelgallery.com. VAT: Spec.

The Parker Gallery   BADA
28 Pimlico Rd. SW1W 8LJ. (Thomas H. Parker Ltd). SLAD. Est. 1750. Open 9.30-5.30, Sat. by appointment. SIZE: Medium. *STOCK: Historical prints, £45-£1,200; English paintings, £1,000-£30,000; ship models, £95-£30,000.* LOC: 5 minutes from Sloane Sq. TEL: 020 7730 6768; fax - 020 7259 9180; website - www.theparker gallery.com. SER: Restorations (as stock); mounting; framing. VAT: Stan/Spec.

Michael Parkin Fine Art Ltd
Studio 4, Sedding St., 1/6 Sloane Sq. SW1W 8EE. SLAD. By appointment only. *STOCK: British paintings, watercolours, drawings and prints, 1860-1960, £50-£10,000.* PARK: Easy. TEL: 020 7730 9784; fax - 020 7730 9718. FAIRS: 20th-21st C British Art. VAT: Spec.

Trevor Philip and Sons Ltd   BADA
75a Jermyn St., St. James's. SW1Y 6NP. (T. and R. Waterman). Est. 1972. Open 9.30-6, Sat. by appointment only. SIZE: Medium. *STOCK: Early scientific instruments, globes, barometers and ships models; silver and vertu.* PARK: At rear. TEL: 020 7930 2954; fax - 020 7321 0212; e-mail - globe@trevorphilip.com; website - www.trevorphilip.com. SER: Valuations; restorations (clocks and scientific instruments); buys at auction. VAT: Stan/Spec.

Portland Gallery
9 Bury St., St. James's. SW1Y 6AB. SLAD. Est. 1985. Open 10-6. CL: Sat. SIZE: Medium. *STOCK: Scottish pictures, 20th C, £500-£250,000.* TEL: 020 7321 0422. SER: Valuations; buys at auction. VAT: Spec.

Pullman Gallery
14 King St., St. James's. SW1Y 6QU. (Simon Khachadourian). Est. 1980. Open 10-6, Sat. by appointment. SIZE: Medium. *STOCK: Objets de luxe, 19th-20th C, £200-£20,000; automobile art, pre-1950, £1,000-£20,000; collectable cocktail shakers, bar accessories, cigar memorabilia, 1880-1950, £250-£25,000; René Lalique glass, 1900-1940, from £3,000.* LOC: Corner of Bury St., adjacent Christie's. PARK: Easy. TEL: 020 7930 9595; fax - 020 7930 9494; mobile - 07973 141606; e-mail - sk@pullmangallery.com; website - www.pullmangallery.com. VAT: Stan.

Mark Ransom Ltd
62 and 105 Pimlico Rd. SW1W 8LS. Est. 1989. Open 10-6. SIZE: Medium. *STOCK: Furniture - French Empire and Russian, early 19th C; Continental, decorative, from late 18th C, all to £1,000+.* LOC: Close to Sloane Sq. underground - turn left left, 5 minute walk. PARK: Side streets. TEL: 020 7259 0220; fax - 020 7259 0323. VAT: Stan/Spec.

Steven Rich & Michael Rich
39 Duke St., St. James's. SW1Y 6DF. SLAD. Open daily, Sat. by appointment. SIZE: Medium. *STOCK: Master paintings, 16th-19th C; collectors items.* LOC: Just off Piccadilly. PARK: St. James's Sq. TEL: 020 7930 9308; fax - 020 7930 2088. SER: Valuations. VAT: Spec.

Rogier et Rogier
20A Pimlico Rd. SW1W 8LJ. (Miss Lauriance Rogier). Est. 1980. Open 10-6, Sat. 11-4. SIZE: Small. *STOCK: French and Continental painted and country furniture, 18th-19th C, £1,000-£5,000; lamps and wall sconces, 19th C, from £500; decorative antique and reproduction items, from £300.* LOC: 5 minutes walk from Sloane Sq. PARK: Meters. TEL: 020 7823 4780; e-mail - rogier @easynet.co.uk. SER: Restorations (decoration, painted effects, murals, trompe l'oeil). VAT: Spec.

Rossi & Rossi Ltd
91c Jermyn St., St James's. SW1Y 6JB. (Anna Maria and Fabio Rossi). Est. 1984. Open 10-5, Sat. and Sun. by appointment. SIZE: Medium. *STOCK: Himalayan art, 12th-17th C, to £10,000+; Indian art, 1st-13th C, to £10,000+.* LOC: Off Piccadilly. PARK: Meters. TEL: 020 7321 0208; fax - 020 7321 0546. SER: Valuations; buys at auction. VAT: Spec.

Julian Simon Fine Art Ltd   BADA
70 Pimlico Rd. SW1W 8LS. (M. and J. Brookstone). Open 10-6, Sat. 10-4 or by appointment. *STOCK: Fine English and Continental pictures, 18th-20th C.* LOC: Sloane Sq. TEL: 020 7730 8673; fax - 020 7823 6116; e-mail - julian simon@compuserve.com; website - www.19th centurypaintings.com. FAIRS: Olympia.

THE PARKER GALLERY

(ESTABLISHED 1750)

28, PIMLICO ROAD, LONDON SW1W 8LJ

TEL: 0207-730 6768   FAX: 0207-259 9180

Action off Cape François, 21st October 1757
Coloured line engraving by Smith after Swaine, published 1758
Size 7 x 11¾ inches (17.8 x 29.9cms)

The Royal Scots Greys, Chobham 1853
Coloured lithograph by Butler after de Prades, published 1854
Size 11½ x 17 inches (29.2 x 43 cms)

DEALERS IN PRINTS, PAINTINGS AND WATERCOLOURS OF
THE 18th, 19th & 20th CENTURY, COVERING MARINE,
MILITARY, TOPOGRAPHICAL AND SPORTING
SUBJECTS, MAPS & SHIP MODELS

Sims, Reed Ltd
43a Duke St., St James's. SW1Y 6DD. Open 10-6, Sat. 10-4. *STOCK: Illustrated, rare and in-print books on the fine and applied arts; leather-bound literary sets; contemporary books.* TEL: 020 7493 5660; fax - 020 7493 8468; e-mail - info@sims reed.com; website - www.simsreed.com.

Peta Smyth - Antique Textiles
42 Moreton St., Pimlico. SW1V 2PB. LAPADA. Est. 1977. Open 9.30-5.30. CL: Sat. *STOCK: European textiles and needlework, 17th-19th C, £50-£10,000; tapestries and cushions.* PARK: Easy. TEL: 020 7630 9898; fax - 020 7630 5398; e-mail - petasmyth@uk.online.co.uk. FAIRS: Olympia. VAT: Spec.

Somlo Antiques   BADA
7 Piccadilly Arcade. SW1Y 6NH. Est. 1972. Open 10-5.30, Sat. 10.30-5. SIZE: Medium. *STOCK: Vintage wrist and antique pocket watches, from £1,000.* **LOC: Between Piccadilly and Jermyn St. PARK: Meters. TEL: 020 7499 6526. SER: Restorations.**

Henry Sotheran Ltd
80 Pimlico Rd. SW1W 8PL. Open 10-6, Sat. 10-4. *STOCK: Fine and rare antique prints of architecture, decorative, natural history, travel and topography.* TEL: 020 7730 8756; fax - 020 7823 6090. VAT: Stan.

Robin Symes Ltd
3 Ormond Yard, Duke of York St., St. James's. SW1. Open by appointment only. SIZE: Large. *STOCK: Antiquities, ancient art.* PARK: Meters. TEL: 020 7930 9856/7; 020 7930 5300.

thesilverfund.com
40 Bury St. SW1Y 6AU. (Alastair Crawford and Michael James). Open daily, Sat. and Sun. by appointment. SIZE: Large. *STOCK: Old Georg Jensen silver, £500-£100,000.* LOC: Opposite Christies (King St/Bury St). PARK: NCP Mayfair. TEL: 020 7839 7664; fax - 020 7839 8935; e-mail - dealers@thesilverfund.com. SER: Valuations; restorations. VAT: Stan/Spec.

Bill Thomson - Albany Gallery
1 Bury St., St. James's. SW1Y 6AB. (W.B. Thomson). Open Mon.-Fri. 9-6 by appointment. *STOCK: British drawings, watercolours and paintings, 1700-1850 and some 20th C.* TEL: 020 7839 6119; fax - 020 7839 6614.

Trafalgar Galleries   BADA
35 Bury St., St. James's. SW1Y 6AY. Open 9.30-6. CL: Sat. *STOCK: Old Master paintings.* **LOC: Just south of Piccadilly. TEL: 020 7839 6466.**

Tryon Gallery (incorporating Malcolm Innes)
7 Bury St.,St James's. SW1Y 6AL. (Malcolm Innes and Oliver Swann). SLAD. Open 10-6, CL: Sat. (except during some exhibitions). *STOCK: Sporting, wildlife and natural history subjects; Scottish landscape and military pictures; paintings, bronzes, books, £150-£50,000.* TEL: 020 7839 8083; fax - 020 7839 8085. SER: Valuations; framing; advising; commission buying. FAIRS: Game. VAT: Spec.

Un Francais á Londres
202 Ebury St. SW1W 8UN. Est. 1990. Open 10-6, Sat. 10-4, or by appointment. SIZE: Large. *STOCK: 18th to early 19th C French and Continental furniture.* LOC: Near Pimlico Rd. PARK: Easy. TEL: 020 7730 1771/1881; fax - 020 7730 1661; e-mail - eburystreet@aol.com; website - www.unfrancaisalondres.com. SER: Valuations; restorations; buys at auction. VAT: Spec

Rafael Valls Ltd   BADA
11 Duke St., St. James's. SW1Y 6BN. SLAD. Est. 1976. Open Mon.-Fri. 9.30-6. *STOCK: Old Master paintings.* **TEL: 020 7930 1144; fax - 020 7976 1596. VAT: Spec.**

Rafael Valls Ltd   BADA
6 Ryder St., St. James's. SW1Y 6QB. SLAD. Open Mon.-Fri. 9.30-6. *STOCK: Fine European paintings.* **TEL: 020 7930 0029; fax - 020 7976 1596. VAT: Spec.**

Johnny Van Haeften Ltd   BADA
13 Duke St., St. James's. SW1Y 6DB. (J. and S. Van Haeften). SLAD, TEFAF. Est. 1978. Open 10-6, Sat. and Sun. by appointment. SIZE: Medium. *STOCK: Dutch and Flemish Old Master paintings, 16th-17th C, £5,000-£5m.* **LOC: Middle of Duke St. TEL: 020 7930 3062/3; fax - 020 7839 6303. SER: Valuations; restorations (Old Masters); buys at auction (paintings including Old Masters). FAIRS: Grosvenor House; Maastricht. VAT: Spec.**

Waterman Fine Art Ltd
75A Jermyn St., St. James's. SW1Y 6NP. Open 9-6, Sat. 10-4. *STOCK: 20th C paintings and watercolours.* TEL: 020 7839 5203; fax - 020 7321 0212.

Westenholz Antiques Ltd
76-78 Pimlico Rd. SW1W 8PL. Open 10-6, Sat. by appointment. *STOCK: 18th-19th C furniture, pictures, objects, lamps, mirrors.* TEL: 020 7824 8090.

ANTIQUARIUS

131-141 King's Road, London SW3

"A fine example of what the best antiques centre can offer"

Antique Dealer and Collectors Guide

Enquiries: Mike Spooner/Neil Jackson

Tel: 020-7969 1500   Fax: 020-7969 1639

Whitford Fine Art
6 Duke St., St. James's. SW1Y 6BN. (Adrian Mibus). Est. 1973. Open 10-6. CL: Sat. *STOCK: Oil paintings and sculpture, late 19th to 20th C; Modernism, post war abstract and pop art.* TEL: 020 7930 9332; fax - 020 7930 5577; e-mail - whitfordfineart@btinternet.com; website - www. artnet.com/whitford.html. VAT: Spec.

Arnold Wiggins and Sons Ltd   BADA
4 Bury St., St. James's. SW1Y 6AB. (M. Gregory). Open Mon.-Fri 9-5.30. *STOCK: Picture frames, 16th-19th C.* TEL: 020 7925 0195.

Wildenstein and Co Ltd
46 St. James's Place. SW1A 1NS. SLAD. Est. 1934. By appointment only. *STOCK: Impressionist and Old Master paintings and drawings.* TEL: 020 7629 0602; fax - 020 7493 3924.

SW3

Norman Adams Ltd   BADA
8/10 Hans Rd., Knightsbridge. SW3 1RX. Est. 1923. Open 9-5.30, Sat. and Sun. by appointment. SIZE: Large. *STOCK: English furniture, 18th C, £650-£250,000; objets d'art (English and French) £500-£50,000; mirrors, glass pictures, 18th C; clocks and barometers.* LOC: 30yds. off the Brompton Rd., opposite west side entrance to Harrods. TEL: 020 7589 5266; fax - 020 7589 1968; e-mail - antiques@normanadams.com; website - www.normanadams.com. FAIRS: Grosvenor House; BADA. VAT: Spec.

After Noah
261 King's Rd. Chelsea. SW3 5EL. (M. Crawford and Z. Candlin). *STOCK: Arts and Craft oak and similar furniture, leather sofas and chairs, 1880's to 1950's, £1-£5,000; iron, iron and brass beds; decorative items, bric-a-brac including candlesticks, mirrors, lighting, kitchenalia and jewel-lery.* TEL: 020 7351 2610; fax - same; e-mail - enquiries@afternoah.com; website - www. afternoah.com. SER: Restorations. VAT: Stan.

The Andipa Gallery
162 Walton St. SW3 2JL. LAPADA. Est. 1969. Open Tues.-Sat. 11-6. *STOCK: Icons from Byzantium, Greece, Russia, Eastern Europe, Asia Minor and North Africa; Italian Masters and Old Masters, all from 14th-19th C; Asian art and antiquities, from 500 BC; modern and contemporary prints, drawings, paintings and sculpture.* LOC: Knightsbridge. TEL: 020 7589 2371; fax - 020 7225 0305; e-mail - art@andipa.com; website - www.andipa.com. SER: Valuations; restorations; research; collections.

Antiquarius
131/141 King's Rd. SW3. (Atlantic Antiques Centres Ltd). Est. 1970. Open 10-6. LOC: On the corner of King's Rd. and Flood St., next to Chelsea Town Hall. TEL: Enquiries - 020 7969 1500; fax - 020 7969 1639; e-mail - antique@ dial.pipex.com. Below are listed some of the many specialist dealers at this market.

225 Jewellery Exchange
Stand V36. (Mrs. Michelle Rowan). LAPADA. *Jewellery and silver.* TEL: 020 7352 8744.

Jaki Abbott
Stand M12. *Jewellery.* TEL: 020 7352 7989; mobile - 07774 864442.

Aesthetics   BADA
Stand V2. (Peter and Philip Jeffs). LAPADA. *Silver, ceramics and decorative arts, 1860-1960.* TEL: 020 7352 0395.

Alzubeidi
Stand V10. LAPADA. *African artefacts.*

AM-PM
Stand V35. (T.J. Yeganeh) *Vintage watches.* TEL: 020 7351 5654.

Francois Amato
Stand V3/4. *18th-20th C furniture and works of art.*
TEL: 020 7352 0809.

Alexia Amato
Stand V8. LAPADA. *Decorative antiques, Bohemian glass.* TEL: 020 7352 3666.

S. Arena
Stand E5. *General antiques, silver plate, ivory.* TEL: 020 7352 7989.

The Art Deco Pavillion
Stand V9. (Maxime Boulanger). *Art Deco furniture.* TEL: Mobile - 07960 321668.

Beauty & The Beast
Stands Q9/10. (J. Rothman). *Costume jewellery, BP Austrian bronzes, handbags.* TEL: 020 7351 5149.

Alexandra Bolla
Stand J1. *Jewellery.* TEL: 020 7352 7989.

Brown & Kingston
Stands V5/6. (Dennis Kingston). *Furniture, Imari, blue and white, Staffordshire porcelain.* TEL: 020 7376 8881.

Mrs T. Buchinger
Stand Q2. *Jewellery.* TEL: 020 7352 8734.

Jasmine Cameron
Stands M1/2/16. *Inkpots and pens, artists materials, glass.* TEL: 020 7351 4154.

Vivian Carroll
Stand N1. *General antiques.* TEL: 020 7352 8734.

G. Chancelier
Stand Q5. *Period costume jewellery, mirrors, lamps, objet d'art.*

Chelsea Antiques Rug Gallery
Stand V15. (N. Somnez). *Oriental carpets and Persian rugs.* TEL: 020 7351 6611.

Chelsea Military Antiques
Stand N13/14. (Dominic Abbott and Richard Black). *Militaria, swords, revolvers, uniforms, medals (WWII and British Empire).* TEL: 020 7352 0308; mobile - 07889 600844.

The Cufflink Shop
Stand G2/3. (John Szwarc). *Jewellery and cufflinks.* TEL: 020 7352 8201.

Glen Dewart
Stands P7/8. *Prints and paintings.* TEL: 0120 7352 4777.

D. Donaghue
Stands P9/10/11. *Jewellery and objets de vertu.* TEL: 020 7352 8734.

Makiko Featherstone
Stands J9/11. *Silver jewellery, small objets d'art.* TEL: 020 7376 8845.

Ferguson Fine Art
Stand V13. (Serena Ferguson). *Sporting collectables.* TEL: 020 7352 5272.

Flight of Fancy
Stands A9-A11. (Jesse Davis). LAPADA. *General antiques.* TEL: 020 7352 4314.

French Glass House
Stands P14/15/16, N4/5. (M. Aboudara). *Art Deco and Art Nouveau glass.* TEL: 020 7376 5394.

Anthony J. Gibb
Stand D3. *Militaria.* TEL: Mobile - 0780 378 3857.

Angelo Gibson
Stand M10. *Silver plate, general antiques.* TEL: 020 7352 4690.

Brian Gordon
Stand G1. LAPADA. *Silver and plate.* TEL: 020 7352 5808.

Hayman & Hayman
Stands K2-K5. *Photo frames, scent bottles.* TEL: 020 7351 6568.

Michael Kelleher
Stand V7. *Decorative prints.* TEL: 020 7581 8739

Don Kelly
Stand L3, M13. *Antiquarian and reference books.* TEL: 020 7352 4690.

The Lace Shop
Stand Q7/8. (Mrs Williamson). *Lace, textiles and decorative antiques.* TEL: Mobile - 07778 659783.

Claude & Martine Latreville
Stand V16. *Fine silver and jewellery.* TEL: 020 7352 5964.

Le Shop
Stand L9. (A. Canetti and J. Galisson). *Jewellery and decorative accessories.* TEL: 020 7352 4690; mobile - 07771 601100.

E. Lehane
Stand V19. LAPADA. *Tortoiseshell and collectables.* TEL: 020 7349 8638.

Michael Lexton
Stand N8-11. *Silver.* TEL: 020 7351 5980.

Little River
Stands D1/2 and D5/6. (David Dykes). *Asian prints, Oriental china and porcelain.* TEL: 020 7349 9080. SER: Restorations (Oriental furniture).

Mrs. A. Lopari (Sormeh)
Stand V20. Jewellery. TEL: 020 7352 5592.

Mrs. V. Luu
Stand P12. Chinese antiques. TEL: 20 7352 8734.

Mr. Martinez-Negrilo
Stand P1/2/3. *Jewellery, porcelain, glass, paintings, objets de vertu.* TEL: 020 7349 0038; mobile - 0956 406954.

Gerald Mathias
Stand R3-6. *Victorian, Edwardian furniture, clocks, boxes.* TEL: 020 7351 0484.

Sue Mautner
Stand N15. *'40's and '50's costume jewellery.* TEL: 020 7376 4419.

Mrs N. McDonald-Hobley
Stand L7. *Jewellery.* TEL: 020 7351 0154.

William McLeod-Brown
Stand L5/6. *Prints.* TEL: 020 7352 4690; workshop - 020 7730 3547.

Mrs. T. Molloy
Stands A12/13. *Oil paintings.*

Mrs. D. Mousavi
Stand D4. *Gold and silver, jade, netsuke.* TEL: 020 7352 8734.

Myriad Antique Jewellery
Stand V38. (Mrs M. McLean). LAPADA. *Vienna bronzes and jewellery.* TEL: 020 7351 9526.

Nicholson Jewellery
Stand V37. (James Nicholson). *Jewellery and silver.* TEL: Mobile - 0976 567992.

Sue Norman
Stand L4. (Mr and Mrs Alloway). *Blue and white china.* TEL: 020 7352 7217.

Roger Painter
Stand V12. *Silver and jewellery..* TEL: 020 73521231; fax - 020 7351 1646.

Maria Perez
Stand V23/24. *Jewellery.* TEL: 020 7351 1986.

Phillipa & John
Stands J4/5. (Mrs. P.M. Miller). *Jewellery and objet d'art.* TEL: 020 7352 4690/7351 0294.

Abdul Rabi
Stand P4. TEL: 020 7352 8734. SER: Jewellery and watch repairs.

Robert Raymond
Stands J2/3. LAPADA. *Fine jewellery.* TEL: 020 7349 0809.

Keiron Reilly
Stands K1/6. *Art Nouveau and Art Deco.* TEL: 020 7352 2099.

Ronco Antiques
Stand V1. (Alex Ronco). *Bronzes.* TEL: 020 7376 8116.

Simar Antiques
Stand A18/19 and H1/2. (A. Cohen). *Silver.* TEL: 020 7352 7155.

D. M. Simpson
Stand E1. *Ivory.* TEL: 020 7352 7989.

Miwa Thorpe
Stand M8/9. *Silver and jewellery.* TEL: 020 7351 2911.

Graham Tomlinson & Sotiris Papadimitriou
Stand T3/4. LAPADA. *Decorative antiques and garden ornaments.* TEL: Mobile - 07778 470983.

William Wain
Stand J6. *Vintage costume jewellery.* TEL: 020 7351 4905.

Geoffrey Waters
Stands F1-6. LAPADA. *Oriental porcelain and silver.* TEL: 020 7376 5467.

West Country Jewellery
Stand M5/6/7. (David Billing). *Jewellery, objects, silver.* TEL: 020 7376 8252.

XS Baggage
Stand A1-4, B1-5, C1/2. (Mr and Mrs Lehane). *Antique luggage and travel requisites including Louis Vuitton and Asprey; sporting memorabilia.* TEL: 020 7352 7989/7376 8781.

Ziggy
Stand E3/4. (S. Aritake). *Watches and lighters.* TEL: 020 7376 5628.

Apter Fredericks Ltd   BADA
265-267 Fulham Rd. SW3 6HY. Open 9.30-5.30, Sat. and evenings by appointment. SIZE: 6 showrooms. STOCK: *English furniture, 17th to early 19th C.* TEL: 020 7352 2188; fax - 020 7376 5619; e-mail - antiques@apter-fredericks.com. FAIRS: Grosvenor House. VAT: Stan/Spec.

Joanna Booth   BADA
247 King's Rd., Chelsea. SW3 5EL. Est. 1963. Open 10-6. SIZE: Medium. STOCK: *Sculpture, 12th-17th C; tapestries, textiles, 16th-18th C; Old Master drawings, £50-£50,000; early furniture, works of art.* PARK: Meters. TEL: 020 7352 8998; fax - 020 7376 7350; e-mail - joannabooth@londonweb.net. SER: Buys at auction. FAIRS: Olympia; BADA (Chelsea). VAT: Spec.

Bourbon-Hanby Antiques Centre
151 Sydney St. Chelsea. SW3 6NT. Open 10-6, Sun. 11-5. LOC: Just off Kings Road, opposite town hall. TEL: 020 7352 2106.

Butler and Wilson
189 Fulham Rd. SW3 6JN. *STOCK: Jewellery, Art Deco, vintage bags and clothes, 1950's jewellery, objects and accessories.* TEL: 020 7352 3045.

Campbell's of Walton Street
164 Walton St. SW3 2JL. Open 9.30-5.30. *STOCK: 20th C impressionist and modern British oils and watercolours.* TEL: 020 7584 9268; fax - 020 7581 3499; website - www.campbellsof waltonstreet.co.uk. SER: Master framing, carving, gilding and restorations.

Classic Fabrics with Robin Haydock
Unit 18 Bourbon-Hanby Antiques Centre, 151 Sydney St. SW3 6NT. LAPADA. Est. 1996. Open Wed.-Sat. 10.30-5.30, Sun. 11-5. *STOCK: Decorative antiques and 17th-19th C textiles.* TEL: 020 7349 9110; fax - same; mobile - 07770 931240; e-mail - robinhaydock@talk21.com. SER: Restorations; shipping. FAIRS: Olympia (June); Decorative Antiques & Textile.

Richard Courtney Ltd   BADA
112-114 Fulham Rd. SW3 6HU. Est. 1959. Open 9.30-1 and 2-6. CL: Sat. SIZE: Large. *STOCK: English furniture, 18th C, £5,000-£50,000.* PARK: Easy. TEL: 020 7370 4020. FAIRS: Grosvenor House; BADA. VAT: Spec.

Robert Dickson and Lesley Rendall Antiques   BADA
263 Fulham Rd. SW3 6HY. Est. 1969. Open 10-6, Sat. 10-4.30. SIZE: Medium. *STOCK: Late 18th to early 19th C furniture and works of art, £500-£100,000.* PARK: Easy. TEL: 020 7351 0330. VAT: Spec.

Dragons of Walton St. Ltd
23 Walton St. SW3 2HX. (R. Fisher). *STOCK: Mainly painted and decorated furniture; hand decorated children's furniture, decorative items.* LOC: Close to Harrods. PARK: Hasker St. or First St. TEL: 020 7589 3795; fax - 020 7584 4570.

Michael Foster   BADA
118 Fulham Rd., Chelsea. SW3 6HU. (Margaret and Michael Susands). Est. 1963. Open 9.30-5.30, Sat. by appointment. *STOCK: 18th C English furniture and works of art.* PARK: Rear of premises. TEL: 020 7373 3636/3040. SER: Valuations. FAIRS: Grosvenor House.

Gallery Lingard
PO Box 33705, Chelsea Manor St. SW3 3FD. SLAD. Open by appointment only. *STOCK: Architectural drawings, watercolours, paintings, prints and books.* TEL: 020 7352 6034; fax - same.

Gallery Yacou
127 Fulham Rd. SW3 6RT. LAPADA. Open 10.30-6, Sat. 11.30-5. *STOCK: Decorative and antique Oriental and European carpets (room-size and over-size).* TEL: 020 7584 2929; fax - 020 7584 3535. FAIRS: Olympia.

General Trading Co Ltd
2 Symons St. SW3 2TJ. LAPADA. Est. 1920. Open 10-6.30. SIZE: Medium. *STOCK: English furniture, £100-£10,000; objects, both 18th-20th C.* LOC: Near Sloane Sq. TEL: 020 7730 0411, 020 7823 5426; e-mail - enquiries@general-trading.co.uk; website - www.general-trading.co.uk. VAT: Stan/Spec.

David Gill
60 Fulham Rd. SW3 6HH. LAPADA. Est. 1986. Open 10-6. SIZE: Medium. *STOCK: Decorative and fine arts, Picasso, Cocteau ceramics and drawings, 1900 to present day.* PARK: Onslow Sq. TEL: 020 7589 5946; fax - 020 7584 9184. VAT: Stan.

Godson and Coles   BADA
92 Fulham Rd. SW3 6HR. Est. 1978. Open 9.30-5.30. CL: Sat. *STOCK: Fine 17th to early 19th C English furniture and works of art.* TEL: 020 7584 2200; fax - 020 7584 2223; e-mail - godsonandcoles@aol.com; website - www. godsonandcoles.co.uk.

Green and Stone
259 Kings Rd. SW3 5EL. (R.J.S. Baldwin). Est. 1927. Open 9-5.30, Wed. 9-7, Sat. 9.30-6, Sun. 12-5. *STOCK: 18th-19th C writing and artists' materials, glass and china.* LOC: At junction with Old Church St. PARK: Meters. TEL: 020 7352 0837; e-mail - greenandstone@enterprise.net. SER: Restorations (pictures). VAT: Stan.

James Hardy and Co
235 Brompton Rd. SW3 2EP. Est. 1853. Open 10-5.30. *STOCK: Silver including tableware, and jewellery.* PARK: Meters. TEL: 020 7589 5050; fax - 020 7589 9009. SER: Valuations; repairs.

Stephanie Hoppen Ltd
17 Walton St. SW3 2HX. Est. 1962. Open 10-6, Sat. 12-4. *STOCK: Decorative picture specialist - watercolours, oils, drawings and prints, antique and modern.* TEL: 020 7589 3678.

TIARAS
A History of Splendour
by Geoffrey C. Munn

Tiaras have always inspired a great fascination and the most beautiful and influential women have been painted, photographed and admired whilst wearing them. Even in the 21st century they are still worn and continue to inspire special poise and elegance. This lavishly illustrated book includes new photographs of a variety of Royal tiaras together with those of French and Russian Imperial provenances. Geoffrey Munn has been granted special access to the photographic archives of many famous jewellers, including Cartier, Boucheron and Fabergé, for his research. Other makers include Garrards, Castellani, Giuliano, Lalique, Fouquet and Tiffany. Many of these stunning tiaras also have great historical significance and their provenance is explained fully by the author, who is a specialist in jewellery and metalwork. Among the contemporary pieces illustrated are tiaras belonging to Jamie Lee Curtis, Vivienne Westwood, Elton John and Madonna, made by Slim Barratt, Galliano and Versace. This awe-inspiring, sublime text, which incorporates more than 300 majestic colour plates, includes chapters on tiaras as crown jewels, Russian style tiaras, tiaras as a work of art and the relationship between the tiara and the costume ball.

Geoffrey Munn is the Managing Director of Wartski Ltd, a firm of antique dealers in London specialising in European precious metalwork. He is co-author of *Pre-Raphaelite to Arts and Crafts Jewellery* and author of both *Castellani and Giuliano – Revivalist Jewellers of the 19th Century* and *The Triumph of Love – Jewellery 1530-1930*. He is also the jewellery specialist on the BBC's *Antiques Roadshow*.

11 x 9¼in./280 x 234mm., 432pp., c.350 col., & 100 b.&w. illus. **£45.00**

Available from the
ANTIQUE COLLECTORS' CLUB
Sandy Lane, Old Martlesham,
Woodbridge, Suffolk IP12 4SD, UK.
For your free copy of the catalogue:
Tel: **01394 389950** or Fax: **01394 389999**
Email: sales@antique-acc.com
Website: www.antique-acc.com

Hungry Ghost
122 Fulham Rd. SW3 6HU. (Virginia Kern). Est. 1998. Open 10-5.30. CL: Mon. *STOCK: Chinese furniture and artefacts, 18th-19th C, to £15,000.* TEL: 020 7370 6673; fax - same; e-mail - virginia kern@aol.com; website - www.hungry-ghost.co.uk. FAIRS: Decorative (Battersea). VAT: Stan.

Anthony James and Son Ltd   BADA
88 Fulham Rd. SW3 6HR. CINOA. Est. 1949. Open 9.30-5.45, Sat. by appointment. SIZE: Large. *STOCK: Furniture, 1700-1880, £200-£50,000; mirrors, bronzes, ormolu and decorative items, £200-£20,000.* PARK: Easy. TEL: 020 7584 1120; fax - 020 7823 7618; e-mail - anthony. james10@virgin.net; website - www.anthony-james.com. SER: Valuations; buys at auction. FAIRS: Olympia (June & Nov). VAT: Spec.

Peter Jones at PJ2
1st Floor, Draycott Ave. SW3 2NA. (The John Lewis Partnership). Est. 1915. Open 9.30-7. *STOCK: 18th-19th C furniture, mirrors and pictures.* LOC: Chelsea. TEL: 020 7730 3434, ext. 5734.

John Keil Ltd   BADA
1st Floor, 154 Brompton Rd. SW3 1HX. Est. 1959. Open 9.30-5.30. CL: Sat. except by appointment. *STOCK: Fine English furniture, 18th to early 19th C.* LOC: Near Knightsbridge underground station. PARK: 200 yds. TEL: 020 7589 6454; fax - 020 7823 8235; e-mail - antiques@johnkeil.com; website - www. johnkeil.com. VAT: Spec.

Peter Lipitch Ltd   BADA
120/124 Fulham Rd. SW3 6HU. Est. 1954. Open 9.30-5.30. SIZE: Large. *STOCK: Fine English furniture and mirrors.* TEL: 020 7373 3328; fax - 020 7373 8888. FAIRS: BADA; Grosvenor House. VAT: Spec.

The Map House   BADA
54 Beauchamp Place. SW3 1NY. (P. Curtis and P. Stuchlik). Est. 1907. Open 9.45-5.45, Sat. 10.30-5 or by appointment. *STOCK: Antique and rare maps, atlases, engravings and globes.* TEL: 020 7589 4325/7584 8559; fax - 020 7589 1041; e-mail - maps@themaphouse.com; website - www.themaphouse.com. VAT: Stan.

McKenna and Co
28 Beauchamp Place. SW3 1NJ. (C. and M. McKenna). LAPADA. Est. 1982. Open 10-6. SIZE: Medium. *STOCK: Fine jewellery, Georgian to post war, £250-£25,000; some silver and objects.* Not Stocked: Pictures and furniture. LOC: Off Brompton Rd., near Harrods. PARK: Meters. TEL: 020 7584 1966; fax - 020 7225 2893; e-mail - info@mckennajewels.com; website - www. mckennajewels.com. SER: Valuations; restorations. VAT: Stan/Margin.

No. 12
12 Cale St., Chelsea Green. SW3 3QU. Open 10-6. *STOCK: French country furniture and accessories.* TEL: 020 7581 5022; fax - 020 7581 3966.

Old Church Galleries
98 Fulham Rd., Chelsea. SW3 6HS. (Mrs M. Harrington). FATG. ABA. Open 10-6. *STOCK: Maps and engravings, from 16th C; sporting and decorative prints.* TEL: 020 7591 8790; fax - 020 7591 8791; e-mail - sales@old-church-galleries. com; website - www.old-church-galleries.com. SER: Framing.

Orientalist
152-154 Walton St. SW3 2JJ. (E., H. and M. Sakhai). LAPADA. Open 10.30-5, appointment advisable. SIZE: Large. *STOCK: Oriental, European, antique and reproduction rugs, Aubusson, tapestries, cushions and contemporary rugs.* TEL: 020 7581 2332; e-mail - mikijan@orientalist. demon.co.uk; website - www. orientalist.demon. co.uk. SER: Valuations; restorations (cleaning and repairing rugs, carpets and tapestries).

Perez
199 Brompton Rd. SW3 1LA. (Mr Tyran). LAPADA. Est. 1983. Open 10-6. SIZE: Large. *STOCK: Antique carpets, rugs, tapestries and Aubussons.* LOC: 50 yards from Harrods. PARK: Easy. TEL: 020 7589 2199 (ansaphone). SER: Valuations; restorations; buys at auction. VAT: Stan/Spec.

Prides of London
15 Paultons House. Paultons Sq. SW3 5DU. Open by appointment only. *STOCK: Fine 18th-19th C English and Continental furniture; objets d'art.* TEL: 020 7586 1227. SER: Interior design.

Rogers de Rin Antiques

76

Specialists in **WEMYSS WARE**

76 Royal Hospital Road   London SW3 4HN
Tel: 020 7352 9007 Fax: 020 7351 9407

OPEN 10AM TO 5.30PM, SAT. 10AM TO 1PM. NOW OPEN SUNDAY BY APPOINTMENT.
We would like to buy collections of Wemyss Ware or individual pieces
Email: rogersderin@rogersderin.co.uk

Rogers de Rin   BADA
76 Royal Hospital Rd., Chelsea. SW3 4HN. (V. de Rin). Est. 1950. Open 10-5.30, Sat. 10-1, Sun. by appointment, SIZE: Small. *STOCK: Wemyss pottery, objets d'art, decorative furnishings (Regency taste), collectors' specialities, 18th-19th C, £50-£10,000.* LOC: Just beyond Royal Hospital, corner of Paradise Walk. PARK: Easy. TEL: 020 7352 9007; fax - 020 7351 9407; e-mail - rogersderin@rogersderin. co.uk; website - www. rogersderin.co.uk. VAT: Spec.

Russell Rare Books
239A Fulham Rd., Chelsea. SW3 6HY. (C. Russell). ABA, PBFA. Est. 1978. Open 11-6. *STOCK: Antiquarian books.* LOC: At junction Old Church St. TEL: 020 7351 5119; fax - 020 7376 7227; e-mail - c.russell@russellrarebooks. com; website - www.russellrarebooks.com.

Charles Saunders Antiques
255 Fulham Rd. SW3 6HY. Open 9.30-5.30, Sat. 10-5. *STOCK: Decorative furniture, objects and lamps, 18th-19th C.* TEL: 020 7351 5242. VAT: Spec.

Christine Schell
15 Cale St. SW3 3QS. LAPADA. Est. 1973. Open 10-5.30. SIZE: Small. *STOCK: Unusual tortoiseshell, silver and enamel objects, late 19th to early 20th C, £150-£2,500.* LOC: North of King's Rd., between Sloane Ave. and Sydney St. PARK: Easy. TEL: 020 7352 5563; e-mail - c.schell@ eidosnet.co.uk. SER: Valuations; restorations (tortoiseshell, ivory, shagreen, crocodile, leather, enamels, silver and hairbrush re-bristling). VAT: Stan/Spec.

Robert Stephenson
1 Elystan St. Chelsea Green. SW3 3NT. Open 9.30-5.30, Sat. 10.30-2. *STOCK: Antique and decorative room-sized carpets and kilims; antique Oriental rugs, European tapestries and Aubussons, textiles, needlepoints and cushions; modern Bessarabian kilims, traditional and own contemporary designs.* TEL: 020 7225 2343; fax - same.

Gordon Watson Ltd
50 Fulham Rd. SW3 6HH. LAPADA. Est. 1977. Open 11-6. *STOCK: Art Deco and 1940's glass, jewellery and furniture, £1,000-£50,000; silver by Jensen and Jean E. Puiforcat, 1920's, £500-£30,000.* LOC: At junction with Sydney St. PARK: Sydney St. TEL: 020 7589 3108/7584 6328. VAT: Stan/Spec.

Clifford Wright Antiques Ltd.
Antiques and Works of Art

Telephone 020-7589 0986
Fax 020-7589 3565

104 & 106 Fulham Road,
London SW3 6HS

A good pair of George II carved giltwood mirrors retaining the original Vauxhall bevelled glasses (re-silvered). English Circa 1740. Height 51" (130cm) Width 25" (64cm)

O.F. Wilson Ltd   **BADA**
Queen's Elm Parade, Old Church St. (corner Fulham Rd.), Chelsea. SW3 6EJ. (P. and V.E. Jackson and K.E. Simmonds). LAPADA. Est. 1935. Open 9.30-5.30, Sat. 10.30-1. SIZE: 6 showrooms. *STOCK: English and French furniture, mirrors, mantelpieces, objets d'art.* TEL: 020 7352 9554; fax - 020 7351 0765. SER: Valuations. VAT: Spec.

Clifford Wright Antiques Ltd   **BADA**
104-106 Fulham Rd. SW3 6HS. Est. 1964. Open Mon.-Fri. 9-5.30 or by appointment. *STOCK: Furniture, period giltwood, looking glasses and consoles, 18th to early 19th C.* TEL: 020 7589 0986; fax - 020 7589 3565. VAT: Spec.

SW4

Antiques and Things
(Mrs V. Crowther). Est. 1986. Open by appointment only. SIZE: Medium. *STOCK: Decorative curtain furniture and fittings; linen, lace, textiles, Victorian to Edwardian, £1-£500; china, glass, kitchenalia, 18th-19th C, £5-£500; English and French furniture, decorative items, 19th C, £20-£2,000.* LOC: Off Lavender Hill, near Clapham junction. TEL: 020 7498 1303; fax - same; mobile - 07767 262096; website - www.antiques andthings.co.uk.

Places and Spaces
30 Old Town, Clapham. SW4 0LB. (Paul Carroll and Nick Hannam). Est. 1996. Open 10.30-6, Sun. 12-4. CL: Mon. SIZE: Small. *STOCK: Furniture, lighting, art and ceramics, 20th C, £45-£2,000.* LOC: Near Clapham Common underground station. PARK: Meters. TEL: 020 7498 0998; fax - 020 7627 2625. SER: Valuations.

SW5

Beaver Coin Room
Beaver Hotel, 57 Philbeach Gdns. SW5 9ED. (J. Lis). Est. 1971. Open by appointment. SIZE: Small. *STOCK: European coins, 10th-18th C; commemorative medals, 15th-20th C; all £5-£5,000.* LOC: 2 mins. walk from Earls Court Rd. PARK: Easy. TEL: 020 7373 4553; fax - 020 7373 4555; e-mail - hotelbeaver@hotmail.com. SER: Valuations; buys at auction (coins and medals). FAIRS: London Coin and Coinex. VAT: Stan.

O.F. WILSON LTD.

LAPADA MEMBER

QUEEN'S ELM PARADE

OLD CHURCH STREET LONDON SW3 6EJ

Tel: 020 7352 9554
Fax: 020 7351 0765

English and Continental period decorative furniture, mirrors, objets d'art; period English & French mantelpieces

Mon.–Fri.
9.30–5.30
Sat. 10.30–1
Valuations given

SW6

20th Century Gallery
821 Fulham Rd. SW6 5HG. (E. Brandl and H. Chapman). Open 10-6, Sat. 10-1. SIZE: Small. *STOCK: Post impressionist and modern British oils and watercolours; original prints.* LOC: Near Munster Rd. junction. PARK: Easy. TEL: 020 7731 5888. SER: Restorations (paintings); framing. VAT: Spec.

275 Antiques
275 Lillie Rd., Fulham. SW6 7LL. (David Fisher). Open 10-5.30. SIZE: Medium. *STOCK: English and Continental decorative furniture, £200-£1,200; decorative objects and mirrors, £50-£500; unique American Lucite 1960's table lamps and furniture, £250-£800.* PARK: Easy. TEL: 020 7386 7382.

291 Antiques
291 Lillie Rd., Fulham. SW6 7LL. SIZE: Large. *STOCK: Highly decorative antiques, Gothic style and 18th C splendour; mirrors, garden statuary and textiles.* TEL: 020 7381 5008. SER: Lavish interior design.

313 Antiques
313 Lillie Rd., Fulham. SW6 7LL. (Marc Costantini Art & Antiques). Open 10.30-5.30. *STOCK: 17th-19th C furniture, £200-£3,000; decorative and interesting objects, £20-£500; pictures especially portrait oils; decorative wood frames, mirrors, carpets.* LOC: From Old Brompton Rd., west for half a mile after crossing Northend Rd. PARK: Easy and nearby. TEL: 020 7610 2380; fax - same;. SER: Shipping arranged.

(55) For Decorative Living
55 New King's Rd., Chelsea. SW6 4SE. (Mrs J. Rhodes). Open 10.30-5.30. *STOCK: Furniture, lighting and decorative items.* TEL: 020 7736 5623. SER: Design.

And So To Bed Limited
638/640 King's Rd. SW6. Est. 1970. Open 10-6. SIZE: Large. *STOCK: Brass, lacquered and wooded beds.* LOC: End of King's Rd., towards Fulham. PARK: Easy. TEL: 020 7731 3593/4/5; freephone - 0808 1444343; fax - 020 7371 5272; e-mail - enquiries@andsotobed.co.uk; website - www.andsotobed.co.uk. SER: Restorations; spares; interior design. VAT: Stan.

The Antique Lamp Shop
at Christopher Wray Lighting, 591-593 King's Rd. SW6 2YW. Est. 1964. Open 10-6. SIZE: Large. *STOCK: Victorian and Edwardian oil lamps, 19th C French and English decorative light fittings, Art Deco wall brackets and pendants, piano candle sconces; also door furniture, old signage and some furniture.* LOC: From Sloane Sq. over Stanley Bridge. TEL: 020 7751 8701; fax - 020 7751 8699. VAT: Stan.

Christopher Bangs   BADA
P O Box 6077. SW6 7XS. LAPADA, CINOA. Est. 1971. Open by appointment only. *STOCK: Domestic metalwork and metalware, works of art, decorative objects.* TEL: 020 7381 3532 (24 hrs); fax - 020 7381 2192 (24 hrs); mobile - 07836 333532; e-mail - cbangs@beeb.net. SER: Research; commission buys at auction; finder. VAT: Stan/Spec.

Sebastiano Barbagallo
661 Fulham Rd. SW6 5PZ. Est. 1975. Open 10.30-6 including Sun., Sat. 9-7. *STOCK: Chinese furnitures; antiques and handicrafts from India, Tibet, SE Asia and China.* TEL: 020 7751 0691.

Barclay Samson Ltd
65 Finlay St. SW6 6HF. (Richard Barclay). IVPDA. Open by appointment only. *STOCK: Pre 1950 original lithographic posters: French, German, Swiss, American, British and Russian Constructivist schools.* TEL: 020 7731 8012; fax - 020 7731 8013; mobile - 07785 306401; e-mail - richard@barclaysamson.com. FAIRS: Olympia (June); USA. VAT: Spec.

Robert Barley Antiques
(R.A. Barley). Est. 1965. Open by appointment. SIZE: Medium. *STOCK: Rare and bizarre objects, sculpture and pictures, 2000BC-2000AD.* TEL: 020 7736 4429; fax - same. VAT: Stan/Spec.

Big Ben Antique Clocks
5 Broxholme House, New King's Rd. SW6 4AA. (R.Lascelles). Est. 1978. *STOCK: Longcase painted dial clocks, from £1,500; also decorative antiques and accessories.* LOC: At junction of Wandsworth Bridge Rd. and New King's Rd. TEL: 020 7736 1770; fax - 020 7384 1957; e-mail - info@lasc.demon.co.uk; website - www.rogerlascelles.com. SER: Buys at auction.

Julia Boston
588 King's Rd. SW6 2DX. LAPADA, CINOA. Est. 1976. Open 10-6, Sat. 10-5, other times by appointment. SIZE: Large. *STOCK: 18th-19th C Furniture, tapestry cartoons, antiquarian prints and decoration.* TEL: 020 7610 6783; fax - 020 7610 6784; e-mail - julia@juliaboston.com; website - www.juliaboston.com. VAT: Spec.

Alasdair Brown
3/4 The Cranewell, The Gas Works, 2 Michael Rd. SW6 2AD. Est. 1986. Open Wed. and Thurs. 10-6, other days by appointment. SIZE: Medium. *STOCK: Furniture, to £15,000; decorative items, to £10,000; upholstery, lighting and the unusual.* LOC: Behind Christopher Wray (King's Road). PARK: Easy. TEL: 020 7736 6661; fax - 020 7384 3334; e-mail - ab@alasdairbrown.com; website - www.alasdairbrown.com. SER: Valuations; restorations; finder. FAIRS: Olympia (Feb., June and Nov). VAT: Stan/Spec.

I. and J.L. Brown Ltd
632-636 King's Rd. SW6 2DU. Open 9-5.30. SIZE: Large. *STOCK: English and French provincial furniture including tables, country chairs, dressers, armoires, side tables and servers; decorative items.* TEL: 020 7736 4141; fax - 020 7736 9164; e-mail - sales@ brown antiqueslondon. com. SER: Restorations; chair re-rushing.

Rupert Cavendish Antiques
610 King's Rd. SW6 2DX. Est. 1980. Open 10-6. SIZE: Large. *STOCK: Louis XVI (Gustavian), Empire, Biedermeier and Art Deco furniture; 20th C oil paintings.* LOC: Just before New King's Rd. PARK: Easy. TEL: 020 7731 7041; fax - 020 7731 8302; e-mail - RCavendish@ aol.com; website - www.rupertcavendish.co.uk. SER: Valuations. VAT: Spec.

Chelminski
616 King's Rd., Chelsea. SW6 2DU. (Hilary Chelminski). Est. 1970. Open 10-6, Sat. 11-5. SIZE: Medium. *STOCK: Architectural antiques, garden ornaments and sculpture especially stone, 18th-19th C, £5,000-£250,000; English and Continental terracotta, £500-£50,000; marble, stone and bronze, £100-£250,000.* LOC: Near corner with Maxwell Rd. PARK: Easy. TEL: 0207 384 2227; fax - 0207 384 2229; mobile - 07989 033831. SER: Restorations (architectural and garden items and sculpture); buys at auction.

John Clay
263 New King's Rd., Fulham. SW6 4RB. Est. 1974. Open 10-6. SIZE: Medium. *STOCK: Furniture, £50-£10,000; objets d'art and animal objects, silver and clocks, £10-£5,000; all 18th-19th C. Not Stocked: Pine.* LOC: Close to Parsons Green, A3. PARK: Easy. TEL: 020 7731 5677; e-mail - johnclayantiques@btconnect.com. SER: Restorations (furniture, objets d'art). VAT: Stan/Spec.

JULIA BOSTON

18th & 19th CENTURY ENGLISH & CONTINENTAL FURNITURE TAPESTRY CARTOONS, ANTIQUE PRINTS & OBJETS D'ART

588 KING'S ROAD LONDON SW6 2DX
TEL. +44 020 7610 6783   FAX. +44 020 7610 6784
www.juliaboston.com
E-mail: julia@juliaboston.com

Fergus Cochrane and Leigh Warren Antiques

570 King's Rd. SW6 2D. Est. 1981. Open 10-5. SIZE: Medium. *STOCK: Decorative lighting, furniture and objects, 1700-1930, £100-£3,000.* PARK: Easy. TEL: 020 7736 9166.

Decorative Antiques

284 Lillie Rd., Fulham. SW6 7PX. (Anthony Harley). LAPADA. Est. 1991. Open 10-5.30. SIZE: Medium. *STOCK: French country furniture, 18th C; decorative items.* PARK: Easy. TEL: 020 7610 2694; fax - 020 7386 0103. SER: Valuations; restorations. VAT: Spec.

Charles Edwards   BADA

19A Rumbold Rd. SW6 2HX. Est. 1972. Open 9.30-6, Sat. 10-5. SIZE: Medium. *STOCK: Antique and reproduction light fixtures; furniture, 18th-19th C; decorative items, mirrors, British oil paintings, garden furniture.* LOC: Just off King's Rd. PARK: Meters. TEL: 020 7736 7172; fax - 020 7731 7388; e-mail - charles @charlesedwards.com. VAT: Stan/Spec.

Nicole Fabre

592 King's Rd. SW6 2DX. CINOA Est. 1989. Open 10.30-6, Sat. 11-6, Sun. by appointment only. SIZE: Medium. *STOCK: French furniture, provincial style, French textiles, decorative objects, to 1870.* PARK: Meters. TEL: 020 7384 3112; fax - 020 7610 6410. VAT: Spec.

Fairfax Antiques and Fireplaces

568 King's Rd. SW6 2DY. Open 10-5.30. *STOCK: Cast iron and pine fireplaces, architectural items, balustrades and railings, decorative furniture and collectables.* TEL: 020 7736 5023; fax - 020 7731 5436.

Hector Finch Lighting

88-90 Wandsworth Bridge Rd. SW6 2TF. (Mr and Mrs H. Finch). Est. 1988. Open 10-5.30. SIZE: Medium. *STOCK: Antiques and period lighting, early 20th C contemporary and reproduction.* LOC: Off New King's Rd. PARK: Side streets or Pay and Display. TEL: 020 7731 8886; fax - 020 7731 7408; e-mail - hector@hectorfinch.com; website - www.hectorfinch.com. SER: Restorations (period lighting). VAT: Global.

George Floyd Ltd

592 Fulham Rd. SW6 5UA. Open 8.30-5.30. SIZE: Large. *STOCK: 18th to early 19th C furniture and accessories.* TEL: 020 7736 1649. VAT: Stan/Spec.

Birdie Fortescue Antiques

Studio GJ, Cooper House, 2 Michael Rd. SW6 2AD. LAPADA. Open by appointment only. SIZE: Large. *STOCK: French and Italian fruitwood furniture, 18th to early 19th C, £500-£10,000.* LOC: Off King's Rd. TEL: 01206 337557; fax - same; mobile - 07778 263467. FAIRS: Olympia (Feb. and June): Decorative (Sept). VAT: Spec.

Fulham Antiques

318-320 Munster Rd., Fulham. SW6 6BH. (Adrian Eves). Est. 1998. Open 10-5.30. SIZE: Large. *STOCK: English, Continental and decorative antique furniture, mirrors and lighting.* TEL: 020 7610 3644.

Judy Greenwood

657-659 Fulham Rd. SW6 5PY. Est. 1978. Open 10-5.30, Sat. 10-5. *STOCK: French decorative furniture including armoires, tables and chairs, commodes, lighting, mirrors, beds, quilts, all 1900's.* LOC: Fulham Broadway, nearest tube station. TEL: 020 7736 6037; fax - 020 7736 1941; e-mail - judyg@dial.pipex.com.

Robin Greer

434 Fulham Palace Rd. SW6 6HX. ABA, PBFA. Est. 1965. Open by appointment. *STOCK: Children's and illustrated books, original illustrations.* TEL: 020 7381 9113; fax - 020 7381 6499; e-mail - rarerobin @yahoo.com. SER: Catalogues issued.

Gregory, Bottley and Lloyd

13 Seagrave Rd. SW6 1RP. Est. 1858. SIZE: Medium. *STOCK: Mineral specimens, £1-£5,000; fossils, £5-£500.* LOC: Nearest tube station - West Brompton. PARK: Easy. TEL: 020 7381 5522; fax - 020 7381 5512. VAT: Stan.

Guinevere Antiques

574/580 King's Rd. SW6 2DY. Open 9.30-6, Sat. 10-5.30 (warehouse by appointment only). SIZE: Large + trade warehouse. *STOCK: Period decorative antiques and accessories.* TEL: 020 7736 2917; fax - 020 7736 8267; e-mail - sales@ guinevere.co.uk; website- www.guinevere. co.uk.

Gutlin Clocks and Antiques

606 King's Rd. SW6 2DX. Est. 1990. Open 10-6. SIZE: Large - two floors. *STOCK: Longcase clocks, £2,000-£8,000; mantel clocks, £300-£6,000; furniture and lighting, £500-£3,000; all 18th-19th C.* LOC: 200 yards from beginning of New King's Rd. PARK: Maxwell Rd. TEL: 020 7384 2439; fax - same; home - 020 8740 6830; e-mail - mark@gutlin.com; website - www.gutlin. com. SER: Valuations; restorations (clocks and clock cases); buys at auction (clocks).

CHARLES EDWARDS

19A RUMBOLD ROAD,
LONDON, SW6 2HX

TEL: +44 (0) 20 7736 7172
FAX: +44 (0) 20 7731 7388
www.charlesedwards.com

Hollingshead and Co
56 Tasso Rd., Fulham. SW6. (D. Hollingshead). Est. 1946. Open 8.30-5, Sat. 9-1. SIZE: Medium. *STOCK: Marble and wood mantelpieces, grates, fenders, fire irons, chandeliers, including repro-duction, £50-£20,000.* TEL: 020 7385 8519. SER: Valuations; restorations (marblework and wood mantelpieces). VAT: Stan.

House of Mirrors
597 King's Rd. SW6 2EL. (G. Witek). Est. 1960. Open 10-6. *STOCK: Mirrors.* TEL: 020 7736 5885; fax - 020 7610 9188.

HRW Antiques (London) Ltd
26 Sulivan Rd. SW6 3DT. LAPADA. Open 9-5. CL: Sat. SIZE: Large. *STOCK: Furniture and objects of art, 18th-19th C.* LOC: Within easy reach of the King's Rd. and Chelsea Harbour. TEL: 020 7371 7995; fax - 020 7371 9522; e-mail - iain@hrw-antiques.com; website - www.hrw-antiques.com.

P.L. & M. James
590 Fulham Rd. SW6 5NT. LAPADA. Open 8.30-6, Sat. by appointment only. *STOCK: 18th-19th C furniture and objects.* TEL: 020 7736 0183; e-mail - info@plj-antiques.com; website - www.plj-antiques.com. SER: Restorations (polishing and cabinet work, painted and lacquer furniture, gilding and carving). VAT: Stan/Spec.

Christopher Jones Antiques
618-620 King's Rd. SW6 2DU. Open 10-5.30. *STOCK: Continental and British decorative objects and furniture, screens and mirrors, 18th-19th C, £500-£10,000.* TEL: 020 7731 4655; fax - 020 7371 8682. VAT: Spec.

King's Court Galleries
949/953 Fulham Rd. SW6 5HY. (Mrs J. Joel). Est. 1983. Open 10-5.30. *STOCK: Antique maps, engravings, decorative and sporting prints.* TEL: 020 7610 6939; e-mail - sales@kingscourt galleries.co.uk; website - www.kingscourtgalleries.co.uk. SER: Framing (on site).

L. and E. Kreckovic
559 King's Rd. SW6 2EB. Open 10-6. *STOCK: 18th-19th C furniture.* TEL: 020 7736 0753; fax - 020 7731 5904. SER: Restorations.

Lewin
638 Fulham Rd. SW6 5RT. (David and Harriett Lewin). Open 10.30-6. SIZE: Medium. *STOCK: Original Dutch colonial furniture and teak and mahogany reproduction colonial-style designs.* TEL: 020 7731 1616. VAT: Stan.

Lunn Antiques Ltd
86 New Kings Rd., Parsons Green. SW6 4LU. Est. 1976. Open 10-6. *STOCK: Antique lace, antique and modern bed linen, nightdresses, christening robes.* TEL: 020 7736 4638; fax - 020 7371 7113; e-mail - lunnantiques@aol.com. SER: Laundry and restoration (antique linen and lace). VAT: Margin.

Michael Luther Antiques
590 King's Rd., Chelsea. SW6 2DX. (Michael Luther and Peter Goodwin). Est. 1967. Open 10-6. SIZE: Large. *STOCK: Furniture - 18th-19th C, £500-£10,000; early 20th C, £300-£3,000; lighting, 19th-20th C, £300-£5,000.* LOC: Between Lots Rd. and Wandsworth Bridge Rd. PARK: Nearby. TEL: 020 7371 8492; fax - same. SER: Valuations; buys at auction (furniture). VAT: Spec.

Michael Marriott Ltd
588 Fulham Rd. SW6 5NT. Est. 1979. Open 10-5.30. CL: Sat. pm. and Sun. except by appoint-ment. SIZE: Large. *STOCK: English furniture, 1700-1850, £400-£15,000.* LOC: Junction of Fulham Rd. and Parsons Green Lane. PARK: Easy. TEL: 020 7736 3110; fax - 020 7736 0568. SER: Valuations; restorations. VAT: Stan/Spec.

David Martin-Taylor Antiques
558 King's Rd. SW6 2DZ. LAPADA. Open 10-6, Sat. 11-5. SIZE: Medium. *STOCK: Classic and decorative furniture and unusual objects, 18th-19th C.* PARK: Easy. TEL: 020 7731 4135; fax - 020 7371 0029; e-mail - dmt@davidmartintaylor. com; website - www.davidmartintaylor.com. SER: Hire. FAIRS: Olympia (June). VAT: Stan/Spec.

Mark Maynard Antiques
651 Fulham Rd. SW6 5PU. Est. 1977. Open 10-5, Sun. by appointment. SIZE: Medium. *STOCK: Decorative items, £25-£300.* LOC: Near Fulham Broadway underground. PARK: Easy. TEL: 020 7731 3533; home - 020 7373 4681. VAT: Stan/Spec.

Mora & Upham Antiques
584 King's Rd. SW6 2DX. (Matthew Upham). Est. 1976. Open 10-6. SIZE: Medium. *STOCK: Furniture, pictures, decorative objects and chan-deliers, 18th-19th C.* LOC: Corner premises. PARK: Easy. TEL: 020 7731 4444; fax - 020 7736 0440. SER: Valuations; restorations (pictures, china and furniture). VAT: Spec.

Sylvia Napier Ltd
554 King's Rd. SW6 2DZ. Est. 1972. Open 10-6. SIZE: Large. *STOCK: Furniture - decorative European, 18th-19th C, £100-£15,000; decor-*

ative Oriental, 17th-19th C, £200-£7,000; garden, 19th C, £150-£7,000; objets d'art; unusual chandeliers. LOC: Near junction with Lots Rd. PARK: Easy. TEL: 020 7371 5881. SER: Restorations. VAT: Spec.

Nimmo & Spooner

277 Lillie Rd., Fulham. SW6 7LL. (Catherine Nimmo and Myra Spooner). Est. 1996. Open 10.30-5.30. SIZE: Medium. STOCK: Objects and furniture including painted dressers and chests of drawers, tables, mirrors, 18th-20th C, to £3,500. LOC: Between Fulham Broadway and Hammersmith. PARK: Nearby. TEL: 020 7385 2724; fax - same.

Old World Trading Co

565 King's Rd. SW6. (R.J. Campion). Est. 1970. Open 9.30-6. STOCK: Fireplaces, chimney pieces and accessories, chandeliers, mirrors, furniture including decorative, works of art. TEL: 020 7731 4708; fax - 020 7731 1291; e-mail - oldworld @btinternet.com.

Ossowski   BADA

595 King's Rd. SW6 2EL. Est. 1960. Open 9.30-5.30. SIZE: Large. STOCK: Furniture, 18th C. TEL: 020 7731 0334. SER: Valuations; restorations. FAIRS: Olympia (June); Palm Beach. VAT: Spec.

M. Pauw Antiques

Cooper House, 2 Michael Rd. SW6 2AD. Est. 1981. SIZE: Medium. STOCK: English and Continental furniture, leather chairs, 18th-19th C; decorative items, lighting fixtures, cast iron, zinc and lead planters. PARK: Easy. TEL: 020 7731 4022; fax - 020 7731 7356; e-mail - info@ mpauw; website - www.mpauw.com. VAT: Stan.

Perez Antique Carpets Gallery

150 Wandsworth Bridge Rd., Fulham. SW6 2UH. (K. Dinari). Est. 1984. Open 10-6.30, Wed. 10-7.30. SIZE: Large. STOCK: Carpets, 19th C, £400-£40,000; rugs, 18th-20th C, £300-£3,000; textiles, 19th C, £70-£1,500. PARK: Easy. TEL: 020 7371 9619/9620. SER: Valuations; restorations; buys at auction (Oriental and European carpets, rugs and textiles, tapestries). VAT: Stan/Spec.

The Pine Mine (Crewe-Read Antiques)

100 Wandsworth Bridge Rd., Fulham. SW6 2TF. (D. Crewe-Read). Est. 1971. Open 9.45-5.45, Sat. till 4.30. SIZE: Large. STOCK: Georgian and Victorian pine, Welsh dressers, farmhouse tables, chests of drawers, boxes and some architectural items. LOC: From Sloane Sq., down King's Rd., into New King's Rd., left into Wandsworth Bridge Rd. PARK: Outside. TEL: 020 7736 1092. SER: Furniture made from old wood; stripping; export.

Daphne Rankin and Ian Conn

608 King's Rd. SW6 2DX. LAPADA. Est. 1979. Open 10.30-6. SIZE: Medium. STOCK: Oriental porcelain including Chinese, Japanese, Imari, Cantonese, Satsuma, Nanking, Famille Rose, £500-£25,000; Dutch Delft; tortoiseshell tea caddies. PARK: Maxwell Rd. adjacent to shop. TEL: 020 7384 1847; fax - same; mobile - 07774 487713; e-mail - daphnerankin@aol.com; website - www.rankin-conn-chinatrade.com. SER: Valuations; buys at auction (as stock). FAIRS: Olympia (June and Nov). VAT: Stan/Spec.

Redroom

72 Farm Lane, Fulham. SW6 1QA. (Lei Jia). Est. 1997. Open Wed.-Fri. 10-5, Sat. 10-1. SIZE: Medium. STOCK: Chinese furniture and works of art, late 17th-19th C, to £1,500. LOC: Near Fulham Broadway. PARK: Easy. TEL: 020 7386 8777; fax - 020 7385 3747; mobile - 07798 801707. FAIRS: Decorative, Battersea. VAT: Margin.

Reffold

572 King's Rd. SW6 2DY. (K. Jackson). Est. 1968. Open Mon.-Fri. 10-5. SIZE: Medium. STOCK: Early furniture, works of art and paintings. PARK: Easy. TEL: 020 7736 7145; fax - 020 7736 0029. VAT: Spec.

Richardson and Kailas Icons   BADA

65 Rivermead Court, Ranelagh Gardens. SW6 3RY. (C. Richardson). LAPADA. Open by appointment. STOCK: Icons and frescoes. TEL: 020 7371 0491; e-mail - chris.richardson 1@virgin.net.

Rogers & Co

604 Fulham Rd. SW6 5RP. (M. and C. Rogers). LAPADA. Est. 1971. Open 10-6. SIZE: Large. STOCK: Furniture, 18th-19th C, £100-£3,000; upholstery. LOC: Near Fulham library, Parsons Green Lane. PARK: Side streets. TEL: 020 7731 8504; fax - 020 7610 6040. SER: Valuations. VAT: Stan/Spec.

George Sherlock Antiques

588 King's Rd. SW6 2DX. Est. 1968. Open 9.30-5.30. SIZE: Large. STOCK: General antiques, decorative furniture and upholstery, 1650-1900, £20-£15,000. PARK: Easy. TEL: 020 7736 3955; fax - 020 7371 5179. VAT: Stan/Spec.

Simon Horn Furniture Ltd

117-121 Wandsworth Bridge Rd. SW6 2TP. IDDA. Est. 1981. Open 9.30-5.30, Sun. by appointment. SIZE: Large. STOCK: Wooden classical style bedframes, £1,500-£6,000; bedside tables, £450-£1,100; all 1790-1910 or recent larger copies. LOC: South from New King's Rd., towards river down Wandsworth Bridge Rd., premises on left at first zebra crossing. PARK: Easy. TEL: 020 7731 1279; fax - 020 7736 3522; e-mail - sales@simonhorn.com; website - www. simonhorn.com. SER: Restorations (as stock). FAIRS: House & Garden. VAT: Stan.

Sleeping Beauty Antique Beds
579/581 King's Rd. SW6 2EH. Open 10-5.30. *STOCK: Brass, iron and French wooden beds, 19th C, £500-£15,000.* TEL: 020 7471 4711; e-mail - info@antiquebeds.com; website - www. antiquebeds.com.

Stephen Sprake
283 Lillie Rd., Fulham. SW6 7LL. Open 10.30-5.30. *STOCK: 18th-20th C lighting and furniture.* LOC: 10 mins. from Hammersmith roundabout. PARK: Easy. TEL: 020 7381 3209; fax - 020 7381 9502. VAT: Spec.

Trowbridge Gallery
555 King's Rd. SW6 2EB. (M. Trowbridge). LAPADA. Est. 1980. Open 9.30-6, Sat. 10-5.30. SIZE: Large. *STOCK: Decorative prints, 17th-19th C, £35-£3,000.* LOC: Near Christopher Wray Lighting. PARK: Easy. TEL: 020 7371 8733. SER: Valuations; restorations; buys at auction (antiquarian books and prints); hand-made frames; decorative mounting. FAIRS: Decorative Antiques and Textiles, Olympia, LAPADA, City of London. VAT: Stan.

Whiteway and Waldron Ltd
305 Munster Rd., Fulham. SW6 6BJ. (M. Whiteway and G. Kirkland). Est. 1976. Open 10-6, Sat. 11-4. SIZE: Large. *STOCK: Religious antiques including candlesticks, statuary, gothic and carved church woodwork.* LOC: At junction with Lillie Rd. PARK: On forecourt for loading, or Strode Rd. TEL: 020 7381 3195; fax - same; e-mail - sales@whiteway-waldron.co.uk; website-www.whiteway-waldron.co.uk. SER: Buys at auction (religious items). VAT: Stan.

York Gallery Ltd
569 King's Rd. SW6 2EB. (Jane and Gerd Beyer). Est. 1984. Open 10.30-5.30. SIZE: Medium. *STOCK: Antique prints.* TEL: 020 7736 2260; fax - same; e-mail - prints@yorkgallery. co.uk; website - www.yorkgallery.co.uk. SER: Bespoke framing. VAT: Stan.

SW7

Anglo Persian Carpet Co
6 South Kensington Station Arcade. SW7 2NA. Est. 1910. Open 9.30-6. *STOCK: Carpets and rugs.* TEL: 020 7589 5457. SER: Valuations; restorations (carpets and rugs); cleaning.

Atlantic Bay Carpets Gallery   BADA
14 Gloucester Rd. SW7 4RB. (W. Grodzinski). CINOA. Est. 1945. Open 9-4, Sat. by appointment. SIZE: Medium. *STOCK: Antique Oriental and European carpets and textiles; Islamic and Indian art.* TEL: 020 7689 8489; fax - 020 7581 8189; e-mail - atlanticbaygallery@btinternet. com; website - www.btinternet.com/~atlantic baygallery/. SER: Valuations; restorations; buys at auction (as stock). VAT: Stan/Spec.

Julie Collino
15 Glendower Place, South Kensington. SW7 3DR. Est. 1971. Open 11-5, Sat. 2-5, Sun. by appointment. *STOCK: Watercolours, oils, etchings, £25-£1,000; china, £25-£500; both 19th-20th C; furniture, £50-£2,000.* LOC: Off Harrington Rd. TEL: 020 7584 4733; home - 020 8568 7440.

The Gloucester Road Bookshop
123 Gloucester Rd., South Kensington. SW7 4TE. (Nicholas Dennys). Est. 1983. Open 9.30-10.30 pm, Sat. and Sun. 10.30-6.30. SIZE: Medium. *STOCK: Second-hand hardback and paperback books, all genres, mainly 19th-20th C, £1-£50; modern first editions, mainly 20th C, £5-£500; rare books, 17th-20th C, £70-£1,000.* LOC: 150 yards Gloucester Road underground station. Come out of station, cross road and turn right. PARK: Loading; easy weekends. Meters nearby. TEL: 020 7370 3503; fax - 020 7373 0610. SER: Valuations; book search.

M.P. Levene Ltd   BADA
5 Thurloe Place. SW7 2RR. Est. 1889. Open 9.30-6. CL: Sat. pm. *STOCK: Silver, old Sheffield plate, scale silver models, various, all prices.* LOC: Few minutes past Harrods near South Kensington station. PARK: Easy. TEL: 020 7589 3755; fax - 020 7589 9908; e-mail - silver@mplevene.co.uk; website - www. mplevene.co.uk. SER: Valuations. VAT: Stan/ Spec.

A. & H. Page (Est. 1840)
66 Gloucester Rd. SW7 4QT. Open 9-5.45, Sat. 10-2. *STOCK: Silver, jewellery, watches.* TEL: 020 7584 7349. SER: Valuations; repairs; silversmith; goldsmith.

The Taylor Gallery Ltd
1 Bolney Gate. SW7 1QW. (Jeremy Taylor). Est. 1986. Open by appointment only. *STOCK: Irish, British, China Trade and marine paintings, 19th-20th C.* TEL: 020 7581 0253; fax - 020 7589 4495; e-mail - jeremy@taylor-gallery-london. com; website - www.taylor-gallery-london.com. FAIRS: Olympia (June); Palm Beach (Feb); Hong Kong (Oct).

The Wyllie Gallery
44 Elvaston Place. SW7 5NP. (J.G. Wyllie). Open by appointment. *STOCK: 19th-20th C marine paintings and etchings, especially works by the Wyllie family.* TEL: 020 7584 6024; e-mail - jgwyllie@hotmail.com.

SW8

The French House (Antiques) Ltd
125 Queenstown Rd. SW8 3PH. (S.B. and M.J. Hazell). Est. 1995. Open Thurs., Fri., and Sat., other days by appointment. SIZE: Medium. *STOCK: Wooden beds, 18th-19th, £900-£2,500; gilt mirrors, 19th C, £300-£2,000; lighting, 19th-20th C, £200-£1,000; all French.* LOC: Short drive from Victoria station. PARK: Sidestreets. TEL: 020 7978 2228; fax - 020 7978 2340; website - www.thefrenchhouse.co.uk. SER: Restorations; cabinet making, upholstery, French polishing and painting. VAT: Stan/Spec.

Heskia
BADA
Est. 1877. Open by appointment only. *STOCK: Oriental carpets, rugs and tapestries.* **TEL: 020 7373 4489. SER: Valuations; cleaning and repairs.**

Fay Lucas Artmetal
BADA
Christies Fine Art Security, 42 Ponton Rd. SW8 5BA. LAPADA. Est. 1977. Open by appointment only. *STOCK: Fine signed silver holloware, 20th C, £200-£50,000; signed furniture, 20th C, £5,000-£50,000; antique military and sporting jewellery, £100-£3,000.* **TEL: 020 7371 4404; fax - same; mobile - 07767 660550; e-mail - info@faylucas.com. SER: Valuations; restorations; buys at auction. FAIRS: Olympia (Feb., June, Nov). VAT: Stan/Spec.**

Paul Orssich
2 St. Stephen's Terrace, South Lambeth. SW8 1DH. Open by appointment only. *STOCK: Old, rare and out of print books on Spain and Hispanic studies; old maps of all parts of the world, from £20.* TEL: 020 7787 0030; fax - 020 7735 9612; e-mail - paulo@orssich.com; website - www.orrssich.com.

SW9

Rodney Franklin Antiques
Est. 1968. Open by appointment only. *STOCK: French and English mirrors and beds, furniture, lighting, architectural and garden items.* TEL: 020 7274 0729. VAT: Stan/Spec.

SW10

Iftikhar Bokhari
57 Uverdale Rd., Chelsea. SW10 0SN. Est. 1963. Open 10-6. SIZE: Large. *STOCK: Rare tapestries, carpets, textiles.* TEL: 020 7351 3296/7376 3136; fax - 020 7376 4876; e-mail - ibokhari@ freeserve. SER: Valuations; restorations; cleaning; part exchange. VAT: Stan.

Carlton Davidson Antiques
507 King's Rd., Chelsea. SW10 0TX. Est. 1981. Open 10-6. *STOCK: Lamps, chandeliers, mirrors and decorative items, £500-£5,000.* TEL: 020 7795 0905.

Jonathan Clark & Co
18 Park Walk, Chelsea. SW10 0AQ. SLAD. Open 10-6.30, Sat. by appointment. *STOCK: Modern British paintings and sculpture.* TEL: 020 7351 3555; fax - 020 7823 3187.

Collins and Hastie Ltd
5 Park Walk, Chelsea. SW10 0AJ. (Caroline Hastie and Diana Collins). Open 10-6, Sat. 11-4. SIZE: Large. *STOCK: 20th C contemporary and modern paintings, European and British, £500-£30,000.* LOC: Park Walk runs between King's Rd. and Fulham Rd. PARK: Easy. TEL: 020 7351 4292. SER: Restorations (pictures). VAT: Spec.

The Furniture Cave
533 King's Rd. SW10 0TZ. Est. 1967. Open 10-6, Sun. 11-4. SIZE: Large. LOC: Corner of Lots Rd. PARK: Meters. TEL: 020 7352 4229/5478. SER: Shipping; forwarding. VAT: Stan/Spec. Below are listed the dealers trading from this address.

Paul Andrews Antiques
Basement. *English and Continental decorative furniture; sculpture, Old Master paintings, prints and drawings.* TEL: 020 7352 4584; fax - 020 7351 78165.

Brown's Antique Furniture
First Floor. *Library and dining, and decorative objects, from early 18th C.* TEL: 020 7352 2046; fax - 020 7352 3654.

The Classic Library
First Floor. *Continental furniture specialising French Empire; antiquarian books, maps and prints.* TEL: 020 7376 7653; fax - 020 7352 3654.

Stuart Duggan
First Floor. *Georgian and Victorian furniture especially 19th-20th C pianos.* TEL: 020 7352 2046; fax - 020 7352 3654.

Kenneth Harvey
Ground Floor. LAPADA. *Decorative furniture, mirrors, chandeliers, light fittings.* TEL: 020 7352 8645; fax - 020 7376 3225.

Simon Hatchwell Antiques
Ground Floor. Est. 1961. *English and Continental decorative furniture and objets d'art.* TEL: 020 7351 2344; fax - 020 7351 3520.

Hill Farm Antiques
General antiques, large tables. TEL: 020 7352 2046.

Lamberty
Unusual English and Continental furniture, chandeliers, works or art, £500-£50,000. TEL: 020 7352 3111; fax - 020 7351 5833; mobile - 07768 736687; e-mail - mail@lamberty.co.uk; website - www.lamberty.co.uk VAT: Spec.

David Loveday
English Georgian large furniture. TEL: 020 7352 1100.

Phoenix Trading Company
Furniture including Indian, porcelain, bronzes. TEL: 020 7351 6543; fax - 020 7352 9803.

Preston Antiques
Ground Floor. *Early 19th C and Regency furniture.* TEL: 020 7352 3775; fax - 020 7352 3759.

Anthony Redmile
Basement. *Marble resin neo-classical Grand Tour objects.* TEL: 020 7351 3813; fax - 020 7352 8131.

York Whiting
Ground Floor. LAPADA. *17th-20th C furniture, English and Continental, paintings, carpets and textiles.* TEL: 020 7376 8530; fax - 020 7352 7994.

Granville Antiques   BADA
15 Langton St. SW10 0JL. (I.E.G. Miller). Est. 1979. Open 10-5.30 or by appointment. *STOCK: Period furniture, pre-1940, £50-£15,000; accessories and pictures.* **TEL: 020 7351 2108; mobile - 07966 279761. SER: Valuations; restorations (furniture). FAIRS: BADA. VAT: Spec.**

Hünersdorff Rare Books
P.O. Box 582. SW10 9RU. ABA. Est. 1969. Open by appointment only. *STOCK: Continental books in rare editions, early printing, science and medicine, illustrated books, Latin America, natural history.* TEL: 020 7373 3899; fax - 020 7370 1244; e-mail - huner.rarebooks@dial. pipex.com; website - www.abebooks.com/home/ hunersdorff. FAIRS: Olympia (June).

Thomas Kerr Antiques Ltd
at L'Encoignure, 517 King's Rd. SW10 0TX. Est. 1977. Open 10-6. SIZE: Large. *STOCK: French country furniture, paintings, mirrors and decorative items.* TEL: 020 7351 6465; fax - 020 7351 4744. VAT: Stan/Spec.

Lane Fine Art Ltd
8 Drayton Gardens. SW10 9SA. (C. Foley). Open by appointment only. *STOCK: Oil paintings, 1500-1850, principally English, major works by the main artists of the period, £10,000-£1million+.* TEL: 020 7373 3130; fax - 020 7373 2277; e-mail - cf@lanefineart.co.uk. SER: Valuations. VAT: Stan/Spec.

Langford's Marine Antiques   BADA
The Plaza, 535 King's Rd. SW10 0SZ. (L.L. Langford). LAPADA. Est. 1941. *STOCK: Ships models, marine instruments, globes, steam engine models.* **TEL: 020 7351 4881; fax - 020 7352 0763; e-mail - langford@dircon.co.uk; website - www. langfords.co.uk. VAT: Stan/ Spec.**

Langton Street Gallery
13 Langton St. SW10 1JR. (P. and C. Kennaugh). Open 10.30-7.30, Sat. 10-4. *STOCK: Oils, watercolours, prints, 19th-20th C, £200-£3,000.* LOC: Worlds End, Chelsea. TEL: 020 7351 1973.

Stephen Long
348 Fulham Rd. SW10 9UH. Est. 1966. Open 9.30-1 and 2.15-5. CL: Sat. pm. and Sun. except by appointment. SIZE: Small. *STOCK: English pottery, 18th-19th C, to £400; English painted furniture, 18th to early 19th C; toys and games, household and kitchen items, chintz, materials and patchwork, to £1,000. Not Stocked: Stripped pine, large brown furniture, fashionable antiques.* LOC: From South Kensington along road on right between Ifield Rd. and Billing Rd. PARK: Easy. TEL: 020 7352 8226. VAT: Spec.

McVeigh & Charpentier
498 King's Rd. SW10. (Maggie Charpentier). LAPADA. Est. 1979. Open 10.30-5, weekends by appointment only. SIZE: Medium. *STOCK: Continental furniture, mirrors, garden ironwork and stone, 17th-19th C.* LOC: Two blocks down from Earls Court. PARK: In cul de sac adjacent. TEL: 020 7351 1442/7352 6084; home - 020 7937 6459; mobile - 07801 480167. FAIRS: Olympia (June); Harvey (Sept., Jan. and March). VAT: Spec.

McWhirter
22 Park Walk, Chelsea. SW10 0AQ. (James McWhirter). Open 9-6, Sat. by appointment. SIZE: Medium. *STOCK: Works of art, objects, unusual furniture.* LOC: Near Fulham Road Cinema. PARK: Meters. TEL: 020 7351 5399; fax - 020 7352 9821. VAT: Spec.

Offer Waterman and Co. Fine Art
11 Langton St. SW10 0JL. Est. 1996. Open 10-6.30, Sat. 11-4, Sun. by appointment. SIZE: Small. *STOCK: Modern British paintings, 1900 to date, £500-£5,000.* LOC: Off Kings Rd. PARK: Easy. TEL: 020 7351 0068; fax - 020 7351 2269; e-mail - info@waterman.co.uk; website - www.waterman.co.uk. SER: Valuations; restorations (as stock); framing; buys at auction (Modern British paintings). FAIRS: Art 2002; 20th/21st C Art, Olympia. VAT: Stan/Spec.

Orientation
2 Park Walk. SW10 0AD. (Evelyne Soler). Est. 1990. Open 10-5.30, Sat. by appointment. SIZE: Medium. *STOCK: Continental furniture, 18th-19th C; Chinese porcelain, ceramics, works of art, China trade items, to £20,000.* LOC: Off Fulham Rd. TEL: 020 7351 0234; fax - 020 7351 7535. FAIRS: Olympia. VAT: Spec.

Park Walk Gallery   BADA
20 Park Walk, Chelsea. SW10 0AQ. (J. Cooper). Est. 1988. Open 10-6.30, Sat. 11-4. SIZE: Medium. STOCK: Paintings, £250-£100,000; watercolours, £250-£20,000; drawings, £200-£15,000; all 19th-20th C English and Continental. LOC: Off Fulham Rd. PARK: Easy. TEL: 020 7351 0410; fax - same; website - www.jonathancooper.co.uk. SER: Valuations; restorations. FAIRS: Olympia; Watercolours and Drawings, Art London; Art 2002; 20th/21st C Art. VAT: Spec.

H.W. Poulter and Son
279 Fulham Rd. SW10 9PZ. Est. 1946. Open 9.30-5. CL: Sat. pm. SIZE: Large. *STOCK: English and French marble chimney pieces, grates, fenders, fire-irons, brass, chandeliers.* PARK: Meters. TEL: 020 7352 7268. SER: Restorations (marble work). VAT: Stan/Spec.

John Thornton
455 Fulham Rd. SW10 9UZ. Open 10-5.30. *STOCK: Antiquarian books especially theology.* TEL: 020 7352 8810.

Vaughan Ltd
G1 Chelsea Harbour Design Centre, Chelsea Harbour. SW10 0XE. Est. 1980. Open 9-5.30. CL: Sat. SIZE: Large. *STOCK: Reproduction 18th-19th C lighting, furniture, decorative objects.* PARK: Easy. TEL: 020 7349 4600. VAT: Stan/Spec.

SW11

Artchaos
176 Northcote Rd., Battersea. SW11 6RE. (John C. Butt). Est. 1991. Open 10-6. CL: Wed. SIZE: Medium. *STOCK: Furniture and lights, £200-*£1,000; 1950's and 1960's Italian design, £100-£500; modern paintings, £500-£2,500; all 20th C.* PARK: Nearby. TEL: 020 7924 5856. SER: Valuations; buys at auction.

Braemar Antiques
113 Northcote Rd., Battersea. SW11 6PW. (Maria Elisabeth Ramos-de-Deus and Elizabeth Henderson). Est. 1995. SIZE: Small. *STOCK: Painted furniture including armoires, chests of drawers, mirrors and lamps; quilts, eiderdowns, china and glass.* LOC: Near Clapham junction. PARK: Easy. TEL: 020 7924 5628. FAIRS: Brocante, Kensington.

Eccles Road Antiques
60 Eccles Rd., Battersea. SW11. (H. Rix). Open 10-5. *STOCK: General antiques, pine furniture and smalls.* LOC: Off Clapham Common. TEL: 020 7228 1638.

Christopher Edwards
36 Roseneath Rd. SW11 6AH. Est. 1982. Open by appointment. SIZE: Medium. *STOCK: Architecturally inspired furniture, unusual works of art, 19th C, £100-£10,000.* TEL: 020 7223 9962; fax - same; mobile - 07831 707043. SER: Valuations; buys at auction. VAT: Stan/Spec.

Garland Antiques
74 Chatham Rd., Battersea. SW11 6HG. (Garland Beech). Open 10-6, Sun. 12-5. CL: Mon. SIZE: Small. *STOCK: Furniture, 19th C; decorative objects, 18th-19th C.* PARK: Easy. TEL: 020 7924 4284.

Gideon Hatch Rugs
1 Port House, Plantation Wharf, Battersea. SW11 3TY. Est. 1985. Open by appointment. SIZE: Small. *STOCK: Oriental and European rugs, 19th to early 20th C, £500-£25,000.* LOC: Off York Rd., behind Homebase. PARK: Easy. TEL: 020 7223 3996; fax - 020 7223 3997; e-mail - info@gideonhatch.co.uk; website - www.gideonhatch.co.uk. SER: Valuations; restorations; cleaning; buys at auction (rare rugs). FAIRS: Olympia; Battersea. VAT: Stan/Spec.

Northcote Road Antiques Market
155A Northcote Rd., Battersea. SW11 6QB. Open 10-6, Sun. 12-5. SIZE: 30 dealers. *STOCK: Victoriana and Art Deco collectables, silver, glass, furniture, lighting, jewellery, prints, mirrors, flatware.* TEL: 020 7228 6850.

Overmantels
66 Battersea Bridge Rd. SW11 3AG. (Seth Taylor). BCFA. Est. 1980. Open 9.30-5.30. SIZE: Medium. *STOCK: English giltwood mirrors,*

£400-£3,000; French giltwood mirrors, £700-£3,000; both 18th-19th C. Furniture, 19th C, £200-£2,000. LOC: 200m south of Battersea Bridge. PARK: Outside shop. TEL: 020 7223 8151; fax - 020 7924 2283. SER: Valuations; restorations (gesso work and gilding). VAT: Stan/Spec.

Pairs Antiques Ltd

Unit 6 Parkfields Industrial Estate, Culvert Rd., Battersea. SW11 5BA. (Iain M. Brunt). Est. 1994. Open by appointment. SIZE: Large. *STOCK: Pairs only - 18th-19th C furniture, decorative objects and paintings, £500-£20,000.* PARK: Easy. TEL: 020 7622 6446; mobile - 07798 684694; fax - 020 7622 3663; e-mail - mail@pairsantiques.co.uk; website - www.pairsantiques. co.uk. SER: Valuations; restorations; buys at auction. VAT: Stan/Spec.

Regent House Gallery

223 St John's Hill. SW11 1TH. (Nick & Jayne Underwood Thompson). Est. 1988. Open 10-6, Thurs. 10-7.30. CL: Mon. SIZE: Small. *STOCK: Watercolours and paintings, 19th-20th C, £50-£500; prints, drawings, cartoons, 18th-20th C, £10-£200; small antiques, books, 19th to early 20th C, £10-£200.* LOC: Top of St John's Hill, mid-way between Clapham Junction and Wandsworth Town. PARK: Pay and display. TEL: 020 7228 9344; home and fax - 020 7228 9344; e-mail - nick@regenthousegallery.com; website - www.regenthousegallery.com. SER: Framing.

The Woodpigeon

71 Webbs Rd. SW11 6SD. (John Taylor and Barbara Cunnell). Est. 1995. Open Tues.-Sat. 10.30-5.30. SIZE: Small. *STOCK: Country furniture, mainly French - painted armoires, chests, wardrobes and beds; small decorative items and country antiques, mainly mid to late 19th C, £5-£1,500.* LOC: Parallel with Northcote Rd. PARK: Side roads. TEL: 020 7223 8668; mobile - 07958 787676. SER: Furniture painting and re-upholstery. VAT: Spec.

Robert Young Antiques   BADA

68 Battersea Bridge Rd. SW11 3AG. Est. 1974. Open 10-6, Sat. 10-5. CL: Mon. SIZE: Medium. *STOCK: English oak and country furniture, 17th-18th C, £500-£20,000; English and European treen and objects of folk art, £20-£10,000; English and European provincial pottery and metalwork, £20-£2,500.* **LOC: Turn off King's Rd. or Chelsea Embankment into Beaufort St., cross over Battersea Bridge Rd., 9th shop on right. PARK: Opposite in side street. TEL: 020 7228 7847; fax - 020 7585 0489; e-mail - office@robertyoungantiques. com. SER: Valuations; buys at auction (treen and country furniture). FAIRS: Olympia, Chelsea. VAT: Stan/Spec.**

The Kilim Warehouse Ltd

28A Pickets St. SW12 8QB. (J. Luczyc-Wyhowska). Est. 1982. Open 10-5.30, Sat. 10-4. SIZE: Medium. *STOCK: Kilims from Eastern Europe, Asia Minor and beyond, £50-£8,000.* LOC: Near Clapham South tube station and Nightingale Lane. PARK: Easy after 11.30am. TEL: 020 8675 3122; fax - 020 8675 8494; website - www.kilim-warehouse.co.uk; e-mail - info@kilim-warehouse.co.uk. SER: Restorations; cleaning. VAT: Stan.

Twentieth Century

(M. Taylor). Est. 1986. By appointment only. *STOCK: Art Deco, Art Nouveau, Arts and Crafts, decorative arts items, £50-£500.* PARK: Easy. TEL: 020 8675 6351; fax - same; e-mail - martin@nbscoms.co.uk. FAIRS: Battersea Art Deco; Loughborough Art Deco; Manchester; Birmingham. VAT: Stan.

Christine Bridge   BADA

78 Castelnau, Barnes. SW13 9EX. LAPADA, CINOA. Est. 1972. Open anytime by appointment only. SIZE: Medium. *STOCK: Glass - 18th C collectors and 19th C coloured, engraved and decorative, £50-£15,000; small decorative items - papier mâché, bronzes, needlework, ceramics.* **LOC: Main road from Hammersmith Bridge. PARK: Easy. TEL: 020 8741 5501; fax - 020 8255 0172; mobile - 07831 126668; e-mail - christine@bridge-antiques. com; website - www.bridge-antiques.com. SER: Valuations; restorations (glass - cutting, polishing, declouding); buys at auction; shipping. FAIRS: Olympia (June & Nov.); BADA; Brussels; Tokyo; Melbourne; Sydney; Singapore; Santa Monica. VAT: Stan/Spec.**

Simon Coleman Antiques

40 White Hart Lane, Barnes. SW13. Est. 1974. SIZE: Large. *STOCK: Country furniture, oak, fruitwood, pine, French and English farm tables, 18th-19th C.* PARK: Easy. TEL: 020 8878 5037; e-mail - colemansimon@aol.com. VAT: Stan/Spec.

The Dining Room Shop

62/64 White Hart Lane, Barnes. SW13 0PZ. (K. Dyson). Est. 1985. Open 10-5.30, Sun. by appointment. SIZE: Medium. *STOCK: Formal and country dining room furniture, 18th-19th C; glasses, china, pottery, cutlery, damask and lace table linen, 19th C; associated small and decorative items.* LOC: Near Barnes railway

Kate Dyson

THE DINING ROOM SHOP

62-64 White Hart Lane • London SW13 0PZ
Tel: 020-8878 1020   Fax: 020-8876 2367   Website: www.thediningroomshop.co.uk

Antique tables and sets of chairs, glass, china, cutlery, prints,
table linen and lace – all for the dining room

bridge, turning opposite White Hart public house. PARK: Easy. TEL: 020 8878 1020; fax - 020 8876 2367; website - www.thediningroom shop.co.uk. SER: Valuations; restorations; bespoke furniture; finder; interior decorating. FAIRS: Olympia (June). VAT: Stan/Spec.

Joy McDonald Antiques
50 Station Rd., Barnes. SW13 0LP. Resident. Est. 1966. Open 10.30-5.30 prior telephone call advisable. CL: Mon. SIZE: Small. *STOCK: 19th-20th C mirrors, chandeliers and lighting; decorative items and upholstered chairs.* TEL: 020 8876 6184.

New Grafton Gallery
49 Church Rd., Barnes. SW13 9HH. (D. Wolfers). Est. 1968. Open 10-5.30. CL: Mon. SIZE: Medium. *STOCK: British paintings and drawings, £150-£3,000.* LOC: Off Castelnau which runs from Hammersmith Bridge. PARK: Easy. TEL: 020 8748 8850; home - 020 8876 6294. SER: Valuations; restorations; buys at auction. VAT: Stan/Spec.

John Spink   BADA
9 Richard Burbridge Mansions, 1 Brasenose Drive, Barnes. SW13 8RB. Est. 1972. Open by appointment. *STOCK: Fine English water-colours and selected oils, 1720-1920.* **TEL: 020 8741 6152; e-mail - john@johnspink.com. FAIRS: World of Watercolours; Olympia (Summer and Winter).**

Tobias and The Angel
68 White Hart Lane, Barnes. SW13 0PZ. (A. Hughes). Est. 1985. Open 10-6. SIZE: Large. *STOCK: Quilts, textiles, furniture, country and painted beds, decorative objects, from 1800.* LOC: Parallel to Barnes High St. PARK: Easy. TEL: 020 8878 8902; home - 01206 391003. SER: Interior design. VAT: Stan/Spec.

SW14

The Arts & Crafts Furniture Co Ltd
49 Sheen Lane, East Sheen. SW14 4AB. (Patrick Rogers). Est. 1985. Open 10-6, Sat. 10-5. SIZE: Medium. *STOCK: Arts and Crafts furniture and effects, Gothic and Aesthetic movement, 1850-1950, £500-£5,000.* LOC: Sheen Lane is off Upper Richmond Road (South Circular A205). PARK: Nearby. TEL: 020 8876 6544; fax - same; website - www.acfc.co.uk. SER: Valuations; restorations including French polishing and upholstery; buys at auction. VAT: Spec.

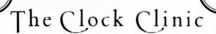

The Clock Clinic

Antique Clocks

A Regency period striking bracket clock
signed Handley and Moore London

Open Tues – Fri 9-6, Sat 9-1, Closed Mondays

85, Lower Richmond Road, Putney, London, SW15 1EU
Tel: 020-8788 1407 Fax: 020-8780 2838

Website: www.clockclinic.co.uk
Email: clockclinic@btconnect.com

Mary Cooke Antiques Ltd   BADA
12 The Old Power Station, 121 Mortlake High St. SW14 8SN. LAPADA. Open by appointment. *STOCK: Silver.* TEL: 020 8876 5777; fax - 020 8876 1652. SER: Valuations; restorations. FAIRS: Chelsea (Autumn); BADA; LAPADA; Olympia. VAT: Stan/Spec.

Paul Foster's Bookshop
119 Sheen Lane, East Sheen. SW14 8AE. ABA, PBFA. Est. 1983. Open 10.30-6. SIZE: Medium. *STOCK: Books - antiquarian, 17th-19th C, £100-£1,000; out of print, 19th-20th C, £1-£500; general, 50p-£100.* LOC: 20 yards from South Circular. PARK: Easy. TEL: 020 8876 7424; fax - same. FAIRS: Hotel Russell, PBFA monthly.

SW15

The Clock Clinic Ltd   BADA
85 Lower Richmond Rd., Putney. SW15 1EU. (R.S. Pedler). LAPADA, FBHI. Est. 1971. Open 9-6, Sat. 9-1. CL: Mon. *STOCK: Clocks and barometers.* TEL: 020 8788 1407; fax - 020 8780 2838; e-mail - clockclinic@btconnect. com; website - www.clockclinic.co.uk. SER: Valuations; restorations (as stock); buys at auction. VAT: Stan/Spec.

Hanshan Tang Books
Unit 3 Ashburton Centre, 276 Cortis Rd. SW15 3AY. (John Constable, John Cayley and Myrna Chug). ABA. Open by appointment only. *STOCK: Second-hand, antiquarian and new books and periodicals on Chinese, Japanese, Korean and Central Asian art and culture.* TEL: 020 8788 4464; fax - 020 8780 1565; e-mail - hst@hanshan. com; website - www.hanshan.com/. SER: Regular and special catalogues; wants lists welcome.

Jorgen Antiques
40 Lower Richmond Rd., Putney. SW15 1JP. (A.J. Dolleris). Est. 1960. Open 11-5. CL: Mon. and Sat. SIZE: Large. *STOCK: English and Continental furniture, 18th to early 19th C, £50-£5,000.* LOC: Between Putney Bridge and Putney Common. PARK: Easy. TEL: 020 8789 7329. VAT: Spec.

Thornhill Galleries Ltd. in association with A. & R. Dockerill Ltd
Rear of 78 Deodar Rd., Putney. SW15 2NJ. (Graham and Anthony Wakefield and Lindy Greig). Est. 1880. Open 9-5.15, Sat. 10-12. SIZE: Large. *STOCK: English and French period panelling, chimneypieces in wood, marble and stone; architectural items, wood carvings, 17th-19th C firegrates and fenders, fireplace accessories and iron interiors.* LOC: Off Putney Bridge Rd. PARK: Easy. TEL: 020 8874 2101/5669; fax - 020 8877 0313; e-mail - sales@thornhill galleries.co.uk; website - www.thornhillgalleries. co.uk. SER: Valuations; restorations (architectural items); buys at auction (architectural items). VAT: Stan/Spec.

SW16

H.C. Baxter and Sons   BADA
40 Drewstead Rd. SW16 1AB. (T.J., J. and G.J. Baxter and T.J. Hunter). LAPADA. Est. 1928. Open Wed. and Thurs. 8.30-5.15 or by appointment. SIZE: Medium. *STOCK: English furniture, 1730-1830, £1,000-£35,000.* LOC: Near Streatham Hill station. PARK: Easy. TEL: 020 8769 5869/5969; fax - 020 8769 0898; e-mail - partners@hcbaxter.co.uk; website - www.hcbaxter.co.uk.

A. and J. Fowle
542 Streatham High Rd. SW16 3QF. Est. 1962. Open 9.30-7. SIZE: Large. *STOCK: General antiques, Victorian and Edwardian furniture.* LOC: From London take A23 towards Brighton. PARK: Easy. TEL: 020 8764 2896; mobile - 07968 058790.

SW17

Ted Few
97 Drakefield Rd. SW17 8RS. Resident. Est. 1975. Open by appointment. SIZE: Medium. *STOCK: Paintings and sculpture, 1700-1940, £500-£5,000.* LOC: 5 mins. walk from Tooting Bec underground station. TEL: 020 8767 2314. SER: Valuations; buys at auction. VAT: Spec.

SW18

Earlsfield Bookshop
513 Garratt Lane, Wandsworth. SW18 4SW. (Charles Dixon). Est. 1985. Open 4-6, Fri. 11-6, Sat. 10-5. SIZE: Small. *STOCK: Books, £1-£50.* LOC: Next to Earlsfield station. PARK: Limited. TEL: 020 8946 3744.

Just a Second
284 Merton Rd., Wandsworth. SW18 5JN. (James Ferguson). Est. 1980. Open 9.30-5.30. CL: Mon. SIZE: Medium. *STOCK: Victorian, Edwardian, pre-1920's and reproduction furniture and bric-a-brac.* LOC: 5 minutes from Southfields underground station. PARK: Easy. TEL: 020 8874 2520. SER: Valuations; restorations.

Mr Wandle's Workshop Ltd
202 Garratt Lane, Wandsworth. SW18 4ED. (S. Zoil). Open 9-5.30. *STOCK: Victorian and Edwardian fireplaces and surrounds especially cast iron.* TEL: 020 8870 5873. SER: Shot-blasting.

SW19

Adams Room Antiques
20 Ridgway, Wimbledon Village. SW19 4LN. LAPADA. Est. 1971. Open 10-5. SIZE: Large. *STOCK: 18th-19th C English and French furniture especially dining; decorative Regency chairs, silver.* LOC: 4 miles from King's Rd., Chelsea; 1 mile off Kingston by-pass, M3. TEL: 020 8946 7047/8947 4784; fax - 020 8946 7476. SER: Export orders arranged. VAT: Spec.

Corfield Potashnick
39 Church Rd., Wimbledon Village. SW19 5DQ. Open Thurs.-Sat. 10.30-5 or by appointment. *STOCK: Fine antique furniture.* TEL: 020 8944 9022.

Coromandel
SW19. (P. Lang and B. Leigh). Resident. Open at any time by appointment. SIZE: Small. *STOCK: Boxes, table cabinets and decorative items,* Anglo-Indian and European Colonial, 17th-19th C, £250-£5,000. *PARK: Easy. TEL: 020 8543 9115; fax - 020 8543 6255; mobile - 07932 102756; e-mail - info@antiqueboxes.com. SER: Restorations (ivory and tortoiseshell).

The David Curzon Gallery
35 Church Rd., Wimbledon Village. SW19 5DQ. Open 10-6. CL: Mon. SIZE: Medium. *STOCK: Paintings and watercolours, from 1900, £350-£10,000.* LOC: 7 min. walk from Wimbledon Underground/BR. PARK: Reasonable. TEL: 020 8944 6098; fax - same; e-mail - davidcurzon@barclays.net. VAT: Spec.

Shaikh and Son (Oriental Rugs) Ltd
139 Arthur Rd. SW19 8AB. (M. Shaikh). Open 10-6. CL: Sat. pm. *STOCK: Persian carpets, rugs, £100-£10,000.* TEL: 020 8947 9232. SER: Repairing and cleaning.

Mark J. West - Cobb Antiques Ltd
BADA
39B High St., Wimbledon Village. SW19 5BY. Open 10-5.30. SIZE: Large. STOCK: Antique glass, £5-£5,000. PARK: Easy. TEL: 020 8946 2811. SER: Valuations; buys at auction. FAIRS: Olympia; Grosvenor House.

SW20

W.G.T. Burne (Antique Glass) Ltd
BADA
PO Box 9465. (Formerly of Chelsea) SW20 9ZD. (Mrs G. and A.T. Burne). Est. 1936. By appointment only. STOCK: English and Irish glassware, Georgian and Victorian decanters; chandeliers, candelabra and lustres. TEL: 020 8543 6319; fax - same; mobile - 07774 725834. SER: Valuations; restorations. VAT: Stan/Spec.

W. F. Turk Antique Clocks
355 Kingston Rd., Wimbledon Chase. SW20 8JX. LAPADA, CINOA. Est. 1970. Open Tues.-Fri. 9-5.30, Sat. 9-4. SIZE: Medium. *STOCK:*

Clocks, including longcase, 17th-19th C, £4,000-£60,000; bracket, 17th-19th C, £2,000-£40,000; mantel and carriage, 19th C, £450-£20,000. LOC: Off A3. PARK: Easy. TEL: 020 8543 3231; fax - same. SER: Valuations; restorations. FAIRS: Olympia; LAPADA. VAT: Stan/Spec.

SE1

Antique Trade Warehouse
64 Druid St., Bermondsey. SE1 3LW. (Margaret McCarthy). Est. 1983. Open 9.30-5. SIZE: Warehouse. *STOCK: General antiques and shipping goods.* PARK: Easy. TEL: 020 7394 7856. SER: Valuations.

Antiques Exchange
170-172 Tower Bridge Rd. SE1 3LS. (Mr and Mrs R. Draysey). Est. 1972. Open 10.30-6 including Sun. SIZE: Large. *STOCK: Furniture, smalls, lighting, decorative items, from 1700.* PARK: Nearby. TEL: 020 7403 5568; fax - 020 7378 8828; e-mail - jo.draysey@virgin.net; website - www.antiquesexchange.com. SER: Restorations (furniture).

Bermondsey Antiques Market
Corner of Long Lane and Bermondsey St. SE1. (Bath Antiques Markets Ltd). Est. 1959. Open Fri. 5 am-2 pm. *STOCK: Wide range of general antiques and collectables including specialist dealers in most fields especially jewellery and silver.* LOC: Borough, Tower Hill or London Bridge tube stations. TEL: Enquiries - 020 7969 1500; fax - 020 7969 1639. SER: Valuations; book binding.

Victor Burness Antiques and Scientific Instruments
241 Long Lane, Bermondsey. SE1 4PR. (V.G. Burness). Est. 1975. Open Fri. 6am-1pm or by appointment. SIZE: Small. *STOCK: Scientific instruments, marine items, 19th C, £20-£1,500.* PARK: Easy. TEL: Home - 01732 454591. SER: Valuations. FAIRS: Portman Hotel.

Robert Bush - Antique & Decorative Furniture
Open by appointment only. *STOCK: Furniture.* TEL: Mobile - 07836 236911; e-mail - bush.antiques@virgin.net.

Europa House Antiques
160-164 Tower Bridge Rd. SE1 3LS. (G. Viventi). Est. 1976. Open 9.30-6.30. CL: Sat. and Sun. except by appointment. SIZE: Large. *STOCK: Furniture and general antiques.* TEL: 020 7357 8951/7394 1001/7403 0022; e-mail - viventi@btinternet.com.

The Galleries
157 Tower Bridge Rd., Bermondsey. SE1 3LW. (Alan Bennett). LAPADA. Open 9.30-5.30, Fri. 8-4.30, Sat. and Sun. 12-6. SIZE: Very large. *STOCK: Georgian and Victorian English and Continental furniture, some collectables.* PARK: Easy. TEL: 020 7407 5371; fax - 020 7403 0359. VAT: Stan/Spec.

Tower Bridge Antiques
47 and 71 Tanner St. SE1 3PL. Open 9-5.30, Sat. 10.30-6, Sun. 11-5. SIZE: Large. *STOCK: Victorian, Georgian and Edwardian furniture, shipping goods.* TEL: 020 7403 3660; e-mail - towerbridgeant@aol.com. VAT: Stan.

SE3

Michael Silverman
PO Box 350. SE3 0LZ. ABA, ILAB. Est. 1989. By appointment only. *STOCK: Manuscripts, autograph letters, historical documents.* PARK: Free. TEL: 020 8319 4452; fax - 020 8856 6006; e-mail - ms@michael-silverman.com; website - www.michael-silverman.com. SER: Catalogue available. FAIRS: ABA - Olympia (June) and Chelsea (Nov).

Vale Stamps and Antiques
21 Tranquil Vale, Blackheath. SE3 0BU. (H.J. and R.P. Varnham). Est. 1952. Open 10-5.30. CL: Thurs. SIZE: Small. *STOCK: Georgian and Victorian jewellery, £25-£500; ancient and medieval coins, £20-£500.* LOC: Village centre, 100yds. from station. PARK: Nearby. TEL: 020 8852 9817. SER: Valuations. VAT: Stan/Spec.

Wallace Antiques Ltd
56 Tranquil Vale, Blackheath. SE3 0BD. Open 9.30-5.30. *STOCK: Furniture including reproduction.* TEL: 020 8852 2647.

SE5

Camberwell Architectural Salvage & Antiques
47 Southampton Way, Camberwell. SE5 7SW. (J. Swan and M. Tree). Est. 1993. Open Tues.-Sat. 10-5. SIZE: Large. *STOCK: Architectural salvage including doors, floorboards, radiators, baths, sinks and taps, 19th-20th C, £15-£600; furniture, 19th-20th C.* LOC: From Camberwell Green towards Peckham - 6th turning on left, just past College of Art. PARK: Easy. TEL: 020 7277 0315.

Coats Oriental Carpets
116 Grove Lane. SE5 8BJ. (A. Coats). Est. 1973. Open by appointment only. *STOCK: Oriental carpets and rugs, kelims, £50-£2,000; Oriental*

textiles and embroideries, £10-£100; all 19th C.
TEL: 020 7274 6471. SER: Valuations; restorations
(re-weaving); buys at auction. VAT: Stan/Spec.

Robert E. Hirschhorn BADA
LAPADA. CINOA. Est. 1979. Open by appointment. *STOCK: Distinctive English, Welsh and Continental country furniture, mainly oak, elm, walnut and fruitwood, and interesting objects, 18th C and earlier; European ceramics, especially delfware; textiles, and metalwork.* PARK: Easy. TEL: 020 7703 7443; mobile - 07831 405937; e-mail - hirschhornantiques @macunlimited.net. FAIRS: BADA (March); Olympia (June and Nov).

SE6

Wilkinson plc
5 Catford Hill. SE6 4NU. Est. 1947. Open 9-5.
CL: Sat. SIZE: Medium. *STOCK: Glass especially chandeliers, 18th C and reproduction, art metal work.* LOC: Opposite Catford Bridge railway station. Entrance through Wickes D.I.Y. car park. PARK: Easy. TEL: 020 8314 1080; fax - 020 8690 1524; e-mail - enquiries@wilkinson-plc.com; website - www.wilkinson-plc.com. SER: Restorations and repairs (glass, metalwork).

SE7

Ward Antiques
267 Woolwich Rd., Charlton. SE7. (T. and M. Ward). Est. 1981. Open 10-5, Sun. 11-2. SIZE: Medium. *STOCK: Victorian fireplaces, Victorian and Edwardian furniture, £50-£1,000.* LOC: From A102 M take Woolwich/Woolwich ferry turn, 100yds. from roundabout, immediately under railway bridge across the road. PARK: Easy. TEL: 020 8305 0963; home - 020 8698 0771.

SE8

Antique Warehouse
9-14 Deptford Broadway. SE8 4PA. Est. 1986.
Open 10-6, Sun. 11-4. SIZE: Large. *STOCK: Fine furniture, 1750 to 20th C; sofas, chairs, mirrors and lighting.* PARK: Opposite. TEL: 020 8691 3062; website - www.antiquewarehouse.co.uk. VAT: Stan.

SE9

Cobwebs
73 Avery Hill Rd., New Eltham. SE9 2BJ. (Martin Baker). Est. 1991. Open 10-5.30, Sun. 10-2. CL: Mon. am and Thurs. SIZE: Medium.

STOCK: Furniture, smalls, Oriental items. LOC: Between A20 and A2 and 5 minutes from New Eltham BR station. PARK: Easy. TEL: 020 8850 5611; website - wwwantique-dealers.eu.com/ cobwebs. SER: Valuations.

The Fireplace
257 High St., Eltham. SE9 1TY. (A. Clark). Est. 1978. Open daily. SIZE: Medium. *STOCK: Fireplaces, 19th-20th C, £100-£1,000.* PARK: Adjacent side streets. TEL: 020 8850 4887. SER: Restorations (fireplaces). VAT: Stan.

R.E. Rose FBHI
731 Sidcup Rd., Eltham. SE9 3SA. Est. 1976. Open 9-5. SIZE: Small. *STOCK: Clocks and barometers, 1750-1930, £50-£5,000.* LOC: A20 from London, shop on left just past fiveways traffic lights at Green Lane. PARK: Easy. TEL: 020 8859 4754. SER: Restorations (clocks and barometers); spare parts for antique clocks and barometers. VAT: Stan/Spec.

SE10

Creek Antiques
23 Greenwich South St. SE10 8NW. Est. 1986. Open 11-5, appointment advisable. SIZE: Small. *STOCK: Jewellery and silver, from Victorian, £5-£500.* LOC: 200 yards from British Rail station. PARK: Easy. TEL: 020 8293 5721; mobile - 07778 427521; e-mail - creekantiques@aol.com.

Greenwich Antiques Market
Greenwich High Rd. SE10. Est. 1972. Open Sun. 7.30-4.30, and Sat. (June-Sept.). SIZE: 80 stalls. *STOCK: General antiques and bric-a-brac.* LOC: Almost opposite railway station. PARK: Adjacent.

The Greenwich Gallery
9 Nevada St. SE10 9JL. (R.F. Moy). Est. 1965. Open 10-5.30 including Sun. *STOCK: Mainly English oil paintings and watercolours, 18th C to 1950.* PARK: Opposite. TEL: 020 8305 1666. SER: Restorations; framing; exhibitions. VAT: Spec.

The Junk Box
151 Trafalgar Rd., Greenwich. SE10 9TX. (Robert Dodd and Marilyn Allen). Est. 1993. Open 10-5.30 including Sun. SIZE: Small. *STOCK: Furniture, pictures and prints, collectables, 19th-20th C, £5-£1,000.* LOC: ½ mile east of centre of Greenwich. PARK: Easy. TEL: 020 8293 5715.

The Junk Shop
47 Old Woolwich Rd. SE10 8NW. (T. and R.

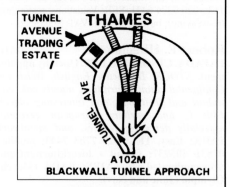
Moy). Est. 1985. Open 10-5.30 including Sun. SIZE: Large. *STOCK: Larger antique and decorative items, 18th C to 1950's; furniture, architectural antiques, bric-a-brac.* LOC: A202. From London follow A2, then turn left at Deptford - or follow riverside road from Tower Bridge. PARK: Meters. TEL: 020 8305 1666, ext. 25. SER: Restorations (furniture). VAT: Stan/Spec.

Lamont Antiques Ltd
Tunnel Avenue Antique Warehouse, Tunnel Avenue Trading Estate, Greenwich. SE10 0QH. (N. Lamont and F. Llewellyn). LAPADA. Open 9-5.30. CL: Sat. SIZE: Large. *STOCK: Architectural fixtures and fittings, bars, stained glass, pub mirrors and signs, shipping furniture, £5-£25,000.* PARK: Own. TEL: 020 8305 2230; fax - 020 8305 1805. SER: Container packing.

Peter Laurie Antiques
28 Greenwich Church St. SE10 9BQ. Open 10-5 including Sun. CL: Fri. am. *STOCK: Nautical items, navigational instruments, maritime curiosities, weapons and photographic items.* TEL: 020 8853 5777; fax - same; e-mail - plaurie@maritime antiques-uk.com; website - www.maritime antiques-uk.com.

The Warwick Leadlay Gallery
5 Nelson Rd., Greenwich. SE10 9JB. Est. 1974. Open 9.30-5.30, Sun. and public holidays 11-5.30. SIZE: Large. *STOCK: Antique maps, prints, fine arts, Nelson specialists, 17th-20th C.* LOC: Head of Greenwich Market. PARK: Nearby. TEL: 020 8858 0317; fax - 020 8853 1773; e-mail - wlg @easynet.co.uk; website - www.wlgonline.com. SER: Framing; restorations; valuations. VAT: Stan.

Marcet Books
4A Nelson Rd., Greenwich. SE10 9JB. (Martin Kemp). PBFA. Est. 1980. Open 10-5.30 including Sun. SIZE: Small. *STOCK: General second-hand and antiquarian books.* LOC: In alley off Nelson Rd., leading to Greenwich market. PARK: 200 yards. TEL: 020 8853 5408; fax - same; e-mail - marcet@dircon.co.uk; website - www.marcet books.co.uk. SER: Valuations. FAIRS: PBFA 12 monthly at Russell Hotel.

Rogers Turner Books
23a Nelson Rd., Greenwich. SE10 9JB. Est. 1975. Open Thurs.-Fri. 10-6 or by appointment. *STOCK: Antiquarian books especially on clocks and scientific instruments.* TEL: 020 8853 5271; fax - same; Paris - 0033 13912 1191; e-mail -

rogersturner@compuserve.com; website - www.
rogersturner@abebooks.com. SER: Buys at auction
(British and European); catalogues available.

Spread Eagle Antiques
1 Stockwell St. SE10 9JL. (R.F. Moy). Est. 1954.
Open 10-5.30 including Sun. SIZE: Large.
*STOCK: Furniture, pictures and decorative
items, 18th-19th C.* PARK: Opposite. TEL: 020
8305 1666; home - 020 8692 1618. SER:
Valuations; restorations (pictures, furniture).
VAT: Stan/Spec.

Spread Eagle Book & Curio Shop
8 Nevada St. SE10 9JL. (R.F. Moy). Est. 1954.
Open 10-5.30 including Sun. SIZE: Large.
*STOCK: Antiquarian and secondhand books,
period costume, curios, china, bric-a-brac,
prints, postcards.* Not Stocked: Furniture. LOC:
A202. From London follow A2, then turn left at
Deptford - or follow riverside road from Tower
Bridge. TEL: 020 8305 1666. SER: Valuations;
restorations (furniture, china, pictures). VAT:
Stan/Spec/Global.

The Waterloo Trading Co.
Unit D Tunnel Ave. Trading Estate, Tunnel Ave.,
Greenwich. SE10 0QH. Est. 1989. Open 9-5. CL:
Sat. SIZE: Large. *STOCK: Victorian, Edwardian
and shipping furniture.* TEL: 020 8858 3355; fax
- 020 8858 3344; e-mail - boysship@ftech.co.uk.
SER: Robert Boys Shipping; packing. VAT: Stan.

Robert Whitfield Antiques
Tunnel Avenue Antique Warehouse, Tunnel
Avenue Trading Estate, Greenwich. SE10 0QH.
LAPADA. Open 10-5. CL: Sat. *STOCK:
Edwardian, Victorian and secondhand furniture,
especially bentwood chairs.* TEL: 020 8305 2230;
fax - 020 8305 1805. SER: Container packing.

SE13

Robert Morley and Co Ltd   **BADA**
34 Engate St. SE13 7HA. Est. 1881. Open 9-5.
STOCK: Pianos, harpsichords, clavichords,
spinets, virginals, harps; stools, music cabinets
and stands. PARK: Own. TEL: 020 8318 5838;
e-mail - jvm@morley-r.u-net.com; website -
www.morleypianos.com. SER: Restorations
(musical instruments). VAT: Stan.

The Old Station
72 Loampit Lane, Lewisham. SE13 7SX. (Robert
Jacob). Open 10-5.30, Sun. 11-4. SIZE: Medium.
*STOCK: Architectural items including doors,
baths, panelling and sinks; antique furniture.*
LOC: A20. PARK: Easy. TEL: 020 8694 6540;

mobile - 07710 489895; e-mail - theoldstation@
btinternet.com; website - www.the-old-station.
co.uk. SER: Valuations; pine stripping. FAIRS:
Ardingly, Newark, Swinderby.

SE18

The Walpole Galleries
Commonwealth Buildings, Woolwich Church St.
SE18 5NS. (Graham Walpole). Est. 1975. By
appointment. SIZE: Very large. *STOCK:
Paintings, 1770-1940, £500-£50,000; works of
art, 1700-1920, £250-£10,000; furniture, 1780-
1920, £500-£25,000.* LOC: Immediately off
A206; main road through London through
Greenwich and east to Woolwich. .25 of mile
before Woolwich Ferry. PARK: Own. TEL: 020
8316 7324; fax - same; mobile - 07831 561042.
FAIRS: Olympia (June). VAT: Stan/Spec.

SE20

Bearly Trading of London
202 High St., Penge. SE20 7QB. (Jake and Guy
Aust). Open Sat. 10-6. *STOCK: Old bears, artist
bears, rocking horses, antique furniture.* LOC:
Opposite Kent House Rd., Beckenham, Kent.
PARK: Opposite. TEL: 020 8659 0500; 020 8466
6696; fax - 020 8460 3166. SER: Repairs (bears).

SE21

Acorn Antiques
111 Rosendale Rd., West Dulwich. SE21 8EZ.
(Mrs G. Kingham). Est. 1976. Open 10-6, Sat. 10-
5.30. *STOCK: Furniture, sterling silver, jewellery, ceramics, glassware and fireplace accessories.* TEL: 020 8761 3349.

Francis Jevons
80 Dulwich Village. SE21 7AJ. Est. 1983.
Usually open 9.30-1 and 2.30-5.30, Sat. until 5,
other times by appointment. CL: Wed. *STOCK:
China and small furniture, late 18th to 19th C;
interior design, lamps and decorative items.*
LOC: Off South Circular leading down from
either Gallery or College roads. PARK: Easy.
TEL: 020 8693 1991. SER: Valuations; restorations. VAT: Stan/Spec.

SE22

Melbourne Antiques & Interiors
67 and 161 Lordship Lane, East Dulwich. SE22
8EW. (Ian Peters). Est. 1990. Open 10-6

including Sun. SIZE: Large. *STOCK: French beds and armoires, £300-£1,000+; mirrors, £50-£1,000+; commodes, £500-£1,000+: all 19th C; French linen.* LOC: Off South Circular at Dulwich. PARK: Easy. TEL: 020 8299 6565; fax - 020 8299 4257. SER: Restorations (furniture).

SE24

Under Milkwood
379-381 Milkwood Rd., Herne Hill. SE24 0HA. (Nick and Sue Williams). Est. 1988. Open 9-5.30. SIZE: Medium. *STOCK: Victorian, Edwardian and reproduction mantelpieces, £200-£2,000.* LOC: At rear of Herne Hill station. PARK: Easy. TEL: 020 7733 3921. SER: Valuations; restorations; installations; gas fires; slate hearths.

SE25

Engine 'n' Tender
19 Spring Lane, Woodside Green. SE25 4SP. (Mrs Joyce M. Buttigieg). Est. 1957. Open Thurs. and Fri. 12-5.30, Sat. 10-5.30. SIZE: Small. *STOCK: Model railways, mainly pre 1939; Dinky toys, to 1968; old toys, mainly tinplate.* PARK: Easy. TEL: 020 8654 0386. FAIRS: Local toy.

North London Clock Shop Ltd
Rear of 60 Saxon Rd. SE25 5EH. (D.S. Tomlin). Est. 1960. Open 9-6. CL: Sat. SIZE: Medium. *STOCK: Clocks, longcase, bracket, carriage, skeleton, 18th-19th C.* PARK: Easy. TEL: 020 8664 8089. SER: Restorations (clocks and barometers); wheel cutting, hand engraving, dial painting, clock reconversions. FAIRS: Olympia. VAT: Stan.

SE26

Abbott Antiques and Country Pine
109 Kirkdale, Sydenham. SE26 4QJ. Est. 1972. Open 10-5.30, Sat. 10-5. *STOCK: Victorian and Edwardian pine furniture, general antiques and interesting items.* LOC: ½ mile from South Circular Rd. at Forest Hill. TEL: 020 8699 1363; e-mail - abbottantiques@btinternet.com.

Behind the Boxes - Art Deco
98 Kirkdale, Sydenham. SE26 4BG. (Ray Owen). Est. 1987. Open 10.30-5, Sun. and Mon. by appointment. SIZE: Large. *STOCK: Furniture, lighting and costume jewellery, 1930's, from £25.* LOC: 1 mile from Crystal Palace. BR station Forest Hill. PARK: Loading, otherwise Fransfield Rd. TEL: 020 8291 6116. SER: Valuations; buys at auction. FAIRS: Decorama and Deco.

Oola Boola Antiques London
139-147 Kirkdale. SE26 4QJ. (R. Scales and S. Bramley). Est. 1968. Open 10-6, Sat.10-5, Sun. 11-5. SIZE: Large. *STOCK: Furniture, £5-£3,000; mahogany, oak, walnut, Victorian, Arts & Crafts, Art Nouveau, Edwardian, Art Deco, retro and shipping goods.* PARK: Forecourt. TEL: 020 8291 9999; fax - 020 8291 5759; e-mail - oola.boola@telco4u.net.

Sydenham Antiques Centre
48 Sydenham Rd., Sydenham. SE26 5QF. (Mrs L. Cockton). Est. 1996. Open 10-5. SIZE: Medium. *STOCK: China, glass, silver, collectables, furniture and jewellery, 19th-20th C, £5-£500.* LOC: 2 doors down from Post Office in High St. PARK: Easy and nearby. TEL: 020 8778 1706. SER: Valuations; restorations (china).

Vintage Cameras Ltd
256 Kirkdale, Sydenham. SE26 4NL. (J. and M. Jenkins). Est. 1959. Open 9-5. SIZE: Large. *STOCK: Vintage and classic cameras, £50-£5,000; general photographica, £5-£500; all 1840-2001.* LOC: Near South Circular Rd. PARK: Nearby. TEL: 020 8778 5416; fax - 020 8778 5841; e-mail - i@vintagecameras.co.uk; website - www.vintagecameras.co.uk. SER: Valuations. VAT: Stan.

E1

La Maison
107/108 Shoreditch High St. E1 6JN. (Guillaume and Louise Bacou). Open 10-6. SIZE: Large. *STOCK: Beds.* TEL: 020 7729 9646; fax - 020 7729 6399. SER: Restorations. VAT: Margin.

E2

George Rankin Coin Co. Ltd
325 Bethnal Green Rd. E2. Open 10-5. *STOCK: Coins, medals, medallions and jewellery.* TEL: 020 7739 1840/7729 1280; fax - 020 7729 5023.

E4

Record Detector
3 & 4 Station Approach, Station Rd., North Chingford. E4 6AL. (N. Salter). Est. 1992. Open 10-6. CL: Thurs. SIZE: Small (2 shops). *STOCK: Secondhand and collectable records, L.P's, E.P's, singles and CD's.* LOC: In forecourt of North Chingford railway station. PARK: Easy. TEL: 020 8529 6361/2938; website - www.salter.co.uk.

Nicholas Salter Antiques

8 Station Approach, Station Rd., North Chingford. E4 6AL. (Sherley Salter). Est. 1971. Open Tues. and Wed. 10-5, Fri. and Sat. 10-6. SIZE: Large. *STOCK: Furniture, 1850-1930, £150-£1,500; china and linen, 1870-1950, £30-£150; antiquarian and secondhand books; vintage clothes and accessories, 1860's-1970's, £5-£500.* LOC: Next to North Chingford station. PARK: Easy. TEL: 020 8529 2938; website - www.Salter.co.uk.

E8

Boxes and Musical Instruments

2 Middleton Rd., Hackney. E8 4BL. (A. and J.O'Kelly). Est. 1974. Open any time by appointment. SIZE: Medium. *STOCK: Boxes - caddies, sewing, writing, snuff, vanity, jewellery and desk, £300-£5,000; musical instruments, plucked string, £1,000-£3,000; all 18th-19th C.*

LOC: Off Kingsland Rd., continuation of Bishopsgate. PARK: Easy. TEL: 020 7254 7074; home - same; fax - 0870 125 7669; e-mail - boxes@hygra.com; website - www.hygra.com. SER: Valuations; restorations (exceptional instruments only). Registered with the Conservation Unit of the Museums and Galleries Commission.

E11

Old Cottage Antiques

8 High St., Wanstead. E11 2AJ. (P. Blake and B. Hawkins). LAPADA. Est. 1920. Open Fri. and Sat. 10-5. SIZE: Medium. *STOCK: Furniture, clocks, paintings, 19th-20th C.* LOC: Near Wanstead and Snaresbrook Central Line stations. PARK: Easy. TEL: 020 8989 2317/8504 9264; mobile - 07710 031079; e-mail - brianhawkins antiques@hotmail.com. SER: Buys at auction. VAT: Stan/Spec.

'A Picardy Market', pencil, watercolour and gouache, 10in. x 14in., signed. This is typical of the plein-air *compositions for which William became famous. In March 1931 The Times wrote of his watercolours: 'The essentially descriptive drawing is concealed by a certain freedom of handling which never goes so far as to interfere with accuracy.'*

Writing in the Tenth Annual Investment Issue (July/August 1985) of **Antique Collecting** Anthony J. Lester thought works by William Lee-Hankey (1869-1952) 'still have some way to go up the price ladder'. Here he looks in depth at the artist's work and life. From an article entitled "William Lee-Hankey (1869-1952) – A British Impressionist" which appeared in the December 2001/January 2002 issue of **Antique Collecting**. For more details and to subscribe see page 21.

A.R. ULLMANN LTD.
10 HATTON GARDEN
LONDON EC1N 8AH
TEL: 020 7405 1877
FAX: 020 7404 7071

e-mail: ar_ullmann27@hotmail.com
website:
http://freespace.virgin.net/ar.ullmann

ANTIQUE AND SECONDHAND JEWELLERY SILVER OBJETS D'ART BOUGHT, SOLD & REPAIRED

OPEN: Monday – Fri 9am-5pm
Sat 9.30am – 5pm
REPAIRS – VALUATIONS

E17

Collectors Centre - Antique City
98 Wood St. E17. Est. 1978. Open 9.30-5.30. CL: Thurs. SIZE: Large. *STOCK: Antiques, collectables, 40's, 50's, 60's, £1-£500.* PARK: Opposite. TEL: 020 8520 4032. *Trade Only.*

Georgian Village Antiques Market
100 Wood St., Walthamstow. E17 3HX. Est. 1972. Open 10-5. CL: Thurs. SIZE: 10 shops. *STOCK: Clocks, barometers, postcards, collectables, jewellery, brass, copper, stamps, silver, silver plate, crafts.* LOC: 50yds. from Dukes Head. PARK: Adjacent. TEL: 020 8520 6638.

E18

Victoria Antiques
166A George Lane, South Woodford. E18 2HL. (M. A. Holman). Est. 1998. Open 11-5. CL: Tues.and Thurs. SIZE: Small. *STOCK: Clocks and carved chairs, 18th-19th C, £100-£1,000; pictures, 19th C, £50-£500; silver, £20-£500; bronze figures, £100-£1,000.* LOC: 2 mins. walk from South Woodford station. PARK: George Lane. TEL: 020 8989 1002. SER: Valuations. VAT: Stan.

EC1

City Clocks
31 Amwell St. EC1R 1UN. (J. Rosson). FBHI. Est. 1960. Open Tues.-Fri. 8.30-5.30, Sat. 9.30-2.30 or by appointment. SIZE: Medium. *STOCK: Clocks, some furniture, 18th-20th C, £100-£12,000.* PARK: Easy. TEL: 020 7278 1154; website - www.cityclocks.co.uk. SER: Valuations; restorations (clocks and watches, house calls to longcase); buys at auction. VAT: Spec.

Eldridge London
99-101 Farringdon Rd. EC1R 3BT. (B. Eldridge). Est. 1953. Open 12-5, 1st Sat. in month 11-5. CL: Wed. SIZE: Large. *STOCK: Furniture, treen and items of social and historical importance.* PARK: Easy. TEL: 020 7837 0379. VAT: Spec.

Finecraft Workshop Ltd
10 Greville St. EC1N 8SB. (Martyn J. Pummell). NAG. Est. 1955. Open 10.15-5, Sat. 10.15-4.30, Sun. 10.15-2. SIZE: Medium. *STOCK: Jewellery, 19th-20th C, £100-£8,000+.* LOC: Between Farringdon Rd. and Hatton Garden. PARK: Nearby. TEL: 020 7242 3825; fax - 020 7404 0170. SER: Valuations; restorations; re-making and repairing; insurance claims undertaken; buys at auction. FAIRS: Europe and USA. VAT: Stan.

C.R. Frost and Son Ltd
60-62 Clerkenwell Rd. EC1M 5PX. BCWMG; BHI. Est. 1932. Open 10-5. CL: Sat. *STOCK: Quality vintage clocks, watches and barometers.* TEL: 020 7253 0315; fax - 020 7253 7454; website - www.crfrost.co.uk. SER: Repairs (clocks and watches).

Jonathan Harris (Jewellery) Ltd
63-66 Hatton Garden (office). EC1N 8LE. (E.C., D. I. and J. Harris). Est. 1958. Open 9.30-4.30. CL: Sat. *STOCK: Antique and secondhand rings, brooches, pendants, bracelets and other jewellery, from £100.* PARK: Nearby. TEL: 020 7242 9115/7242 1558; fax - 020 7831 4417. SER: Valuations; export. VAT: Stan/Spec.

Hirsh Ltd
10 Hatton Garden. EC1N 8AH. (A. Hirsh). Open 10-5.30. *STOCK: Fine jewellery, silver and objets d'art.* TEL: 020 7405 6080; fax - 020 7430 0107; e-mail - enquiries@hirsh.co.uk. SER: Valuations; jewellery designed and re-modelled.

R. Holt and Co. Ltd
98 Hatton Garden. EC1N 8NX. (R. and J. Holt). GMC, BJA, London Diamond Bourse. Est. 1948. Open 9.30-5.30. CL: Sat. *STOCK: Gemstone specialists.* TEL: 020 7405 5286/0197; fax - 020

7430 1279; e-mail - info@rholt.co.uk. SER: Valuations; restorations (gem stone cutting and testing; bead stringing; inlaid work).

Joseph and Pearce Ltd
63-66 Hatton Garden. EC1. LAPADA. Est. 1896. Open by appointment. *STOCK: Jewellery, 1800-1960, £100-£5,000.* TEL: 020 7405 4604/7; fax - 020 7242 1902. FAIRS: Earls Court, NEC, Inhorgenta, New York. VAT: Stan/Spec. *Trade Only.*

A.R. Ullmann Ltd
10 Hatton Garden. EC1N 8AH. (J.S. Ullmann). Est. 1939. Open 9-5, Sat. 9.30-5. SIZE: Small. *STOCK: Jewellery, gold, silver and diamond; silver and objets d'art.* LOC: Very close to Farringdon and Chancery Lane tube stations. PARK: Multi-storey in St. Cross St. TEL: 020 7405 1877; fax - 020 7404 7071; home - 020 8346 2546. SER: Valuations; restorations. VAT: Stan/Spec.

EC2

D. Horton
69 Moorgate. EC2R 6BH. *STOCK: Modern British paintings.* TEL: 020 7588 6004; fax - 020 7588 6005; website - www.hortonlondon.co.uk. SER: Valuations.

LASSCo
St. Michael's, Mark St. (off Paul St.). EC2A 4ER. LAPADA. Est. 1977. Open 10-5. *STOCK: Architectural antiques including panelled rooms, chimney pieces, garden ornaments, lighting, door furniture, stained glass, columns and capitals, stonework, relics and curiosities.* TEL: 020 7749 9944; fax - 020 7749 9941; website - www.lassco. co.uk.

Westland London
St. Michael's Church, Leonard St. EC2A 4ER. (Geoffrey Westland). SALVO. Est. 1969. Open 9-6, Sat. 10-5, Sun. by appt. SIZE: Large. *STOCK: Period and prestigious chimneypieces, architectural elements, panelled rooms, light fittings, statuary, paintings and furniture, £100-£100,000.* LOC: Off Gt. Eastern St. PARK: Easy. TEL: 020 7739 8094; fax - 020 7729 3620; e-mail - westland @westland.co.uk; website - www. westland.co.uk. SER: Restorations; installations; shipping.

EC3

Ash Rare Books
153 Fenchurch St. EC3M 6BB. (L. Worms). ABA, ILAB. Est. 1946. Open 10-5. CL: Sat. SIZE: Small. *STOCK: Books, 1550-1980, £20-£10,000; maps, 1550-1850, £25-£2,000; prints, 1650-*

1900, £20-£1,000. LOC: First floor office opposite top of Rood Lane. TEL: 020 7626 2665; fax - 020 7623 9052; e-mail - books@ashrare. com; website - www.ashrare.com. SER: Buys at auction (books and maps). VAT: Stan.

Halcyon Days   BADA
4 Royal Exchange. EC3V 3LL. (Peter Norman). Est. 1950. Open 10-5.30. *STOCK: 18th to early 19th C enamels, Georgian and Victorian scent bottles, papier mâché, tôle, objects of vertu, treen, unusual small Georgian furniture.* **TEL: 020 7626 1120; fax - 020 7283 1876; e-mail - info@halcyondays.co.uk; website - www.halcyondays.co.uk. FAIRS: Grosvenor House. VAT: Stan/Spec.**

Nanwani and Co
2 Shopping Arcade, Bank Station, Cornhill. EC3V 3LA. Est. 1958. CL: Sat. *STOCK: Precious and semi-precious stones, Oriental items, objets d'art.* TEL: 020 7623 8232; fax - 020 7283 2548. VAT: Stan.

Searle and Co Ltd
1 Royal Exchange, Cornhill. EC3V 3LL. NAG. Est. 1893. Open 9-5.30. SIZE: Medium. *STOCK: Georgian, Victorian, Art Nouveau, Art Deco and secondhand silver and jewellery; novelty pieces and collectibles.* LOC: Near Bank Underground - exits 3 & 4. PARK: Meters. TEL: 020 7626 2456; fax - 020 7283 6384; e-mail - mail@searleandco. ltd.uk; website - www.searleandco.ltd.uk. SER: Commissions; valuations; restorations; repairs; engraving. VAT: Stan/Spec.

EC4

Gladwell and Company
68 Queen Victoria St. EC4N 4SJ. (Anthony Fuller). LAPADA. SLAD. Open 9.30-5.30, Sat. and Sun. by appointment. SIZE: Small. *STOCK: Oil paintings, watercolours, drawings, etchings and bronzes, £50-£50,000.* LOC: Near St Paul's cathedral and Bank of England. PARK: Easy. TEL: 020 7248 3824; fax - 020 7236 6875. SER: Valuations; restorations; buys at auction. FAIRS: LAPADA; NEC; Manchester, Glasgow and Tatton Watercolours and Drawings.

N1

After Noah
121 Upper St., Islington. N1 1QP. (M. Crawford and Z. Candlin). Est. 1990. Open 10-6, Sun. 12-5. SIZE: Medium. *STOCK: Arts and Craft oak and similar furniture, leather sofas and chairs, 1880's to 1950's,* £1-£5,000; iron, iron and brass beds; decorative items, bric-a-brac including candlesticks, mirrors, lighting, kitchenalia and jewellery. PARK: Side streets. TEL: 020 7359 4281; fax - same; e-mail - enquiries@afternoah.com; website - www.after noah.com. SER: Restorations. VAT: Stan.

Angel Arcade
116-118 Islington High St., Camden Passage. N1 8EG. Open Wed. and Sat. SIZE: Large. *STOCK: Decorative items, some antique.*

Annie's Vintage Costume & Textiles
12 Camden Passage, Islington. N1 8ED. (A. Moss). Open 11-6 including Sun. PARK: Nearby and meters. TEL: 020 7359 0796.

The Antique Trader
The Millinery Works, 85/87 Southgate Rd. N1 3JS. (B. Thompson and D. Rothera). Est. 1968. Open Tues.-Sat. 11-6, Sun. 12-5 or by appointment. SIZE: Large. *STOCK: Arts & Crafts, Art furniture and effects; £100-£15,000.* LOC: Close to Camden Passage Antiques Centre. PARK: Free. TEL: 020 7359 2019; fax - 020 7359 5792; e-mail - antiquetrader@millinery.demon.co.uk; website - www.milleryworks.co.uk. VAT: Stan/ Spec.

Banbury Fayre
6 Pierrepont Row Arcade, Camden Passage, Islington. N1. (N. Steel). Est. 1984. Open Wed. and Sat. SIZE: Small. *STOCK: Collectables including commemoratives, shipping, Boy Scout movement, Boer War, air line travel.* PARK: 200yds. TEL: Home - 020 8852 5675.

Camden Passage Antiques Market and Pierrepont Arcade Antiques Centre
12 Camden Passage, Islington. N1 8ED. Est. 1960. Open Wed. and Sat. 7.30-3.30. Thurs. - book market. SIZE: Over 400 dealers. *STOCK: Wide range of general antiques and some specialists.* LOC: Behind the Angel, Islington. TEL: 020 7359 0190.

Patric Capon   BADA
350 Upper St., Islington. N1 0PD. Est. 1970. Open Wed. and Sat. or by appointment. SIZE: Medium. *STOCK: Unusual carriage clocks, 19th C, £450-£6,000; 8-day and 2-day marine chronometers, 19th C, £850-£4,500; clocks and barometers, 18th-19th C, £400-£6,500.* **LOC: Adjacent Camden Passage. PARK: Easy. TEL: 020 7354 0487; fax - 020 8295 1475; home - 020 8467 5722. SER: Valuations; restorations. FAIRS: Olympia. VAT: Stan/Spec.**

Peter Chapman Antiques and Restoration
10 Theberton St., Islington. N1 0QX. (P.J. and Z.A. Chapman). LAPADA, CPTA. Est. 1971. Open 9.30-

6. CL: Sun. and public holidays except by appointment. SIZE: Medium. *STOCK: Furniture and decorative objects, 1700-1900; paintings, drawings and prints, 17th to early 20th C; stained glass, hall lanterns; Grand Tour items.* LOC: 5 mins. walk from Camden Passage down Upper St. PARK: Easy. TEL: 020 7226 5565; mobile - 07831 093662; fax - 020 8348 4846; e-mail - pchapman antiques@easy net.co.uk; website - www.antiques-peterchapman. co.uk. SER: Valuations; restorations (furniture and period objects); buys at auction. VAT: Stan/Spec.

Chapter One
2 Pierrepont Row Arcade, Camden Passage. N1 9EG. (Yvonne Gill). Est. 1993. Open Wed. 9-3, Sat. 9-5 or by appointment. SIZE: Small. *STOCK: Handbags, costume jewellery, vintage accessories, fabrics, bric-a-brac, 1880-1960, £5-£300.* TEL: 020 7359 1185. SER: Jewellery repairs; search.

Charlton House Antiques
18/20 Camden Passage, Islington. N1 8ED. Open Wed. and Sat. 8-5, Tues. and Fri. 10-4. SIZE: Large. *STOCK: European and Scandinavian furniture, 1840-1930, £100-£5,000; general antiques.* LOC: Near Angel underground station. PARK: Easy. TEL: 020 7226 3141; fax - 020 7226 1123; e-mail - charlhse@aol.com. VAT: Stan/Spec.

Chest of Drawers
281 Upper St., Islington. N1 2TZ. (J. Delf). Open 10-6 including Sun. *STOCK: Pine and oak.* TEL: 020 7359 5909.

Rosemary Conquest
4 Charlton Place, Camden Passage. N1 8AJ. Open 11-5.30, Wed. and Sat. 9-5.30. SIZE: Small. *STOCK: Chandeliers, European decorative items, copper and brass.* PARK: Easy. TEL: 020 7359 0616; home - 020 7254 1208.

Carlton Davidson Antiques
33 Camden Passage, Islington. N1 8EA. Est. 1981. Open Wed.-Sat. 10-4. SIZE: Medium. *STOCK: Lamps, chandeliers, mirrors and decorative items, £100-£3,000.* LOC: Near Charlton Place. PARK: Meters. TEL: 020 7226 7491. VAT: Stan.

Donay Games & Pastimes
3 Pierrepont Row, Camden Passage, Islington. N1 8EF. (Carol E. Goddard). Est. 1980. Open Wed. and Sat. 9.30-3.30, office Mon.-Fri. SIZE: Medium. *STOCK: Board and mechanical games - horse racing, cricket, golf and football; treen, paper and metal puzzles including Journet and mechanical Hoffman; chess, backgammon, cribbage, dominoes; card games and scorers; tinplate including Schuco; dice, shakers, mah-jong, marbles, artists' colourboxes; animal bronzes; Punch & Judy puppets including ephemera, 1780-1950, £5-£5,000.* LOC: Near Angel tube station. PARK: Charlton Place, Colebrook Row. TEL: 020 7359 1880; office - 01444 250230; fax - 01444 250231; e-mail - donay games@aol.com; website - www. donaygames.com.

Copper-green lead glazes. (Left) E.B. Fishley of Fremington c.1900, 'Within this jug there is good lqr. / Fit for Parson or for Vicar' etc. (Centre) Probably Staffordshire mid-18th century, inscribed 'WT'. (Right) Yearsley, N.E. Yorks, inscribed 'John Wedg Wood 1691'. Maximum height 7¼in. (Trustees of the Victoria & Albert Museum)

From an article entitled "Strong Ale, Wet Joke – Puzzle Jugs through the Ages" by Robin Hildyard which appeared in the September 2001 issue of **Antique Collecting**. For more details and to subscribe see page 21.

Eclectica
2 Charlton Place. N1 8AJ. (Liz Wilson). Est. 1988. Open Tues. Thurs. and Fri. 11-6, Wed. and Sat. 9-6. *STOCK: Vintage costume jewellery.* TEL: 020 7226 5625; fax - same.

Feljoy Antiques
3 Angel Arcade, Camden Passage, Islington. N1 8EA. (J. Humphreys and F. Finburgh). Est. 1985. Open Wed. and Sat. 8-4. *STOCK: Chintzware, decorative antiques and textiles.* TEL: 020 7354 5336; e-mail - joy@feljoy-antiques.demon.co.uk. FAIRS: Brocante.

The Fleamarket
7 Pierrepont Row Arcade, Camden Passage, Islington. N1 8EE. Open 9.30-6. CL: Mon. SIZE: Large. 26 stand-holders. *STOCK: Jewellery, furniture, objets d'art, militaria, guns, swords, pistols, porcelain, coins, medals, stamps, 18th-19th C, £1-£500; antiquarian books, prints, fine art, china, silver, glass and general antiques.* PARK: Easy. TEL: 020 7226 8211. SER: Valuations; buys at auction; weapon repairs.

Vincent Freeman
1 Camden Passage, Islington. N1 8EA. Est. 1966. Open 10-5. CL: Mon. and Thurs. SIZE: Large. *STOCK: Music boxes, furniture and decorative items, from £100.* TEL: 020 7226 6178; fax - 020 7226 7231. VAT: Stan/Spec.

Furniture Vault
50 Camden Passage, Islington. N1 8AE. (David Loveday). Est. 1969. Open Tues.-Sat. 9.30-4.30. SIZE: Large. *STOCK: Furniture, 18th-20th C.* TEL: 020 7354 1047.

Georgian Village
30-31 Islington Green. N1. Open 10-4, Wed. and Sat. 7-5. PARK: Nearby. TEL: 020 7226 1571.

Get Stuffed
105 Essex Rd., Islington. N1 2SL. Est. 1975. Open 1-5, Sat. 1-3. *STOCK: Stuffed birds, fish, animals, trophy heads; rugs; butterflies, insects.* TEL: 020 7226 1364; mobile - 07831 260062; fax - 020 7359 8253; e-mail - taxidermy@theget stuffed. co.uk; website - www.thegetstuffed.co. uk. SER: Restorations; taxidermy; glass domes and cases supplied.

Gordon Gridley
28 & 41 Camden Passage, Islington. N1 8EA. Est. 1968. CL: Mon., Tues. and Thurs. SIZE: Large + warehouse at rear. *STOCK: English and Continental furniture, paintings, decorative objects, metalwork, glass and ceramics, statuary and garden furniture, 17th-19th C, £50-£20,000.* PARK: Business Design Centre or Charlton Place. TEL: 020 7226 0643. SER: Valuations; restorations. FAIRS: Olympia (June). VAT: Stan/Spec.

David Griffiths Antiques
17 Camden Passage, Islington. N1 8EA. Open Tues., Wed., Fri. and Sat. 10-4 or by appointment. *STOCK: Decorative antiques including military and campaign furniture, leather chairs, pub accessories, club fenders and other fittings from hotels and gentlemen's clubs; quality vintage luggage.* TEL: 020 7226 1126; fax - 020 7226 1991.

Rosemary Hart
8 Angel Arcade, 116 Islington High St. N1 8EG. Est. 1980. Open Wed. and Sat. 9.30-4.30, Thurs. and Fri. 10.30-3. SIZE: Small. *STOCK: Victorian silver plated tableware and decorative serving pieces, £5-£500; small silver gifts, from £50.* LOC: Near Angel tube station. PARK: Business Design Centre. TEL: 020 7359 6839; e-mail - contact @Rosemaryhart.co.uk; website - www.Rosemary hart.co.uk. SER: Restorations; replating.

House of Steel Antiques
400 Caledonian Rd. N1 1DN. (J. Cole). Est. 1974. Open 11-6, Sat. by appointment. SIZE: Warehouse. *STOCK: Metal items - fireplaces, 18th-19th C, £50-£1,000; spiral staircases, £300-£1,000; balconies, railings, garden furniture, £50-£500; all 19th C.* LOC: Near King's Cross. PARK: Own. TEL: 020 7607 5889. SER: Valuations; restorations (welding, polishing, sandblasting); steel furniture manufactured, items made to order. VAT: Stan.

Diana Huntley
8 Camden Passage, Islington. N1 8ED. LAPADA. Est. 1970. Open Tues. and Fri. 10-4, Wed. 7.30-5, Thurs. by appointment, Sat. 9-5. *STOCK: European porcelain, £50-£10,000; objets d'art; all 19th C.* TEL: 020 7226 4605; fax - 020 7359 0240; e-mail - diana@dianahuntley antiques.co.uk; website - www.dianahuntley antiques.co.uk. SER: Valuations. VAT: Stan/Spec.

Intercol London
Gallery, 114 Islington High St. (within Camden Passage). Correspondence - 43 Templars Crescent, N3 3QR. N1. (Yasha Beresiner). Est. 1977. Open Wed.-Sat. 9-5, other times by appointment. SIZE: Large. *STOCK: Playing cards, maps and banknotes and related literature, £5-£1,000+.* PARK: Easy. TEL: 020 8349 2207; fax - 020 8346 9539; e-mail - yasha@compuserve. com; website - www. intercol.co.uk. SER: Valuations; restorations (maps including colouring); buys at auction (playing cards, maps, banknotes and books). FAIRS: Major specialist European, U.S.A. and Far Eastern. VAT: Stan/Spec.

Jonathan James
52/53 Camden Passage, Islington. N1 8EA. (James and Norman Petre). LAPADA. Est. 1970. Open 10-4.30, Wed. 9.30-4.30. CL: Mon. SIZE: Medium. *STOCK: Furniture, 18th-19th C, £1,000-£20,000.* PARK: 100 yds. TEL: 020 7704 8266; fax - same. SER: Valuations. VAT: Stan/Spec.

Japanese Gallery
23 Camden Passage, Islington. N1 8EA. Open 10-6. *STOCK: Japanese woodcut prints; books, porcelain, screens, kimonos, scrolls, furniture.* TEL: 020 7226 3347; fax - 020 7229 2934. SER: Framing; free authentification; interior design, ie. Tatami.

Jubilee Photographica
10 Pierrepont Row Arcade, Camden Passage, Islington. N1 8E. (Richard Meara). Est. 1966. Open Wed. and Sat. 10-4 or by appointment. SIZE: Small. *STOCK: Photographica - images, daguerreotypes, ambrotypes, tintypes, vintage paper prints, stereoscopic cards and viewers, magic lanterns and slides, topographical and family albums, cabinet cards and cartes de visite, 10p-£1,000.* LOC: From Piccadilly Circus, take 19 bus to Angel, Islington. PARK: Meters. TEL: Home - 01932 863924; e-mail - meara@ btconnect.com. SER: Buys at auction. FAIRS: London Photograph; Photographica, Bièvres, France; American Photo Historical Society, New York.

Carol Ketley Antiques
PO Box 16199. N1 7WD. LAPADA. Est. 1979. Open by appointment. SIZE: Medium. *STOCK: Mirrors, decanters, drinking glasses, decorative furniture and objects, 1780-1900, £10-£10,000.* LOC: Showroom close to Camden Passage. PARK: Easy. TEL: 020 7359 5529; mobile - 07831 827284; fax - 020 7226 4589. FAIRS: Olympia; LAPADA; Decorative Antiques and Textile. VAT: Global.

Judith Lassalle
7 Pierrepont Row Arcade, Camden Passage, Islington. N1 8EF. Est. 1765 Cornhill. Open Wed. 7.30-4, Sat. 9.30-4, other times by appointment. *STOCK: Books, children's games, optical toys and rocking horses, 17th C to 1914, £25-£5,000.* PARK: Nearby. TEL: 020 7607 7121; shop - 020 7354 9344. SER: Valuations; restorations; buys at auction. FAIRS: Ephemera; PBFA; American Ephemera.

THE MALL
ANTIQUES ARCADE
Camden Passage, London N1

Over 35 Dealers in
London's premier centre for dealers,
decorators and collectors.

Enquiries: Mike Spooner/Neil Jackson
Tel: 020-7969 1500 Fax: 020-7969 1639

John Laurie (Antiques) Ltd
351/352 Upper St., Islington. N1 0PD. (R. Gewirtz). LAPADA. Est. 1962. Open 9.30-5. SIZE: Large. *STOCK: Silver, Sheffield plate.* TEL: 020 7226 0913/6969; fax - 020 7226 4599. SER: Restorations; packing; shipping. VAT: Stan.

Michael Lewis Antiques
6-7 Peabody Yard, Greenman St. N1 8SB. LAPADA. Est. 1977. Open 9-6, Sun. 12-5. CL: Mon. SIZE: Small. *STOCK: Pine and country furniture, British and Irish, 18th-19th C, £100-£6,500.* LOC: 100yds. north of Camden Passage. PARK: Easy. TEL: 020 7359 7733. VAT: Stan/Spec.

London Militaria Market
Angel Arcade, Camden Passage, Islington. N1. (S. Bosley and M. Warren). Est. 1987. Open Sat. 8-2. SIZE: Large. 35 dealers. *STOCK: Militaria, 1800 to date.* LOC: Near Angel tube station. PARK: Meters and nearby. TEL: 01628 822503 or 01455 556971.

The Mall Antiques Arcade
359 Upper St., Islington. N1. (Atlantic Antiques Centres Ltd). Est. 1979. Open 10-5, Wed. 7.30-5, Sat. 9-6. CL: Mon. LOC: 5 mins. from Angel tube station. PARK: Meters. TEL: 020 7969 1500; enquiries - 020 7969 1634; e-mail - antique@dial.pipex.com. Below are listed the dealers at this Arcade.

Alexandra Alfandary
Stand G9. LAPADA. *Meissen porcelain.* TEL: 020 7354 9762.

R. Arantes
Stand G27. *Lalique glass.* TEL: 020 7253 5303.

Audley Art Ltd
Stand G20. (A. Singer). *Meissen porcelain and oil paintings.* TEL: 020 7704 9507.

Banana Dance Ltd.
Stand G16. (Jonathan Daltrey). *20th C decorative arts including Clarice Cliff.* TEL: Mobile - 07976 296987.

Mario Barazi
Stand G23. *Porcelain including Meissen, and glass.* TEL: 020 7226 2426.

David Bowden
Stand G12. *Oriental and European works of art, watches.* TEL: 020 7226 3033.

Chancery Antiques
Stand G10. (R. & D. Rote). *Oriental and Continental works of art.* TEL: 020 7359 9035.

P. Collingridge
Stand G6. *Lighting, brass and furniture.* TEL: 020 7354 9189.

Steven Donnelly
Stand G17. *French decorative furniture.* TEL: 020 8523 5870; mobile - 07712 322269.

Chris Dunn St. James
Stand G7. *Vintage jewellery.* TEL: 020 7704 0127.

John Harvey
Stand G21. *Art Deco and Art Nouveau.* TEL: 020 7354 3349.

Leon's Militaria
Stand G25. *Militaria.* TEL: Mobile - 07989 649972.

Andrew Lineham   BADA
Stand G19. *Glass and porcelain.* TEL: 020 7704 0195.

Paul Mayhew
Stand G28. Clocks. TEL: 020 7704 6510.

Linda Morgan Antiques
Stand G26. *Jewellery.* TEL: 020 7359 0654.

Nadine Okker
Stand G8. LAPADA. *Porcelain, glass and bronzes.* TEL: 020 7354 9496.

John Pearman
Stand G24. *Glass and porcelain.* TEL: 020 7359 0591.

Tom Pelc
Stand G1. *Watches and clocks.* TEL: 020 7704 6510.

Sylvia Powell
Stand G18. LAPADA. *Decorative arts, art pottery, 1870-1894.* TEL: 020 7354 2977; mobile - 07802 714998.

Rumours
Stand G4/5. (J. Donovan). LAPADA. *Art Nouveau and Art Deco china and objets d'art.* TEL: 020 7704 8416.

Robert Tredwen
Stand G11. *Military antiques.* TEL: 020 7359 2224.

Count Alexander von Beregshasy
Stand G13. *Jewellery, French paste and tiaras (reproduction crown jewels).* TEL: 020 7354 0059.

Michael Young
Stand G22. *Decorative items, model boats.* TEL: 020 7226 2225.

Lower Mall

The Antique Barometer Co.
Stand B5. (Jill Liddell). *Antique barometers, scientific and medical instruments, furniture and related accessories.* TEL: 020 7226 4992.

Patricia Baxter
Stand B3. *Furniture.* TEL: 020 7354 0886.

Malcolm D. Stevens
Stand B2. LAPADA. *Furniture.* TEL: 020 7359 1020; home - 01992 574607.

Turner Brown Antiques
Stand B9/10. (V. Brown). *Furniture and general antiques.* TEL: 020 7359 9402.

Charles Woodage
Stand B4/6/7. *Furniture.* TEL: Mobile - 07767 304317.

Graham Woodage
Stand B1. *Furniture and accessories.*

Laurence Mitchell Antiques Ltd
27 Camden Passage, Islington. N1 8EA. (L.P.J. Mitchell). LAPADA. Est. 1972. Open 10-5, Wed. 8-5, Mon. by appointment. *STOCK: European and English porcelain; Oriental works of art, Chinese export and Japanese porcelain; Meissen, 18th and especially 19th C.* TEL: 020 7359 7579; fax - 020 7226 1738; e-mail - lawrence.mitchell @ntlworld.com; website - www.121antiques. com. VAT: Stan/Spec.

Michel André Morin
7 Charlton Place, Camden Passage, Islington. N1 8AQ. Open Wed. 8.30-4.30, Sat. 9-4.30, other days by appointment. SIZE: Medium. *STOCK: French decorative furniture, 18th-19th C; French chandeliers.* PARK: Easy. TEL: 020 7226 3803; fax - 020 7704 0708; mobile - 07802 832496. FAIRS: Olympia; Decorative, Battersea. VAT: Spec.

Chris Newland Antiques
Lower Ground Floor, Georgian Village, 30/31 Islington Green. N1. Est. 1964. Open 9-5.30. SIZE: Large. *STOCK: Mahogany furniture, 19th C, £300-£1,000; office furniture, 19th-20th C; shipping furniture, marble, works of art.* PARK: NCP 100 yards. TEL: 020 7359 9805. SER: Valuations; restorations (furniture, French polishing). VAT: Stan/Spec.

Kevin Page Oriental Art
2, 4 and 6 Camden Passage, Islington. N1 8ED. LAPADA. Est. 1968. Open 10-4. CL: Mon. SIZE: Large. *STOCK: Oriental porcelain and furniture, cloisonné, bronzes, ivories.* LOC: 1 min. from Angel tube station. PARK: Easy. TEL: 020 7226 8558. SER: Valuations. VAT: Stan.

Regent Antiques
Barpart House, North London Freight Depot, York Way. N1 0UZ. (T. Quaradeghini). Est. 1983. Open 9-5.30, other times by appointment. SIZE: Large. *STOCK: Furniture, 18th C to Edwardian.* LOC: ¼ mile from Kings Cross Station. PARK: Own. TEL: 020 7833 5545; fax - 020 7278 2236; e-mail - regentantiques@aol.com. SER: Restorations (furniture). VAT: Stan/Spec. *Trade Only.*

Relic Antiques at Camden Passage
21 Camden Passage, Islington. N1 8EA. (Malcolm Gliksten). Est. 1968. Open 10-4.30. CL: Mon. *STOCK: Decorative antiques and painted furniture, childhood memorabilia and paintings, Black Forest carving, fairground art, marine items, period shopfittings, architectural ornaments, trade signs and naive art.* PARK: Meters. TEL: 020 7359 2597; fax - 020 7388 2691; mobile - 07831 785059. FAIRS: Chelsea Decorative. VAT: Stan.

Restall Brown and Clennell Ltd
Adelaide Wharf, 120 Queensbridge Rd. (S. Brown). Open Mon.-Fri. 9-5.30 appointment advisable. *STOCK: English furniture, 17th-19th C.* TEL: 020 7739 6626; fax - 020 7739 6123; e-mail - sales@rbc-furniture.co.uk. VAT: Stan/Spec.

Marcus Ross Antiques
16 Pierrepont Row Arcade, Camden Passage, Islington. N1 8EF. Est. 1972. Open 10.30-4.30.

CL: Mon. *STOCK: Oriental porcelain, general antiques, Victorian walnut furniture.* TEL: 020 7359 8494.

Keith Skeel Antiques

The Merchants Hall, 46 Essex Rd. N1 8LN. LAPADA. SIZE: Very large. *STOCK: Funny, fantastic and fatalistic furniture.* TEL: 020 7359 5633; fax - 020 7226 3780. *Trade Only.*

Style Gallery

1 Ground Floor, Georgian Village, Camden Passage. N1. (M. Webb and P. Coakley-Webb). Open Wed. and Sat. 9.30-4 or by appointment. *STOCK: Art Nouveau, WMF and Liberty pewter, Art Deco bronzes including Preiss and Chiparus, ceramics and glass.* TEL: 020 7359 7867; home - 020 8361 2357; fax - same; mobile - 07831 229640; website - www.styleantiques.co.uk; e-mail - coakleywebb@madasafish.com.

Sugar Antiques

8-9 Pierrepont Arcade, Camden Passage, Islington. N1 8EF. (Elayne and Tony Sugarman). Est. 1990. Open Wed. and Sat. 7.30-3.30. SIZE: Medium. *STOCK: Wrist and pocket watches, 19th-20th C, £25-£2,000; fountain pens and lighters, early 20th C to 1960's, £15-£1,000; costume jewellery and collectables, 19th-20th C, £5-£500.* LOC: 5 minutes walk from the Angel Underground station (Northern Line). PARK: Meters. TEL: 020 7354 9896; fax - 020 8931 5642; mobile - 0793 179 980; e-mail - tony@sugarantiques.com; website - www.sugarantiques.com. SER: Repairs (as stock); buys at auction (as stock). VAT: Stan.

Swan Fine Art

120 Islington High St., Camden Passage. N1 8EG. (P. Child). Open 10-5, Wed. and Sat. 9-5 or by appointment. SIZE: Medium. *STOCK: Paintings, fine and decorative sporting and animal, portraits, 17th-19th C, £500-£25,000+.* PARK: Easy, except Wed. and Sat. TEL: 020 7226 5335; fax - 020 7359 2225; mobile - 07860 795336. VAT: Spec.

Tadema Gallery   BADA

10 Charlton Place, Camden Passage, Islington. N1. (S. and D. Newell-Smith). LAPADA. Est. 1978. Open Wed. and Sat. 10-5 or by appointment. SIZE: Medium. *STOCK: 20th C abstract art and jewellery, from Art Nouveau to 1960's artist designed pieces.* PARK: Reasonable. TEL: 020 7359 1055; fax - same. SER: Valuations. VAT: Spec.

C. Tapsell

Christopher House, 5 Camden Passage, Islington. N1 8EA. Est. 1970. Open Wed. 9-4.30, Sat. 9-5,

other times by appointment. SIZE: Medium. *STOCK: English mahogany and walnut furniture, 18th-19th C, £300-£15,000; Oriental china, 17th-19th C, £20-£5,000; French furniture, 18th-19th C, £500-£5,000.* LOC: Near Angel underground station. PARK: Opposite. TEL: 020 7354 3603. VAT: Stan/Spec.

The Textile Company

P.O Box 2800. N1 4DQ. (Judy Wentworth). Est. 1982. Open by appointment only. *STOCK: 18th C silks, British and French printed cottons, lace, 1600-1850; Paisley and Kashmir shawls, period costume and accessories.* Not Stocked: Tapestries, upholstery and cushions. TEL: 020 7254 3256; e-mail - jwentworth@beeb.net. SER: Buys at auction; hire; photographic archive. VAT: Stan/Spec.

M. Tisdall Antiques

49 Camden Passage, Islington. N1 8EA. Est. 1984. Open Wed. 7-3.30, Sat. 9-3.30, other days by appointment. SIZE: Medium. *STOCK: Sheffield plate, 18th-19th C, £20-£2,000; Victorian plate, 19th to early 20th C, £20-£3,000; silver, 18th-20th C, £50-£5,000.* PARK: NPC nearby. TEL: 020 7354 1860; mobile - 07768 263546; e-mail - marktisdall@aol.com. SER: Valuations; restorations (replating, gilding, repairs); buys at auction (as stock). FAIRS: Newark. VAT: Stan/Spec

Turn On Lighting

116/118 Islington High St., Camden Passage. N1 8EG. Est. 1976. *STOCK: Lighting, 1840-1940.* TEL: 020 7359 7616; fax - same.

Vane House Antiques

15 Camden Passage, Islington. N1 8EA. (Michael J. Till). Est. 1950. Open 10-5. CL: Mon. and Thurs. *STOCK: 18th to early 19th C furniture.* TEL: 020 7359 1343; fax - same. VAT: Stan/Spec.

Mike Weedon

7 Camden Passage, Islington. N1 8EA. (Mike and Hisako Weedon). LAPADA. Est. 1977. Open Wed. 9-5, Sat. 10-5. *STOCK: Large selection Art Nouveau glass - Gallé, Daum, Lötz; antique glass by artists and designers, from 1880 to 1939; Art Deco sculpture - bronze, bronze and ivory - including Chiparus, Preiss, Lorenzl.* TEL: Wed and Sat. only - 020 7226 5319; fax - 020 7700 6387; home - 020 7609 6826; e-mail - info@mikeweedonantiqu.plus.com.

Agnes Wilton

3 Camden Passage, Islington. N1 8EA. Est. 1974. Open 9.30-3. *STOCK: Furniture, decorative items including perfume bottles, collectables, silver and boxes.* TEL: 020 7226 5679.

Yesterday Child
Angel Arcade, Camden Passage, 118 Islington High St. N1. (D. and G. Barrington). LAPADA. Est. 1970. Open Wed. and Sat. 8.30-3. SIZE: Small. *STOCK: Dolls, miniatures and toys, 1800-1925, £25-£5,000.* PARK: Easy. TEL: 020 7354 1601; home and fax - 01908 583403. SER: Valuations; restorations. FAIRS: Kensington Town Hall Doll. VAT: Stan/Spec.

Yingguoren Ltd
54 Duncan St. N1 8BW. (Rachel Hayward and Damian Hubsch). Open 10.30-6.30, Sun. 11-4. CL: Mon. SIZE: Medium. *STOCK: Chinese country furniture, 19th C to mid-20th C, £500-£1,000; Chinese porcelain, 19th C, £50-£150; accessories, late 19th C to mid-20th C, £50-£100.* LOC: Off Upper Street, Angel end, turn right before Camden Passsage. PARK: Easy. TEL: 020 7833 0835; fax - 020 7833 5881.

York Gallery Ltd
51 Camden Passage. N1 8EA. (Jane and Gerd Beyer). Est. 1984. Open Wed. and Sat. 10-5. *STOCK: Antique prints.* TEL: 020 7354 8012. SER: Bespoke framing.

N2

Amazing Grates - Fireplaces Ltd
61-63 High Rd., East Finchley. N2. (T. Tew). Resident. Est. 1971. Open 10-6. SIZE: Large. *STOCK: Mantelpieces, grates and fireside items, £200-£5,000; Victorian tiling, £2-£20; early ironwork, all 19th C.* LOC: 100yds. north of East Finchley tube station. PARK: Own. TEL: 020 8883 9590/6017. SER: Valuations; reproduction mantelpieces in stone and marble; restorations (ironwork, welding of cast iron and brazing, polishing); installations. VAT: Stan.

Martin Henham (Antiques)
218 High Rd., East Finchley. N2 9AY. Open 10-6. SIZE: Medium. *STOCK: Furniture and porcelain, 1710-1920, £5-£3,500; paintings, 1650-1940, £10-£4,000.* PARK: Easy. TEL: 020 8444 5274. SER: Valuations; restorations (furniture); buys at auction.

Barrie Marks Ltd
24 Church Vale, Fortis Green. N2 9PA. ABA, PBFA. Open by appointment only. *STOCK: Antiquarian books - illustrated, private press, colourplate, colour printing; modern first editions.* TEL: 020 8883 1919; fax - 020 8374 8079.

Lauri Stewart - Fine Art
36 Church Lane. N2 8DT. Open Mon. and Tues. 10.30-4.30. *STOCK: Modern British oils and watercolours.* TEL: 020 8883 7719; e-mail - lste 181072@aol.com.

N4

Alexander Juran and Co   BADA
at Nathan Azizollahoff, OCC, Top Floor & Lift, Building A, 105 Eade Rd. N4 1TJ. Est. 1951. Open 9.15-5.30. CL: Sat. STOCK: Caucasian rugs, nomadic and tribal; carpets, rugs, tapestries. TEL: 020 7435 0280; fax - same. SER: Valuations; repairs. VAT: Stan/Spec.

Kennedy Carpets
OCC Building 'G', 105 Eade Rd. N4 1TJ. (M. Kennedy and V. Eder). Est. 1974. Open 9.30-6. SIZE: Large. *STOCK: Decorative carpets, collectable rugs and kelims, mid-19th C to new, £500-£50,000.* LOC: Off Seven Sisters Road. PARK: Free. TEL: 020 8800 4455; fax - 020 8800 4466. SER: Valuations; making to order. FAIRS: Domotex. VAT: Stan.

Joseph Lavian
OCC, Building E, Ground Floor, 105 Eade Rd. N4 1TJ. LAPADA. Est. 1950. Open 9.30-5.30. SIZE: Large. *STOCK: Oriental carpets, rugs, kelims, tapestries and needlework, Aubusson, Savonnerie and textiles, 17th-19th C.* TEL: 020 8800 0707; fax - 020 8800 0404; mobile - 07767 797707; e-mail - Lavian@Lavian.com; website - www.Lavian.com. SER: Valuations; restorations.

Teger Trading
318 Green Lanes. N4 1BX. *STOCK: Reproduction bronzes, furniture, marble figures, paintings, mirrors, porcelain and unusual items.* TEL: 020 8802 0156; fax - 020 8802 4110. SER: Restorations; film hire. *Trade Only.*

N5

Nicholas Goodyer
15 Calabria Rd., Highbury Fields. N5 1JB. Est. 1951. Open 9.30-5, but prior telephone call advisable. CL: Sat. *STOCK: Antiquarian books especially illustrated.* PARK: Nearby. TEL: 020 7226 5682; fax - 020 7354 4716; e-mail - email@ nicholasgoodyer.com; website - www.nicholas goodyer.com. FAIRS: International ILAB (London, Boston, San Francisco); monthly PBFA, London.

Strike One   BADA
48a Highbury Hill. N5 1AP. (J. Mighell). Est. 1968. Open by appointment. SIZE: Medium. STOCK: Clocks, pre-1870, especially early

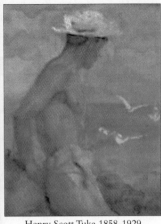

Finchley Fine Art Galleries

983 High Road, North Finchley, London N12 8QR
Telephone: 020-8446-4848 Mobile: 07712 629282
E-mail: finchleyfineart@onetel.net.uk

200 plus fine 18th-20th Century English watercolours and paintings in a constantly changing stock. Four galleries of good quality Georgian, Victorian and Edwardian furniture, pottery, porcelain, smalls, etc.

OPENING TIMES:
MON, TUES, THURS, FRI,
SAT, SUN, 1.00-7.00.
WEDNESDAY
BY APPOINTMENT

Henry Scott Tuke 1858-1929
A Young Man Sun Bathing in a White Hat
4¾ x 4 inches

English wall and Act of Parliament, £2,000-£25,000; English longcase, 1675-1820, £3,000-£40,000; English bracket, lantern, skeleton and French carriage; Vienna regulators; barometers, music boxes. PARK: Easy. TEL: **020 7354 2790**; fax - same; e-mail - **milo@strikeone.co.uk**; website - **www.strikeone.co.uk**. SER: Valuations; restorations (clocks, barometers); catalogue available. VAT: Stan/Spec.

N6

At the Sign of the Chest of Drawers
164 Archway Rd. N6 5BB. (A. Harms). Open Tues.-Sat. 10-6. *STOCK: Pine and country furniture.* TEL: 020 8340 7652

Fisher and Sperr
46 Highgate High St. N6 5JB. (J.R. Sperr). Est. 1945. Open daily 10.30-5. SIZE: Large. *STOCK: Books, 15th C to date.* LOC: From centre of Highgate Village, nearest underground stations Archway (Highgate), Highgate. PARK: Easy. TEL: 020 8340 7244; fax - 020 8348 4293. SER: Valuations; restorations (books). VAT: Stan.

Betty Gould and Julian Gonnermann Antiques
408-410 Archway Rd., Highgate. N6 5AT. Est. 1964. Open 10-5.30, Sat. 9.30-5.30. CL: Mon. and Thurs. SIZE: Medium. *STOCK: Furniture, 18th-20th C, £50-£5,000.* LOC: On A1, just below Highgate tube station (corner of Shepherds Hill). TEL: 020 8340 4987. SER: Restorations; French polishing; upholstery.

N7

Dome Antiques (Exports) Ltd
40 Queensland Rd., Islington. N7 7AJ. (Adam and Louise Woolf). LAPADA. Est. 1961. Open Mon.-Fri. and Sat. morning. SIZE: Large. *STOCK: 19th C furniture, £250-£10,000.* LOC: Near junction of Holloway and Hornsey roads. PARK: Easy. TEL: 020 7700 6266; mobile - 07831 805888; fax - 020 7609 1692; e-mail - dome.antiques@dial.pipex.com. SER: Valuations; restorations (furniture). FAIRS: LAPADA (April - NEC: June - Olympia; Oct. - Earls Court). VAT: Stan/Spec.

N8

Solomon
49 Park Rd., Crouch End. N8 8SY. (Solomon Salim). Est. 1984. Open 9.30-6. SIZE: Medium. *STOCK: Furniture including upholstered and Arts and Crafts, £200-£4,000; decorative items, £100-£500; all 1800-1920.* LOC: 20 minutes off North Circular at Muswell Hill turn-off. PARK: Easy. TEL: 020 8341 1817; e-mail - solomon@ solomonantiques.fsnet.co.uk. SER: Valuations; restorations (furniture including upholstery). VAT: Spec.

N11

The Collector Limited
4 Queens Parade Close, Friern Barnet. N11 3FY. (Tom Power). Est. 1973. Open 9.30-5.30. SIZE: Large. *STOCK: Decorative ceramics especially Royal Doulton, from 1900, £50-£3,000; Beswick,*

from 1920, £40-£1,000; Moorcroft, £150-£750. LOC: Near Arnos Grove. PARK: Easy. TEL: 020 8361 7787; fax - 020 8361 4143. SER: Valuations. FAIRS: Specialist Decorative Art, mainly Royal Doulton. VAT: Stan.

N12

Finchley Fine Art Galleries
983 High Rd., North Finchley. N12 8QR. (Sam Greenman). Est. 1972. Open 1-7, Sun. by appointment. SIZE: Large. *STOCK: 18th-20th C watercolours, paintings, etchings, prints, mostly English, £25-£10,000; Georgian, Victorian, Edwardian furniture, £50-£10,000; china and porcelain - Moorcroft, Doulton, Worcester, Clarice Cliff, £5-£2,000; musical and scientific instruments, bronzes, early photographic apparatus, fire-arms, shotguns.* LOC: Off M25, junction 23, take Barnet road. Gallery on right 3 miles south of Barnet church, opposite Britannia Road. PARK: Easy. TEL: 020 8446 4848. SER: Valuations; restorations; picture re-lining, cleaning and framing.

Frames Direct
218 Woodhouse Rd., Friern Barnet. N12 0RS. (D. Georgiou and S. Kerr). Est. 1976. Open 10-5.30. SIZE: Small. *STOCK: General antiques, mirrors and frames.* LOC: Near Muswell Hill. PARK: Nearby. TEL: 020 8446 8409. SER: Restorations.

Zeno Booksellers
57a Nether St. North Finchley. N12 7NP. (Maria and Loui Loizou). Est. 1944. Open 9.30-5.30, Sat. 10-4.30. *STOCK: Antiquarian books on Greece, Cyprus, Byzantium, Turkey, Middle East and the Balkans.* TEL: 020 8446 1985/6; fax - 020 8446 1985; e-mail - info@thegreekbookshop.com; website - www.thegreekbookshop.com.

N13

Palmers Green Antiques Centre
472 Green Lanes, Palmers Green. N13 5PA. (Michael Webb). Est. 1976. Open 10-5.30, Sun. 11-5. CL: Tues. SIZE: Large. *STOCK: Furniture, general antiques and collectables.* PARK: Nearby. TEL: 020 8350 0878. SER: Valuations. FAIRS: Alexandra Palace; Wembley.

N14

C.J. Martin (Coins) Ltd
85 The Vale, Southgate. N14 6AT. LAPADA. Open by appointment. *STOCK: Ancient and medieval coins and ancient artefacts.* TEL: 020 8882 1509/4359.

Southgate Antiques & Collectables
48 Chaseside, Southgate. N14 5PA. Open 10-5. SIZE: Medium - 10 dealers. *STOCK: Gramophones, radios, records, sci-fi, militaria and military medals, blazer badges, general small antique and collector's items including named porcelain and glass, china tableware, silver and gold jewellery, watches, stone necklets; period furniture.* LOC: Near Southgate underground station. TEL: 020 8447 8017. SER: Medals mounted and framed; watch and clock repairs ((John Cant - 07977 202542). VAT: Stan.

N19

Chesney's Antique Fireplace Warehouse
734-736 Holloway Rd. N19 3JF. Est. 1983. Open 9-5.30, Sat. 10-5. SIZE: Large. *STOCK: 18th-19th C marble, stone and timber chimney pieces, £1,000-£150,000; reproduction chimney pieces, £250-£7,500.* LOC: South of Archway roundabout on A1. PARK: Side streets adjacent. TEL: 020 7561 8280; fax - 020 7561 8288. SER: Valuations. VAT: Stan/Spec.

Old School (Gardens & Interiors)
130c Junction Rd., Tufnel Park. N19 5LB. Open 11-7 including Sun. *STOCK: Decorative objects, original pine and reclaimed furniture, period garden furniture and some reproduction, tools and general antiques.* TEL: 020 7272 5603.

N20

Julian Alexander Antiques
40 Totteridge Lane. N20 9QJ. (Julian A. Gonnermann). Est. 1991. Open 9.30-5. CL: Mon. and Thurs. SIZE: Medium. *STOCK: 18th-20th C furniture, £50-£5,000.* LOC: Close to Totteridge and Whetstone tube station. TEL: 020 8446 6663; e-mail - julian@jag.uk.com; website - www.jag.uk.com. SER: French polishing; re-upholstery.

The Totteridge Gallery
61 Totteridge Lane. N20 0HD. Est. 1886. Open daily, Sun. by appointment. SIZE: Small. *STOCK: Oil paintings, £1,000-£25,000; watercolours, £300-£10,000; both 18th to early 20th C. Limited edition Russell Flint prints, 20th C, £500-£3,000.* LOC: Opposite Totteridge and Whetstone tube station. PARK: Easy. TEL: 020 8446 7896; website - www.totteridgegallery.com. SER: Valuations; restorations; frame repairs. VAT: Stan/Spec.

N21

Dolly Land
864 Green Lanes, Winchmore Hill. N21 2RS. Est. 1987. Open 9.30-4.30. CL: Mon. and Wed. *STOCK: Dolls, teddies, trains, die-cast limited editions.* PARK: Easy. TEL: 020 8360 1053; fax - 020 8364 1370; website - www.dollyland.com. SER: Restorations; part exchange; dolls' hospital. FAIRS: Doll and Bear.

NW1

Art Furniture
158 Camden St. NW1 9PA. Open 12-5 including Sun. SIZE: Warehouse. *STOCK: Decorative arts 1851-1951, Arts & Crafts furniture by Heal's, Liberty and others.* LOC: Under railway bridge on Camden St. going south. PARK: Easy. TEL: 020 7267 4324; fax - 020 7267 5199; e-mail - arts-and-crafts@artfurniture.co.uk; website - www.artfurniture.co.uk. SER: Export; hire. VAT: Stan/Spec.

Barkes and Barkes
76 Parkway, Camden Town. NW1 7AH. (J. N. and P. R. Barkes). Est. 1976. Open Thurs. 12-7.30, Fri. and Sat. 12-6, and every day during exhibitions. *STOCK: Post-war Russian paintings; British artists - Nick Botting and Mark Pearson.* LOC: Just north of Regents Park. PARK: Next street. TEL: 020 7284 1550; website - www.artrussia.com. VAT: Spec.

Madeline Crispin Antiques
95 Lisson Grove. NW1 6UP. Est. 1971. Open 10-5. *STOCK: General antiques and shipping goods.* TEL: 020 7402 6845. VAT: Stan. *Trade Only.*

Angela Hone Watercolours
LAPADA, CINOA. Open by appointment only. *STOCK: English and French watercolours and pastels, 1850-1930.* TEL: 020 7402 2901. FAIRS: Chelsea; Olympia; LAPADA.

Laurence Corner
62-64 Hampstead Rd. NW1 2NU. Est. 1955. Open 9.30-6. SIZE: Large. *STOCK: Uniforms, helmets, militaria, theatrical costumes, props, fancy dress, flags.* LOC: From Tottenham Court Rd. - Warren St. end - continue into Hampstead Rd., then Drummond St. is first turning on right by traffic lights. PARK: Easy. TEL: 020 7813 1010; fax - 020 7813 1413. SER: Hire; catalogue on request.

Relic Antiques Trade Warehouse
127 Pancras Rd. NW1 1UN. (Malcolm and Matthew Gliksten). Est. 1968. Open 10-5.30, Sat. and Sun. by appointment. *STOCK: English and French decorative and country; architectural and garden; mirrors and French posters; fairground art, trade signs and marine antiques; shopfittings and showcases.* PARK: Meters. TEL: 020 7387 6039; fax - 020 7388 2691; mobile - 07831 785059. VAT: Stan.

This and That (Furniture)
50 and 51 Chalk Farm Rd. NW1 8AN. (M.P. Fraser). Est. 1974. Open 10.30-6 including Sun. SIZE: Medium. *STOCK: Country furniture, stripped pine, oak and walnut, 1890-1930.* LOC: Between Roundhouse and Camden Lock. PARK: Easy. TEL: 020 7267 5433. VAT: Stan.

David J. Wilkins
27 Princess Rd., Regents Park. NW1 8JR. Est. 1974. Open by appointment only. SIZE: Large, warehouses. *STOCK: Oriental rugs.* LOC: Off Regent's Park Rd., near St Mark's church. PARK: Free. TEL: 020 7722 7608; home - 01799 542246; website - www.orientalrugexperts.com. SER: Valuations; restorations; Oriental rug broker. VAT: Stan.

NW2

G. and F. Gillingham Ltd
62 Menelik Rd. NW2 3RH. Est. 1960. Open by appointment. *STOCK: Furniture, 1750-1950.* TEL: 020 7435 5644; fax - same; mobile - 017958 484140. SER: Valuations; export.

Sabera Trading Co
2 Oxgate Parade, Crest Rd. NW2 7EU. (Sabera Nawrozzadeh). Open 10-6. SIZE: Large. *STOCK: Oriental carpets, 19th-20th C, £100-£12,000; porcelain, early 20th C, £100-£1,000; antiques and fine art, jewellery.* PARK: Easy. TEL: 020 8450 0012; fax - same; home - 020 8450 4058. SER: Valuations.

Soviet Carpet & Art Galleries
303-305 Cricklewood Broadway. NW2 6PG. (R. Rabilizirov). Est. 1983. Open 10.30-5, Sun. 10.30-5.30. CL: Sat. SIZE: Large. *STOCK: Hand-made rugs, £100-£1,500; Russian art, £50-£5,000; all 19th-20th C.* LOC: A5. PARK: Side road. TEL: 020 8452 2445. SER: Valuations; restorations (hand-made rugs). VAT: Stan.

NW3

Patricia Beckman Antiques
(Patricia and Peter Beckman). LAPADA. Est.

1968. Open by appointment. *STOCK: Furniture, 18th-19th C.* LOC: Hampstead. TEL: 020 7435 5050/0500. VAT: Spec.

Tony Bingham
11 Pond St. NW3 2PN. LAPADA. Est. 1964. *STOCK: Musical instruments, books, music, oil paintings, engravings of musical interest.* TEL: 020 7794 1596; fax - 020 7433 3662; e-mail - tbingham@easynet.co.uk. VAT: Stan/Spec.

P.G. de Lotz
20 Downside Cres., Hampstead. NW3 2AP. Est. 1967. *STOCK: Antiquarian books on history warfare - naval, military and aviation.* TEL: 020 7794 5709; fax - 020 7284 3058. SER: Catalogue available; search. *Mail Order only.*

Keith Fawkes
1-3 Flask Walk, Hampstead. NW3 1HJ. Est. 1970. Open 10-5.30. SIZE: 2 shops. *STOCK: Antiquarian and general books.* LOC: Near Hampstead tube station. TEL: 020 7435 0614.

Otto Haas (A. and M. Rosenthal)
49 Belsize Park Gardens. NW3 4JL. Est. 1866. By appointment only. CL: Sat. *STOCK: Manuscripts, printed music, autographs, rare books on music.* TEL: 020 7722 1488; fax - 020 7722 2364.

Hampstead Antique and Craft Emporium
12 Heath St., Hampstead. NW3 6TE. Est. 1967. Open 10.30-5, Sat. 10-6, Sun. 11.30-5.30. CL: Mon. SIZE: 24 units. *STOCK: General antiques, craft work and gifts.* LOC: 2 mins. walk from Hampstead underground. TEL: 020 7794 3297.

Klaber and Klaber   BADA
PO Box 9445. NW3 1WD. (Mrs B. Klaber and Miss P. Klaber). Est. 1968. Open by appointment. *STOCK: English and Continental porcelain and enamels, 18th-19th C.* TEL: 020 7435 6537; fax - 020 7435 9459; e-mail - info@klaber.com; website - wwwklaber.com and e-antique porcelain.com. FAIRS: Grosvenor House. VAT: Spec.

Leask Ward
LAPADA. Open by appointment. *STOCK: Oriental and European antiques and paintings.* TEL: 020 7435 9781; fax - same; e-mail - wardl5@aol.com. SER: Consultancy. VAT: Spec.

Duncan R. Miller Fine Arts   BADA
17 Flask Walk, Hampstead. NW3 1HJ. CINOA. Open 10-6. SIZE: Small. *STOCK: Modern British and European paintings, drawings and sculpture, especially Scottish Colourist paintings.* LOC: Off Hampstead High St., near underground station. PARK: Nearby. TEL: 020 7435 5462. SER: Valuations; conservation and restoration (oils, works on paper and Oriental rugs); buys at auction. FAIRS: Grosvenor House; BADA; Olympia. VAT: Spec.

Newhart (Pictures) Ltd
PO Box 1608. NW3 3LB. (Ann and Bernard Hart). Open by appointment only. *STOCK: Oil paintings and watercolours, 1850-1930, from £500.* TEL: 020 7722 2537; fax - 020 7722 4335. SER: Valuations; restorations; framing. VAT: Spec.

Malcolm Rushton - Early Oriental Art
13 Belsize Grove. NW3 4UX. (Dr Malcolm Rushton). Est. 1997. By appointment only, mainly evenings and weekends. SIZE: Small. *STOCK: Fine early Oriental art, neolithic to Tang dynasty, to £15,000.* LOC: Near Belsize Park tube station, off Haverstock Hill. PARK: Easy. TEL: 020 7722 1989. SER: Valuations; restorations (ceramics, sculpture mounting). VAT: Stan.

M. and D. Seligmann   BADA
26 Belsize Park Gardens. NW3 4LH. CINOA Est. 1948. Open by appointment only. *STOCK: Fine vernacular furniture, mainly English, 17th to early 19th C; antiquities and objets d'art.* PARK: Meters. TEL: 020 7722 4315; fax - same; mobile - 07946 634429. FAIRS: Olympia (June and Nov). VAT: Stan/Spec.

David Wainwright
28 Rosslyn Hill. NW3 1NH. Est. 1989. Open 10-6, Sun. 11-5. SIZE: Large. *STOCK: Furniture from the sub-continent and Far East, 15th-20th C including 18th-19th C cupboards, dining tables and architectural pieces, £5-£2,000; stonework - urns, mortars and water containers, to 19th C; contemporary ironwork.* LOC: Hampstead, on corner of Downshire Hill. PARK: Easy. TEL: 020 7431 5900. FAIRS: Olympia. VAT: Stan.

NW4

Talking Machine
30 Watford Way, Hendon. NW4 3AL. Open 10-5, Sat. 9.30-1.30, prior telephone call advisable. *STOCK: Mechanical music, old gramophones, phonographs, vintage records and 78's, needles and spare parts, early radios and televisions, typewriters, sewing machines, juke boxes, early telephones.* LOC: 1 minute Hendon Central underground station. TEL: 020 8202 3473; mobile - 07774 103139; e-mail - davepaul50@hotmail.

com and talkingmachine@gramophones.ndirect. co.uk; website - www.gramophones. ndirect.co.uk. SER: Buys at auction. VAT: Spec.

NW5

Acquisitions (Fireplaces) Ltd
24-26 Holmes Rd., Kentish Town. NW5. (K. Kennedy). NFA; GMC. Est. 1974. Open 9-5. SIZE: Large. *STOCK: Fireplaces in marble, wood, cast-iron and stone, Georgian, Victorian, Edwardian reproduction, fire-side accessories, £195-£5,000.* LOC: 3 mins. walk from Kentish Town tube station. PARK: Forecourt. TEL: 020 7485 4955. SER: Bespoke manufacture of chimney pieces. VAT: Stan.

Orientalist
74-78 Highgate Rd. NW5 1PB. (E. and H. Sakhai). Est. 1885. SIZE: Large. *STOCK: Rugs, carpets, needlepoints, tapestries and Aubussons, including reproduction.* PARK: Easy and nearby. TEL: 020 7482 0555; fax - 020 7267 9603. SER: Valuations; restorations (cleaning and repairing rugs, carpets and tapestries); buys at auction (Oriental carpets, rugs and textiles). VAT: Stan/Spec.

NW6

H. Baron
76 Fortune Green Rd. NW6 1DS. ABA. PBFA. Est. 1949. Open Fri. and Sat. 1-6. SIZE: Small. *STOCK: Antiquarian music, books on music and iconography, autograph music and letters.* TEL: 020 7794 4041; office and fax - 020 8459 2035.

John Denham Gallery
50 Mill Lane, West Hampstead. NW6 1NJ. Est. 1981. Open 10-5. CL: Sat. *STOCK: Paintings, drawings and prints, 17th-20th C, £5-£5,000.* PARK: Easy. TEL: 020 7794 2635. SER: Restorations; conservation; re-framing. VAT: Spec.

Gallery Kaleidoscope incorporating Scope
64-66 Willesden Lane. NW6 7SX. (K. Barrie). Est. 1965. Open 10-6. SIZE: Large. *STOCK: Oils, watercolours, prints, ceramics and sculpture, 19th-20th C.* LOC: 10 mins. from Marble Arch. PARK: Easy. TEL: 020 7328 5833; fax - 020 7624 2913. SER: Restorations; framing. VAT: Stan/Spec.

Hosains Books and Antiques
12 Honeybourne Rd., West Hampstead. NW6 1JJ. (K.S. and Mrs. Y. Hosain). Est. 1979. Open by appointment only. *STOCK: Secondhand and antiquarian books on India, Middle East, Central Asia; miniatures; prints of India and Middle East.* TEL: 020 7794 7127; fax - 020 7433 3126.

NW8

Alfies Antique Market
13-25 Church St. NW8. Open Tues.-Sat. 10-6. SIZE: 300 stands with 180+ dealers on 4 floors. TEL: 020 7723 6066; fax - 020 7724 0999; e-mail - post@Alfies.com. Below are listed the dealers at this market.

Accurate Trading Co. Ltd.
Stand G30/G23. *Jewellery.* TEL: 020 7723 1513.

Beth Adams
Stand G43/44. *Decorative arts, 1860-1950's, £8-£750.* TEL: 020 7723 5613; fax - 020 7262 1576.

M. R. Allahyari
Stand F100. TEL: 020 7723 1370.

David and Diana Bennett Antiques
Stand G104/5. *Boxes, scent bottles, small furniture, silver inkwells, fish servers, clocks, brass scales, glasses, decanters, wooden watch stands, 1800-1900, £20-£300.* TEL: 020 7724 2229.

Bibliopola
Stand F17 & F106. (Jo Del-Grosso). *Antiquarian illustrated, childrens books; modern first editions, 1600-1940.* TEL: 020 7724 7231.

M. J. Black
Stand F59/61. *Decorative and unusual objects.* TEL: 020 7723 0687.

Shelley Blake
Stand G109. TEL: 020 7723 1513.

Paolo Bonino
Stand S1. TEL: 020 7723 6105.

Peter Brooks
Stand G103. *Jewellery, figures, mugs and objets d'art, Georgian to 1960, £25-£1,500.* TEL: 020 7723 0564; mobile - 07785 786395.

Ian Broughton
Stand 48/49. *1950's items.* TEL: 020 7723 6105.

Bernie Bruno
Stand G115. *Clocks and watches.* TEL: 020 7723 0564

Vincenzo Cafferella
Stand G33/34 & 37. *Oil paintings.* TEL: 020 7724 3701.

Sheila Cameron
Stand G135. TEL: 020 7723 0564.

William Campbell
Stand B33/34. *Period picture framer, original frames cut to size, 18th-20th C, £20-£1,000.* TEL: 020 7723 7730.

Wendy Carmichael
Stand S126-129. *Country furniture and decorative antiques, 18th-20th C.* TEL: 020 7723 5731.

Mia Cartwright
Stand G52/53. TEL: 020 7723 0449.

Castaside
Stand B37-42. (David Smith). *Theatre memorabilia.* TEL: 020 7723 7686.

Linda Chan
Stand G120. *Jewellery.* TEL: 020 7724 0362.

Collectors World
Stand G101/130/143. (Jo Khan). *Toys including tin plate, Dinky, Meccano, lead soldiers; clocks, watches, cameras, film and TV memorabilia.* TEL: 020 7723 0564; mobile - 07860 791588.

V. Da Silva
Stand G75/76. TEL: 020 7723 0449.

Gill Danz
Stand 48/49. *Architectural fittings, brass, lighting including chandeliers, decorative items.* TEL: 020 7723 0678.

Dodo
Stand F73/83/84. (Liz Farrow). *Posters, tins and advertising signs, 1890-1940.* TEL: 020 7706 1545.

Gerald Dougall
Stand F16/18/19. *Decorative antiques, 18th-20th C, £20-£1,000.* TEL: 020 7723 0678.

Antonio Durante
Stand S55/56/57. *Decorative items.* TEL: 020 7723 6105.

East-West Antiques
Stand G113/114/117. (Colin Thomson). *Books and Oriental objects, from 1800, £5-£500.* TEL: 020 7723 0564.

Eastgate Antique
Stand S7/9. (Joan Latford) *China teasets, wall plates, cups and saucers; Victorian coloured and Art Deco pressed glass; oil lamps and silver, 19th-20th C, £15-£1,500.* TEL: 020 7723 6105.

George Enoch
Stand S11/52. TEL: 020 7723 6105.

Ellis Fahimian
Stand G30. TEL: 020 7723 1515.

R. Ferrari
Stand G54/55. TEL: 020 7723 0449.

Julia Foster-Fogle
Stand F56. *19th C decorative antiques.* TEL: 020 7723 0678; mobile - 07973 146610.

Gardiner and Gardiner
Stand F13/24. (Helen Gardiner). *Ornamental antiques, 18th-19th C.* TEL: 020 7723 5595.

Goldsmith and Perris
Stand G59-61. (Gloria Goldsmith). LAPADA. *Silver and plate.* TEL: 020 7724 7051.

Theresa Gore
Stand S10. TEL: 020 7723 6105.

Marie Gottlieb
Stand F40/45. TEL: 020 7723 2688.

Patricia Gould
Stand F70. *Textiles, 1400-1900, £5-£1,500.* TEL: 020 7723 0429.

Linette Greco
Stand G26/27. *Jewellery.* TEL: 020 7262 0766.

Guillou-Emary
Stand F71/72. (Jean Gillou). *General decorative antiques, 18th-20th C, £25-£800.* TEL: 020 7723 0429.

Stephen Hall
Stand F77/78. TEL: 020 7723 0678.

Goya Hartogs
Stand S2/4. TEL: 020 7723 6105.

Henry Hay
Stand S54. *Art Deco, chrome and brass lamps, bakelite telephones, 20th C, £25-£500.* TEL: 020 7723 2548.

George Hepburn
Stand B43/44. *Paintings, 18th-20th C, £50-£2,000.* TEL: 020 7723 3437; mobile - 07721 598487.

Frances Houlding
Stand G122/123. *Silver and jewellery.* TEL: 020 7723 1513.

Huxtable's Old Advertising
Stand S3/5. (David Huxtable). *Advertising, collectables, tins, signs, bottles, commemoratives, old packaging, from late Victorian, 50p to £1,000.* TEL: 020 7724 2200; fax - 01727 833445.

Rod Jones
Stand B28-32. TEL: 020 7723 7730.

Kitchen Bygones
Stand B51-53. (N. Oakley). *Kitchen antiques - working and decorative, 1800-1940's, £1.50-£500.* TEL: 020 7258 3045; fax - 01923 260453.

Barry Landsman
Stand G9/10/11. *Watercolours, 18th-19th C, £50-£1,000.* TEL: 020 7723 1513.

Legacy
Stand G50/51. (J. Rosser and W. Garraway). *Postcards, old tins, ephemera, commemoratives, decorative and miniature objects.* TEL: Mobile - 078555 164 954.

Sarah Lewis
Stand S40. *Textiles - cushions, curtains, tapestries and embroideries; trims, tassels, prints, linen and lace, silk, shawls and clothes, 19th-20th C, £10-£10,000.* TEL: 020 7723 6105.

Marie Antiques
Stand G107/136-138. (Marie Warner). TEL: 020 7706 3727.

Nigel Martin
Stand G49. *Textiles.* TEL: 020 7723 0449.

Francesca Martire
Stand F131-7. *Arts and Crafts, 20th C paintings, costume jewellery, decorative arts.* TEL: 020 7724 4802.

Robert McCoy
Stand F20. *Paintings, 19th-20th C, £50-£500.* TEL: 020 7723 0678.

Claire Mills
Stand F57/58. TEL: 020 7724 0678.

Moji Mohamadi
Stand G31. *Jewellery.* TEL: 020 7723 1513.

Bruna Naufal
Stand B58/59. *Modernist furniture, from 1920.* TEL: 020 7724 3439.

Noe & Chiesa
Stand S50/51. *Art Deco and bakelite, 20th C, from £4.* TEL: 020 7723 6105.

Kenneth Norton-Grant
Stand F109-111. *Brass, pewter, pottery and china, 16th-20th C, £1-£250.* TEL: 020 7723 1370.

NS Watches
Stand G12/13. (Mo Heidarieh). *Watches, clocks, prints, pens and silver, from 1850, from £10.* TEL: 020 7723 1513.

G. Payder
Stand G24/25. TEL: 020 7723 1513.

M. Payne
Stand S53. *Jewellery, collectables.* TEL: 020 7723 6105.

Stevie Pearce
Stand G144/5. *Costume jewellery, fashion accessories, 1900-1970, from £10.* TEL: 020 7723 2526.

Persiflage
Stand S6-8. (G. Trefor Jones). *Costume.* TEL: 020 7724 7366.

Katharine Pole
Stand F54/55. *Textiles and decorative antiques, 18th-19th C, £5-£500.* TEL: 020 7723 0678.

Geoffrey Robinson
Stand G77/78/91/92. *Glass, lighting, chrome, Art Deco, 1925-1960's.* TEL: 020 7723 0449; fax - 020 7 706 3254.

Hoshang Samii
Stand S105. *French decorative antiques, 18th-19th C, £10-£600.* TEL: 020 7723 5731.

Christiaan Scholtz
Stand B48/49. TEL: 020 7724 3439.

O. Scremini
Stand S109. TEL: 020 7723 5731.

Kyra Segal
Stand S11. TEL: 020 7723 6105.

A. Sharpe
Stand F46/47. TEL: 020 7723 0678.

Gloria Sinclair
Stand F23. *Porcelain and jewellery, 18th-19th C.* TEL: 020 7724 7118.

Connie Speight
Stand G121/124. TEL: 020 7723 5613.

Robert Steer
Stand S123/4/31/32. TEL: 020 7723 5731.

Textilean
Stand S14. (Sam Peters). *Cushion repair/making.* TEL: 020 7723 4990.

Eugene Tiernan
Stand F14. *Decorative antiques, 19th-20th C, £50-£1,500.* TEL: 020 7723 8964; fax - same.

David Tileke
Stand G6-8. *Prints and engravings, 17th-20th C, £5-£500.* TEL: 020 7724 3722.

Tin Tin Collectables
Stand G40/41/42. (Peter Pinnington). *Antique luggage, ceramics.* TEL: 020 7258 1305.

Travers Antiques
Stand F80-82. (Paula Kluth). TEL: 020 7258 0662.

Rhona Valentine
Stand S12. TEL: 020 7723 6105.

Ruth Van Leon
Stand F79. TEL: 020 7706 1545.

Leslie Verrinder
Stand G38/39. TEL: 020 7258 1305.

June Victor
Stand S41-43. *Decorative textiles and linen, 17th-20th C, £5-£500.* TEL: 020 7723 6105.

D. F. Wallis
Stand F15. *Medical and scientific items, cork-screws, 19th C, £1-£500.* TEL: 020 7402 1038; fax - same.

G. Wetzel
Stand S110. TEL: 020 7723 5731. SER: Restorations.

Fiona Wicks
Stand G70-74. TEL: 020 7723 0449.

Woolfbridge
Stand S16. (Nigel Brooke). TEL: 020 7723 9755.

Beverley
30 Church St., Marylebone. NW8 8EP. Open 10-6 or by appointment. *STOCK: Art Nouveau, Art Deco, decorative objects.* TEL: 020 7262 1576.

D. and A. Binder
34 Church St. NW8 8EP. Open 10-6. *STOCK: Traditional shop-fittings, counters, cabinets, vitrines and display stands.* LOC: Near Lisson Grove. TEL: 020 7723 0542; fax - 020 7724 0837.

Bizarre
24 Church St., Marylebone. NW8 8EP. (A. Taramasco and V. Conti). Open 10-5. *STOCK: Art Deco and Art Nouveau.* TEL: 020 7724 1305; fax - 020 7724 1316.

Camden Art Gallery
22 Church St. NW8 8EP. (Allen and Anne Silver). Est. 1968. Open 10-5. SIZE: Medium. *STOCK: Oil paintings and furniture, 18th-19th C, £300-£10,000.* LOC: Off Edgware Rd. PARK: Easy. TEL: 020 7262 3613; fax - 020 7723 2333. SER: Valuations; restorations (furniture, picture framing and cleaning). FAIRS: Barbican. VAT: Spec.

Church Street Antiques
8 Church St. NW8 8ED. (Stuart Shuster). Est. 1975. Open 10-5.30. CL: Mon. SIZE: Medium. *STOCK: English brown furniture, 18th to early 20th C, £500-£2,000.* LOC: Between Edgware Rd. and Lisson Grove. PARK: Meters. TEL: 020 7723 7415; fax - 020 7723 7415; home - 020 8952 2249. SER: Valuations; restorations (polishing). FAIRS: NEC. VAT: Stan.

Deuxieme
44 Church St. NW8 8BT. (Victoria Harvey and Jerome Zanotti). *STOCK: Decorative and unusual items, French and English furniture.* TEL: 020 7724 0738; fax - same.

Nicholas Drummond/Wrawby Moor Art Gallery Ltd
6 St. John's Wood Rd. NW8 8RE. (J.N. Drummond). Est. 1972. Open by appointment only. *STOCK: English and European oils, £250-£30,000; works on paper.* LOC: Pass Lords entrance and next lights, house last bow front on left, facing down Hamilton Terrace. TEL: 020 7286 6452; home - same; fax - 020 7266 9070; e-mail - drummonds@nixpix.fsnet.co.uk. SER: Valuations; restorations (oils); buys at auction. VAT: Spec.

Robert Franses and Sons
Est. 1969. Open by appointment only. *STOCK: European and Oriental carpets, tapestries, needle-work, Turkish village and early Chinese rugs.* TEL: 020 7328 0949. SER: Restorations. VAT: Stan/Spec.

Gallery of Antique Costume and Textiles
2 Church St., Marylebone. NW8 8ED. Est. 1975. Open 10-5.30. *STOCK: Curtains, needleworks, paisley shawls, original clothing up to 1940's and English quilts, 19th-20th C; tassles, decorative borders, silk panels, velvets and brocades, £5-£20,000.* LOC: 500yds. from Marylebone tube and ½ mile from Marble Arch. PARK: Easy. TEL: 020 7723 9981 (ansaphone); e-mail - info@gact.co.uk; website - www.gact.co.uk. FAIRS: Hali; Vintage Fashion and Textiles; New York.

James Bond *special magazine published to publicise* Goldfinger. *Highly collected by Bond fans and worth around £25.*

From an article entitled "Periodically Valuable" by Adrian Greenwood which appeared in the December 2001/January 2002 issue of **Antique Collecting**. For more details and to subscribe see page 21.

**PERIOD AND
REPRODUCTION
OFFICE
BOARDROOM
AND STUDY
FURNITURE**

20, Church Street, London, NW8 8EP
Tel 020 7723 7976
Fax 020 7402 6416

JUST DESKS OFFICE INTERIORS

**Showrooms open Monday-Saturday
Brochure available**

Patricia Harvey Antiques and Decoration

42 Church St., Marylebone. NW8 8EP. LAPADA. Est. 1961. Open 10-5.30. SIZE: Medium. *STOCK: Decorative furniture, objets, accessories and paintings, £100-£20,000.* LOC: Between Lisson Grove and Edgware Rd., shop is near Alfies Antique Market. TEL: 020 7262 8989; fax - same; home - 020 7624 1787. SER: Valuations; buys at auction; interior decoration. FAIRS: Decorative Antiques and Textiles. VAT: Stan.

Just Desks

20 Church St. NW8 8EP. (G. Gordon and N. Finch). LAPADA. Est. 1967. Open 9.30-6, Sat. 9.30-5 or by appointment. *STOCK: Victorian, Edwardian and reproduction desks, writing tables, bureaux, chairs, filing cabinets and roll tops.* PARK: Meters/Pay & Display. TEL: 020 7723 7976; fax - 020 7402 6416. VAT: Stan.

Andrew Nebbett Antiques

35-37 Church St., Marylebone. NW8 8ES. Est. 1986. Open 10-5.30. CL: Mon. SIZE: Large. *STOCK: Shop fittings, leather chesterfields, decorative, military and ships furniture; cream-ware and glass.* LOC: 50m from Alfie's Antique Market. TEL: 020 7723 2303; e-mail - anebbett @aol.com. FAIRS: Decorative, Battersea. VAT: Stan/Spec.

No. 28 Antiques

28 Church St. NW8 8EP. (David Tulissio, Dominic de Beaumont and Alan Isenberg). Est. 1998. Open 10-6. SIZE: Medium. *STOCK: Chandeliers, wall lights and lamps, 18th-20th C, £200-£3,000; bronzes and sculpture, 18th-19th C, £200-£4,000; general decorative antiques, 18th-20th C, £100-£5,000; furniture, 19th-20th C, £300-£5,000.* LOC: Opposite Alfie's Antique Market, between Lisson Grove and Edgware Rd. (nearest tube - Edgware Road). TEL: 020 7724 4631; mobiles - 07973 186305/07770 920405/07802 425835. VAT: Stan/Spec.

The Studio

(John Beer). Open by appointment only. *STOCK: British Arts and Crafts, Gothic and Art Deco, especially furniture, 1830-1960's.* TEL: 01242 576080; mobile - 07976 704306. SER: Valuations; buys at auction.

Tara Antiques

6 Church St. NW8 8ED. (G. Robinson). Est. 1971. Open 10-6. CL: Mon. SIZE: Medium. *STOCK: Unusual marble and bronze statuary; Vienna bronzes, silver, furniture, paintings, ivory and tortoiseshell.* PARK: Easy. TEL: 020 7724 2405. SER: Buys at auction. VAT: Stan.

Townsends

81 Abbey Rd., St. John's Wood and 106 Boundary Rd. NW8 0AE. (M. Townsend). Est. 1972. Open 10-6. SIZE: Large + warehouse 96A Clifton Hill. *STOCK: Fireplaces, £250-£6,000; stained glass, £80-£1,000; architectural and garden antiques, £50-£2,000; all mainly 18th-19th C.* LOC: Corner of Abbey Rd. and Boundary Rd. PARK: Easy. TEL: 020 7624 4756; warehouse - 020 7372 4327; fax - 020 7372 3005. SER: Valuations; site surveys; free delivery. VAT: Stan.

Wellington Gallery

1 St John's Wood High St. NW8 7NG. (Mrs K. Barclay). LAPADA. Open 10.30-6. *STOCK: Furniture, 18th-19th C; paintings, Georgian glass, fine porcelain, silver and Sheffield plate, general antiques.* TEL: 020 7586 2620; fax - 020 7483 0716. SER: Valuations; restorations (silver and plate, furniture, paintings, glass and porcelain); curtain making, upholstery, gilding, engraving.

Young & Son

12 Church St. NW8 8EP. (L. and S. Young). Est. 1990. Open 10-6. CL: Mon. SIZE: Medium. *STOCK: Furniture, paintings, £1,000-£5,000; lighting and mirrors, £200-£500; decorative items, £100-£5,000; all 18th-20th C.* LOC: Off

Lisson Grove and Edgeware Rd. PARK: Easy. TEL: 020 7723 5910; fax - same; mobile - 07958 437043; e-mail - leon@dircon.co.uk. SER: Valuations; restorations (gilding, framing, French polishing, paintings lined, cleaned and restored). VAT: Stan/Spec.

NW9

B.C. Metalcrafts
69 Tewkesbury Gardens. NW9 0QU. (F. Burnell). LAPADA. Est. 1946. Open by appointment only. *STOCK: Lighting, ormolu and marble lamps; Oriental and European vases; clocks, pre-1900, £5-£500.* Not Stocked: Silver. TEL: 020 8204 2446; fax - 020 8206 2871. SER: Restorations and conversions; buys at auction. VAT: Stan/Spec. *Trade Only.*

NW10

David Malik and Son Ltd
5 Metro Centre, Britannia Way, Park Royal. NW10 7PA. Open 9-5. CL: Sat. *STOCK: Chandeliers, wall lights.* PARK: Easy. TEL: 020 8965 4232; fax - 020 8965 2401. VAT: Stan.

Willesden Green Architectural Salvage
189 High Rd.,Willesden. NW10 2SD. (D. Harkin). Est. 1996. *STOCK: Architectural items.* TEL: 020 8459 2947; fax - 020 8415 1515; mobile - 07971 176547.

NW11

Christopher Eimer
P.O. Box 352. NW11 7RF. BNTA; IAPF. *STOCK: Commemorative and historical medals and related art.* TEL: 020 8458 9933; fax - 020 8455 3535; e-mail - art@christophereimer.co.uk; website - www.christophereimer.co.uk. VAT: Global/Margin.

WC1

Abbott and Holder
30 Museum St. WC1A 1LH. (Philip Athill). Est. 1936. Open 9.30-6, Thurs. till 7. SIZE: 3 floors. *STOCK: English watercolours, drawings, oils and prints, 1760-2000.* LOC: Opposite British Museum. TEL: 020 7637 3981; fax - 020 7631 0575; e-mail - abbott.holder@virgin.net; website - www.abbottandholder.co.uk. VAT: Spec.

Atlantis Bookshop
49a Museum St. WC1A 1LY. Open 11-6. *STOCK: Antiquarian books on the occult and paranormal; occasional related artefacts and paintings.* TEL: 020 7405 2120

Austin/Desmond Fine Art
Pied Bull Yard, 68/69 Great Russell St. WC1B 3BN. (J.Austin). SLAD. Open 10.30-5.30. *STOCK: Modern and contemporary British paintings and prints.* TEL: 020 7242 4443; fax - 020 7404 4480; website - www.austindesmond. com.

Book Art & Architecture & Volume Gallery
12 Woburn Walk, Bloomsbury. WC1. (Prof. Dennis Sharp and Y. Shariff). Est. 1964. Open 11-6 or by appointment. SIZE: Small. *STOCK: Rare, out-of-print and second-hand architectural books and prints, 20th C, £3.50-£350; art, design, planning of modern movement; books published by Book Art Ltd.* LOC: Pedestrian street off Tavistock Sq., opposite Euston. PARK: Nearby. TEL: 020 7387 5006; fax - 020 7787 8286; e-mail - sharpd@globalnet.co.uk; website - sharp architects.co.uk. SER: Valuations; restorations; buys at auction (books and prints). FAIRS: Various book; Historic Buildings Show. VAT: Stan.

A half-pint can of Lassell & Sharman's 'Famous Strong Ale' brewed in the late 1930s. £25. Halls Fine Art, Chester.

From a feature on Saleroom Prices which appeared in the October 2001 issue of **Antique Collecting.** For more details and to subscribe see page 21.

Cinema Bookshop
13-14 Great Russell St. WC1B 3NH. (F. Zentner). Est. 1969. Open 10.30-5.30. SIZE: Small. *STOCK: Books, magazines, posters and stills.* LOC: First right off Tottenham Court Rd. PARK: Easy. TEL: 020 7637 0206; fax - 020 7436 9979. SER: Mail order. VAT: Stan.

George and Peter Cohn
Unit 21, 21 Wren St. WC1X 0HF. Est. 1947. Open 9-5, Sat. and Fri. pm. by appointment. *STOCK: Decorative lights.* PARK: Forecourt. TEL: 020 7278 3749. SER: Restorations (chandeliers and wall-lights). *Trade Only.*

Sebastian D'Orsai Ltd
39 Theobalds Rd. WC1X 8NW. (A. Brooks). Open 9-5. CL: Sat. *STOCK: Framed watercolours.* TEL: 020 7405 6663. SER: Restorations (paintings and prints); framing; gilding. VAT: Stan.

Fine Books Oriental
38 Museum St. WC1A 1LP. (Jeffrey Somers). PBFA. Est. 1970. Open 9.30-6, Tues. and Thurs. 9.30-5.30. SIZE: Medium. *STOCK: Books.* LOC: Near British Museum. PARK: Meters. TEL: 020 7242 5288; fax - 020 7242 5344.

Michael Finney Antique Prints and Books
31 Museum St. WC1A 1LG. (Michael and Mirka Finney). ABA. PBFA. Est. 1979. Open 10-6. SIZE: Large. *STOCK: Prints, 17th-19th C; decorative plate books and watercolours especially David Roberts, Piranesi and Spain; caricatures.* PARK: Meters. TEL: 020 7631 3533; fax - 020 7637 1813; e-mail - prints@michaelfinney.co.uk; website - www. michaelfinney. co.uk. FAIRS: ABA Olympia (June).

Robert Frew Ltd
106 Gt. Russell St. WC1B 3NB. ABA, PBFA. Open 10-6, Sat. 10-2. *STOCK: Books, 15th-20th C, £5-£25,000; maps and prints, 15th-19th C, £5-£5,000.* LOC: Turn right off Tottenham Court Rd. to British Museum, shop on left past YMCA. PARK: Easy. TEL: 020 7580 2311; fax - 020 7580 2313; e-mail - shop@robertfrew.com; website - www.robert frew. com. FAIRS: ABA Olympia, Chelsea; PBFA, Hotel Russell; various USA. VAT: Stan.

Jessop Classic Photographica
67 Great Russell St. WC1B 3BN. Open 9-5.30. *STOCK: Classic photographic equipment, cameras and optical toys.* TEL: 020 7831 3640; fax - 020 7831 3956.

The Museum Bookshop
36 Gt. Russell St. WC1B 3QB. (Ashley Jones). Est. 1982. Open 10-5.30. *STOCK: Books on antiquities - Egyptian, Middle Eastern, classical; glass, ceramics, conservation.* LOC: 3 minutes from Tottenham Court Rd. underground station. PARK: Easy. TEL: 020 7580 4086; fax - 020 7436 4361; e-mail - mbooks@btconnect.com; website - www.museumbooks.org. SER: Catalogues, mail order.

Nortonbury Antiques
BCM Box 5345. WC1N 3XX. LAPADA. Open by appointment. *STOCK: Silver, 17th-19th C.* TEL: 01984 631668; fax - same; mobile - 07774 174092; e-mail - nortonbury.antiques@virgin.net; websites - www.antiquesweb.co.uk/nortonbury; antiquesweb.co.uk/silver.

Rennies
13 Rugby St. WC1. (Paul and Karen Rennie). Open Tues.-Sat. 12-6.30. *STOCK: Decorative arts, 1880-1960; vintage posters, mainly British; ceramics by Ravilious; vintage scarves.* TEL: 020 7405 0220; e-mail - info@rennart.co.uk; website - www.rennart.co.uk.

Simmons Gallery
53 Lambs Conduit St. WC1N 3NB. (Howard and Frances Simmons). BNTA. Est. 1982. Open 10.30-5.30, Wed. 10.30-7. CL: Sat. SIZE: Small. *STOCK: Coins and medals, from 2000BC to contemporary; scales and weights, ancient to 1900; contemporary jewellery and sculpture.* LOC: Off Theobalds Rd, Holborn. Close to Gt Ormond St. Hospital. PARK: Meters. TEL: 020 7831 2080; fax - 020 7831 2090; e-mail - info@ simmonsgallery.co.uk; website - www.simmons gallery.co.uk. SER: Valuations; buys at auction (coins and medals). FAIRS: London Coin (Feb., June, Nov); ANA Midsummer Convention (Aug). VAT: Stan/Spec/Global.

Skoob Russell Square
10 Brunswick Centre, Off Bernard St. WC1N 1AE. (C.Y. Loh). Est. 2001. Open 10.30-7.30, Sun. 12-5. SIZE: Large. *STOCK: Secondhand books specialising in philosophy, cultural studies, literature, psychology, science. Art house videos.* LOC: Near Russell Sq. underground. PARK: Easy. TEL: 020 7278 8760; fax - 020 7278 3137; e-mail - books@skoob.com; website - www. skoob.com. SER: Publishers of Skoob Seriph, Esoterica and Pacifica series.

Spink and Son Ltd   BADA
69 Southampton Row. WC1B 4ET. BNTA. IAPN. Est. 1666. Open 9.30-5.30. CL: Sat. STOCK: Coins, medals, stamps, bank notes, and related books. TEL: 020 7563 4000; fax - 020 7563 4066; e-mail - info@spinkandson.com; website - www.spink-online.com. SER: Valuations. VAT: Stan/Spec.

WC2

Anchor Antiques Ltd

Suite 31, 26 Charing Cross Rd. WC2H 0DG. (K.B. Embden and H. Samne). Est. 1964. Open by appointment. *STOCK: Continental and Oriental ceramics, European works of art and objets de vertu.* TEL: 020 7836 5686. VAT: Spec. *Trade Only.*

Apple Market Stalls

Covent Garden Market. WC2E 8RF. Est. 1980. Open every Monday 10-6.30. SIZE: 48 stalls. *STOCK: General antiques and quality collectables.* TEL: 020 7836 9136; e-mail - info@covent gardenmarket.co.uk; website - www.coventgarden market.co.uk.

A.H. Baldwin and Sons Ltd   BADA

11 Adelphi Terrace. WC2N 6BJ. IAPN, BNTA. Est. 1872. Open 9-5. CL: Sat. SIZE: Medium. STOCK: Coins, 600 BC to present; commemorative medals, 16th C to present, numismatic literature. LOC: Off Robert St., near Charing Cross. TEL: 020 7930 6879; fax - 020 7930 9450; e-mail - coins@baldwin.sh. SER: Valuations; auctioneers and auction agents for selling and purchasing. VAT: Stan/Spec.

Bell, Book and Radmall

4 Cecil Court. WC2N 4HE. Est. 1974. Open 10-5.30, Sat. 11-4. *STOCK: 20th C first editions English and American literature including detective fiction.* TEL: 020 7240 2161; fax - 020 7379 1062; e-mail - bellbr@dial.pipex.com.

Blackwell's

100 Charing Cross Rd. WC2H 0JG. SIZE: Small. *STOCK: Antiquarian and rare modern books.* TEL: 020 7292 5100.

M. Bord (Gold Coin Exchange)

16 Charing Cross Rd. WC2H 0HR. Est. 1969. Open 9.30-6. SIZE: Small. *STOCK: Gold, silver and copper coins, Roman to Elizabeth II, all prices.* LOC: Near Leicester Sq. underground station. TEL: 020 7836 0631/7240 0479. SER: Valuations; buys at auction. FAIRS: All major coin. VAT: Stan/Spec.

Philip Cohen Numismatics

20 Cecil Court. WC2N 4HE. BNTA. Est. 1977. SIZE: Medium. *STOCK: English coins, 16th-20th C, £1-£1,000.* LOC: Off Charing Cross Road. TEL: 020 7379 0615; fax - 020 7240 4300. SER: Valuations.

Covent Garden Flea Market

Jubilee Market, Covent Garden. WC2E 8RB. (Sherman and Waterman Associates Ltd). Est. 1975. Open Mon. and Bank Holidays 5-5. SIZE: 200 stalls. *STOCK: General antiques.* LOC: South side of piazza, just off The Strand, via Southampton St. PARK: Easy and N.C.P. Drury Lane. TEL: 020 7836 2139/7240 7405.

David Drummond at Pleasures of Past Times

11 Cecil Court, Charing Cross Rd. WC2N 4EZ. Est. 1962. Open 11-2.30 and 3.30-5.45 and usually 1st Sat. monthly, other times by appointment. SIZE: Medium. *STOCK: Scarce and out-of-print books of the performing arts; early juvenile and illustrated books; vintage postcards, valentines, entertainment ephemera.* Not Stocked: Coins, stamps, medals, jewellery, maps, cigarette cards. LOC: In pedestrian court between Charing Cross Rd. and St. Martin's Lane. TEL: 020 7836 1142; fax - same; e-mail - drummond@poptfsnet. co.uk. VAT: Stan.

Stanley Gibbons

399 Strand. WC2R 0LX. Est. 1856. Open 9-5.30, Sat. 9.30-5.30. SIZE: Large. *STOCK: Popular and specialised stamps, postal history, catalogues, albums, accessories; autographs and memorabilia.* LOC: Opposite Savoy Hotel. TEL: 020 7836 8444; fax - 020 7836 7342. SER: Valuations; auctions. VAT: Stan/Spec.

Gillian Gould at Ocean Leisure

Embankment Place, 11-14 Northumberland Avenue. WC2N 5AQ. Est. 1988. Open 9.30-6, Thurs. 9.30-7, Sat. 9.30-5.30 or by appointment. SIZE: Small. *STOCK: Marine antiques and collectables, scientific instruments, £30-£1,000.* PARK: Meters. TEL: 020 7930 5050; fax - 020 7930 3032; home - 020 7419 0500; fax - 020 7419 0400; mobile - 07831 150060; e-mail - gillgould@ dealwith.com. SER: Valuations; restorations; hire; sources gifts for personal and corporate presentation; buys at auction. VAT: Stan.

Grosvenor Prints

28 Shelton St., Covent Garden. WC2H 9JE. Est. 1975. Open 10-6, Sat. 11-4. SIZE: Large. *STOCK: 18th-19th C topographical and decorative prints, specialising in portraits, dogs and British field sports.* LOC: One street north of Covent Garden tube. PARK: Easy. TEL: 020 7836 1979; fax - 020 7379 6695; website - www. grosvenorprints.com; e-mail - grosvenorprints@ btinternet.com. SER: Valuations; restorations; buys at auction. VAT: Stan/Spec.

P. J. Hilton (Books)

12 Cecil Court. WC2N 4HE. (Paul Hilton). Est. 1980. Open 11-6, Sat. 11-5. SIZE: Medium. *STOCK: Antiquarian books, 16th-20th C, £75-*

KOOPMAN LTD & RARE ART (LONDON) LTD

A FINE SET OF FOUR
GEORGE III SILVER
CANDLESTICKS

MADE IN LONDON, 1774
BY **JOHN CARTER**

Height :
10³/4 in. (27.3 cm.).
Weight :
91 oz. (2,830.1 g.).

*Colour brochure
available upon request*

53/64 CHANCERY LANE, LONDON WC2A 1QS
TELEPHONE : 020-7242 7624   FAX : 020-7831 0221
E-mail : rareart@compuserve.com   Website : www.rareartlondon.com

£500; secondhand books; leather cloth bindings by the yard. LOC: Off Charing Cross Rd. TEL: 020 7379 9825. SER: Valuations.

Lee Jackson
2 Southampton St., Covent Garden. WC2E 7HA. PBFA. Est. 1996. Open 10-5.30. SIZE: Large. *STOCK: Maps and views of the world, 16th-19th C, £10-£3,000.* LOC: Off the Strand, opposite the Savoy Hotel. PARK: Meters. TEL: 020 7240 1970; e-mail - leejackson@btinternet.com; website - www.leejackson.btinternet.co.uk. FAIRS: London Map; Miami International Map. VAT: Stan.

S. and H. Jewell Ltd
26 Parker St. WC2B 5PH. Est. 1830. Open 9-5.30, Sat. by appointment. SIZE: Large. *STOCK: Furniture.* TEL: 020 7405 8520. SER: Valuations; restorations. VAT: Stan/Spec.

Thomas Kettle Ltd
53a Neal St. WC2H 9PJ. Est. 1974. Open 11-6 and most Sundays 1.30-5. SIZE: Medium. *STOCK: Watches, 1930-1965, £500-£5,000; bespoke and platinum jewellery, £100-£10,000.* LOC: Near Covent Garden tube. PARK: Leicester Sq. TEL: 020 7379 3579. SER: Valuations; restorations (wrist watches). VAT: Stan.

Koopman Ltd & Rare Art (London) Ltd
BADA
Entrance to London Silver Vaults, Ground Floor, 53/64 Chancery Lane. WC2A 1QS. (Michael Koopman and Lewis Smith). Open 9-5.30, Sat. 10-1. *STOCK: Fine quality English Georgian and Continental silverware.* TEL: 020 7242 7624; fax - 020 7831 0221; e-mail - rareart @compuserve.com; website - www.rareart london.com. FAIRS: Milan, Olympia, New York, Tefaf (Maastricht).

The London Silver Vaults
Chancery House, 53-64 Chancery Lane. WC2A 1QS. Est. 1892. Open 9-5.30, Sat. 9-1. SIZE: 34 shops. *STOCK: Antique and modern silver, plate, jewellery, objets d'art, clocks, watches, collectors' items.* TEL: 020 7242 3844. The following are some of the dealers at these vaults.

A. M. W. Silverware
Vault 52-53. TEL: 020 7242 3620; fax - 020 7831 3923.

Argenteus Ltd
Vault 2. LAPADA. TEL: 020 7831 3637; fax - 020 7430 0126. VAT: Stan/Spec.

Belmonts

A. Bloom

Vault 27. *Victorian and Edwardian silver miniatures to monumental table centres.* TEL: 020 7242 6189; fax - same; e-mail - bloomvault@aol. com; website - www.bloomvault.com.

Luigi Brian Antiques

Vault 17. *Fine English and European silver, objets d'art and icons.* TEL: 020 7405 2484; fax - same.

B.L. Collins

Vault 20. (Barry Collins). TEL: 020 7404 0628; fax - 020 7404 1451; e-mail - b.collins@silvervaults. idps.co.uk; website - www.blcollins.co.uk.

Crown Silver

Vault 30. TEL: 020 7242 4704. *Trade Only.*

P. Daniels

Vault 51. TEL: 020 7430 1327.

Bryan Douglas

Vault 12/14. (Ian Bryan). LAPADA. *Antique, old and modern silverware.* TEL: 020 7242 7073; fax - same; e-mail - sales@bryandouglas.co.uk; website - www.bryandouglas.co.uk.

R. Feldman Ltd

Vault 6. LAPADA. *Unusual and rare items, old Sheffield and Victorian plate, silver centrepieces, candelabra, epergnes combined with argenteus specialising in all patterns of flatware.* TEL: 020 7405 6111; fax - 020 7430 0126; e-mail - rfeldman @rfeldman.co.uk; website - www.rfeldman.co.uk.

I. Franks

Vault 9/11. Est. 1926. LAPADA. *Old and antique English silver and plate especially tableware, teasets, cutlery, epergnes, candlesticks and candelabra.* TEL: 020 7242 4035; fax - same; e-mail - info@ifranks.com; website - www.ifranks. com.

M. & J. Hamilton

Vault 25. *17th -20th C silver including cutlery.* TEL: 020 7831 7030; fax - 020 7831 5483; e-mail - hamiltonsilver@hotmail.com.

Gary Hyams

Vault 48-50. *Silver and Sheffield Plate.* TEL: 020 7831 4330.

Stephen Kalms

Vault 15, 31, 32. LAPADA. TEL: 020 7430 1265; fax - 020 7405 6206; e-mail - stephen@skalms. freeserve.co.uk; website - www.kalmsantiques. com.

B. Lampert

Vault 19. TEL: 020 7242 4121.

Langfords

Vault 8/10. (Adam and Joel Langford). Est. 1940. LAPADA. *Silver and plate especially cutlery.* TEL: 020 7242 5506; fax - 020 7405 0431; e-mail - vault@langfords.com; website - www.langfords. com. SER: Valuations. VAT: Stan/Spec.

Leon Antiques

Vault 57.

Nat Leslie Ltd

Vault 21-23. (Mark Hyams). Est. 1940. *Victorian and 20th C silverware especially flatware and contemporary designers, especially Stuart Devlin.* TEL: 020 7242 4787; fax - 020 7242 4504; e-mail - nat.leslie@which.net; website - www.natleslie.co. uk. VAT: Stan/Spec.

Linden and Co. (Antiques) Ltd

Vault 7. (H, F, H.M. and S. C. Linden). *Silver and plate, specialising in gift items for weddings, christenings, silver weddings and retirements, £100-£750.* TEL: 020 7242 4863; fax - 020 7405 9946; e-mail - lindenandco@aol.com; website - www. lindenantiquesilver.com. VAT: Stan/Spec.

C. and T. Mammon

Vault 55-64. (Claude Mammon). *Victorian and old Sheffield plate, Continental and English silver and cutlery, mirror plateaux and centrepieces.* TEL: 020 7405 2397; fax - 020 7405 4900; e-mail - claudemammon@btinternet.com; website - www. candtmammon.com.

I. Nagioff (Jewellery)

Vault 63 and 69. (I. and R. Nagioff). Est. 1955. *Jewellery, 18th-20th C, £5-£2,000+; objets d'art, 19th C, to £200.* TEL: 020 7405 3766. SER: Valuations; restorations (jewellery). VAT: Stan.

Percy's (Silver Ltd).

Vault 16. (David and Paul Simons). LAPADA. *Fine decorative silver especially claret jugs, and candelabra, candlesticks, flatware and collectables.* TEL: 020 7242 3618; fax - 020 7831 6541; e-mail - sales@percys-silver.com; website - www. percys-silver.com.

Terry Shaverin

Vault 143. TEL: 020 8368 5869; fax - 020 8361 7659; e-mail - terryshaverin@silverflatware.co.uk; website - www.silverflatware.co.uk.

David S. Shure and Co

Vault 1. (Lynn Bulka). Est. 1900. Author. *Antique and modern silverware, old Sheffield plate, cutlery and jewellery.* TEL: 020 7405 0011; fax - same. SER: Valuations. VAT: Stan.

Silstar (Antiques Ltd)

Vault 29. (B. Stern). Est. 1955. TEL: 020 7242 6740; fax - 020 7430 1745; e-mail - antique@ silstar.fsnet.co.uk. VAT: Stan/Spec.

B. Silverman   BADA

Vault 26. Est. 1927. *Fine antique silver including flatware.* TEL: 020 7242 3269; fax - 020 7430 1949; e-mail - robin@silverman-london.com; website - www.silverman-london.com. SER: Valuations; buys at auction. VAT: Stan/Spec.

Jack Simons (Antiques) Ltd

Vault 35-37. (David and Paul Simons). Est. 1955.

LAPADA. *Fine English and European silver.* TEL: 020 7242 3221; fax - 020 7831 6541; e-mail - sales@percys-silver.com; website - www.percys-silver.com. VAT: Stan/Spec.

S. and J. Stodel BADA
Vault 24. (Jeremy Stodel). *Chinese export to English Art Deco silver including flatware.* TEL: 020 7405 7009; fax - 020 7242 6366; e-mail - stodel @msn.com; website - www.chinesesilver. com.

J. Surtees
Vault 65. *Silver.* TEL: 020 7242 0749.

William Walter Antiques Ltd BADA
Vault 3/5. (Elizabeth Simpson). Est. 1927. LAPADA. *Georgian silver, old Sheffield plate; also modern silver.* TEL: 020 7242 3284; fax - 020 7404 1280; e-mail - enq@wwantiques.prestel.co. uk; website - www.williamwalter.co.uk. SER: Valuations; restorations (silver, plate).

Peter K. Weiss
Vault 18. Est. 1955. *Watches, clocks.* TEL: 020 7242 8100; fax - 020 7242 7310. VAT: Stan.

Wolfe (Jewellery)
Vault 41. (John Petrook). TEL: 020 7405 2101; fax - same. VAT: Stan/Spec.

Marchpane

16 Cecil Court, Charing Cross Rd. WC2N 4HE. (Kenneth Fuller). ABA. PBFA. Est. 1984. Open 10-6. SIZE: Medium. *STOCK: Antiquarian children's and illustrated books, from 18th C to date.* TEL: 020 7836 8661; fax - 020 7497 0567; e-mail - k-fuller@btclick.com.

Arthur Middleton

12 New Row, Covent Garden. WC2N 4LF. Est. 1968. Open 10-6, Sat. by appointment only. SIZE: Medium. *STOCK: Globes, 1720-1950, from miniatures to large library pairs; scientific instruments - navigation, astronomy, surveying, microscopes, 18th-19th C, £100-£50,000.* LOC: New Row runs between Leicester Sq. and Covent Garden. Shop 300yds. east from Leicester Sq. TEL: 020 7836 7042/7062; fax - 020 7497 2486. SER: Valuations; buys at auction; prop hire. VAT: Stan.

Henry Pordes Books Ltd

58-60 Charing Cross Rd. WC2H 0BB. Open 10-7. *STOCK: Secondhand, antiquarian and remainder books on most subjects including antiques.* TEL: 020 7836 9031; fax - 020 7240 4232; e-mail - henrypordes@clara.net; website - www.home. clara.net/henrypordes.

The Rae-Smith Gallery

8 Cecil Court. WC2N 4HE. (John and Felicity Rae-Smith). Est. 1992. Open 11.30-6, Mon. by appointment. SIZE: Medium. *STOCK: 20th C original cartoon artwork and book illustrations, £30-£3,000.* LOC: Between Charing Cross Road and St. Martin's Lane - Leicester Square underground. PARK: Meters or NCP. TEL: 020 7836 7424; fax - same; e-mail - raesmithg@aol.com. SER: Valuations. FAIRS: Watercolours and Drawings. VAT: Margin.

Reg and Philip Remington

18 Cecil Court, Charing Cross Rd. WC2N 4HE. ABA. Est. 1979. Open 10-5, Sat. by appointment. SIZE: Medium. *STOCK: Voyages and travels, 17th-20th C, £5-£1,000.* LOC: Near Trafalgar Sq. TEL: 020 7836 9771. SER: Buys at auction. FAIRS: London Book, Olympia. VAT: Stan.

Bertram Rota Ltd

1st Floor, 31 Long Acre. WC2E 9LT. Est. 1923. Open 9.30-5.30. CL: Sat. *STOCK: Antiquarian and secondhand books, especially first editions, private presses, English literature, and literary autographs.* TEL: 020 7836 0723.

The Silver Mouse Trap

56 Carey St. WC2A 2JB. (A.Woodhouse). Est. 1690. Open 10-5. CL: Sat. SIZE: Medium. *STOCK: Jewellery, silver.* LOC: South of Lincoln's Inn Fields. TEL: 020 7405 2578. SER: Valuations; restorations. VAT: Spec.

Stage Door Prints

9 Cecil Court, Charing Cross Rd. WC2N 4EZ. (A. Reynold). Open 11-6. *STOCK: Prints of performing arts, sports and topographical; signed photographs, maps, Victorian cards, valentines; film shop - posters, stills, books, memorabilia; performing arts book room and bargain basement.* TEL: 020 7240 1683.

Storey's Ltd

3 Cecil Court, Charing Cross Rd. WC2N 4EZ. (T. Kingswood). Est. 1929. Open 10-6. *STOCK: Antiquarian prints and engravings, especially naval and military; natural history and topography, including David Roberts; antiquarian maps and books.* LOC: Between Charing Cross Rd. and St. Martin's Lane. PARK: Trafalgar Square garage. TEL: 020 7836 3777; fax - 020 7836 3788; e-mail - storeysltd@btinternet.com; website - www. storeysltd.co.uk.

Tomtom

42 New Compton St. WC2H 8DA. (T. S. Roberts). Est. 1990. Open 12-7, Sat. 11-6. CL: Mon. SIZE: Medium. *STOCK: Post war design furniture, art, glass and ceramics, 1940-1980, to £1,000+.* LOC: Adjacent Charing Cross Rd.

PARK: Meters. TEL: 020 7240 7909; fax - same; e-mail - sales@tomtomshop.co.uk; website - www.tomtomshop.co.uk. SER: Valuations; buys at auction (designer furniture and post war art). FAIRS: Pier Show, New York. VAT: Spec.

Trafalgar Square Collectors Centre
7 Whitcomb St. WC2H 7HA. (D.C. Pratchett and R.D. Holdich). Est. 1979. Open 10-5. CL: Sat. *STOCK: Coins and military medals, bonds, banknotes, badges and militaria, 18th-20th C, £5-£10,000.* LOC: Next to National Gallery. PARK: NCP. TEL: 020 7930 1979; fax - 020 7930 1152; e-mail - rdhmedals@aol.com. SER: Valuations; buys at auction (coins and military medals). VAT: Stan/Spec.

Travis and Emery
17 Cecil Court, Charing Cross Rd. WC2N 4EZ. ABA, PBFA. Est. 1960. Open 11-6 including Sun. SIZE: Medium. *STOCK: Musical literature, music and prints.* LOC: Between Charing Cross Rd. and St. Martin's Lane. PARK: Meters. TEL: 020 7240 2129; fax - 020 7497 0790; e-mail - enqasb@travis-and-emery.com.

Watkins Books Ltd
19 Cecil Court, Charing Cross Rd. WC2N 4EZ. Est. 1880. Open 10-6, Thurs. 10-8, Sat. 10.30-6. *STOCK: Mysticism, occultism, Oriental religions, astrology, psychology, complementary medicine and a wide selection of books in the field of mind, body and spirit - both new and secondhand.* LOC: Near Leicester Sq. underground station. TEL: 020 7836 2182; fax - 020 7836 6700; e-mail - service @watkinsbooks.com; website - www.watkins books.com.

Nigel Williams Rare Books
22 & 25 Cecil Court, Charing Cross Rd. WC2N 4HE. ABA. Est. 1988. Open 10-6. SIZE: Medium. *STOCK: Books - literature first editions, 18th-20th C; collectable children's and illustrated, original artwork and prints.* LOC: Near Leicester Sq. underground. TEL: 020 7836 7757; fax - 020 7379 5918; e-mail - sales@nigelwilliams.com; website - www.nigelwilliams.com. FAIRS: ABA, Olympia.

The Witch Ball
2 Cecil Court, Charing Cross Rd. WC2N 4HE. (R. Glassman). Resident. Est. 1969. Open 10.30-6.30. SIZE: Small. *STOCK: Prints relating to the performing arts, from 17th C; 20th C posters.* LOC: 2 mins. from Leicester Sq. underground. PARK: NCP nearby. TEL: 020 7836 2922; e-mail - thewitchball@btinternet.com; website - www. thewitchball.co.uk.VAT: Stan.

Zwemmer
24 Litchfield St. WC2H 9NJ. Est. 1921. Open 10-6.30, Thurs. 10-8, Sat. 10-6. SIZE: Large. *STOCK: Books on art and fine art; rare and out-of-print catalogue raisonnés.* LOC: Just south of Cambridge Circus, Leicester Sq. underground. TEL: 020 7240 4158.

Harry Potter fans went wild for this collection of tarot cards and crystals from the Ken Paul archive, which had featured in '...the Philosopher's Stone'. They might have cost £10 from a back-alley head shop, but at Sotheby's sale they made £1,100.

From an Auction Report by Christopher Wight on Prop Art held at Sotheby's, New Bond Street 13th-15th March 2002 which appeared in the May 2002 issue of **Antique Collecting**. For more details and to subscribe see page 21.

AMPTHILL

Ampthill Antiques
Market Sq. MK45 2EH. (A. Olney). Est. 1980. Open 11-4, Sun. 2-5. SIZE: Large. *STOCK: Furniture, collectables, jewellery, clocks, china, glass, pictures.* LOC: Town centre. PARK: Easy and at rear. TEL: 01525 403344.

Ampthill Antiques Emporium
6 Bedford St. MK45 2NB. (Marc Legg). Est. 1979. Open 10-5 every day except Tues. SIZE: Large - 40 dealers. *STOCK: Antique furniture, fireplaces, architectural items, smalls, ceramics, glass and jewellery.* LOC: 5 mins. from Junction 13, M1. PARK: Easy. TEL: 01525 402131; fax - 01582 737527; e-mail - info@ampthillantiques.co.uk; website - www.ampthillantiquesemporium.co.uk. SER: Restorations (pine stripping and upholstery).

Antiquarius of Ampthill
107 Dunstable St. MK45 2NG. (Peter Caldwell). Est. 1997. Open 10.30-5, Sun. 1-5. SIZE: Small. *STOCK: Sitting and dining room furniture, 1800-1900, to £3,000.* LOC: Town centre. PARK: Nearby. TEL: 01525 841799; e-mail - peter. caldwell@tesco.net. SER: Restorations including pine stripping.

House of Clocks
102-104 Dunstable St. MK45 2JP. (John and Helga Ginty and Ian and Hazel Proud). Resident. Est. 1957. Open 9-5, Sun. 11-5. SIZE: Medium. *STOCK: Clocks including longcase, bracket, carriage and wall, £150-£12,000.* PARK: Behind Market Sq. TEL: 01525 403136; fax - 01525 402680; e-mail - ian@houseofclocks102 freeserve.co.uk. SER: Valuations; restorations (clocks). FAIRS: Manchester; Birmingham: Uxbridge: Kettering: Luton. VAT: Stan/Spec.

David Litt Antiques
The Old Telephone Exchange, Claridges Lane. MK45 2NG. (David and Helen Litt). Est. 1967. Open 7.30-5, weekends by appointment. SIZE: Large. *STOCK: French country items especially armoires, farmhouse tables, sets of chairs, chandeliers and mirrors.* LOC: Off Woburn St. PARK: Easy. TEL: 01525 404825; fax - 01525 404563; mobile - 07802 449027; home - 01525 750359; e-mail - litt@ntlworld.com. SER: Restorations (cabinet work). FAIRS: Decorative Antique & Textile, Battersea; House & Garden; Olympia.

Paris Antiques
97B Dunstable St. MK45 2NG. (Paul and Elizabeth Northwood). Est. 1985. Open 9.30-5. CL: Mon. SIZE: Medium. *STOCK: Furniture,* 18th to early 20th C, £250-£4,000; brass and copper, silver and plate, pictures and smalls.* LOC: Off junction 12, M1. PARK: Opposite. TEL: 01525 840488; home - 01525 861420; mobile - 07802 535059. SER: Valuations; restorations (mainly furniture, some metal); buys at auction.

Pilgrim Antiques
111 Dunstable St. MK45 1BY. (Gary Lester). Est. 1982. Open 10-5.30 including Sun. SIZE: Large. *STOCK: Furniture including dining tables, bookcases, chairs, wardrobes, 18th-20th C, £500-£5,000.* LOC: Town centre. PARK: Rear of premises. TEL: 01525 633023; home - 01525 403266. SER: Restorations.

The Pine Parlour
82a Dunstable St. MK45 2LF. (Lynn Barker). Est. 1989. Open 10-5 including Sun. CL: Mon. SIZE: Small. *STOCK: Pine furniture, 19th C, £200-£800; kitchenalia, £5-£60.* PARK: Easy. TEL: 01525 403030; home - same. SER: Valuations.

Transatlantic Antiques & Fine Art Ltd
101 Dunstable St. MK45 2NG. (I.J. and D. M. Higgins). Est. 1995. Open 10.30-5, Sun. 12-5. SIZE: Large. *STOCK: 19th C furniture, £150-£4,000; glass, ceramics, silver and metalware, 19th C, £5-£3,000; pictures and interesting objects, 18th-19th C, £50-£1,000.* LOC: Main street. PARK: Easy and nearby. TEL: 01525 403346; fax - same; e-mail - transatlantic@talk 21.com; website - www.transatlanticantiques. com. SER: Restorations; buys at auction. VAT: Spec.

BEDFORD

Architectural Antiques
70 Pembroke St. MK40 3RQ. (Paul and Linda Hoare). Est. 1989. Open 12-5, Sat. 10-5. SIZE: Medium. *STOCK: Early Georgian to early 20th C fireplaces, £500-£1,000; sanitary ware, from late Victorian, £100-£500; doors, panelling, pews, chimney pots and other architectural items, Georgian and Victorian, £50-£100.* LOC: Follow signs to town centre, turn on The Embankment or Castle Rd., shop is off Castle Rd., near Post Office. PARK: Easy. TEL: 01234 213131/ 343421; fax - 01234 309858. SER: Valuations; restorations; installations, particularly period fireplaces.

BIGGLESWADE

Old Mother Hubbard's
38 Shortmead St. SG18 0AP. (Derry Anne Dynes). Est. 1994. Open 10-5, Sat. 9.30-5. CL: Thurs. SIZE: Medium. *STOCK: China, 1920's-*

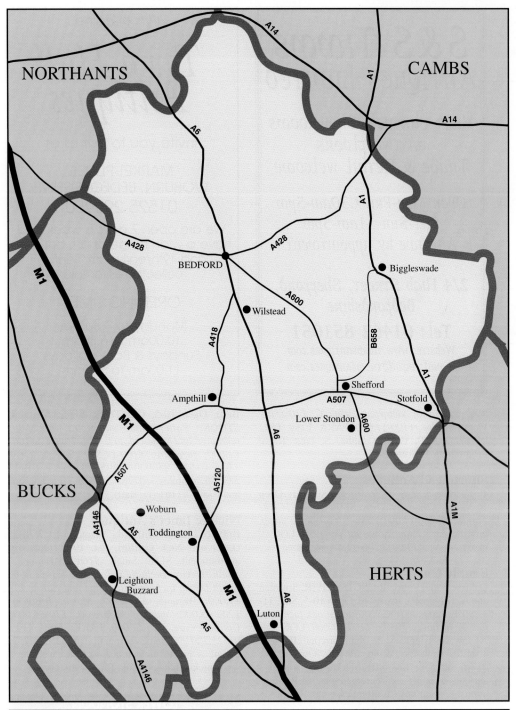

Dealers and Shops in Bedfordshire

				Shefford	1	
				Stotfold	1	
Ampthill	9	Leighton Buzzard	2	Toddington	1	
Bedford	1	Lower Stondon	1	Wilstead	1	
Biggleswade	3	Luton	3	Woburn	4	

30's, £15-£100; Victoriana, 19th C, £10-£500; Victorian pine, £100-£1,000. PARK: Easy. TEL: 01767 600959. FAIRS: Janba, St Ives; Regal Promotions, Dunstable.

Shortmead Antiques
46 Shortmead St. SG18 0AP. (S.E. Sinfield). Open 10.30-4. CL: Mon. and Thurs. SIZE: Small. STOCK: Furniture, £50-£1,000; boxes, porcelain, silver, bronzes, copper and brass, all pre-1930. LOC: ½ mile from A1. TEL: 01767 601780 (ansaphone).

Simply Oak
Oaktree Farm, Potton Rd. SG18 0EP. (R. Sturman and A. Kilgarriff). Est. 1996. Open 10-5, Sun. 11-4. SIZE: Large. STOCK: Restored oak furniture, late Victorian to 1930's, £100-£2,000. LOC: Off A1 towards Biggleswade, right turn onto B1040 - 3 miles towards Potton. PARK: Own. TEL: 01767 601559; fax - 01767 312855; e-mail - antiques@simplyoak.freeserve.co.uk. SER: Valuations; restorations (furniture especially oak).

LEIGHTON BUZZARD

Baroq & David Ball Antiques
59 North St. LU7 7EQ. (Brian Dawson and David

Ball). Open 10-5. CL: Thurs. SIZE: Medium. STOCK: Pottery and porcelain, £10-£500; paintings and watercolours, 18th-20th C, £100-£1,000; furniture, £100-£4,500. PARK: Easy. TEL: 01525 850900/382954; home - 01908 587766; mobiles - 07767 303501 (B. Dawson) and 07831 11161 (D. Ball).

Nick & Janet's Antiques
Buffalo House, Mill Rd., Slapton. LU7 9BT. (Janet and Nick Griffin). Est. 1992. Open by appointment. SIZE: Small. STOCK: Pottery - South Devon including Torquay, £1-£2,000; North Devon including Brannam and Baron, £1-£1,000; Wesuma, £20-£400; Martin Brothers, £200-£5,000; modern Moorcroft, £30-£4,000; Cobridgeware, £20-£1,000. PARK: Easy. TEL: 01525 220256; home - same; fax - 01525 220757; e-mail - janet@nickandjanets.co.uk; website - www.nickandjanets.co.uk. SER: Valuations.

LOWER STONDON

Memory Lane Antiques
14 Bedford Rd. SG16 6EA. (Elizabeth Henry). Est. 1985. Open 10.30-5, Sun. 11-4. CL: Wed. and Thurs. SIZE: Medium. STOCK: General

antiques including 19th oak, silver and plate, glass including coloured. LOC: On A600 near RAF Henlow. PARK: Easy. TEL: 01462 811029/812716; fax - same. SER: Valuations.

LUTON

Bargain Box
4 & 6a Adelaide St. LU1 5BB. Open 9-6, Wed. 9-1. *STOCK: General antiques and collectables.* TEL: 01582 423809.

Bernadette's Antiques & Collectables & Auctioneers
19a Adelaide St. LU1 5BB. Open 9-6, Wed. 9-1. *STOCK: General antiques.* TEL: 01582 423809.

Foye Gallery
15 Stanley St. LU1 5AL. Est. 1960. Open 9.30-5 or by appointment. *STOCK: Engravings, etchings, drawings, watercolours, paintings, maps, books.* TEL: 01582 738487. VAT: Stan.

SHEFFORD

S. and S. Timms Antiques Ltd
2/4 High St. SG17 5DG. LAPADA. Est. 1976. Open 9.30-5, Sat. and Sun. 11-5 or by appointment. SIZE: Large. *STOCK: 18th-19th C town and country furniture.* LOC: A507, centre of village. PARK: Easy. TEL: 01462 851051; mobile - 07885 458541. FAIRS: LAPADA (London and NEC); Chelsea; Battersea. VAT: Stan/Spec.

STOTFOLD, Nr. Hitchin

Ayuka Ltd
3 Fen End, Astwick Rd. SG5 4BA. (Mune Ota). Open by appointment. SIZE: Medium. *STOCK: Pine and oak furniture, Victorian to 1950, £100-£700; smalls, £10-£500.* PARK: Easy. TEL: Mobile - 07796 804032; home - 01438 362494. SER: Buys at auction; shipping. *Trade Only.*

TODDINGTON

Books for Collectors Ltd.
Unit 1, Rear 24/26 High St, LU5 6BY. (Frank and Shirley Horn). Open 10-4, prior telephone call advisable. *STOCK: New and secondhand collectors books.* PARK: Easy. TEL: 01525 875100/ 01582 738624; fax - 01525 877600.

WILSTEAD (WILSHAMSTEAD) Nr. Bedford

Manor Antiques
The Manor House, Cottonend Rd. MK45 3BT. (Mrs S. Bowen). Est. 1976. Open Tues.-Sat. 10-5, Sun. by appointment. SIZE: Large. *STOCK: Furniture, 19th C to Edwardian, £100-£5,000; lighting, mirrors, decorative objects.* LOC: Just off A6, 4 miles south of Bedford. PARK: Own. TEL: 01234 740262; home - same. SER: Restorations (furniture); buys at auction. FAIRS: Olympia. VAT: Stan/Spec.

WOBURN

Christopher Sykes Antiques
The Old Parsonage. MK17 9QL. (C. and M. Sykes). Est. 1949. Open 9-5. SIZE: Large. *STOCK: Collectors' items - attractive, early brass, copper and pewter; scientific and medical instruments; specialist in rare corkscrews, £10-£800; silver decanter labels, tastvins and funnels, pottery barrels and bin labels, glass decanters and tantalus.* LOC: In main street opposite Post Office on A50. PARK: Easy. TEL: 01525 290259/290467; fax - 01525 290061; e-mail - sykes.corkscrews@sykes-corkscrews.co.uk; website - www.sykes-corkscrews.co.uk. SER: 130 page illustrated mail order catalogue on corkscrews and wine related antiques available £7 each. VAT: Stan/Spec.

Town Hall Antiques
Market Place. MK17 9PZ. (Elfyn and Elaine Groves). Est. 1993. Open 10-5.30, Sun. 11-5.30. SIZE: Medium. *STOCK: Furniture, £50-£5,000; lighting, clocks, ceramics, glass, silver and plate, £10-£2,000; prints and pictures, £5-£2,000; all 18th to early 20th C; mirrors, domestic metalware; some antiquities; cigarette cards, tools, sporting memorabilia.* LOC: Off A5 and off junction 12 or 13, M1. PARK: Easy. TEL: 01525 290950; e-mail - elfyngroves@tinyworld. co.uk. SER: Valuations; framing.

The Woburn Abbey Antiques Centre

MK17 9WA. Est. 1967. Open every day (including Bank Holidays) 10-5.30. CL: Christmas holidays. SIZE: Over 60 shops and showcases on two floors. *STOCK: English and Continental furniture, porcelain, glass, paintings, silver and decorative items.* Not Stocked: Reproduction items. LOC: Exits 12 and 13, M1. On A5 follow signs to Woburn Abbey and after entering grounds, follow signs, The Antiques Centre is in the South Courtyard. PARK: Easy. TEL: 01525 290350; fax - 01525 292102; e-mail - antiques@ woburnabbey.co.uk. SER: Carriage for large items; worldwide shipping.

Woburn Fine Arts

12 Market Place. MK17 9PZ. (Z. Bieganski). Est. 1983. Open Tues.-Sun. 2-5. SIZE: Medium. *STOCK: Post-impressionist paintings, 1880-1940; European paintings, 17th-18th C; British paintings, 20th C.* PARK: Easy. TEL: 01525 290624. SER: Restorations (oils and watercolours); framing.

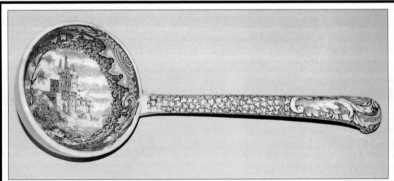

Copeland & Garrett, c.1840. Earthenware sauce ladle decorated with part of the blue printed pattern Byron's Views. (Private collection)

From an article entitled "Spode-Copeland-Spode Art & Design" by Vega Wilkinson which appeared in the March 2002 issue of **Antique Collecting**. For more details and to subscribe see page 21.

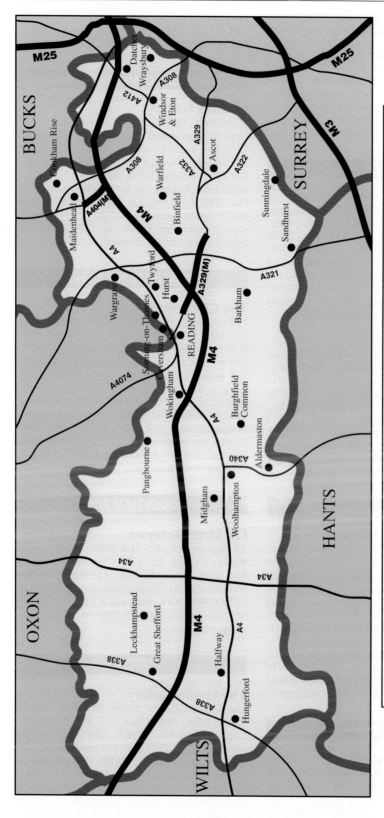

Dealers and Shops in Berkshire

Aldermaston		Caversham	1	Horton	
Ascot		Cookham Rise	2	Hungerford	14
Barkham		Datchet	1	Hurst	
Binfield		Great Shefford	1	Leckhampstead	1
Burghfield Common		Halfway	1	Maidenhead	1
				Midgham	1
				Pangbourne	1
				Reading	2
				Sandhurst	1

Sonning-on-Thames	1
Sunningdale	1
Twyford	1
Warfield	1
Wargrave	1
Windsor and Eton	17
Wokingham	1
Woolhampton	1
Wraysbury	2

ALDERMASTON, Nr. Reading

Aldermaston Antiques
The Old Dispensary. RG7 4LW. (Vivian and Roger Green). Est. 1994. Open 10-5.30. SIZE: Small + yard. *STOCK: Longcase clocks, furniture, lamps, desks, mainly 19th C; architectural and garden items.* LOC: A340, village centre. PARK: Easy and at rear. TEL: 01189 712370; home -same.

ASCOT

Melnick House of Ascot
16 Brockenhurst Rd. SL5 9DL. (Jackie Collins and Vic Day). Open 10-5, Sat. 10.30-4. CL: Mon. SIZE: Small. *STOCK: Furniture, 19th-20th C, £50-£2,000; maps and prints, 17th-19th C, £50-£2,000; decorative items, 18th-20th C, £20-£500.* LOC: 5 mins. from South Ascot station. PARK: Easy. TEL: 01344 297517; fax - 01344 291800; home - 01344 628383. SER: Restorations (furniture including upholstery and French polishing). VAT: Stan.

Omell Galleries
The Corner House, Course Rd. SL5 7HL. (Omell Galleries (Windsor) Ltd). Est. 1947. Open Tues.-Sat. 9.30-1 and 2-5 or by appointment. SIZE: Medium. *STOCK: Contemporary oils, £400-£6,000.* LOC: Off High St. opposite garage. PARK: Easy. TEL: 01344 873443; fax - 01344 873467; home - 01344 625958; e-mail - aomell@aol.com; website - www.omellgalleries.co.uk. SER: Valuations; restorations (cleaning, repair - oils, watercolours and frames). VAT: Spec.

BARKHAM, Nr. Wokingham

Barkham Antique Centre
Barkham St. RG40 4PJ. (Len and Mary Collins). Open 10.30-5 including Sun. SIZE: Large - 50+ dealers. *STOCK: General antiques including furniture, china, kitchenalia, coins, Dinky toys, paintings, glassware, scientific instruments and brass; collectables including Beswick, Moorcroft, Royal Doulton, Wade.* LOC: Off M4, junction 10, A329M to Wokingham, over station crossing to Barkham (B3349), left at Bull public house, centre 300 yds. on left. PARK: Easy. TEL: 0118 976 1355. SER: Valuations; restorations (china, French polishing, upholstery, cabinet making).

BINFIELD

Ulla Stafford Antiques   BADA
Binfield Lodge. RG42 5QB. Open by appointment. *STOCK: Georgian and Continental furniture; European ceramics, 17th-18th C.* TEL: 0118 934 3208; fax - same. FAIRS: Olympia (June). VAT: Spec.

BURGHFIELD COMMON, Nr. Reading

Graham Gallery
Highwoods. RG7 3BG. (J. Steeds). Est. 1976. Open by appointment at any time. SIZE: Medium. *STOCK: English watercolours, £50-£1,500; English oil paintings, £200-£8,000; English prints, £25-£200; mainly 19th to early 20th C.* LOC: 4 miles from Reading on Burghfield road. PARK: Easy. TEL: 0118 9832320; fax - 0118 9831070; e-mail - grahamgallery@freeuk.com; website - www.grahamgallery.freeuk.com. SER: Valuations; restorations (cleaning, framing).

CAVERSHAM, Nr. Reading

The Clock Workshop
17 Prospect St. RG4 8JB. (J. M. Yealland FBHI). LAPADA. TVADA. CINOA. Est. 1980. Open 9.30-5.30, Sat. 10-1. SIZE: Small. *STOCK: Clocks, late 17th to late 19th C, £350-£60,000; barometers, 18th-19th C, £500-£12,000.* LOC: Prospect St. is the beginning of main Reading to Henley road. PARK: Behind shop in North St. TEL: 0118 9470741; e-mail - theclockworkshop @supanet.com. SER: Valuations; restorations (clocks, barometers, chronometers, barographs); buys at auction. FAIRS: TVADA; LAPADA; Olympia. VAT: Stan/Spec.

COOKHAM RISE

Cookham Antiques
35 Station Parade. SL6 9BR. (Gary Lloyd Wallis). TVADA. Est. 1990. Open daily including Sun. SIZE: Large. *STOCK: Furniture including bookcases, desks, chests of drawers, 18th-20th C, £50-£1,000.* PARK: Easy and at rear. TEL: 01628 523224; mobile - 07778 020536. SER: Valuations; restorations.

DATCHET

The Studio Gallery
The Old Bank, The Green, SL3 9JH. (Julian Bettney). Est. 1990. Open 11-7, until 6 Sun. CL: Tues. am. and Fri. *STOCK: Fine paintings and prints, 1740-1940.* LOC: Off junction 5, M4, opposite Manor Hotel. PARK: Horton Rd. or railway station. TEL: 01753 544100; fax - same; mobile - 07770 762468; e-mail - Julianbettney@

talk21.com. SER: Landscape paintings in oils painted to commission; bespoke framing (hand built, coloured, gilded, marbled, veneered).

GREAT SHEFFORD, Nr. Hungerford

Alan Hodgson

No 2 Ivy House, Wantage Rd. RG16 7DA. *STOCK: Boxes, country and general antiques, collectors' items.* LOC: A338, 10 minutes from Hungerford towards Wantage. TEL: 01488 648172; e-mail - alanh.ivy@pop3.hiway.co.uk. SER: Restorations (furniture).

HALFWAY, Nr. Newbury

Alan Walker   BADA
Halfway Manor. RG20 8NR. TVADA. Open by appointment. SIZE: Large. STOCK: Fine barometers and weather instruments. LOC: 4 miles west of Newbury on A4. PARK: Easy. TEL: 01488 657670; mobile - 07770 728397; website - www.alanwalker-barometers.com. SER: Restorations.

HORTON, Nr. Windsor

John A. Pearson Antiques   BADA
Horton Lodge, Horton Rd. SL3 9NU. (Mrs J.C. Sinclair Hill). Est. 1902. By appointment only. SIZE: Large. STOCK: English and Continental furniture, 1700-1850, £50-£30,000; oil paintings, 17th-19th C, £50-£50,000; decorative objects. Not Stocked: Items after 19th C. LOC: From London turn off M4, exit 5, past London Airport; from M25 take exit 14. 10 mins from Heathrow. PARK: Easy. TEL: 01753 682136; fax - 01753 687151.

HUNGERFORD

Beedham Antiques Ltd   BADA
Charnham Close. RG17 0EJ. Open 10-5 or by appointment. STOCK: English oak furniture, 16th-18th C; objects and works of art. TEL: 01488 684141; fax - 01488 684050. VAT: Spec.

Below Stairs of Hungerford
103 High St. RG17 0NB. (S.L. Hofgartner). Est. 1974. Open 10-6, including Sun. and Bank Holidays. SIZE: Large. *STOCK: Kitchen and decorative garden items, bedroom furniture, lighting, collectables, sporting items and memorabilia, interior fittings and taxidermy, mainly 19th C English, £20-£2,500. Not Stocked: Reproductions.* LOC: Main street. PARK: Easy.

TEL: 01488 682317; fax - 01488 684294; e-mail - hofgartner@belowstairs. co.uk; website - www. belowstairs.co.uk. SER: Valuations. VAT: Stan.

Sir William Bentley Billiards (Antique Billiard Table Specialist Company)
Standen Manor Farm. RG17 0RB. Open by appointment seven days a week. SIZE: Large. *STOCK: Billiard tables, billiard/dining tables; antique and modern accessories including panelling and brass lights.* PARK: Easy. TEL: 01488 681711; 020 8940 1152; fax - 01488 685197; website - www.billiards.co.uk. SER: Restorations; removals and storage. FAIRS: House & Garden; Ideal Home; Period Living; Decorex.

Bow House
3-4 Faulkner Sq., Charnham St. RG17 0HH. (Jo Preston). Open 9.30-5.30, Sun. 10-4. SIZE: 2 floors. *STOCK: 18th-19th C furniture and decoratives, contemporary accessories and gifts.* LOC: First shop in Hungerford from Newbury A4. PARK: Own. TEL: 01488 680826. VAT: Spec.

The Fire Place (Hungerford) Ltd
Hungerford Old Fire Station, Charnham St. RG17 0EP. (E.B. and E.M. Smith). Est. 1976. Open 10-1.30 and 2.15-5. SIZE: Large. *STOCK: Fireplace furnishings and metalware especially fenders; paintings.* LOC: A4. TEL: 01488 683420. VAT: Stan/Spec.

Garden Art
Barrs Yard, 1 Bath Rd. RG17 0HE. (Susan and Arnie Knowles). Est. 1980. Open 10-6, Sun. 11-4. SIZE: Large. *STOCK: Period garden items.* PARK: Easy. TEL: 01488 681881; home - 01488 681882; website - www.bigbronze.co.uk. VAT: Stan/Spec.

Great Grooms of Hungerford
Riverside House, Charnham St. RG17 0EP. Open 9.30-5.30, Sun. 10-6. SIZE: Large. *STOCK: Wide variety of specialist dealers in 18th-19th C English and Continental town and country furniture, pottery and porcelain, silver and plate, works of art, metalware, glass, clocks, Oriental, oils and watercolours, prints, clocks and watches.* PARK: Easy. TEL: 01488 682314; fax - 01488 686677; e-mail - antiques@great-grooms.co.uk; website - www. great.grooms.co.uk. SER: Valuations; restorations (furniture including upholstery, pictures, silver, jewellery, ceramics). VAT: Spec.

Hungerford Arcade
High St. RG17 0NF. (Wynsave Investments Ltd). Est. 1972. Open 9.30-5.30, Sun. 11-5. SIZE: Over 80 stallholders. *STOCK: General antiques and period furniture.* PARK: Easy. TEL: 01488 683701.

Roger King Antiques
111 High St. RG17 0NB. (Mr and Mrs R.F. King). Est. 1974. Open 9.30-5. SIZE: Large. *STOCK: Furniture, 1750-1910, £100-£2,000; china, 19th C; oil paintings.* Not Stocked: Silver, jewellery. LOC: Opposite Hungerford Arcade. PARK: Easy. TEL: 01488 682256; website - www.king antiques.co.uk. VAT: Spec.

The Old Malthouse   BADA
15 Bridge St. RG17 0EG. (P.F. Hunwick). CINOA. Est. 1963. Open 10-5.30. SIZE: Large. *STOCK: 18th to early 19th C walnut and mahogany furniture - dining tables, sets of chairs, mirrors, chests of drawers; clocks, barometers, decorative items and glass.* Not Stocked: Orientalia. LOC: A338, left at Bear Hotel, shop is approx. 120 yds. on left, just before bridge. PARK: Front of premises. TEL: 01488 682209; fax - same; e-mail - hunwick@oldmalthouse30 .freeserve.co.uk. SER: Valuations. VAT: Spec.

Principia Fine Art
35A High St. RG17 0NF. (Michael Forrer). Est. 1970. Open 9.30-5.30. *STOCK: Collectors items, scientific instruments, maritime, country furniture, treen, pictures, Oriental china, porcelain, books and clocks.* TEL: 01488 682873. FAIRS: Scientific Instrument.

Styles Silver
12 Bridge St. RG17 0EH. (P. and D. Styles). LAPADA. Est. 1974. Open 9.30-5.30, other times by appointment. SIZE: Medium. *STOCK: Antique, Victorian and secondhand silver including cutlery.* PARK: Easy. TEL: 01488 683922; home - same; fax - 01488 683488; mobile - 07778 769559; e-mail - dpgstyles@btinternet.com; website - www.styles-silver.co.uk. SER: Repairs; finder.

Turpins Antiques   BADA
17 Bridge St. RG17 0EG. (Jane Sumner). LAPADA. CINOA. Open Wed., Fri. and Sat. or by appointment. SIZE: Small. *STOCK: 17th-18th C walnut, oak and mahogany furniture and metalware.* TEL: 01488 681886; home - 01672 870727. FAIRS: Olympia. VAT: Spec.

Youll's Antiques
27 and 28 Charnham St. RG17 0EJ. (B. Youll). Est. 1935. Open 10.30-5.30, Sun. 11-5. *STOCK: French and English furniture and decorative items.* TEL: 01488 682046; fax - 01488 684335; e-mail - bruce.youll@talk21.com; website - www.youll.com. FAIRS: Newark.

HURST, Nr. Reading

Peter Shepherd Antiques
Penfold, Lodge Rd. RG10 0EG. Est. 1962. Open by appointment only. *STOCK: Glass, rarities and books.* TEL: 0118 934 0755.

LECKHAMPSTEAD, Nr. Newbury

Hill Farm Antiques
Hill Farm, Shop Lane. RG20 8QG. (Mike Beesley). Open 9-5, Sun. by appointment. *STOCK: 19th C dining tables, chairs and library furniture.* LOC: Off B4494 between Stag public house and church. PARK: Own at rear. TEL: 01488 638541/638361. SER: Restorations; shipping arranged; buys at auction.

MAIDENHEAD

Widmerpool House Antiques
7 Lower Cookham Rd., Boulters Lock. SL6. Open by appointment only. *STOCK: English furniture, oil paintings, watercolours, prints; porcelain and Swansea pottery, glass, silver, 18th-19th C.* PARK: Nearby. TEL: 01628 623752.

MIDGHAM, Nr. Reading

Berkshire Antiques Centre
Unit 1 Kennetholme Farm Buildings, Bath Rd. RG7 5UX. (J. Bradley). Est. 1996. Open 10.30-4.30 including Sun. CL: Wed. SIZE: Medium. *STOCK: Antique and reproduction furniture, smalls including china, glass and collectables; garden art and artifacts.* LOC: A4 London to Newbury road. PARK: Easy. TEL: 01189 710477; fax - same. FAIRS: Ardingly, Kempton.

PANGBOURNE

Rita Butler
4a Station Rd. RG8 7AN. TVADA. Est. 1999. Open 10-5. *STOCK: General antiques including brass and bronze; early 19th C to early 20th C ceramics especially Art Deco; glass, early 1800's.* PARK: Opposite. TEL: 0118 984 5522; mobile - 07752 936327. FAIRS: TVADA; Thames.

READING

Rupert Landen Antiques
Church Farm, Reading Rd., Woodcote. RG8 0QX. TVADA. Open by appointment only. *STOCK: Late 18th to early 19th C furniture.* TEL: 01491 682396; mobile - 07974 732472.

P.D. Leatherland Antiques
68 London St. RG1 4SQ. (Susan, Paul and Peter Leatherland). Est. 1970. Open 9-6, Sun. 10-5.30. SIZE: Large. *STOCK: Furniture, 18th C to 1920's; decorative china, clocks, metalware, mirrors and pictures, £5-£4,000.* LOC: 1/2 mile from station. PARK: Easy. TEL: 0118 958 1960. VAT: Stan/Spec.

SANDHURST

Berkshire Metal Finishers Ltd
3 Factory, Vulcan Close. GU47 9DD. (J.A. and Mrs. J. Sturgeon). Est. 1957. Open 8-1 and 2-6, Sat. 8-1 and 2-4, Sun. 9-1. SIZE: Large. *STOCK: Brass, copper and steel metalware; silver plate.* LOC: Off A30 towards Wokingham on A321, after 1.25 miles turn left into Swan Lane, estate 1st turning right, last factory near car park. PARK: Easy. TEL: 01252 873475; fax - 01252 875434. SER: Restorations (metalware polishing and lacquering).

SONNING-ON-THAMES

Cavendish Fine Arts   **BADA**
The Dower House. RG4 6UL. (Janet Middlemiss and Guy Hazel). LAPADA. TVADA. Est. 1972. Open by appointment only. *STOCK: Fine Queen Anne and English Georgian furniture, glass and porcelain.* TEL: 01189 691904; mobile - 07831 295575. SER: Valuations; shipping; interior decoration. FAIRS: Olympia; Chelsea; BADA; TVADA. VAT: Stan/Spec.

SUNNINGDALE

The Coworth Gallery
9 Coworth Rd. SL5 0NX. (Stephen Paddon). Est. 1985. Open most times, subject to a 'phone call. SIZE: Small. *STOCK: Garden ornaments, French country furniture, large pots, statuary, decorative items.* LOC: Turn right into Bedford Lane off A30 from London, after I Gladiatori. PARK: Easy. TEL: 01344 626532; mobile - 07831 182076. SER: Restorations; garden design.

TWYFORD, Nr. Reading

Bell Antiques
2B High St. RG10 9AE. (Nigel, Chris and Russell Timms). Est. 1989. Open 9.30-5.30, Sun. 10-5.30. SIZE: Small. *STOCK: General antiques including china and glass, silver and plate, small furniture, 18th-20th C, £10-£300.* LOC: Village centre on crossroads. PARK: Nearby. TEL: 0118 934 2501. VAT: Spec.

WARFIELD

Moss End Antique Centre
Moss End Garden Centre. RG12 6EJ. TVADA. Est. 1988. Open 10.30-5. CL: Mon. SIZE: Large - 25 dealers. *STOCK: General antiques and collectables.* LOC: A3095. PARK: Own. TEL: 01344 861942. FAIRS: TVADA (Spring and Autumn).

WARGRAVE

John Connell - Wargrave Antiques
66 High St. RG10 8BY. Est. 1979. Open Wed.-Sun. other times by appointment. SIZE: Large - several dealers. *STOCK: Furniture, Georgian-Edwardian; small items, china, glass, metal.* PARK: Nearby. TEL: 01189 402914. SER: Restorations (furniture); silver plating; metal polishing.

Ferry Antiques
70 High St. RG10 8BY. (Kate and Peter Turner). Est. 1982. Open 10-5.30, Sun. 10.30-4.30. CL: Mon. and Tues. SIZE: Medium. *STOCK: Furniture, 18th-19th C, £250-£5,000; glass and porcelain, 18th-19th C, £25-£500; silver and plate, 19th C, £50-£1,000.* LOC: At crossroads. PARK: 100 yards. TEL: 01189 404415; e-mail - kasiapj@aol.com. SER: Valuations; restorations (furniture and clocks). FAIRS: East Berkshire Antiques, Burchetts Green.

WINDSOR AND ETON

Art & Antiques and Bridge Miniatures
69 High St., Eton. SL4 6AA. (Vivien and Eddie Rand). Est. 1982. Open 10.30-5.30, Sat. 10.30-6, Sun. 2.30-6. SIZE: Medium. *STOCK: Collectors' items, jewellery, furniture, dolls house miniatures, from Victorian, £1-£600.* LOC: Ist shop over Thames from Windsor at Eton. PARK: Nearby. TEL: 01753 855727; home - 01628 527127. SER: Restorations (furniture, dolls houses, jewellery).

Roger Barnett Antiques
91 High St., Eton. SL4 6AF. Est. 1975. Open by appointment. *STOCK: Mahogany furniture and clocks.* TEL: 01753 867785/541861.

Berkshire Antiques Co Ltd
42 Thames St., Windsor. SL4 1YY. Est. 1980. Open 10.30-5.30 including Sun. (Jan. to April - Sun. by appointment). SIZE: Large. *STOCK: Antique and modern designer jewellery; general antiques, china, porcelain and glass, silver and plate, Royal commemoratives, toys and dolls,*

£10-£25,000. LOC: Opposite George Vth memorial fountain. PARK: Nearby. TEL: 01753 830100; fax - 01753 832278; e-mail - sales@jewels2go.co.uk; website - www.jewels2go.co.uk. SER: Valuations; repairs.

Dee's Antique Pine
89 Grove Rd. SL4 1HT. (Dee Waghorn). Est. 1975. Open 10.30-6, other times by appointment. *STOCK: 19th C pine furniture.* TEL: 01753 865627; mobile - 07711 902887.

Eton Antique Bookshop
88 High St., Eton. SL4 6AF. TEL: 01753 855534.

Eton Antiques Partnership
80 High St., Eton. SL4 6AF. (Mark Procter). Est. 1967. Open 10-5, Sun. 11-5.30. SIZE: Large. *STOCK: Mahogany and rosewood furniture, 18th-19th C.* LOC: Slough East exit from M4 westbound. PARK: Nearby. TEL: 01753 860752; home - same. SER: Exporting; interior design consultants. VAT: Stan/Spec.

Eton Gallery
(Josephine Smith). LAPADA. By appointment only. *STOCK: Fine 18th to early 19th C furniture.* TEL: 01753 860963.

Marcelline Herald Antiques
41 High St., Eton. SL4 6BD. LAPADA, TVADA. Est. 1993. Open Tues.,Thurs., Fri. and Sat. 10-5, other days by appointment. SIZE: Medium. *STOCK: Furniture, £500-£15,000; mirrors, pelmets and screens, £200-£2,500; ceramics, lamps and prints, £50-£1,000; all 18th to early 19th C.* PARK: Loading only. TEL: 01753 833924; fax - 0118 971 4683; home - same; e-mail - marcelline.herald@virgin.net. FAIRS: TVADA; Decorative Antiques and Textiles. VAT: Spec.

J. Manley
27 High St., Eton. SL4 6AX. Est. 1891. Open 10-5. *STOCK: Watercolours, old prints.* TEL: 01753 865647. SER: Restorations; framing, mounting.

Peter J. Martin
40 High St., Eton. SL4 6BD. TVADA. Est. 1963. Open 9-1 and 2-5. CL: Sun. SIZE: Large and warehouse. *STOCK: Period, Victorian and decorative furniture and furnishings, £50-£20,000; metalware, £10-£500, all from 1800.* PARK: 50yds. opposite. TEL: 01753 864901; home - 01753 863987. SER: Restorations; shipping arranged; buys at auction. VAT: Stan/Spec.

Mostly Boxes
93 High St., Eton. SL4 6AF. (G.S. Munday). Est. 1977. Open 10-6.30. *STOCK: Wooden, mother of*

pearl and tortoiseshell boxes. PARK: 100 yds. TEL: 01753 858470. SER: Restorations (boxes). VAT: Spec.

O'Connor Brothers
Trinity Yard, 59 St. Leonards Rd., Windsor. SL4 3BX. (Bernard O'Connor). Est. 1970. Open 10-5.30. *STOCK: Furniture and general antiques.* LOC: 5 Minutes from the castle. PARK: Easy. TEL: 01753 866732/869852. SER: Restorations; upholstery. VAT: Stan.

Oriental Rug Gallery Ltd
115-116 High St., Eton. SL4 6AN. (Richard Mathias and Julian Blair). BORDA. Open 10-5. *STOCK: Russian, Afghan, Turkish and Persian carpets, rugs and kelims; Oriental objets d'art.* PARK: Behind showroom. TEL: 01753 623000; fax - same; e-mail - rugs@orientalruggallery.com; website - www.orientalruggallery.com.

Rules Antiques
62 St Leonard's Rd. SL4 3BY. (Sue Rule and Kathryn Cale). Open 10.30-6. *STOCK: Lighting, door furniture, period fixtures & fittings; unusual small furniture.* LOC: Next to Arts Centre. TEL: 01753 833210.

Studio 101
101 High St., Eton. SL4 6AF. (Anthony Cove). Est. 1959. SIZE: Medium. *STOCK: Mahogany furniture, some 18th C, mainly 19th C, £50-£1,000; brass, silver plate, 19th C, £10-£200.* LOC: Walk over Windsor Bridge from Windsor and Eton Riverside railway station. PARK: Public, at rear of premises. TEL: 01753 863333.

Times Past Antiques
59 High St., Eton. SL4 6BL. (P. Jackson). MBHI. Est. 1970. Open 10-6, Sun. 12-5. SIZE: Medium. *STOCK: Clocks and music boxes, £100-£3,000; furniture, all 18th-19th C; silver, 19th C, £5-£500.* PARK: Reasonable. TEL: 01753 857018; home - same. SER: Valuations; restorations (clocks and watches); buys at auction (clocks). VAT: Stan/Spec.

Turks Head Antiques
98 High St., Eton. SL4 6AF. Open 10-5. CL: Mon. *STOCK: Silver and plate, porcelain, glass and interesting collectables.* TEL: 01753 863939.

WOKINGHAM

Wokingham Antiques Centre
152 London Rd. RG40 1SU. (Janice Charlton). Est. 1998. Open 10.30-5.30, 1st Sun. monthly 10.30-4.30, other times by appointment. CL: Wed. SIZE: Small. *STOCK: Furniture, 18th C to 1950's, £50-£2,500; curios, £1-£1,000; porcelain, pottery and silver, to modern collectables, £1-£500.* LOC: Off A329, follow signs for town centre, first shop on right opposite St. Crispin's school. PARK: Easy. TEL: 0118 9790202; e-mail - wokingham.antiques@btinternet.com. SER: Restorations (caning, small upholstery, wood); buys at auction.

WOOLHAMPTON, Nr. Reading

The Old Bakery Antiques
Bath Rd. RG7 5RE. (S. Everard). Resident. Est. 1969. *STOCK: Furniture, objets d'art, collectors' items, general antiques.* TEL: 0118 9712116.

WRAYSBURY

Wyrardisbury Antiques
23 High St. TW19 5DA. (C. Tuffs). Est. 1978. Open 10-5. CL: Mon. except by appointment. SIZE: Small. *STOCK: Clocks, £100-£6,000; barometers, small furniture, £100-£1,500.* LOC: A376 from Staines by-pass (A30) or from junction 5 M4/A4 via B470, then B376. PARK: Easy. TEL: 01784 483225. SER: Restorations (clocks).

The top drawer of a serpentine chest, fitted with a hinged mirror supported by a ratchet, and thirteen lidded compartments. (Sotheby's)

When paying a return visit to Alice at her Virtual Antiques Emporium in search of a chest of drawers, Peter Philp is offered some basic information. From an article entitled "Choosing a Chest of Drawers" which appeared in the November 2001 issue of **Antique Collecting**. For more details and to subscribe see page 21.

The Cupboard Antiques
80 High St., Old Amersham. HP7 0DS. (N. Lucas). LAPADA. Est. 1965. Open 10-5. CL: Fri. SIZE: 4 showrooms. *STOCK: Georgian, Regency and early Victorian furniture and decorative items.* PARK: Easy. TEL: 01494 722882. FAIRS: Olympia (June).

Michael and Jackie Quilter
38 High St. HP7 0DJ. Est. 1970. Open 10-5. *STOCK: General antiques, stripped pine, copper, brass, unusual objects.* PARK: Easy. TEL: 01494 433723. VAT: Stan.

Sundial Antiques
19 Whielden St. HP7 0HU. (A. and Mrs M.Macdonald). Est. 1970. Open 9.30-5.30. CL: Thurs. SIZE: Small. *STOCK: English and European brass, copper, metalware, fireplace equipment, 18th-19th C, £5-£500; small period furniture, 1670-1910, £25-£1,500; horse brasses, £10-£300; decorative items, 1750-1910, £5-£500; pottery, porcelain, curios, pre-1914, £10-£750.* Not Stocked: Jewellery, clocks, coins, oil paintings, stamps, books, silver, firegrates. LOC: On A404, in Old Town 200yds. from High St. on right; from High Wycombe, 500yds. from hospital on left. PARK: Easy. TEL: 01494 727955.

Buck House Antique Centre
47 Wycombe End, Old Town. HP9 1LZ. (C. and B. Whitby). Est. 1979. Open 10-5, Sun. 12-5. CL: Wed. SIZE: Medium - 10 dealers. *STOCK: Wide variety of general antiques including English and Oriental porcelain, clocks, barometers, oak and mahogany furniture, stripped pine, boxes and beds, to 1930's, £5-£5,000.* LOC: A40. PARK: Easy. TEL: 01494 670714; e-mail - bachantiques@supanet.com. SER: Valuations.

June Elsworth - Beaconsfield Ltd
Clover House, 16 London End. HP9 2JH. (Mrs J. Elsworth). Est. 1983. CL: Mon. SIZE: Small. *STOCK: Fine English furniture, 18th-19th C; decorative accessories and silver, 19th C.* LOC: In old town, on A40. PARK: Easy. TEL: 01494 675611; fax - 01494 671273. VAT: Spec.

Grosvenor House Interiors
51 Wycombe End, Beaconsfield Old Town. HP9 1LX. (T.I. Marriott). Est. 1970. Open 10-1 and 2-5. CL: Wed. SIZE: Large. *STOCK: 18th-19th C furniture especially upholstered and mid-19th C walnut; fireplaces and accessories; 19th C watercolours and oils.* PARK: Easy. TEL: 01494 677498. SER: Interior architectural design, fireplace specialists. VAT: Stan/Spec.

Period Furniture Showrooms
49 London End. HP9 2HW. (R.E.W. Hearne and N.J. Hearne). TVADA. Est. 1965. Open Mon.-Sat. 9-5.30. SIZE: Large. *STOCK: Furniture, 1700-1900, £50-£5,000.* LOC: A40 Beaconsfield Old Town. PARK: Own. TEL: 01494 674112; fax - 01494 681046; e-mail - sales@periodfurniture.net; website - www.periodfurniture.net. SER: Restorations (furniture). VAT: Stan/Spec.

The Spinning Wheel
86 London End. HP9 2JD. (Mrs M. Royle). Est. 1945. Open 9.30-4.30. CL: Mon. and Wed. *STOCK: English furniture, 18th-19th C, mahogany and oak items, porcelain, glass.* TEL: 01494 673055; home - 01494 873294.

Bourne End Antiques Centre
67 The Parade. SL8 5SB. (S. Shepheard). Est. 1995. Open 10-5.30, Sun. 12-4. SIZE: Large. *STOCK: Furniture - pine, £100-£900, darkwood, £100-£800; both from 19th C; china and glass, £1-£250.* LOC: A4155, 2 miles from Marlow. PARK: Easy. TEL: 01628 533298; home - 01300 320125. VAT: Stan.

La Maison
The Crossings, Cores End Rd. SL8 5AL. (Jeremy D. Pratt). Est. 1995. Open 9.30-5.30, Mon. 1-5, Sat. 10-5.30, Sun. 11-5. SIZE: Medium. *STOCK: French antiques including beds and chandeliers, 19th C, to £1,000.* LOC: Take Marlow by-pass from junction 3, M40. PARK: Easy. TEL: 01628 525858; fax - 01494 670363. SER: Valuations; restorations (re-upholstery). FAIRS: Burchetts Green. VAT: Stan/Spec.

Buckingham Antiques Centre
5 West St. MK18 1HL. (Peter Walton). Est. 1975. Open 9.15-5.30, Sat. 9-5.30, Wed. and Sun. by appointment. SIZE: Medium. *STOCK: Furniture, 19th C, £50-£1,000; clocks, 18th-20th C, £50-£2,000; general antiques, £2-£500.* LOC: On A422 towards Brackley, near town centre. PARK: Nearby. TEL: 01280 824464; home - same. SER: Valuations; restorations (clocks).

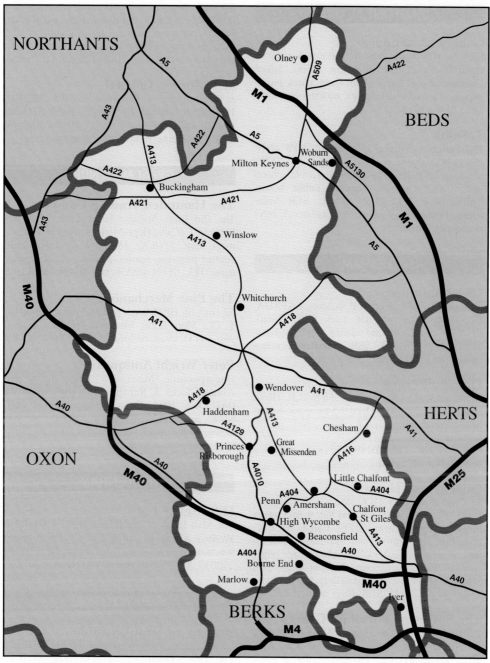

Dealers and Shops in Buckinghamshire

Amersham	3	Great Missenden	3	Milton Keynes	1
Beaconsfield	5	Haddenham	1	Olney	4
Bourne End	2	High Wycombe	2	Penn	2
Buckingham	1	Iver	1	Princes Risborough	1
Chalfont St. Giles	2	Little Chalfont	1	Wendover	3
Chesham	6	Marlow	3	Whitchurch	1
				Winslow	1

CHALFONT ST. GILES

Gallery 23 Antiques
High St. HP9 4QH. (Mrs A. Vollaro). Est. 1991. Open 10-5. *STOCK: Furniture, clocks, silver, Continental and English porcelain, glass, paintings, prints and watercolours, tapestry cushions.* TEL: 01494 871512.

T. Smith
The Furniture Village, London Rd. HP8 4NN. Est. 1982. Open 10-5 including Sun. SIZE: Medium. *STOCK: Antique pine and architectural items.* LOC: Opposite Pheasant public house. PARK: Easy. TEL: 01494 873031. SER: Valuations; restorations (including upholstery); buys at auction (furniture).

CHESHAM

Chess Antiques
85 Broad St. HP5 3EF. (M.P. Wilder). LAPADA. Est. 1966. Open 9-5, Sat. 10-5. SIZE: Small. *STOCK: Furniture and clocks.* PARK: Easy. TEL: 01494 783043. SER: Valuations; restorations. VAT: Stan/Spec.

Omniphil Prints
Germains Lodge, Fullers Hill. HP5 1LR. (Ross Muddiman). Est. 1953. Open 9-5 by appointment. SIZE: Warehouse. *STOCK: Rare prints on all subjects and Illustrated London News from 1842.* PARK: Easy. TEL: 01494 771851; e-mail - omniphil@talk21.com.

Queen Anne House
57 Church St. HP5 1HY. (Miss A.E. Jackson). Est. 1918. Open Wed., Fri. and Sat. 9.30-5, other times by appointment. SIZE: Large. *STOCK: Furniture, decorative and furnishing pieces, porcelain figures, other china, glass, silver plate, copper, brass, Victoriana, Persian rugs. Not Stocked: Silver, weapons, jewellery.* PARK: Easy. TEL: 01494 783811. SER: Buys at auction.

The Sovereign Furniture Gallery
115 High St. HP5 1DE. (Mr and Mrs Leadbeater). Est. 1999. Open 10-5.30, Sun. 12-4. CL: Wed. SIZE: Large. *STOCK: Furniture, 18th to early 20th C, £25-£1,500.* LOC: A41 - Chesham turning on to A416 to High St. PARK: Nearby. TEL: 01494 783103. SER: Valuations; restorations (furniture including upholstery). FAIRS: NEC; Milton Keynes Centre.

Stuff and Nonsense
68-70 Broad St. HP5. (Elaine and Helen Robb). Open 9.30-5.30, Sun. 11-5.30. SIZE: Medium.

STOCK: General antiques and collectables - furniture including reproduction mahogany, books, commemoratives, records and clocks. LOC: Just out of High St., on main road. PARK: Easy and at rear. TEL: 01494 775988; fax - same.

M.V. Tooley, CMBHI
at Chess Antiques, 85 Broad St. HP5 3EF. Est. 1960. Open 9-6, Sat. 10-5. SIZE: Small. *STOCK: Clocks and barometers.* TEL: 01494 783043. SER: Valuations; restorations; spare parts.

GREAT MISSENDEN

The Hampden Trading Company
The Old Barn, Solinger Farm, Little Hampden. HP16 9PT. (Callie Hope-Morley). Open by appointment only. *STOCK: 18th-19th C country and painted furniture, textiles, pictures and decorative items.* TEL: 01494 488538; fax - 01494 488818.

The Pine Merchants
52 High St. HP16 0AU. (Mrs J. Peters). Open 10-5. CL: Mon. SIZE: Medium. *STOCK: Stripped pine and Victorian bedsteads.* TEL: 01494 862002.

Peter Wright Antiques
(Incorporating Missenden Restorations and Abbey Clocks & Repairs), 32b High St. HP16 0AU. Est. 1992. Open by appointment only. SIZE: Small. *STOCK: Clocks, curios and furniture.* LOC: A413. TEL: 01494 891330. SER: Restorations; clock repairs.

HADDENHAM

H.S. Wellby Ltd
The Malt House, Church End. HP17 8AH. (C.S. Wellby). ABPR. Est. 1820. Open by appointment 9-6. *STOCK: 18th-19th C paintings.* TEL: 01844 290036. SER: Restorations. VAT: Spec.

HIGH WYCOMBE

Browns' of West Wycombe
Church Lane, West Wycombe. HP14 3AH. Est. Pre 1900. Open 8-5.30. CL: Sat. *STOCK: Furniture.* LOC: On A40 approximately 3 miles west of High Wycombe on Oxford Rd. PARK: Easy. TEL: 01494 524537; fax - 01494 439548. SER: Restorations and hand-made copies of period chairs.

Windmill Fine Art
2 Windmill Drive, Widmer End. HP15 6BD. (Ray White). Open by appointment only. *STOCK: Fine*

DERBY PORCELAIN

1748-1848

John Twitchett

- *Certain to establish itself as the standard work on the Derby factory*

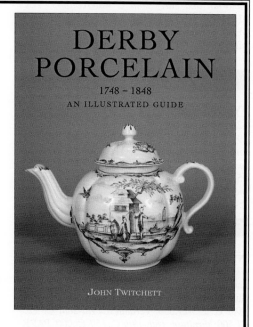

Derby Porcelain contains a good deal of new information and a large quantity of hitherto unpublished illustrations. Much of the documentary evidence is also published for the first time, including an illustrated twenty page appendix of cup shapes.

The author deals comprehensively with the Nottingham Road, Derby factory, its staff and its wares, with detailed biographies on anyone and everyone connected with production and sales during the period 1748-1848.

John Twitchett has specialised in the history of Derby porcelain and china for more than thirty years and is the leading authority on the Derby China Works. He has been Curator of the Royal Crown Derby Museum since 1982. Published works include numerous articles for antiques magazines and specialist journals and titles comprise *Derby Porcelain; Landscapes on Derby and Worcester Porcelain* (with Henry Sandon); *Royal Crown Derby* (with Betty Bailey); *Painters and the Derby China Works* (with John Murdoch). He also produced the catalogue for an exhibition staged at the Victoria and Albert Museum in 1987.

Specifications: **320pp., 256 col. illus., 217 b.&w. illus. 11x8¼in./279x216mm. £45.00**

Available from the
ANTIQUE COLLECTORS' CLUB
Sandy Lane, Old Martlesham,
Woodbridge, Suffolk IP12 4SD, UK.
For your free copy of the catalogue:
Tel: **01394 389950** or Fax: **01394 389999**
Email: sales@antique-acc.com
Website: www.antique-acc.com

Victorian and early 20th C watercolours. TEL: 01494 713757; fax - same; mobile - 07885 370408. SER: Valuations; commission search. FAIRS: Most major.

IVER

"Yester-year"
12 High St. SL0 9NG. (P.J. Frost). Resident. Est. 1969. Open 10-6. SIZE: Small. *STOCK: Furniture, porcelain, pottery, glass, metalwork, 18th to early 20th C.* PARK: Easy. TEL: 01753 652072. SER: Valuations; restorations (furniture, pictures); framing; buys at auction.

LITTLE CHALFONT

Nightingale Antiques
17 Nightingale's Corner. HP7 9PZ. (Lee Andreou and Alan Truss). Est. 1995. Open Tues.-Sat. 10-5.30, Sun. 10-4. SIZE: Medium. *STOCK: Silver, 18th-19th C, £25-£1,500; ceramics, 19th-20th C, £25-£1,500; furniture, 18th-19th C, £50-£5,000.* PARK: Easy. TEL: 01494 762163. SER: Valuations; restorations (silver plating, furniture and ceramics).

MARLOW

Glade Antiques   BADA
(Sonia Vaughan). LAPADA. CINOA. Open by appointment only. *STOCK: Fine Oriental ceramics, bronzes and jades: Chinese items from Han, Tang, Song, Ming and Quing periods; Japanese items - mainly Kakiemon, Nabeshima, Kutani, Satsuma and Imari; also Korean Koryo, Yi and Choson periods.* TEL: 01628 487255; fax - 01628 487255; mobile - 07771 552328; e-mail - sonia@gladeantiques. com; website - www.gladeantiques.com. FAIRS: BADA; Olympia; LAPADA; NEC; Harrogate.

Jack Harness Antiques
Westfield Farm, Henley Rd., Medmenham. SL7. Est. 1981. Open 9-5 or by appointment. SIZE: Large warehouse. *STOCK: Pine and country furniture, especially period pine and original painted French provincial furniture.* PARK: Easy. TEL: 01491 410691; fax - same; mobile - 07768 666833; home - 01628 471775. SER: Restorations; courier. VAT: Stan/Spec. *Mainly Trade.*

Marlow Antique Centre
35 Station Rd. SL7 1NW. TVADA. Est. 1995. Open 10.30-5, Sun. 11-4. SIZE: 30+ dealers. *STOCK: 18th-20th C furniture, collectors' china from Worcester to Clarice Cliff, Staffordshire figures and*

dogs, chandeliers, silver, decorative glass, writing slopes, tea caddies, postcards, pens, cuff-links, equestrian items, jewellery. LOC: Town centre. PARK: Nearby. TEL: 01628 473223; fax - 01628 478989. SER: International shipping and packing.

MILTON KEYNES

Temple Lighting (Jeanne Temple Antiques)
Stockwell House, Wavendon. MK17 8LS. Est. 1968. Open 10-5, Sun. by appointment. CL: Mon. SIZE: Medium. *STOCK: Victorian, Edwardian and 1930's light fittings; 19th C furniture; decorative items.* LOC: Just off A5130 Woburn Sands to Newport Pagnell road. PARK: Easy. TEL: 01908 583597; fax - 01908 281149. FAIRS: Luton; Mid-Beds.

OLNEY

The Antiques Centre at Olney
13 Osborns Court, Off High Street South. MK46 4LA. (Robert Sklar). Open 10-5, Sun. 12-5. CL: Mon. SIZE: Large, 50 dealers. *STOCK: General antiques, furniture, porcelain.* LOC: Town centre. PARK: Easy. TEL: 01234 710942; fax - 01234 710947.

Archer's Antique and Country Furniture
19 High St. MK46 4EB. (Katherine Haslam and Neil Carter). Est. 1999. Open 10-5, Sun. 2-5. CL: Wed. SIZE: Medium. *STOCK: 19th C English and Continental pine, mahogany, French and upholstered furniture, to £2,000.* LOC: Past market square on A509. PARK: Easy. TEL: 01234 713050; fax - same. SER: Restorations. VAT: Stan/Spec.

Pine Antiques
10 Market Place. MK46 4EA. (Linda Wilkinson). Est. 1976. Open 10-5, Sat. 9.30-5.30, Sun. 12-5. SIZE: 3 floors. *STOCK: Pine furniture, antique and reclaimed.* PARK: Easy. TEL: 01234 711065; 01908 510226; e-mail - pine-antiques@hotmail.com.

Robin Unsworth Antiques
1 Weston Rd. MK46 5BD. (R. and Z. M. Unsworth). Est. 1971. Open 9-5, Sun. 9-4.30. SIZE: Small. *STOCK: Longcase and wall clocks, £500-£15,000; period and Victorian furniture, £1,000-£10,000; objects of art, £200-£5,000.* LOC: 6 miles from junction 14, M1. PARK: Easy. TEL: 01234 711210; home - 01908 617193. VAT: Spec.

ANTIQUES AT...WENDOVER
Datelined Antiques Centre
Established 1987
30 dealers offering quality town and country
antiques in a period building.
Garden antiques & car park

Monday – Saturday 10-5.30 Sundays & B. Hols 11-5.00

The Old Post Office, 25 High Street, Wendover, Bucks HP22 6DU
Tel: 01296 625335   www.antiquesatwendover.co.uk
Email: antiques@antiquesatwendover.co.uk

PENN, Nr. High Wycombe

Country Furniture Shop
3 Hazlemere Rd., Potters Cross. HP10 8AA. (M. and
V. Thomas). LAPADA. Est. 1955. Open 9.30-1 and
2-5. SIZE: Large. *STOCK: Furniture, Georgian,
£100-£5,000; Victoriana, £5-£2,500; large Victorian
dining tables, Victorian dining chairs.* LOC: B474.
PARK: Easy. TEL: 01494 812244; home - same.
SER: Valuations. VAT: Stan/Spec.

Penn Barn
By the Pond, Elm Rd. HP10 8LB. (P. J. M. Hunnings).
Est. 1968. Open Tues.-Sat.10.30-4, (sometimes closed
1-2). SIZE: Medium. *STOCK: Antiquarian books,
maps and prints, 19th C, £5-£500; watercolours and
oils, 19th-20th C, £50-£1,500.* LOC: B474. PARK:
Easy. TEL: 01494 815691.

PRINCES RISBOROUGH

Well Cottage Antiques Centre
20-22 Bell St. HP27 0AD. Open 9.30-5.30, Sun.
and Bank Holidays 1-5. SIZE: Medium. *STOCK:
Furniture including pine; silver, jewellery, china,
glass, brass, copper, silhouettes, miniatures,
treen, pictures and collectables.* LOC: A4010.
TEL: 01844 342002.

WENDOVER

Antiques at . . .Wendover Antiques Centre
The Old Post Office, 25 High St. HP22 6DU. (N.
Gregory). Est. 1987. Open 10-5.30, Sun. and Bank
Holidays 11-5. SIZE: Large - 30 dealers + barn
housing. *STOCK: General antiques dateline
1940/50 - town and country furniture, flatware,
kitchenalia, gardenalia, pottery and porcelain,
jewellery, Art Deco, Belleek, silver, lamps and
lighting, clocks, barometers, telescopes, scientific
and medical instruments, beds and bathroom*
*fittings, decorative items, glass, metalware, lace and
linen, garden statuary, architectural salvage and
antiquities.* LOC: A431. PARK: Own. TEL: 01296
625335; fax - 01296 620401; e-mail - antiques@
antiquesatwendover.co.uk; website - www.antiques
atwendover.co.uk. SER: Restorations (china,
furniture); metal polishing.

Bowood Antiques
Wendover Dean Farm, Bowood Lane. HP22 6PY.
(Miss P. Peyton-Jones). LAPADA. Est. 1963.
Open 9.30-5, Sat. 10-4.30 - prior telephone call
advisable. SIZE: Large. *STOCK: Period fur-
niture, 17th-19th C, £500-£10,000; decorative
items, £50-£1,500.* LOC: A413, midway between
Amersham and Aylesbury and Gt Missenden and
Wendover. PARK: Easy. TEL: 01296 622113;
home/fax - 01296 696598. VAT: Spec.

Sally Turner Antiques
Hogarth House, High St. HP22 6DU. LAPADA.
TVADA. Open 10-5. CL: Wed. and Sun. except
Dec. SIZE: 7 showrooms + barn. *STOCK: Decorative and period furniture, general antiques and
jewellery.* PARK: Rear of shop. TEL: 01296
624402; fax - same; mobile - 07860 201718.

WHITCHURCH

Deerstalker Antiques
28 High St. HP22 4JT. (R.J. and L.L. Eichler). Est.
1980. Open 10-5.30. CL: Mon. SIZE: Small. *STOCK:
General antiques.* PARK: Easy. TEL: 01296 641505.
SER: Restorations (furniture pre 1880).

WINSLOW

Winslow Antiques Centre
15 Market Sq. MK18 3AB. Est. 1992. Open 10-5,
Sun. 1-5. CL: Wed. SIZE: 20 dealers. *STOCK:
Furniture, English pottery, silver and jewellery,
general antiques.* LOC: A413. TEL: 01296
714540; fax - 01296 714556.

BALSHAM, Nr. Cambridge

Ward Thomas Antiques
7 High St. CB1 6DJ. (Christian Ward Thomas). Est. 1997. Open 9-5, Sat. 10-5, Sun. 10-4. *STOCK: Pine furniture, £210-£950.* LOC: Village centre, opposite primary school. TEL: 01223 892431; fax - 01223 892367; mobile - 07887 986566; e-mail - christian@ward-thomas.freeserve.com. SER: Valuations; restorations (pine).

BARTON, Nr. Cambridge

Bagatelle Antiques
Burwash Manor Barns, New Rd. CB3 7AY. (A. M. and M. H. Jeffery). Est. 1998. Open 10-5, Sat. 2-5, Sun. by appointment. SIZE: Medium. *STOCK: Furniture, 19th C, £100-£2,000; decorative items, 19th C to 1930's, £10-£250.* LOC: Signed from New Rd. PARK: Easy. TEL: 01223 264400; fax - 01223 264445. SER: Restorations (furniture including re-caning).

BOTTISHAM, Nr. Cambridge

Cambridge Pine
Hall Farm, Lode Rd. CB5 9DN. (Mr and Mrs D. Weir). Est. 1980. Open seven days. SIZE: Large. *STOCK: Pine, 18th-19th C and reproduction, £25-£2,000.* LOC: Midway between Bottisham and Lode, near Anglesey Abbey. PARK: Easy. TEL: 01223 811208; home - same; e-mail - cambridgepine@btconnect.com; website - www.cambridgepine.co.uk. SER: Copies made in old timber with or without painted finish.

BRAMPTON, Nr. Huntingdon

David's
The Old Forge, 41 High St. PE28 4TG. (David Clark and David Collet). Est. 1957. Open Fri. and Sat. 10-4.30, Sun. 11-4. SIZE: Medium. *STOCK: English furniture, 18th-19th C.* PARK: Easy. TEL: 01480 434389; fax - same. SER: Valuations; buys at auction. VAT: Spec.

BURWELL

Peter Norman Antiques and Restorations
Sefton House, 55 North St. CB5 0BA. (P. Norman and A. Marpole). Est. 1975. Open 9-12.30 and 2-5.30. SIZE: Medium. *STOCK: Furniture, clocks, arms and Oriental rugs, 17th-19th C, £250-*£10,000. PARK: Easy. TEL: 01638 616914. SER: Valuations; restorations (furniture, oil paintings, clocks, arms). VAT: Stan/Spec.

CAMBRIDGE

20th Century
169 Histon Rd. CB4 3JD. (S. Charles). Open Wed., Thurs. and Fri. 12-5, Sat. 10-5. *STOCK: Decorative arts, 1880-1980.* TEL: 01223 359482.

Jess Applin Antiques   BADA
8 Lensfield Rd. CB2 1EG. Est. 1968. Open 10-5. *STOCK: Furniture, 17th-19th C; works of art.* LOC: At junction with Hills Rd., opposite church. PARK: Pay and display nearby. TEL: 01223 315168. VAT: Spec.

John Beazor and Sons Ltd   BADA
78-80 Regent St. CB2 1DP. Est. 1875. Open 9.15-5, Sat. 10-4 or by appointment. *STOCK: English furniture, late 17th to early 19th C; clocks, barometers and decorative items.* TEL: 01223 355178; fax - 01223 355183; e-mail - martin@ johnbeazorantiques.co.uk; website - www.john beazorantiques.co.uk. SER: Valuations.

The Bookshop
24 Magdalen St. CB3 0AF. (Hugh Harding and Peter Bright). Open 10.30-5.30. SIZE: Medium. *STOCK: Secondhand and antiquarian books.* LOC: North of river. PARK: Meters. TEL: 01223 362457; e-mail - harding@btinternet.com.

Buckies
31 Trinity St. CB2 1TB. (G. McClure-Buckie). LAPADA. NAG, GMC. Est. 1972. Open 9.45-5. CL: Mon. SIZE: Medium. *STOCK: Jewellery, silver, objets d'art.* PARK: Multi-storey nearby. TEL: 01223 357910. SER: Valuations; restorations and repairs. VAT: Stan/Spec.

Cambridge Fine Art Ltd
Priesthouse, 33 Church St., Little Shelford. CB2 5HG. (R. and J. Lury). LAPADA. Resident. Est. 1972. Open daily 10-6, Sun. by appointment. SIZE: Large. *STOCK: British and European paintings, 1780-1900; modern British paintings, 1880-1940; British prints by J.M. Kronheim to the Baxter Process.* LOC: Next to church. PARK: Easy. TEL: 01223 842866/843537. SER: Valuations; restorations; buys at auction. VAT: Stan/Spec.

Gabor Cossa Antiques
34 Trumpington St. CB2 1QY. (D. Theobald). Est. 1948. Open 10-6. *STOCK: English ceramics, glass, bijouterie.* LOC: Opposite Fitzwilliam Museum. PARK: 400yds. TEL: 01223 356049. VAT: Global.

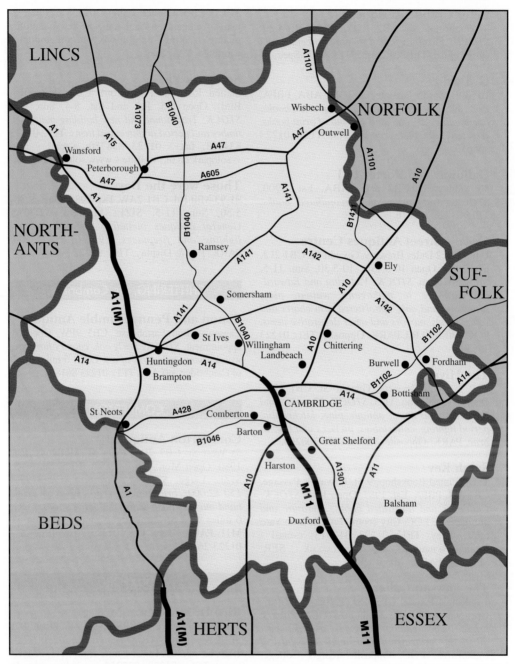

Dealers and Shops in Cambridgeshire

Balsham	1	Chittering	1	Harston	1	Somersham	1
Barton	1	Comberton	1	Huntingdon	2	St. Ives	1
Bottisham	1	Duxford	1	Landbeach	1	St. Neots	1
Brampton	1	Ely	6	Outwell	1	Wansford	1
Burwell	2	Fordham	1	Peterborough	4	Willingham	1
Cambridge	17	Great Shelford	2	Ramsey	2	Wisbech	4

Peter Crabbe Antiques
3 Pembroke St. CB2 3QY. Open 10-4.30. *STOCK: Furniture and Oriental porcelain and works of art.* TEL: 01223 357117. VAT: Spec.

G. David
16 St. Edward's Passage. CB2 3PJ. ABA, PBFA. Est. 1896. Open 9-5. *STOCK: Antiquarian books, fine bindings, secondhand and out of print books, selected publishers remainders.* TEL: 01223 354619.

Galloway and Porter Ltd
30 Sidney St. CB2 3HS. ABA. Est. 1900. *STOCK: Antiquarian and secondhand books.* TEL: 01223 367876.

Gwydir Street Antiques Centre
Units 1 & 2 Dales Brewery, Gwydir St. CB1 2LJ. Est. 1994. Open 10-5, Sat. 10-5.30, Sun. 11-5. SIZE: Medium. *STOCK: Victorian and Edwardian furniture in mahogany, walnut, pine, satinwood and oak; upholstered arm chairs and sofas; lamps, mirrors and other decorative items.* LOC: Off Mill Rd. PARK: Opposite. TEL: 01223 356391.

The Hive
Unit 3, Dales Brewery, Gwydir St. CB1 2LG. Open 10-5.30, Sun. 11-5. *STOCK: Victorian and Edwardian furniture, antique pine, kitchenalia, period lighting, collectables, pictures and bric-a-brac.* PARK: Opposite. TEL: 01223 300269.

Sarah Key
The Haunted Bookshop, 9 St. Edward's Passage. CB2 3PJ. PBFA. Est. 1987. Open 10-5. *STOCK: Children's and illustrated books, literature and antiquarian.* LOC: City centre. PARK: Lion Yard multi-storey. TEL: 01223 312913; e-mail - sarahkey@hauntedbooks.demon.co.uk. SER: Shipping. FAIRS: Major UK.

The Lawson Gallery
7-8 King's Parade. CB2 1SJ. FATG. Est. 1967. Open 9.30-5.30. SIZE: Medium. *STOCK: Posters, prints, limited editions, original artwork, specialists in antiquarian and modern prints of Cambridge.* LOC: Opposite King's College. PARK: Lion Yard. TEL: 01223 313970. VAT: Stan.

Sebastian Pearson Paintings Prints and Works of Art
3 Pembroke St. CB2 3QY. Est. 1989. Open 10.30-5.30. CL: Mon. SIZE: Medium. *STOCK: Oil paintings and watercolours, £300-£3,500; 20th C British prints (etchings and wood engravings), £60-£600.* LOC: City centre. PARK: Nearby. TEL: 01223 323999; home - 01438 871364; e-mail - sebpearson@aol.com. SER: Valuations; picture framing; exhibitions of contemporary paintings. VAT: Spec.

Solopark Plc
Station Rd., Nr. Pampisford. CB2 4HB. (R.J. Bird). Open 8-5, Fri. and Sat. 8-4, Sun. 9-1. *STOCK: Traditional and new building materials, timber and period architectural items.* TEL: 01223 834663; fax - 01223 834780; e-mail - info @solopark.co.uk; website - www.solopark. co.uk.

Those were the Days
91-93 Mill Rd. CB1 2AW. Est. 1984. Open 9.30-5.30, Sun. 11-5. SIZE: Medium. *STOCK: General antiques including furniture, period lighting and fireplaces, 19th C, £5-£1,500.* PARK: Pay & Display. TEL: 01223 300440.

Simon and Penny Rumble Antiques
Causeway End Farmhouse. CB5 9PW. Open by appointment. *STOCK: Early oak, country furniture, woodcarving and works of art.* LOC: 6 miles north of Cambridge, off A10. TEL: 01223 861831.

Comberton Antiques
5a West St. CB3 7DS. (Mrs M. McEvoy). Est. 1980. Open Mon., Fri. and Sat. 10-5, Sun. 2-5. SIZE: Large. *STOCK: Furniture, 1780-1920, £50-£2,000; bric-a-brac, 1830-1920, £5-£100; hand-made Turkish kelims; shipping goods.* LOC: 6 miles west of Cambridge, 2 miles junction 12 M11. PARK: Easy. TEL: 01223 262674; home - 01223 263457.

Riro D. Mooney
4 Moorfield Rd. CB2 4PS. Est. 1946. Open 9-7. SIZE: Medium. *STOCK: General antiques, 1780-1920, £5-£1,200.* LOC: 1 mile from M11. PARK: Easy. TEL: 01223 832252; website - www. riromooney-antiques.com. SER: Restorations (furniture). VAT: Stan/Spec.

Sara Lemkow Antiques
Waterside Antiques Centre, The Wharf. CB7 4AU. Est. 1962. Open 9.30-5.30 including Bank

Holidays, Sun. 11-4.30. SIZE: Small. *STOCK: French enamel and English kitchenalia, copper and brass, scales and weights, oil lamps.* LOC: River edge. PARK: Easy. TEL: 01353 667066; fax - 01284 735161; mobile - 07789 405635; e-mail - rachel.lemkow@btinternet.com; website - www.antique-kitchenalia.co.uk. FAIRS: Newark.

Mrs Mills Antiques
1a St. Mary's St. CB7 4ER. Est. 1968. Open 10-5. CL: Tues. SIZE: Small. *STOCK: China, jewellery, silver.* Not Stocked: Furniture. LOC: Near cathedral. PARK: Nearby. TEL: 01353 664268.

Rookery Farm Antiques
Waterside Antiques Centre, The Wharf. CB7 4AU. (Rachel Lemkow). Est. 1972. Open 9.30-5.30 including Bank Holidays, Sun. 11-4.30. SIZE: Small. *STOCK: Stripped and painted pine and decorative items.* LOC: River edge. PARK: Easy. TEL: 01353 667066; fax - 01294 735161; mobile - 07789 405635; e-mail - rachel.lemkow@btinter net.com; website - www.antique. kitchenalia. co.uk. FAIRS: Newark.

Valued History
9 Market Place. CB7 4NP. (Paul Murawski). Est. 1995. Open 10-5. CL: Mon. SIZE: Small. *STOCK: Antiquities, ancient to Tudor, £25-£1,000+; coins and other artifacts, £5-1,000.* TEL: 01353 654080. SER: Valuations. FAIRS: Cumberland Coin. VAT: Spec.

Waterside Antiques Centre
The Wharf. CB7 4AU. Est. 1986. Open 9.30-5.30 including Bank Holidays, Sun. 11.30-5.30. SIZE: Large. *STOCK: General antiques.* LOC: Waterside area. PARK: Easy. TEL: 01353 667066.

Marie West Antiques
Waterside Antiques Centre, The Wharf. CB7 4AU. Open 9.30-5.30 including Bank Holidays, Sun. 11-4.30. SIZE: Small. *STOCK: Decorative furniture and smalls; painted and stripped pine.* LOC: River edge. PARK: Easy. TEL: 01353 667066; home - 01799 586305; e-mail - marie west@sellarwest.fsnet.co.uk. FAIRS: Newark.

FORDHAM, Nr. Ely

Phoenix Antiques
1 Carter St. CB7 5NG. Est. 1966. Open by appointment only. SIZE: Medium. *STOCK: Early European furniture, domestic metalwork, pottery and delft, carpets, scientific instruments, treen and bygones.* LOC: Centre of village. PARK: Own. TEL: 01638 720363. SER: Valuations.

GREAT SHELFORD, Nr. Cambridge

The Store Antiques
134 Cambridge Rd. CB2 5JU. (Mick Lambourn-Brown and Warren Dosanjh). Est. 1980. Open 10-4, Sun. 11-4. CL: Mon. SIZE: Medium. *STOCK: Furniture, collectables, architectural and decorative items, bygones, 18th C to Victorian, £5-£1,000.* LOC: Adjacent to Scotsdale's Garden Centre, main road into village. PARK: Easy. TEL: 01223 841070; fax - 01223 839102; home - 01223 276243. SER: Valuations; restorations; buys at auction. FAIRS: Newark.

Storm Fine Arts Ltd
Church Street Barns. CB2 5EL. (Bill & Sue Mason). Resident. Est. 1998. Open by appointment. SIZE: Medium. *STOCK: Paintings and pictures, 1500 to date, £500-£100,000; porcelain, pottery and glass, 1800-1900, £150-£1,500; decorative arts, 1700 to date, £100-£15,000; textiles, 1700-1900, £1,000-£30,000.* PARK: Easy. TEL: 01223 844786; fax - 01223 847871; website - www.stormfinearts.com. SER: Valuations; restorations; buys at auction. VAT: Stan.

HARSTON

Antique Clocks
1 High St. CB2 5PX. (C.J. Stocker). Open every day. LOC: On A10, 5 miles south of Cambridge. PARK: Easy. TEL: 01223 870264.

HUNTINGDON

Adams Furniture Centre
Rear of The Old Post Office, George St. PE18 6AW. (Stephen Copsey). Est. 1977. Open 9.30-5.30. CL: Thurs. SIZE: Large. *STOCK: Mainly furniture.* LOC: Off Huntingdon ring road. PARK: Easy. TEL: 01480 435100; fax - 01480 454387. SER: Valuations; buys at auction. VAT: Stan/Spec.

Huntingdon Trading Post
1 St Mary's St. PE29 3PE. (Mrs D. J. A. De'Ath). Est. 1980. Open daily. SIZE: Large. *STOCK: Wide range of general antiques, to £10,000.* PARK: Easy. TEL: 01480 450998; fax - 01480 431142; website - www.huntingdontradingpost.co.uk.

LANDBEACH

J.V. Pianos and Cambridge Pianola Company
The Limes, 85 High St. CB4 8DR. (F.T. Poole). Est. 1972. Open Mon.-Fri., evenings and week-

ends by appointment. SIZE: Medium. *STOCK: Pianos, pianolas and pianola rolls.* LOC: First building on right in Landbeach from A10. PARK: Easy. TEL: 01223 861348/861507; home - same; fax - 01223 441276; website - www.cambridge pianolacompany.co.uk. SER: Valuations; restorations. VAT: Stan.

OUTWELL, Nr. Wisbech

A.P. and M.A. Haylett
Glen-Royd, 393 Wisbech Rd. PE14 8PG. Open 9-6 including Sun. *STOCK: Country furniture, pottery, treen and metalware, 1750-1900, £5-£500.* Not Stocked: Firearms. LOC: A1101. PARK: Easy. TEL: 01945 772427; home - same. SER: Buys at auction.

PETERBOROUGH

Antiques & Curios
249 Lincoln Rd., Millfield. PE2 5NZ. (M. and Mrs R. Mason). Est. 1990. Open 10-5. SIZE: Medium. *STOCK: Pine furniture, 19th C, £50-£500; mahogany and oak furniture, 19th to early 20th C, £50-£500; fireplaces, 19th C, £50-£1,000; collectables, 19th-20th C, £10-£100.* LOC: North from city centre. PARK: Easy. TEL: 01733 314948; home - same. SER: Valuations; restorations (furniture stripping and polishing, fireplaces). FAIRS: Peterborough Festival of Antiques.

Francis Bowers Chess Suppliers
138 Reeves Way, Eastfield. PE1 5LY. Resident. Est. 1991. Open by appointment only. SIZE: Small. *STOCK: Chess books, boards, sets and timers; clocks.* PARK: Easy. TEL: 01733 562778; e-mail - chessbower@aol.com.

Fitzwilliam Antiques Centre
Fitzwilliam St. PE1 2RX. Open 10-5. SIZE: 25 dealers. *STOCK: General antiques.* LOC: Near city centre. PARK: Easy. TEL: 01733 565415/ 566346.

Ivor and Patricia Lewis Antique and Fine Art Dealers
30 Westwood Park Rd. PE3 6JL. LAPADA. Open by appointment. *STOCK: Decorative English and French furniture, 19th to early 20th C.* TEL: 01733 344567; mobile - 07860 553388.

RAMSEY, Nr. Huntingdon

Abbey Antiques
63 Great Whyte. PE26 1HL. (R. and J. Smith). Est. 1977. Open 10-5 including Sun. CL: Mon.

SIZE: Medium. *STOCK: Furniture including pine, 1850-1930, £50-£500; porcelain, Goss and crested china, 1830-1950, £3-£500; Beswick, Wade and Fen pottery, Mabel Lucie Attwell, Disney and small collectables.* PARK: Easy. TEL: 01487 814753. SER: Mabel Lucie Attwell Museum and Collectors' Club: Memories UK (Enesco Memories of Yesterday figurines sold). FAIRS: Alexandra Palace.

Antique Barometers
Wingfield, 26 Biggin Lane. PE26 1NB. (William and Helen Rae). Open by appointment. *STOCK: Fine barometers, 18th-19th C, barographs, £400-£10,000.* PARK: Easy. TEL: 01487 814060; home/fax - same; e-mail - antiquebarometers@talk21.com. SER: Valuations; restorations.

SOMERSHAM, Nr. Huntingdon

T. W. Pawson - Clocks
31A High St. PE28 3JA. BWCG. Est. 1981. Open by appointment. SIZE: Small. *STOCK: Antique clocks, £150-£5,000; mercury barometers, to mid-19th C.* LOC: Main road through village. PARK: Easy. TEL: 01487 841537; home - same; e-mail - thomas.pawson@btinternet.com. SER: Restorations, overhauls, repairs (clocks and barometers).

ST. IVES

B.R. Knight and Sons
Quay Court, Bull Lane, Bridge St. PE17 4AU. (M. Knight). Est. 1972. Open Mon., Wed., Fri. 11-2, Sat. 10.30-4.30 or by appointment. SIZE: Medium. *STOCK: Porcelain, pottery, jewellery, paintings, watercolours, prints, decorative arts.* LOC: Off Bridge St. PARK: Nearby. TEL: 01480 468295/300042; e-mail - michaelknight9@hot mail.com.

ST. NEOTS

Tavistock Antiques
Cross Hall Manor, Eaton Ford. PE19 7GB. Open by appointment. *STOCK: Period English furniture.* TEL: 01480 472082. *Trade Only.*

WANSFORD, Nr. Peterborough

Starlight Period Lighting
16 London Rd. PE8 6JB. (Lynne Ayres and Richard P. Rimes). Resident. Est. 1989. Open Tues.-Fri. 9.30-1 and 2.15-5 and most Sats. 10-1

and 2.30-5. SIZE: Medium. *STOCK: Period and new lighting.* LOC: On A1 near A47 junction. PARK: Easy. TEL: 01780 783999; fax - same; e-mail - starlight@lampsandcandles.freeserve.co. uk; website - www.starlight-rpr.co.uk. SER: Restorations (period lighting).

WILLINGHAM

Q Antiques
27 Green St. CB4 5JA. (Helen H. Dunne and Amy King). Est. 2000. Open 10.30-5, Sun. 10.30-4. CL: Tues. SIZE: Medium. *STOCK: Paintings, furniture, porcelain, silver and jewellery, brass and copper, fishing items, racing memorabilia, rugs, early oak, to Edwardian, £5-£2,000.* LOC: A14. PARK: Easy. TEL: 01954 260280; home - 01954 231220 and 01354 741199. SER: Valuations; restorations (furniture, silver, porcelain); buys at auction.

WISBECH

Antiques & Curios (Steve Carpenter)
95-96 Norfolk St. PE13 2LF. Est. 1985. Open 9-5, Sun., Mon. and Wed. by appointment. SIZE: Medium. *STOCK: Georgian and Victorian longcase clocks, £1,000-£3,000; Georgian,* *Victorian and Edwardian furniture, 19th C, £100-£5,000; bygones and collectables, 18th-20th C, £5-£3000.* LOC: Town centre, just off A47. PARK: Easy. TEL: 01945 588441; e-mail - scarpenterantiques@amserve.net. SER: Valuations; restorations (structural, veneering and polishing); shipping.

Peter A. Crofts
117 High Rd., Elm. PE14 0DN. Est. 1949. Open by appointment. *STOCK: General antiques, furniture, porcelain, silver, jewellery.* LOC: A1101. TEL: 01945 584614. VAT: Stan/Spec.

Granny's Cupboard
34 Old Market. PE13 1NF. (R.J. Robbs). Est. 1982. Open Tues. and Thurs. 10.30-4, Sat. 10.30-3. SIZE: Small. *STOCK: China, glass, small furniture, Victorian to 1950's, £5-£500.* PARK: Easy. TEL: 01945 589606; home - 01945 870730. FAIRS: The Maltings, Ely.

R. Wilding
Lanes End, Gadds Lane, Leverington. PE13 5BJ. Resident. *STOCK: Bamboo furniture and mirrors; period furniture including walnut chests; gilt/polished mirrors.* TEL: 01945 588204; fax - 01945 475712. SER: Veneering; polishing; compo carving; gilding; conversions; replicas. *Trade Only.*

A group of Magic Roundabout *character stick puppets sold in June 1999: Florence for £129, Mr Rusty for £106 and Dougal, Zebedee and Brian sold together for £223.*

From an article entitled "Yours Puppetually!" by Dick Henrywood which appeared in the July/August 2001 issue of **Antique Collecting**. For more details and to subscribe see page 21.

CHESHIRE

ALDERLEY EDGE

Sara Frances Antiques
32 South St. SK9 7ES. (Mrs. F.S. Waterworth). Est. 1990. Open Tues. 10-1, Thurs., Fri. and Sat. 10-4. SIZE: Small. *STOCK: Furniture, 17th-19th C, £100-£6,000; silver, 19th-20th C, £50-£500; decorative items, 17th-20th C, £100-£2,500.* LOC: Off London Rd. PARK: Easy. TEL: 01625 585549/584516; mobile - 07801 458852. SER: Valuations; restorations (furniture and silver).

D.J. Massey and Son
51a London Rd. SK9 7DY. Est. 1900. Open 9.15-5.15, Wed. 9.15-4.45. SIZE: Large. *STOCK: Victorian jewellery, silverware, gold and diamond jewellery.* LOC: On A34. PARK: Easy. TEL: 01625 583565. VAT: Stan/Spec.

ALSAGER, Nr. Crewe

Trash 'n' Treasure
48 Sandbach Rd. South. ST7 2LP. (G. and D. Ogden). Est. 1979. Open Tues., Thurs., Fri. and Sat. 10-4. SIZE: Medium. *STOCK: Late Georgian to 1930's furniture, pictures, ceramics, £5-£10,000.* LOC: 10 minutes junction 16, M6. PARK: Nearby. TEL: 01270 872972/873246. SER: Valuations; lectures.

ALTRINCHAM

Bizarre Decorative Arts North West
116 Manchester Rd. WA14 4PY. (Malcolm C. and Rebecca Lamb). Resident. Est. 1986. Open 10-6, Sun. by appointment. SIZE: Large. *STOCK: Furniture and lighting, £100-£15,000; figurines, bronzes, ceramics including Clarice Cliff, and jewellery, £5-£2,000; all Art Nouveau and Art Deco.* LOC: A56. PARK: Own. TEL: 0161 926 8895; home - same; fax - 0161 929 8310. SER: Valuations; restorations (furniture and lighting; silver and chrome plating, pewter polishing). FAIRS: NEC (Aug); Loughborough Art Deco; Kensington Decorative Arts. VAT: Stan/Spec.

Church Street Antiques
4/4a Old Market Place. WA14 4NP. (Alex Smalley and Nick Stanley). LAPADA. Est. 1991. Open 10-5.30, Sun. 12-4. CL: Tues. SIZE: Large. *STOCK: Furniture, 18th-19th C, £100-£10,000; silver and plate, 19th C, £50-£1,000; paintings, 19th C to contemporary, £100-£5,000.* PARK: Easy. TEL: 0161 929 5196; fax - same; mobile - 07768 318661; website - www.churchstreetantiques.com. SER: Valuations; restorations. FAIRS: Tatton; Chester; GMex; Arley; Harrogate. VAT: Spec.

Robert Redford Antiques & Interiors
48 New St. WA14 2QS. (S. and R. Redford). Est. 1989. By appointment. *STOCK: General antiques, furniture, small silver, porcelain, glass.* PARK: Easy. TEL: 0161 929 8171; home - 0161 926 8232; fax - 0161 928 4827.

Squires Antiques
25 Regent Rd. WA14 1RX. (V. Phillips). Est. 1977. Open 10-5. CL: Mon. and Wed. SIZE: Medium. *STOCK: Small furniture, 1800-1930, £60-£1,500; small silver, 1850-1970, £20-£400; brass, copper and bric-a-brac, 1850-1940, £10-£400; jewellery, porcelain, fire accessories, light fittings and interior design items.* Not Stocked: Large furniture, coins and badges. LOC: Adjacent hospital and large car park. PARK: Easy. TEL: 0161 928 0749. SER: Valuations.

BARTON, Nr. Malpas

Derek and Tina Rayment Antiques
BADA
Orchard House, Barton Rd. SY14 7HT. (D.J. and K.M. Rayment). LAPADA. Est. 1960. Open by appointment every day. STOCK: Barometers, 18th-20th C, from £100. LOC: A534. PARK: Easy. TEL: 01829 270429; home - same; e-mail - raymentantiques@aol.com. SER: Valuations; restorations (barometers only); buys at auction (barometers). FAIRS: Olympia; Chelsea; LAPADA - NEC and London; BADA. VAT: Stan/Spec.

BOLLINGTON, Nr. Macclesfield

House of St Clair
Clarence Mill, Clarence Rd. SK10 5JZ. Est. 1970. Open Thurs., Fri. and Sat. 10-5, Sun. 11-5. SIZE: Small. *STOCK: Jewellery, silver, ceramics and glass, 18th to early 20th C, £2-£500.* LOC: Off Macclesfield Silk Rd., through village, left after traffic lights. PARK: Easy. TEL: 0161 449 9978. SER: Valuations; restorations. FAIRS: Buxton, Deanwater Hotel, Stockport Town Hall.

BOWDON

Richmond Antiques
Richmond Rd. WA14 2TT. (Joe Freeman). Est. 1992. Open 12-6, Sun. by appointment. CL: Mon. *STOCK: Mirrors, 19th C, £300-£2,000; French decorative furniture, 19th C, £150-£500; chandeliers, early 20th C, £200-£700.* LOC: Near Manchester airport, junction 7, M56, junction 19, M6. PARK: Easy. TEL: 01619 281229; home - same. SER: Restorations. VAT: Spec.

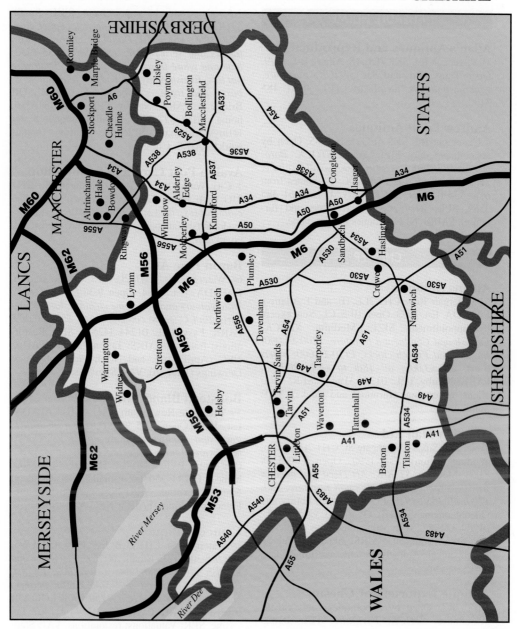

Dealers and Shops in Cheshire

Alderley Edge	2	Davenham	1	Mobberley	1	Tarporley	1
Alsager	1	Disley	1	Nantwich	8	Tarvin	1
Altrincham	4	Hale	2	Northwich	1	Tarvin Sands	1
Barton	1	Haslington	1	Plumley	1	Tattenhall	1
Bollington	1	Helsby	1	Poynton	2	Tilston	1
Bowdon	1	Knutsford	6	Ringway	1	Warrington	1
Cheadle Hulme	2	Littleton	1	Romiley	1	Waverton	1
Chester	25	Lymm	2	Sandbach	1	Widnes	1
Congleton	2	Macclesfield	4	Stockport	12	Wilmslow	1
Crewe	2	Marple Bridge	1	Stretton	1		

Allan's Antiques and Reproductions
10 Ravenoak Rd. SK8 7DL. (S. Allan). Est. 1979. Open Thurs., Fri. and Sat. *STOCK: Furniture, general antiques, metalware.* TEL: 0161 485 3132.

Andrew Foott Antiques
4 Claremont Rd. SK8 6EG. Est. 1985. Open by appointment only. SIZE: Small. *STOCK: Barometers, 18th-20th C, £200-£2,500; small furniture, 18th-20th C, £500-£3,000.* LOC: 5 minutes from new A34 by-pass. PARK: Easy. TEL: 0161 485 3559. SER: Restorations (barometers and furniture). FAIRS: NEC Antiques for Everyone.

Adams Antiques
65 Watergate Row. CH1 2LE. (B. and T. Adams). LAPADA. Est. 1973. Open 10-5. CL: Sun. except by appointment. SIZE: Medium. *STOCK: English and Continental furniture, £200-£4,000; English and French clocks, £150-£4,000; objets d'art, £10-£3,000; all 18th to early 20th C.* PARK: Nearby. TEL: 01244 319421. SER: Valuations; restorations (furniture and clocks). VAT: Stan/Spec.

Aldersey Hall Ltd
Town Hall Sq., 47 Northgate St. CH1 2HQ. (Kim Wilding-Welton). Est. 1990. Open 8.30-5.30. SIZE: Medium. *STOCK: Art Deco and general British ceramics, £5-£500; small furniture, £50-£200; all 1880-1940.* LOC: Between library and Odeon cinema. PARK: Own 100 yards. TEL: 01244 324885. SER: Valuations; buys at auction (Art Deco ceramics). FAIRS: Alexandra Palace, Loughborough, Ardingly, Newark and Birmingham. VAT: Stan/Spec.

Antique Exporters of Chester
CH3 7RZ. Open by appointment only. SIZE: Warehouse. *STOCK: Furniture.* TEL: 01829 741001; home - 01244 570069. SER: Packing.

The Antique Garden
Grosvenor Garden Centre, Wrexham Rd. CH4 9EB. (Maria Hopwood). Est. 1991. Open 10-4.30 including Sun. *STOCK: Garden-related bygones.* LOC: A483. PARK: Easy. TEL: 01244 629191; mobile - 07976 539990. SER: Valuations.

The Antique Shop
40 Watergate St. CH1 2LA. (Peter Thornber). Est. 1985. Open 10-5.30, Sat. 10-6, Sun. (May-Dec.) 1-5, other times by appointment. SIZE: Small. *STOCK: Metalware - brass, pewter, copper, iron, 1700-1900, £35-£350; Doulton - character jugs, figures and series ware, 1890-1960, £35-£350; blue and white transfer printed ware; Prattware pot lids, British Army cap badges; fountain pens; boxes and treen; cranberry glass.* LOC: Off Bridge St. PARK: Nearby. TEL: 01244 316286; home - 0151 327 1725; email - antiqueschester @tinyworld.co.uk. SER: Restorations (metalwork). FAIRS: Cheshire.

Avalon Post Card and Stamp Shop
1 City Walls, Rufus Court, Northgate St. CH1 2JG. (G.E. Ellis). *STOCK: Postcards, stamps and collectables.* TEL: 01244 318406; e-mail - avalon@fsbdial.co.uk; website - www.postcard. co. uk/npf.

Baron Fine Art
68 Watergate St. CH1 2LA. (S. and R. Baron). LAPADA. Est. 1984. Open 9.30-5.30. *STOCK: Watercolours and oils, some etchings, late 19th to early 20th C, some contemporary, £50-£60,000.* PARK: Easy. TEL: 01244 342520. SER: Restorations; framing. FAIRS: Tatton Park; LAPADA; NEC (April, Aug. and Nov); Watercolours & Drawings (Jan/Feb). VAT: Stan/Spec.

Boustead-Bland Antiques
59 Watergate Row South. CH1 2LE. LAPADA. Est. 1985. Open 10-5.30. *STOCK: 17th-19th C town and country furniture; portraits, clocks, metalware, pottery, porcelain and lighting.* LOC: City centre. PARK: Nearby. TEL: 01244 342300; home - 01244 350366; e-mail - bousteadbland @attglobal.net.uk. SER: Restorations (furniture, French polishing). FAIRS: NEC. VAT: Spec.

Cameo Antiques
19 Watergate St. CH1 2LB. Est. 1994. Open 9-5, Sat. 9-5.30. SIZE: Small. *STOCK: Jewellery and English silver, 1800-1990, £20-£2,000; English (including Moorcroft and Sally Tuffin pottery) and Continental porcelain, 1750-1960.* LOC: Off Bridge St. PARK: Easy. TEL: 01244 311467; fax - same. SER: Valuations; restorations. VAT: Stan/Spec.

Farmhouse Antiques
21-23 Christleton Rd., Boughton. CH3 5UF. (K. Appleby). Est. 1973. Open 9-5. SIZE: Large. *STOCK: Farmhouse furniture, longcase clocks, Staffordshire pottery, country bygones, mechanical music, Manchester United football programmes.* LOC: 1 mile from City centre on A41. PARK: Easy. TEL: 01244 322478; evenings - 01244 318391. SER: Export. VAT: Stan/Spec.

Grosvenor Antiques and Interiors
61 Watergate Row. CH1 2LE. (John R. Martin).
Est. 2002. Open 10-5.30. SIZE: Medium.
*STOCK: Dining and bedroom furniture,
paintings, silver plate, lighting and interior
design.* LOC: City centre, 200 metres west of
Cross. PARK: Multi-storey nearby. TEL: 01244
342300. SER: Interior design; restorations
(furniture including polishing). FAIRS: NEC.

Guildhall Fair - Chester
Watergate St. CH1. Open Thurs. 10-4. SIZE:
Several dealers. *STOCK: General antiques.*

Harris & Holt
Grange Farm, Parkgate Rd., Mollington. CH1
6NP. (Sandra Harris). Est. 1978. Open 10-5, Mon.,
Tues and Wed. by appointment. SIZE: Medium.
*STOCK: English and Continental furniture, £500-
£10,000; oil paintings including portraits, £1,000-
£10,000; works of art, £100-£5,000; all 17th-19th
C.* LOC: A540 Chester to Parkgate road, opposite
Banastre Hotel. PARK: Easy. TEL: 01244 851180;
fax - 0151 353 8107; mobile - 07860 560875. SER:
Valuations; buys at auction. FAIRS: Battersea;
Olympia (June). VAT: Spec.

J. Alan Hulme
Antique Maps & Old Prints, 52 Mount Way,
Waverton. CH3 7QF. Est. 1965. Open Mon.-Sat.
by appointment. *STOCK: Maps, 16th-19th C;
prints, 18th-19th C.* TEL: 01244 336472.

Jamandic Ltd
22 Bridge St. Row. CH1 1NN. Est. 1975. Open
9.30-5.30, Sat. 9.30-1. SIZE: Medium. *STOCK:
Decorative furniture, mirrors, lighting, pictures
and prints.* TEL: 01244 312822. SER: Interior
design and decoration; export. VAT: Stan/Spec.

K D Antiques
11 City Walls. CH1 1LD. (Dorothea Gillett). Est.
1990. Open 10-5. SIZE: Small. *STOCK: Staffordshire figures, 18th-19th C, £50-£500; wooden
boxes, 18th-19th C, £20-£300; collectables, £5-
£50.* LOC: Town centre, next to Eastgate Clock,
wall level. PARK: Nearby. TEL: 01244 314208.

Kayes of Chester
9 St. Michaels Row. CH1 1EF. (A.M. Austin-Kaye
and N.J. Kaye). LAPADA. NAG. Est. 1948. Open
9-5.30. SIZE: Medium. *STOCK: Diamond rings
and jewellery, 1850-1950, £20-£20,000; silver and
plate, 1700-1930, £20-£8,000; small objects and
ceramics, 19th to early 20th C, £50-£1,000.*
PARK: Nearby. TEL: 01244 327149; fax - 01244
318404; website - www.Kayeschester. com. SER:
Valuations; restorations (silver, jewellery and
plate); buys at auction. VAT: Stan/Spec.

Lowe and Sons
11 Bridge St. Row. CH1 1PD. Est. 1770. *STOCK:
Jewellery and silver, Georgian, Victorian and
Edwardian; unusual collectors' items.* TEL:
01244 325850. VAT: Stan/Spec.

Made of Honour
11 City Walls. CH1 1LD. (E. Jones). Est. 1971.
Open 10-5. *STOCK: Staffordshire figures, British
ceramics, boxes, prints and pictures, decorative
and collectable items, 18th-19th C.* LOC: Next to
Eastgate clock, wall level. TEL: 01244 314208;
e-mail - eric.antiques@btinternet.com.uk. FAIRS:
Anglesey.

Melody's Antiques
The Old School House, Kinnerton Rd., Lower
Kinnerton. CH4 9AE. (M. and M. Melody).
LAPADA. Est. 1977. Open 10-5.30 by appoint-
ment. SIZE: Large. *STOCK: 18th-20th C oak,
mahogany, walnut and pine furniture; porcelain,
lighting, decorative items.* LOC: 3 miles from
Chester. TEL: 01244 660204. SER: Courier;
container packing. FAIRS: Newark; NEC. VAT:
Stan/Spec.

Moor Hall Antiques
27 Watergate Row. CH1 2LE. (John Murphy).
Resident. Est. 1992. Open 10-5.30, Mon., Fri. and
Sat. 10.30-5.30. SIZE: Large. *STOCK: Furniture,
18th-19th C, £1,000-£2,000; prints, 19th C, £50-
£200; modern decorative items, £20-£100.* LOC:
City centre. PARK: Easy. TEL: 01244 340095.
SER: Restorations (oils, watercolours and furniture). VAT: Stan/Spec.

The Old Warehouse Antiques
7 Delamere St. CH1 4DS. (Mr and Mrs M.
O'Donnell). Est. 1990. Open 10-5. SIZE: Large.
*STOCK: Victorian and Edwardian furniture, £50-
£1,000.* LOC: Opposite Delamere bus station.
PARK: Nearby. TEL: 01244 383942; mobile -
07790 533850. SER: French polishing. VAT: Spec

Stothert Old Books
4 Nicholas St. CH1 2NX. (Alan and Marjory
Checkley). GADAR. Est. 1977. Open 10-5.
SIZE: Medium. *STOCK: Books, 17th-20th C, £2-
£1,000.* LOC: At junction with Watergate St.
TEL: 01244 340756.

Watergate Antiques
56 Watergate St. CH1 2LD. (A. Shindler). Est.
1968. Open 9.30-5.30. SIZE: Medium. *STOCK:
Porcelain and pottery, jewellery; specialist in
silver and silver plate to the Trade.* LOC: From
Liverpool first set of traffic lights past Waterfall
Roundabout, turn left. PARK: At rear. TEL:
01244 344516; fax - 01244 320350; e-mail -
watergate.antiques@themail.co.uk. VAT: Stan.

Wheatsheaf Antiques
57 Christleton Rd., Boughton. CH3. Est. 1988.
Open 11-4, Sun. 12-4. SIZE: Medium. *STOCK: Furniture, 18th C to 1930's, £500-£2,000; vintage clothing, Victorian to 1970's; prints, 18th C to 1930's.* PARK: Adjacent. TEL: 01244 403743; fax - 01244 351713; e-mail - info@antiques onlineuk.com; website - www.antiquesonlineuk. com. SER: Restorations. VAT: Spec.

CONGLETON

W. Buckley Antiques Exports
35 Chelford Rd. CW12 4QA. Open 7 days by appointment. *STOCK: Mainly shipping and Victorian furniture.* TEL: 01260 275299. SER: Shipping.

Littles Collectables
8/10 Little St. CW12 1AR. (Mrs .J. Storey). Est. 1989. CL: Wed. SIZE: Medium. *STOCK: Pottery and glass, Doulton, £5-£1,000.* LOC: Town centre. PARK: Nearby. TEL: 01260 299098.

CREWE

Steven Blackhurst
102 Edleston Rd. CW2 7HD. Est. 1988. Open 9.30-5, Sat. 10-5, Sun. by appointment. CL: Wed. SIZE: Small. *STOCK: Stripped pine, 19th to early 20th C, £25-£600; satinwood furniture, 1900, £100-£500.* LOC: Turn off Nantwich Rd. (A534), shop 250 yards on left. TEL: 01270 258617; home - 01270 665991.

Copnal Books
18 Meredith St. CW1 2PW. (P. Ollerhead). Est. 1980. Open Mon. and Fri. 9.30-4.30, Sat. 9.30-5. SIZE: Small. *STOCK: Books, £1-£50.* LOC: 200 yards north of market. PARK: Easy. TEL: 01270 580470; home - 01270 585622. SER: Valuations; buys at auction.

DAVENHAM, Nr. Northwich

Davenham Antiques Centre
461 London Rd. CW9 8NA. Est. 1985. Open 10-5, Sun. 11-5. CL: Wed. SIZE: 15 dealers. *STOCK: Victorian and Edwardian furniture, china, pictures, silver, clocks, books and collectables.* LOC: Village centre, off A566. TEL: 01606 44350; fax - 01606 782317; e-mail - maxwells@ connectfree.co.uk; website - www.antiques-atlas.com/davenham.htm. SER: Shipping.

DISLEY

Mill Farm Antiques
50 Market St. SK12 2DT. (F.E. Berry). Est. 1968. Open every day. SIZE: Medium. *STOCK: Pianos, clocks, mechanical music, shipping goods, general antiques, £50-£10,000.* LOC: A6, 7 miles south of Stockport. PARK: Easy. TEL: 01663 764045; fax - 01663 762690. SER: Valuations; restorations (clocks, watches, barometers, music boxes). VAT: Stan/Spec.

HALE, Nr. Altrincham

Affordable Antiques
25 Stamford Park Rd. WA15 9EL. (Joel and Kate Freeman). Est. 1996. Open Mon.-Sat. SIZE: Large. *STOCK: Furniture, mid to late Victorian, £100-£600; mirrors, to Victorian, £300-£500.* LOC: From Hale Rd. turn right down Hawthorn Rd., left at bottom, first shop on right. PARK: Own. TEL: 0161 929 0700; fax - same; home - 01625 525367; mobile - 0780 888 6982. SER: Valuations; restorations (French polishing, paint effects, upholstery). FAIRS: Lille & Montpellier, France.

French Countrystyle
61 Stamford Park Rd. WA15 9EZ. (Bernard and Margaret Ernstone). Open Tues.-Sat.10-5. SIZE: Small. *STOCK: French decorative furniture, beds, lighting, mirrors and unusual items, 1800-1910, £150-£2,000.* PARK: Easy. TEL: 0161 927 9041; fax - 0161 904 8949; e-mail - bernard@ frenchcountrystyle.co.uk; website - www.french countrystyle.co.uk.

HASLINGTON, Nr. Crewe

J. Luffman
Bank House, 13 Bradeley Rd. CW1 5PW. Open by appointment. *STOCK: Longcase, bracket and mantel clocks, music boxes, country furniture, paintings and militaria, £5-£20,000.* TEL: 01270 500199; mobile - 07836 592898. SER: Valuations; buys at auction (militaria and paintings). VAT: Spec.

HELSBY

Sweetbriar Gallery
Robin Hood Lane. WA6 9NH. (Mrs A. Metcalfe). Est. 1986. Open 9-5.30 or by appointment to see

full stock. *STOCK: Antique and modern paperweights, £5-£8,000.* LOC: Off M56, junction 14. First left at traffic lights, first right after Elf Garage, past three right turns. Premises on hillside with long, low sandstone wall in front. PARK: Easy. TEL: 01928 723851; home - same; fax - 01928 724153; mobile - 07860 907532; e-mail - sweetbr@globalnet.co.uk; website - www.sweetbriar.co.uk. SER: Valuations; buys at auction (paperweights). FAIRS: Glass (May and Nov.); National Motorcycle Museum (Birmingham); Great Antiques; Shepton Mallet; Newark; Ardingly. VAT: Stan/Spec.

KNUTSFORD

Antiques, Collectables and Crafts
35 King St. WA16 6DW. (Lindsey Bowman). Est. 1997. Open 10.30-4.30, Sun. 12.30-5.30. CL: Wed. SIZE: Medium. *STOCK: English and Continental furniture, wall, mantel and longcase clocks, paintings, prints and collectables, decorative lighting, marine and naval antiques and replicas.* PARK: Easy. TEL: 01565 653599; fax - same. SER: Valuations; restorations (upholstery and clocks).

B.R.M. Coins
3 Minshull St. WA16 6HG. (Brian Butterworth). Est. 1968. Open 11-3, Sat. 11-1 or by appointment. SIZE: Small. *STOCK: Coins, medals and banknotes, worldwide, BC to date, from 5p; money boxes, coin scales and weights.* LOC: A50. PARK: Nearby. TEL: 01565 651480; home - 01606 74522. SER: Valuations; buys at auction (as stock).

Cranford Galleries
10 King St. WA16 6DL. (M.R. Bentley). Est. 1964. Open 11-5. CL: Wed. SIZE: Small. *STOCK: Pictures, prints and Victoriana.* Not Stocked: Glass. LOC: Main St. PARK: Easy. TEL: 01565 633646. SER: Framing and mounting. VAT: Stan.

Glynn Interiors
92 King St. WA16 6ED. Est. 1963. Open 10-4. CL: Mon. and Wed. SIZE: Large. *STOCK: Furniture, 1750-1900, £50-£2,000; Victorian chairs, £50-£650.* Not Stocked: Porcelain. LOC: 10 mins. drive after leaving M6 at Exit 19. PARK: Own. TEL: 01565 634418. SER: Restorations (re-upholstery) and cabinet repairs. VAT: Stan/Spec.

Knutsford Antiques Centre

113 King St. WA16 6EH. (David and Patricia McLeod). Est. 1995. Open 10-5, Sun. 12-5. CL: Mon. SIZE: 20+ dealers. *STOCK: Furniture, 18th C, £100-£2,000; pine, £200-£600; early British porcelain, ceramics and collectables, £10-£2,000; British silver, £10-£1,000; books, £1-£50; glass, £10-£500; jewellery, £25-£500.* LOC: Main street, 5 minutes from junction 19, M6. PARK: Easy. TEL: 01565 654092; website - www. knutsfordantiques.com. SER: Valuations.

Lion Gallery and Bookshop

15a Minshull St. WA16 6HG. (R.P. Hepner). Est. 1964. Open Fri. 10.30-4.30, Sat. 10-4.30. *STOCK: Antiquarian maps, prints and books, watercolours and oils, 16th-20th C; O.S. maps and early directories.* LOC: King St. 3 mins. M6. PARK: Nearby. TEL: 01565 652915; mobile - 07850 270796; fax - 01565 750142. SER: Restorations; binding, cleaning, framing and mounting. VAT: Stan.

LITTLETON, Nr. Chester

John Titchner and Sons

Littleton Old Hall, Little Heath Rd. CH3 7DW. LAPADA. Open 9-5. CL: Sat. *STOCK: Furniture, 18th-19th C.* TEL: 01244 336986.

LYMM

Reflections

11 The Cross. WA13 0HR. (John and Jennie Sprague). Est. 1970. Open 9.30-5, Sun. by appointment. CL: Mon. SIZE: Medium. *STOCK: Furniture and smalls, 1850-1950, £5-£1,000.* LOC: Village centre, in yard opposite 'Wine Sellers'. TEL: 01925 753555; home - 01925 757331. SER: Valuations; restorations (polishing, repairs; upholstery, modern and traditional).

Willow Pool Garden Centre

Burford Lane. WA13 0SH. (S. Brunsveld). Open 9-6, including Sun. *STOCK: Architectural and general antiques.* TEL: 01925 757827; fax - 01925 758101.

MACCLESFIELD

Gatehouse Antiques

72 Chestergate. SK11 6QQ. (W.H. Livesley). Est. 1973. Open 9-5. CL: Sun. except by appointment and Wed. pm. *STOCK: Small furniture, silver and plate, glass, brass, copper, pewter, jewellery, 1650-1880.* PARK: At rear. TEL: 01625 426476; home - 01625 612841.

Hills Antiques

Indoor Market, Grosvenor Centre. SK11 6SY. (D. Hill). Est. 1968. Open 9.30-5.30. *STOCK: Small furniture, jewellery, collectors' items, stamps, coins, postcards.* LOC: Town Centre. PARK: Easy. TEL: 01625 420777/420467; e-mail - hills antiques@tinyworld.co.uk; website - www.hills antiques.co.uk.

D.J. Massey and Son

47 Chestergate. SK11 6DG. Est. 1900. Open 9.30-5.15. *STOCK: Jewellery, gold and diamonds, all periods.* TEL: 01625 616133.

Mereside Books

75 Chestergate. SK11 6DG. (Miss S. Laithwaite and K. S. Kowalski). Est. 1996. Open 10-5, Mon. and Tues. by appointment. SIZE: Small. *STOCK: Books - secondhand, 20th C, £2-£100; antiquarian, 19th C, £10-£300; illustrated, 20th C, £10-£1,000.* TEL: 01625 425352; home - 01625 431160. SER: Valuations; restorations (books including re-binding). FAIRS: Buxton Book.

MARPLE BRIDGE, Nr. Stockport

Town House Antiques

21 Town St. SK6 5AA. (Paul and Jeri Buxcey). Open 10-6 most days. *STOCK: Antique pine, French beds and decorative items.* PARK: Forecourt. TEL: 0161 427 2228; home - 0161 427 1343.

MOBBERLEY

David Bedale

WA16 7HR. Est. 1977. By appointment. SIZE: Medium. *STOCK: 18th-19th C furniture, unusual and decorative items.* TEL: 01565 872270; mobile - 07836 623021. VAT: Stan/Spec.

NANTWICH

Adams Antiques   BADA

Churche's Mansion, Hospital St. CW5 5RY. (Sandy Summers). LAPADA. Resident. Est. 1975. Open by appointment. SIZE: Large. *STOCK: Mainly oak and walnut country furniture, dressers, corner cupboards, tables and chairs; longcase clocks, Mason's Ironstone.* **LOC: A500 to Nantwich to town centre, shop on left. PARK: Own. TEL: 01270 625643; fax - same. SER: Valuations. FAIRS: BADA LAPADA; NEC. VAT: Stan/Spec.**

Tim Armitage

99 Welsh Row. CW5 5ET. (T.J. Armitage). Est. 1967. Open by appointment. SIZE: Small. *STOCK: Tin toys, steam models and early advertising.* LOC: Main road into town from Chester. PARK: Easy. TEL: 01270 626608; home - same. SER: Valuations; buys at auction (toys and models).

Barn Antiques

8 The Cocoa Yard, Pillory St. CW5 5BL. (J.B. Lee). Est. 1993. CL: Wed. SIZE: Small. *STOCK: Carltonware, Beswick, Royal Doulton and Shelley china and collectables.* LOC: Town centre. TEL: 01270 627770.

Chapel Antiques

47 Hospital St. CW5 5RL. (Miss D.J. Atkin). Est. 1983. Open 9.30-5.30, Wed. 9.30-1 or by appointment. CL: Mon. SIZE: Medium. *STOCK: Oak, mahogany and pine furniture, Georgian and Victorian, £100-£3,000; longcase clocks, pre-1830, £1,000-£3,000; copper, brass, silver, glass, porcelain, pottery and small items, 19th C, £10-£500.* LOC: Enter town via Pillory St., turn right into Hospital St. PARK: Easy. TEL: 01270 629508; home - same. SER: Valuations; restorations (furniture, clocks).

Roderick Gibson

70 Hospital St. CW5 5RP. (R. and L. Gibson). Est. 1975. Open 9-5. *STOCK: Furniture and decorative collectors' pieces.* TEL: 01270 625301; website - www.sfc.co.uk/antiques. SER: Valuations. VAT: Stan/Global.

Love Lane Antiques

Love Lane. CW5 5BH. (M. Simon). Open 10-5. CL: Wed. SIZE: Small. *STOCK: General antiques, 19th-20th C, £5-£500.* LOC: Two minutes walk from town square. PARK: Nearby. TEL: 01270 626239.

Pillory House

18 Pillory St. CW5 5BD. (D. Roberts). Est. 1968. Open 9-5. CL: Wed. *STOCK: Hand-carved chimney pieces and oak.* TEL: 01270 623524.

Richardson Antiques Ltd

90 Hospital St. CW5 5RP. (Terry Richardson). Est. 1981. Open daily, Sun. by appointment. SIZE: Medium. *STOCK: Furniture, collectables and china.* TEL: 01270 625963; home - 01270 628348. SER: Valuations; restorations (French polishing, upholstery, clocks). VAT: Spec.

Coppelia Antiques

Valerie and Roy Clements

Holford Lodge, Plumley Moor
Road, Plumley, Nr. Knutsford,
Cheshire WA16 9RS
Telephone: 01565 722197
Fax: 01565 722744
4 miles from J.19, M6

Fine quality mahogany longcase clock, c.1770, London maker, ht. 7ft. 8in. Dial with chapter ring and spandrels with strike-silent in the arch

We currently have one of the finest selections of quality longcase clocks in the U.K. We also stock mantel, bracket, English and Vienna wall clocks. Established 1970, all our clocks are fully restored and guaranteed 1 year. Free delivery U.K. mainland. Why not pay us a visit, you will receive a warm welcome, free coffee and constructive, expert advice.

OPEN 7 DAYS BY APPOINTMENT

NORTHWICH

Northwich Antiques Centre
132 Witton St. (F.J. Cockburn). Est. 1990. Open 10-5 including Sun. SIZE: Large. *STOCK: Georgian, Victorian and Edwardian furniture, £50-£1,000+; china, clocks and barometers; Royal Doulton, Beswick, Moorcroft; prints, paintings, books, jewellery.* LOC: Town centre. PARK: Easy. TEL: 01606 47540; fax - 01606 889262.

PLUMLEY

Coppelia Antiques
Holford Lodge, Plumley Moor Rd. WA16 9RS. (V. and R. Clements). Resident. Est. 1970. Open 10-6 every day by appointment. SIZE: Medium. *STOCK: Over 500 clocks (mainly longcase and wall), £1,000-£50,000; tables - Georgian mahogany, wine, oak gateleg and side; bureaux, desks, chests of drawers, lowboys, coffers.* LOC: 4 miles junction 19, M6. PARK: Easy. TEL: 01565 722197; fax - 01565 722744. FAIRS: Buxton (May). VAT: Spec.

POYNTON, Nr. Stockport

Harper Fine Paintings
"Overdale", Woodford Rd. SK12 1ED. (P.R. Harper). Est. 1967. Open by appointment. SIZE: Large. *STOCK: Watercolours, £100-£35,000; oils including European, £250-£60,000.* LOC: From A523 centre of Poynton lights, turn into Chester Rd., over railway. After ¼ mile turn right, 1st drive on left after railway bridge. PARK: Easy. TEL: 01625 879105; home - same; fax - 01625 850128; e-mail - Peteevette@aol.com. SER: Valuations; restorations; buys at auction (as stock). VAT: Stan/Spec.

Recollections
69 Park Lane. SK12 1RD. (Angela Smith). Open 10-5. SIZE: Medium. *STOCK: Antique, pre-war and secondhand furniture; costume jewellery and decorative collectables.* PARK: Own at rear and Civic Centre. TEL: 01625 859373.

RINGWAY, Nr. Altrincham

Cottage Antiques
Hasty Lane. WA15 8UT. (J. and J. M. Gholam). Est. 1967. SIZE: Medium. *STOCK: Furniture, metalware, ceramics, glass, early 18th-mid 19th C.* Not Stocked: Jewellery, jade and ivory. LOC: Off junction 6, M56, off A538, very close to airport. PARK: Easy. TEL: 0161 980 7961. SER: Valuations.

ROMILEY, Nr. Stockport

Romiley Antiques & Jewellery
42 Stockport Rd. SK6 3AA. (P. Green). Est. 1983. Open Thurs., Fri. and Sat. 9-5. SIZE: Medium. *STOCK: Furniture, 18th-19th C, £100-£2,000; ceramics, 18th-19th C, £5-£1,000; jewellery, 19th C, £5-£1,000.* LOC: 5 miles from Stockport. PARK: Nearby. TEL: 0161 494 6920; home - same. SER: Valuations. VAT: Stan/Spec.

SANDBACH

Saxon Cross Antiques Emporium
Town Mill, High St. CW11 1AH. (John and Christine Jones). Est. 1972. Open 10-5, Tues. 10-4.30, Sun. 11-4, Mon. by appointment only. SIZE: Large. *STOCK: Furniture, 16th to early 20th C, £50-£1,000; glass, silver, china and porcelain, 19th-20th C, £50-£1,000;* LOC: .75 miles off junction 17, M6. PARK: Easy and nearby. TEL: 01270 753005; fax - same. SER: Valuations; restorations; buys at auction. FAIRS: Cheshire Show. VAT: Stan/Spec.

STOCKPORT

Antique Furniture Warehouse
Units 3/4 Royal Oak Buildings, Cooper St. SK1 3QJ. Est. 1982. Open 9-5. SIZE: Large. *STOCK: English and Continental mahogany, walnut and inlaid furniture, paintings, clocks, shipping goods, pottery, porcelain and curios, decorative items, architectural.* LOC: 5 mins. off M56 towards town centre, 2 mins. off M60. PARK: Easy. TEL: 0161 429 8590; fax - 0161 480 5375. SER: Courier; packing. VAT: Stan.

Antiques Import Export
20 Buxton Rd., Hevley. SK2 6NU. Open 9.30-5.30. SIZE: Large. *STOCK: American and pre-1930 English furniture, to £5,000.* PARK: Easy. TEL: 0161 476 4013; fax - 0161 285 2860; e-mail - paul@antiquesimportexport.freeserve.co.uk. SER: Valuations; restorations. FAIRS: Newark.

E. R. Antiques Centre
122 Wellington St., off Wellington Rd. South. SK1 1YH. (E. Warburton). Est. 1979. Open 12.30-7.30. SIZE: Medium - 6 dealers. *STOCK: China, pottery, glass, silver, EPNS, costume jewellery, 1820-1960, £5-£200.* LOC: Turn into Edwards St. by the Town Hall, at 'T' junction turn left, shop 500yds. on left at bollards. PARK: Easy. TEL: 0161 429 6646; home - 0161 292 2296.

Flintlock Antiques
28 and 30 Bramhall Lane. SK2 6HD. (F. Tomlinson and Son). Est. 1968. Open 9-5. SIZE: Large. *STOCK: Furniture, clocks, pictures, scientific instruments.* TEL: 0161 480 9973. VAT: Stan/Spec.

Halcyon Antiques
435/437 Buxton Rd., Great Moor. SK2 7HE. (Mrs Jill A. Coppock). Est. 1980. Open 10-5. SIZE: Large. *STOCK: Porcelain and glass, £1-£2,000; furniture, £50-£2,000; both 1750-1940: jewellery, silver and plate, linen and lace.* LOC: A6, 2 miles south of town. PARK: Easy. TEL: 0161 483 5038; home - 0161 439 3524.

Imperial Antiques
295 Buxton Rd., Great Moor. SK2 7NR. (A. Todd). LAPADA. Est. 1972. Open 10-5, Sun. by appointment. SIZE: Large. *STOCK: Silver and plate, 19th-20th C; porcelain especially Japanese and Chinese, 18th-19th C; both £10-£1,000.* LOC: A6 Buxton Rd., 1.5 miles south of town centre. PARK: Easy. TEL: 0161 483 3322; e-mail - Alfred.todd@imperial antiques.com; website - www.imperialantiques.com. SER: Buys at auction (as stock). VAT: Stan/Spec.

Sue Ledger Antiques
370 Buxton Rd. SK2 7BY. (Sue Ledger and M. Shipley). Open 10.30-5. CL: Wed. SIZE: Medium.

STOCK: Pine furniture, decorative items, smalls, £25-£1,000. LOC: A6. PARK: Easy. TEL: 0161 483 6603.

Limited Editions
35 King St. East. SK1 1XJ. (C.W. Fogg). Est. 1978. Open 9.45-6, Sat. 9.30-5.30. SIZE: Large. *STOCK: Furniture, 19th C, especially dining tables and chairs, £100-£5,000; arm chairs and couches for re-upholstery.* LOC: Off Warren St., next to Sainsbury's. PARK: Own at rear. TEL: 0161 480 1239; e-mail - info@ltd-editions.co.uk; website - www.ltd-editions.co.uk. SER: Valuations; restorations (furniture). VAT: Stan/Spec.

Manchester Antique Company
MAC House, St Thomas's Place. SK1 3TZ. Open 9.30-4.30. SIZE: Large. *STOCK: Antique furniture, English, Continental and shipping goods, mainly walnut and mahogany.* TEL: 0161 355 5566/5577; e-mail - sales@manchesterantique. co.uk; website - www. manchester-antique.co.uk.

Nostalgia Architectural Antiques
Holland's Mill, Shaw Heath. SK3 8BH. (D. and E. Durrant). LAPADA. Est. 1975. Open Tues.-Fri. 10-6, Sat. 10-5. SIZE: Large. *STOCK: Fireplaces, £200-£50,000; bathroom fittings and architectural items, £50-£2,000; all 18th-19th C.* PARK: At rear. TEL: 0161 477 7706; fax - 0161 477 2267; website - www.nostalgia-uk.com. SER: Valuations. VAT: Stan/Spec.

The Old Curiosity Shop
123 Stockport Rd. West, Bredbury. SK6 2AN. (Sandra Crook). Est. 1984. Open 10-6, Sun. 12-5. CL: Wed. SIZE: Medium. *STOCK: 1920's, 1930's oak furniture, especially barley twist; brass coal buckets, fire tools.* LOC: 2 miles from M60. PARK: Forecourt or opposite. TEL: 0161 494 9469; home - same. SER: Restorations (furniture - hand stripping).

Victoria Imports
MAC House, St. Thomas's Place. SK1 3TZ. (S. Harris and T. Finn). Est. 1973. Open 8-5. CL: Sat. *STOCK: General antiques especially decorative lighting and four-poster beds.* TEL: 0161 285 1167; mobile - 07946 417074. SER: Valuations; restorations; export. VAT: Stan/Spec.

STRETTON, Nr. Warrington

Antiques Etc.
Shepcroft House, London Rd. WA4 5PJ. (M. Clare). Est. 1978. Resident, usually available. SIZE: Medium. *STOCK: Furniture, pine, barometers, clocks, instruments and items of interest, £5-£2,000.* LOC: A49, towards Warrington,

through Stretton traffic lights, next turning on left. PARK: Easy. TEL: 01925 730431; mobile - 07836 570663.

TARPORLEY

Tarporley Antique Centre
76 High St. CW6 0DP. Est. 1992. Open 10-5, Sun. 11-4. SIZE: 9 dealers on two floors. *STOCK: Furniture, ceramics, commemoratives, treen, Studio pottery, glass, oils, watercolours, prints.* LOC: Main road, near Crown public house. PARK: In front of premises and opposite. TEL: 01829 733919. SER: Buys at auction.

TARVIN, Nr. Chester

Antique Fireplaces
The Manor House, Church St. CH3. (Mrs G. O'Toole). Est. 1979. Open Fri., Sat. and Sun. 10-5 or by appointment. SIZE: Medium. *STOCK: Fireplaces and ranges, 18th-19th C, £150-£3,000.* LOC: At junction of A556 and A51. PARK: Easy. TEL: 01829 740936; home - 01606 46717. SER: Valuations; restorations; installations (fireplaces and ranges); new tiles and fenders ordered from suppliers on request. FAIRS: Tatton Park, Knutsford.

TARVIN SANDS, Nr. Chester

Cheshire Brick and Slate Co
Brook House Farm, Salters Bridge. CH3 8HL. (Malcolm and Jason Youde). Est. 1978. Open 8-5.30, Sat. 8-4.30, Sun. 10-4. SIZE: Large. *STOCK: Reclaimed conservation building materials, 16th-20th C; architectural antiques - garden statuary, stonework, lamp posts, gates, fireplaces, bathroom suites, chimney pots and ironwork, 18th-20th C, £50-£1,000; furniture, pews, leaded lights, pottery, 18th-20th C, £5-£1,000.* LOC: Directly off A54 just outside Tarvin. PARK: Own. TEL: 01829 740883; fax - 01829 740481; e-mail - enquiries@cheshire brickandslate.co.uk; website - www.cheshire brickandslate.co.uk. SER: Valuations; restorations (fireplaces, timber treatment); building/construction and demolition; renovations. VAT: Stan/Global.

TATTENHALL, Nr. Chester

The Great Northern Architectural Antique Company Ltd
New Russia Hall, Chester Rd. CH3 9AH. Open 9.30-5 including Sun. SIZE: Large. *STOCK: Period doors, fire surrounds, stained glass, sanitary ware, garden statuary, furniture and curios.* LOC: Off

A41. PARK: Easy. TEL: 01829 770796; fax - 01829 770971. SER: Stripping; restorations (stained glass); repairs (metalwork). VAT: Stan.

TILSTON, Nr. Malpas

Well House Antiques
The Well House. SY14 7DP. (S. French-Greenslade). Est. 1968. Open by appointment only. SIZE: Small. *STOCK: Collectors' items, china, glass, silver.* PARK: Easy. TEL: 01829 250332.

WARRINGTON

The Rocking Chair Antiques
Unit 3, St. Peter's Way. WA2 7BL. (M. and N.J. Barratt). Est. 1976. Open 8-5.30, Sat. 10-4. SIZE: Large. *STOCK: Furniture and bric-a-brac.* LOC: Off Orford Lane. PARK: Easy. TEL: 01925 652409; fax - same; mobile - 07774 492891. SER: Valuations; shipping, packing. VAT: Stan.

WAVERTON, Nr. Chester

The White House
Whitchurch Rd. CH3 7PB. (Mrs Elizabeth Rideal). Resident. Est. 1979. Open 10-5. SIZE: Medium. *STOCK: Stripped pine furniture, 19th-20th C, £50-£2,000; Victorian china, 19th C, £5-£100; bric-a-brac.* LOC: A41, 2.5 miles south of Sainsbury's roundabout on Whitchurch Rd. PARK: Easy. TEL: 01244 335063; home - same; fax - 01244 335098. VAT: Margin.

WIDNES

Iain Campbell
Unit A5, Moor Lane Business Centre, WA8 7AQ. Moor Lane. PBFA. Est. 1970. Open by appointment. SIZE: Small. *STOCK: Prints, 18th-19th C, £1-£100; drawings and watercolours, printed ephemera, books, 19th C, £1-£500.* LOC: On B5419. PARK: Easy. TEL: 0151 420 5545. FAIRS: Newark DGM; PBFA - London, Oxford, Cambridge, York, Haydock Park, Chester; Ephemera, London (June and Dec.). VAT: Stan.

WILMSLOW

Wilmslow Antiques
5 Church St. SK9 1AX. (G.M. and S.M. Dale). Est. 1996. Open 10-5. SIZE: Medium - 18 dealers. *STOCK: Wide range of general antiques and fine furniture, 18th-20th C, £5-£1,000+.* LOC: Town centre. PARK: At rear. TEL: 01625 540472; e-mail - pmdale99@aol.com.

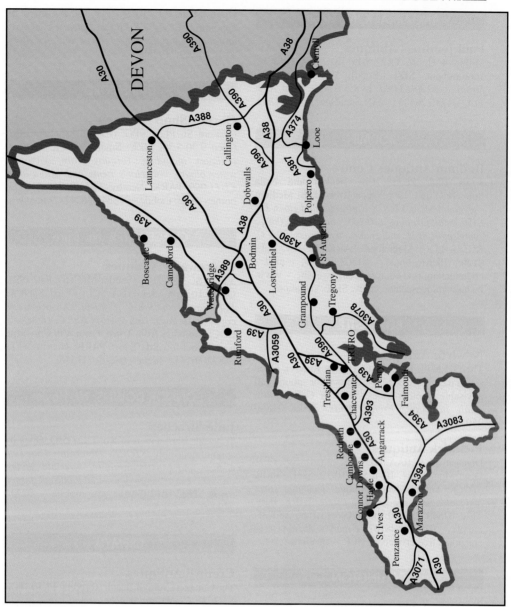

Dealers and Shops in Cornwall

				Penzance	10
Angarrack	1	Dobwalls	1	Polperro	2
Bodmin	1	Falmouth	4	Redruth	1
Boscastle	2	Grampound	2	Rumford	1
Callington	1	Hayle	1	St. Austell	1
Camborne	1	Launceston	2	St. Ives	3
Camelford	1	Looe	2	Tregony	1
Connor Downs	1	Lostwithiel	2	Tresillion	1
Chacewater	1	Marazion	1	Truro	6
Cremyll	1	Penryn	2	Wadebridge	2

ANGARRACK, Nr. Hayle

Paul Jennings Antiques
Millbrook House. TR27 5HY. Est. 1974. Open by
appointment. SIZE: Small. *STOCK: Clocks,
furniture, £100-£3,000.* LOC: ½ mile from A30.
TEL: 01736 754065. VAT: Stan/Spec. *Trade Only.*

BODMIN

Bodmin Antiques Centre
Town End. PL31 1LN. (Ralph and Nola
Solomons). Est. 1996. Open 10-4. SIZE: Medium
- several dealers. *STOCK: Ceramics and glass, £5-
£350, small furniture, £10-£350, both 19th-20th C;
commemoratives, kitchenalia, toys, brass, 20th C,
£5-£75.* LOC: Main road. PARK: Nearby. TEL:
01208 78661; home - 01208 74609; e-mail -
bodminantiques@hotmail. com; website - www.
bodminantiquescentre. co.uk. SER: Valuations.

BOSCASTLE

Newlyfe Antiques
The Old Mill. PL35 0AQ. (Harry Ruddy). Open
seven days a week May-Sept. - prior 'phone call
advisable at other times. *STOCK: Collectables,
small furniture, French beds.* TEL: 01840
250230.

Pickwick Antiques
Dunn St. PL35 0AA. (David Lamond). Est. 1970.
Open Mon.-Thurs. 10-4, Sat. 10-12. SIZE: Small.
*STOCK: General small antiques including silver
and plate, glass, pre 1950, £5-£500+.* PARK: Easy.
TEL: 01840 250770; home/fax - 01566 880085;
mobile - 07971 648107; e-mail - david-peter@
craigmoor.freeserve.co.uk. SER: Valuations.

CALLINGTON

Country Living Antiques
Weston House, Haye Rd. PL17 7JJ. (Ian Baxter
CBE). Resident. Est. 1990. Open 10-6. SIZE:
Large - including barn. *STOCK: 19th C oak and
pine country furniture, general antiques, £1-
£2,000.* LOC: Town centre. PARK: Own. TEL:
01579 382245; fax - same. SER: Valuations; buys
at auction.

CAMBORNE

Victoria Gallery & Bookshop
28 Cross St. TR14 8EX. (B.J. and J.P. Maker).

Open Mon.-Fri. 10.30-5.15, other times by
appointment. *STOCK: Books, pictures, general
antiques, small furniture, silver and jewellery.*
TEL: 01209 719268.

CAMELFORD

Corner Shop Antiques
68 Fore St. PL32 9PG. (P.J. Tillett). Est. 1982.
Open 9.30-5.30. SIZE: Small. *STOCK: General
antiques including Torquay ware, Victorian
watercolours, collector's items and bric-a-brac,
£2-£1,000.* PARK: Nearby. TEL: 01840 212573;
home - same; mobile - 07884 456247. *Trade Only.*

CHACEWATER, Nr. Truro

Chacewater Antiques
5 Fore St. TR4 8PS. (Sandra McCall). Est. 1991.
Open 10.30-4, Sat. 10-1. CL: Wed. *STOCK:
Furniture, 17th-19th C, £100-£1,000; brass and
copper, paintings, 19th to early 20th C, £80-£450.*
LOC: 5 minutes from Truro. From A30 Chiverton
roundabout towards Truro. PARK: Nearby. TEL:
01872 561411; home - 01209 711545.

CONNOR DOWNS, Nr. Hayle

Julie Strachey
Trevaskis Barn, Gwinear Rd. TR27 5JQ. Open by
appointment only. *STOCK: Decorative 18th-19th
C farm and country furniture, especially tables,
dressers, chests, wrought iron and unusual garden
items.* TEL: 01207 613750; mobile - 07711
249939.

CREMYLL

Cremyll Antiques
The Cottage, Cremyll Beach, Torpoint. PL10 1HX.
*STOCK: Clocks and watches, small items, jewell-
ery.* TEL: 01752 823490. SER: Repairs (barometers, barographs, watches, clocks, jewellery).

DOBWALLS, Nr. Liskeard

Olden Days
Five Lanes. PL14 6JD. (F. J. C. Nancarrow and K.
E. C. Trevellian). Est. 1980. Open 9.30-5.30, Sun.
11-4. SIZE: Medium. *STOCK: Period furniture,
£50-£1,500; reclaimed and new pine furniture;
bric-a-brac and collectables.* LOC: A38 between
Liskeard and Bodmin. PARK: Easy and private
behind shop. TEL: 01579 321577; home - same; e-

mail - dobwallsantiques@talk21.com; website - www.oldendays.org. SER: Restorations; furniture made to order. VAT: Stan/Spec.

FALMOUTH

John Maggs
54 Church St. TR11 3DS. (C.C. Nunn). Est. 1900. Open 10-5. SIZE: Medium. *STOCK: Antiquarian prints and maps, exclusive limited editions.* LOC: Main street. PARK: At rear of shop. TEL: 01326 313153; fax - same; website - www.johnmaggs. co.uk. SER: Restorations; framing.

Old Town Hall Antiques
3 High St. TR11 2AB. (Mary P. Sheppard and Terence J. Brandreth). Est. 1986. Open 10-5.30, Sun. by appointment. SIZE: Large + trade store. *STOCK: Furniture including French, beds and mirrors, 19th-20th C, £100-£2,000; country smalls, china and collectables, 19th-20th C, £10-£60.* LOC: From edge of Falmouth follow signs towards marina, shop situated on right under road arch (one-way street). PARK: Easy. TEL: 01326 319437; home - 01326 377489. SER: Storage and deliveries. VAT: Global.

Rosina's
4 High St. TR11 2AB. (Mrs R. Gealer). Open 11-4.30. *STOCK: Old dolls, bears, including limited edition, Steiff and artist bears, toys, linen and lace, clothes; modern miniatures. Fairies especially designed for Rosina's.* TEL: 01326 311406; home - 01326 317739. SER: Restorations.

Waterfront Antiques Market
1st Floor, 4 Quay St. TR11 3HH. Open 10-5. SIZE: 20 dealers. *STOCK: Furniture, pottery, porcelain, glass, silver, metalware, kitchenalia, pictures, books, clocks, jewellery, decorative and collectors' items.* TEL: 01326 311491.

GRAMPOUND, Nr. Truro

Pine and Period Furniture
Fore St. TR2 4QT. (S. Payne). Est. 1971. Open 10.30-5. *STOCK: Pine and period furniture.* TEL: 01726 883117. SER: Restorations.

Radnor House
Fore St. TR2 4QT. (P. and G. Hodgson). Est. 1972. Open 10-5. SIZE: Medium. *STOCK: Furniture and accessories, pre-1900.* Not Stocked: Jewellery, coins and weapons. LOC: A390. PARK: Easy. TEL: 01726 882921; home - same. SER: Valuations; buys at auction.

HAYLE

Copperhouse Gallery - W. Dyer & Sons
14 Fore St. TR27 4DX. (A.P. Dyer). Est. 1900. Open 9-5.30. SIZE: Medium. *STOCK: Watercolours and oils, including Newlyn and St. Ives schools; small antiques, Art Deco and studio pottery.* LOC: Main road. PARK: Easy. TEL: 01736 752787; home - 01736 752960. SER: Framing.

LAUNCESTON

Antique Chairs and Museum
Colhay Farm, Polson. PL15 9QS. (Tom and Alice Brown). Est. 1988. Open seven days. SIZE: Large. *STOCK: Chairs, 18th-20th C.* LOC: Signed from A30. PARK: Easy. TEL: 01566 777485; fax - same; home - same. SER: Restorations; buys at auction.

Todd's
2 High St. and 8 Tower St. PL15 8ER. (B. Gallant and T. Mead). Est. 1997. Open 9-5, Sat. 9-4. SIZE: Medium and small. *STOCK: Furniture, from 18th C, £100-£2000; ceramics, from 18th C, £10-£400; reproduction period lighting, £40-£500.* PARK: Nearby. TEL: 01566 775007/ 772749; fax - 01566 775007. SER: Restorations. VAT: Stan/Spec.

LOOE

Dowling and Bray
Fore St., East Looe. PL13 1AE. Est. 1920. *STOCK: General antiques, furniture and brassware.* TEL: 01503 262797.

Tony Martin
Fore St. PL13 1AE. Est. 1965. Open 9.30-1 and 2-5 appointment advisable. CL: Thurs. pm. SIZE: Medium. *STOCK: Porcelain, 18th C; silver, 18th-19th C, both £20-£200; glass, furniture, oils and watercolours.* LOC: Main street. TEL: 01503 262734; home - 01503 262228.

LOSTWITHIEL

John Bragg Antiques
35 Fore St. PL22 0BN. Open 10-5. CL: Wed. pm. *STOCK: Furniture, mainly period mahogany and Victorian.* LOC: 100yds. off A390. TEL: 01208 872827.

Old Palace Antiques

Old Palace, Quay St. PL22 0BS. (D. Bryant). Open 10-1 and 2-5. CL: Wed. pm. *STOCK: Pine, general antiques, books, postcards and collectors' items.* TEL: 01208 872909.

Antiques

The Shambles, Market Place. TR17 0AR. (Andrew S. Wood). Est. 1988. Open Mon.-Fri. 10.15-5.30, also Sats. 1 Nov.-31 March. SIZE: Medium. *STOCK: General antiques and collectors' items including 19th-20th C pottery and porcelain; Victorian to 20th C glass including pressed; blue and white china, Art Deco ceramics, Devon pottery, commemorative ware, Goss and crested china, 1950's-60's pottery and glass, bottles.* LOC: Main street. PARK: Easy. TEL: 01736 711381; home - same.

Old School Antiques

Church Rd. TR10 8DA. (J.M. Gavin). Open 8.30-6. *STOCK: General antiques.* TEL: 01326 375092.

Neil Willcox & Mark Nightingale

Jobswater, Mabe. TR10 9BT. Open by appointment. *STOCK: Sealed wine and other bottles, British and Continental 1650-1850, and related items.* TEL: 01326 340533; fax - same; e-mail - nightdes@aol.com; website - www.earlyglass.com. SER: Valuations; mail order - catalogue and photos supplied.

Antiques & Fine Art

1 Queens Buildings, The Promenade. TR18 4DL. (Elinor Davies and Geoffrey Mills). Est. 1985. Open 10-4. SIZE: Medium. *STOCK: Furniture, 17th C to Edwardian, to £4,000; some decorative pieces, to £250.* LOC: Next to Queen's Hotel. PARK: Nearby. TEL: 01736 350509; home - 01736 350677; e-mail - antiquesandfineart@tinyworld.co.uk. SER: Valuations; restorations (furniture including upholstery); buys at auction (furniture).

Chapel Street Antiques Arcade

61/62 Chapel St. TR18 4AE. Open 9.30-5. SIZE: 20 dealers. *STOCK: Furniture, pottery, porcelain, glass, silver, metalware, kitchenalia, pictures, books, clocks, jewellery, decorative and collectors' items.* TEL: Mobile - 07890 542708.

Daphne's Antiques

17 Chapel St. TR18 4AW. Est. 1976. Open 10-5. SIZE: Medium. *STOCK: Early country furniture, Georgian glass, Delft, pottery and decorative objects.* TEL: 01736 361719.

Peter Johnson

62 Chapel St. TR18 4AE. (Peter Chatfield-Johnson). Est. 1961. Open 9.30-5, Mon. by appointment. SIZE: Small. *STOCK: Lighting, 19th-20th C, £25-£500; Oriental ceramics and furniture, 18th-19th C, £25-£2,000; handmade silk lampshades, 20th C, £25-£250.* LOC: Left at top of Market Jew St. PARK: Easy. TEL: 01736 363267; home - 01736 368088. SER: Valuations; restorations (soft furnishings).

Little Jem's

69 Causewayhead. TR18 2SR. (J. Lagden). Open 9.30-5. *STOCK: Antique and modern jewellery (specialising in opal and amber), gem stones, objets d'art, paintings, clocks and watches.* TEL: 01736 351400. SER: Repairs; commissions.

New Street Bookshop

4 New St. TR18 2LZ. (K.E. Hearn and C.J. Bradley). Open 10-5. *STOCK: Books and ephemera.* LOC: Close to town centre, just off Chapel St. TEL: 01736 362758; e-mail - eankelvin@yahoo.com.

The Old Custom House

53 Chapel St. TR18 4AF. (Manfred Baker and Ulrich Grote). Est. 1997. Open 9-5.30. SIZE: Medium. *STOCK: Porcelain and glass, silver and small furniture, contemporary paintings.* TEL: 01736 331030.

Penzance Rare Books

43 Causewayhead. TR18 2SS. (Patricia Johnstone). Est. 1990. Open 10-5. SIZE: Small. *STOCK: Anitquarian and secondhand books.* LOC: Top of Causewayhead. PARK: Nearby. TEL: 01736 362140; home - 01736 367506; e-mail - patricia. johnstone@btinternet.com. SER: Valuations.

Tony Sanders Penzance Gallery and Antiques

14 Chapel St. TR18 4AW. Est. 1972. Open 9-5.30. SIZE: 3 floors. *STOCK: Oils and watercolours, 19th-20th C, £50-£5,000; glass, silver, china and small furniture; specialist in Newlyn and J F Pool of Hayle copper; contemporary art, paintings and bronzes.* TEL: 01736 366620/368461. VAT: Stan.

Ursus

1 Arcade Steps. TR18 2LX. (Mrs J. Piper). Est. 1999. Open summer only Wed.-Sat. 10-3 or other times by appointment. SIZE: Small. *STOCK: Teddy bears and toys, 1900-1960, £5-£2,000.*

LOC: Town centre, just off main street. TEL: 01736 364605; home - 01736 871537; e-mail - piper@tredavoe.freeserve.co.uk; website - ursus. co.uk. SER: Valuations; restorations (bears); buys at auction (bears and dolls).

POLPERRO

Gentry Antiques
c/o Rod & Line, Little Green. PL13 2RF. (Marilyn Gentry). Est. 2000. Open 10-5. SIZE: Small. *STOCK: Ceramics, mainly blue and white; country furniture especially stickback chairs, Cornishware, kitchenalia, brass and copper, £10-£1,000.* PARK: At entrance to village. TEL: 01503 272361; home - 01503 272796; website - www.cornishware collector.co.uk. SER: Valuations.

Past & Presents inc. Upstairs, Downstairs
1 Lansallos St. PL13 2QU. (Joe Askew and Melanie Jane Wray). Est. 1998. Open Nov.-Mar. 10-4, summer months 9-7. SIZE: Small. *STOCK: Oak and pine country furniture, oil lamps, Victorian kitchen enamelware and utensils, Staffordshire pottery, Beswick, Beatrix Potter, Royal Doulton character jugs, crested china.* PARK: Nearby. TEL: 01503 272737; home - 01503 272984; e-mail - info@polperro-antiques .com; website - www.polperro-antiques.com.

REDRUTH

The Old Steam Bakery
60A Fore St. TR14 7NU. (Stephen J. Phillips). Est. 1986. Open 10.30-5. SIZE: Large. *STOCK: Furniture including oak, 19th to early 20th C, £50-£100+; china and glass, early 20th C.* LOC: Next to main Post Office. PARK: Easy. TEL: 01209 315099; home - 01209 710650. SER: Valuations; restorations (furniture). VAT: Stan.

RUMFORD

Henley House Antiques
PL27 7SS. (J.L. Neale). Open any time by appointment. SIZE: Small. *STOCK: Juvenilia, small antiques, bric-a-brac.* PARK: Easy. TEL: 01841 540322; e-mail - nealej@talk21.com.

ST. AUSTELL

Mrs. Margaret Chesterton
33 Pentewan Rd. PL25 5BU. Est. 1965. Open 10-5.30, appointment advisable. CL: Sat. pm.

STOCK: Victoriana, Edwardiana, 1800-1915; some furniture, porcelain, glass, £1-£500; brass, copper, pewter, jewellery, clocks, watercolours. LOC: Coming from Plymouth, travel direct to St. Austell. Keep on main by-pass until roundabout for Mevagissey and Pentewan Rd. House is 100yds. on left down this road. PARK: Easy. TEL: 01726 72926.

ST. IVES

Courtyard Collectables
Cyril Noall Sq., Fore St. TR26 1HE. (Janice Mosedale). Est. 1994. Open June to end Sept. 7 days 10-10; Oct., April and May 7 days 10-6; Nov. to March, Tues.-Sun. 10.30-4.30. SIZE: Medium. *STOCK: 20th C collectables.* TEL: 01736 798809. SER: Valuations; buys at auction.

Mike Read Antique Sciences
1 Abbey Meadow, Lelant. TR26 3LL. Est. 1974. Open by appointment. SIZE: Small. *STOCK: Scientific instruments - navigational, surveying, mining, barometers, telescopes and microscopes, medical, 18th-19th C, £10-£5,000; maritime works of art and nautical artifacts.* LOC: Turn left on hill in village, heading towards St. Ives. PARK: Easy. TEL: 01736 757237. SER: Valuations; restorations.

Tremayne Applied Arts
Street-an-Pol. TR26 2DS. (Roger and Anne Tonkinson). Est. 1998. Summer - Open 10.30-4.30, Sat. 10-1.30. CL: Wed. Winter - Open Mon., Fri., Sat. morning. *STOCK: Furniture, china, glass, paintings and prints, late 19th to late 20th C, £50-£3,000.* LOC: Central, close to tourist information office. PARK: Station. TEL: 01736 797779; fax - 01736 793222; home - 01736 753537.

TREGONY, Nr. Truro

Tregony Antiques
The Old Rectory, Fore St. TR2 5RW. (The Oliver Family). Open 10.30-5, (extended in summer), evenings and Sun. by appointment. SIZE: Medium. *STOCK: Ceramics, including Doulton stoneware, £10-£500; paintings and prints, 19th to early 20th C, £50-£1,000; furniture, 18th to early 20th C, £75-£3,000; brass, copper and treen, £10-£300.* Not Stocked: Silver and jewellery. LOC: Village centre, B3287. PARK: Easy. TEL: 01872 530225; home - same.

ALAN BENNETT

18th and 19th century Furniture, Porcelain Silver, Jewellery and Paintings

NEW BRIDGE HOUSE NEW BRIDGE STREET TRURO CORNWALL
Truro 273296

TRESILLIAN, Nr. Truro

Tresillian Antiques
The Elms. TR2 4BA. (Philip and Linda Buddell). Est. 1972. Open 9.30-5.30, Sun. by appointment. SIZE: Small. *STOCK: Oak and mahogany furniture, Georgian, Victorian and Edwardian; collectables including china, ivory, silver and teddy bears; oils and watercolours, mainly landscape and marine.* LOC: A390. PARK: Easy. TEL: 01872 520173; home - same; mobile - 0797 4022893; e-mail - lindabudd@aol.com. SER: Valuations; restorations (furniture, canework and paintings).

TRURO

Alan Bennett
24 New Bridge St. TR1 2AA. Est. 1954. Open 9-5.30. SIZE: Large. *STOCK: Furniture, £50-£5,000; jewellery and porcelain, to 1900, £5-£1,000; paintings and prints, £20-£2,000.* LOC: Eastern side of cathedral. PARK: 100yds. from shop. TEL: 01872 273296. VAT: Stan/Spec.

Blackwater Pine Antiques
Blackwater. TR4 8ET. (J.S.Terrett). Open 9-6. *STOCK: Pine and country furniture.* TEL: 01872 560919. SER: Restorations; stripping; furniture made to order.

Bonython Bookshop
16 Kenwyn St. TR1 3BU. (Rosemary Carpenter). Est. 1996. Open 10.30-4.30. SIZE: Small. *STOCK: Cornish books, £5-£200; topography, £5-£50; art, £5-£100.* TEL: 01872 262886; e-mail - bonython books@mobooks.freeserve.co. uk; website - www. abebooks.com. SER: Valuations; booksearch.

Bric-a-Brac
16A Walsingham Place. TR1 2RP. (Lynne and Richard Bonehill). Est. 1991. SIZE: Small. *STOCK: Militaria, £5-£2,000; small furniture, £20-£1,000; commemorative and crested china, £5-£150; collectors' items and bric-a-brac, 50p-£2,000; all 19th-20th C.* LOC: Town centre, just off Victoria Sq. PARK: Multi-storey nearby. TEL: 01872 225200; e-mail - richard@bonehill3.freeserve.co.uk; website - www.bonehill3.freeserve.co.uk. FAIRS: Lostwithiel.

The Coinage Hall Antiques Centre
1 Boscawen St. TR1 2QU. (Graham and Pippa Kennedy). Est. 1994. Open 10-4.30. SIZE: Medium. *STOCK: Fine art, furniture, paintings, sculpture, lighting, architectural items, collectables including postcards.* LOC: City centre. PARK: Easy. TEL: 01872 262520; fax - same. SER: Valuations; restorations (fine art, furniture). FAIRS: Newark, Shepton Mallet, Westpoint.

Collector's Corner
45-46 Pannier Market, Back Quay. TR1 2LL. (Alan McLoughlin and John Lethbridge). Est. 1980. Open 9.30-4.30, Sat. 9-4. SIZE: Small. *STOCK: Stamps, coins, postcards, medals, postal history, militaria, £5-£500.* LOC: City centre. PARK: Nearby. TEL: 01872 272729; home - 01326 573509; mobile - 07815 668551. SER: Valuations.

WADEBRIDGE

St. Breock Gallery
St. Breock Churchtown. PL27 7JS. (R.G.G. Haslam-Hopwood). Est. 1970. Open 10-5. *STOCK: Oils and watercolours, 20th-21st C; furniture, general antiques and objets d'art, £20-£2,000.* LOC: Near Royal Cornwall Showground. PARK: Own. TEL: 01208 812543; fax - 01208 814671; e-mail - hopscotch@stbroeck.freeserve. co.uk; website - www.tomorrows-antiques.com. SER: Restorations; buys at auction; furniture copies made to order. VAT: Spec.

Victoria Antiques
21 Molesworth St. PL27 7DQ. (M. and S. Daly). Open Mon.-Sat. SIZE: Large. *STOCK: Furniture, 17th-19th C, £25-£10,000.* LOC: On A39 between Bude and Newquay. PARK: Nearby. TEL: 01208 814160. SER: Valuations; restorations.. VAT: Stan/Spec/Global.

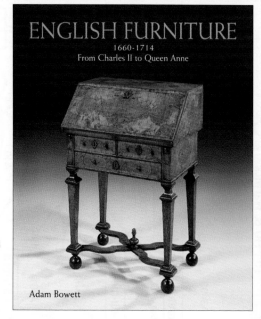

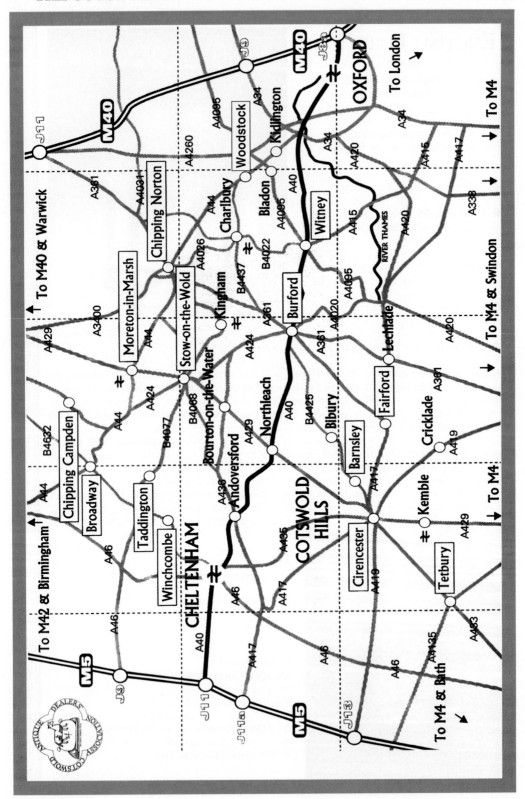

THE COTSWOLD ANTIQUE DEALERS' ASSOCIATION

Buy Fine Antiques and Works of Art at provincial prices in England's lovely and historic countryside

The Cotswolds, one of the finest areas of unspoilt countryside in the land, have been called "the essence and the heart of England." The region has a distinctive character created by the use of honey-coloured stone in its buildings and dry stone walls. Within the locality the towns and villages are admirably compact and close to each other and the area is well supplied with good hotels and reasonably priced inns. The Cotswolds are within easy reach of London (1½ hour by road or rail) and several major airports.

Cotswold sheep – which inspired the logo for the Cotswold Antique Dealers' Association – a quatrefoil device with a sheep in its centre – have played an important part in the region's history with much of its wealth created by the woollen industry. As for antiques, shops and warehouses of the CADA offer a selection of period furniture, pictures, porcelain, metalwork, and collectables unrivalled outside London.

With the use of the CADA directory on the following pages, which lists the names of its members, their specialities and opening times, visitors from all over the world can plan their buying visit to the Cotswolds. CADA members will assist all visiting collectors and dealers in locating antiques and works of art. They will give you advice on where to stay in the area, assistance with packing, shipping and insurance and the exchange of foreign currencies. They can advise private customers on what can realistically be bought on their available budgets, and if the first dealer does not have the piece which you are selecting he will know of several other members who will. The CADA welcomes home and overseas buyers in the certain knowledge that there are at least fifty dealers with a good and varied stock, a reputation for fair trading and an annual turnover in excess of £15,000,000.

179

BARNSLEY, Nr. Cirencester

Denzil Verey
Barnsley House. GL7 5EE. CADA. Resident. Est. 1980. Open 9.30-5.30, Sat. 10-5.30, other times by appointment. SIZE: Large. *STOCK: Country furniture, including pine, 18th-19th C; decorative and unusual items, treen, copper, brass, domestic and rural objects, kitchenalia.* LOC: 4 miles from Cirencester on B4425 to Burford, 1st large house in village, set back off road on the right. PARK: Easy. TEL: 01285 740402; fax - 01285 740628. VAT: Stan/Spec.

BROADWAY

Fenwick and Fenwick Antiques
88-90 High St. WR12 7AJ. (George and Jane Fenwick). CADA. Est. 1980. Open 10-6 and by appointment. SIZE: Large. *STOCK: Furniture, oak, mahogany and walnut, 17th to early 19th C; samplers, boxes, treen, Tunbridgeware, Delft, decorative items and corkscrews.* PARK: Easy and own by arrangement. TEL: 01386 853227; after hours - 01386 841724; fax - 01386 858504. VAT: Spec.

Haynes Fine Art of Broadway   BADA
Picton House Galleries, 42 High St. WR12 7DT. (A. C. Haynes). LAPADA. CADA. Open 9-6. SIZE: Large - 12 showrooms. *STOCK: Over 2000 British and European 16th-21st C oil paintings and watercolours.* LOC: From Lygon Arms, 100 yds up High St. on left. PARK: Easy. TEL: 01386 852649; fax - 01386 858187; e-mail - enquiries@haynes-fine-art.co.uk; website - www. haynesfineart.com. SER: Free valuations; restorations; framing; catalogue available (£10). VAT: Spec.

H. W. Keil Ltd   BADA
Tudor House. WR12 7DP. CADA. Est. 1925. Open 9. 15-12. 45 and 2. 15-5. 30. SIZE: Large. *STOCK: Walnut, oak, mahogany and rosewood furniture; early pewter, brass and copper, tapestry, glass and works of art, 17th-18th C.* LOC: By village clock. TEL: 01386 852408; fax - 01386 852069. VAT: Spec.

John Noott Galleries   BADA
58 High St. , 14 Cotswold Court, and at The Lygon Arms, High St. WR12 7AA. LAPADA. CADA. Est. 1972. Open 9. 30-1 and 2-5. SIZE: Large. *STOCK: Paintings, watercolours and bronzes, 19th C to Contemporary.* PARK: Easy. TEL: 01386 854868/858969; fax - 01386 854919. SER: Valuations; restorations; framing. VAT: Stan/Spec.

BURFORD

Jonathan Fyson Antiques
50 High St. OX18 4QF. (J.R.Fyson). CADA. Est. 1970. Open 9.30-1 and 2-5.30. SIZE: Medium. *STOCK: English and Continental furniture, decorative brass and steel including lighting and fireplace accessories; club fenders, mirrors, porcelain, glass, jewellery.* LOC: At junction of A40/A361 between Oxford and Cheltenham. PARK: Easy. TEL: 01993 823204; fax - same; home - 01367 860223; e-mail - j@fyson.co.uk. SER: Valuations. VAT: Spec.

Gateway Antiques
Cheltenham Rd., Burford Roundabout. OX18 4JA. (M.C. Ford and P. Brown). CADA. Est. 1986. Open 10-5.30 and Sun. 2-5. SIZE: Large. *STOCK: English and Continental furniture, 18th to early 20th C; decorative accessories.* LOC: On roundabout (A40) Oxford/Cheltenham road, adjacent to the Cotswold Gateway Hotel. PARK: Easy. TEL: 01993 823678/822624; fax - 01993 823857; e-mail - enquiries@gatewayantiques. co.uk; website - www.gatewayantiques.co.uk. SER: Courier (multi-lingual). VAT: Stan/Spec.

David Pickup   BADA
115 High St. OX18 4RG. CADA. Est. 1977. Open 9.30-1 and 2-5.30, Sat. 10-1 and 2-4. SIZE: Medium. *STOCK: Fine furniture, works of art, from £500+; decorative objects, from £100+; all late 17th to mid 20th C, specialising in Arts and Crafts.* PARK: Easy. TEL: 01993 822555. FAIRS: Olympia. VAT: Spec.

Richard Purdon Antique Carpets
**   BADA**
158 The Hill. OX18 4QY. CADA. Open 10-5. SIZE: Medium. *STOCK: Antique Eastern and European carpets, village and tribal rugs, needle-work, textiles and related items.* TEL: 01993 823777; fax - 01993 823719; e-mail - rp@richardpurdon.demon.co.uk; website - www.purdon.com. SER: Valuations; restorations. FAIRS: Hali (Olympia). VAT: Stan/Spec.

Manfred Schotten Antiques
109 High St. OX18 4RG. CADA. Est. 1974. Open 9.30-5.30 or by appointment. *STOCK: Sporting antiques and library furniture.* TEL: 01993 822302; fax - 01993 822055; e-mail - antiques@schotten.com; website - www.schotten. com. SER: Restorations. FAIRS: Olympia (Spring, Summer and Winter). VAT: Stan/Margin.

Brian Sinfield Gallery
150 High St. OX18 4QU. CADA. Est. 1972. Open 10-5.30, Mon. by appointment. *STOCK: Mainly contemporary and late 20th C paintings, watercolours and sculpture; contemporary Indian miniatures.* TEL: 01993 824464; fax - 01993 824525; e-mail - gallery@briansinfield. com; website - www.briansinfield.com. SER: 8 exhibitions annually.

Swan Gallery
High St. OX18 4RE. (D. Pratt). CADA. Est. 1966. Open 10-5.30. SIZE: Large. *STOCK: Country furniture in oak, yew, walnut and fruitwood, 17th-19th C, £300-£12,000; Staffordshire figures and small decorative items, 18th-20th C, £50-£800.* PARK: Easy. TEL: 01993 822244. VAT: Mainly Spec.

CHIPPING CAMPDEN

The Titian Gallery
London House, High St. GL55 6AG. (Ilona Johnson Gibbs). LAPADA. CADA. CINOA. Est. 1976. Open 10-1 and 2-5, Sun. by appointment. SIZE: 2 showrooms. *STOCK: Fine 18th-19th C British and European oil paintings and watercolours, to £40,000.* LOC: Near centre of town square. PARK: Easy. TEL: 01386 841789; fax - 01386 849151; e-mail - ilona@titiangallery.co.uk; website - www. titiangallery.co.uk. SER: Valuations; buys at auction (oils and watercolours). VAT: Spec.

CHIPPING NORTON

Antique English Windsor Chairs BADA
at Bugle Antiques 9 Horse Fair. OX7 5AL. CINOA. CADA. Est. 1971. Open 10-5 (prior telephone call advisable). CL: Mon. and Tues. except by appointment. *STOCK: 18th-19th C Windsor chairs, including sets.* TEL: 01608 643322; fax - 01608 644322; e-mail - michael @antique-english-windsor-chairs.com; website - www.antique-english-windsor-chairs. com. FAIRS: BADA; Olympia (June, Nov). VAT: Stan/Spec.

Key Antiques
11 Horse Fair. OX7 5AL. (J. Riley). LAPADA, CADA. Open 10-5.30 or by appointment. CL: Mon. and Tues. SIZE: Medium. *STOCK: English period oak and country furniture, 17th-19th C; domestic metalware, pottery and associated items.* LOC: On main road. PARK: Easy. TEL: 01608 644992. VAT: Spec.

CIRENCESTER

William H. Stokes   BADA
The Cloisters, 6/8 Dollar St. GL7 2AJ. (W.H. Stokes and P.W. Bontoft). CADA. Est. 1968. Open 9.30-5.30, Sat. 9.30-4.30. *STOCK: Early oak furniture, £1,000-£30,000; brassware, £150-£5,000; all 16th-17th C.* LOC: West of parish church. TEL: 01285 653907; fax - 01285 640533. VAT: Spec.

Rankine Taylor Antiques
34 Dollar St. GL7 2AN. LAPADA. CADA. Est. 1969. Open 9-5.30, Sun. by appointment. SIZE: Large. *STOCK: Furniture, 17th to early 19th C, £300-£35,000; silver, glass, rare and interesting objects.* Not Stocked: Victoriana. LOC: From church, turn right into West Market Place, via Gosditch St. into Dollar St. PARK: Own - private opposite. TEL: 01285 652529; website - www. antiquesnews.co.uk/rankin-taylor. VAT: Spec.

Patrick Waldron Antiques
18 Dollar St. GL7 2AN. Resident. CADA. Est. 1965. Open 9.30-1 and 2-6, Sun. by appointment. SIZE: Medium. *STOCK: Town and country furniture, 17th to early 19th C.* LOC: In street behind church. PARK: Easy and public behind shop. TEL: 01285 652880; home - same; workshop - 01285 643479; e-mail - patrick.waldron @virgin.net. SER: Restorations (furniture); buys at auction. VAT: Stan./Spec.

FAIRFORD

Blenheim Antiques
Market Place. GL7 4AB. (N. Hurdle). CADA. Resident. Est. 1972. Open 9.30-6.30. SIZE: Medium. *STOCK: 18th-19th C furniture and accessories.* PARK: Easy. TEL: 01285 712094. VAT: Stan/Spec.

MORETON-IN-MARSH

Astley House - Fine Art
Astley House, High St. GL56 0LL. (David, Nanette & Caradoc Glaisyer). LAPADA. CADA. Est. 1973. Open 9-5.30 and by appointment. SIZE: Medium. *STOCK: Oil paintings and botanical watercolours, 19th-21st C, £400-£20,000.* LOC: Main street. PARK: Easy. TEL: 01608 650601; fax - 01608 651777; e-mail - astart333@aol.com; website - www.art-uk.com. SER: Restorations (oils and watercolours); framing. VAT: Spec.

Astley House - Fine Art
Astley House, London Rd. GL56 0LE. (David, Nanette & Caradoc Glaisyer). LAPADA. CADA. Est. 1973. Open 10-1 and 2-5 and by appointment. CL: Wed. SIZE: Large. *STOCK: Oil paintings, 19th-21st C; large decorative oils and portraits.* LOC: Town centre. PARK: Easy. TEL: 01608 650608; fax - 01608 651777; e-mail - astart333@aol.com; website - www.art-uk.com. SER: Restorations (oils and watercolours); porcelain framing. VAT: Spec.

Jon Fox Antiques
High St. GL56 0AD. CADA. Est. 1982. Open 9.30-5.30, Sun. 11-4, Tues. by appointment. SIZE: Large - 2 adjacent shops. *STOCK: 19th C garden items including urns, seats, troughs and tools, £50-£5,000+; 18th -19th C country furniture £300-£3,000; treen, bygones, metalware, fireplace items.* PARK: Easy. TEL: 01608 650325/650714. VAT: Spec.

Seaford House Antiques
Seaford House, High St. GL56 0AD. (Derek and Kathy Young). LAPADA. CINOA. CADA. Est. 1988. Open 10-5.30, Tues. by appointment. SIZE: Medium. *STOCK: Furniture, 18th C to Edwardian especially upholstered, £500-£5,000; English and Continental porcelain including Worcester, Coalport, Meissen, Sitzendorf, Sampson and Copeland, mirrors and paintings, 19th C, £100-£3,000.* PARK: Easy. TEL: 01608 652423; fax - same. VAT: Spec.

STOW-ON-THE-WOLD

Duncan J. Baggott
Woolcomber House, Sheep St. GL54 1AA. LAPADA. CADA. Est. 1967. Open 9-5.30 or by appointment. SIZE: Large. *STOCK: 17th-20th C English furniture, paintings, domestic metalwork and decorative items; garden statuary and ornaments.* PARK: Sheep St. or Market Sq. TEL: 01451 830662; fax - 01451 832174.

Baggott Church Street Ltd   BADA
Church St. GL54 1BB. (D.J. and C.M. Baggott). CADA. Est. 1978. Open 9.30-5.30 or by appointment. SIZE: Large. *STOCK: English furniture, 17th-19th C; portrait paintings, metalwork, pottery, treen and decorative items.* LOC: South-west corner of market square. PARK: In market square. TEL: 01451 830370; fax - 01451 832174.

Christopher Clarke Antiques Ltd
The Fosseway. GL54 1JS. (I.D., D.S. and S.F. Clarke). LAPADA. CADA. Est. 1961. Open 9.30-5.30 or by appointment. SIZE: Large. *STOCK: Furniture including campaign, 17th-20th C; works of art, metalware, treen, pictures, decorative items, animal antiques.* LOC: Corner of The Fosseway and Sheep St. PARK: Easy. TEL: 01451 830476; fax - 01451 830300; e-mail - cclarkeantiques @aol.com; website - www.antiques-in-england.com. FAIRS: Olympia (June).

Cotswold Galleries
GL54 1AB. (Richard and Cherry Glaisyer). CADA. Est. 1961. Open 9-5.30 or by appointment. SIZE: Large. *STOCK: Oil paintings especially 19th-20th C landscape.* TEL: 01451 870567; fax - 01451 870678. SER: Restorations; framing.

The John Davies Gallery
Church St. GL54 1BB. CADA. Est. 1977. Open 9.30-1.30 and 2.30-5.30. SIZE: Large. *STOCK: Contemporary and late period paintings; limited edition bronzes.* PARK: In square. TEL: 01451 831698; fax - 01451 832477; e-mail - daviesant@aol.com; website - www.the-john-davies-gallery.co.uk. SER: Restoration and conservation to museum standard.

Keith Hockin Antiques   BADA
The Square. GL54 1AF. CADA. Est. 1968. Open Thurs., Fri., Sat., 10-5, other times by appointment or ring the bell. SIZE: Medium. *STOCK: Oak furniture, 1600-1750; country furniture in oak, fruitwoods, yew, 1700-1850; pewter, copper, brass, ironwork, all periods.* Not Stocked: Mahogany. PARK: Easy. TEL: 01451 831058; fax - same; keithhockin@aol.com. SER: Buys at auction (oak, pewter, metalwork). VAT: Stan/Spec.

Huntington Antiques Ltd
Church St. GL54 1BE. (M.F. and S.P. Golding). LAPADA. CADA. CINOA. Resident. Est. 1974. Open 9.30-5.30 or by appointment. SIZE: Large. *STOCK: Early period and fine country furniture,*

metalware, treen and textiles, tapestries and works of art. LOC: Opposite main gates to church. TEL: 01451 830842; fax - 01451 832211; e-mail - info@huntington-antiques.com; website - www.huntington-antiques.com. SER: Valuations; buys at auction. FAIRS: LAPADA. VAT: Spec.

Roger Lamb Antiques & Works of Art
The Square. GL54 1AB. LAPADA. CADA. Open 10-5. *STOCK: 18th to early 19th C furniture especially small items, lighting, decorative accessories, oils and watercolours.* TEL: 01451 831371. SER: Search.

Antony Preston Antiques Ltd   BADA
The Square. GL54 1AB. CADA. Est. 1965. Open 9.30-5.30 or by appointment. *STOCK: 18th-19th C English and Continental furniture and objects; barometers and period lighting.* **TEL: 01451 831586; fax - 01451 831596. VAT: Stan/Spec.**

Queens Parade Antiques Ltd   BADA
The Square. GL54 1AB. (Antony Preston Antiques Ltd). CADA. Est. 1965. Open 9.30-5.30. SIZE: Large. *STOCK: 18th-19th C furniture, papier mâché, tôle peinte, needlework and period lighting.* **LOC: Off Fosse Way. PARK: Easy. TEL: 01451 831586. VAT: Stan/Spec.**

Ruskin Decorative Arts
5 Talbot Court. GL54 1DP. (Anne and William Morris). CADA. Est. 1990. Open 10-1 and 2-5.30. SIZE: Small. *STOCK: Interesting and unusual decorative objects, Arts and Crafts furniture, Art Nouveau, Art Deco, glass and pottery, metalwork, 1860-1940.* LOC: Between The Square and Sheep Street. PARK: Nearby. TEL: 01451 832254; fax - 01451 832167; home - 01993 831880; e-mail - william.anne@ruskin decarts.co.uk. SER: Valuations. FAIRS: NEC.

Samarkand Galleries
7 & 8 Brewery Yard, Sheep St. GL54 1AA. (Brian MacDonald). LAPADA. CADA. CINOA. FRGS. Est. 1979. Open 10-5.30, Sun. by appointment. SIZE: Medium. *STOCK: Tribal and village rugs and artefacts, 19th C, £100-£10,000; fine decorative carpets, 19th-20th C, £1,000-£10,000+; kelims, 19th-20th C, £200-£2,000; also unique contemporary rugs and carpets.* LOC: Street adjacent to Market Sq. PARK: Easy. TEL: 01451 832322; fax - same; e-mail - mac @samarkand.co.uk; website - www.samarkand. co.uk. SER: Exhibitions; valuations; restorations; cleaning. FAIRS: Hali, Olympia (June). VAT: Stan/Spec.

Stow Antiques
The Square. GL54 1AF. (Mr and Mrs J. Hutton-Clarke). LAPADA. CADA. Resident. Est. 1969. Open Mon.-Sat. 10-5.30 other times by appointment. SIZE: Large. *STOCK: Furniture, mainly Georgian, £500-£30,000; decorative items, gilded mirrors, £50-£10,000.* PARK: Easy. TEL: 01451 830377; fax - 01451 870018; e-mail - hazel@stow antiques.co.uk. SER: Shipping worldwide.

STRETTON-ON-FOSSE

Astley House - Fine Art
The Old School. GL56 9SA. (David, Nanette and Caradoc Glaisyer). LAPADA. CADA. Est. 1973. Open by appointment. SIZE: Large. *STOCK: Large decorative oil paintings, 19th-21st C.* LOC: Village centre. PARK: Easy. TEL: 01608 650601; fax - 01608 651777; e-mail - astart333 @aol.com; website - www.art-uk.com. SER: Exhibitions; mailing list. VAT: Spec.

TADDINGTON, Nr. Cutsdean

Architectural Heritage
Taddington Manor. GL54 5RY. CADA. Est. 1978. Open 9.30-5.30, Sat. 10.30-4.30. SIZE: Large. *STOCK: Oak and pine period panelled rooms; stone and marble chimney pieces; stone, marble, bronze and terracotta statuary; garden ornaments, fountains, temples, well-heads, seats, urns, cisterns, sundials and summer houses.* PARK: Easy. TEL: 01386 584414; fax - 01386 584236; e-mail - puddy@architectural-heritage. co.uk; website - www.architectural-heritage.co. uk. SER: Worldwide delivery; shipping; bespoke ornament, chimneypieces and panelled rooms. FAIRS: Chelsea Flower Show. VAT: Stan.

TETBURY

Breakspeare Antiques
36 and 57 Long St. GL8 8AQ. (M. and S. Breakspeare). LAPADA. CADA. Resident. Est. 1962. Open 10-5 or by appointment. CL: Thurs. SIZE: Medium. *STOCK: English period furniture - early walnut, 1690-1740, mahogany, 1750-1835.* PARK: Own. TEL: 01666 503122; fax - same. VAT: Stan/Spec.

Day Antiques   BADA
5 New Church St. GL8 8DS. CADA. TADA. Est. 1975. Open 10-5.30. SIZE: Medium. *STOCK: Early oak furniture and related items.* **PARK: Easy. TEL: 01666 502413; fax - 01666 505894; e-mail - dayantiques@lineone.net; website - www.dayantiques.com VAT: Spec.**

Witney Antiques

LSA & CJ JARRETT AND RR SCOTT
96-100 CORN STREET, WITNEY,
OXON OX28 6BU, ENGLAND.
TEL: 01993 703902. FAX: 01993 779852.
E-mail: witneyantiques@community.co.uk
Website: www.witneyantiques.com

*A fine bracket clock by Haley & Son, London.
English. Circa 1830.*

Antique Furniture, Clocks,
Samplers & Early Needlework.

Bobbie Middleton

58 Long St. GL8 8AQ. CADA. TADA. Open 10-1 and 2.30-5, Sun. by appointment. *STOCK: Classic country house furniture, mirrors and upholstered furniture, 18th-19th C.* LOC: On corner with New Church St. TEL: 01666 502761; e-mail - bobbiemiddleton@lineone.net. VAT: Spec.

WINCHCOMBE

Prichard Antiques

16 High St. GL54 5LJ. (K.H. and D.Y. Prichard). CADA. Est. 1979. Open 9-5.30, Sun. by appointment. SIZE: Large. *STOCK: Period and decorative furniture, £10-£20,000; treen and metalwork, £5-£5,000; interesting and decorative accessories.* LOC: On B4632 Broadway to Cheltenham road. PARK: Easy. TEL: 01242 603566. VAT: Spec.

WITNEY

Colin Greenway Antiques

90 Corn St. OX28 6BU. CADA Resident. Est. 1975. Open 9.30-5, Sat. 10-4, Sun. by appointment. SIZE: Large. *STOCK: Furniture, 17th-20th*

C; metalware, decorative and unusual items. LOC: Along High St. to town centre, turn right, shop 400yds. on right. PARK: Easy. TEL: 01993 705026; mobile - 07831 585014. VAT: Stan/Spec.

W.R. Harvey & Co (Antiques) Ltd BADA

86 Corn St. OX28 6BU. CADA. GMC. Open 9.30-5.30, and by appointment. SIZE: Large. *STOCK: Fine English furniture, £500-£50,000; clocks, mirrors, objets d'art, £250-£20,000; all 1680-1830.* LOC: 300 yds. from Market Place. PARK: Easy. TEL: 01993 706501; fax - 01993 706601; e-mail - antiques@wrharvey.co.uk; website - www.wrharvey.co.uk. SER: Valuations; restorations; consultancy. FAIRS: BADA; Chelsea (March & Sept.); Olympia (June). VAT: Stan/Spec.

Witney Antiques BADA

96/100 Corn St. OX28 6BU. (L.S.A. and C.J. Jarrett and R.R. Jarrett-Scott). LAPADA, CADA. Est. 1962. Open 10-5, Mon. and Tues. by appointment. SIZE: Large. *STOCK: English furniture, 17th-18th C; bracket and longcase clocks, mahogany, oak and walnut, needleworks and works of art.* LOC: From Oxford on old A40 through Witney via High St., turn right at T-junction, 400yds. on right. PARK: Easy. TEL: 01993 703902/703887; fax - 01993 779852; e-mail - witneyantiques@ community.co.uk; website - www.witney antiques.com. SER: Restorations. FAIRS: BADA; Grosvenor House. VAT: Spec.

WOODSTOCK

John Howard BADA

19 High St. OX20 1TE. LAPADA. TVADA. CADA. Open 10-5.30. SIZE: Small. *STOCK: 18th-19th C British pottery especially rare Staffordshire animal figures, bocage figures, lustre, 18th C creamware and unusual items.* PARK: Easy. TEL: 0870 4440678; fax - same; mobile - 07831 850544; e-mail - john@john howard.co.uk; website - www.antiquepottery. co.uk and www.Staffordshires.com. SER: Packing; insurance service to USA. FAIRS: Olympia; BADA. VAT: Spec.

Little explored and virtually inaccessible, the Tsangpo Gorge in South-east Tibet is the world's deepest gorge. Through it twists the Yarlong Tsangpo, Tibet's great river, emerging far below on the plains of India. This is the story of its exploration and the rich plant and animal life found there.

Riddle of the Tsangpo Gorges, first published in 1926, is the fascinating account of plant-hunter and explorer Frank Kingdon Ward's most important expedition. Kenneth Cox, Kenneth R. Storm Jr. and Ian Baker have spent the last ten years retracing the route of the 1924-25 expedition and have managed to reach further into this magical and only partly explored land.

This new edition contains the original Kingdon Ward text (with about fifty of his own photographs from the archive at the Royal Geographical Society) and extensive additional material including a brief biography of Kingdon Ward, a new foreword by his widow, Jean Rasmussen, a history of the exploration, geography and religious significance of the area and more than 250 colour photographs with detailed captions on the plants of the area, most of which are described by Kingdon Ward in the original text.

There are first person accounts of recent expeditions to the area by Ken Cox and Ken Storm, Jr. and a photographic essay documents for the first time in a book the 'new' Hidden Falls located in the portion of the gorge left unexplored by Frank Kingdon Ward and Lord Cawdor in 1924.

ISBN 1 85149 371 9
320pp., 258 col. illus., 51 b.&w. illus. **£35.00**

Available from the
ANTIQUE COLLECTORS' CLUB
Sandy Lane, Old Martlesham,
Woodbridge, Suffolk IP12 4SD, UK.
For your free copy of the catalogue:
Tel: **01394 389950** or Fax: **01394 389999**
Email: sales@antique-acc.com
Website: www.antique-acc.com

TETBURY ANTIQUE DEALERS' ASSOCIATION

The Antiques Emporium
The Old Chapel, Long St. GL8 8AA. (D. Sayers). TADA. Est. 1993. Open 10-5, Sun. 1-5. SIZE: Large - 38 dealers. *STOCK: Fruitwood and country furniture, fine oak and mahogany, clocks, china, porcelain, treen, copper and brass, jewellery, silver, kitchenalia, £1-£15,000.* Not Stocked: Reproductions. PARK: Nearby. TEL: 01666 505281; fax - 01666 505661. SER: Export. VAT: Stan/Spec.

Arkangel Antiques
33 Long St. GL8 8AA. (Jacqueline Hall). TADA. LAPADA. Est. 1976. Open 10-5. CL: Sun. except by appointment. SIZE: Large. *STOCK: Furniture, painted English and Continental, mirrors; £500-£4,500; decorative items and objects, 18th-19th C.* PARK: Nearby. TEL: 01666 505820/500247; e-mail - j.hall.antiques@talk21.com. SER: Valuations. FAIRS: BABAADA Decorative, Bath; Decorative Antiques & Textiles, Battersea. VAT: Stan/Spec.

Artique
Talboys House, Church St. GL8 8JG. (George Bristow). TADA. Open 9-5. *STOCK: Interiors, textiles, carpets and kelims and objets d'art from the Orient.* TEL: 01666 503597; fax - same; e-mail - george@artique.demon.co.uk.

Ball and Claw Antiques
45 Long St. GL8 8AA. (Chris Kirkland). TADA. Est. 1994. Open 10-5 and most Sundays 2-5. SIZE: Medium. *STOCK: 17th-19th C furniture, engravings, pictures, ceramics and general antiques.* PARK: Easy. TEL: 01666 502440; mobile - 07957 870423; e-mail - chris@balland claw.co.uk; website - www.ballandclaw.co.uk. SER: Finder.

Balmuir House Antiques
14 Long St. GL8 8AQ. (P. Whittam). LAPADA. TADA. Open 9.30-5.30. SIZE: Large. *STOCK: Furniture, paintings, mirrors, 19th C, £500-£5,000.* LOC: Town centre. PARK: Easy. TEL: 01666 503822; home - same. SER: Restorations (furniture, upholstery, paintings). VAT: Spec.

The Chest of Drawers
24 Long St. GL8 8AQ. (A. and P. Bristow). TADA. Resident. Est. 1969. Open Tues.-Fri. 9.30-6, Mon. by appointment. SIZE: Medium. *STOCK: Late Georgian and Regency furniture; country pieces, 17th-18th C; walnut and other woods, 18th C; pictures.* LOC: On A433. PARK: Easy. TEL: 01666 502105; home - same. VAT: Spec.

Day Antiques
BADA
5 New Church St. GL8 8DS. CADA. TADA. Est. 1975. Open 10-5.30. SIZE: Medium.
STOCK: Early oak furniture and related items. **PARK: Easy. TEL: 01666 502413; fax - 01666 505894; e-mail - dayantiques@lineone.net; website - www.dayantiques.com VAT: Spec.**

The Decorator Source
39a Long St. GL8 8AA. (Colin Gee). TADA. Open 10-5 or by appointment. SIZE: Large. *STOCK: French provincial furniture - armoires, farm tables, buffets; decorative items and accessories of interest to interior decorators.* PARK: Easy. TEL: 01666 505358. VAT: Stan/Spec.

Fowler and Bateson
51A Long St. GL8 8AA. TADA. Est. 1995. Open 10-5, Sun. 11-5 and most Bank Holidays. SIZE: Medium. *STOCK: Mainly French provincial and painted furniture, porcelain, ceramics, silver and pictures; interior design items.* TEL: 01666 505083.

Jester Antiques
10 Church St. GL8 8JG. (Lorna Coles and Peter Bairsto). TADA. Open 10-5.30, including Sun. *STOCK: Longcase and wall clocks, also oil portraits and pictures, Oriental objects, lamps, furniture, decorative items, outside statuary and architectural.* TEL: 01666 505125.

Lyon Oliver Antiques
Laynes House, Oaksey. SN16 9SE. TADA. Prior telephone call advisable. *STOCK: English and Irish country house furniture, large mirrors, upholstery and decorative sculpture.* TEL: 01666 577603; e-mail - lyon@lyon-oliver.demon.co.uk.

Bobbie Middleton
58 Long St. GL8 8AQ. CADA. TADA. Open 10-1 and 2.30-5, Sun. by appointment. *STOCK: Classic country house furniture, mirrors and upholstered furniture, 18th-19th C.* LOC: On corner with New Church St. TEL: 01666 502761; e-mail - bobbie middleton@lineone.net. VAT: Spec.

Peter Norden Antiques
61 Long St. GL8 8AA. (Peter and Jenny Norden). TADA. LAPADA. Est. 1960. Open 10-5.30, Sun. by appointment. SIZE: Medium. *STOCK: Early oak furniture, 16th-17th C, £250-£20,000; country furniture, 17th-19th C, £75-£10,000; early carvings, metalware, pewter, pottery, treen, 14th-19th C, £10-£10,000.* PARK: Nearby. TEL: 01666 503854; fax - 01666 505595; home - 01452 770536; e-mail - peternorden-antiques@ linone.net; website - www.peter-norden-antiques. co.uk. SER: Valuations. VAT: Spec.

The Tetbury Antique Dealers Association aims to promote and encourage trade in the Tetbury area and to assist all visiting antique dealers and collectors.

Over twenty shops with over fifty dealers

For further details contact the secretary:
Colin Gee, 39A Long Street, Tetbury, Glos. GL8 8AA
Telephone (+44) 01666 505358

Panache

32 Long St. GL8 8AQ. (Linda Biggs). TADA. Open 10-5 or by appointment. SIZE: Medium. *STOCK: French provincial and painted furniture, mirrors, chandeliers, garden and decorative accessories.* PARK: Easy. TEL: 01666 502423.

Sharland & Lewis

52 Long St. GL8 8AQ. (Ali Sharland). TADA. Open 10.30-5, Sat 10-5 or by appointment. SIZE: Medium. *STOCK: Painted furniture, textiles and decorative objects.* PARK: Easy. TEL: 01666 500354.

Sieff

49 Long St. GL8 8AA. LAPADA. TADA. Est. 1994. Open 10-5.30, Sun. by appointment. SIZE: Large. *STOCK: English and French 18th-20th C furniture and objets, £100-£10,000.* PARK: Easy. TEL: 01666 504477; fax - 01666 504478; e-mail - sieff@sieff.co.uk; website - www.sieff.co.uk. SER: Valuations; buys at auction. FAIRS: Harvey Decorative Antique & Textile. VAT: Stan/Spec.

The Sporting Gallery

12 Church St. (B. Hulftegger). TADA. Open 10-5. SIZE: Medium. *STOCK: Period and contemporary sporting pictures, engravings, watercolours, oils and associated sporting items.* PARK: Easy. TEL: 01666 504605; e-mail - info@ sporting-gallery.com.

Tetbury Gallery

18 Market Place. GL8 8DD. (Jane Maile). FATG. TADA. Open every day. *STOCK: Original and limited edition prints, from Victorian watercolours and oils to contemporary artists including Russell Flint, David Shepherd and Ben Maile.* TEL: 01666 503412.

Tetbury Old Books & Coach House Antiques

4 The Chipping. GL8 8ET. (Tetbury Old Books Ltd). TADA. Open 10-6, Sun. 11-5. *STOCK: Antiquarian and secondhand books and prints.* TEL: 01666 504330; fax - 01666 504458; e-mail - oldbooks@tetbury.co.uk.

Westwood House Antiques and Beehive Antiques

29 Long St. GL8 8AA. (Richard Griffiths and Lynne Petersen). TADA. Resident. Est. 1993. Open 10-5.30 or by appointment. SIZE: Large. *STOCK: Oak, elm and ash country furniture especially dressers, dresser bases and tables, 17th-19th C; occasional French pieces; decorative pottery, pewter and treen.* TEL: 01666 502328; fax - same; mobile - 07774 952909; e-mail - richardgriffiths@tinyworld.co.uk. VAT: Spec.

ALLONBY

Cottage Curios
Main St. CA15 6PX. (B. Pickering). Est. 1965.
Open Sat. and Sun. 2-5.

ALSTON

Alston Antiques
Front St. CA9 3HU. (Mrs J. Bell). Est. 1976.
Open 10-5. CL: Tues. SIZE: Medium. *STOCK:
General antiques.* PARK: Easy. TEL: 01434
382129; mobile - 07876 501929.

Just Glass
Cross House, Market Place. CA9 3HS. (M.J.
Graham). Est. 1987. Open Wed., Thurs., Sat. 11-
4, Sun. 12-4. *STOCK: Glass, 1780-1920's, to
£800.* LOC: Town centre. PARK: Easy. TEL:
Home - 01434 381263; mobile - 07833 994948.
FAIRS: Narworth Castle.

BEETHAM, Nr. Milnthorpe

Peter Haworth
Temple Bank. LA7 7AL. Open by appointment.
*STOCK: English and Scottish paintings and
watercolours, 1850-1950, £100-£30,000.* LOC: 2
miles south of Milnthorpe on A6 to Lancaster.
PARK: Easy. TEL: 015395 62352; fax - 015395
63438; e-mail - prhaworth@yahoo.com. SER:
Valuations; restorations; commissions. VAT: Spec.

BOWNESS ON WINDERMERE

Something Old Something New
(Behind Royal Hotel), St Martin's Parade. Open
11-5.30 including Sun. SIZE: 3 rooms. *STOCK:
Rare vinyl, books, collectables, antiques, bric-a-
brac.* TEL: 01524 781718.

J.W. Thornton Antiques Supermarket
North Terrace. LA23 3AU. Est. 1972. Open by
appointment. SIZE: Large. *STOCK: Fine art,
general antiques, furniture, shipping and
architectural items, pine, bric-a-brac, paintings,
decorators items.* PARK: Nearby. TEL: 01229
580284; mobile - 07974 788525. SER: Valuations;
buys at auction; fairs vetting. VAT: Stan/Spec.

BRAMPTON

The Cumbrian Antiques Centre
St Martin's Hall, Front St. CA8 1NT. (S.T.

Summerson-Wright). Est. 1976. Open 10-5, Sun.
12-5. SIZE: Large. *STOCK: Wide range of
general antiques from silver and china to
longcase clocks and furniture.* LOC: A69 Carlisle
to Newcastle road into village, premises on right
as road forks. PARK: Easy. TEL: 016977 42515;
fax - same; home - 07889 924843; e-mail -
cumbrian antiques@hotmail.com. SER: Valuations;
restorations.

Something Old, Something New
46 Main St. CA8 1SB. (Joan Potts). Est. 1980.
Open 10-4.30. SIZE: Medium. *STOCK: Victorian
stripped pine, £50-£500; oak and mahogany
country furniture, smalls.* LOC: A69. PARK:
Easy. TEL: 01697 741740; home - 01228 675587.
SER: Valuations; buys at auction.

CARLISLE

Carlisle Antiques Centre
Cecil Hall, Cecil St. CA1 1NT. Open 9-4.30.
SIZE: Large plus trade warehouse (Basement -
Fri. and Sat. indoor market - bric-a-brac,
collectibles). *STOCK: Furniture, porcelain,
clocks, silver, jewellery, quilts and textiles.* LOC:
M6 junction 43. PARK: Easy. TEL: 01228
536910; fax - same; e-mails - wendymitton
@aol.com; websites - www.carlisleantiques
centre.co.uk and carlisle-antiques.co.uk. Below
are listed the dealers at this centre. SER: Repairs
(clocks). FAIRS: Naworth Castle, Brampton
(March and August).

> **Fine Pine**
> *Old and original stripped pine furniture; mahogany
> and oak bedroom suites, large furniture, china,
> quilts.*

> **It's About Time**
> (B. and W. Mitton). Est. 1985. *Longcase, bracket
> and carriage clocks, watches; period furniture;
> Royal Worcester fine porcelain, jewellery, textiles.*
> TEL: 01228 536910.

> **Warwick Antiques**
> (J. T. Wardrope). CMBHI. *Period furniture, wall
> and bracket clocks.* SER: Valuations; restorations
> (clocks).

**Saint Nicholas Galleries Ltd.
(Antiques and Jewellery)**
39 Bank St. CA3 8HJ. (C.J. Carruthers). Open
10-5. CL: Mon. SIZE: Medium. *STOCK: Jewellery, silver, plate, Rolex and pocket watches,
clocks; collectables; Royal Doulton; Dux, Oriental
vases; pottery, porcelain; watercolours, oil
paintings; brass and copper.* LOC: City centre.
PARK: Nearby. TEL: 01228 544459.

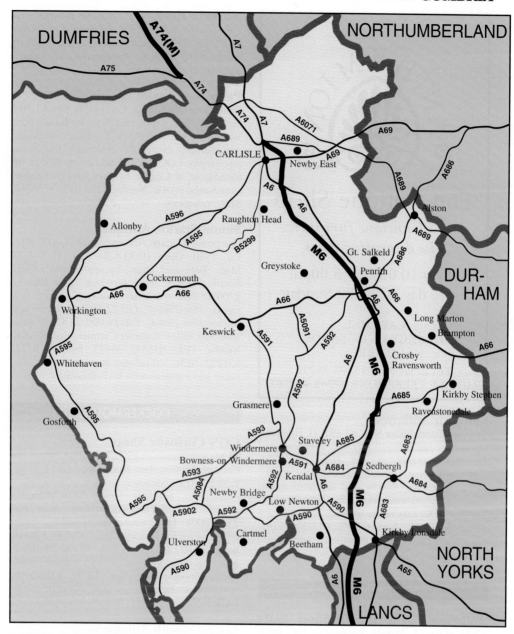

Dealers and Shops in Cumbria

Allonby	1	Grasmere	2	Newby East	1
Alston	2	Great Salkeld	1	Penrith	8
Beetham	1	Greystoke	1	Raughton Head	1
Bowness-on-Windermere	2	Kendal	7	Ravenstonedale	2
Brampton	2	Keswick	4	Sedbergh	2
Carlisle	3	Kirkby Lonsdale	1	Staveley	1
Cartmel	4	Kirkby Stephen	2	Ulverston	2
Cockermouth	3	Long Marton	1	Whitehaven	1
Crosby Ravensworth	1	Low Newton	2	Windermere	1
Gosforth	1	Newby Bridge	1	Workington	1

The Antique Shop

English antique furniture, also decorative items

Open 10.00am – 5.00pm
every day including Sunday

CARTMEL
GRANGE-OVER-SANDS
CUMBRIA

TELEPHONE 015395-36295
MOBILE TELEPHONE 07768 443757

Souvenir Antiques
Treasury Court, Fisher St. CA3 8RF. (J. Higham).
Open 10-5. SIZE: Small. *STOCK: Porcelain and pottery, Victorian to Art Deco, £5-£500; coronation ware, crested china, local prints, maps, postcards, Roman and medieval coins, antiquities, costume jewellery.* Not Stocked: Textiles. LOC: City centre between Fisher St. and Scotch St. PARK: Nearby. TEL: 01228 401281; websites - www.souvenirantiques.co.uk and www.cumbriamaps.co.uk.

CARTMEL

Anthemion - The Antique Shop BADA
LA11 6QD. (J. Wood). LAPADA. Est. 1982.
Open 10-5 including Sun. SIZE: Large. *STOCK: English period furniture, 17th to early 19th C, £100-£30,000; decorative items, 17th-19th C, £20-£2, 000.* Not Stocked: Victoriana, bric-a-brac. LOC: Village centre. PARK: Easy. TEL: 01539 536295; mobile - 07768 443757. FAIRS: Olympia; LAPADA; NEC; Harrogate. VAT: Stan/Spec.

Norman Kerr - Gatehouse Bookshop
The Square. LA11 6PX. (H. and J.M. Kerr).
PBFA. Est. 1933. Open weekend afternoons or by appointment. *STOCK: Antiquarian and second-hand books.* TEL: 01539 536247.

Peter Bain Smith (Bookseller)
Bank Court, Market Sq. LA11 6QB. Open 1.30-5 including Sun. From mid Nov. to Easter open Wed.-Sat. 1.30-4.30.*STOCK: Books including antiquarian, especially children's and local topography.* LOC: A590 from Levens Bridge, off roundabout at Lindale by-pass through Grange-over-Sands. PARK: Nearby. TEL: 01539 536369. SER: Valuations.

Simon Starkie Antiques
Gatehouse Cottage, Cavendish St. LA11 6QA.
Est. 1980. Open 10.30-4.30, Sun. 11.30-4.30, Mon., Tues. and Thurs. by appointment. SIZE: Small. *STOCK: Oak furniture, 17th-19th C, £100-£8,000; painted country furniture and clocks, 18th-19th C, £50-£2,500; Delftware and pewter, 18th-19th C, £30-£1,000.* LOC: 10 miles from M6, follow signs for Cartmel priory. PARK: Nearby. TEL: 015395 36453; home - 01229 861222. SER: Valuations; buys at auction (furniture and earthenware). VAT: Stan/Spec.

COCKERMOUTH

CG's Curiosity Shop
43 Market Place. CA13 9LT. (Colin Graham and Corinne Ritchie). Est. 1985. Open 10-12.30 and 1.30-5. SIZE: Medium. *STOCK: China, glass, collectables, militaria, books, linen, furniture, advertising, radios and unusual items, from 1800, £5-£1,000+.* LOC: End of main street, over the bridge. PARK: Nearby. TEL: 01900 824418; home - 01697 321108; mobile - 07712 206786; e-mail - cgcuriosity@hotmail.com; website - www. cgcuriosityshop.fws1.com. SER: Valuations; restorations; buys at auction; internet search. FAIRS: Newark.

Cockermouth Antiques
5 Station St. CA13 9QW. (E. Bell and G. Davies).
Est. 1983. Open 10-5. SIZE: Large. *STOCK: General antiques especially jewellery, silver, ceramics, furniture, pictures, glass, books, metalware, quilts.* LOC: Just off A66, in town centre. PARK: Easy. TEL: 01900 826746; e-mail - elainebell54@aol.com.

Cockermouth Antiques Market
Courthouse, Main St. CA13 9LU. Est. 1979. Open 10-5. SIZE: Large - 4 stallholders. *STOCK: Victorian, Edwardian and Art Deco items, furniture,*

A Can shape coffee pot, height 8in., milk and sugar decorated with the Black Fruit pattern (C.893-989), from about 1958.

From an article entitled "Susie Cooper Bone China 1950-1966" by Ann Eatwell which appeared in the March 2002 issue of **Antique Collecting**. For more details and to subscribe see page 21.

printed collectables, postcards, books, linen, china, glass, textiles, jewellery and pictures. LOC: Town centre, just off A66. PARK: 50 yds. TEL: 01900 824346. SER: Restorations (furniture); stripping (pine). VAT: Stan/Spec.

Jennywell Hall Antiques
CA10 3JP. (Mrs M. Macadie). Resident. Est. 1975. Open most days but 'phone call advisable. SIZE: Medium. *STOCK: Oak and mahogany furniture, paintings, interesting objects.* LOC: 5 miles from junction 39, M6. PARK: Easy. TEL: 01931 715288; home - same.

Archie Miles Bookshop
Beck Place. CA20 1AT. (Mrs C.M. Linsley). Open 10-5, Sun. 1-5.30, out of season opening times may vary. CL: Mon. *STOCK: Secondhand, antiquarian and out-of-print books, maps and prints.* TEL: 01946 725792.

Lakes Crafts & Antiques Gallery
3 Oak Bank, Broadgate. LA22 9TA. (Joe and Sandra Arthy). Est. 1990. Open 15th Mar. - 31st Oct. 9.30-6 including Sun., other times 10-4.30. CL: 5th Jan. - 1st Feb. SIZE: Medium. *STOCK: Books, 18th-20th C, £1-500; collectables and postcards, £1-£100; general antiques, 17th-20th C, £5-£250.* LOC: North side of village, off A591 on Ambleside to Keswick road. PARK: Easy. TEL: 01539 435037; fax - 01539 444271; home - 01539 444234. VAT: Stan.

The Stables
College St. LA22 9SW. (J.A. and K.M. Saalmans). Est. 1971. Open daily 10-6 Easter-November, other times telephone call advisable. SIZE: Small. *STOCK: Brass and copper items, oil lamps, domestic bygones; pottery, silver, prints, books.* Not Stocked: Weapons, furniture. LOC: By the side of Moss Grove Hotel. PARK: Easy. TEL: 01539 435453; home - same; e-mail - andrew.saalmans@btinternet.com.

GREAT SALKELD, Nr. Penrith

G.K. Hadfield

Beck Bank. CA11 9LN. (G.K. and J.V. Hadfield
(Hon. FBHI) and D.W. and N.R. Hadfield-Tilly).
Est. 1972. Open 9-5. *STOCK: Clocks - longcase,
dial, Act of Parliament, skeleton, Black Forest,
American and carriage; unrestored antique
clocks; secondhand, new and out of print
horological books; secondhand workshop tools
and materials.* LOC: From M6, junction 40 take
A686 towards Alston for 3 miles, left on B6412
signed Great Salkeld, about 1.5 miles, turn left at
sign for Salkeld Dykes, 1st house on right. TEL:
01768 870111; fax - same; e-mail - gkhadfield
@dial.pipex.com. SER: Restoration materials
(antique clocks); valuations (clocks and horological books). VAT: Stan/Spec.

GREYSTOKE

Roadside Antiques

Watsons Farm, Greystoke Gill. CA11 0UQ. (K.
and R. Sealby). Resident. Est. 1988. Open 10-6
including Sun. SIZE: Medium. *STOCK: Ceramics,
longcase clocks, glass, Staffordshire figures, pot-
lids, paintings, furniture, small collectables,
jewellery, mainly 19th C, £5-£2,000.* LOC: B5288
Penrith/Keswick road to Greystoke, through
village, first left then left again, premises second
on right. PARK: Easy. TEL: 01768 483279.

KENDAL

Architectural Antiques

146 Highgate. LA9 4HW. (G. Fairclough). Est.
1984. Open 9.30-5. SIZE: Medium. *STOCK:
Fireplaces, hobs, grates, marble and wooden
chimney pieces, cast-iron inserts; Victorian tiles
and kitchen ranges, unusual architectural items,
clocks, Flemish brass chandeliers.* PARK: Easy.
TEL: 01539 737147; fax - same; mobile - 07801
440031; e-mail - gordonfairclough@cs.com;
website - www.architecturalantiques.co.uk. SER:
Valuations; restorations (cast-iron).

Below Stairs

125 Stricklandgate. LA9 4RF. (S. and T. Ritchie).
Est. 1982. Open 10-4. SIZE: Medium. *STOCK:
China, brass, copper, coloured glass, silver and
collectables.* LOC: Main street on road towards
Windermere. TEL: 01539 741278.

Dower House Antiques
40 Kirkland. LA9 5AD. Open 10-6. *STOCK: Pottery, porcelain, paintings, furniture.* TEL: 01539 722778.

Granary Collectables
29 All Hallows Lane. LA9 4JH. (B. J. Cross). Est. 1998. Open 10-4.30. CL: Mon. SIZE: Small. *STOCK: Small collectables, pictures, kitchenalia, pottery, advertising and unusual items, £5-£100.* LOC: 100 yards from town centre, off main road. PARK: Easy. TEL: 01539 740770. SER: Valuations.

Kendal Studios Antiques
2/3 Wildman St. LA9 6EN. (R. Aindow). Est. 1950. Open 10.30-4, prior telephone call advisable. SIZE: Medium. *STOCK: Ceramics, maps and prints, paintings, oak furniture, art pottery.* LOC: Leave M6 at junction 37, follow one-way system, shop on left. PARK: Nearby. TEL: 01539 723291 (24 hrs. answering service). SER: Finder; shipping. VAT: Stan/Spec.

Shambles Antiques
17-19 New Shambles. LA9 4TS. (John G. and Janet A. Smyth). Est. 1992. Open Tues.-Sat. 10-5. SIZE: Medium. *STOCK: Arts and Crafts, art pottery, paintings, furniture; English pottery and porcelain, 18th-19th C; 20th C Scandinavian ceramics and glass; collectors' items, silver, all £5-£5,000.* LOC: Off Market Place. PARK: Multi-storey nearby. TEL: 01539 729947; home - 01539 821590; mobile - 07710 245059; e-mail - jansmyth @btinternet.com; website - kendalantiques.co.uk. SER: Valuations.

The Silver Thimble
39 All Hallows Lane. LA9. (V. Ritchie). Est. 1980. Open 10-4. SIZE: Large. *STOCK: Jewellery, silver, glass, linen and lace, porcelain, copper and brass.* LOC: Turn left at second set of traffic lights on main road into Kendal from south, shop 200yds. on right. PARK: Easy. TEL: 01539 731456; e-mail - gmvritchie@aol.com. VAT: Spec.

KESWICK

Cat in the Window
29 Station St., (Beneath Ravensworth Hotel). CA12 5HH. (E. Fell). Est. 1980. Open 10.30-4.30. CL: Mon-Wed. SIZE: Small. *STOCK: Porcelain and pottery, copper, brass and pewter, small furniture.* LOC: Near Fitz Park. PARK: Easy and nearby. TEL: Mobile - 07989 717088. SER: Valuations; buys at auction. FAIRS: Colin Caygill in Cumbria.

The Country Bedroom
Lake Rd. CA12 5BZ. (W.I. Raw). Est. 1981. Open 9.30-5. *STOCK: Brass beds, iron and brass beds, mattress and base sets for antique beds, mirrors, linen, quilts, £150-£2,000.* LOC: Top of Main St. TEL: 017687 74881; fax - 017687 71424. VAT: Stan.

Keswick Bookshop
4 Station St. CA12 5HT. (Jane and John Kinnaird). PBFA. Est. 1994. Open April to end Oct. 10.30-5, prior telephone call essential in winter months. SIZE: Medium. *STOCK: Books, 18th-20th C; prints and maps, 18th-20th C.* LOC: Town centre. PARK: Nearby. TEL: 01768 775535; fax - 01228 528567; home - same. VAT: Stan/Spec.

John Young and Son (Antiques)
12-14 Main St. CA12 5JD. LAPADA. Est. 1890. Open 9-5. SIZE: Large. *STOCK: 17th-20th C. furniture, clocks and decorative items for the home and garden.* LOC: Town centre. PARK: At rear. TEL: 017687 73434; fax - 017687 73306. VAT: Stan/Spec.

KIRKBY LONSDALE

Architus Antiques
14 Main St. (J. Pearson). Est. 1990. Open 10-4.30, Sat. 10-5.30. SIZE: Medium. *STOCK: Victorian oil lamps, £100-£250; china and glass, jewellery and silver, Victorian to early 20th C.* LOC: First antique shop on left in village from A65 towards Kendal. TEL: 015242 72409; home - 015242 71517. SER: Valuations.

A Limehouse sauceboat supported on three claw feet, c.1746-47, (interior), £9,410.

From an article entitled "18th century English Porcelain" by Simon Spero which appeared in the October 2001 issue of **Antique Collecting**. For more details and to subscribe see page 21.

KIRKBY STEPHEN

Haughey Antiques
28/30 Market St. CA17 4QW. (D.M. Haughey).
LAPADA. Est. 1969. Open 10-5 or by appointment.
SIZE: Large. *STOCK: Furniture, 17th-19th C;
garden furniture and statuary.* PARK: Own. TEL:
017683 71302; fax - 017683 72423; e-mail -
haugheyantiques@aol.com. SER: Valuations.
FAIRS: Olympia; LAPADA, NEC. VAT: Stan/ Spec.

David Hill
36 Market Sq. CA17 4QT. Est. 1965. Open
Thurs., Fri. and Sat. 9.30-4. SIZE: Medium.
*STOCK: Country clocks and furniture, £10-
£1,000; both 18th-19th C; glassware, £5-£75;
curios, £5-£50; shipping goods, kitchenalia, iron
and brassware.* LOC: On A685; M6 junction 38.
PARK: Easy. TEL: 017683 71598.

LONG MARTON, Nr. Appleby

Ben Eggleston Antiques
The Dovecote. CA16 6BJ. (Ben and Kay
Eggleston). Est. 1976. Open strictly by appointment. SIZE: Large. *STOCK: Pine furniture,*
unstripped and unrestored for the trade, £5-
£2,500. LOC: 2 miles east of A66 between
Appleby and Penrith. PARK: Easy. TEL: 017683
61849; home and fax - same; e-mail - ben@
beneggletonantiques.co.uk. FAIRS: Newark.
VAT: Stan/Spec. *Strictly Trade Only.*

LOW NEWTON, Nr. Grange-over-Sands

Utopia Antiques Ltd
Yew Tree Barn. LA11 6JP. (P.J. and Mrs J.
Wilkinson). Est. 1970. Open 10-5 including Sun.
SIZE: Large + warehouse. *STOCK: Indian Colonial
furniture including reproduction, handicrafts and
fabrics.* LOC: A590, 2 miles south of Newby
Bridge. PARK: Easy. TEL: 015395 30065; e-mail
- utopiaantique@utopiaantique.com; website -
www.utopiaantique.com. VAT: Stan.

W.R.S. Architectural Antiques
Yew Tree Barn. LA11 6JP. (Clive Wilson). Open
10-5, Sun. 12-6 (winter 11-5). *STOCK: General
architectural antiques including fireplaces;
period furniture.* TEL: 01539 531498.

NEWBY BRIDGE

Townhead Antiques
LA12 8NP. (E.M. and C.P. Townley). LAPADA. Est. 1960. Open 10-5. SIZE: Large. *STOCK: 18th-19th C furniture, silver, porcelain, glass, decorative pieces; clocks, pictures.* LOC: A592. 1 mile from Newby Bridge on the Windermere road. PARK: Easy. TEL: 01539 531321; fax - 01539 530019; e-mail - Townhead@aol.com; website - www.Townhead-Antiques.co.uk. SER: Valuations. VAT: Stan/Spec.

NEWBY EAST, Nr. Carlisle

Country Seat Antiques
Irthing Villa. CA4 8QX. (David Notman). Est. 2000. Open 9.30-4.30 and by appointment. CL: Wed. and Sat. SIZE: Medium. *STOCK: 18th-20th C furniture, paintings and collectables.* LOC: 5 miles from Carlisle, 1 mile from A69 Hexham road. PARK: Easy. TEL: 01228 57368; mobile - 07760 120431; e-mail - country-seat@lineone. net. SER: Upholstery.

PENRITH

Antiques of Penrith
4 Corney Sq. CA11 7PX. (Sylvia Tiffin and Lilian Cripps). Est. 1964. Open 10-12 and 1.30-5, Sat. 10-12.30. CL: Wed. SIZE: Large. *STOCK: Early oak and mahogany furniture, clocks, brass, copper, glass, china, silver plate, metal, Staffordshire figures, curios, paintings and collectables.* Not Stocked: Jewellery, books, rugs. LOC: Near Town Hall. PARK: Easy. TEL: 01768 862801. VAT: Stan/Spec/Global.

Brunswick Antiques
8 Brunswick Rd. CA11 7LU. (M. and L. Hodgson). Est. 1985. Open 10-5. SIZE: Small. *STOCK: Furniture, clocks, pottery, glass, metalware, 19th-20th C.* PARK: Easy. TEL: 01768 899338; home - 01768 867164. VAT: Spec.

The Gallery
54 Castlegate. CA11 7HY. (K.G. Plant). Est. 1969. Open by appointment only. SIZE: Small. *STOCK: Paintings and watercolours, 17th-20th C, £500-£50,000.* LOC: From town centre towards the railway station. TEL: 01768 865538; home - same. SER: Valuations. VAT: Stan/Spec.

Hearth & Home
6 Brunswick Rd. CA11 7LU. Open 9-5. *STOCK: Reproduction furniture and decorative accessories, fireplaces, multi-fuel and gas stoves.* TEL: 01768 867200.

Joseph James Antiques
Corney Sq. CA11 7PX. (G.R. Walker). Est. 1970. Open 9-5. CL: Wed. SIZE: Medium. *STOCK: Furniture and upholstery, 18th C and Victorian, £10-£3,000; porcelain and pottery, £5-£1,000; silver and plate, pictures, £2-£800; all 18th-19th C.* LOC: On the one-way system in the town, 100yds. from the main shopping area (Middlegate), 50yds. from the town hall. PARK: Easy and 100yds. TEL: 01768 862065. SER: Re-upholstery; soft furnishings. VAT: Stan.

Penrith Coin and Stamp Centre
37 King St. CA11 7AY. (Mr and Mrs A. Gray). Resident. Est. 1974. Open 9-5.30. CL: Wed. Sept.-May. SIZE: Medium. *STOCK: Coins, B.C. to date, 1p-£500; jewellery, secondhand, £5-£500; Great Britain and Commonwealth stamps.* LOC: Just off town centre. PARK: Behind shop. TEL: 01768 864185; fax - same. SER: Valuations; jewellery repairs. FAIRS: Many coin. VAT: Stan.

Sandgate Antiques
21 Sandgate. CA11 7TJ. (Steve Bates). Est. 1983. Open Mon., Tues., Fri. and Sat. 10-5 or by appointment. SIZE: Medium. *STOCK: Oak and country furniture, 17th to early 19th C; longcase clocks, Delft, decorative items.* LOC: Near town centre, past bus station up hill on right. PARK: Easy. TEL: 01768 899599; fax - same. VAT: Stan/Spec

RAUGHTON HEAD, Nr. Carlisle

Cumbria Architectural Salvage
Birkshill. CA5 7DH. (K. Temple). SALVO. Est. 1988. Open 9-5, Sat. 9-12. SIZE: Medium. *STOCK: Fireplaces, 1700-1930, £150-£1,500; kitchen ranges, cast-iron radiators, bathroom fittings, doors, bricks and granite setts, building materials, sandstone, flags, balusters and staircase parts.* LOC: 9 miles from Carlisle. PARK: Easy. TEL: 01697 476420; home - same; fax - 01697 476754. SER: Valuations; restorations (fireplaces and ranges).

RAVENSTONEDALE, Nr. Kirkby Stephen

The Book House
Grey Garth. CA17 4NQ. (C. and M. Irwin). PBFA. Est. 1963. Open 9-5. CL: Tues. *STOCK: Books, mainly 19th-20th C, £1-£1,000; some postcards, 20th C, 25p-£20.* LOC: Off A685. Square house across road triangle from village school. PARK: Easy. TEL: 015396 23634; fax - 015396 23434; e-mail - enquiries@thebookhouse.co.uk. SER: Valuations. FAIRS: Northern PBFA. VAT: Stan.

Winton Hall Antiques

Rowfoot Farm. CA17 4NN. (S. Baldwick). Resident. Est. 1975. Open 9-5 including Sun. SIZE: Large. *STOCK: Oak and country furniture, 1600-1800, £100-£7,000; mahogany, 1750-1830, £100-£4,000.* LOC: Midway between village and The Fat Lamb Inn, 1.5 miles from A685. PARK: Easy. TEL: 015396 23669. SER: Valuations; buys at auction. VAT: Stan/Spec. *Trade Only.*

SEDBERGH

R. F. G. Hollett and Son

6 Finkle St. LA10 5BZ. (R. F. G. and C. G. Hollett). Est. 1951. Open Wed.-Sat. 10-5. SIZE: Large. *STOCK: Antiquarian books, 15th-20th C, £20-£20,000+; maps, prints and paintings, 17th-19th C, £20-£5,000.* LOC: Town centre. PARK: Free nearby. TEL: 015396 20298; fax - 015396 21396; e-mail - hollett@sedbergh.demon.co.uk; website - www.holletts-rarebooks.co.uk. SER: Valuations. VAT: Stan.

Stable Antiques

Wheelwright Cottage, 15-16 Back Lane. LA10 5AQ. Est. 1970. Open 10-6 or by appointment. *STOCK: Small furniture, brass, copper, silver, china, prints, small collectors' items, treen.* LOC: 5 miles from exit 37, M6. PARK: Easy. TEL: 015396 20251.

STAVELEY

Staveley Antiques

27/29 Main St. LA8 9LU. (P. John Corry). Est. 1991. Open 10-5, Sun. by appointment. SIZE: Large. *STOCK: Brass and iron bedsteads, 1830-1930, £200-£1,200; French walnut bedsteads, from 1880, £500-£2,000; lighting, 1880-1935,*

A Lenci pottery figure, 15¼in. high. £5,170. Wintertons, Lichfield, Staffordshire.

From a feature on Saleroom Prices which appeared in the July/August 2001 issue of **Antique Collecting**. For more details and to subscribe see page 21.

from £50; fire-irons, kerbs and metalware, from 1850, from £50. LOC: Between Kendal and Windermere on A591 (now bypassed). PARK: Easy. TEL: 01539 821393; home - 01539 821123. SER: Valuations; restorations (brass and iron bedsteads, metalware)

ULVERSTON

A1A Antiques

59B Market St. LA12 7LT. (J.W. Thornton). Est. 1960. Telephone for appointment, preferably before 8am or between 8-11pm. SIZE: Large. *STOCK: Bric-a-brac, clocks, furniture, shipping items, pictures, decorators items.* PARK: Easy. TEL: 01229 580284; mobile - 07974 788525. SER: Valuations; restorations; buys at auction; fairs vetting.

Elizabeth and Son

Market Hall. (J.R. Bevins). Est. 1960. Open 9-5. CL: Wed. SIZE: Medium. *STOCK: Victorian and Edwardian glass, silver, brass and copper, gold and silver jewellery, books.* LOC: Town centre. PARK: Easy. TEL: 01229 582763.

WHITEHAVEN

Michael Moon - Antiquarian Booksellers

19 Lowther St. CA28 7AL. (M. and S. Moon). SBA, PBFA. Open 9.30-5. SIZE: Large. *STOCK: Antiquarian books including Cumbrian topography.* LOC: Opposite Clydesdale Bank. PARK: Nearby. TEL: 01946 599010. FAIRS: PBFA Northern. VAT: Stan.

WINDERMERE

Joseph Thornton Antiques

4 Victoria St. LA23 1AB. (J.W. Thornton). Est. 1971. Open by appointment. SIZE: Large. *STOCK: General antiques, art, architectural and decorators' items, clocks, bric-a-brac.* LOC: 50yds. from railway station. PARK: Easy. TEL: 01229 580284. SER: Valuations; buys at auction; fairs vetting.

WORKINGTON

Castle Antiques Bookstore

18 Pow St. CA14 3AG. SIZE: Medium. *STOCK: Books and related ephemera, vintage posters, cigarette cards, postcards, sporting programmes, comics, pictures and prints.* LOC: Just off A66 coming into town. PARK: Opposite. TEL: 01900 607499/601387. SER: Publishers of local histories.

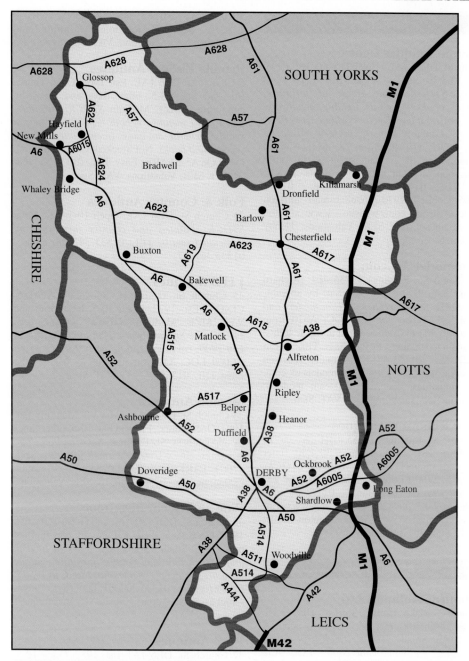

Dealers and Shops in Derbyshire

Alfreton	3	Derby	5	Long Eaton	1
Ashbourne	10	Doveridge	1	Matlock	1
Bakewell	5	Dronfield	1	Newmills	1
Barlow	2	Duffield	1	Ockbrook	1
Belper	3	Glossop	1	Ripley	1
Bradwell	1	Hayfield	2	Shardlow	1
Buxton	5	Heanor	1	Whaley Bridge	2
Chesterfield	3	Killamarsh	1	Woodville	1

Alfreton Antiques Centre

11 King St. DE55 7AF. (Helen Dixon). Est. 1996. Open 10-4.30, Sun. 11-4.30. SIZE: Large - 40 dealers. *STOCK: Wide range of furniture, ceramics, books, postcards, lighting, metalware, glass, collectables, Deco, costume jewellery, pictures, Langley Artware pottery, militaria, silver.* LOC: Off junction 28, M1, A38 to Alfreton, King St. is main street up to traffic lights, shop on right before the lights. PARK: Easy. TEL: 01773 520781; home - 01773 852695; mobile - 07970 786968; e-mail - alfreton antiques@supanet.com; website - www. alfreton antiques.supanet.com. SER: Valuations; Denby replacement service.

Steammodels.uk.com

31-32 South St., Riddings. DE55 4EJ. (Richard Evison). Est. 1990. Open 9-5, Sat. by appointment. SIZE: Small. *STOCK: Steam models and advertising figures, 20th C.* LOC: A610 from junction 26, M1 to Codnor. Right at traffic lights, right again to Riddings. PARK: Easy. TEL: 01773 541527; fax - 01773 541527; e-mail - raevison @aol.com; website - www.steammodels.uk.com. SER: Valuations; restorations (steam models); buys at auction (steam models). VAT: Stan.

Taylor Robinson Antiques

31 George St. Riddings. DE55 4BH. (A. and B. Robinson). Est. 1973. Open 9.30-4.30 (later closing in summer). SIZE: Medium. *STOCK: Furniture, £100-£1,000; ceramics, copper, £5-£200, all 19th C.* TEL: Home - 01773 603659; mobile - 07885 507420; website - www.taylor robinsonantiques.co.uk. FAIRS: Shepton Mallet (DMG); Stafford (Bowmans).

Ashbourne Antiques Ltd

Warehouse, Blake House, Shirley. DE6 3AS. (Robert Allsebrook). Est. 1977. Open by appointment. SIZE: Small. *STOCK: English furniture, 17th-20th C, and hand-made copies.* LOC: A52 Ashbourne/Derby. PARK: Easy. TEL: 01335 361236; mobile - 07970 094883. SER: Restorations; cabinet makers; removals, packing and shipping. VAT: Stan.

Daniel Charles Antiques

33 Church St. DE6 1AE. (Keith and Hayley Phillips-Moul). Est. 2000. Open 10-5.30. SIZE: Medium. *STOCK: Furniture and fine art, 17th-18th C, to £1,000+.* PARK: Easy. TEL: 01335 300002; fax - 01335 348200; mobile - 07050 129250. SER: Restorations (furniture and porcelain); buys at auction. VAT: Stan/Spec.

Pamela Elsom - Antiques

5 Church St. DE6 1AE. Est. 1963. Open Thurs., Fri. and Sat. 10-5, other days and times by appointment. SIZE: Medium. *STOCK: Furniture, £20-£5,000, metalware, both 17th-19th C; period smalls, general antiques, treen, pottery, glass, secondhand books.* Not Stocked: Coins, militaria. LOC: On A52. PARK: Easy. TEL: 01335 343468/ 344311. SER: Valuations. VAT: Spec.

Folk & Country Antiques

21 Church St. DE6 1AE. Open 10-5. CL: Mon. *STOCK: Painted and country furniture and associated smalls.* TEL: 01335 342598; home - 01335 361217.

J H S Antiques

45 Church St. (Julian H. Snodin). LAPADA. CINOA. Est. 1972. Open 10-5. CL: Mon. and Wed. SIZE: Medium. *STOCK: 17th C oak, £1,000-£7,000; metalware, 17th to early 19th C, £50-£400; carvings, 17th to early 18th C, £300-£1,000.* LOC: A52 from junction 25, M1. PARK: Easy. TEL: 01335 347733. VAT: Spec.

Manion Antiques

23 Church St. DE6 1AE. (Mrs V.J. Manion). Est. 1984. Open Thurs., Fri. and Sat. 10-5, other times by appointment. SIZE: Small. *STOCK: Porcelain, paintings, silver, jewellery, small furniture, £50-£100+.* PARK: Easy. TEL: 01335 343207; home - same; mobile - 07968 067316. SER: Valuations.

Pine and Decorative Items

38 Church St. DE6 1AJ. (M. and G. Bassett). Est. 1980. Open 10-5, Wed. and Sun. by appointment only. SIZE: Small + warehouse. *STOCK: English and French pine and country furniture; garden furniture, ironwork, kitchenalia, 18th C to 1950's, from £10.* TEL: 01335 300061; fax - same; e-mail - mgbassett@aol.com; website - www.antiques-atlas.com. VAT: Stan.

Rose Antiques

37 Church St. DE6 1AJ. Est. 1982. Open 10-5. SIZE: Medium. *STOCK: Furniture, silver, porcelain, jewellery, copper, brass and pine.* LOC: A52. PARK: Easy. TEL: 01335 343822; home - 01283 575301.

Spurrier-Smith Antiques

28, 30 and 39 Church St. DE6 1AJ. (I. Spurrier-Smith). LAPADA. Est. 1973. Open 10-5, Wed. and Sun. by appointment. SIZE: Large (8 showrooms) + warehouse. *STOCK: Furniture, oils, water-*

colours, porcelain, pottery, metalware, instruments, Oriental bronzes, collectables, pine, decorative items. Warehouse - pine and American export goods. PARK: Easy. TEL: 01335 343669/342198; home - 01629 822502; e-mail - ivan@spurrier-smith.fsnet.co.uk; website - www.spurrier-smith.co.uk. SER: Valuations; restorations (furniture). VAT: Stan/Spec.

Kenneth Upchurch
30B Church St. DE6 1AE. Est. 1972. *STOCK: Oil paintings and watercolours, mainly 19th C; pottery and porcelain.* TEL: 01332 754499.

BAKEWELL

Peter Bunting Antiques   BADA
Harthill Hall, Alport. DE45 1LH. LAPADA. Est. 1980. Open by appointment. SIZE: Medium. *STOCK: Early oak, country furniture, portraits and period decoration.* **LOC: On B5056. PARK: Own. TEL: 01629 636203; fax - 01629 636101; mobile - 07860 540870. VAT: Stan/Spec.**

Chappells Antiques Centre
King St. DE45 1DZ. BADA; LAPADA. Est. 1992. Open 10-5, Sun. 12-5. *STOCK: Period furniture, decorative and collectors' items, 17th-20th C.* LOC: King St is signposted B5055, Monyash, off the A6. PARK: Agricultural Centre (entrance off A6) and Smith's Island (off Baslow Rd.) 5 mins walk from Centre. TEL: 01629 812496; fax - 01629 814531; website - www.chappellsantiquescentre.com. Below are listed the dealers at this market.

Allens
20th C ceramics and secondhand books.

Barbara Austin
Linen, lace and small textile items.

Rex Boyer Antiques
LAPADA. *18th-19th C furniture and decorative objects.*

Chappell's Antiques & Fine Art   BADA
Est. 1940. LAPADA. *17th-19th C English furniture, oil paintings, porcelain, pottery, metalwork, clocks and decorative items.* **VAT: Stan/Spec.**

Clocks in the Peak
Longcase clocks, specialising in Derbyshire makers.

Compton House
LAPADA. *Fine 19th C furniture.*

Cottage Antiques
LAPADA. *18th-19th C furniture, glass, treen, textiles, furnishing and decorative items.*

Stephanie Davison Antiques
Early English oak and country furniture.

Roger de Ville
19th C pottery and porcelain, specialising in commemoratives.

J. Dickinson
Maps, prints and books.

Elizabeth Ann Antiques
Furniture and decorative items.

Elizabeth Antiques
General antiques and collectables.

G.W. Ford & Son Ltd
(I.G.F. Thomson). Est. 1890. LAPADA. *Mahogany and country furniture, 18th-19th C, £50-£5,000; sculpture, 19th to early 20th C, £50-£3,000; collectable and decorative items, 18th-19th C, £10-£1,200.* TEL: Home - 01246 410512; fax - same; SER: Valuations; restorations (furniture, silver and EP). VAT: Stan/Spec.

Ganymede Antiques
18th-19th C clocks, furniture, silver and plate, pewter, brass, pharmaceutical and scientific instruments.

J.H.S. Antiques
LAPADA. *17th to early 19th C country furniture, Staffordshire, treen and metalware.*

Peter Kelsey Antiques
Furniture and works of art.

Shirley May Antiques & Collectables
Kitchenalia, Cornish, Denby and textiles.

Millennium Antiques
Fine English silver, silver plate, glass and bijouterie.

Walter Moores & Son
18th-19th C furniture and decorative items.

M.F. Morris Antiques
Fine Derby, Royal Crown Derby and Lynton porcelain.

Newton Fine Art
19th-20th C oil paintings and watercolours.

Old Country Antiques
Sporting antiques, luggage and Beswick animals.

Paraphernalia Lighting
Antique lighting and decorative arts.

Peak Antiques, Glossop
Victorian and Edwardian furniture.

Judy Portway
(Benjamin Henry & Co). *Vintage and designer costume jewelley and accessories.*

Pye Antiques
Early blue and white, ironstone, Dux, wall clocks and barometers.

Renaissance Antiques
Pottery, papier-mâché, metals, glass and objects d'art.

Scarlett Antiques
Victorian to 1930's jewellery, clocks and watches.

Sandra Wallhead Antiques
19th to early 20th C furniture, cranberry glass, dolls, jewellery and objets d'art.

N.I. Wilkinson
19th-20th C collectables.

Michael Wisehall Antiques   BADA
Furniture, plate, glass, pictures, metalware and pottery.

Martin and Dorothy Harper Antiques
King St. DE45 1DZ. LAPADA. Est. 1973. Open 10-5, Sun. and other times by appointment. CL: Mon. and Thurs. SIZE: Medium. *STOCK: Furniture, £75-£7,500; metalware, £30-£300; glass, £15-£150; all 17th to late 19th C; needlework,*

19th C. PARK: Easy. TEL: 01629 814757; mobile - 07885 347134. SER: Valuations; restorations; buys at auction. VAT: Stan/Spec.

Thornbridge Antiques
King St. DE45 1DZ. (Peter Hunt). LAPADA. Open 10-5, Sun. 11-4. CL: Bank Holidays. SIZE: Large. *STOCK: Town and country furniture, 17th-19th C, from £500; clocks, 18th-19th C; objets d'art, porcelain, treen and metalware.* LOC: Near Rutland Hotel. PARK: Easy and nearby. TEL: 01629 814224; fax - same. VAT: Spec.

Water Lane Antiques
Water Lane. DE45 1EU. (M.J. Pembery). Est. 1967. Open 10-5. SIZE: Medium. *STOCK: Furniture, £500-£4,000; metalware, £100-£1,000; objets d'art, £100-£1,500; all 18th-19th C.* LOC: Off Market Sq. PARK: Nearby. TEL: 01629 814161. SER: Valuations; restorations. VAT: Stan/Spec.

BARLOW

Byethorpe Furniture
Shippen Rural Business Centre, Church Farm. S18. Est. 1977. Open 9.30-5.30. SIZE: Medium. *STOCK: Oak, mahogany and pine country and classical furniture.* PARK: Easy. TEL: 01142 899111; fax - same; website - www.byethorpe. com. SER: Restorations (furniture); specialist woodwork; upholstery; French polishing; handmade reproductions. VAT: Stan/Spec.

Hackney House Antiques
Hackney Lane, S18 7TD. (Mrs J.M. Gorman). Resident. Est. 1984. Open Tues.-Sun. 9-6. SIZE: Small. *STOCK: Furniture, 18th-19th C; prints, clocks, linen, silver.* LOC: B6051 NW of Chesterfield. PARK: Easy. TEL: 01142 890248.

BELPER

Derwentside Antiques
Derwent St. DE56 1WN. Est. 1995. Open 8.30-5.30, Sun. 8.30-5. SIZE: Large. *STOCK: General antiques mainly furniture.* LOC: Just off A6. PARK: Own. TEL: 01773 828008; fax - 01773 828983; e-mail - enquires@derwentsidehomecentre.co.uk; website - www.derwentside homecentre.co. uk. SER: Restorations; sourcing of period furniture.

Sweetings (Antiques 'n' Things)
1 & 1a The Butts. DE56 1HX. (K.J. and J.L. Sweeting). Est. 1971. Open daily. SIZE: Large. *STOCK: Pre 1940's furniture including stripped pine, oak, mahogany, satinwood, £20-£1,000.* LOC:

Off A6, near Market Place. PARK: Easy. TEL: 01773 825930/822780. SER: Valuations; restorations (pine and satinwood); shipping. VAT: Stan.

Neil Wayne "The Razor Man"
The Cedars (rear of 55 Field Lane), DE56 1DD. Resident. Est. 1969. Open every day 9.30-6, prior telephone call essential. SIZE: Medium. *STOCK: Razors and shaving items, 18th to early 19th C, £20-£300.* PARK: Easy. TEL: 01773 824157; fax - 01773 825573; e-mail - neil.wayne@derbyshire-holidays.com.

BRADWELL

Bradwell Antiques Centre
Newburgh Hall, Netherside. Est. 2000. Open 10-5, Sun. 11-5. SIZE: 30 dealers. *STOCK: Wide range of general antiques, 18th-20th C, £5-£5,000.* LOC: A625 Hope Valley road, turn opposite Travellers Rest public house on to B6049. PARK: Own. TEL: 01433 621000; fax - same; e-mail - info@bradwell antiques.com; websites - www.bradwellantiques. com and www. antiquestrail.com. SER: Restorations (furniture); buys at auction.

BUXTON

The Antiques Warehouse
25 Lightwood Rd. SK17 7BJ. (N.F. Thompson). Est. 1983. Open 10.30-4 or by appointment. SIZE: Large. *STOCK: British furniture, mainly mahogany, rosewood and walnut, 17th-20th C; paintings, silver, metalware, smalls, clocks including longcase, Victorian brass and iron bedsteads.* LOC: Off A6. PARK: Own at rear. TEL: 01298 72967; home/fax - 01298 22603; mobile - 07947 050552. SER: Valuations; restorations; buys at auction.

Maggie Mays
Unit 10, Cavendish Arcade. SK17. (Mrs. J. Wild). Est. 1993. Open 10.30-5. CL: Mon. *STOCK: Victorian furniture and effects, £35-£800; Art Deco glassware, mirrors, pottery, £20-£500; Edwardian furniture, £100-£800.* LOC: Opposite Turners Memorial on Terrace Road. PARK: Easy. TEL: Mobile - 07831 606003; home - 01663 733935. SER: Valuations; buys at auction.

The Penny Post Antiques
9 Cavendish Circus. SK17 6AT. (D. and R. Hammond). Est. 1978. Open 10-4.30, Sat. 10-5. SIZE: Small. *STOCK: Pictures, commemoratives, crested china, shaving mugs and other collectables; furniture; general antiques.* LOC: Town centre, opposite Palace Hotel. PARK: Easy. TEL: Home - 01298 25965.

West End Galleries
8 Cavendish Circus. SK17 6AT. (A. and A. Needham). Est. 1955. Open 9-5, Sat. 9-4. SIZE: Medium. *STOCK: French and English furniture; clocks, paintings, works of art, bronzes.* LOC: A6. PARK: Easy. TEL: 01298 24546. VAT: Spec.

What Now Antiques
Cavendish Arcade, The Crescent. SK17 6BQ. (L. Carruthers). Est. 1987. Open 10-5, Sun. 2-5. CL: Mon. SIZE: Small. *STOCK: General antiques and collectables including Art Deco pottery, small silver items, jewellery, textiles, lighting, clocks, Victorian and Edwardian furniture, £1-£1,000.* LOC: Central. PARK: Nearby. TEL: 01298 27178; mobile - 07977 369878; e-mail - ally4antiques@ic24.net. SER: Export; valuations; foreign trade.

CHESTERFIELD

Anthony D. Goodlad
26 Fairfield Rd., Brockwell. S40 4TP. Est. 1974. Open by appointment only. SIZE: Small. *STOCK: General militaria, WWI and WWII.* LOC: Close to town centre. PARK: Easy. TEL: 01246 204004. FAIRS: Major UK Arms.

Ian Morris
479 Chatsworth Rd. S40 3AD. Est. 1970. Open 1-5 or by chance or appointment. SIZE: Medium. *STOCK: Furniture, 18th-20th C, £50-£2,000; pictures, small items.* LOC: A619 to Baslow and Chatsworth House. PARK: Easy. TEL: 01246 235120. VAT: Stan/Spec.

Marlene Rutherford Antiques
401 Sheffield Rd., Whittington Moor. S41 8LS. Est. 1985. Open Mon. and Thurs. 10-4, Tues. 12-4, Fri. and Sat. 1-4. *STOCK: Furniture, pottery, clocks and lamps, £5-£1,000.* PARK: Easy. TEL: 01426 450209; mobile - 07885 665440. SER: Valuations. FAIRS: Bowman, Newark. Pandora.

DERBY

Abbey House
115 Woods Lane. DE22 3UE. (Shirley White). Resident. Est. 1959. Open by appointment. *STOCK: Dolls, teddy bears and all things juvenile.* TEL: 01332 331426; fax - same; e-mail - shirley.white1@btinternet.com. SER: Repairs (dolls and teddies); restorations (furniture).

Derventio Books
43a Sadler Gate. DE1 1NR. (D. A. Harper). Est. 1996. Open 10.15-5. SIZE: Medium. *STOCK:*

Out-of-print, secondhand and antiquarian books especially modern first editions, Derbyshire, science fiction, mainly 19th-20th C, 50p to £500; some antiquarian maps and prints. LOC: 1st floor via short passageway off Sadler Gate. PARK: Nearby. TEL: 01332 343538; website - www.derventio-books.co.uk SER: Valuations.

Finishing Touches
224 Uttoxeter Old Rd., The Rowditch. DE1 1NF. (Lynne Robinson). Est. 1994. Open 10-5.30, Sun. by appointment. CL: Mon. SIZE: Small. *STOCK: Fire surrounds, £200-£800; pine furniture, £50-£500; kitchenalia and pottery, £1-£25; all late 19th to early 20th C.* LOC: Off A38 at junction with A52. PARK: Rear of church. TEL: 01332 721717; website - www.derbyantiques.co.uk. SER: Restorations.

Friargate Pine Company Ltd
The Pump House, Friargate Goods Wharf, Stafford St. Entrance. DE1 1JL. (N. J. Marianski). Open 9-5. *STOCK: Antique and reproduction pine furniture.* TEL: 01332 341215.

Brian Matsell
1 Friar Gate Court, Friar Gate. DE1 1HE. Resident. Est. 1965. Open by appointment. SIZE: Small. *STOCK: Georgian and Regency furniture, decorative antiques, Oriental porcelain and objects; oil paintings and watercolours.* LOC: Town centre. PARK: Easy. TEL: 01332 365211; fax - 01332 367572; mobile - 07747 702741. SER: Valuations; buys at auction; consultancy. VAT: Stan/Spec.

DOVERIDGE

Pine Antiques Workshop
Bell Farm, Yelt Lane. DE6 5JU. (M.A. and A. Groves). Open Tues.-Sat. 9-5.30, other times by appointment. *STOCK: English and Welsh pine, pottery, linen and kitchenalia.* TEL: 01889 564898; fax - same.

DRONFIELD

Bardwell Antiques
51 Chesterfield Rd. S18 6XA. (S. Bardwell). Open Tues., Wed., Thurs. 10-4, Sat. 9-2. *STOCK: General antiques.* TEL: 01246 412183; fax - same.

DUFFIELD, Nr. Derby

Wayside Antiques
62 Town St. DE56 4GG. (Mrs J. Harding). Est. 1975. *STOCK: Furniture, 18th-19th C, £50-£5,000; porcelain, pictures, boxes and silver.* TEL: 01332 840346. VAT: Stan/Spec.

GLOSSOP

Derbyshire Clocks
104 High St. West. SK13 8BB. (J.A. and T.P. Lees). Est. 1975. CL: Tues. *STOCK: Clocks.* PARK: Easy. TEL: 01457 862677. SER: Restorations (clocks and barometers). VAT: Spec.

HAYFIELD, Nr. New Mills

Michael Allcroft Antiques
1 Church St. Open Sat. 2-5, Sun. 1-5, other times by appointment. *STOCK: Pine furniture and decorative items.* TEL: 01663 742684; mobile - 07798 781642; fax - 01663 744014.

Paul Pickford Antiques
Top of the Town, Church St. SK22 2JE. Est. 1975. Open Tues., Thurs. and Sat. 11-4, Sun. 1-5, other times by appointment. SIZE: Medium. *STOCK: 19th C furniture, stripped pine, lighting and general antiques, £50-£500.* LOC: Off A6 at Newtown, near Disley, take A6015. PARK: Easy. TEL: 01663 747276; home - 01663 743356; e-mail - paul@pickfordantiques.co.uk; website - www.pickfordantiques.co.uk.

HEANOR

Heanor Antiques Centre
1-3 Ilkeston Rd. (Jane Richards). Est. 1998. Open 10.30-4.30. SIZE: Large. *STOCK: Wide range of general antiques and collectables.* PARK: Easy. TEL: 01773 531181. SER: Valuations; restorations.

KILLAMARSH

Havenplan's Architectural Emporium
The Old Station, Station Rd. S21 1EN. Est. 1972. Open Tues., Wed., Thurs. and Sat. 10-2.30. SIZE: Large. *STOCK: Architectural fittings and decorative items, church interiors and furnishings, fireplaces, doors, decorative cast ironwork, masonry, bygones, garden ornaments, 18th to early 20th C.* LOC: M1, exit 30. Take A616 towards Sheffield, turn right on to B6053, turn right on to B6058 towards Killamarsh, turn right between two railway bridges. PARK: Easy. TEL: 01142 489972; home - 01246 433315. SER: Hire.

LONG EATON

Miss Elany
2 Salisbury St. NG10 1BA. (D. and Mrs Mottershead). Est. 1977. Open 9-5. SIZE: Medium.

STOCK: Pianos, 1900 to date, £50-£500; general antiques, Victorian and Edwardian, £25-£200. PARK: Easy. TEL: 0115 9734835. VAT: Stan.

MATLOCK

Matlock Antiques and Collectables Centre

7 Dale Rd. DE4 3LT. (W. Shirley). Open 10-5 including Sun. SIZE: Large - 70 dealers. *STOCK: Furniture, clocks, art and general antiques.* LOC: Town centre. PARK: Easy. TEL: 01629 760808; e-mail - bmatlockantiques@aol.com; website - www. matlockantiques.f9.co.uk.

NEWMILLS, Nr. Stockport

Michael Allcroft Antiques

203 Buxton Rd., Newtown. Open Tues.-Fri. 12-6, Sat. 10-5, other times by appointment. SIZE: Large. *STOCK: Edwardian and 1930's furniture.* LOC: A6 south of Stockport. TEL: Mobile - 07798 781642; fax - 01663 744014.

OCKBROOK

The Good Olde Days

6 Flood St. DE72 3RP. (Mr and Mrs S. Potter). Est. 1992. Open 10-5, Wed. 12-5. CL: Mon. SIZE: Medium. *STOCK: Beswick, Doulton, Wedgwood, Moorcroft, small furniture.* LOC: Village centre. PARK: Rear of shop. TEL: 01332 544244; home - 01332 663586. SER: Valuations. FAIRS: Cheltenham Racecourse, Coventry, Kettering, Wickstead Park, RAF Swinderby, Ipswich, Norwich.

RIPLEY

Memory Lane Antiques Centre

Nottingham Rd. DE5 3AS. (James Cullen). Est. 1994. Open 10.30-4 including Sun. SIZE: Large. *STOCK: Victoriana and 20th C collectables, pine furniture, specialist in old Denby, Bourne and Langley, lighting.* LOC: 200 yds from town centre - 500 yds from A610 (Sainsburys) roundabout. PARK: Easy. TEL: 01773 570184; mobile - 07703 115626. SER: Valuations; pine stripping; old Denby replacement service. FAIRS: Derby University; Newark; Abacus; Kedleston Hall; Swinderby.

SHARDLOW, Nr. Derby

Shardlow Antiques Warehouse

24 The Wharf. DE72 2GH. (Nigel Critchlow). Est. 1986. Open 10.30-5, Sun. 12-5. CL: Fri. SIZE: Large. *STOCK: Furniture, Georgian to shipping.* LOC: Off M1, junction 24. PARK: Own. TEL: 01332 792899/662899. VAT: Spec.

WHALEY BRIDGE

Richard Glass

Hockerley Old Hall, Hockerley Lane. Resident. Est. 1985. Open by appointment only. SIZE: Small. *STOCK: Oak furniture, 17th-18th C, £1,000-£5,000; paintings, drawings, metal and stoneware, 17th-19th C, £200-£2,000.* LOC: From town centre towards Stockport, turn left at station car park, up hill and 2nd right into Hockerley Lane, up farm track at the end of the lane, house on left. PARK: Easy. TEL: 0161 236 1520; fax - 0161 237 5174. SER: Valuations. VAT: Spec.

Nimbus Antiques

Chapel Rd. (L.M. and H.C. Brobbin). Est. 1978. Open 9-5.30, Sun. 2-5.30. SIZE: Large. *STOCK: Furniture, mainly mahogany, including desks, dining tables, clocks, chests, 18th-19th C.* LOC: A6. PARK: Easy. TEL: 01663 734248; home - 01663 733332; e-mail - nimbusantiques@hotmail.com; website - www.antiques-atlas.com/ nimbus.htm. SER: Valuations; restorations. VAT: Stan/Spec.

WOODVILLE

Wooden Box Antiques

32 High St. DE11 7EH. (Mrs R. Bowler). Est. 1982. Open 10-5 including some Sun. SIZE: Medium. *STOCK: Furniture, Georgian-Edwardian, £75-£400; original cast-iron fireplaces, surrounds, £50-£600; Victorian tiles, country pine furniture, pine doors.* LOC: A511 (was A50), between Ashby-de-la-Zouch and Burton-on-Trent. PARK: Easy. TEL: 01283 212014; home - same.

A 15th century oak and iron alms box which fetched £7,500.

From an Auction Report by Christopher Wight on the contents of Nyetimber Manor held at Sotheby's Olympia, 27th September 2001 which appeared in the November 2001 issue of **Antique Collecting**. For more details and to subscribe see page 21.

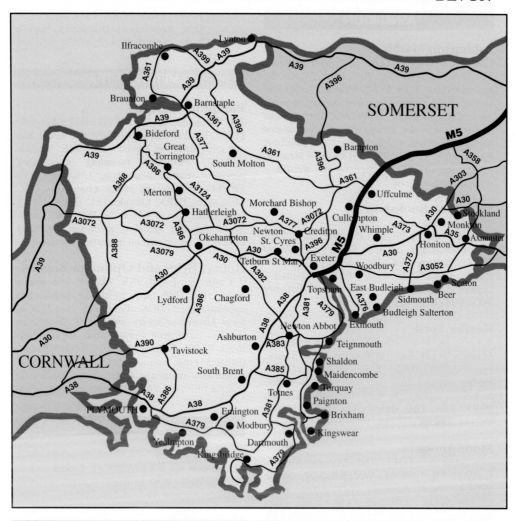

Dealers and Shops in Devonshire

Ashburton	5	Great Torrington	1	Plymouth	6
Axminster	1	Hatherleigh	1	Seaton	1
Bampton	2	Honiton	22	Shaldon	2
Barnstaple	6	Ilfracombe	1	Sidmouth	5
Beer	1	Kingsbridge	1	South Brent	1
Bideford	3	Kingswear	1	South Molton	6
Braunton	1	Lydford	1	Stockland	1
Brixham	2	Lynton	2	Tavistock	2
Budleigh Salterton	3	Maidencombe	1	Tedburn St Mary	1
Chagford	3	Merton	1	Teignmouth	3
Crediton	1	Modbury	2	Topsham	3
Cullompton	5	Monkton	1	Torquay	5
Dartmouth	1	Morchard Bishop	1	Totnes	7
East Budleigh	1	Newton Abbot	2	Uffculme	1
Ermington	1	Newton St. Cyres	1	Whimple	1
Exeter	11	Okehampton	1	Woodbury	1
Exmouth	2	Paignton	2	Yealmpton	1

ASHBURTON

Ashburton Marbles
Great Hall, North St. TQ13 7DU. (Adrian Ager). Est. 1976. Open 8-5, Sat. 10-4. SIZE: Warehouse and showroom. *STOCK: Marble and wooden fire-surrounds, decorative cast iron inserts; scuttles, fenders, overmantels, 1790-1910; architectural decorative antiques, garden statuary and related items, chandeliers, soft furnishings and furniture.* PARK: Easy. TEL: 01364 653189; fax - same; e-mail - enquiries@adrianager.co.uk; website - www.adrianager.co.uk.

Dartmoor Bookshop
2 Kingsbridge Lane. TQ13 7DX. (Paul and Barbara Heatley). PBFA. Est. 1982. Open 9.30-5.30. SIZE: Large. *STOCK: Books - secondhand and antiquarian.* LOC: On lane facing car park. PARK: Easy. TEL: 01364 653356; e-mail - Dartmoorbks@aol.com; website - www.dartmoorbks.dabsol.co.uk. SER: Valuations.

Kessler Ford
9 North St. TQ13 7QJ. (Elisabeth Kessler and Matthew Ford). Est. 1999. Open Tues., Thurs., Fri. 10-5, Sat. 10.30-5. SIZE: Medium. *STOCK: Period oak and Georgian mahogany furniture; pictures, carvings, bronzes.* LOC: Main street. PARK: Easy. TEL: 01364 654310; fax - 01364 652141. SER: Valuations. VAT: Spec.

Moor Antiques
19a North St. TQ13 7QH. (T. and Mrs D. Gatland). Est. 1984. CL: Wed. pm. SIZE: Small. *STOCK: Small furniture, 1780-1900, £250-£2,500; clocks, 1830-1910, £150-£2,000; silver and china, 1800-1900, £25-£500; jewellery, £30-£250.* LOC: A38 town centre, 100 yards past town hall. PARK: Nearby. TEL: 01364 653767. SER: Valuations.

The Shambles
24 North St. TQ13 7QD. Est. 1982. Open 10-5, Sat. 10-4. SIZE: 8 dealers. *STOCK: Country and general antiques and decorative items, £5-£2,000.* LOC: Town centre. PARK: Opposite. TEL: 01364 653848. SER: Valuations. FAIRS: Sandown Park; Westpoint Exeter; Shepton Mallet. VAT: Stan/Spec.

AXMINSTER

W.G. Potter and Son
1 West St. EX13 5HS. Est. 1863. Open 9-5. CL: Sat. pm. SIZE: Medium. *STOCK: Pine, 19th-20th C; some mahogany and oak.* LOC: In main street

(A35) opposite church. PARK: Easy. TEL: 01297 32063. SER: Restorations (furniture); buys at auction. VAT: Stan/Spec.

BAMPTON, Nr. Tiverton

Bampton Gallery
2-4 Brook St. EX16 9LY. (Gerald Chidwick). FRICS. Est. 1997. Open 9.30-5.30, Sat. 9.30-1, Sun. and other times by appointment. SIZE: Medium. *STOCK: Furniture including upholstered, porcelain, pottery and glass, 1750-1900, £10-£10,000; pictures and prints, £10-£1,000.* LOC: Main street. PARK: Outside. TEL: 01398 331119; fax - same; home - 01398 331354. SER: Restorations (furniture including traditional upholstery, ceramics); buys at auction (porcelain and furniture).

Robert Byles and Optimum Brasses
7 Castle St. EX16 9NS. (Robert and Rachel Byles). Est. 1966. Open by chance, knocking or appointment. *STOCK: Furniture, 16th-18th C; local farmhouse tables and settles, metalwork, pottery, unstripped period pine, architectural items.* PARK: Nearby. TEL: 01398 331515; fax - 01398 331164; website - www.obida.com. SER: Restoration materials; replica brass handles for antique furniture. VAT: Stan/Spec.

BARNSTAPLE

Barn Antiques
73 Newport Rd. EX32 9BG. (T. Cusack). Open 9.30-5, Wed. 9.30-1. SIZE: Large. *STOCK: General antiques.* TEL: 01271 323131.

Medina Gallery
80 Boutport St. EX31 1SR. (R. Jennings). Est. 1972. Open 9.30-5. SIZE: Small. *STOCK: Maps, prints, photographs, oils and watercolours, £1-£500.* TEL: 01271 371025. SER: Picture framing, mounting. VAT: Stan.

North Devon Antiques Centre
The Old Church, 18 Cross St. EX31 1BD. (P. Broome). Est. 1985. Open 10-4.30. SIZE: Large. *STOCK: Furniture, china, clocks, 18th C to 1960's, £5-£2,500; Victorian and Art Deco fireplaces, £100-£900.* LOC: 40 yards off High St. PARK: Nearby. TEL: 01271 375788. SER: Valuations; restorations (woodwork and clocks). FAIRS: Newark, Shepton Mallet, Exeter Westpoint.

Mark Parkhouse Antiques and Jewellery
106 High St. EX31 1HP. Est. 1976. CL: Wed. *STOCK: Jewellery, furniture, silver, paintings,*

clocks, glass, porcelain, small collectors' items, 18th-19th C, £100-£10,000. PARK: Nearby. TEL: 01271 374504; fax - 01271 323499. SER: Valuations; buys at auction. VAT: Stan/Spec.

Selected Antiques & Collectables
19 Newport Rd. EX32 9BG. (Helen Chugg). Est. 1994. Open Tues.-Sat. 10-4. SIZE: Medium. *STOCK: North Devon pottery, 19th C; porcelain and ceramics, glass, collectables, 19th-20th C; linen, books, memorabilia, toys.* PARK: Easy. TEL: 01271 321338 (24hr. answerphone). SER: Valuations; restorations (ceramics). FAIRS: Specialist pottery.

Tudor House
115 Boutport St. EX31 1TD. (C. and D. Pilon). Est. 1980. Open 9.30-3.30, Wed. 9.30-1. SIZE: Large. *STOCK: Furniture and bric-a-brac, late 18th C and reproduction.* LOC: Off M5, Tiverton link road to town centre. PARK: Easy. TEL: 01271 375370; home - 01271 371750. SER: Valuations; restorations (furniture).

BEER

Beer Collectables
Dolphin Courtyard. EX12 3EQ. (L. R. Forkes). Est. 1985. Open 10-5 including Sun. SIZE: Medium. *STOCK: Antique fishing tackle, from £25; jewellery, £50-£2,000; china and smalls, £2-£50.* PARK: Easy. TEL: 01297 24362; home - 01460 65294. SER: Valuations; buys at auction. FAIRS: Taunton, Torquay, Beaminster and some local.

BIDEFORD

J. Collins and Son   BADA
The Studio, 28 High St. EX39 2AN. (J. and P. Biggs). LAPADA, CINOA. Est. 1953. Open by appointment. SIZE: Large. *STOCK: Georgian and Regency furniture; general antiques including framed and restored 19th-20th C oils and watercolours, £100-£100,000.* PARK: Easy. TEL: 01237 473103; fax - 01237 475658; home - 01237 476485; e-mail - biggs@collinsantiques. co.uk; website - www.collinsantiques.co.uk. SER: Valuations; restorations (period furniture, paintings and watercolours); cleaning and framing. FAIRS: BADA (March); Olympia (Nov).

Cooper Gallery
Cooper St. EX39 2DA. (Mrs. J. Bruce). Est. 1975. Open 10-4.30, Wed. 10-1.30, Sat. 10-2.30. SIZE: Small. *STOCK: Watercolours, mainly West Country views, late 19th to early 20th C, £200-*£2,500.* LOC: Just off the quay, opposite HSBC bank. PARK: Nearby. TEL: 01237 477370; fax - same; home - 01237 423415; e-mail - cooper gallery@freecall-uk.co.uk; website - www. coopergallery.f2s.com. SER: Valuations; restorations (watercolours and oils). VAT: Spec.

Medina Gallery
20 Mill St. EX39 2JR. (R. Jennings). Est. 1973. Open 9.30-5. SIZE: Medium. *STOCK: Maps and prints, photographs, oils, watercolours, £1-£500.* PARK: Easy. TEL: 01237 476483. SER: Picture framing, mounting. VAT: Stan.

BRAUNTON

Timothy Coward Fine Silver
Marisco, Saunton. EX33 1LG. LAPADA. Open by appointment. *STOCK: Antique and early 20th C silver.* TEL: 01271 890466.

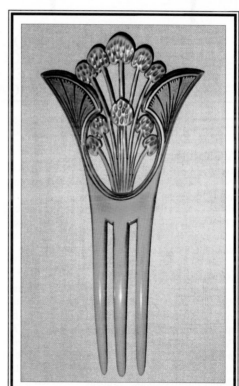

Hair comb; celluloid imitating ivory, lily pads open work decoration, Art Nouveau, 1900-10.

From an article entitled *"Collectable Hair Ornaments"* by Nancy Lyons which appeared in the February 2002 issue of **Antique Collecting**. For more details and to subscribe see page 21.

BRIXHAM

Around the Clock
Ye Olde Coffin House, King St. TQ5 9TF. (Dr. Paul Strickland). Est. 1996. Open by appointment. SIZE: Small. *STOCK: Antique and early electric clocks.* PARK: Loading only and nearby. TEL: 01803 856307; website - www.forall.fsnet. co.uk. SER: Valuations; restorations; buys at auction (clocks and mechanical items).

John Prestige Antiques
1 and 2 Greenswood Court. TQ5 9HN. (John and Patricia Prestige). Est. 1971. Open 8.45-6, appointment advisable. CL: Sat. and Sun. except by appointment. SIZE: Large + warehouse. *STOCK: Period and Victorian furniture; shipping goods; decorative smalls.* TEL: 01803 856141; home - 01803 853739; fax - 01803 851649; e-mail - sales @john-prestige.co.uk; website - www.john-prestige.co.uk. SER: Restorations (furniture); desk re-lining. VAT: Stan/Spec.

BUDLEIGH SALTERTON

Days of Grace
15 Fore St. EX9 6NH. (L. Duriez). *STOCK: Antique lace, vintage textiles and costume, china, jewellery, furniture, interesting decorating items.* TEL: 01395 443730.

Alison Gosling Antiques
46a High St. EX9 6LJ. Est. 1983. Open Mon. 11-5, Tues. and Wed. 3-5, Fri. 1.30-5 or by appointment. SIZE: Medium. *STOCK: Furniture, early 18th to early 19th C , £400-£8,500; porcelain and decorative items, early 18th to early 20th C, £20-£1,000.* LOC: Next to Barclay's Bank. PARK: Easy. TEL: 01395 443737; home - 01395 271451; mobile - 07773 911867. SER: Valuations.

David J. Thorn
2 High St. EX9 6LQ. Est. 1950. Open Tues., Fri. and Sat. 10-1. SIZE: Small. *STOCK: English, Continental and Oriental pottery and porcelain, 1620-1850, £5-£5,000; English furniture, 1680-1870, £20-£5,000; paintings, silver, jewellery, £1-£1,000.* PARK: Easy. TEL: 01395 442448. SER: Valuations. VAT: Stan/Spec.

CHAGFORD

Godolphin Antiques
68 The Square. TQ13 8AE. (S. Freeman). Est. 2000. Open 10-4.30, Sun. by appointment. SIZE:

Medium. *STOCK: Watercolours and oils, 18th to early 20th C, £200-£35,000; oak and country furniture, 17th-19th C; clocks.* LOC: Off The Square, turn opposite Easton Court Hotel on A382. PARK: Easy. TEL: 01647 433999; website - www-godolphinfineart.com. SER: Buys at auction (watercolours and oils).

Rex Antiques
The Old Cinema. TQ13 8AB. (John Meredith). Est. 1979. Open by appointment. SIZE: Large. *STOCK: Country oak, 16th-19th C, £5-£2,000; Oriental brass and copper, weapons, large unusual items, granite, architectural items, old iron work.* PARK: Easy. TEL: 01647 433405. SER: Buys at auction. VAT: Stan/Spec. *Trade only.*

Whiddons Antiques and Tearooms
6 High St. TQ13 8AJ. (D. Meldrum). Est. 1979. Open 10-5.30, Sun. 12-5.30. SIZE: Medium. *STOCK: General and country items - furniture including pine, clocks, prints, paintings, copper, brass, books and collectables.* LOC: Opposite church. PARK: Easy. TEL: 01647 433406; home - 01647 433303.

CREDITON

Musgrave Bickford Antiques
15 East St. EX17 3AT. (Mr and Mrs. D.M. Bickford). Est. 1983. Open by appointment. SIZE: Small. *STOCK: Clocks, barometers, small furniture, mainly 19th C, from £400.* LOC: From Exeter on A377 on right entering one-way system, towards Tiverton. PARK: Easy and at rear by arrangement. TEL: 01363 775042. SER: Restorations (longcase, mantel, wall clock and barometer movements, dials, cases). VAT: Stan/Spec.

CULLOMPTON

Cobweb Antiques
The Old Tannery, Exeter Rd. EX15 1DT. (R. Holmes). Est. 1980. Open 10-5. SIZE: Large. *STOCK: Pine and country furniture, painted, decorative and mahogany items, £5-£5,000.* LOC: Half a mile from junction 28, M5. PARK: Easy. TEL: 01884 855748. SER: Stripping; restorations; packing; courier.

Cullompton Old Tannery Antiques
Exeter Rd. EX15 1DT. (Cullompton Antiques Ltd). Est. 1989. Open 10-5, Sun. by appointment. SIZE: Large. *STOCK: Pine, oak, mahogany and fruitwood country furniture; beds, china, decorative items and mirrors.* LOC: Off M5, junction 28, through town centre, premises on right, approximately 1 mile.

PARK: Easy. TEL: 01884 38476; fax - same; e-mail - cullompton-antiques@lineone.net; website - www.cullompton-antiques.ltd.uk.

Miller Antiques
The Old Tannery, Exeter Rd. EX15 1DT. (Nick Miller). Open 10-5.30, Sat. 10-5, Sun. by appointment. SIZE: Large. *STOCK: Furniture, 18th-19th C, £25-£2,000, country, 17th-19th C, £25-£3,000; decorative accessories, £5-£2,000.* LOC: M5 junction 28, bottom of the High St. opposite Somerfield. PARK: Easy. TEL: 01884 38476; fax - same. SER: Valuations; buys at auction.

Mills Antiques
The Old Tannery, Exeter Rd. EX15 1DT. Est. 1979. Open 10-5.30, Sat. 10-5. *STOCK: 17th C to Edwardian furniture; French bedroom suites, country furniture and decorative items.* PARK: Easy. TEL: 01392 860945.

R.C. Associates
The Old Tannery, Exeter Rd. EX15 1DT. Open 10-5.30, Sat. 10-5. *STOCK: French provincial furniture - beds, armoires, tables, buffets.* PARK: Easy.

DARTMOUTH

Chantry Bookshop and Gallery
11 Higher St. TQ6 9RB. (M.P. Merkel). Est. 1969. Open 10.30-5. CL: 15th Jan.-20th Mar. SIZE: Small. *STOCK: Antiquarian books and watercolours; decorative maps, town plans, prints, sea charts and battle plans.* LOC: Next to 'The Cherub' public house. PARK: Nearby. TEL: 01803 832796; home - 01803 834208.

EAST BUDLEIGH

Antiques at Budleigh House
Budleigh House. EX9 7ED. (W. Cook). Est. 1982. Open 10-5, Sat. 10-1. CL: Mon. and Wed. SIZE: Small. *STOCK: 18th-19th C small furniture and decorative objects, porcelain, glass, silver and metalware, £5-£1,000.* LOC: Opposite Sir Walter Raleigh public house. PARK: Easy. TEL: 01395 445368; home - same. SER: Valuations; buys at auction.

ERMINGTON, Nr. Ivybridge

Mill Gallery
PL21 9NT. (Christopher Trant). Resident. Est. 1984. CL: Sat. SIZE: Small. *STOCK: Oils and watercolours, 18th-20th C, £300-£1,000.* LOC:

209

From A38 take Ivybridge exit, follows signs, 1st premises in village. PARK: Easy. TEL: 01548 830172; website - www.millgallery.com. SER: Valuations; restorations (oils). VAT: Spec.

EXETER

The Antique Centre on the Quay
The Quay. EX2 4AP. Open 10-5 winter, 10-6 summer including Sun. SIZE: 20+ dealers. *STOCK: Antiques - small furniture, ceramics, glass, collectables, books, pictures, postcards, records, tools and jewellery.* PARK: Nearby. TEL: 01392 493501; website - www.exeterquay antiques.co.uk.

Electique
Cellars 18 & 23, The Quay. EX2 4AP. (E.J. Henson and C. Frank). Est. 1992. Open 7 days 11-5. SIZE: Medium. *STOCK: Mainly Victorian and Edwardian furniture including pine and oak; dining tables, chests of drawers, chairs and pictures.* LOC: Town centre. PARK: Nearby. TEL: 01392 250799; e-mail - sales@eclectique.co.uk; website - www.eclectique.co.uk.

Exeter Rare Books
Guildhall Shopping Centre. EX4 3HG. (R.C. Parry). ABA. PBFA. Est. 1975. Open 10-1 and 2-5. SIZE: Small. *STOCK: Books, antiquarian, secondhand, out-of-print, 17th-20th C; Devon and West Country topography. £5-£500.* LOC: City centre. PARK: Easy. TEL: 01392 436021. SER: Valuations; buys at auction. FAIRS: ABA Chelsea, Bath and Edinburgh.

Fagins Antiques
The Old Whiteways Cider Factory, Hele. EX5 4PW. (C.J. Strong). Open 9.15-5, Sat. 11-5. SIZE: Large. *STOCK: Furniture, decorative items, pictures, porcelain, garden furniture, architectural and shipping items.* PARK: Easy. TEL: 01392 882062; fax - 01392 882194; e-mail - cstrong@ fagins-antiques.co.uk; website - www.fagins-antiques.co.uk. SER: Stripping (pine); pine furniture made to order.

Gold and Silver Exchange
Eastgate House, Princesshay. EX4 3JT. *STOCK: Jewellery, watches including Rolex.* TEL: 01392 217478.

The House that Moved
24 West St. EX1 1BA. (L. Duriez). Est. 1980. Open 10-5. SIZE: 3 floors and courtyard. *STOCK: Lace, shawls, babywear, linen, 1920's costume, Victorian and Edwardian bridal wedding dresses.* LOC: West Quarter. PARK: Easy. TEL: 01392 432643.

McBains Antiques
Exeter Airport Industrial Estate, Westcott Lane. EX5 2BA. LAPADA. Est. 1975. Open 9-6, Sat. 10-1. SIZE: Large warehouse complex. *STOCK: Georgian, Victorian and Edwardian furniture; Arts and Crafts; Continental, decorated and painted furniture.* LOC: 3 miles from junction 29, M5. Below are listed the dealers trading from this address. PARK: Easy. TEL: 01392 366261; fax - 01392 365572; e-mail -mcbains@netcomuk.co.uk. SER: Container packing; courier; shipping. FAIRS: Newark. VAT: Spec/Global.

Ash Brothers Antiques
Shipping furniture and decorative items. TEL: 01392 364483; fax - same.

J. Buchanan Antiques

M. Burbidge Antiques

J. Huggett Antiques

McBain Antique Exports
(I.S., G., R. and M. McBain). Est. 1963. *English, French and Belgium furniture suitable for export worldwide.* TEL: 01392 466304; fax - 01392 447304; e-mail - mcbain.exports@zetnet.co.uk SER: Container packing; European courier service.

Miscellany Antiques
Shipping goods. TEL: 01684 566671.

P & A

Portobello Antiques

P. Reynolds Antiques

Leon Robertson Antiques
Furniture. TEL: Mobile - 07971 171909.

Tredantiques
Fine quality period furniture and decorative items. TEL: Mobile - 07967 447082; website - www. tredantiques.com.

Wilford Antiques

Youll's Antiques

Mortimers
87 Queen St. EX4 3RP. (B. Mortimer). Est. 1970. Open 9-5. SIZE: Small. *STOCK: Jewellery, silver, clocks, watches and objet d'art.* LOC: City centre. PARK: Easy. TEL: 01392 279994. SER: Valuations; repairs. VAT: Stan/Spec.

John Nathan Antiques
1st floor, Ivor Doble Ltd. 24 Sidwell St. EX4 1AS. (I. Doble). Est. 1950. Open 9-5.30. SIZE: Small. *STOCK: Silver and jewellery, £5-£5,000; clocks, including Georgian and Victorian, £25-*

£3,000. PARK: Easy. TEL: 01392 210864. SER: Valuations; restorations (silver and jewellery); buys at auction. VAT: Stan.

Phantique
47 The Quay. EX2 4AN. (Patsy Bliss). Est. 1996. Open daily - summer 10.30-5.30, winter 10.30-5. SIZE: Several dealers. *STOCK: Antiques, collectables, prints, books, toys, jewellery.* PARK: Nearby. TEL: 01392 498995; website - www.phantique.co.uk.

The Quay Gallery Antiques Emporium
43 The Quay. EX2 4AP. (James and Stephanie Gould). Est. 1984. Open 10-5 including Sun. SIZE: Large - 15 dealers. *STOCK: 18th-20th C oak and mahogany furniture, marine items, porcelain, silver, plate, glass, paintings, prints, antiquities, carpets and decorative items.* LOC: Next to Old Customs House. PARK: Easy. TEL: 01392 213283.

EXMOUTH

Boase Antiques
5 High St. EX8 1NN. Open 10-5. *STOCK: Jewellery, silver, Victorian collectables.* LOC: Town centre. PARK: Easy. TEL: 01395 271528.

Treasures
34 Exeter Rd. EX8 1PS. (L. Treasure). Open 9-5. *STOCK: General antiques.* TEL: 01395 279512.

GREAT TORRINGTON

C Short Antiques
12 Potacre St. EX38 8BH. (C. J. Short). Est. 1985. Open 10-4, Sat. 10-1. SIZE: Small. *STOCK: Victorian pine furniture, £100-£500.* TEL: 01805 624796; home - 01805 624105. SER: Valuations; restorations (pine stripping and polishing). VAT: Stan.

HATHERLEIGH

Hatherleigh Antiques   BADA
15 Bridge St. EX20 3HU. (M. Dann). Open 9-5, prior telephone call advisable. SIZE: Medium. *STOCK: Collectors' furniture and works of art, pre-1700.* **PARK: Easy. TEL: 01837 810159/ 810500. VAT: Spec.**

HONITON

Jane Barnes Antiques & Interiors
59 High St. EX14 8PW. (J.A.C. and S.J. Barnes). Open 10-4. CL: Wed. SIZE: Medium. *STOCK: General antiques and country pine, glass, clocks.* LOC: Main St. PARK: Easy. TEL: 01404 41712. SER: Furniture copies made to order.

Roderick Butler   BADA
Marwood House. EX14 1PY. (Roderick and Valentine Butler). Est. 1948. Open 9.30-5 (during August by appointment only). SIZE: Large. *STOCK: 17th-18th C and Regency furniture, curiosities, unusual items, early metalwork.* **LOC: Adjacent to roundabout at eastern end of High St. PARK: In courtyard. TEL: 01404 42169. SER: Restorations (furniture). VAT: Spec.**

C & S Antiques
159 High St. EX14 1LJ. (I. Crackston and H. Sledge). Est. 1986. Open 10-5. SIZE: Medium. *STOCK: Oak and period country antiques, copper, brass, samplers, ceramics, 17th-19th C.* PARK: Nearby. TEL: 01404 43436.

Fountain Antiques
132 High St. EX14 1JP. (J. Palmer and G. York). Est. 1980. Open 9.30-5.30. *STOCK: General antiques including pictures, books and linen.* PARK: Nearby. TEL: 01404 42074; fax - 01404 44993; e-mail - antiques@gyork.co.uk.

The Grove Antiques Centre
55 High St. EX14 1PW. (Lesley V. Phillips). Est. 1998. Open 10-5, Sun. 11-4 (April-Dec.). SIZE: Large. *STOCK: Regency, Victorian and country furniture; iron and mahogany beds; glass, porcelain, Staffordshire, silver and jewellery, pictures, tinplate toys and bears, carpets.* PARK: Easy. TEL: 01404 43377; fax - 01404 43390; e-mail - info@grove antiquescentre.com; website - www.groveantiques centre.com. SER: Shipping; deliveries.

Hermitage Antiques
37 High St. EX14 1PJ. Open 10-5 or by appointment. *STOCK: Collectables and general antiques.* TEL: 01404 44406; fax - 01404 42471.

High Street Books
150 High St. EX14 8JB. (G. Tyson). PBFA. Est. 1978. Open 10-5. SIZE: Medium. *STOCK: Books, prints and maps, 18th-20th C, £1-£1,000.* LOC: Opposite police station. PARK: Easy. TEL: 01404 45570; fax - same; home - 01404 41771. SER: Valuations. FAIRS: Major London Book.

Honiton Antique Centre

Abingdon House, 136 High St. EX14 8JP. (N.D.A. and E.K. Thompson). Est. 1985. Open 9.30-5.30. SIZE: Large - 20 dealers. *STOCK: 17th-20th C furniture, metalwork, copper, brass, tools, sporting items, pottery, porcelain, pictures and collectables.* LOC: Exeter end of High St. PARK: Nearby. TEL: 01404 42108.

Honiton Antique Toys

38 High St. EX14 1PJ. (L. and S. Saunders). Est. 1986. Open 10.30-5. CL: Mon. and Thurs. *STOCK: Toys, dolls, teddies and children's books.* PARK: Easy. TEL: 01404 41194; e-mail - honitonantiquetoys38 @hotmail.com.

Honiton Clock Clinic

16 New St. EX14 1EY. (David Newton). Est. 1992. Open 10-12.30 and 1.30-4, Sat. 10-1. CL: Thurs. SIZE: Small. *STOCK: Clocks and barometers.* PARK: Nearby. TEL: 01404 47466.

Honiton Fine Art

189 High St. EX14 8LQ. (C.B. and P.R. Greenberg). Est. 1974. Open 11.30-5. SIZE: Medium. *STOCK: English watercolours and oil paintings, 18th-20th C, £300-£5,000; Old Master drawings, Dutch, Italian and French, 16th-18th C, £300-£1,500.* LOC: Town centre. PARK: Easy. TEL: 01404 45942. SER: Valuations; restorations (oil paintings and watercolours).

The Honiton Lace Shop

44 High St. EX14 8PJ. (Jonathan Page). Est. 1983. Open 9.30-1 and 2-5. SIZE: Medium. *STOCK: Lace including wedding veils, specialist and collectors; quilts, shawls and other textiles, bobbins and lace making equipment.* PARK: Limited. TEL: 01404 42416; fax - 01404 47797; e-mail - shop@honitonlace.com; website - www. honitonlace.com. SER: Valuations; repairs. VAT: Stan.

Honiton Old Bookshop

Felix House, 51 High St. EX14 1PW. (R. Collicott). ABA. PBFA. Est. 1991. Open 10-5.30. *STOCK: Books - travel, childrens' illustrated, topography, natural history, antiquarian, sciences; West Country maps; bindings; all £5-£2,000.* LOC: Main street. PARK: Easy. TEL: 01404 47180. SER: Catalogues available (2 per annum). FAIRS: London PBFA; Chelsea and Olympia ABA. VAT: Stan.

Lombard Antiques

14 High St. EX14 8PU. Est. 1984. Open 10-5.30. SIZE: Small. *STOCK: 18th-19th C English furniture, porcelain and decorative items.* PARK: Easy. TEL: 01404 42140.

Maya Antiques

46 High St. EX14 1PJ. (Antonio Briglia and Pauline Brown). Est. 1996. Open 10-5. SIZE: Medium. *STOCK: Furniture, 18th C, £500-£1,000.* PARK: Easy. TEL: 01404 46009.

Merchant House Antiques

19 High St. EX14 1PR. (C. Giltsoff and R. Kirk). Open 10-5, Sun. by appointment. SIZE: Large. *STOCK: English and French fine and provincial furniture, 17th-19th C; works of art, ironstone and later china, collectables and decorative items, upholstery and furnishings, £10-£20,000+.* PARK: Easy. TEL: 01404 42694; fax - 01404 42471; home - 01884 820944; mobile - 07768 960144. SER: Valuations. VAT: Stan/Spec.

Otter Antiques

69 High St. EX14 1PW. (Kate Skailes). Open 9.30-5. CL: Thurs. p.m. *STOCK: Fine antique silver and plate including flatware; modern silver.* TEL: 01404 42627; e-mail - otterantiques@jspencer.co.uk.

Pilgrim Antiques

145 High St. EX14 8LJ. (G. and J.E. Mills). LAPADA. Est. 1970. Open 9-5.30. SIZE: Large - trade warehouse. *STOCK: Period English and Continental furniture.* PARK: Easy. TEL: 01404 41219/45316; fax - 01404 45317. SER: Packing and shipping. VAT: Stan/Spec.

Jane Strickland & Daughters

71 High St. EX14 1PW. LAPADA. Est. 1977. Open 10-5. SIZE: Medium. *STOCK: 18th-19th C furniture; 19th C English and French mirrors; 19th C armchairs, sofas and chaise longues; lighting, needlepoint and Aubusson rugs and cushions; decorative items.* PARK: Easy. TEL: 01404 44221; e-mail - jsanddaughtersUK@aol.com. SER: Restorations (upholstery). FAIRS: Decorative Antique Textile, Battersea. VAT: Stan/Spec.

Upstairs, Downstairs

12 High St. EX14 8PU. Open 10-5.30. SIZE: Large. *STOCK: 18th-19th C furniture, porcelain, metalware, pictures and clocks.* PARK: Easy. TEL: 01404 44481/42140.

Geoffrey M. Woodhead

53 High St. EX14 1PW. Est. 1950. Open 10-5. SIZE: Medium. *STOCK: Secondhand books and magazines, general antiques.* LOC: A30 opposite largest tree in street. PARK: Limited. TEL: 01404 42969. FAIRS: Shepton Mallet; Marsh Barton and West Point, Exeter.

Graham York Rare Books

225 High St. EX14 1LB. ABA, ILAB, PBFA. Est. 1982. Open 9.30-5. SIZE: Medium. *STOCK:*

Travel especially Spain and South Africa; art - fine and applied, especially lace, costume and textiles; literature, natural history, history, biography, children's, British topography especially West Country, gypsies, George Borrow; also maps and prints. LOC: Last shop at west end of High St. PARK: Nearby. TEL: 01404 41727; fax - 01404 44993; mobile - 07831 138011; e-mail - books @gyork.co.uk; website - www.gyork.co.uk. FAIRS: Monthly (Hotel Russell, Bloomsbury); ABA Chelsea; International Book, Olympia (June); PBFA Bath (April).

ILFRACOMBE

Relics
113 High St. EX34 9ET. (Nicola D. Bradshaw). Resident. Est. 1977. Open 10-5. SIZE: Small. *STOCK: General antiques and small collectables, Victorian and Edwardian.* LOC: Opposite The Bunch of Grapes. PARK: Nearby. TEL: 01271 865486; home/fax - same; e-mail - nikkibradshaw @ukonline.co.uk. SER: Valuations.

KINGSBRIDGE

Avon House Antiques/Hayward's Antiques
13 Church St. TQ7 1BT. (D.H. and M.S. Hayward). Est. 1969. Open 10-1 and 2-5. SIZE: Small. *STOCK: General antiques.* PARK: Limited. TEL: 01548 853718. SER: Valuations; pine stripping. FAIRS: Devon County.

KINGSWEAR, Nr. Dartmouth

David L.H. Southwick Rare Art BADA
Beacon Lodge, Beacon Lane. TQ6 0BU. Open by appointment. *STOCK: Chinese and Japanese works of art.* TEL: 01803 752533; fax - 01803 752535; e-mail - rareart@ewobell. co.uk.

LYDFORD, Nr. Okehampton

Skeaping Gallery
Townend House. EX20 4AR. Est. 1972. Open by appointment. *STOCK: Oils and watercolours.* TEL: 01822 820383; fax - same. VAT: Spec

LYNTON

Farthings
Churchill House. EX35 6NF. (Mrs L. R. Farthing and Miss I. J. Farthing). Est. 1996. Open 10-4.30

(4pm in winter) including Sun. SIZE: Small. *STOCK: Pictures, 19th-20th C, £50-£5,000; small furniture, Victorian and Edwardian, £50-£1,000; collectibles, 19th-20th C, £5-£2,000.* LOC: Opposite church. PARK: Easy. TEL: 01598 753744; home - 01598 753465. SER: Valuations; restorations; buys at auction.

Wood's Antiques
29A Lee Rd. EX35 6BS. (Pat and Brian Wood). Est. 1994. Open 9-5.30; in winter Sun. 9.30-2. CL: Thurs. *STOCK: General antiques including small furniture, mainly Victorian, £10-£8,000.* PARK: Easy. TEL: 01598 752722.

MAIDENCOMBE, Nr. Torquay

G.A. Whiteway-Wilkinson
Sunsea, Teignmouth Rd. TQ1 4TP. Est. 1943. Open by appointment only. *STOCK: General antiques, fine art and jewellery.* LOC: Approximately half-way on main Torquay/Teignmouth road. TEL: 01803 329692. VAT: Spec.

MERTON, Nr. Okehampton

Barometer World Ltd
Quicksilver Barn. EX20 3DS. Est. 1979. Open Tues.-Sat. 9-5. SIZE: Medium. *STOCK: Mercurial wheel and stick barometers, 1780-1900, £650-£12,500; aneroid barometers, 1850-1930, £100-£1,500.* LOC: Between Hatherleigh and Torrington on A386. PARK: Easy. TEL: 01805 603443; fax - 01805 603344; e-mail - enquiries@barometer world.co.uk; website - www.barometerworld.co. uk. SER: Valuations; restorations (barometers). VAT: Stan/Spec.

MODBURY, Nr. Ivybridge

Collectors Choice
27 Church St. PL21 0QR. (Allan Jenkins). Resident. Est. 1994. Open 10-5.30. CL: Some Wed. SIZE: Small. *STOCK: Clocks, £20-£1,000; valve radios, ceramics, fountain pens and small furniture, £5-£500; all 19th-20th C.* LOC: A379 between Plymouth and Kingsbridge. PARK: Easy. TEL: 01548 831111. SER: Valuations; restorations (clocks, fountain pens); clock repairs, cleaning, re-silvering.

Wild Goose Antiques
34 Church St. PL21 0QR. (Mr and Mrs T.C. Freeman). Open 10-5.30. *STOCK: Old pine, country furniture, decorative items.* TEL: 01548 830715. VAT: Stan.

MONKTON, Nr. Honiton

Pugh's Farm Antiques
Pugh's Farm. EX14 9QH. (G. Garner and C. Cherry). Est. 1974. Open 9-5.30. SIZE: Large. *STOCK: French furniture, armoires, farm tables, country furniture, neo-rustique, especially wooden beds; Victorian and Edwardian furniture.* LOC: A30 2 miles from Honiton. PARK: Easy. TEL: 01404 42860; home - same; fax - 01404 47792; e-mails - sales@pughsantiques.com, and sales@antiquebeds.com; websites - www.pughs-antiques-export.com; www.pughsantiques.com and www.antiquebeds.com. SER: Importers and exporters. VAT: Stan.

MORCHARD BISHOP, Nr. Crediton

Morchard Bishop Antiques
Meadowbank. EX17 6PD. (J.C. and E.A. Child). Resident. Est. 1970. Open by appointment. SIZE: Small. *STOCK: General antiques.* LOC: 8 miles west of Crediton, off A377 at Morchard Rd. PARK: Easy. TEL: 01363 877456.

NEWTON ABBOT

The Attic
9 Union St. TQ12 2JX. (G.W. Gillman). Est. 1976. CL: Mon. and Thurs., prior telephone call advisable. SIZE: Medium. *STOCK: General antiques, to £1,000.* LOC: Town centre. PARK: Easy. TEL: 01626 355124. SER: Valuations.

St Leonards Antiques & Craft Centre
Wolborough St. TQ12 1JQ. (Derick Wilson). Est. 1970. Open 10-4.30 including Sun., Tues. 9.30-4.30. SIZE: Large. *STOCK: General antiques, 19th C, £5-£1,000.* LOC: At start of main road to Totnes. PARK: Adjacent and opposite. TEL: 01626 335666; fax - same. SER: Valuations; restorations; buys at auction (furniture, decorative items). FAIRS: All major.

NEWTON ST. CYRES, Nr. Exeter

Gordon Hepworth Fine Art
Hayne Farm, Sand Down Lane. EX5 5DE. (C.G. and I.M. Hepworth). Est. 1990. Open Wed.-Sat. during exhibitions or by appointment. SIZE: Large barn - 2 floors. *STOCK: Modern British paintings, post-war and contemporary especially West*

Country - West Cornwall and St. Ives School,
£300-£5,000. LOC: A377, 3 miles nw. of Exeter
turn left by village sign, into Sand Down Lane,
farm entrance on left, after last white house.
PARK: Easy. TEL: 01392 851351; home - same.

OKEHAMPTON

Alan Jones Antiques
Fatherford Farm. EX20 1QQ. Est. 1971. Open
anytime by appointment. SIZE: Large - warehouse and showroom. *STOCK: Furniture, oak,*
walnut and mahogany, some pine; copper, brass,
barometers, clocks. LOC: On A30, one mile from
Okehampton. PARK: Easy. TEL: 01837 52970;
home - 01409 231428. SER: Valuations. VAT:
Stan/Spec.

PAIGNTON

Hyde Road Antiques
23 Hyde Rd. TQ4 5BW. (David Pentecost). Est.
1975. Open 10-5, Thurs. 10-12.30 and 1.30-5.
SIZE: Medium. *STOCK: Collectables and general*
antiques, 16th-20th C, £1-£5,000. LOC: Off
Torquay Rd. PARK: Opposite. TEL: 01803 554000.
SER: Valuations; restorations (clocks, furniture,
china); buys at auction. FAIRS: Westpoint and
Matford, Exeter.

The Pocket Bookshop
159 Winner St. TQ3 3BP. (L. and A.R. Corrall).
Est. 1985. Open Tues.-Sat. 10.30-5.30. SIZE:
Small. *STOCK: Books, secondhand and out of*
print. LOC: Outskirts. PARK: Nearby. TEL:
01803 529804.

PLYMOUTH

Annterior Antiques
22 Molesworth Rd., Millbridge. PL1 5LZ. (A.
Tregenza and R. Mascaro). Est. 1987. Open 9.30-
5.30, Sat. 10-5 or by appointment. SIZE: Small.
STOCK: Stripped pine, 18th-19th C, £50-£3,000;
some painted, mahogany and decorative furniture;
brass and iron beds, 19th C, £250-£1,500;
decorative small items. LOC: Follow signs to
Torpoint Ferry from North Cross roundabout, turn
left at junction of Wilton St. and Molesworth Rd.
PARK: Easy. TEL: 01752 558277; fax - 01752
564471; e-mail - info@annterior.co.uk. SER: Buys
at auction; finder. VAT: Stan/Spec.

Antique Fireplace Centre
30 Molesworth Rd., Stoke. PL1 5NA. (Brian
Taylor). Est. 1988. Open 10-5 or by appointment.

STOCK: Fire surrounds - timber, marble, slate,
cast iron, £100-£3,500; Georgian and Victorian
fire grates, £100-£1,500; original accessories
including scuttles, coal boxes, fire irons and
overmantels, lamps and lanterns. LOC: 50yds.
from Victoria Park, map sent on request. PARK:
Easy. TEL: 01752 559441; fax - 01752 605964;
website - www.2vu.com/antique.fireplaces. SER:
Valuations. VAT: Stan/Spec.

Barbican Antiques Centre
82-84 Vauxhall St., Barbican. PL4 0EX. (T.
Cremer-Price). Est. 1971. Open 9.30-5 every day.
SIZE: 60+ dealers. *STOCK: Silver and plate, art*
pottery, porcelain, glass, jewellery, furniture,
pictures, clocks, collectables. PARK: Own. TEL:
01752 201752; fax - 020 8546 1618.

New Street Antique Centre
27 New St., The Barbican. PL1 2LS. (Turner
Properties). Est. 1980. Open 10-5. SIZE: Medium.
STOCK: Clocks, silver, jewellery, weapons,
general antiques. PARK: Nearby. TEL: 01752
661165. VAT: Stan/Spec.

Parade Antiques Market
17 The Parade, The Barbican. PL1 2JW. (John
Cabello). Est. 1982. Open 10-5 including Sun.
SIZE: Medium. *STOCK: Collectables, 19th-20th*
C, £1-£1,000; militaria, 18th-20th C, £1-£7,000.
PARK: Easy. TEL: 01752 221443; fax - 01752
291208.

Michael Wood Fine Art
The Gallery, 1 Southside Ope, The Barbican, PL1
2LL. Est. 1967. Open 10-6, Sun. and Mon. by
appointment. SIZE: Medium. *STOCK: Oils, water-*
colours, original prints, sculptures, ceramics, art
glass and books, contemporary, RA exhibitors,
modern British, Newlyn, St Ives and Victorian,
£100-£100,000. LOC: Harbour front. PARK:
Nearby. TEL: 01752 225533; mobiles - 07971
847722/ 07764 377899; e-mail - michael@michael
woodfineart.com. SER: Valuations; conservation/
preservation/security advice. FAIRS: Most major.
VAT: Spec/ Stan.

SEATON

Etcetera Etc Antiques
12 Beer Rd. EX12 2PA. (Michael and Deborah
Rymer). Est. 1969. Open 10-1 and 2-5. CL: Thurs.
except by appointment. SIZE: Medium. *STOCK:*
General antique furniture and shipping goods.
PARK: Own. TEL: 01297 21965; mobile - 07780
840507.

SHALDON

Leigh C. Extence
49 Fore St. TQ14 0EA. Open 10-1 and 2.15-5, prior telephone call advisable. CL: Thurs. pm. *STOCK: Clocks, 1730-1880; barometers.* LOC: Opposite Royal Standard public house. PARK: Outside shop. TEL: 01626 872636; mobile - 07967 802160; e-mail clocks@extence.co.uk; website - www.extence.co.uk. SER: Buys at auction; clock finding service; horological research.

W. J. Woodhams
28 Fore St. TQ14 0DE. (P.J. and Mrs. K.M. Richards). Est. 2000. Open Tues.-Sat. 10-5. SIZE: Small. *STOCK: Furniture, £5-£500; silver and porcelain, bric-a-brac, £5-£200; 19th-20th C.* TEL: 01626 871098.

SIDMOUTH

Gainsborough House Antiques
Libra Court, Fore St. EX10 8AJ. (K.S. Scratchley). Est. 1935. Open 9-5, Sat. 9-12.45. CL: Thurs. pm. except by appointment. SIZE: Small. *STOCK: Small general antiques, 1750-1950, £1-£1,000; medals and militaria, 1700 to date, £1-£1,500.* LOC: Down Fore St., 50 yds from seafront, left down York St., entrance to premises on left. PARK: 100 yds. TEL: 01395 514394; home - 01395 515112; e-mail - kss@kscratchley.freeserve.co.uk. SER: Valuations.

The Lantern Shop Gallery
5 New St. EX10 8AP. (Miss J.M. Creeke). Est. 1974. Open 10-4.45. SIZE: Medium. *STOCK: Lighting including table lamps, 1750-1960, £50-£2,000; shades, £50-£250; English porcelain, 1780-1970, £5-£1,500; watercolours and oils, 1800-1950, £15-£2,000; small furniture, decorative items and collectables, 1750-1970, £5-£1,000; topographical and decorative prints, especially East Devon, 1780-1930, maps, 1620-1880, £10-£700.* LOC: Town centre between Fore St. and Market Place. PARK: Nearby - disabled opposite. TEL: 01395 578462. SER: Silk lampshade-making. VAT: Stan.

The Old Curiosity Shop
Old Fore St. EX10 8LP. (Thomas and Sally Koch). Est. 1994. Open 9.30-5, Sun. 11-5. SIZE: Medium. *STOCK: Glass and china, including Moorcroft, Clarice Cliff, Lalique, Royal Doulton, Beswick; Oriental rugs, furniture; mantel and grandfather clocks; paintings.* LOC: Down High St. towards sea, in pedestrianised Old Fore St. PARK: Nearby. TEL: 01395 515299. FAIRS: Exeter; Shepton Mallet.

Sidmouth Antiques and Collectors Centre
All Saints Rd. EX10 8ES. Open 10-5 (Easter-end Oct. 10-5.30). SIZE: 10 dealers. *STOCK: Wide range of antiques and collectables, collectors' records, antiquarian and out of print books, postcards, stamps, limited edition plates, pictures and prints, linen, lace and crochet items.* TEL: 01395 512588.

The Vintage Toy and Train Shop
Sidmouth Antiques and Collectors Centre, All Saints Rd. EX10 8ES. (R.D.N., M.E. and J.W. Salisbury). Est. 1995. Open 10-5. *STOCK: Hornby Gauge 0 and Dublo trains, Dinky toys, Meccano and other die-cast and tinplate toys, wooden jig-saw puzzles.* LOC: Near main Post Office. PARK: Limited and opposite. TEL: 01395 512588; home - 01395 513399.

SOUTH BRENT

P.M. Pollak
Moorview, Plymouth Rd. TQ10 9HT. (Dr. P.M. Pollak). ABA. Est. 1973. Open by appointment. SIZE: Small. *STOCK: Antiquarian books especially medicine and science; prints, some instruments, £50-£5,000.* LOC: On edge of village, near London Inn. PARK: Own. TEL: 01364 73457; fax - 01364 649126; e-mail - patrick@rarevols.co.uk; website - www.rarevols.co.uk. SER: Valuations; buys at auction; catalogues issued, computer searches.

SOUTH MOLTON

The Antique & Interior Centre
14a Barnstaple St. EX36 3BQ. (R.M. Golding). Est. 1992. Open Tues.-Sat.10-5. SIZE: Large. *STOCK: Wide range of general antiques.* LOC: On old A361, 100 yards from town centre. PARK: Nearby. TEL: 01769 573401. SER: Valuations.

The Dragon
80 South St. EX36 3AG. (Mrs J E Aker). Est. 1994. Open 9.30-4.30. SIZE: Small. *STOCK: Pine and country furniture, from 19th C; bric-a-brac, books and pictures.* LOC: Near town centre. PARK: Limited or nearby. TEL: 01769 572374; mobile - 07712 079818. SER: Restorations (furniture).

The Dragon and the Phoenix
24 East St. EX36 3DB. (Paul Williams and Caroline Bennett). Open 10-4. SIZE: Small. *STOCK: Antique Chinese and Tibetan furniture.* PARK: Easy. TEL: 01769 574104; e-mail - antiques@dragonphoenix.co.uk; website - www. antiquechinesefurniture.co.uk.

Snap Dragon
77 South St. EX36 3AG. (Mrs J. E. Aker). Est. 1994. Open 9.30-4.30. SIZE: Small. *STOCK: Pine and country furniture, kitchenalia and tools, architectural and garden artefacts.* LOC: Near town centre. PARK: Limited and opposite. TEL: 01769 572374; mobile - 07712 079818. SER: Restorations (furniture).

J.R. Tredant
50/50a South St. EX36 4AG. Usually open. *STOCK: General antiques.* TEL: 01769 573006; home - 01769 572416. SER: Valuations.

R M Young Bookseller
17 Broad St. EX36 3AQ. (Mark Young). Est. 1970. Open 10-5, Thurs., Fri. and Sat. 9-5. SIZE: Medium. *STOCK: Books especially Exmoor, the countryside, Henry Williamson, £5-200.* LOC: Main street. PARK: Free nearby. TEL: 01769 573350. SER: Restorations; out-of-print booksearch.

STOCKLAND, Nr. Honiton

Colystock Antiques
Rising Sun Farm. EX14 9NH. (D.C. McCollum). Est. 1975. Open seven days. SIZE: Large. *STOCK: Pine and oak including English, Irish and Continental, 18th-19th C.* TEL: 01404 861271. SER: Container packing and documentation; courier.

TAVISTOCK

King Street Curios
5 King St. PL19 0DS. (T. and P. Bates). Est. 1979. Open 9-4. SIZE: Medium. *STOCK: Pine furniture, postcards, cigarette cards, china, glass, general collectables, jewellery, to £100.* LOC: Town centre. TEL: 01822 615193.

Tavistock Books
5 Pepper St. PL19 0BD. (D.T. and D.J. Byass). Est. 1993. Open 10-5. CL: Mon. and Wed. SIZE: Small. *STOCK: Antiquarian and secondhand books, £10-£1,000.* LOC: Just off main street, opposite market. PARK: Easy. TEL: 01822 616077. SER: Valuations; buys at auction.

TEDBURN ST. MARY, Nr. Exeter

A. E. Wakeman & Sons Ltd
Newhouse Farm. EX6 6AL. (A.P., G.M. and A. A. Wakeman). Est. 1967. Open Mon.-Fri. 9-5.30 or by appointment. SIZE: Medium. *STOCK: Mahogany, walnut and rosewood furniture, mainly 19th C, £200-£5,000; some 18th C mahogany and oak, £300-£5,000.* LOC: 6 miles from Exeter. PARK: Easy. TEL: 01647 61254; home/fax - same; mobile - 07836 284765; e-mail - a.e.wakeman@hotmail.com. FAIRS: Newark. *Trade Only.*

TEIGNMOUTH

Extence Antiques
2 Wellington St. TQ14 8HH. (T.E. and L.E. Extence). Est. 1928. Open 9.30-5. SIZE: Medium. *STOCK: Jewellery, silver, objets d'art.* PARK: Limited. TEL: 01626 773353. VAT: Stan/Spec.

Queen's House Emporium
27 Fore St. TQ14 8DZ. (Teresa Nicholls). Est. 1982. Open Tues.-Sat. 10-1 and 1.30-5. SIZE: Small. *STOCK: Furniture, china, brass, general antiques and collectables.* LOC: Main street. PARK: Nearby. TEL: 01626 776675; mobile - 07768 076360. FAIRS: Westpoint; Marsh Barton.

Timepiece
125 Bitton Park Rd. TQ14 9BZ. (Clive and Willow Pople). Est. 1988. Open Tues.-Sat. 9.30-5.30, Sat. 9.30-6. SIZE: Medium. *STOCK: Country furniture, clocks, 19th C, £25-£2,000; kitchenalia and collectables, 19th-20th C, £1-£100; Torquay pottery, £5-£120.* LOC: On A379 next to Bitton Park. TEL: 01626 770275.

These two Jumeau tête bébé dolls are included in Phillips Knowle Collectors' Sale on 28th November where they are expected to realise £2,000-£3,000 and £1,500-£2,000 respectively.

From an Auction Report of Phillips Knowle Collectors' Sale on 28th November 2001 which appeared in the November 2001 issue of **Antique Collecting**. For more details and to subscribe see page 21.

TOPSHAM, Nr. Exeter

Mere Antiques
13 Fore St. EX3 0HF. (Marilyn Reed). LAPADA. Resident. Est. 1986. Open 9.30-5.30, Sat. 10-4.30, Sun. by appointment. SIZE: Small. *STOCK: English and Continental porcelain, 19th C, £50-£5,000; Japanese Satsuma - Meiji period, £350-£5,000; furniture, 18th-19th C, £200-£5,000.* PARK: Easy and nearby. TEL: 01392 874224; e-mail - bob@ntlbusiness.com. SER: Valuations. FAIRS: NEC; LAPADA. VAT: Spec.

A pair of creamware figures, possibly intended to represent Ophelia and Hamlet. The same figures are illustrated in Early English Figure Pottery *by Sir Harold Mackintosh, pub. Chapman & Hall 1938; here they are attributed by him to Ra Wood. This pair has been attributed to Leeds because of the relief decorations, and dated c.1775. 12¾in. high. (See also* A Collection of Early English Pottery. Part VIII, *Jonathan Horne.) (Jonathan Horne Antiques)*

From an article entitled "Cream Coloured Earthenware" by Griselda Lewis which appeared in the September 2001 issue of **Antique Collecting**. For more details and to subscribe see page 21.

Pennies
40 Fore St. EX3 0HU. (Michael Clark). Open 10-5. *STOCK: Antiques and collectables.* TEL: 01392 877020. VAT: Stan/Spec.

Topsham Quay Antiques Centre
The Quay. EX3 0JA. (Stonewall Ltd). Est. 1993. Open seven days 10-5. SIZE: Large. *STOCK: Furniture, 18th-19th C, £100-£3,000+; ceramics, 18th-20th C, £5-£1,000+; collectables, 20th C, £5-£200; silver and plate, 18th-20th C, £10-£1,500+.* PARK: Easy. TEL: 01392 874006; fax - same; e-mail - office@antiquesontopshamquay.co.uk; website - www.antiquesontopshamquay.co.uk. SER: Valuations; buys at auction. FAIRS: Local.

TORQUAY

Birbeck Gallery
45 Abbey Rd. TQ2 5NQ. (Stephen and Ross Birbeck). Est. 1952. Open by appointment. SIZE: Medium. *STOCK: Paintings, watercolours and prints, 19th to early 20th C, to £10,000.* LOC: 200yds. up Abbey Rd. from main street roundabout at Torquay GPO. TEL: 01803 291658/297144/324449.

The Old Cop Shop
Castle Lane. TQ1 3AN. (L. Rolfe). Est. 1971. Open 9-5. SIZE: Medium. *STOCK: General antiques and shipping items.* PARK: Easy. TEL: 01803 294484; fax - 01803 316620; e-mail - rolfebrown@tinyworld.co.uk. SER: Valuations. FAIRS: Local.

The Schuster Gallery
P O Box 139. TQ1 2XX. ABA. Est. 1973. Open by appointment. *STOCK: Antique prints, maps, medieval manuscripts, fine and rare colour plate books, atlases; children's illustrated books including Beatrix Potter, Kate Greenaway and Alice in Wonderland and related items.* TEL: 01803 211422; fax - 01803 211290; e-mail - tschuster@easynet.co.uk; website - www.acid.co.uk/acid/schus.htm.

Sheraton House Antiques
Sheraton House, 1 Laburnum Row, Torre. TQ2 5QX. (I.S. Hutton). Open 9.30-4.45. *STOCK: General antiques.* TEL: 01803 293334.

Toby's Architectural Antiques
Torre Station, Newton Rd. TQ2 2DD. (Paul and John Norrish). SALVO. Est. 1985. Open 10.30-5 seven days. SIZE: Large. *STOCK: Furniture, £15-£3,000; pianos, fireplaces, lighting, collectables, 19th-20th C, £5-£2,000.* LOC: Main Newton Abbott road, 1 mile from sea front.

PARK: Easy. TEL: 01803 212222; fax - 01803 200523; e-mail - paul4tobys@yahoo.co.uk; website - www.tobysreclamation.co.uk. SER: Valuations; buys at auction. VAT: Spec.

TOTNES

Bogan House Antiques
43-45 High St. TQ9 5NP. (Chris Mitchell). Est. 1977. Open Fri. 10-1 and 2-4, Sat. 10.30-1 and 2-4.30, some Tues., otherwise by appointment. SIZE: Small. *STOCK: Silver flatware, £5-£200; metalware, Victorian and Delft tiles, £5-£40; Japanese woodblock prints, £20-£400.* PARK: Nearby. TEL: 01803 862075; home - 01803 865386; mobile - 07813 750610.

Collards Books
4 Castle St. TQ9 5NU. (B. Collard). Est. 1970. Open 10.30-5, restricted opening in winter. *STOCK: Antiquarian and secondhand books.* LOC: Opposite castle. PARK: Nearby. TEL: Home - 01548 550246.

The Exchange
76 High St. TQ9 5SN. (J. and M. Caley). Est. 1997. Open 10-5.SIZE: Small. *STOCK: Antiquarian and secondhand books, papers and ephemera; general antiques and curios.* LOC: Town centre. PARK: Nearby. TEL: 01803 866836; home - 01803 868598; e-mail - bookworm1700@yahoo.co.uk. SER: Valuations.

Fine Pine Antiques
Woodland Rd., Harbertonford. TQ9 7SX. (Nick and Linda Gildersleve). Est. 1973. Open 9.30-5, Sun. 11-4. SIZE: Large. *STOCK: Stripped pine and country furniture.* LOC: A381. PARK: Easy. TEL: 01803 732465; home - 01548 821360; e-mail - info@fine-pine-antiques.co.uk; website - www.fine-pine-antiques.co.uk. SER: Restorations; stripping.

Past and Present
94 High St. TQ9 5SN. (James Sturges). CL: Lunch-times. SIZE: Large. *STOCK: Furniture, £100-£2,000; smalls, bygones, £5-£300; all 18th-20th C.* LOC: A38. PARK: 150 yards. TEL: 01803 866086. FAIRS: Sandown Park.

Pedlars Pack Books
4 The Plains. TQ9 5DR. (P. D. and A. Elliott). PBFA. Est. 1991. Open 9-5. SIZE: Medium. *STOCK: Books, £5-500.* LOC: Near river. PARK: Nearby. TEL: 01803 866423; e-mail - pedlar@aol.com. SER: Valuations; buys at auction.

Rotherfold Antiques
The Rotherfold. TQ9 5ST. (Mrs S. M. van Heck). Est. 1999. Open 10-1 and 2-5. CL: Thurs. SIZE: Medium. *STOCK: Furniture and fine art, 19th C; objets d'art, ceramics, mirrors.* LOC: At the end of The Narrows. PARK: Easy. TEL: 01803 840303.

UFFCULME, Nr. Cullompton

English Country Antiques
The Old Brewery, High St. EX15 3AB. (M.C. Mead). Est. 1996. Open 9-5, prior telephone call preferred. SIZE: Large. *STOCK: Country and decorating antiques: furniture, pine including painted, fruitwoods, oak and mahogany, bamboo, bentwood, leather and upholstered; metalware including lighting, brass, copper and iron, gardenalia, architectural; china and glass, mainly 19th-20th C; textiles, leatherwork, bric-a-brac, basketware, wooden items, model yachts, pictures and paintings, mirrors.* LOC: Village centre. PARK: Own. TEL: 01884 841110; home/fax - 01803 845480; mobile - 07768 328433; e-mail - mike@englishcountryantiques.co.uk; website - www.englishcountryantiques.co.uk. FAIRS: NEC.

WHIMPLE, Nr. Exeter

Anthony James Antiques
Brook Cottage, The Square. EX5 2SL. Open by appointment. *STOCK: 17th-19th C furniture and works of art.* LOC: A30 between Exeter and Honiton. PARK: Easy. TEL: 01404 822146. SER: Valuations. VAT: Spec.

WOODBURY, Nr. Exeter

Woodbury Antiques
Church St. EX5 1HN. (H. Ballingall). Est. 1966. Open Mon., Tues., Fri. 10-3, Sat. 10-1. SIZE: Large. *STOCK: Victorian and Edwardian furniture and items.* PARK: Easy. TEL: 01395 232727. VAT: Stan/Spec.

YEALMPTON, Nr. Plymouth

Carnegie Paintings & Clocks
15 Fore St. PL9 2JN. (Chris Carnegie). Open 10-5.30, Thurs. 10-7.30 or by appointment. *STOCK: Clocks, barometers, paintings and small furniture.* TEL: Mobile - 07970 968337; website - www. paintingsandclockscom. SER: Restorations (paintings, clocks and barometers).

Dorset Reclamation
Cow Drove. BH20 7JZ. Open 8-5, Sat. 9-4. *STOCK: Decorative architectural and garden antiques.* TEL: 01929 472200; fax - 01929 472292.

Legg of Dorchester
The Old Mill Antiques, West St. BH20 7HS. (W. and H. Legg & Sons). Est. 1930. *STOCK: General antiques, Regency and decorative furniture, stripped pine.* TEL: 01929 472051.

BLANDFORD FORUM

Ancient and Modern Bookshop (including Garret's Antiques)
84 Salisbury St. DT11 7QE. (Mrs P. Davey). Open 9.30-12.30 and 1.30-4.30. CL: Wed. *STOCK: Books and small antiques.* TEL: 01258 455276; e-mail - pegdavey@tinyworld.co.uk; websites - www.ancientandmodernbooks.co.uk; www.calcraft.co.uk;www.ukbookworld.com/ members/ ancient.

Antiques for All
Higher Shaftesbury Rd. DT11 7TA. Est. 1998. Open 9.30-5, Sun. 10.30-5. SIZE: Large. *STOCK: Furniture, 18th-20th C, £100-£10,000; ceramics and collectables, 18th-20th C, £5-£1,000; clocks and barometers, oil lamps, 18th-19th C, £100-£1,000.* LOC: A354 and A350 roundabout on by-pass; town exit, 3rd turning on right, 1st left. PARK: Easy. TEL: 01258 458011; fax - 01258 458022. SER: Buys at auction (furniture, oil lamps and ceramics).

Milton Antiques
Market Place. DT11 7HU. Open 9-5. CL: Wed pm. SIZE: Medium. *STOCK: Furniture, 18th-19th C, £50-£2,000; decorative items, 18th-20th C, £5-£200.* LOC: Opposite parish church, adjacent to town museum. PARK: Easy. TEL: 01258 450100. SER: Valuations; restorations including polishing.

BOURNEMOUTH

Antiques and Furnishings
339 Charminster Rd. BH8 9QR. (P. Neath). Open 10-5.30. *STOCK: Furniture, brass, copper, china, textiles and decorative objects.* TEL: 01202 527976.

Antiques Exchange
873-877 Christchurch Rd., Boscombe. BH7 6AT. (Mr and Mrs R. Draysey). Est. 1972. Open 10.30-6. SIZE: Medium. *STOCK: Furniture, smalls, lighting, decorative, from 1700.* PARK: Easy. TEL: 01202 433456; e-mail - jo.draysey@virgin.net; website - www.antiquesexchange.com. SER: Restorations (furniture).

Arcade Antiques
6 Westbourne Arcade, Westbourne. BH4 9AY. (Richard Samuel). Est. 1984. Open 10-4.30, Wed. 10-1, Fri. and Sat. 9.30-5. SIZE: Medium. *STOCK: Pottery and porcelain, general antiques, furniture, collectors' items.* LOC: Just off A35 between Bournemouth and Poole. PARK: Easy. TEL: 01202 764800; fax - 01202 769537. SER: Valuations. VAT: Spec.

Boscombe Militaria
86 Palmerston Rd., Boscombe. BH1 4HU. (E.A. Browne). Est. 1981. Open 10-1 and 2-5. CL: Wed. *STOCK: German militaria, £10-£500; British and American militaria, £5-£300, all 1914-1918 and 1939-1945.* LOC: Just off Christchurch Rd. PARK: Easy. TEL: 01202 304250; fax - 01202 733696. FAIRS: Farnham; Cheshunt; major South of England Arms.

Boscombe Models and Collectors Shop
802c Christchurch Rd., Boscombe. BH7 6DD. (Sylvia Hart). Open Thurs., Fri. and Sat. 10-1 and 2-4.30. *STOCK: Collectors' toys, 19th-20th C, £1-£1,000.* LOC: On Somerset Rd. TEL: 01202 398884.

Chorley-Burdett Antiques
828-830 Christchurch Rd., Pokesdown. BH7 6DF. (Raymond Burdett). Open 9-5.30. SIZE: Large. *STOCK: Furniture, pine furniture including reclaimed, late 19th to early 20th C, £50-£1,000.* LOC: Corner of Warwick Rd. PARK: Easy. TEL: 01202 423363; fax - same. VAT: Stan/Spec.

Lionel Geneen Ltd
811 Christchurch Rd., Boscombe. BH7 6AP. LAPADA. Est. 1902. Open 9-5, Sat. 9-12, other times by appointment. CL: Lunchtimes. SIZE: Large. *STOCK: English, Continental and Oriental furniture, china and works of art including some bronzes, enamels, ivories, jades, all mainly 19th C, Art Nouveau and Art Deco; specialising in tea, dinner and dessert services.* LOC: Main road through Boscombe. PARK: Own. TEL: 01202 422961; home - 01202 520417; mobile - 07770 596781. SER: Valuations. VAT: Stan/Spec.

H.L.B. Antiques
139 Barrack Rd. BH23 2AW. (H.L.Blechman). Est. 1969. SIZE: Large. *STOCK: Collectable items.* PARK: Easy. TEL: 01202 429252/482388.

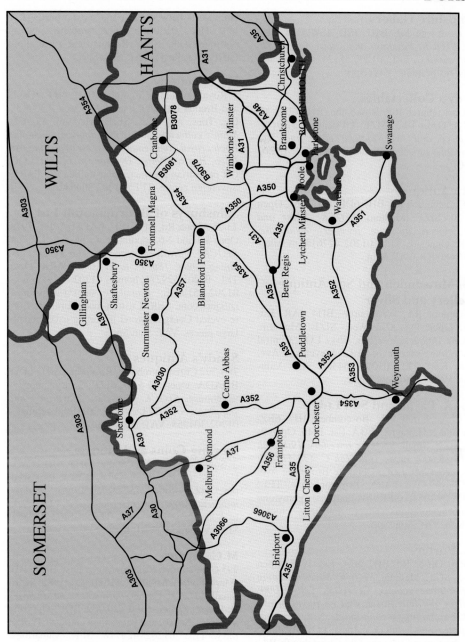

Dealers and Shops in Dorset

				Poole	3
Bere Regis	2	Dorchester	7	Puddletown	1
Blandford Forum	3	Fontmell Magna	1	Shaftesbury	2
Bournemouth	24	Frampton	1	Sherborne	14
Branksome	3	Gillingham	1	Sturminster Newton	1
Bridport	4	Litton Cheney	1	Swanage	2
Cerne Abbas	1	Lytchett Minster	1	Wareham	2
Christchurch	4	Melbury Osmond	1	Weymouth	5
Cranborne	1	Parkstone	3	Wimborne Minster	3

Hampshire Gallery
18 Lansdowne Rd. BH1 1SD. LAPADA. Est. 1971. *STOCK: Paintings and watercolours, 17th to early 20th C.* TEL: 01202 551211. SER: Valuations; restorations. VAT: Spec.

Hardy's Collectables
862 Christchurch Rd., Boscombe. BH7 6DQ. (J. Hardy). Open 10-5. SIZE: 20 dealers. *STOCK: Art Deco and Art Nouveau glass and 50's collectables especially Poole pottery.* TEL: 01202 422407.

Libra Antiques
916 Christchurch Rd. BH7 6DL. Est. 1967. Open 10-4.30. SIZE: Medium. *STOCK: Silver and plate, objects, furniture, jewellery, metalware.* PARK: Opposite. TEL: 01202 427615; mobile - 07836 680928. VAT: Stan.

G.B. Mussenden and Son Antiques, Jewellery and Silver
24 Seamoor Rd., Westbourne. BH4 9AR. Est. 1948. Open 9-5. CL: Wed. SIZE: Medium. *STOCK: Antiques, jewellery, silver.* LOC: Central Westbourne, corner of R.L. Stevenson Ave. PARK: Easy. TEL: 01202 764462. SER: Valuations. VAT: Stan/Global/Spec.

Geo. A. Payne and Son Ltd
742 Christchurch Rd., Boscombe. BH7 6BZ. (H.G. and N.G. Payne). FGA. Est. 1946. Open 9-5.30. SIZE: Small. *STOCK: Jewellery, 19th-20th C, £10-£3,000; silver, 18th-20th C, £30-£1,000; plate, £10-£200.* LOC: Opposite Browning Ave. and Chessel Ave. PARK: Browning Ave. TEL: 01202 394954. SER: Valuations; gemstone testing; restorations (silver, jewellery, clocks, watches). VAT: Stan/Spec.

R.E. Porter
2-6 Post Office Rd. BH1 1BA. Est. 1934. Open 9.30-5. SIZE: Medium. *STOCK: Silver including early antique spoons, Georgian, £20-£5,000; jewellery, pot lids, Baxter and Le Blond prints, clocks including second-hand.* Not Stocked: Furniture, arms, armour, carpets. LOC: Walking from the Square, take the Old Christchurch Rd., then the first turning on the left. PARK: 300yds. at top of Richmond Hill. TEL: 01202 554289. SER: Valuations. VAT: Stan/Spec.

Portique
15/16/17 Criterion Arcade. BH1 1BU. (N. and E. Harkness). NAG. Est. 1968. Open Tues.- Fri. 9.30-5, Sat. 9.30-4.30. *STOCK: Silver, jewellery, Derby china, glass paperweights, cloisonné, clocks.* LOC: Coming from the square take the Old Christchurch Rd. from roundabout, arcade entrance is between first and second turnings on left. TEL: 01202 552979; website - www. portique.co.uk. SER: Repairs and restorations (silver, jewellery). VAT: Stan/Spec.

Recollections
5 Royal Arcade, Boscombe. BH1 4BT. (David and Brenda Francis). Est. 1994. Open 9.30-4.30. CL: Tues. and Wed. SIZE: Medium. *STOCK: Mainly collectables, 1920's to modern, including Poole, royal commemoratives, crested china, Art Deco, Beatrix Potter, Doulton, to £1,000.* LOC: Off pedestrian precinct, opposite Sea Rd. PARK: Sovereign centre. TEL: 01202 304441.

Sainsburys of Bournemouth Ltd
23-25 Abbott Rd. BH9 1EU. LAPADA. Est. 1918. Open 8-1 and 2-6, appointment advisable. CL: Sat. *STOCK: Furniture especially bookcases and dining tables, 18th C, to £15,000.* PARK: Own. TEL: 01202 529271; home - 01202 763616; fax - 01202 510028; e-mail - sales@sainsburys-antiques.com. SER: Custom-made furniture from re-cycled Georgian wood including exceptionally large pieces. VAT: Stan/Spec.

Sandy's Antiques
790-792 Christchurch Rd., Boscombe. BH7 6DD. BDADA. Open 10-5.30. SIZE: 2 large shops + warehouse. *STOCK: Victorian, Edwardian and shipping goods.* TEL: 01202 301190; evenings - 01202 304955. VAT: Stan/Spec.

Sterling Coins and Medals
2 Somerset Rd., Boscombe. BH7 6JH. (W.V. Henstridge). Est. 1969. Open 9.30-4. CL: Wed. pm. SIZE: Small. *STOCK: Coins, medals, militaria, World War II German items.* LOC: Next to 806 Christchurch Rd. TEL: 01202 423881. SER: Valuations. VAT: Stan.

M.C. Taylor
995 Christchurch Rd., Boscombe East. BH7 6BB. (Mark Taylor). MAPH, CMBHI. Est. 1982. SIZE: Small. *STOCK: Clocks, barometers, music boxes and turret clocks, £500-£20,000.* LOC: Opposite St. James' School and Kings Park entrance. PARK: Easy. TEL: 01202 429718. SER: Valuations; restorations. VAT: Stan/Spec.

Tregoning Antiques
57 Westover Rd. BH1 2BZ. (Barry Papworth). NAG. Est. 1969. Open Mon., Tues., Fri. and Sat. SIZE: Small. *STOCK: Fine jewellery, 18th-19th C, £50-£24,000; silver, 18th-19th C, £10-£5,000; collectables, 19th C, £10-£200.* LOC: At junction with Bath Rd., opposite Royal Bath Hotel. PARK: Easy. TEL: 01202 312100; fax - same; mobile - 07813 820624. SER: Valuations; restorations (jewellery and silver). VAT: Stan.

Victorian Chairman
883 Christchurch Rd., Boscombe. BH7 6AU. (M. Leo). Open 10-5. *STOCK: Furniture especially chairs, sofas and tables.* TEL: 01202 420996. SER: Upholstery restoration.

Vintage Clobber
874 Christchurch Rd., Boscombe. BH7 6DQ. (R.A. Mason). Open 10-5. *STOCK: Clothing and fabrics, from Victorian.* TEL: 01202 429794; website - www.vintageclobber.com.

Yesterday Tackle and Books
42 Clingan Rd., Boscombe East. BH6 5PZ. (David and Alba Dobbyn). Open by appointment. *STOCK: Fishing tackle and associated items including taxidermy; books; ephemera and prints.* TEL: 01202 476586. SER: Catalogues issued.

BRANKSOME

Allen's (Branksome) Ltd
447/449 Poole Rd. BH12 1DH. (D.L and P.J. D'Ardenne). Est. 1948. Open 9-5.30. SIZE: Large. *STOCK: Furniture.* TEL: 01202 763724; fax - 01202 763724. VAT: Stan/Spec.

Branksome Antiques
370 Poole Rd. BH12 1AW. (B.A. Neal). Est. 1973. Open 10-5. CL: Wed. and Sat. SIZE: Medium. *STOCK: Scientific and marine items, furniture and general small items.* PARK: Easy. TEL: 01202 763324; home - 01202 679932. SER: Buys at auction (as stock). VAT: Stan/Spec.

David Mack Antiques
434-436 Poole Rd. and 21 Crommer Rd. BH12 1DF. Est. 1963. Open 9-5.30. SIZE: Large. *STOCK: 18th-19th C tables, chairs, display cabinets, desks, bureaux, bookcases; later furniture.* LOC: 2 doors from Branksome rail station. PARK: Own. TEL: 01202 760005; fax - 01202 765100; website - www. davidmack antiques.co. uk. SER: Restorations. VAT: Stan/Spec.

BRIDPORT

Batten's Jewellers
26 South St. DT6 3NQ. (R. Batten). Open 9.30-5. *STOCK: Jewellery and silver.* TEL: 01308 456910. SER: Valuations; repairs.

Benchmark Antiques
West Allington. DT6 5BJ. (Megan Standage). BAFRA. Est. 1992. Open by appointment. SIZE: Small. *STOCK: English furniture and related items, 1700-1880, £100-£15,000.* LOC: B3167

(West Street) 450yds from town centre. PARK: Easy. TEL: 01308 420941; home - same. SER: Valuations; restorations; buys at auction. FAIRS: NEC; Olympia.

Bridport Antiques Centre
5 West Allington. DT6 5BJ. (J.L. and R.M. Higgins). Est. 1985. Open 9-5. SIZE: 10 dealers. *STOCK: Pine and country furniture, lace, linen, porcelain, glass, books, prints, watercolours, oils, postcards, jewellery, classical garden ornaments, taxidermy.* TEL: 01308 425885.

Bridport Old Books
11 South St. DT6 3NR. PBFA. Est. 1998. Open 10-5. SIZE: Small. *STOCK: Antiquarian and secondhand books and prints.* LOC: Town centre. PARK: Nearby. TEL: 01308 425689. FAIRS: PBFA, Hotel Russell, London; Oxford; Bath; Glasgow; Edinburgh; Aberdeen.

CERNE ABBAS

Cerne Antiques
DT2 7LA. (I. Pulliblank). Est. 1972. Open 10-1 and 2-5, Sun. 2-5. CL: Mon. and Fri. SIZE: Medium. *STOCK: Silver, porcelain, furniture including unusual items, mainly 19th C, £1-£400.* LOC: A352. PARK: Easy. TEL: 01300 341490; home - same.

CHRISTCHURCH

J.L. Arditti
20 Twynham Ave. BH23 1QU. Est. 1964. Open by appointment only. SIZE: Medium. *STOCK: Oriental carpets and rugs, 18th to early 20th C, £500-£8,000.* LOC: From town centre take road towards Hurn airport, left turn. PARK: Twynham Avenue. TEL: 01202 485414/481500. SER: Valuations; restorations; cleaning (Persian rugs). VAT: Stan/Spec.

Christchurch Carpets
55/57 Bargates. BH23 1QE. (J. Sheppard). Est. 1963. Open 9-5.30. SIZE: Large. *STOCK: Persian carpets and rugs, 19th-20th C, £100-£5,000.* LOC: Main road. PARK: Adjacent. TEL: 01202 482712. SER: Valuations; repairs; cleaning. VAT: Stan/Spec.

Hamptons
12 Purewell. BH23 1EP. (G. Hampton). Open 10-6. CL: Sat. am. SIZE: Large. *STOCK: Furniture, 18th-19th C; general antiques, clocks, china, instruments, metalware, oil paintings, Chinese and Persian carpets and rugs.* PARK: Easy. TEL: 01202 484000.

Tudor House Antiques

420 Lymington Rd., Highcliffe, BH23 5HE. (P. Knight and D. Burton). LAPADA. Est. 1940. Open 10-5. CL: Mon. and Wed. SIZE: Medium. *STOCK: General antiques.* LOC: Main road, A337. PARK: Easy. TEL: 01425 280440. VAT: Stan/Spec.

CRANBORNE, Nr. Wimborne

Tower Antiques

The Square. BH21 5PR. (P.W. Kear and P. White). Est. 1975. Open 8.30-5.30. CL: Sat. *STOCK: Georgian and Victorian furniture.* TEL: 01725 517552.

DORCHESTER

Box of Porcelain

51d Icen Way. DT1 1EW. (R.J. and Mrs. S.Y. Lunn). Est. 1984. Open 10-5. *STOCK: Porcelain including Worcester, Doulton, Spode, Coalport, Beswick.* LOC: Close town centre, near Dinosaur Museum. TEL: 01305 267110; fax - 01305 263201; e-mail - rlunn@btconnect.com; website - www.boxofporcelain.com. SER: Beswick/ Doulton collectors' finder service.

Colliton Antique Centre

Colliton St. DT1 1XH. Open daily, Sun. by appointment. SIZE: 14 dealers. *STOCK: 18th-20th C furniture, £25-£5,000; brass, bric-a-brac, pictures, china, pine, clocks, jewellery and silver, toys.* LOC: By town clock. PARK: Easy. TEL: 01305 269398/260115. SER: Restorations (cabinet work and metalware). VAT: Stan/Spec.

Finesse Fine Art

Empool Cottage, West Knighton. DT2 8PE. (Tony Wraight). Open by appointment only. *STOCK: Pre-war motoring accessories - metal mascots and Lalique glassware, including mascots, fine bronzes, automobilia, picnic hampers, £500-£50,000.* TEL: 01305 854286; fax - 01305 852888; mobile - 07973 886937.

Michael Legg Antiques

8 Church St. DT1 1JN. (E.M.J. Legg). Open 9-5.30 or any time by appointment. SIZE: Medium. *STOCK: 17th-19th C furniture, clocks, porcelain, pictures, silver, glass.* TEL: 01305 264596. SER: Lectures on the Arts. VAT: Stan/Spec.

Legg of Dorchester

Regency House, 51 High East St. DT1 1HU. (W. and H.Legg & Sons). Est. 1930. *STOCK: General antiques, Regency and decorative furniture, stripped pine.* TEL: 01305 264964. VAT: Stan/Spec.

The Poet's Eye

52 High West St. DT1 1UT. (John Walker). Open 9.30-5 or by appointment. SIZE: Small. *STOCK: Early furniture, textiles, metalwork, ceramics, wood carvings, 16th-18th C; British folk art, 16th-19th C; 20th C and contemporary British arts and crafts.* LOC: Main street. PARK: Easy. TEL: 01305 260324. SER: Valuations; buys at auction. VAT: Spec.

Words Etcetera

2 Cornhill. DT1 1BA. (Julian Nangle). PBFA, ABA. Est. 1970. Open 9.30-5.30. SIZE: Medium. *STOCK: Antiquarian and quality second-hand books and prints; remainders on all subjects.* LOC: Close to museum. TEL: 01305 251919; fax - 01305 266898; home - 01258 820415. SER: Buys at auction (books). FAIRS: ABA London (June).

FONTMELL MAGNA

Quarterjack Antiques

The Old Coach House, Lurmer St. SP7 0PA. (Jon Neilson). Est. 1969. Open 9-5.15, Sun. 9.30-5. SIZE: Small. *STOCK: 18th-19th C glassware, furniture, pictures, corkscrews, walking sticks and horse brasses.* LOC: A350 between Blandford Forum and Shaftesbury. PARK: Easy. TEL: 01747 812222; website - www.quarterjack.com.

FRAMPTON, Nr. Dorchester

Georgina Ryder

Frampton House, DT2 9NH. LAPADA. Est. 1977. Open by appointment. SIZE: Medium. *STOCK: 18th-19th C French furniture and decorative objects.* PARK: Easy. TEL: 01300 320308; fax - 01300 321600; mobile - 07785 391710; e-mail - maynardryder@aol.com. SER: Valuations; restorations (upholstery). FAIRS: Olympia; LAPADA; Decorative & Textile, Battersea. VAT: Spec.

GILLINGHAM

Talisman

The Old Brewery, Wyke. SP8 4NW. LAPADA. Open 9-5, Sat. 10-4. SIZE: Large. *STOCK: Unusual and decorative items, garden furniture, architectural fittings, 18th-19th C; English and Continental furniture.* PARK: Easy. TEL: 01747 824423/824222; fax - 01747 823544. FAIRS: Olympia (June). VAT: Stan/Spec.

LITTON CHENEY, Nr. Dorchester

F. Whillock

Court Farm. DT2 9AU. Est. 1979. Open by

appointment. *STOCK: Maps and prints.* LOC: Village centre. PARK: Easy. TEL: 01308 482457. SER: Framing.

LYTCHETT MINSTER

Old Button Shop Antiques
BH16 6JF. (T. Johns). Est. 1970. Open Tues.-Fri. 2-5, Sat 11-1. *STOCK: Small antiques, brass, copper, curios, unusual items and antique Dorset buttons.* TEL: 01202 622169.

MELBURY OSMOND, Nr. Dorchester

Hardy Country
Meadow View. DT2 0NA. (Steven and Caroline Groves). Est. 1980. Open by appointment. SIZE: Large. *STOCK: Georgian, Victorian, Edwardian pine and country furniture, £40-£2,500.* LOC: Off A37. PARK: Easy. TEL: 01935 83440; website - www.hardycountry.com.

PARKSTONE, Nr. Poole

Derek J. Burgess - Horologist
470 Ashley Rd. BH14 0AD. Est. 1980. Open Tues.-Fri. 9-1.30. *STOCK: Clocks, watches.* TEL: 01202 730542. SER: Restorations (clocks and watches of all periods); parts made.

Dorset Coin Company
193 Ashley Rd. BH14 9DL. (E.J. and C.P. Parsons). BNTA, IBNS. Est. 1977. Open 9.30-4, Sat. 9.30-1. *STOCK: Coins, 19th-20th C, £1-£50; banknotes, 20th C, £3-£50.* LOC: Main road through Upper Parkstone. PARK: Easy. TEL: 01202 739606; fax - 01202 739230. SER: Valuations. FAIRS: BNTA Harrogate & London. VAT: Stan/Global/Exempt

Christopher Williams Antiquarian Bookseller
19 Morrison Ave. BH12 4AD. *STOCK: Books especially on antiques, art, needlework, lacemaking and leatherbound volumes and sets.* TEL: 01202 743157; fax - same; e-mail - cw4finebooks @lineone.net. FAIRS: Various. *Postal only.*

POOLE

G.D. and S.T. Antiques
(G.D. and S.T.Brown). Open by appointment. *STOCK: General antiques.* TEL: 01202 676340.

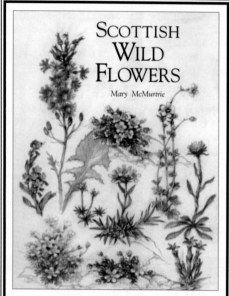

Laburnum Antiques

Lonbourne House, 250 Bournemouth Rd. BH14 9HZ. (Doreen Mills). Est. 1998. Open Tues.-Sat. 10-5.30. *STOCK: Fine Georgian and Victorian furniture, smalls, decorative items.* PARK: Forecourt. TEL: 01202 746222; fax - same.

Stocks and Chairs

11 Bank Chambers, Penn Hill Ave. BH14 9NB. (Mrs C.E. Holding-Parsons). Est. 1992. Open Tues., Thurs. and Fri. 11-5, Sat. 9.30-5 and by appointment. SIZE: Medium. *STOCK: Furniture, 18th to early 20th C, mainly £500-£5,000; specialist in hand-dyed leather chairs and settees.* PARK: Easy. TEL: 01202 718618; mobile - 07970 010512; e-mail - stocksand.chairs@virgin.net; website - www.stocksandchairsantiques.com. SER: Restorations (cabinet work, polishing).

PUDDLETOWN, Nr. Dorchester

Antique Map and Bookshop

32 High St. DT2 8RU. (C.D. and H.M.Proctor). ABA. PBFA. Est. 1976. Open 9-5. *STOCK: Antiquarian and secondhand books, maps, prints and engravings.* PARK: Easy. TEL: 01305 848633; fax - 01305 848992; e-mail - proctor@puddletown. demon.co.uk; website - www.abebooks.com/home/proctorbooks. SER: Postal; catalogues.

SHAFTESBURY

Mr. Punch's Antique Market

33 Bell St. SP7 8AE. Est. 1994. Open 10-5.30. CL: Mon. SIZE: Large. *STOCK: Wide variety of general antiques, fine art and collectables. Also Punch and Judy collection.* LOC: On corner with Muston's Lane. PARK: Easy 100 yards. TEL: 01747 855775; fax - same. SER: Valuations; restorations; deliveries.

Shaston Antiques

16A Bell St. SP7 8AE. (J. D. Hine). Resident. Est. 1996. Open 9.30-1 and 2-5, Wed. 9.30-1. SIZE: Medium. *STOCK: Furniture, 18th-19th C, £300-£5,000.* LOC: From town centre, turn right opposite Grosvenor Hotel into Bell St. TEL: 01747 850405; home - same. SER: Restorations (furniture).

SHERBORNE

Abbas Antiques

at Sherborne World of Antiques, Long St. DT9 3BS. Open 9.30-5. *STOCK: Small collectables and furniture.* TEL: 01935 816451.

Antiques of Sherborne

1 The Green. DT9 3HZ. (C. and L. Greenslade). LAPADA. CINOA. Est. 1988. Open 10-5. *STOCK: 18th-19th C furniture, sofas and armchairs, chess sets and linen.* LOC: Top of Cheap St., just off A30. PARK: Nearby. TEL: 01935 816549; mobile - 07971 019173; e-mail - clive@ antiquesofsherborne.fsnet.co.uk. SER: International deliveries arranged. VAT: Spec.

Chapter House Books

Trendle St. DT9 3NT. (Carol and Robert Hutchison). PBFA. Est. 1988. Open 10-5. SIZE: Large. *STOCK: Out-of-print, secondhand and antiquarian books, to £400.* LOC: Next to Almshouse and Abbey. TEL: 01935 816262. SER: Valuations; restorations (bookbinding and repair); book search.

Dodge and Son

28-33 Cheap St. DT9 3PU. (S. Dodge). LAPADA. Est. 1918. Open 9-5.30, Sun. by appointment. SIZE: Large. *STOCK: Furniture, including dining, all periods.* PARK: At rear. TEL: 01935 815151; e-mail - sales@ dodgesherborne.co.uk. SER: Restorations; furniture makers; worldwide delivery. VAT: Stan/Spec.

Greystoke Antiques

Swan Yard, Off Cheap St. DT9 3AX. (F.L. and N.E. Butcher). Est. 1970. Open 10-4.30. *STOCK: Silver, Georgian, Victorian and later; early 19th C English blue transfer printed pottery.* LOC: Off main street. PARK: Adjacent to Swan Yard or outside shop. TEL: 01935 812833. VAT: Stan/Margin/Global.

Heygate Browne Antiques

South St. DT9 3NG. (M. and W. Heygate Browne). Open 10-5. SIZE: Large. *STOCK: 18th-19th C furniture, pottery and porcelain.* LOC: Off Cheap St. towards station. PARK: Easy. TEL: 01935 815487. SER: Valuations; restorations. VAT: Stan/Spec.

Keeble Antiques

2 Tilton Court, Digby Rd. DT9 3NL. (C.P. Keeble). Est. 1965. Open 9-6, Sat. 8.30-6, Sun. 9.30-5.30. SIZE: Medium. *STOCK: Clocks, 19th C, £250-£850; Venetian mirrors, 19th C, £500-£900; books, 16th-20th C, £1-£800; maps, 17th-19th C, £100-£750.* LOC: Adjacent tourist information centre, near abbey. PARK: Easy. TEL: 01935 816199; fax - same; e-mail - info@keeble antiques.co.uk; website - www.keebleantiques. co.uk. SER: Valuations (books and maps).

The Nook

South St. DT9 3LX. (J. Morley). *STOCK: General antiques - furniture, china, glass, brass and copper.* TEL: 01935 813987.

Phoenix Antiques

21 Cheap St. DT9 3PU. (Sally and Neil Brent Jones). Est. 1998. Open 9.30-5.30. SIZE: Medium. *STOCK: Furniture, 17th-20th; lighting, mirrors and furnishings.* LOC: Town centre. PARK: Easy. TEL: 01935 812788. SER: Valuations; restorations. VAT: Spec.

Piers Pisani Antiques

The Courtyard, Newland. Open 10-5. SIZE: Medium. *STOCK: 17th-19th C furniture and furnishings.* TEL: 01935 815209; fax - same; e-mail - pp@pierspisani.com. SER: Restorations; upholstery; chairs copied; cabinet-making. VAT: Spec.

Sherborne World of Antiques

Long St. DT9 3BS. Open 9.30-5. SIZE: 40+ dealers. *STOCK: Fine arts, painting, furniture, rugs, objets d'art, jewellery, ceramics, glass.* LOC: From A30 via Greenhill. PARK: Easy - opposite. TEL: 01935 816451; fax - 01935 816240; e-mail - info@sherborneworldantiques.co.uk. SER: Restorations; upholstery; delivery; book search.

The Swan Gallery

51 Cheap St. DT9 3AX. (S. and Mrs K. Lamb). Est. 1977. Open 9.30-5, Wed. 9.30-1. SIZE: Large. *STOCK: Watercolours, 18th to early 20th C; oil paintings, antiquarian maps and prints.* PARK: Easy, at rear. TEL: 01935 814465; fax - 01308 868195. SER: Valuations; restorations (paintings, watercolours and prints); framing. FAIRS: Watercolours and Drawings, Park Lane, London. VAT: Stan/Spec.

Timecraft Clocks

Unit 2, 24 Cheap St. DT9 3PX. (Gordon M. Smith). Grad. BHI. Est. 1993. Open 10-5.30. SIZE: Small. *STOCK: Clocks, 18th-20th C, £200-£4,000; barometers, 18th-20th C, £80-£1,200; telephones, 20th C, £80-£250.* PARK: Easy. TEL: 01935 817771. SER: Restorations (clock and barometer movements, cases and dials).

Henry Willis (Antique Silver)

38 Cheap St. DT9 3PX. Est. 1973. Open 10-5. SIZE: Small. *STOCK: Silver, 16th-20th C, £15-£15,000.* LOC: Town centre, just off A30. PARK: Nearby. TEL: 01935 816828. SER: Valuations; restorations (silver); buys at auction (silver). FAIRS: Olympia (June). VAT: Stan/Spec.

STURMINSTER NEWTON

Tom Tribe and Son

Bridge St. DT10 1BZ. CMBHI. Resident. Open 9-5, Sat. 9-1 and by appointment. *STOCK: Longcase and mantel clocks, barometers.* PARK: At side of shop. TEL: 01258 472311. VAT: Stan/ Spec.

SWANAGE

Georgian Gems Antique Jewellers

28 High St. BH19 2NU. (Brian Barker). NAG. Est. 1971. Open 9.30-1 and 2.30-5 or by appointment. SIZE: Small. *STOCK: Jewellery, £5-£2,000; silver, £5-£500; both from 1700.* LOC: Town centre. PARK: Nearby. TEL: 01929 424697; freephone - 0800 471 0242. SER: Valuations; repairs; gem testing; special search.

Reference Works Ltd.

at The Last Resort, 9 Commercial Rd. BH19 1DF. (B. and J.E. Lamb). Est. 1984. Open 10-4, Sat.

Copeland, c.1930s. Collection of jade figures. (Private collection)

From an article entitled "Spode Copeland Spode Art And Design" by Vega Wilkinson which appeared in the March 2002 issue of **Antique Collecting**. For more details and to subscribe see page 21.

10-1. *STOCK: Reference books and catalogues on ceramics, all subjects, new and out-of-print; small range of ceramics, 18th-20th C.* TEL: 01929 424423; fax - 01929 422597; e-mail - sales@referenceworks.co.uk; website - www.referenceworks.co.uk. SER: Mail order, catalogue available; six newsletters each year; ceramic research and consultancy.

WAREHAM

Heirlooms Antique Jewellers and Silversmiths
21 South St. BH20 4LR. (M. and Mrs G. Young). FGA, DGA, RJDip. Est. 1986. Open 9.15-5. CL: Wed. SIZE: Medium. *STOCK: Jewellery, £30-£1,000; silver, £20-£500; both Georgian to Edwardian.* LOC: On main thoroughfare. PARK: At rear. TEL: 01929 554207. SER: Valuations; restorations; repairs; gem testing.

Yesterdays
32 South St. BH20 4EN. Est. 1995. Open 10-4, Wed. 10-1. *STOCK: Pottery and porcelain - Dennis, Poole, blue and white, Beswick, Isle of Wight, Wade, Carlton and Spode; okra glass.* LOC: Near Tourist Information Centre. PARK: Nearby. TEL: 01929 550505; home - 01929 556381. SER: Valuations; buys at auction. FAIRS: Shepton Mallet, Exeter and Winchester. VAT: Stan.

WEYMOUTH

Books Afloat
66 Park St. DT4 7DE. (J. Ritchie). Est. 1983. Open 9.30-5.30. SIZE: 2 floors. *STOCK: Rare and secondhand books especially nautical; maritime ephemera, liner memorabilia, ship models, paintings, prints.* LOC: Near railway station. TEL: 01305 779774.

Books & Bygones
Great George St. DT4 7AR. (Mrs Denise Nash). Est. 1981. Open 11-5.30, Sun. 12-5. SIZE: Medium. *STOCK: Books including antiquarian, 50p to £1,000; antiques and collectables, from 18th C, £1-£750; ephemera, from 50p.* LOC: Near King's statue, on esplanade. PARK: Easy. TEL: 01305 777231; home - 01305 771529. SER: Valuations; buys at auction.

The Crows Nest
3 Hope Sq. DT4 8TR. (Julia Marko). Open 10-5 including Sun. SIZE: Medium. *STOCK: Collectables including china, glass and nautical items.*

LOC: Follow signs for Brewers Quay, shop opposite. PARK: Brewers Quay. TEL: 01305 786930. FAIRS: Shepton Mallet.

Nautical Antique Centre
3a Cove Passage, off Hope Sq. DT4 8TR. (D.C. Warwick). Est. 1989. Open 10-1 and 2-5 - prior 'phone call advisable, Sat., Sun. and Mon. by appointment. SIZE: Medium. *STOCK: Exclusively nautical, including sextants, logs, clocks, flags, blocks, old sails, rope, bells, ship models, telescopes, ship badges, portholes and memorabilia, also restaurant/pub decorative items, 19th-20th C, £5-£2,000.* LOC: Near Hope Square opposite Brewers Quay, adjacent harbour. PARK: Nearby. TEL: 01305 777838; home - 01305 783180; e-mail - nauticalantiques@tinyworld.co.uk; website - www.nauticalantiquesweymouth.co.uk. SER: Buys at auction (nautical items).

The Treasure Chest
29 East St. DT4 8BN. (P. Barrett). Open 10-1 and 2.30-5. CL: Wed. pm. *STOCK: Maps, prints, coins, medals; army, RN and RAF badges.* PARK: Next door. TEL: 01305 772757. SER: Lost medals replaced; medal mounting - full size or miniature, brooches and new ribbons.

WIMBORNE MINSTER

Four Seasons Gallery
24 West Borough. BH21 1NF. (Nigel Cox). Est. 1996. Open Wed.- Sat. 10-5.30. SIZE: Small. *STOCK: Small 18th-19th furniture, paintings, collectables; contemporary art gallery with regular exhibitions.* LOC: Near minster. PARK: Easy and nearby. TEL: 01202 882204; website - www. fourseasonsgallery.co.uk.

J.B. Antiques
10A West Row. BH21 1LA. (J. Beckett). Est. 1978. Open 10-4, Fri. and Sat. 9.30-4. CL: Wed. SIZE: Small. *STOCK: Copper, £5-£360; brass, £1-£350; furniture, £30-£1,200; all 18th-20th C.* LOC: 2 mins. from Sq. PARK: Nearby. TEL: Home - 01202 882522. SER: Valuations; restorations (metalware); buys at auction (copper).

Minster Books
12 Corn Market. BH21 1HW. (John and Angela Child). Est. 1970. Open 10-5. SIZE: Medium. *STOCK: Books, £5-£100.* LOC: In road at side of minster. PARK: King St. TEL: 01202 883355. SER: Valuations; restorations (book binding).

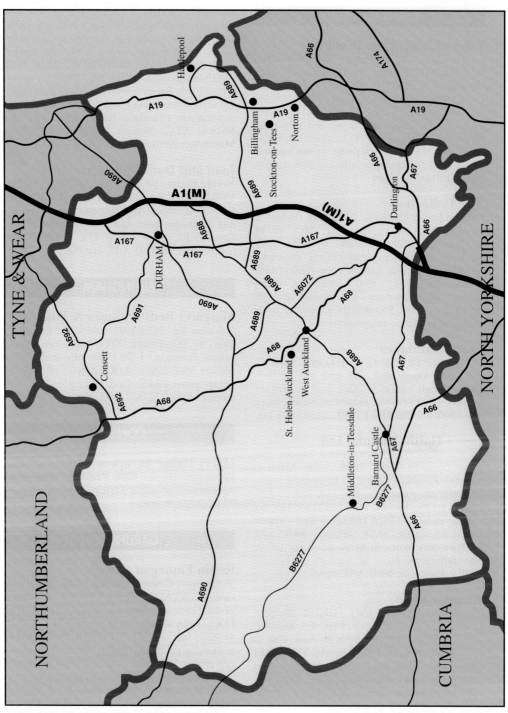

Dealers and Shops in Durham

				Middleton-in-Teesdale	1
				Norton	1
Barnard Castle	7	Darlington	2	St. Helen Auckland	1
Billingham	1	Durham	2	Stockton-on-Tees	1
Consett	1	Hartlepool	1	West Auckland	1

Edward Barrington-Doulby
23 The Bank. (M. A. Venus). Est. 1990. Open Wed.-Sat. 11-5, Sun. 1-5 in summer. SIZE: Warehouse + shop. *STOCK: 18th-20th C unusual tools, implements, kitchenalia, eccentricities, cast-iron, pottery, pictures, £1-£1,000; 17th-20th C pine, oak, mahogany, rustic and provincial furniture.* PARK: Easy. TEL: 01833 630500; home - 01325 264339; website - www.barnard-castle.co.uk/antiques/edwardbarrington-doulby. SER: Delivery arranged.

The Collector
Douglas House, The Bank. DL12 8PH. (Robert A. Jordan). Est. 1970. Open Sat. 10-5 or by appointment. SIZE: Medium. *STOCK: Early furniture and complementary objects, decorative interior fittings and Eastern rugs.* TEL: 01833 637783; fax - same; e-mail - JordanTheCollector @btinternet.com; website - www.barnard-castle.co.uk/antiques. SER: Restorations (especially metal work, early furniture and interiors).

Grant's Antiques
26 Newgate. DL12 8NG. (Carl Grant). Resident. Est. 1976. Open Wed., Fri. and Sat. 10.30-5. SIZE: Small. *STOCK: Oak and mahogany furniture, £100-£4,000; pottery, £15-£500; rugs, £50-£500; all 17th-19th C.* TEL: 01833 695700.

James Hardy Antiques Ltd
12 The Bank. DL12 8PQ. (Alan Hardy). Est. 1994. Open 10-5. CL: Thurs. SIZE: Medium. *STOCK: Furniture, 18th C to Edwardian, £500-£25,000; silver and porcelain, 18th-20th C, £25-£5,000.* PARK: Nearby. TEL: 01833 695135; fax - same; mobile - 07710 162003; e-mail - alan@ jameshardyantiques.co.uk; website - www.james hardyantiques.co.uk. SER: Restorations (silver and furniture); buys at auction (furniture). FAIRS: Harrogate; NEC. VAT: Spec.

Kingsley & Co.
7 Newgate. DL12 8NQ. (David Harper). LAPADA. Est. 1992. Open Wed., Fri. and Sat. 10.30-5. SIZE: Medium. *STOCK: Fine 17th to early 20th C antiques.* PARK: Nearby. TEL: 01833 630522; fax - same; home - 01833 650551; e-mail - kingsleyandco@btopenworld.com; website - www.kingsleyantiques.co.uk. SER: Valuations.

Robson's Antiques
36 The Bank. DL12 8PN. (Anne, David and Dale Robson). Est. 1977. Open 10-5.30, Sun. 1.30-5.30. SIZE: Medium. *STOCK: Smalls including cutlery and canteens; silver perfume bottles, cruets, photograph frames; Victorian and north east glass; pottery including Maling, Carlton-ware and Lesol; Durham and patchwork quilts; Georgian, Victorian and Edwardian fireplaces, ranges, marble and wooden surrounds, inserts.* LOC: Below Market Cross. PARK: Easy. TEL: 01833 690157/638700; mobile - 07977 146584; e-mail - dale.hunter.robson@virgin.net; website - www.robsonantiques.co.uk. SER: Valuations; restorations (fireplace fitting and stripping). FAIRS: NEC; Newark; Birmingham Glass; Manchester Armytage Centre Textile.

Joan and David White Antiques
Neville House, 10 The Bank. DL12 8PQ. Est. 1975. Open Tues., Wed., Fri. and Sat. 11-5. *STOCK: Georgian, Victorian and export furniture and decorative items.* LOC: 100yds. from Market Cross. PARK: Front of shop. TEL: 01833 638329; home - 01325 374303. VAT: Stan/Spec.

Margaret Bedi Antiques & Fine Art
5 Station Rd. TS23 1AG. LAPADA. Est. 1976. Open by appointment. *STOCK: Mainly English period furniture, 1720-1920; oils and water-colours, 19th-20th C.* LOC: 300yds. off A19, by village green. PARK: Easy. TEL: 01642 782346; mobile - 07860 577637. VAT: Stan/Spec.

Harry Raine Antiques
Kelvinside House, Villa Real Rd. DH8 6BL. Appointment advisable. *STOCK: General antiques.* TEL: 01207 503935.

Robin Finnegan (Jeweller)
39 Cornmill Centre. DL1 1LS. NAG. Est. 1974. Open 9-5.30. SIZE: Medium. *STOCK: Jewellery, general antiques, coins and medals, £1-£10,000.* LOC: Town centre. PARK: Easy. TEL: 01325 489820; fax - 01325 357674; website - www. militarybadges.co.uk. SER: Valuations; repairs (jewellery). VAT: Stan.

Alan Ramsey Antiques
Unit 10-11 Dudley Rd, Yarm Road Industrial Estate. DL1 4GG. LAPADA. Est. 1973. Open Mon.-Fri. 9.30-4 or by appointment. SIZE: Warehouse. *STOCK: Victorian, Edwardian and Georgian furniture; interesting pine.* PARK: Easy. TEL: 01325 361679; home - 01642 711311; mobile - 07702 523246. VAT: Stan/Spec. *Trade Only.*

DURHAM

Old & Gold
88 Claypath. DH1 1RG. (Pam and Paul Tracey). Est. 1989. CL: Wed. and Sat. pm. SIZE: Small. *STOCK: Jewellery and china, 19th C, £50-£100.* LOC: 200 yards from Market Place. PARK: Multi-storey nearby. TEL: 0191 386 0728. SER: Valuations; restorations (jewellery); buys at auction. FAIRS: Newark.

J. Shotton Antiquarian Books, Prints and Coins
89 Elvet Bridge. DH1 3AG. Est. 1967. Open 9.30-5. CL: Mon. *STOCK: Antiquarian books, prints, maps and coins.* TEL: 0191 386 4597.

HARTLEPOOL

Antique Fireplace Centre
134 Lyne St. South, TS24 7LX. (D.J. Crowther). Est. 1983. Open 9-5. SIZE: Large. *STOCK: Victorian and Edwardian fireplaces, Victorian 4-panel pine doors, architectural antiques.* TEL: 01429 279007/222433; mobile - 07774 639754.

MIDDLETON-IN-TEESDALE, Nr. Barnard Castle

Brown's Antiques & Collectables
13 Chapel Row. DL12 0SN. (John and Val Brown). Resident. Est. 1990. Open 10-5, Sun. by appointment. SIZE: Medium. *STOCK: Furniture, metalware and collectables, 18th-20th, £20-£2,000.* LOC: North of A66. PARK: Easy. TEL: 01833 640276; e-mail - antiques@13chapelrow. freeserve.co.uk; website - www.browns-antiques. co.uk. SER: Buys at auction.

NORTON, Nr. Stockton-on-Tees

Paraphernalia
12 Harland Place, High St. TS20 1AA. (Rena Thomas). Est. 1982. Open 9.30-5. SIZE: Large. *STOCK: Mainly 19th C mahogany furniture, to £1,000.* LOC: Next to Red Lion public house. PARK: Easy. TEL: 01642 535940. SER: Restorations (furniture and French polishing). VAT: Stan/Spec.

ST. HELEN AUCKLAND

Something Different
34a Maude Terrace. DL14 9BD. Est. 1968. Open 9.30-5.30, Sun. 10-4.30. SIZE: Large. *STOCK:*

Furniture, clocks, decorative items, 19th-20th C. TEL: 01388 664366. SER: Repairs (clocks); deliveries (UK and Europe).

STOCKTON-ON-TEES

T.B. and R. Jordan (Fine Paintings)
Aslak, Eaglescliffe. TS16 0QN. LAPADA. Est. 1974. Open by appointment. *STOCK: Oil paintings and watercolours especially Staithes group, 19th-20th C, £200-£15,000.* LOC: Village centre. PARK: Easy. TEL: 01642 782599; fax - 01642 780473; e-mail - info@tbrjordan.co.uk; website - www. tbrjordan.co.uk. SER: Commissions. VAT: Spec.

WEST AUCKLAND

Eden House Antiques
10 Staindrop Rd. DL14 9JX. (C.W. and M. Metcalfe). Est. 1978. Open daily including Sun. SIZE: Small. *STOCK: Clocks, furniture, 18th-20th C; collectables, bric-a-brac, oak and mahogany reproductions, Continental furniture.* LOC: A68, approx. 7 miles west of A1M. PARK: Easy. TEL: 01388 833013; e-mail - chris@antiques-e.co.uk; website - www.antiques-e.co. uk. SER: Valuations; restorations.

Beryl Cook, 'Oh to be in England', oil on panel, dated 1980, 18in. x 15in. £6,900. Sworder's, Stansted Mountfitchet, Essex.

From Saleroom Prices which appeared in the July/August 2001 issue of **Antique Collecting**. For more details and to subscribe see page 21.

ABRIDGE

Revival
Coach House, Market Place. RM4 1UA. (R. Y. Jefferson). Est. 1988. Open 11-5.30, and some Sun. CL: Fri. SIZE: Large. *STOCK: Furniture, Georgian to Deco, £20-£3,000; china and glass, silver, 1800-1960, £5-£500.* LOC: From London - off M11, junction 5, turn right then left on to A113. From M25, junction 26 follow A121, then B172. PARK: Opposite. TEL: 01992 814000; fax - 01992 814300. SER: Valuations; restorations (ceramics); watch and clock repairs.

BATTLESBRIDGE

Battlesbridge Antique Centre
SS11 7RF. (Jim and Fraser Gallie and Joseph Pettitt). Est. 1967. Open 10-5 including Sun. CL: Mon. SIZE: Over 80 units within adjacent premises (see below). *STOCK: Wide range from large furniture to jewellery, all periods with specialist dealers for most items.* LOC: A130, mid-way between Chelmsford and Southend. Junction 29, M25, east on A127 to A130, then north for 3 miles. By rail: Liverpool St.-Southend-on-Sea, change at Wickford for Battlesbridge. PARK: Own. TEL: Fax

- 01268 575001; e-mail - info @battlesbridge.com; website - www.battlesbridge.com. SER: Restorations (furniture); container facilities; nationwide and overseas delivery service.

Cromwell House Antique Centre
TEL: Management: Jim Gallie - 01268 732927; ground floor dealers - 01268 762612; first floor dealers - 01268 734030.

Haybarn and Bridgebarn Antique Centres
(J.P. Pettitt). TEL: 01268 763500/735884.

Muggeridge Farm Buildings
(Jim Gallie). TEL: 01268 732927.

The Old Granary Antique and Craft Centre
(Jim Gallie). TEL: Office - 01268 575000; showrooms - 01268 764197.

BAYTHORNE END

Swan Antiques
The Swan. CO9 4AF. (Mr and Mrs K. Mercado). Est. 1983. Open 9.30-6 including Sun. SIZE: Medium. *STOCK: Furniture, 18th-19th C and some Edwardian, £50-£2,000; porcelain, 19th C, £5-£1,000; small silver and collectables, 19th-20th C, £5-£500.* LOC: A1017 (formerly A604)

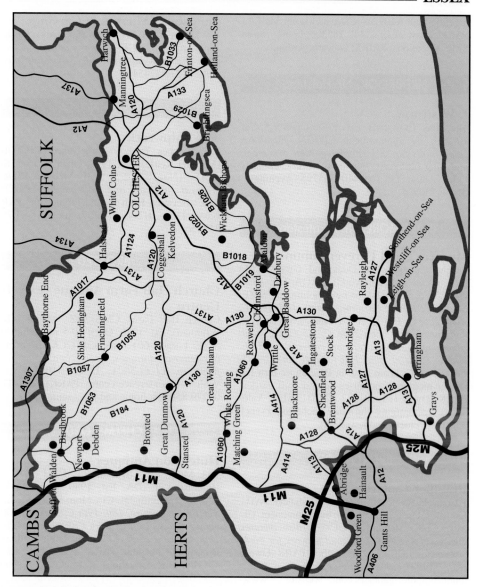

Dealers and Shops in Essex

Abridge	1	Danbury	1	Holland-on-Sea	1	Sible Hedingham	3
Battlesbridge	1	Debden	1	Ingatestone	1	Southend-on-Sea	2
Baythorne End	1	Finchingfield	1	Kelvedon	3	Stansted	3
Birdbrook	1	Frinton-on-Sea	4	Leigh-on-Sea	7	Stock	1
Blackmore	1	Gants Hill	1	Maldon	3	Westcliff-on-Sea	2
Brentwood	3	Grays	1	Manningtree	1	White Colne	1
Brightlingsea	1	Great Baddow	1	Matching Green	1	White Roding	1
Broxted	1	Great Dunmow	1	Newport	2	Wickham Bishops	1
Chelmsford	1	Great Waltham	1	Rayleigh	1	Woodford Green	2
Coggeshall	4	Hainault	1	Roxwell	1	Writtle	1
Colchester	9	Halstead	2	Saffron Walden	7		
Corringham	1	Harwich	1	Shenfield	1		

junction with A1092 to Clare and Long Melford. PARK: Easy. TEL: 01440 785306; home - same. SER: Valuations. FAIRS: Newark; Ardingly.

BIRDBROOK, Nr. Halstead

I. Westrope
The Elms. CO9 4AB. Est. 1958. Open 9-5, Sat. 10-1 or by appointment. *STOCK: Furniture, china, dolls house furniture, garden ornaments including birdbaths, fountains, statues, animals.* LOC: A604. TEL: 01440 785795; evenings - 01440 730594.

BLACKMORE, Nr. Ingatestone

Megarry's and Forever Summer
Jericho Cottage, The Duckpond Green. CM4 0RR. (Peter and Judi Wood). EADA. Est. 1986. Open Wed.-Sun. 11-5 or by appointment. SIZE: Medium. *STOCK: Furniture, mainly 18th-19th C, some 20th C, £60-£3,500; ceramics, glass, treen and metalware, 19th-20th C, £5-£200; small silver and plate, jewellery and collectables, 19th-20th C, £5-£100; pine, 19th to early 20th C, £75-£1,000.* LOC: From A12, in Blackmore turn left at war memorial, premises behind Bull garden. PARK: Own. TEL: 01277 821031. SER: Valuations; restorations (furniture including French polishing, clocks and jewellery).

BRENTWOOD

Brandler Galleries
1 Coptfold Rd. CM14 4BM. (J. Brandler). FATG. Est. 1973. Open 10-5.30, Sun. by appointment. CL: Mon. SIZE: Medium. *STOCK: British pictures, 20th C, £100-£30,000; original artwork for books and comics.* LOC: Near Post Office. PARK: Own at rear. TEL: 01277 222269 (24 hrs); e-mail - john@brandler-galleries.com; website - www-brandler-galleries.com. SER: Valuations (photographs); restorations (watercolour and oil cleaning, relining, framing); buys at auction (pictures); 2-3 free catalogues annually. VAT: Spec.

Neil Graham Gallery
11 Ingrave Rd. CM15 8AP. EADA. FATG. Est. 1977. CL: Mon. SIZE: Large. *STOCK: 19th to early 20th C watercolours, oils and prints, £50-£1,000; Victorian and Edwardian occasional furniture, £100-£1,500; silver, pottery and porcelain, 19th-20th C, £25-£500.* LOC: Near junction of Wilson's Corner, town centre. PARK: Easy and High St. TEL: 01277 215383; fax - same; e-mail - neilgrahamgallery@btinternet.com. SER: Valuations; restorations (paintings); buys at auction. VAT: Stan/Spec.

Simpsons - Mirrors & Carvings
449 Ongar Rd. CM15 9JG. (S. Yardy). Open by appointment. *STOCK: Mirrors - antique including pine and new hand-carved; decorative pieces.* TEL: 01277 374541.

BRIGHTLINGSEA

The Shipwreck
22e Marshes Yard, Victoria Place. CO7 0BX. (Michael Kettle). Est. 1994. Open 10.15-5, Sun. 11.15-5 (Nov.-Feb. 2-5). SIZE: Medium. *STOCK: General antiques and collectables, £1-£100.* LOC: Between High St. and Promenade. PARK: Easy. TEL: 01206 307307; mobile - 07980 357456.

BROXTED

Church Hall Farm Antique & Craft Centre
Church Hall Farm. CM6 2BZ. (Jan and Tony Wildman). Est. 1996. Open 10-5 including Sun. SIZE: Large - 60+ dealers. *STOCK: Wide range of general antiques, from smalls to large furniture, £1-£1,500+.* LOC: B1051 next to Whitehall conference centre. PARK: Easy. TEL: 01279 850858; home and fax - same.

CHELMSFORD

Hutchison Antiques
163 Main Rd., Broomfield. CM1 7DJ. (G. Hutchison). EADA. Est. 1980. Open 11-5.30, Sun. by appointment. CL: Mon. SIZE: Medium. *STOCK: Furniture, 18th-19th C, £300-£1,000+; china, mainly 19th C, from £50; paintings, from 19th C, from £100.* LOC: On main road, near Broomfield hospital. PARK: Easy. TEL: 01245 441184. SER: Valuations; restorations (as stock).

COGGESHALL

Argentum Antiques
1 Church St. CO6 1TU. (Mrs. Dianne M. Carr). Open 10-5. CL: Wed. SIZE: Medium. *STOCK: Silver and Old Sheffield plate, 18th-20th C, £100-£2,000; furniture, mainly oak, 17th-19th C, £200-£3,000; decorative items, object d'art, garden ornaments, 19th C.* LOC: Between A120 and A12, village centre. PARK: Nearby. TEL: 01376 561365. VAT: Spec.

English Rose Antiques
7 Church St. CO6 1TU. (Mark and Iryna Barrett). Est. 1983. Open 10-5.30, Sun. 10.30-5.30. CL: Wed. *STOCK: English and Continental pine*

including dressers, chests, tables and wardrobes, 18th-19th C, £50-£2,000; fruitwood, ash and elm country furniture and kitchenalia. LOC: Town centre. PARK: Loading or 50 yds. TEL: 01376 562683; home - same; fax - 01376 563450; mobile - 07770 880790; e-mail - englishrose antiques@hotmail.com. SER: Valuations; restorations (stripping, repairing and finishing). FAIRS: Newark, Swinderby, Ardingly.

Mark Marchant (Antiques)
3 Market Sq. CO6 1TS. Resident. Est. 1960. Open 11-5, Sun. 2.30-5.30. SIZE: Small. STOCK: Clocks, barometers and music boxes only. LOC: A120. PARK: Market square. TEL: 01376 561188. SER: Valuations; restorations; buys at auction.

Partners in Pine
63/65 West St. CO6 1NS. (W.T. Newton). Resident. Est. 1982. Open 10-5. CL: Wed. SIZE: Small. STOCK: Victorian stripped pine. PARK: Easy. TEL: 01376 561972.

COLCHESTER

Barntiques
Lampitts Farm, Turkeycock Lane, Stanway. CO3 5ND. (A. Jones and S. Doubleday). Resident. Est. 1978. Open weekends. SIZE: Medium. STOCK: General antiques and pine. LOC: Turn left at Eight Ash Green from A604. PARK: Easy. TEL: 01206 210486; home - 01206 212421.

S. Bond and Son
Olivers Orchard, Olivers Lane. CO2 0HH. (R. Bond). Open by appointment. SIZE: Large. STOCK: Furniture and pictures. TEL: 01206 331175; mobile - 07710 823800. SER: Valuations; restorations. VAT: Stan/Spec. Trade only.

Elizabeth Cannon Antiques
85 Crouch St. CO3 3EZ. Open 10-5. STOCK: General antiques including jewellery, silver, glass, porcelain and furniture. PARK: Easy. TEL: 01206 575817.

Castle Bookshop
40 Osborne St. CO2 7DB. (R.J. Green). PBFA STOCK: Antiquarian and secondhand books, maps & prints. TEL: 01206 577520; fax - same.

Dean Antiques
Mill Farm, Harwich Rd., Gt. Bromley. CO7 7JQ. Est. 1947. Open 10-4 including Sun. SIZE: Small. STOCK: Country and pine furniture, 18th-19th C. Not Stocked: Reproductions. LOC: 6 miles from Colchester. 1½ miles off A120 Harwich road, follow signs for Mill Farm camping. PARK: Own. TEL: 01206 250485; home - same; fax - 01206 252040.

Grahams of Colchester
19 Short Wyre St. CO1 1LN. Open 9-5.30. STOCK: Jewellery and silver. TEL: 01206 576808. SER: Valuations; restorations.

E J Markham & Son Ltd
122/3 Priory St. CO1 2PX. (Mrs S. Campbell). NAG, NPA. Open 8.30-5.30. SIZE: Medium. STOCK: Jewellery, 19th-20th C, £25-£8,000; porcelain, 18th-20th C, £25-£2,000; furniture, 19th-20th C, £100-£1,500. LOC: Opposite St Botolph's priory ruins. PARK: NCP Priory St. TEL: 01206 572646. SER: Valuations; restorations (porcelain). VAT: Stan.

Revival
23b Drury Rd. CO2 7UY. (Mrs Barbara Addison). Est. 1999. Open 10.30-4. CL: Mon. and Tues. SIZE: Medium. STOCK: Pine furniture, 19th-20th C, to £300; sofas and chairs, 19th-20th C, to £400; bric-a-brac and smalls, old mirrors and prints, £5-£100. LOC: From town centre Maldon Rd. roundabout, follow Maldon Rd., take 6th left St Helena Rd. Shop at junction with Drury Rd. PARK: Behind shop. TEL: Mobile - 07753 691460. SER: Restorations (wood).

Trinity Antiques Centre
7 Trinity St. CO1 1JN. Est. 1976. Open 9.30-5. SIZE: 7 dealers + cabinets. STOCK: General antiques - small furniture, copper, clocks, brass, porcelain, silver, jewellery, collectors' items, Victoriana, maps and prints, linen, pine furniture. LOC: Town centre, near library. PARK: Nearby. TEL: 01206 577775.

CORRINGHAM, Nr. Stanford-le-Hope

Bush House
Church Rd. SS17 9AP. (F. Stephens). Est. 1976. Open by appointment. STOCK: Staffordshire animals, portrait figures, 1770-1901, £50-£5,000. LOC: Opposite the church. PARK: Own. TEL: 01375 673463; home - same; fax - same; e-mail - francis_j_stephens@hotmail.com. FAIRS: NEC, Birmingham; Westminster Ceramics and Glass.

DANBURY

Danbury Antiques
Eves Corner (by the Village Green). CM3 4QF. (Mrs Pam Southgate). EADA. Est. 1983. Open 10-5, Wed. 10-1, Sun. 10.30-1. CL: Mon. SIZE: Medium. STOCK: Jewellery and silver, ceramics, metalware, furniture, 18th to early 20th C, £5-£3,000. LOC: Off M25, take A12, then A414. PARK: Easy. TEL: 01245 223035. SER: Valuations; restorations (jewellery, upholstery, furniture). FAIRS: Furzehill, Margaretting. VAT: Stan/Spec.

DEBDEN, Nr. Saffron Walden

Debden Antiques
Elder St. CB11 3JY. (Robert Tetlow and Edward Norman). EADA. Est. 1995. Open 10-5.30, Sun. and Bank Holidays 11-4. SIZE: Large. *STOCK: Furniture, 17th-19th C, £100-£10,000; pictures, £50-£5,000, jewellery, silver, glass, porcelain, £5-£500, garden furniture, architectural, £50-£1,000; all 19th C.* LOC: Follow signs to Carver Barracks. PARK: Own. TEL: 01799 543007; fax - 01799 542482. SER: Valuations; restorations. VAT: Stan/Spec.

FINCHINGFIELD

Finchingfield Antiques Centre
The Green. CM7 4JX. (Peter Curry). Est. 1992. Open 10-5.30 including Sun. SIZE: Large - 40 dealers. *STOCK: Wide range of general antiques and collectables.* LOC: From M11, A120 to Gt. Dunmow, then B1057. PARK: Easy. TEL: 01371 810258; fax - same.

FRINTON-ON-SEA

Dickens Curios
151 Connaught Ave. CO13 9AH. (Miss M. Wilsher). Est. 1970. Open 9.45-1 and 2-5.30, Sat. 9.45-1 and 2-5. CL: Wed. pm. SIZE: Small. *STOCK: Postcards and ephemera, Victorian and later items, £5-£200.* Not Stocked: Firearms, watches and clocks. LOC: From Frinton Station quarter of mile down Connaught Ave. PARK: Easy. TEL: 01255 674134.

Number 24 of Frinton
24 Connaught Ave. CO13 9PR. (Chris Pereira). Est. 1993. Open 10-5, Sun. 2-4. CL: Wed. SIZE: Medium. *STOCK: Art Deco and Victorian prints, general antiques, furniture and collectables.* PARK: Easy. TEL: 01255 670505.

Phoenix Trading
130 Connaught Ave. CO13 9AD. (Tom Sheldon). Est. 1996. Open 10-4, Mon. by appointment. SIZE: Large. *STOCK: Pine and painted furniture, 19th C, £500-£1,000.* LOC: Main shopping street. PARK: Easy. TEL: 01255 851094; fax - same. SER: Restorations. FAIRS: Ardingly; Kempton. VAT: Stan/Spec.

GANTS HILL

Antique Clock Repair Shoppe
26 Woodford Ave. IG2 6XG. (K. Ashton). Est. 1971. Open 10-5. *STOCK: Clocks, pictures, bric-a-brac.* TEL: 020 8550 9540.

GRAYS

Atticus Books
8 London Rd. RM17 5XY. (Robert Drake). Est. 1981. Open Thurs.-Sat. 9-4. *STOCK: Books.* LOC: Town centre, 5 mins from station, 10 mins from M25. PARK: Nearby. TEL: 01375 371200.

GREAT BADDOW

Baddow Antique Centre
The Bringey, Church St. CM2 7JW. EADA. Est. 1969. Open 10-5, Sun. 11-5. SIZE: 22 dealers. *STOCK: 18th-20th C furniture, porcelain, silver, paintings, Victorian brass bedsteads, shipping goods.* PARK: Easy. TEL: 01245 476159. SER: Restorations; upholstery; framing; pine stripping.

GREAT DUNMOW

Memories
Starr Corner, 11A Market Place. CM6 1AX. (Peter and Denise Berriman). EADA. Est. 2000. Open 9.30-5. CL: Wed. SIZE: Small. *STOCK: Furniture especially upholstered, Victorian and Edwardian, £500-£1,000; clocks especially longcase, Georgian and Victorian, £2,000-£4,000; books, 19th-20th C, £5-£25.* LOC: Town centre. PARK: Free nearby. TEL: 01371 872331; home - 01279 850915. SER: Buys at auction.

GREAT WALTHAM, Nr. Chelmsford

The Stores
CM3 1DE. (E. Saunders). Est. 1974. Open Wed.-Sat. 10-5, Sun. 11-4. SIZE: Large. *STOCK: Period pine and country furniture.* LOC: Village centre. PARK: At rear. TEL: 01245 360277; home - 01245 360260.

HAINAULT, Nr. Ilford

Gallerie Antiques
62-70 Fowler Rd. IG6 3XE. (M. Johnson). EADA. Est. 1998. Open 10-5.30, Sun. 10-4. SIZE: 80 dealers. *STOCK: Wide range of general antiques including 18th-20th C furniture, £500-£1,000; china, porcelain, glass, linen and lace, books, collectables.* LOC: A1112 Eastern Ave. At Moby Dick public house, turn towards Hainault Forest Country Park. PARK: Easy. TEL: 020 8501 2229; fax - 020 8501 2209. SER: Valuations; restorations (furniture, paintings, ceramics, clocks, re-caning); buys at auction. VAT: Stan/Spec.

Dogsbodies –
a book of canine nonsense
ISBN 1 85149 271 2
Great Mistakes of Civilisation –
Mankind's Mistakes and Faux Pas
ISBN 1 85149 246 1
Handel's Warthog Music
Nonsense in Music
ISBN 1 85149 186 4
Still Warthogs Run Deep and Other
Free Range Nonsense
ISBN 1 85149 087 6

Cat with Piano Tuna and Other
Feline Nonsense
ISBN 1 85149 138 4
The Very Worst of Simon
Drew **£8.50**
ISBN 1 85149 331 X
Simon Drew's Beastly Address Book
for Beastly Friends **£9.95**
ISBN 1 85149 188 0
Simon Drew's Beastly Birthday
Book **£9.95**
ISBN 1 85149 220 8

*All titles are 48pp. and
measure 8¼ x 6in./
210 x 152mm. Colour
illustrated throughout
and priced at £7.50
each unless otherwise
indicated.*

Simon Drew's best-selling offering is a collection of puzzles which, at
first glance, appear to be nonsensical. Upon closer inspection they are
in fact the most excruciating brain teasers – within these pages the
reader will find not only book titles and authors, but also Christmas
carols, composers and film stars to name but a few – all have been
subjected to the genius of Drew. This is a book to exasperate and
annoy; so compelling is it, that it becomes impossible to put down until
every last riddle has been solved. ISBN 1 85149 356 5

Available from the
ANTIQUE COLLECTORS' CLUB
Sandy Lane, Old Martlesham, Woodbridge, Suffolk IP12 4SD, UK.
For your free copy of the catalogue:
Tel: **01394 389950** or Fax: **01394 389999**
Email: sales@antique-acc.com   Website: www.antique-acc.com

HALSTEAD

Antique Bed Shop
Napier House, Head St. CO9 2BT. (Veronica McGregor). Est. 1977. Open Thurs.-Sat., other times by appointment. SIZE: Large. *STOCK: Antique wooden bedsteads - 19th C mahogany, rosewood, chestnut, oak, bergere and painted, £1,295-£3,500.* Not Stocked: Brass, iron or pine beds. LOC: On A131 to Sudbury. PARK: Own. TEL: 01787 477346; fax - 01787 478757. SER: Free UK delivery.

Townsford Mill Antiques Centre
The Causeway. CO9 1ET. (M.T. Stuckey). Open 10-5, Sun. and Bank Holidays 11-5. SIZE: 70 dealers. *STOCK: General antiques and collectables.* LOC: On A131 Braintree/Sudbury road. TEL: 01787 474451.

HARWICH

Harwich Antiques Centre
19 Kings Quay St. CO12 3ER. (Patrick Scholz). Open 10-5, Sun. and Bank Holidays 1-5. CL: Mon. SIZE: Medium. *STOCK: Furniture, porcelain, china, glass, silverware, jewellery, 19th C, £10-£2,000; collectables, 19th-20th C; decorative items.* LOC: Between the pier and Electric Palace cinema. PARK: Nearby. TEL: 01255 554719; e-mail - hac@antiques-access-agency.com; website - www.antiques-access-agency.com. VAT: Stan.

HOLLAND-ON-SEA

Bookworm
100 King's Ave. CO15 5EP. (Andrew M'Garry-Durrant). Est. 1995. Open 9-5 and most Bank Holidays. SIZE: Small. *STOCK: Modern fiction, first editions, 1930-2001, £10-£500; rare and out-of-print, military history, motor and general sport, transport, nautical, £5-£100.* LOC: On junction with Holland Rd. PARK: Easy. TEL: 01255 815984; fax - same; e-mail - sales@adr-comms.demon.co.uk; website - www.adr-comms.demon.co.uk. SER: Valuations.

INGATESTONE

Kendons
122a High St. CM4 0BA. (Mrs Hillary A. O'Connor). Est. 1978. Open 10-5. CL: Wed. and Tues. *STOCK: Jewellery, silver, china, small furniture, clocks, medals, coins, stamps.* PARK: Easy. TEL: 01277 353625. FAIRS: Ardingly; Sandown Park; Alexandra Palace.

KELVEDON, Nr. Colchester

Colton Antiques
Station Rd. CO5 9NP. (Gary Colton). Est. 1993. Open 8-5, Sun. by appointment. SIZE: Medium. *STOCK: Furniture, 17th to early 20th C, £300-£15,000; decorative items.* PARK: Own. TEL: 01376 571504; mobile - 07973 797098. SER: Restorations (furniture). VAT: Stan/Spec.

Chris Papworth Antique Clocks and Watches
2 High St. CO5 9AG. MBHI; BWCG. Open 9-5, Fri. by appointment. SIZE: Medium. *STOCK: Clocks, watches (including pocket) and barometers.* LOC: Near mainline railway station. PARK: Easy - own. TEL: 01376 573434; home - same; mobile - 07802 615461. SER: Repairs. FAIRS: Brunel, Uxbridge, Middx.

G.T. Ratcliff Ltd
Brick House Farm, Braxted Rd. C05 9BS. (F.D. Campbell). Est. 1935. Open by appointment. SIZE: Medium. *STOCK: Furniture, mainly 18th-19th C.* LOC: A12. PARK: Easy. TEL: 01376 570234; fax - 01376 571764. VAT: Stan. *Trade Only, mainly export.*

LEIGH-ON-SEA

K.S. Buchan
135 The Broadway. SS9 1PJ. Open 10-5. *STOCK: Furniture and general antiques.* TEL: 01702 479440.

Collectors' Paradise
993 London Rd. SS9 3LB. (H.W. and P.E. Smith). Est. 1967. Open 10-5.30. CL: Fri. SIZE: Small. *STOCK: Clocks, 1830-1930, from £85; bric-a-brac; postcards, 1900-1930s; cigarette cards, 1889-1939.* LOC: On A13. PARK: Easy. TEL: 01702 473077.

Deja Vu Antiques
876 London Rd. SS9 3NQ. (Stuart D. Lewis). Est. 1990. Open 9.30-5.30. SIZE: Medium. *STOCK: French and English furniture, late 18th to 19th C; antique bedsteads and lighting.* PARK: Easy. TEL: 01702 470829; e-mail - info@deja-vu-antiques.co.uk; website - www.deja-vu-antiques.co.uk. SER: Valuations; restorations. FAIRS: Newark and Ardingly.

Pall Mall Antiques
104c/d Elm Rd. SS9 1SQ. (R. and J. Webb). EADA. Open 10-5. CL: Wed. SIZE: Large. *STOCK: Porcelain, glass, metalware, furniture,*

WEST ESSEX ANTIQUES
Stonehall

Dealer in English and Continental Furniture 18ᵗʰ – 20ᵗʰ C.

e-mail: chris@essexantiques.co.uk

Tel/Fax: 01279 730609

Down Hall Road
Nr. Hatfield Heath
HERTS. CM17 0RA

www.essexantiques.co.uk

Mobile: 07702 492111

15 mins. from M11
15 mins. Stansted Airport
45 mins. London

and collectables. PARK: Own. TEL: 01702 477235; website - www.pallmallantiques.co.uk. FAIRS: Newark.

John Stacey and Sons
86-90 Pall Mall. SS9 1RG. Est. 1946. Open 9-5.30. CL: Sat. pm. *STOCK: General antiques.* TEL: 01702 477051. SER: Valuations; exporters; auctioneers. VAT: Stan.

J. Streamer Antiques
86 Broadway and 212 Leigh Rd. SS9 1AE. Est. 1965. Open 9.30-5.30. CL: Wed. *STOCK: Jewellery, silver, bric-a-brac, small furniture.* TEL: 01702 472895.

Tilly's Antiques
1801 London Rd. SS9 2ST. (S.T. and R.J. Austen). Est. 1972. Open 10-5. CL: Wed. SIZE: Medium. *STOCK: Furniture, 19th C, £100-£500+; Victorian and Edwardian dolls, £100-£500; general antiques, 19th-20th C, £5-£200.* LOC: A13. PARK: Easy. TEL: 01702 557170. SER: Valuations; restorations (furniture and dolls).

MALDON

The Antique Rooms
63D High St. CM9 7EB. (Mrs E. Hedley). Est. 1966. Open 10-4. CL: Wed. SIZE: Medium. *STOCK: Furniture, pottery, porcelain, glass and silver, costume, linen and lace, jewellery, lacemaking equipment, collectors' items.* LOC: Just off High St. PARK: Nearby. TEL: 01621 856985.

Clive Beardall Antiques
104B High St. CM9 5ET. BAFRA, EADA. Est. 1982. Open 8-5.30, Sat 8-4. SIZE: Medium. *STOCK: Furniture, 18th-19th C, £100-£5,000.* LOC: Off High St. up alleyway between Just Fabrics and Peter Foulkes. PARK: Easy. TEL: 01621 857890; fax - 01621 850753; website - www.clivebeardall.co.uk. SER: Restorations (furniture). VAT: Stan/Spec.

Maldon Antiques and Collectors Market
All Saints Church Hall, London Rd. CM9. (Rita Willson). Est. 1975. Open first Sat. every month 9-4. *STOCK: Jewellery, gold and silver, medals and badges, all Victoriana, unusual items.* LOC: Top of High St., opposite Police Station. PARK: Own. TEL: 01702 230746.

MANNINGTREE

Antiques
49 High St. CO11 1AH. (A. Patterson). Open 10-1 and 2-5. *STOCK: General and country antiques.* PARK: Easy. TEL: 01206 396170.

MATCHING GREEN, Nr. Harlow

West Essex Antiques (Stone Hall)
Downhall Rd. CM17 0RA. Est. 1982. Open 9-5, Sat and Sun. by appointment. SIZE: Warehouse. *STOCK: English and Continental furniture, 18th-20th C, £100-£3,000.* LOC: Turning off A1060 at Hatfield Heath. PARK: Own. TEL: 01279 730609; e-mail - chris@essexantiques.co.uk; website - www.essexantiques.co.uk. VAT: Stan.

NEWPORT, Nr. Saffron Walden

Newport Gallery
High St. CB11 3QZ. (W. Kemp and E.C. Hitchcock). Open 9.30-5. CL: Mon. *STOCK: Watercolours, prints and oils.* LOC: On B1383, two miles from Saffron Walden. PARK: At rear. TEL: 01799 540623. SER: Framing.

Omega
High St. CB11 3PF. (Tony Phillips and Sybil Hooper). Est. 1982. Open 10-6, Sat. 10-5.30. CL: Thurs. SIZE: Small. *STOCK: Furniture and lighting, 1880-1960, £20-£1,000; jewellery,*

objects, 1900-1960, £20-£300. LOC: B1383. PARK: Easy. TEL: 01799 540720; home - same. SER: Valuations; restorations (furniture including French polishing, repairs and re-veneering). FAIRS: Art Deco - Battersea, Brighton, Tunbridge Wells.

RAYLEIGH

F.G. Bruschweiler (Antiques) Ltd
41-67 Lower Lambricks. SS6 8DA. LAPADA. Est. 1963. Open 9-5, Sat. by appointment. SIZE: Warehouses. *STOCK: Furniture, 18th-19th C.* LOC: A127 to Weir roundabout through Rayleigh High St. and Hockley Rd., first left past cemetery, then second left, warehouse round corner on left. PARK: Easy. TEL: 01268 773761/773932; home - 0162 182 8152; fax - 01268 773318; e-mail - info@fgbantiques.com; website - www.fgbantiques.com . VAT: Stan.

ROXWELL, Nr. Chelmsford

Freemans Antiques
CM1 4NJ. By appointment only. *STOCK: 17th-18th C oak especially coffers.* TEL: 01245 231286.

SAFFRON WALDEN

Bush Antiques
26-28 Church St. CB10 1JQ. (Mrs J.M. Hosford). EADA. Est. 1962. Open 10.30-4.30. CL: Thurs. SIZE: Medium. *STOCK: English ceramics including blue and white transfer printed pottery, copper lustre and pink lustre, £25-£250; mahogany and country furniture, to £1,000; copper and brass, to £250; all 1800-1860.* LOC: 300 yards north of Market Sq., on crossroads with Museum St. PARK: Nearby. TEL: 01799 523277.

Ickleton Antiques
4A Gold St. CB10 1EJ. (B. Arbery). Est. 1983. Open 10-4, Mon. 10-3, Sat. 10-5. SIZE: Small. *STOCK: Militaria including badges, medals and weapons; advertising and packaging, postcards.* LOC: Just off centre of town. PARK: Nearby. TEL: 01799 513114; home - 01799 527474. SER: Valuations.

The Interior Design Shop
4 & 5 Rose & Crown Walk. CB10 1JH. (Peter Mileham). Est. 1981. Open 9-5. *STOCK: Victorian mahogany, £200-£3,000; upholstered items, Georgian to 1930's, £300-£2,000; oak and early mahogany, 1790-1900, £300-£2,000.* TEL: 01799 516456; fax - 01799 516699. SER: Valuations; restorations; interior design. VAT: Stan/Spec.

Lankester Antiques and Books
Old Sun Inn, Church St., and Market Hill. CB10 1JW. (P. Lankester). Est. 1965. Open 10-5. SIZE: Large. *STOCK: Furniture, porcelain, pottery, metalwork, general antiques, books, prints and maps.* TEL: 01799 522685. VAT: Stan

Littlebury Antiques - Littlebury Restorations Ltd
58/60 Fairycroft Rd. CB10 1LZ. (N.H. D'Oyly). Est. 1962. Open 9-5. CL: Sat. and Sun. except by appointment. SIZE: Medium. *STOCK: Barometers, marine antiques, chess sets, walking sticks and curios.* PARK: Easy. TEL: 01799 527961; fax - same; home - 01279 771530. SER: Valuations; restorations; buys at auction. VAT: Stan/Spec.

Maureen Morris   BADA
CB11 4TA. LAPADA. Open by appointment. *STOCK: Samplers, needleworks, textiles.* TEL: 01799 521338; fax - 01799 522802; e-mail - mm @antiqueembroidery.com.

Saffron Walden Antiques Centre
1 Market Row. CB10 1HA. Est. 1996. Open 10-5.30, Sat. 9-5.30, Sun. 11-5. SIZE: Large - 50+ dealers. *STOCK: Wide range of general antiques.* LOC: Town centre. PARK: Easy. TEL: 01799 524534; fax - 01799 524703.

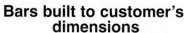

SHENFIELD

The Chart House

33 Spurgate, Hutton Mount. CM13 2JS. (C.C. Crouchman). Est. 1974. Open by appointment only. SIZE: Small. *STOCK: Nautical items.* PARK: Easy. TEL: 01277 225012; home - same. SER: Hire of nautical items and equipment; buys at auction.

SIBLE HEDINGHAM, Nr. Halstead

Hedingham Antiques & Interiors

100 Swan St. CO9 3HP. (P. Patterson). EADA. Est. 1978. Open 1-5, Sat. 10-4, other times by appointment. SIZE: Small. *STOCK: Mainly silver, some plate, china and glass, small furniture.* LOC: On A1017, village centre. PARK: Forecourt. TEL: 01787 460360; home - same; fax - 01787 469109; e-mail - patriciapatterson@ totalise.co.uk; website - www.hedingham antiques. co.uk. SER: Repairs (silver, including re-plating); restorations (furniture).

Lennard Antiques

c/o W.A. Pinn & Sons, 124 Swan St. CO9 3HP. LAPADA. Est. 1978. Open 9.30-6. *STOCK: Oak and country furniture, 17th to early 19th C; English Delftware.* LOC: On A1017 opposite Shell garage in middle of village. PARK: Easy. TEL: 01787 461127. FAIRS: Chelsea; West London; Olympia (June); Harrogate.

W.A. Pinn and Sons   BADA

124 Swan St. CO9 3HP. (K.H. and W.J. Pinn). LAPADA. Est. 1943. Open 9.30-6. CL: Sun. except by appointment. SIZE: Medium. *STOCK: Furniture, 17th to early 19th C, £100-£5,000; Chinese export porcelain, £25-£1,000; interesting items, prior to 1830, £10-£1,500.* LOC: On A1017 opposite Shell Garage. PARK: Easy. TEL: 01787 461127. FAIRS: Chelsea (Spring and Autumn); Olympia (June); Harrogate. VAT: Stan/Spec.

SOUTHEND-ON-SEA

Curio City

Chartwell North, Upper Level, Victoria Plaza Shopping Centre. SS2 5SP. (T.W. Cornforth). Est. 1996. Open 10-5, Sat. 9-5. SIZE: Large - 80 dealers. *STOCK: 18th-20th C furniture, Oriental items, ceramics and collectables.* LOC: Town centre. PARK: Nearby multi-storey. TEL: 01702 611350; fax - 01702 710383; website - www.ridge web.co.uk.

Lonsdale Antiques

86 Lonsdale Rd, Southchurch. SS2 4LR. (H. M. Clark). Est. 1980. Open 9-5.30. CL: Wed. *STOCK: Jewellery, pictures, porcelain, general small antiques.* PARK: Easy. TEL: 01702 462643.

STANSTED

Harris Antiques (Stansted)

40 Lower St. CM24 8LR. (F.A.D. and B.D.A. Harris and E.V. Bradshaw). Resident. BAFRA. EADA. Est. 1956. Open 9-5, Sun. by appointment only. SIZE: Medium. *STOCK: Quality period furniture, ceramics and clocks, 16th-19th C, £200-£20,000+.* LOC: Near M11 and Stansted Airport. PARK: Easy. TEL: 01279 812233; home - same. SER: Valuations; restorations (furniture and ceramics). VAT: Spec.

Linden House Antiques

3 Silver St. CM24 8HA. (A.W. and K.M. Sargeant). Est. 1961. Open 9-5.30. CL: Sun. except by appointment. SIZE: Large. *STOCK: English furniture, 18th-19th C, £100-£10,000; small decorative items, including library and dining room furniture.* LOC: A11. TEL: 01279 812372. VAT: Spec.

Valmar Antiques   BADA

Croft House Cottage, High Lane. CM24 8LQ. (John and Marina Orpin). LAPADA. Resident. Est. 1960. Open by appointment. SIZE: Large. *STOCK: Furniture and decorative items including Arts and Crafts items, £50-£10,000.* TEL: 01279 813201; fax - 01279 816962; mobile - 07831 093701; e-mail - valmar-antiques@ cwcom. net. FAIRS: Major British.

STOCK

Sabine Antiques

38 High St. CM4 9BW. (C.E. Sabine). EADA. Est. 1969. Open 10-5 or by appointment. CL: Mon. *STOCK: Furniture, from £50; china and glass, from £5.* LOC: Village centre on B1007. PARK: Easy. TEL: 01277 840553; fax - 01277 840871. SER: Valuations; restorations (furniture); silver plating; framing.

WESTCLIFF-ON-SEA

It's About Time

863 London Rd. SS0 9SZ. (R. and V. Alps and P. Williams). EADA. Est. 1980. Open 9-5.30. SIZE: Large. *STOCK: Clocks, 18th-19th C, £200-£5,000; barometers, Victorian and Edwardian*

furniture. LOC: A13. PARK: Easy. TEL: 01702 472574; fax - same; home - 01702 205204; e-mail - shop@antiqueclock.co.uk; website - www. antiqueclock.co.uk.

Ridgeway Antiques
66 The Ridgeway. SS0 8NU. (Trevor Cornforth and Charles Jackson). EADA. Est. 1987. Open 10.30-5. SIZE: Small. *STOCK: General antiques, £5-£1,000.* LOC: A13 London road, right at Chalkwell Ave., right to The Ridgeway. PARK: Easy. TEL: 01702 710383. SER: Valuations. FAIRS: Ridgeway and Hallmark.

WHITE COLNE, Nr. Colchester

Fox and Pheasant Antique Pine
CO6 2PS. (J. and J.Kearin). Est. 1978. Open 8-6. SIZE: Small. *STOCK: Stripped pine.* LOC: A604. PARK: Easy. TEL: 01787 223297. SER: Pine stripping; restorations; kitchens; joinery.

WHITE RODING, Nr. Dunmow

White Roding Antiques
'Ivydene', Chelmsford Rd. CM6 1RG. (F. and J. Neill). Est. 1971. Open by appointment. SIZE: Medium. *STOCK: Furniture and shipping goods, 18th-19th C, £10-£1,500.* LOC: A1060 between Bishops Stortford and Chelmsford. PARK: Easy. TEL: 01279 876376; home - same. VAT: Stan/Spec.

WICKHAM BISHOPS

Barling Fine Porcelain Ltd
(S. Parish). Open by appointment only. *STOCK: English porcelain including Royal Worcester, £100-£12,000; watercolours, £300-£2,500.* TEL: 01621 890058; e-mail - stuart@barling.uk.com; website - www.barling.uk.com. FAIRS: Wakefield Ceramic; NEC.

WOODFORD GREEN

Galerie Lev
1 The Broadway. IG8 0HL. Open 10-5. *STOCK: Oils, watercolours, collectors' items, silver plate, porcelain.* LOC: Near Woodford underground station. TEL: 020 8505 2226. SER: Framing (Trade only).

Mill Lane Antiques
29 Mill Lane. IG8 0NG. (Niki Wood and Bonnita Read). Open Tues. and Sun. SIZE: Medium.

STOCK: French lighting, furniture and Venetian mirrors. TEL: 020 8502 9930; fax - same; mobile - 07980 419956. SER: Valuations; restorations. FAIRS: Kempton Park.

WRITTLE, Nr. Chelmsford

Whichcraft Jewellery
54-56 The Green. CM1 3DU. (A. Turner). EADA. Est. 1978. Open 9.30-5.30. CL: Mon. SIZE: Small. *STOCK: Jewellery, silver and watches, 19th C, £30-£5,000.* PARK: Easy. TEL: 01245 420183; fax - 01245 420030. SER: Valuations; restorations (jewellery). VAT: Stan/Spec.

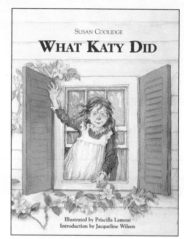

Denzil Verey Antiques

Barnsley House,
Barnsley, near Cirencester,
Gloucestershire. GL7 5EE
Tel: 01285 740402

*18th and 19th century country furniture,
pine, treen, and unusual items*

ANDOVERSFORD, Nr. Cheltenham

Julian Tatham-Losh
Brereton House, Stow Rd. GL54 4JN. (Julian and Patience Tatham-Losh). Resident. Est. 1980. Open Mon.-Fri. 8-6, at any other time by appointment. SIZE: Large. *STOCK: 19th C decorative smalls, bamboo and interesting furniture, majolica, flow blue, Staffordshire figures and animals, boxes and caddies, candlesticks, decorative glass, primitive and folk art items, kitchenalia, mirrors, desk-related items, brass and copper, luggage, £2-£10,000.* Not Stocked: Reproductions and jewellery. LOC: From A40 Oxford to Cheltenham road take A436 to Stow-on-the-Wold, premises first house on left. PARK: Own large. TEL: 01242 820646; fax - 01242 820563; mobile - 07850 574924; e-mail - JTL Antiques@onetel.net.uk. SER: Antique and decorative items supplied to order, especially repeat bulk shipping items; courier (air-conditioned transport); free storage. FAIRS: NEC; Newark. VAT: Stan/Spec. *Trade & Export Only.*

BARNSLEY, Nr. Cirencester

Denzil Verey
Barnsley House. GL7 5EE. CADA. Resident. Est.

1980. Open 9.30-5.30, Sat. 10-5.30, other times by appointment. SIZE: Large. *STOCK: Country furniture, including pine, 18th-19th C; decorative and unusual items, treen, copper, brass, domestic and rural objects, kitchenalia.* LOC: 4 miles from Cirencester on B4425 to Burford, 1st large house in village, set back off road on the right. PARK: Easy. TEL: 01285 740402; fax - 01285 740628. VAT: Stan/Spec.

BERKELEY

Berkeley Antiques Market
GL13 9BP. Open 9.30-1 and 2-5. CL: Mon. SIZE: Large - 10 dealers. *STOCK: General antiques, oak, mahogany, pine, linen and smalls, £1-£1,000.* LOC: Village centre, 1 mile from A38. PARK: Easy. TEL: 01453 511032.

Peter and Penny Proudfoot
16-18 High St. GL13 9BJ. FATG. Est. 1956. Open 9-6, Sun. by appointment. SIZE: Small. *STOCK: Furniture, 1600-1900, £100-£3,000; silver, 1700 to date, £5-£1,000; pictures, 1800 to date, £20-£3,000.* LOC: Village centre. PARK: Easy. TEL: 01453 811513; home - same; fax - 01453 511616; e-mail - BerkPix@aol.com. SER: Valuations; restorations (furniture and oil paintings). VAT: Stan/Spec.

BIBURY, Nr. Cirencester

Mill Antiques of Bibury
Arlington Mill. GL7 5NL. Est. 1999. Open 7 days from 9 am. *STOCK: Antiques, collectables, oils and prints.* PARK: Easy. TEL: 01285 740199; mobile - 07788 681998.

BISHOPS CLEEVE, Nr. Cheltenham

Cleeve Picture Framing
Church Rd. GL52 8RL. (J. Gardner). Open 9-1 and 2-5.30, Sat. 9-1. *STOCK: Prints and pictures.* TEL: 01242 672785. SER: Framing, cleaning, restoring (oils, watercolours and prints).

The Priory Gallery
The Priory, Station Rd. GL52 4HH. (R.M. and E. James). Est. 1977. SIZE: Large. *STOCK: British and European watercolours and oils, late 19th-20th C, £500-£50,000.* LOC: A435. PARK: Easy. TEL: 01242 673226. SER: Buys at auction (as stock). VAT: Stan/Spec.

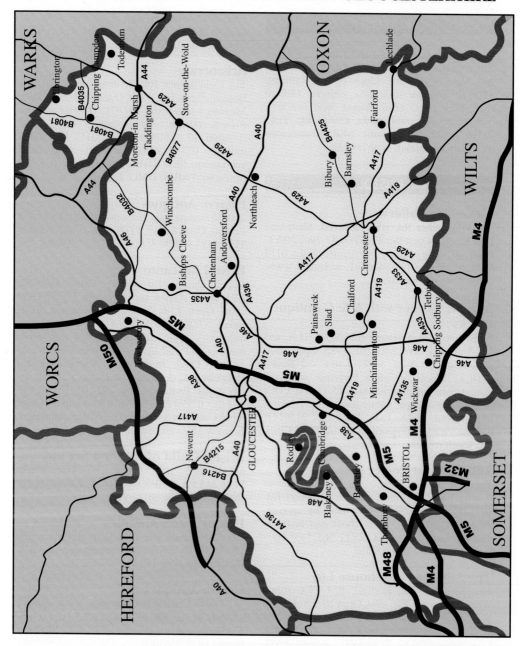

Dealers and Shops in Gloucestershire

Andoversford	1	Chalford	1	Lechlade	3	Stow-on-the-Wold	36
Barnsley	1	Cheltenham	22	Minchinhampton	1	Taddington	1
Berkeley	2	Chipping Campden	6	Moreton-in-Marsh	15	Tetbury	25
Bibury	1	Chipping Sodbury	1	Newent	1	Tewkesbury	3
Bishops Cleeve	2	Cirencester	12	Northleach	3	Thornbury	1
Blakeney	1	Ebrington	1	Painswick	1	Todenham	1
Bristol	29	Fairford	3	Rodley	1	Wickwar	1
Cambridge	1	Gloucester	3	Slad	1	Winchcombe	6

GLOUCESTERSHIRE

BLAKENEY

Lion, Witch and Lampshade

Birmingham House, High St. GL15 4EB. (Mr. and Mrs. N. Dixon). Open by appointment. *STOCK: Unusual decorative objects, 18th to early 20th C, £5-£150; lamps, wall brackets, chandeliers and candlesticks, £50-£1,000.* TEL: 01594 516422; fax - same. SER: Restorations (porcelain and glass); lamp rewiring.

BRISTOL

Alexander Gallery

122 Whiteladies Rd. BS8 2RP. (P.J. Slade and H.S. Evans). Open 9-5.30. *STOCK: 19th-20th C paintings, watercolours and prints.* TEL: 0117 9734692; fax - 0117 9466991; website - www. alexander-gallery.co.uk.

Antique Corner with A & C Antique Clocks

86 Bryants Hill, Hanham. BS5 8QT. (D.A. and J.P. Andrews). BWCMG. Est. 1985. Open 10-4. CL: Mon. and Wed. SIZE: Large - 2 floors. *STOCK: Clocks including longcase, wall and mantel; furniture and ceramics, £5-£5,000.* LOC: Next to The Trooper public house, A431 Bristol to Bath road. PARK: Easy. TEL: 0117 9476141; website - www.antiquecorner.org.uk. SER: Clock and watch repairs.

Antique Four-Poster Beds

The Old Stables, Kennel Lodge Rd., Bower Ashton. BS3 2JT. (Simon and Alicia Poyntz). Est. 1973. Open Mon.-Fri., other times by appointment. *STOCK: Four-poster beds and bedposts and half-tester beds.* TEL: 0117 9632563; fax - same; mobile - 07074 632563.

The Antiques Warehouse Ltd

430 Gloucester Rd., Horfield. BS7 8TX. (Chris Winsor). Resident. Est. 1994. Open 10-6, Sun. 12-4. SIZE: Large. *STOCK: Furniture, 18th to early 20th C, £200-£2,500; mirrors, from 19th C, £60-£1,000; rugs, from 19th C, £150-£600; lighting £100-£1,000.* LOC: On the A38 4 miles from M4/M5 interchange, 2 miles from city centre. PARK: Easy. TEL: 0117 942 4500; fax - 0117 942 4140; mobile - 07785 532173; e-mail - theantiqueswarehouseltd .co.uk. SER: Valuations; restorations (furniture and upholstery). VAT: Stan/Spec.

Arcadia Antiques

4 Boyces Ave., Clifton. BS8 4AA. Est. 1993. Open 10-5.30. CL: Mon. SIZE: Small. *STOCK: General antiques including sofas and chairs, paintings, jewellery and decorative items, £5-£2,500.* LOC: Near The Mall. TEL: 01179 144479; fax - 01179 239308

Aristocratz

115 Coldharbour Rd., Redland. BS6 7SD. (Z. Bouyamourn). Est. 1980. Open 9.30-5.30. SIZE: Medium + warehouse. *STOCK: General antiques, French, Islamic and decorative items.* LOC: Junction 17, M4/M5. TEL: 0117 904 0091; mobile - 07770 393020; e-mail - aristocratz@ yahoo.com. SER: Deliveries arranged (UK and overseas). FAIRS: DMG; Exeter.

Bizarre Antiques

210 Gloucester Rd., Bishopston. BS7 8NZ. (E.J. Parkin). Open 8.15-5. *STOCK: General antiques.* TEL: 0117 9427888; home - 0117 9503498.

Bristol Brocante

123 St. Georges Rd., College Green, Hotwells. BS1 5UW. (David and Elizabeth Durant). Est. 1966. Open 12-6, Sun. by appointment. SIZE: Small. *STOCK: 19th-20th C French decorative antiques - small furniture, crystal and brass, hanging and wall lights and unusual items, £20-£1,000.* LOC: Junction of Anchor Rd. and Hotwells Rd., 3 minutes walk from library and city centre. PARK: Meters. TEL: 0117 909 6688; mobile - 07790 253139. SER: Restorations (small repairs and brass cleaning). FAIRS: Kensington Brocante, Newark, Sandown Park, Ardingly.

Bristol Guild of Applied Art Ltd

68/70 Park St. BS1 5JY. Est. 1908. Open 9-5.30, Mon. and Sat. 9.30-5.30. *STOCK: Furniture, late 19th-20th C.* TEL: 0117 9265548.

Bristol Trade Antiques

192 Cheltenham Rd. BS6 5RB. (L. Dike). Est. 1970. SIZE: Large and warehouse. *STOCK: General antiques.* TEL: 0117 9422790.

Cleeve Antiques

282 Lodge Causeway, Fishponds. BS16 3RD. (T. and S.E. Scull). Est. 1978. Open 9-5.30. *STOCK: Furniture and bric-a-brac.* TEL: 0117 9658366; home - 0117 9567008.

Cotham Antiques

1c Pitville Place, 39 Cotham Hill. BS6 6JZ. (Susan Miller and Cornelius Cummins). Open 10.30-5.30. CL: Mon. SIZE: Small. *STOCK: Jewellery, 1800 to designer modern, £50-£500; ceramics, 19th C to Art Deco, £100-£300; small furniture, 19th to early 20th C, £100-£500.* LOC: Off Whiteladies Rd from Clifton - turn left at Whiteladies shopping centre. PARK: Limited. TEL: 0117 973 3326. SER: Valuations; buys at auction.

Cotham Galleries
22 Cotham Hill, Cotham. BS6 6LF. (D. Jury). Est. 1960. Open 9-5.30. SIZE: Small. *STOCK: Furniture, glass, metal.* LOC: From city centre up Park St. into Whiteladies Rd. Turn right at Clifton Down station. PARK: Easy. TEL: 0117 9736026. SER: Valuations.

Cotham Hill Bookshop
39A Cotham Hill, Cotham. BS6 6JY. (R. Plant). Open 9.30-5. *STOCK: Antiquarian and second-hand books especially fine art; antiquarian prints.* TEL: 0117 9732344.

Dusk 'til Dawn
188 Cheltenham Rd. BS6 5RB. Open Tues.-Sat. 10-5. *STOCK: Antique and traditional bedsteads, iron, brass and wood.* TEL: 0117 944 2388.

Flame and Grate
159 Hotwells Rd., Hotwells. BS8 4RU. Open 9-5. *STOCK: Original cast-iron fireplaces, marble surrounds and fireplace accessories.* PARK: Easy. TEL: 0117 9252560/9292930.

Focus on the Past
25 Waterloo St.,Clifton. BS8 4BT. (K. Walker and A. Roylance). Est. 1976. Open 9.30-5.30, Sat. 9.30-6, Sun. 11-5. SIZE: Large. *STOCK: 19th-20th C furniture including mahogany, country, pine, French, English; ceramics, kitchenalia, glass, silver, plate, jewellery, to £1,000+.* LOC: Off Princess Victoria St. PARK: Nearby. TEL: 0117 973 8080. FAIRS: Shepton Mallet, Newark.

Grey-Harris and Co
12 Princess Victoria St., Clifton. BS8 4BP. Est. 1963. Open 9.30-5.30. *STOCK: Jewellery, Victorian; silver, old Sheffield plate.* TEL: 0117 9737365. SER: Valuations. VAT: Stan/Spec.

Chris Grimes Militaria
13 Lower Park Row. BS1 5BN. Open 11-5.30. *STOCK: Militaria, scientific instruments, nautical items.* TEL: 0117 9298205.

Kemps
9 Carlton Court, Westbury-on-Trym. BS9 3DF. Open 9-5.30. *STOCK: Jewellery.* TEL: 0117 9505090.

Robert Mills Architectural Antiques Ltd
Narroways Rd., Eastville. BS2 9XB. Est. 1969. Open 9.30-5. CL: Sat. SIZE: Large. *STOCK: Architectural items, panelled rooms, shop interiors, Gothic Revival, stained glass, church woodwork, bar and restaurant fittings, 1750-1920, £50-£30,000.* LOC: Half mile from Junction 2, M32. PARK: Easy. TEL: 0117 9556542; fax - 0117 9558146; e-mail - sales@rmills.co.uk; website - www.rmills.co.uk. VAT: Stan.

Jan Morrison
3 Victorian Arcade, Boyce's Avenue, Clifton. BS8 4AA. Est. 1982. Open Tues.-Sat. 10-5.30. SIZE: Small. *STOCK: Silver, 1750 to date; glass, 18th C to Victorian.* PARK: Victoria Square. TEL: 0117 970 6822; fax - same; home - 0117 924 7995; mobile - 07789 094428; e-mail - jan@artibition.com.

Oldwoods
4 Colston Yard. BS1 5BD. (S. Duck). Open 11-5.30, Sat. 11-4. *STOCK: Victorian and Edwardian furniture, pine and other woods.* TEL: 0117 9299023. SER: Restorations.

Pastimes
23 Lower Park Row. BS1 5BN. (A.H. Stevens). Est. 1970. Open 10.30-1.45 and 2.45-5, Sat. 10.30-5. SIZE: Medium. *STOCK: Militaria and military books, £1-£1,000.* LOC: Opposite Christmas Steps, off Colston St. PARK: Meters. TEL: 0117 929 9330.

Period Fireplaces
The Old Station, Station Rd., Montpelier. BS6 5EE. (John Ashton and Martyn Roberts). Est. 1987. Open daily. SIZE: Medium. *STOCK: Fireplaces, original and reproduction, £100-£1,000.* LOC: Just off Gloucester Rd. PARK: Easy. TEL: 0117 9444449; website - www.periodfireplaces.co.uk. SER: Valuations; restorations; fitting. VAT: Stan.

Potter's Antiques and Coins
60 Colston St. BS1 5AZ. (B.C. Potter). Est. 1965. Open 10.30-5.30. SIZE: Small. *STOCK: Antiquities, 500 B.C. to 1600 A.D., £5-£500; commemoratives, 1770-1953, £4-£300; coins, 500 B.C. to 1967, £1-£100; drinking glasses, 1770-1953, £3-£200; small furniture, from 1837, £10-£200.* LOC: Near top of Christmas Steps, close to city centre. PARK: NCP Park Row. TEL: 0117 9262551. SER: Valuations; buys at auction. VAT: Stan/Spec.

Raw Deluxe
148-150 Gloucester Rd. BS7 5NT. (James Stewart). Est. 1998. Open Thurs., Fri. and Sat. 10-5. SIZE: Small. *STOCK: Georgian and Victorian furniture, general smalls, Art Deco, 1950's-1970's furniture and lights.* LOC: Bishopston, 2 miles from city centre. TEL: 0117 942 6998; fax - 0117 942 6998. FAIRS: Kempton Park; Newark; Swinderby.

Relics - Pine Furniture
109 St. George's Rd., College Green. BS1 5UW. (R. Seville and S. Basey). Est. 1972. Open 10-5.30. SIZE: Large. *STOCK: Victorian style and*

reclaimed pine furniture; nauticalia, model yachts and Harmony Kingdom figurines. LOC: Near cathedral, ½ mile from city centre. PARK: Easy. TEL: 0117 9268453; fax - same. VAT: Stan.

St. Nicholas Markets
The Exchange Hall, Corn St. BS1 1JQ. (Steve Morris). Est. 1975. Open 9.30-5. *STOCK: Wide range of general antiques and collectors' items.* TEL: 0117 9224014.

CAMBRIDGE, Nr. Gloucester

Bell House Antiques
Bell House. GL2 7BD. (G. and J. Hawkins). Resident. Open 10-1 and 2-5. SIZE: Medium. *STOCK: Furniture, shipping goods, stripped pine, small items, bygones, £5-£500.* LOC: Near Slimbridge, on main A38. PARK: Easy. TEL: 01453 890463. SER: Valuations.

CHALFORD

J. and R. Bateman Antiques
Green Court, High St. GL6 8DS. LAPADA. Est. 1975. Open 9-6 or by appointment. *STOCK: Furniture, oak and country, 17th-19th C; decorative items.* PARK: Easy. TEL: 01453 883234. SER: Restorations; cabinet making, rushing and caning. VAT: Stan/Spec.

CHELTENHAM

David Bannister FRGS
26 Kings Rd. GL52 6BG. PBFA. Est. 1963. Open by appointment only. SIZE: Medium. *STOCK: Early maps and prints, 1480-1850, from £25; decorative and topographical prints; atlases and colour plate books.* TEL: 01242 514287; fax - 01242 513890; e-mail - db@antiquemaps.co.uk. SER: Valuations; restorations; lectures; buys at auction. FAIRS: Organiser - Antique Map and Print (Bonnington Hotel). VAT: Stan.

Edward Bradbury and Son
32 High St. GL50 1DZ. (O. Bradbury). Resident. Est. 1986. Open by appointment. SIZE: Small. *STOCK: Works of art, tribal art, furniture, 18th-19th C; books on art reference, monographs on artists and photographers, manuscripts.* PARK: Nearby. TEL: 01242 254952; e-mail - hardenhuish53 @hotmail.com. SER: Valuations. VAT: Spec.

Cheltenham Antique Market
54 Suffolk Rd. GL50 2AQ. (K.J. Shave). Est. 1970. Open 9.30-5.30. SIZE: 14 dealers. *STOCK: General antiques.* TEL: 01242 529812.

Cocoa
9 Clarence Parade. GL50 3NY. (Cara Wagstaff). Est. 1973. Open 10-5. SIZE: Small. *STOCK: Lace, antique wedding dresses and accessories, 19th-20th C, £1-£2,000.* TEL: 01242 233588. SER: Re-creations; restorations (period textiles). VAT: Stan.

Giltwood Gallery
30/31 Suffolk Parade. GL50 2AE. (Mrs G. Butt). Resident. Est. 1992. Open 9-5.30, Sat. 10-5.30. SIZE: Large. *STOCK: Furniture, £500-£1,000; mirrors, £500, all 18th to early 20th C.* PARK: Easy. TEL: 01242 512482; fax - same. SER: Valuations; restorations (upholstery); buys at auction. VAT: Stan/Spec.

Greens of Cheltenham Ltd
15 Montpellier Walk. GL50 1SD. Est. 1946. Open 9-5. CL: Wed. SIZE: Large. *STOCK: Jewels, objets, porcelain and silver, some furniture.* LOC: Conjunction of Promenade and main shopping centre. PARK: Easy. TEL: 01242 512088; e-mail - steve@greensofcheltenham. co.uk. SER: Buys at auction. VAT: Stan/Spec.

Latchford Antiques
203 London Rd., Charlton Kings. GL52 6HX. (K. and R. Latchford). Est. 1985. Open 10-5.30. SIZE: Medium. *STOCK: Furniture, china, glass and objets d'art, 18th-19th C, £5-£2,000.* LOC: 2 miles from Cheltenham, on A40 towards London at Sixways Shopping Centre, on right. PARK: Easy. TEL: 01242 226263.

The Loquens Gallery
3 Montpellier Avenue. GL50 1SA. Est. 1992. Open 10.15-5, Sat. 10.15-5.30. SIZE: Small. *STOCK: 18th-20th C watercolours and some oils.* LOC: Adjacent to The Queens Hotel. PARK: Nearby. TEL: 01242 254313; e-mail - stephen @loquensgallery.co.uk. SER: Valuations: framing; restorations.

Manor House Gallery
16 Royal Parade, Bayshill Rd. GL50 3AY. (Geoff Hassell). Resident. Open anytime by appointment. *STOCK: Oils and watercolours, £200-£2,000; prints, under £100; all 20th C.* LOC: Central. PARK: Easy. TEL: 01242 228330; home - same; fax - 01242 228328; e-mail - geoff@ manorhousegallery.net; website - www.manor housegallery.net. SER: Valuations; restorations (oils). VAT: Stan/spec.

Martin and Co. Ltd
19 The Promenade. GL50 1LP. (I.M. and N.C.S. Dimmer). Est. 1890. *STOCK: Silver, Sheffield plate, jewellery, objets d'art.* TEL: 01242 522821; fax - 01242 570430. VAT: Stan/Spec.

Montpellier Clocks   **BADA**
13 Rotunda Terrace, Montpellier. GL50 1SW. (B. Bass and T. Birch). Open 9-5.30. *STOCK: Clocks, 17th-19th C; barometers.* LOC: Close to Queens Hotel. PARK: Easy. TEL: 01242 242178; fax - same. SER: Repairs and restorations by West Dean/BADA Dip. conservator.

Patrick Oliver
4 Tivoli St. GL50 2UW. LAPADA. Est. 1896. SIZE: Large. *STOCK: Furniture and shipping goods.* PARK: Easy. TEL: 01242 519538. VAT: Stan/Spec.

Eric Pride Oriental Rugs
44 Suffolk Rd. GL50 2AQ. Est. 1980. Open by appointment only. SIZE: Medium. *STOCK: Rugs and carpets, £100-£4,000; kilims, £300-£2,000; saddle-bags and horse covers, £150-£800; all 19th to early 20th C.* LOC: A40 near Cheltenham College. PARK: Nearby. TEL: 01242 580822 (answerphone); fax - 01242 700549; e-mail - ericpride@hotmail.com; website - www.antique orientalrugs.co.uk. SER: Valuations; restorations (cleaning and repairs).

Q & C Militaria
22 Suffolk Rd. GL50 2AQ. (J.F. and B.M. Wright). OMRS, MCCOFI, BACSEA. Est. 1970. Open 10-5. CL: Mon. SIZE: Medium. *STOCK: Military memorabilia - British orders, decorations and medals; military drums, edged weapons, cap badges.* LOC: A40 ring road. PARK: At rear, off Old Bath Rd. TEL: 01242 519815; fax - same; mobile - 07778 613977; e-mail - john@qc-militaria.freeserve.co.uk; website - www.qcmilitaria.com. SER: Valuations; restorations (drums and military equipment); framing and mounting (medals); buys at auction. FAIRS: OMRS Convention, Aldershot, Yate, Stratford-upon-Avon; Aldershot Collectors (Farnham).

Michael Rayner
11 St. Luke's Rd. GL53 7JQ. Open 10-6, other times by appointment. CL: Mon. and Tues. *STOCK: Books, antiquarian and secondhand.* PARK: Nearby. TEL: 01242 512806.

Scott-Cooper Ltd   **BADA**
52 The Promenade. GL50 1LY. Est. 1912. *STOCK: Silver, plate, jewellery, clocks, ivory, enamel, objets de vertu.* TEL: 01242 522580. SER: Restorations and repairs (silver and jewellery). VAT: Stan/Spec.

Catherine Shinn Decorative Textiles
7 Suffolk Parade. GL50 2AB. (Catherine Shinn). Open 10-5. SIZE: Small. *STOCK: Antique tapestry cushions, hangings, bell pulls; passe menterie and upholstery pieces, old curtains and table covers, toile.* PARK: Suffolk Sq. TEL: 01242 574546; fax - 01242 578495. SER: Valuations; restorations; buys at auction (European textiles). VAT: Stan.

Sixways Antique Centre
199 London Rd., Charlton Kings. GL52 6HU. Est. 1984. Open 9.30-5.30. SIZE: Large - 11 dealers. *STOCK: General antiques, pine, painted furniture, china, glass, prints, silver, plate, linen, flatware and collectibles, £5-£1,000.* LOC: On A40. PARK: Easy. TEL: 01242 510672.

Tapestry
33 Suffolk Parade. GL50 2AE. Open 10-5.30. SIZE: Medium. *STOCK: Antique and decorative furniture and objects including soft furnishings, garden items, mirrors and lighting.* LOC: 10 mins. walk from The Promenade. PARK: Easy. TEL: 01242 512191.

John P. Townsend
Ullenwood Park Farm, Ullenwood. GL53 9QX. Est. 1969. Open 9-5. CL: Sat. SIZE: Medium. *STOCK: Furniture - stripped pine, country and shipping, to 1940's; books and bric-a-brac.* LOC: 4 miles from Cheltenham. PARK: Easy. TEL: 01242 870169; home - 01242 870223.

Triton Gallery
27 Suffolk Parade. GL50 2AE. (L. Bianco). Resident. Est. 1984. Open 9-5.30, other times by appointment. *STOCK: Period furniture, 18th C paintings, mirrors and lighting.* TEL: 01242 510477.

A rare Staffordshire sign language mug which sold for £300 to a collector.

From an Auction Report by Christopher Wight on Glass, European and Oriental Ceramics and Works of Art at Woolley and Wallis, Salisbury, 28th November 2001 which appeared in the February 2002 issue of **Antique Collecting**. For more details and to subscribe see page 21.

Peter Ward Fine Paintings
Nothill Cowley. GL53 9NJ. Est. 1972. Open 9-5. *STOCK: 17th-19th C paintings.* TEL: 01242 870178; mobile - 07979 857347; website - www. coriniumfinepaintings.co.uk. SER: Valuations; restorations; framing. VAT: Spec.

CHIPPING CAMPDEN

Antique Heritage
High St. GL55 6AT. (D.B. Smith). Est. 1981. Open 10-5, Sun. 11-4. SIZE: Small. *STOCK: Small items, china, porcelain, tables, boxes, Georgian and Victorian, £15-£400.* LOC: Village centre. PARK: Easy. TEL: 01386 840727.

Cottage Farm Antiques
Cottage Farm, Aston sub Edge. GL55 6PZ. (A.E. and E.A. Willmore). Est. 1986. Open 8.30-5.30 including Sun. SIZE: Large. *STOCK: Furniture including 19th C wardrobes, 18th-19th C dressers and tables, to £1,500.* LOC: Follow brown tourist signs. PARK: Easy. TEL: 01386 438263; fax and home - same; e-mail - info@cottagefarmantiques. co.uk; website - www.cottagefarm antiques.co.uk. VAT: Stan/Spec.

Ross Hardie
Lower High St. GL55 6AL. Open 10-5. CL: Mon. SIZE: Small. *STOCK: Antique and secondhand jewellery and silver.* PARK: Easy. TEL: 01386 840539; fax - 01386 841902. SER: Valuations. FAIRS: NEC. VAT: Stan/Spec.

School House Antiques
School House, High St. GL55 6HB. (G.and M. Hammond). Est. 1895. Open 9.30-5 including Sun. (June-Sept.). CL: Thurs. (Oct.-May). SIZE: Large. *STOCK: Clocks, 18th-19th C; Georgian and Victorian furniture; works of art, oils and watercolours.* PARK: At rear. TEL: 01386 841474; e-mail - hamatschoolhouse@aol.com; website - www.schoolhouseantiques.co.uk. SER: Restorations; valuations.

Stuart House Antiques
High St. GL55 6HB. (J. Collett). Est. 1985. Open 10-1 and 2-5.30 including Sun. SIZE: Large. *STOCK: China, 19th C; general antiques, from 18th C; all £1-£1,000.* LOC: Opposite market hall. PARK: Easy. TEL: 01386 840995. SER: Valuations; china search; restorations (ceramics).

The Titian Gallery
London House, High St. GL55 6AG. (Ilona Johnson Gibbs). LAPADA. CADA. CINOA. Est. 1976. Open 10-1 and 2-5, Sun. by appointment. SIZE: 2 showrooms. *STOCK: Fine 18th-19th C British and European oil paintings and watercolours, to £40,000.* LOC: Near centre of town square. PARK: Easy. TEL: 01386 841789; fax - 01386 849151; e-mail - ilona@titiangallery.co.uk; website - www. titiangallery.co.uk. SER: Valuations; buys at auction (oils and watercolours). VAT: Spec.

CHIPPING SODBURY, Nr. Bristol

Sodbury Antiques
70 Broad St. BS37 6AG. (Millicent Brown). Est. 1986. CL: Wed. SIZE: Small. *STOCK: Porcelain and china, mainly 18th-19th C; antique and secondhand jewellery, £5-£1,000.* PARK: Easy. TEL: 01454 273369.

CIRENCESTER

Walter Bull and Son (Cirencester) Ltd
10 Dyer St. GL7 2PF. Est. 1815. Open 9-5. SIZE: Small. *STOCK: Silver, from 1700, £50-£3,000; objets d'art.* LOC: Lower end of Market Place. PARK: At rear. TEL: 01285 653875; fax - 01285 641751. VAT: Stan/Spec.

Cirencester Arcade
25 Market Place. GL7 2NX. (M.J. and P.J. Bird). Open Mon.-Sun. SIZE: 70 dealers. *STOCK: General antiques.* TEL: 01285 644214.

Corner Cupboard Curios
2 Church St. GL7 1LE. (P. Larner). *STOCK: General antiques and gramophonalia.* TEL: 01285 655476.

Forum Antiques
Springfield Farm, Perrotts Brook. GL7 7DT. (W. Mitchell). Est. 1986. Open Mon.-Fri. 8.30-5.30 by appointment only. SIZE: Small. *STOCK: Period furniture, pre-1850.* TEL: 01285 831821. SER: Valuations; restorations. VAT: Spec.

Hares
4 Black Jack St. GL7 2AA. (Allan G. Hare). Est. 1972. Open 10-5.30, Sun. by appointment. SIZE: Large. *STOCK: Furniture, especially dining tables and long sets of chairs, 18th to early 19th C, £100-£50,000; upholstery and decorative objects.* LOC: Near Market Square. PARK: Own. TEL: 01285 640077; mobile - 07860 350097; e-mail - hares@star.co.uk; website - www.hares-antiques.com. SER: Restorations; traditional upholstery. VAT: Spec.

Original Architectural
22 Elliott Rd. GL7 1YS. (Andy Hayward and John Rawlinson). Open 9-5, Sun. 9-4. SIZE:

RANKINE TAYLOR ANTIQUES

Interesting collection of 17th, 18th and 19th century furniture, silver, glass and rare associated objects.

34 DOLLAR STREET, CIRENCESTER, GLOS. GL7 2AN
Telephone: 01285 652529
CUSTOMER CAR PARK OPPOSITE

Large. *STOCK: 19th C fireplaces, £160-£550; 17th C oak doors, £350-£750; stone troughs, £500-£1,000, firebacks, £180-£2,000, both 18th C.* LOC: Ermin Farm, opposite 29th Regiment on A419, 1 mile south of Cirencester. PARK: Easy. TEL: 01285 653532; fax - 01285 644383; email - john@originaluk.com. SER: Valuations; restorations (doors, fireplaces); buys at auction.

Parlour Farm Antiques
Unit 12 Wilkinson Rd., Love Lane Industrial Estate. GL7 1YT. (N. Grunfeld). Est. 1995. Open 10-5.SIZE: Large. *STOCK: Eastern European antique pine.* PARK: Easy. TEL: 01285 885336; fax - 01285 885338; e-mail - info@parlourfarm. com; website - www.parlourfarm.com.

Silver Street Antiques and Things
9 Silver St. GL7 2BJ. (S.A. Tarrant). Resident. Est. 1992. Open 10-5. SIZE: Medium. *STOCK: General antiques including small furniture, £1-£1,500.* LOC: Between Corn Hall and museum. PARK: Nearby. TEL: 01285 641600.

William H. Stokes   BADA
The Cloisters, 6/8 Dollar St. GL7 2AJ. (W.H. Stokes and P.W. Bontoft). CADA. Est. 1968. Open 9.30-5.30, Sat. 9.30-4.30. STOCK: Early

oak furniture, £1,000-£30,000; brassware, £150-£5,000; all 16th-17th C. LOC: West of parish church. TEL: 01285 653907; fax - 01285 640533. VAT: Spec.

Rankine Taylor Antiques
34 Dollar St. GL7 2AN. LAPADA. CADA. Est. 1969. Open 9-5.30, Sun. by appointment. SIZE: Large. *STOCK: Furniture, 17th to early 19th C, £300-£35,000; silver, glass, rare and interesting objects.* Not Stocked: Victoriana. LOC: From church, turn right into West Market Place, via Gosditch St. into Dollar St. PARK: Own - private opposite. TEL: 01285 652529; website - www .antiquesnews.co.uk/rankin-taylor. VAT: Spec.

Patrick Waldron Antiques
18 Dollar St. GL7 2AN. Resident. CADA. Est. 1965. Open 9.30-1 and 2-6, Sun. by appointment. SIZE: Medium. *STOCK: Town and country furniture, 17th to early 19th C.* LOC: In street behind church. PARK: Easy and public behind shop. TEL: 01285 652880; home - same; workshop - 01285 643479; e-mail - patrick.waldron @virgin.net. SER: Restorations (furniture); buys at auction. VAT: Stan./Spec.

Blenheim Antiques

AT FAIRFORD

We Sell Town and Country Furniture, Clocks, Pictures and Decorative Objects.

Market Place, Fairford, Glos.
Telephone: 01285 712094
(Easy parking in the Market Place)

Bernard Weaver Antiques

28 Gloucester St. GL7 2DH. Open by appointment. SIZE: Medium. *STOCK: Furniture, mahogany and oak, 18th-19th C.* LOC: Continuation of Dollar St. PARK: Easy. TEL: 01285 652055. SER: Valuations; restorations.

EBRINGTON, Nr. Chipping Campden

John Burton Natural Craft Taxidermy

21 Main St. GL55 6NL. Est. 1973. Open by appointment. SIZE: Medium. *STOCK: Taxidermy - Victorian and Edwardian cased fish, birds and mammals, from £40-£2,500; glass domes, sporting trophies.* LOC: Village centre. PARK: Easy. TEL: 01386 593231; home - same; mobile - 07850 356354. SER: Valuations; restorations (taxidermy); buys at auction (taxidermy).

FAIRFORD

Blenheim Antiques

Market Place. GL7 4AB. (N. Hurdle). CADA. Resident. Est. 1972. Open 9.30-6.30. SIZE: Medium. *STOCK: 18th-19th C furniture and accessories.* PARK: Easy. TEL: 01285 712094. VAT: Stan/Spec.

Mark Carter Antiques

Gloucester House, Market Place. GL7 4AB. Est. 1979. Open 10-5.30 or by appointment. SIZE: Large. *STOCK: English mahogany, oak and fruitwood furniture, 17th-19th C, £500-£10,000.* PARK: Easy - market place. TEL: 01285 712790; mobile - 07836 260567; e-mail - markcarterantiques@ hotmail. com. SER: Valuations. VAT: Stan/Spec.

Anthony Hazledine

Antique Oriental Carpets, High St. GL7 4AD. Est. 1976. Mon., Fri. and Sat. 9-5, other days by appointment. SIZE: Small. *STOCK: Oriental carpets and textiles, 18th-19th C, £150-£4,000.* PARK: Easy. TEL: 01285 713400; home and fax - same. SER: Sales; purchases; restoration and cleaning. VAT: Stan/Spec.

GLOUCESTER

Gloucester Antique Centre

1 Severn Rd. GL1 2LE. Est. 1949. Open 10-5, Sun. 1-5. SIZE: 140 dealers. 50p admission charge weekends and Bank Hols. - Trade free. *STOCK: General antiques - furniture, jewellery, silver, clocks, ceramics, collectables.* LOC: Within the Dock area. PARK: Easy. TEL: 01452 529716; fax - 01452 307161.

Arthur S. Lewis

LAPADA. Est. 1969. By appointment. *STOCK: Mechanical music, automata, clocks.* TEL: 01452 780258; website - www.arthurlewisantiques.com.

Military Curios, HQ84

(The Curiosity Shop), Southgate. GL1 2DX. (B. Williams). Est. 1964. Open 10-6, including Sun. *STOCK: Medals, badges, (3rd Reich specialities), militaria, blazer badges, Govt. surplus, edged weapons, replicas, air weapons; Jaguar - spares, mascots.* LOC: A38, city centre. PARK: 100 yds (Docks). TEL: 01452 556038; fax - 01452 554056. SER: Valuations; medal find, mounting and framing; costume hire; badge-making; mail order.

LECHLADE

Jubilee Hall Antiques Centre

Oak St. GL7 3AY. Open 10-5, Sun. 11-5. SIZE: Large. *STOCK: 18th-19th C furniture, metalwork, prints, pictures, smalls.* LOC: On left 350 yds from town centre going north towards Burford. PARK: Own. TEL: 01367 253777; website - www.jubileehall.co.uk. SER: Shipping. Listed below are the dealers at this centre.

Ark Antiques

Period oak furniture and metalwork.

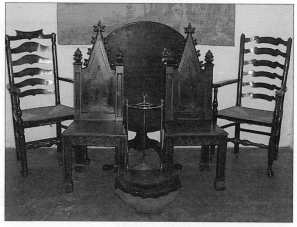
Mandy Barnes
Georgian and Victorian furniture, decorative objects, some textiles.

Keith and Lin Bawden
18th-19th C English furniture, boxes, mirrors, barometers and objects.

John Calgie
Period furniture, mirrors, copper, brass and interesting objects.

Andrew Crawforth
Antique metalwork, treen, glass and unusual items.

Francoise Daniel
Small silver, ivory, shibayama, tortoiseshell, art objects, Tunbridge ware, jewellery and glass.

Marc Drogin
Antiquities, from 2000 years.

Paul Eisler
18th-19th C ceramics, metalware, treen, small furniture, prints and maps.

Peter Gibbons
Period pewter, treen, brass, arms and armour, country furniture.

Maureen Gough
18th-19th C furniture, prints, and decorative objects.

Anita Harris
Porcelain, decorative objects, soft furnishings, small furniture.

Colin and Mary Lee
Glass, porcelain, silver, silhouettes, pottery and objects.

Colin Morris
Country furniture, Staffordshire, brass, copper and period objects.

NAAS Antiques
18th-19th C decorative furnishings, mirrors, pictures, re-upholstered items, Worcester porcelain.

Oak Antiques
(David and Vicky Wilson). Period country oak furniture and metalware.

Clive Payne
LAPADA. Georgian furniture, works of art, blue and white, Masons ironstone.

Mary Pennel
Porcelain, small silver and jewellery.

Judi Pollitt (Times Past)
Ceramics including old blue and white and interesting objects, sewing items.

Red Lane Antiques
(Terry Sparks). 17th-19th C ironwork, treen, copper and brass, Meissen, miniatures, objets d'art.

Lindsey Richardson
Glass, Staffordshire, pottery, porcelain, inkwells.

Keith Robinson
18th-19th C engravings, ceramics, lighting and Japanese and English objects of art.

Jackie & Richard Stent
18th-19th C furniture, prints, pottery, porcelain, chrystoleums, Belleek and small items.

Jollke van den Berg
Antique metalwork and small arms.

Winson Antiques
Georgian and Victorian furniture, lead garden statuary and objects.

Lechlade Arcade
5, 6 and 7 High St. GL7 3AD. (J. Dickson). Est. 1990. Open 9-5 including Sun. SIZE: 40+ dealers. *STOCK: Bric-a-brac, books, furniture (Mexican pine style), collectables, Roman artifacts, militaria, medals, pistols.* PARK: Riverside boat yard. TEL: 01367 252832; mobile - 07949 130875.

The Old Ironmongers Antiques Centre
Burford St. GL7. (Mark A. Serle and Geoff Allen).

Open 10-5 including Sun. *STOCK: Old iron-mongery, £5-£200; furniture including country, £40-£2,000; textiles, £10-£200; Georgian glass, £20-£250; decorative china, £10-£500; treen, £50-£200; militaria including medals, £5-£300; tools and rural implements, £5-£300.* LOC: A361. PARK: Easy. TEL: 01367 252397.

MINCHINHAMPTON, Nr. Stroud

Mick and Fanny Wright
The Trumpet. GL6 9JA. Est. 1979. Open Wed.-Sat. 10.30-5.30. SIZE: Medium. *STOCK: General antiques, decorative items, clocks, furniture, china, silver and plate, 50p-£2,000.* LOC: 200 yards west of crossroads at bottom of High St. PARK: Nearby. TEL: 01453 883027; e-mail - antiques@the trumpet.free-online.co.uk. SER: Valuations. FAIRS: Kempton Park. VAT: Margin.

MORETON-IN-MARSH

Antique Centre
London House, High St. GL56 OAH. Est. 1979. Open 10-5 including Sun. (Sun. 11-5 Nov.-March). SIZE: Large. *STOCK: Furniture, paintings, water-colours, prints, pottery, porcelain (including Chinese), domestic artifacts, clocks, silver, jewellery and plate, mainly 17th-19th C, £5-£3,000.* LOC: Centre of High St. (A429). PARK: Easy. TEL: 01608 651084. VAT: Stan/Spec.

Astley House - Fine Art
Astley House, High St. GL56 0LL. (David, Nanette & Caradoc Glaisyer). LAPADA. CADA. Est. 1973. Open 9-5.30 and by appointment. SIZE: Medium. *STOCK: Oil paintings and botanical watercolours, 19th-21st C, £400-£20,000.* LOC: Main street. PARK: Easy. TEL: 01608 650601; fax - 01608 651777; e-mail - astart333@aol.com; website - www.art-uk.com. SER: Restorations (oils and watercolours); framing. VAT: Spec.

Astley House - Fine Art
Astley House, London Rd. GL56 0LE. (David, Nanette & Caradoc Glaisyer). LAPADA. CADA. Est. 1973. Open 10-1 and 2-5 and by appointment. CL: Wed. SIZE: Large. *STOCK: Oil paintings, 19th-21st C; large decorative oils and portraits.* LOC: Town centre. PARK: Easy. TEL: 01608 650608; fax - 01608 651777; e-mail - astart333@aol.com; website - www.art-uk.com. SER: Restorations (oils and watercolours); porcelain framing. VAT: Spec.

August Antiques and Interiors
3 Fosseway Business Park. GL56 9NQ. (Mike and Maggie Robinson). Open 9.30-5.30, Sun. and other times by appointment. SIZE: Large. *STOCK:*

English and European oak, mahogany and pine furniture, 18th to early 20th C, £100-£5,000; associated items, general antiques and shipping goods. PARK: Easy. TEL: 01608 651515; fax - same; mobile - 07970 429255; e-mail - mike.august antiques@virgin.net. SER: Valuations; restorations.

Benton Fine Art
Regent House, High St. GL56 0AX. (J.G. Benton). LAPADA. Est. 1972. Open 10-5.30, Sun. 11-5.30, Tues. by appointment. SIZE: Large. *STOCK: Paintings, furniture, 18th to early 20th C, £500-£30,000.* PARK: Easy. TEL: 01608 652153; fax - same; mobile - 07885 575139; e-mail - bentonfineart@excite.com. FAIRS: LAPADA; Antiques for Everyone.

Berry Antiques
3 High St. GL56 0AH. (Chris Berry). LAPADA. Est. 1985. Open 10-5.30, Sun. 11-5.30. CL: Tues. SIZE: Medium. *STOCK: Furniture, late 18th to 19th C, £1,000-£15,000; porcelain, £50-£500; paintings, £200-£10,000; both 19th C.* LOC: Near junction with Broadway road. PARK: Easy. TEL: 01608 652929; home - same. SER: Valuations. FAIRS: NEC, LAPADA (NEC). VAT: Spec.

Cox's Architectural Reclamation Yard
Unit 10, Fosseway Industrial Estate. GL56 9NQ. (P. Watson). SALVO. Est. 1991. Open 9-5, Sun. by appointment. SIZE: Large. *STOCK: Architectural antiques, fire surrounds and places, £250-£4,000; doors, £50-£500; all 19th C.* LOC: Just off Fosseway, northern end of Moreton-in-Marsh. PARK: Easy. TEL: 01608 652505; fax - 01608 652881; e-mail - coxs@fsbdial.co.uk. SER: Valuations. VAT: Stan.

Dale House Antiques
High St. GL56 0AD. (N. and A. Allen). Open 10-5.30, Sun. 11-5. SIZE: Large. *STOCK: 17th-19th C town and country furniture, clocks, barometers, pictures, porcelain and pottery, metalwork, objets.* LOC: Main street. PARK: Easy. TEL: 01608 652950; fax - 01608 652424. VAT: Spec.

Jeffrey Formby Antiques   BADA
Orchard Cottage, East St. GL56 0LQ. LAPADA. Resident. Est. 1994. Open by appointment. SIZE: Small. *STOCK: Fine English clocks, pre 1850, £2,000-£15,000; horological books, old and new, £5-£500.* LOC: 100 yards from High St. PARK: Easy. TEL: 01608 650558; website - www.formby-clocks.co.uk. FAIRS: BADA; Olympia; LAPADA (NEC). VAT: Spec.

Jon Fox Antiques
High St. GL56 0AD. CADA. Est. 1982. Open 9.30-5.30, Sun. 11-4, Tues. by appointment.

GARY WRIGHT ANTIQUES LTD TRADE WAREHOUSE

Over 700 pieces of good quality C18th - C19th furniture and unusual objects at trade prices

5 Fosseway Business Park, Stratford Road, Moreton-in-Marsh, Glos. GL56 9NQ

Direct train to London Paddington - 90 mins

Tel/Fax: 01608 652007   Mobile: 07831 653843

Email: info@garywrightantiques.co.uk

SIZE: Large - 2 adjacent shops. *STOCK: 19th C garden items including urns, seats, troughs and tools, £50-£5,000+; 18th -19th C country furniture £300-£3,000; treen, bygones, metalware, fireplace items.* PARK: Easy. TEL: 01608 650325/650714. VAT: Spec.

Grimes House Antiques & Fine Art
High St. GL56 0AT. (S. and V. Farnsworth). FATG. Est. 1978. Open 9.30-1 and 2-5, other times by appointment. *STOCK: Old cranberry and antique coloured glass, fine paintings.* LOC: Town centre. PARK: Free nearby. TEL: 01608 651029; fax - same; e-mail - grimes_house@cix.co.uk; websites - www.grimeshouse.co.uk and www.cranberryglass.co.uk. VAT: Spec/Stan.

Seaford House Antiques
Seaford House, High St. GL56 0AD. (Derek and Kathy Young). LAPADA. CINOA. CADA. Est. 1988. Open 10-5.30, Tues. by appointment. SIZE: Medium. *STOCK: Furniture, 18th C to Edwardian especially upholstered, £500-£5,000; English and Continental porcelain including Worcester, Coalport, Meissen, Sitzendorf, Sampson and Copeland, mirrors and paintings, 19th C, £100-£3,000.* PARK: Easy. TEL: 01608 652423; fax - same. VAT: Spec.

Simply Antiques
at Windsor House Antiques Centre, High St. GL56 0AD. (G. Ellis). Open 10-5, Tues. and Sun. 12-5. *STOCK: Visiting card cases and small period furniture, mainly 18th to early 19th C.* LOC: In large 17th C premises, adjacent town hall. TEL: 01608 650993; e-mail - info@simply-antiques.com; website - www.simply-antiques.com. SER: Finder. FAIRS: NEC. VAT: Spec.

Windsor House Antiques Centre
High St. GL56 0AD. Open 10-5, Tues. and Sun. 12-5. SIZE: 48 dealers. *STOCK: Comprehensive selection of mid-range furniture, from 1650-1914; silver, portrait miniatures, ivory, visiting card cases, French decorative items, English and European porcelain, pottery and glass, objets de vertu, caddies and boxes, brass, copper and pewter.* LOC: Large 17th C premises, adjacent town hall. PARK: Ample. TEL: 01608 650993; fax - 01858 565438; e-mail - windsorhouse@bt internet.com; website - www.windsorhouse.co.uk

Gary Wright Antiques
Unit 5, Fosseway Business Park, Stratford Rd. GL56 9NQ. Est. 1983. Open 9.30-5.30, Sun. by appointment. SIZE: Large. *STOCK: English and Continental furniture, 18th-19th C, £500-£30,000;*

unusual and decorative objects, 17th-20th C, £200-£4,000. LOC: Entrance adjacent to railway bridge on north side of Moreton, on Fosseway (A429). PARK: Easy, TEL: 01608 652007; fax - same; mobile - 07831 653843; e-mail - info@garywright antiques.co.uk; website - www.garywrightantiques. co.uk. SER: Valuations; restorations; buys at auction (furniture). VAT: Stan/Spec.

NEWENT

Jillings Antiques - Distinctive Antique Clocks   BADA
Croft House, 17 Church St. GL18 1PU. (Doro and John Jillings). LAPADA. CINOA. Est. 1986. Open by appointment. *STOCK: 18th-19th C English and Continental clocks including bronze, ormolu, marble and boulle, French, English, longcase and regulators.* PARK: Easy. TEL: 01531 822100; fax - 01531 822666; mobile - 07973 830110; e-mail - clocks@ jillings.com; website - www.jillings.com. SER: Valuations; restorations and repairs; shipping worldwide; free delivery and set up in UK. FAIRS: LAPADA; NEC (Jan); Commonwealth Institute Kensington (April & Oct); BADA (March); Olympia Fine Art and Antiques (June & Nov). VAT: Margin.

NORTHLEACH, Nr. Cheltenham

The Doll's House
Market Place. GL54 3EJ. (Miss Michal Morse). Est. 1971. Open Thurs., Fri. and Sat. 10-5, other times prior telephone call advisable. SIZE: Small. *STOCK: Handmade doll's houses and miniature furniture in one twelfth scale.* LOC: A40. PARK: Easy. TEL: 01451 860431; home and fax - same. SER: Replica houses and special designs to order.

Keith Harding's World of Mechanical Music
The Oak House, High St. GL54 3ET. (K. Harding, FBHI and C.A. Burnett, CMBHI). BHI. Est. 1961. Open 10-6 including Sun. SIZE: Large. *STOCK: Clocks, musical boxes and automata.* PARK: Easy. TEL: 01451 860181; fax - 01451 861133; e-mail - keith@mechanicalmusic.co.uk; website - www.mechanicalmusic.co.uk. SER: Guided tours, demonstrations, and written articles; valuations; restorations (musical boxes, clocks); buys at auction. VAT: Stan/Spec.

Robson Antiques
New Barn Farm, London Rd. GL54 3LX. Est. 1982. Open daily till late. *STOCK: Furniture, from 18th C, £50-£5,000; garden artefacts.* PARK: Easy. TEL: 01451 861071/861006.

PAINSWICK

Nina Zborowska   BADA
Damsels Mill, Paradise. GL6 6UD. Est. 1980. By appointment, except during exhibitions (May-June and Oct.-Nov) 11-5 including Sun. SIZE: Medium. *STOCK: Modern British paintings and drawings, St Ives, Newlyn, NEAC and Bloomsbury schools, 1900-1970, £500-£20,000.* LOC: From Cheltenham towards Stroud on A46, take first turning on left to Sheepscombe. PARK: Easy. TEL: 01452 812460; fax - 01452 812912; e-mail - enquiries@ninazborowska. com; website - www. ninazborowska.com. SER: Valuations; restorations. FAIRS: Art on Paper; 20th/21st C British Art.

RODLEY, Nr. Westbury on Severn

Kelly Antiques
Landeck, Upper Rodley Rd. GL14 1QZ. (G. Kelly). Resident. Always open. *STOCK: Antique pine.* TEL: 01452 760315.

SLAD, Nr. Stroud

Ian Hodgkins and Co. Ltd
Upper Vatch Mill, The Vatch. GL6 7JY. Open by appointment only. *STOCK: Antiquarian books including pre-Raphaelites and associates, the Brontës, Jane Austen; 19th C illustrated, children's art and literature books.* TEL: 01453 764270; fax - 01453 755233; e-mail - i.hodgkins@dial.pipex.com; website - www.ianhodgkins.com.

STOW-ON-THE-WOLD

Ashton Gower Antiques
9/9A Talbot Court, Market Square. GL54 1BQ. (C. Gower and B. Ashton). LAPADA. Est. 1987. Open 10-5. *STOCK: English and Continental furniture, gilt mirrors and decorative accessories, 18th-20th C, £25-£5,000.* LOC: Between the Square and Sheep Street. PARK: Nearby. TEL: 01451 870699; fax - same. SER: Valuations; restorations; buys at auction. VAT: Stan/Spec.

Duncan J. Baggott
Woolcomber House, Sheep St. GL54 1AA. LAPADA. CADA. Est. 1967. Open 9-5.30 or by appointment. SIZE: Large. *STOCK: 17th-20th C English furniture, paintings, domestic metalwork and decorative items; garden statuary and ornaments.* PARK: Sheep St. or Market Sq. TEL: 01451 830662; fax - 01451 832174.

Baggott Church Street Ltd **BADA**
Church St. GL54 1BB. (D.J. and C.M. Baggott). CADA. Est. 1978. Open 9.30-5.30 or by appointment. SIZE: Large. *STOCK: English furniture, 17th-19th C; portrait paintings, metalwork, pottery, treen and decorative items.* LOC: South-west corner of market square. PARK: In market square. TEL: 01451 830370; fax - 01451 832174.

Oonagh Black
Lower Farm House, Coln Rogers. GL54 3LA. (Mr and Mrs Victor Black). LAPADA. Est. 1978. Open by appointment. SIZE: 4 large rooms. *STOCK: Country and French provincial furniture, textiles and related items.* LOC: Just off A429 Fosseway between Cirencester and Stow-on-the-Wold. PARK: Easy. TEL: 01285 720717/720920; fax - 01285 720910; home - 01285 720717; mobile - 07768 568966; e-mail - oonagh @victorblack.co.uk. FAIRS: Olympia; Harvey Decorative; Penman; NEC. VAT: Spec.

Bryden House Clocks & Antiques
Sheep St. GL54 1JS. (J. and D. Hance). Est. 1990. Open 10-5.30, Wed. and Sun. by appointment only. SIZE: Small. *STOCK: Clocks, furniture, barometers, 18th-19th C, £250-£10,000.* LOC: Opposite Unicorn Hotel, junction of Fosseway and Sheep Street. PARK: Opposite. TEL: 01451 832516; home - same. SER: Restorations (clocks and barometers). FAIRS: NEC Antiques for Everyone. VAT: Spec.

Church Street Antiques Centre
3/4 Church St. GL54 1BB. (Mrs G. E. Niner). Est. 1970. Open 9.45-5. SIZE: Medium - 18 dealers. *STOCK: Furniture, 1680-1930, £50-£4,000; pottery especially Staffordshire, porcelain especially 18th C Worcester, silver, metalwork, jewellery, vintage leather, glass, children's furniture and toys.* PARK: Nearby. TEL: 01451 870186. FAIRS: NEC.

Annarella Clark Antiques
11 Park St. GL54 1AQ. Est. 1968. Open 10-5 or by appointment. SIZE: Medium. *STOCK: Wicker and garden, English and French country and painted furniture, needlework, pottery, quilts and decorative objects.* LOC: Park St. leads from Sheep St., 1st right at lights leading into town. PARK: Easy. TEL: 01451 830535; home - same.

Christopher Clarke Antiques Ltd
The Fosseway. GL54 1JS. (I.D., D.S. and S.F. Clarke). LAPADA. CADA. Est. 1961. Open 9.30-5.30 or by appointment. SIZE: Large. *STOCK: Furniture including campaign, 17th-20th C; works of art, metalware, treen, pictures, decorative items,*

animal antiques. LOC: Corner of The Fosseway and Sheep St. PARK: Easy. TEL: 01451 830476; fax - 01451 830300; e-mail - cclarkeantiques @aol.com; website - www. antiques-in-england. com. FAIRS: Olympia (June).

Cotswold Galleries
GL54 1AB. (Richard and Cherry Glaisyer). CADA. Est. 1961. Open 9-5.30 or by appointment. SIZE: Large. *STOCK: Oil paintings especially 19th-20th C landscape.* TEL: 01451 870567; fax - 01451 870678. SER: Restorations; framing.

Country Life Antiques
Grey House, The Square. GL54 1AF. (David and Ann Rosa). Est. 1974. Open 10-5. SIZE: Medium. *STOCK: Scientific instruments, decorative accessories, pewter, brass, copper, furniture; 18th-19th C portraits in oil.* PARK: Easy. TEL: 01451 831564; fax - same.

The John Davies Gallery
Church St. GL54 1BB. CADA. Est. 1977. Open 9.30-1.30 and 2.30-5.30. SIZE: Large. *STOCK: Contemporary and late period paintings; limited edition bronzes.* PARK: In square. TEL: 01451 831698; fax - 01451 832477; e-mail - daviesant@ aol.com; website - www.the-john-davies-gallery. co.uk. SER: Restoration and conservation to museum standard.

Durham House Antiques Centre
Sheep St. GL54 1AA. (Alan Smith). Open 10-5, Sun. 11-5. SIZE: 30+ dealers. PARK: Easy. TEL: 01451 870404; fax - same; e-mail - Durham HouseGB@aol.com. SER: Buys at auction. FAIRS: NEC (Aug); Newark; Ardingly. Below are listed the dealers at this centre.

Acorn Antiques
(Derek Howe, Stanley Taylor). Est. 1987. *19th C Staffordshire figures and animals.*

Ancient and Oriental Ltd
Ancient art and archaeological items, many periods, lands and cultures.

Aston Antiques
Arts and Crafts and Art Deco lighting, decanters, drinking glasses and ceramics, metalwork and furniture.

Avoncroft Antiques
Oak and mahogany furniture; mantel, wall and carriage clocks; ceramics.

Judi Bland Antiques
Toby jugs, Staffordshire, oak furniture, metalware.

Bread and Roses
19th-20th C kitchen, dairy, laundry and garden collectibles.

A Quality Antiques Centre in the Heart of the Cotswolds Over 30 Well Established Trade Dealers

Monday - Saturday 10-5
Sunday 11-5
Tel/Fax: 01451 870404
email: DurhamHouseGB@aol.com

Sheep Street, STOW-ON-THE-WOLD, GL54 1AA

Simon Clarke Antiques
Pictures, prints, metalware and leather items, ceramics and furniture.

Bryan Collyer
English pottery and Staffordshire figures; cork-screws, prints and pictures, small furniture.

Crockwell Antiques
(Philip Dawes). *Longcase clocks, silver, brass and copper, ironstone china, 18th-19th C furniture.*

Lee Elliott
19th-20th C prints and pictures, specialising in country pastimes.

Jane Fairfield
Elegant silver and plate, Continental porcelain and objet d'art.

Tony and Jane Finegan
Traditional English and French furniture and mirrors, lighting, decorative accessories including papier mâché and tole.

Marion Gregg Antiques
19th-20th C Oriental and English furniture and accessories.

Beryl and Brian Harrison
Linen and lace, tableware and bedclothes.

Erna Hiscock and John Shepherd
Samplers and needlework, early ceramics and blue and white, carvings, country furniture and decorative items.

Dorothy Hyatt
Early English porcelain and pottery (Worcester, creamware and blue and white); 18th-19th C drinking glasses.

Corrie Jeffries Antiques
Decorative accessories, stitchery and textiles, pictures and prints.

Ian Kellam
English and Continental porcelain, silver and jewellery, religious objects and objets d'art.

Lineage Antiques
Portrait miniatures, silver and jewellery, tartan and Mauchlineware and objets du vertu.

Little Nells
(Helen Middleton). *Coronation commemoratives, automobilia, Staffordshire and majolica, collectibles and small interesting items.*

Audrey McConnell
Silver and jewellery, picture frames, ceramics, ivory and micromosaics.

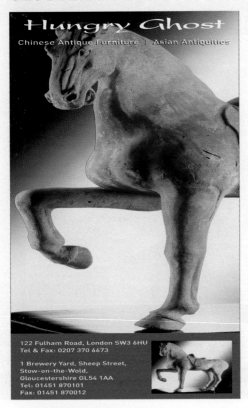

Hungry Ghost

Chinese Antique Furniture | Asian Antiquities

122 Fulham Road, London SW3 6HU
Tel & Fax: 0207 370 6673

1 Brewery Yard, Sheep Street,
Stow-on-the-Wold,
Gloucestershire GL54 1AA
Tel: 01451 870101
Fax: 01451 870012

Atalanti Meyers
Arts and Crafts, ceramics, pewter, small furniture.

Colin Morris
Early carvings, pewter, copper and brass, ceramics, early oak furniture.

Peggy Nichols
Silver and plate, jewellery and glass.

Outram Antiques
(Philip and Dorothy Lipman). *18th-19th C oak and pine country furniture, ironstone china, prints and decorative items.*

Paper Moon Books
19th-20th C bindings including poetry, prose and history; prayer books and bibles.

Pauline Parkes
19th-20th C Mauchlineware, treen and metal sewing ephemera.

Edith and Brian Prosser Antiques
18th-20th C decorative furniture, mirrors, prints, lighting, glass and ceramics.

Quartz and Clay
Arts and Crafts, Art Deco glass and ceramics - Whitefriars, Clarice Cliff and Denby.

Lindsey Richardson Antiques
19th C ceramics including Staffordshire; glass and small decorative items.

Betty Thornley Antiques
Prints and 19th C porcelain, candlesticks and metalware.

Times Past
(Judi Pollitt). *Needlework tools, chatelaines, small silver and objets de vertu*

Yorca Antiques
(Paul and Philippa Hughes). *English porcelain including Derby and Worcester.*

The Fosse Gallery
The Square. GL54 1AF. Est. 1979. Open 10-5.30. SIZE: Large. *STOCK: English and Scottish painters, many RA, RSA and Royal Glasgow Institute members, including Gore, Howard, Ward, Dunstan, Spear, Weight, Morrocco, Donaldson, McClure, Haig, Devlin and Michael Scott.* LOC: Off Fosseway, A429. PARK: Easy. TEL: 01451 831319; fax - 01451 870309. SER: Valuations.

Fox Cottage Antiques
Digbeth St. GL54 1BN. (Sue London). Est. 1995. Open 10-5. SIZE: 9 dealers. *STOCK: Wide variety of general antiques including pottery and porcelain, silver and plate, metalware, prints, small furniture, country and decorative items, mainly pre 1900, £5-£500.* LOC: Left hand side at bottom of narrow street, running down from The Square. PARK: Nearby. TEL: 01451 870307.

Keith Hockin Antiques   BADA
The Square. GL54 1AF. CADA. Est. 1968. Open Thurs., Fri., Sat., 10-5, other times by appointment or ring the bell. SIZE: Medium. STOCK: Oak furniture, 1600-1750; country furniture in oak, fruitwoods, yew, 1700-1850; pewter, copper, brass, ironwork, all periods. Not Stocked: Mahogany. PARK: Easy. TEL: 01451 831058; fax - same; e-mail - keithhockin@ aol.com. SER: Buys at auction (oak, pewter, metalwork). VAT: Stan/Spec.

Hungry Ghost
1 Brewery Yard, Sheep St. GL54 1AA. (Virginia Kern). Est. 1998. Open 9.30-5.30, Sun. 10-4.30. SIZE: Medium. *STOCK: Chinese furniture and artefacts, 18th-19th C, to £15,000.* PARK: Nearby. TEL: 01451 870101; fax - 01451 870012; e-mail - virginiakern@aol.com; website - www.hungry-ghost.co.uk. FAIRS: Decorative Antiques, Battersea. VAT: Stan.

La Chaise Antique

Beauport, Sheep Street, Stow-on-the-Wold, Glos GL54 1AA
Tel: (01451) 830582 Mobile: (07831) 205002

Specialists in leather chairs, upholstery and suppliers of loose leather desk tops. Always available from our new Showroom at Stow-on-the-Wold after 30 years at Faringdon.

Typical example of our leather fully re-upholstered Victorian Chesterfields.

Huntington Antiques Ltd

Church St. GL54 1BE. (M.F. and S.P. Golding). LAPADA. CADA. CINOA. Resident. Est. 1974. Open 9.30-5.30 or by appointment. SIZE: Large. *STOCK: Early period and fine country furniture, metalware, treen and textiles, tapestries and works of art.* LOC: Opposite main gates to church. TEL: 01451 830842; fax - 01451 832211; e-mail - info@huntington-antiques.com; website - www. huntington-antiques.com. SER: Valuations; buys at auction. FAIRS: LAPADA. VAT: Spec.

Kenulf Fine Arts

Digbeth St. GL54 1BN. (E. and J. Ford). LAPADA. Est. 1978. Open 10-5, Sun. 12-5. SIZE: 7 rooms. *STOCK: 19th to early 20th C oils, watercolours and prints; decorative items, fine period walnut and mahogany furniture; bronzes and contemprary paintings.* LOC: Near Barclays Bank. TEL: 01451 870878; mobile - 07774 107269. SER: Valuations; restorations (oils and watercolours, period framing). FAIRS: NEC; LAPADA; Northern; Belgian. VAT: Spec.

T.M. King-Smith & Simon W. Nutter

Wraggs Row, Fosseway. GL54 1JT. Est. 1975. Open 9.30-5.30. *STOCK: 18th-19th C mahogany and oak furniture, £500-£10,000; silver, porcelain, brass and copper.* LOC: Near traffic lights opposite the Unicorn Hotel. TEL: 01451 830658. SER: Buys at auction. VAT: Spec.

La Chaise Antique

Beauport, Sheep St. GL54 1AA. (Roger Clark). LAPADA. Est. 1968. Open 9.30-5.30. CL: Sun. except by appointment. SIZE: Large. *STOCK: Chairs, pre-1860; furniture, 18th-19th C; general antiques, decorators' items.* Not Stocked: Silver, porcelain and glass. PARK: Ample. TEL: 01451 830582; mobile - 07831 205002. SER: Valuations; restorations; upholstery (leather and fabrics); table top liners. FAIRS: NEC (April, Aug., Dec.); LAPADA NEC (Jan.); GAF, Earls Court (Sept./Oct.). VAT: Spec.

Roger Lamb Antiques & Works of Art

The Square. GL54 1AB. LAPADA. CADA. Open 10-5. *STOCK: 18th to early 19th C furniture especially small items, lighting, decorative accessories, oils and watercolours.* TEL: 01451 831371. SER: Search.

Oriental Gallery

GL56 0QW. (Patricia Cater). Open by appointment only. *STOCK: Oriental ceramics and works of art.* TEL: 01451 830944; fax - 01451 870126; e-mail - patriciacaterorg@aol.com; website - www.patricia cater-orientalart.com

Park House Antiques

Park St. GL54 1AQ. (G. and B. Sutton). Est. 1986. Open 10-5, winter - 11-4.30. CL: Tues. and all of May. SIZE: Large. *STOCK: Early dolls, teddy bears, toys, Victorian linen and lace, porcelain, collectables, small furniture and pictures.* PARK: Easy. TEL: 01451 830159; home - same; website - www.TheToymuseum.co.uk. SER: Museum of dolls, teddies, toys, textiles and collectables; teddy bears repaired; antique dolls dressed.

Antony Preston Antiques Ltd BADA

The Square. GL54 1AB. CADA. Est. 1965. Open 9.30-5.30 or by appointment. STOCK: 18th-19th C English and Continental furniture and objects; barometers and period lighting. TEL: 01451 831586; fax - 01451 831596. VAT: Stan/Spec.

Priests Antiques

The Malt House, Digbeth St. GL54 1BN. (A.C. Priest). Est. 1986. Open 10-5. SIZE: Large. *STOCK: English furniture, oak, walnut, fruitwood and mahogany, 17th-19th C.* PARK: Easy. TEL: 01451 830592; fax - 01451 830592. SER: VAT: Spec.

Queens Parade Antiques Ltd BADA

The Square. GL54 1AB. (Antony Preston Antiques Ltd). CADA. Est. 1965. Open 9.30-5.30. SIZE: Large. STOCK: 18th-19th C fur-

niture, papier mâché, tôle peinte, needlework and period lighting. **LOC: Off Fosse Way. PARK: Easy. TEL: 01451 831586. VAT: Stan/Spec.**

Michael Rowland Antiques
Little Elms, The Square. GL54 1AF. Est. 1991. Open 10.45-5. SIZE: Medium. *STOCK: Furniture, including Welsh dressers, farmhouse tables, gate legs, side tables and bureaux, 17th-18th C, £500-£8,000.* PARK: Easy. TEL: 01451 870089; home - same. VAT: Spec.

Ruskin Decorative Arts
5 Talbot Court. GL54 1DP. (Anne and William Morris). CADA. Est. 1990. Open 10-1 and 2-5.30. SIZE: Small. *STOCK: Interesting and unusual decorative objects, Arts and Crafts furniture, Art Nouveau, Art Deco, glass and pottery, metalwork, 1860-1940.* LOC: Between The Square and

A wax mannequin wearing a jewelled bandeau by Cartier that completely encircles the head. This is a style of jewellery that evolved from the shorter coiffures of the 1920s. (Cartier Archives, London)

From an article entitled "Art Deco Tiaras" by Geoffrey C. Munn which appeared in the May 2002 issue of **Antique Collecting**. For more details and to subscribe see page 21.

Sheep Street. PARK: Nearby. TEL: 01451 832254; fax - 01451 832167; home - 01993 831880; e-mail - william.anne@ruskindecarts. co.uk. SER: Valuations. FAIRS: NEC.

Samarkand Galleries
7 & 8 Brewery Yard, Sheep St. GL54 1AA. (Brian MacDonald). LAPADA. CADA. CINOA. FRGS. Est. 1979. Open 10-5.30, Sun. by appointment. SIZE: Medium. *STOCK: Tribal and village rugs and artefacts, 19th C, £100-£10,000; fine decorative carpets, 19th-20th C, £1,000-£10,000+; kelims, 19th-20th C, £200-£2,000; also unique contemporary rugs and carpets.* LOC: Street adjacent to Market Sq. PARK: Easy. TEL: 01451 832322; fax - same; e-mail - mac@samarkand. co.uk; website - www.samarkand.co.uk. SER: Exhibitions; valuations; restorations; cleaning. FAIRS: Hali, Olympia (June). VAT: Stan/Spec.

Arthur Seager Antiques
50 Sheep St. GL54 1AA. Open by appointment. *STOCK: Period oak, carvings and sculpture, £500-£20,000.* TEL: 01451 831605; e-mail - arthur.seager@btconnect.com; website - www. arthurseager.com.

Stow Antiques
The Square. GL54 1AF. (Mr and Mrs J. Hutton-Clarke). LAPADA. CADA. Resident. Est. 1969. Open Mon.-Sat. 10-5.30 other times by appointment. SIZE: Large. *STOCK: Furniture, mainly Georgian, £500-£30,000; decorative items, gilded mirrors, £50-£10,000.* PARK: Easy. TEL: 01451 830377; fax - 01451 870018; e-mail - hazel @stowantiques.co.uk. SER: Shipping worldwide.

Styles of Stow
The Little House, Sheep St. GL54 1JS. (Mr and Mrs W.J. Styles). Est. 1981. Open 10-5.30. SIZE: Medium. *STOCK: Longcase (100+) and bracket clocks, barometers, 18th-19th C, £400-£30,000; fine furniture, 18th-19th C, £250-£15,000; oils and watercolours, 19th-20th C, £25-£20,000.* LOC: Opposite post office. PARK: Easy. TEL: 01451 830455; home and fax - same; e-mail - info@styles ofstow.co.uk; website - www.stylesofstow.co.uk. SER: Valuations; restorations; buys at auction (longcase and bracket clocks). VAT: Margin.

Talbot Court Galleries
Talbot Court. GL54 1BQ. (J.P. Trevers). Est. 1988. Open 9.30-1 and 1.30-5.30. SIZE: Medium. *STOCK: Prints and maps, 1580-1880, £10-£5,000.* LOC: Behind Talbot Hotel in precinct between the Square and Sheep St. PARK: Nearby. TEL: 01451 832169; fax - 01451 832167. SER: Valuations; restorations (cleaning, colouring); framing; buys at auction (engravings). VAT: Stan.

Tudor House

Sheep St. GL54 1AA. (Peter Collingridge and Roy Hooper). Est. 2001. Open 10-5, Sun. by appointment. SIZE: 7 showrooms. *STOCK: Furniture, £500-£10,000; metalware, £50-£2,500; both 1700-1900. Porcelain, 1720-1920, £50-£2,500; watercolours, 1780-1940, £50-£1,000.* LOC: Turn at traffic lights from A429. PARK: At rear. TEL: 01451 830021; fax - same; mobile - 07860 581858. SER: Valuations. VAT: Spec. Below are listed the dealers trading from this address:

Mike & Shirley Allen
19th-20th C glass.

Ashley Antiques
Curios.

Christopher Ashton
French furniture, metalware, lighting, works of art.

Colin Brand
Clocks, porcelain, decorative furniture, militaria.

PeterCollingridge
Metalware, furniture 1700-1900.

Jeremy Collingridge
Fountain pens.

Vienneta Edwards
18th & 19th C pottery, metalware and decorative items.

Roy Hooper
Metalware, Arts & Crafts, Art Nouveau.

Patricia Kleinman
19th to early 20th C English watercolours and drawings.

Atalanti Meyer
Decorative items including pewter, silver, glass and porcelain.

Mark Newsum
Treen, metalware and country bygones.

Tim Olney
18th to early 19th C English porcelain, especially Worcester and Newhall.

Malcolm Potter
17th to early 20th C furniture and accessories.

Iris Walker
Decorative furniture, objets d'art, garden furniture.

Elizabeth Watkiss
Silver and 19th C boxes.

Vanbrugh House Antiques

Park St. GL54 1AQ. (J. and M.M. Sands). Resident. Est. 1972. Open 10-6 or by appoint-

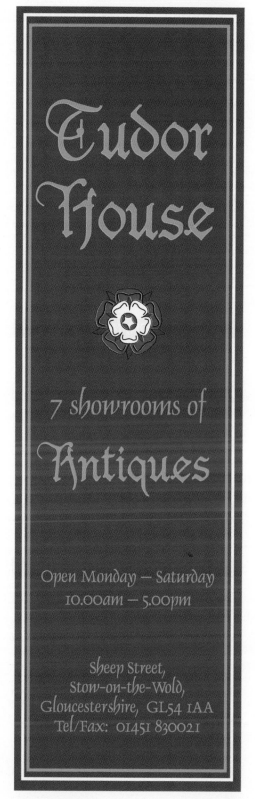

Tudor House

7 showrooms of

Antiques

Open Monday – Saturday
10.00am – 5.00pm

Sheep Street,
Stow-on-the-Wold,
Gloucestershire, GL54 1AA
Tel/Fax: 01451 830021

ment. *STOCK: Furniture and decorative items, 17th to early 19th C; early maps, music boxes, square pianos, clocks and barometers.* LOC: Opposite the Bell Inn. PARK: Easy. TEL: 01451 830797; fax - same. SER: Valuations. VAT: Stan/Spec.

Wyndhams

7a Talbot Court, The Square. GL54 1BQ. (Philip Brown and Kevin Quin). Est. 1988. Open 10-5 or by appointment. SIZE: Medium - 2 showrooms. *STOCK: Fine mid-18th to early 19th C English exotic wood furniture and barometers; fine Art and Crafts and other early 20th C silver; decorative antiques including 19th C Chinese blue and white ceramics, boxes and caddies; brass and ceramic lampbases; late 19th to early 20th C garden watercolours and prints.* LOC: Between The Square and Sheep St. PARK: The Square. TEL: 01451 870067; fax - same; e-mail - antiques@wyndhams.com; website - www. wyndhams.com SER: Valuations. VAT: Spec.

TADDINGTON, Nr. Cutsdean

Architectural Heritage

Taddington Manor. GL54 5RY. CADA. Est. 1978. Open 9.30-5.30, Sat. 10.30-4.30. SIZE: Large. *STOCK: Oak and pine period panelled rooms; stone and marble chimney pieces; stone, marble, bronze and terracotta statuary; garden ornaments, fountains, temples, well-heads, seats, urns, cisterns, sundials and summer houses.* PARK: Easy. TEL: 01386 584414; fax - 01386 584236; e-mail - puddy@architectural-heritage. co.uk; website - www.architectural-heritage.co. uk. SER: Worldwide delivery; shipping; bespoke ornament, chimneypieces and panelled rooms. FAIRS: Chelsea Flower Show. VAT: Stan.

TETBURY

The Antiques Emporium

The Old Chapel, Long St. GL8 8AA. (D. Sayers). TADA. Est. 1993. Open 10-5, Sun. 1-5. SIZE: Large - 38 dealers. *STOCK: Fruitwood and country furniture, fine oak and mahogany, clocks, china, porcelain, treen, copper and brass, jewellery, silver, kitchenalia, £1-£15,000.* Not Stocked: Reproductions. PARK: Nearby. TEL: 01666 505281; fax - 01666 505661. SER: Export. VAT: Stan/Spec.

Arkangel Antiques

33 Long St. GL8 8AA. (Jacqueline Hall). TADA. LAPADA. Est. 1976. Open 10-5. CL: Sun. except

by appointment. SIZE: Large. *STOCK: Furniture, painted English and Continental, mirrors; £500-£4,500; decorative items and objects, 18th-19th C.* PARK: Nearby. TEL: 01666 505820/ 500247; e-mail - j.hall.antiques@talk21.com. SER: Valuations. FAIRS: BABAADA Decorative, Bath; Decorative Antiques & Textiles, Battersea. VAT: Stan/Spec.

Artique

Talboys House, Church St. GL8 8JG. (George Bristow). TADA. Open 9-5. *STOCK: Interiors, textiles, carpets and kelims and objets d'art from the Orient.* TEL: 01666 503597; fax - same; e-mail - george@artique.demon.co.uk.

Ball and Claw Antiques

45 Long St. GL8 8AA. (Chris Kirkland). TADA. Est. 1994. Open 10-5 and most Sundays 2-5. SIZE: Medium. *STOCK: 17th-19th C furniture, engravings, pictures, ceramics and general antiques.* PARK: Easy. TEL: 01666 502440; mobile - 07957 870423; e-mail - chris@balland claw.co.uk; website - www.ballandclaw.co.uk. SER: Finder.

Balmuir House Antiques

14 Long St. GL8 8AQ. (P. Whittam). LAPADA. TADA. Open 9.30-5.30. SIZE: Large. *STOCK: Furniture, paintings, mirrors, 19th C, £500-£5,000.* LOC: Town centre. PARK: Easy. TEL: 01666 503822; home - same. SER: Restorations (furniture, upholstery, paintings). VAT: Spec.

The Black Sheep

51 Long St. GL8 8AA. (Oliver McErlain). Open 10.30-5, Sat. 10-5, Sun. 1-5. SIZE: Small. *STOCK: Traditional English furniture.* PARK: Easy. TEL: 01666 505026.

Breakspeare Antiques

36 and 57 Long St. GL8 8AQ. (M. and S. Breakspeare). LAPADA. CADA. Resident. Est. 1962. Open 10-5 or by appointment. CL: Thurs. SIZE: Medium. *STOCK: English period furniture - early walnut, 1690-1740, mahogany, 1750-1835.* PARK: Own. TEL: 01666 503122; fax - same. VAT: Stan/Spec.

The Chest of Drawers

24 Long St. GL8 8AQ. (A. and P. Bristow). TADA. Resident. Est. 1969. Open Tues.-Fri. 9.30-6, Mon. by appointment. SIZE: Medium. *STOCK: Late Georgian and Regency furniture; country pieces, 17th-18th C; walnut and other woods, 18th C; pictures.* LOC: On A433. PARK: Easy. TEL: 01666 502105; home - same. VAT: Spec.

ARCHITECTURAL HERITAGE

Fine Antique Garden Ornament, Chimney Pieces & Panelled Rooms

Taddington Manor, Taddington, Cheltenham, Glos GL54 5RY

Tel: 01386 584 414   Fax: 01386 584 236

Web - www.architectural-heritage.co.uk
Email - puddy@architectural-heritage.co.uk

Day Antiques   **BADA**
5 New Church St. GL8 8DS. CADA. TADA.
Est. 1975. Open 10-5.30. SIZE: Medium.
STOCK: Early oak furniture and related items.
PARK: Easy. TEL: 01666 502413; fax - 01666
505894; e-mail - dayantiques@lineone.net;
website - www.dayantiques.com VAT: Spec.

The Decorator Source
39a Long St. GL8 8AA. (Colin Gee). TADA. Open
10-5 or by appointment. SIZE: Large. *STOCK:
French provincial furniture - armoires, farm
tables, buffets; decorative items and accessories of
interest to interior decorators.* PARK: Easy. TEL:
01666 505358. VAT: Stan/Spec.

Fowler and Bateson
51A Long St. GL8 8AA. TADA. Est. 1995. Open
10-5, Sun. 11-5 and most Bank Holidays. SIZE:
Medium. *STOCK: Mainly French provincial and
painted furniture, porcelain, ceramics, silver and
pictures; interior design items.* TEL: 01666
505083.

Hampton Gallery
8 Tetbury Upton. GL8 8LP. (P. Downey).
Resident. Est. 1969. Open by appointment. SIZE:
Large. *STOCK: Weapons, arms and armour,
1700-1880, £100-£25,000.* LOC: Off junction 17,
M4. PARK: Easy. TEL: 01666 502971. SER:
Valuations; buys at auction (arms). FAIRS: All
major. VAT: Spec.

Jester Antiques
10 Church St. GL8 8JG. (Lorna Coles and Peter
Bairsto). TADA. Open 10-5.30, including Sun.
*STOCK: Longcase and wall clocks, also oil
portraits and pictures, Oriental objects, lamps,
furniture, decorative items, outside statuary and
architectural.* TEL: 01666 505125.

Merlin Antiques
Shops 4 & 5 Chipping Court Shopping Mall. GL8
8ES. (Miriam and Brian Smith). Est. 1990. Open
9.30-5, Sun. by appointment. SIZE: Medium.
*STOCK: Furniture, Georgian to date, £50-
£2,000; collectables, glass, pictures, china,
jewellery - gold, silver and costume, £2-£500.*
PARK: Nearby. TEL: 01666 505008. SER:
Valuations; restorations.

Bobbie Middleton
58 Long St. GL8 8AQ. CADA. TADA. Open 10-1
and 2.30-5, Sun. by appointment. *STOCK: Classic
country house furniture, mirrors and upholstered
furniture, 18th-19th C.* LOC: On corner with New
Church St. TEL: 01666 502761; e-mail - bobbie
middleton@lineone.net. VAT: Spec.

Paul Nash Antiques

14A The Green. GL8 8DN. LAPADA. Est. 1961. By appointment only. *STOCK: Period furniture, decorative objects and ammonites.* TEL: 01666 503707; mobile - 07785 570701. VAT: Spec.

Peter Norden Antiques

61 Long St. GL8 8AA. (Peter and Jenny Norden). TADA. LAPADA. Est. 1960. Open 10-5.30, Sun. by appointment. SIZE: Medium. *STOCK: Early oak furniture, 16th-17th C, £250-£20,000; country furniture, 17th-19th C, £75-£10,000; early carvings, metalware, pewter, treen, 14th-19th C, £10-£10,000.* PARK: Nearby. TEL: 01666 503854; fax - 01666 505595; home - 01452 770536; e-mail - peternorden-antiques@linone.net; website - www.peter-norden-antiques.co.uk. SER: Valuations. VAT: Spec.

Panache

32 Long St. GL8 8AQ. (Linda Biggs). TADA. Open 10-5 or by appointment. SIZE: Medium. *STOCK: French provincial and painted furniture, mirrors, chandeliers, garden and decorative accessories.* PARK: Easy. TEL: 01666 502423.

Porch House Antiques

40/42 Long St. GL8 8AQ. Est. 1977. Open 10-5. SIZE: Large. *STOCK: 17th-20th C furniture and decorative items.* LOC: Town centre. TEL: 01666 502687. VAT: Spec.

Sharland & Lewis

52 Long St. GL8 8AQ. (Ali Sharland). TADA. Open 10.30-5, Sat 10-5 or by appointment. SIZE: Medium. *STOCK: Painted furniture, textiles and decorative objects.* PARK: Easy. TEL: 01666 500354.

Sieff

49 Long St. GL8 8AA. LAPADA. TADA. Est. 1994. Open 10-5.30, Sun. by appointment. SIZE: Large. *STOCK: English and French 18th-20th C furniture and objets, £100-£10,000.* PARK: Easy. TEL: 01666 504477; fax - 01666 504478; e-mail - sieff@sieff.co.uk; website - www.sieff.co.uk. SER: Valuations; buys at auction. FAIRS: Harvey Decorative Antique & Textile. VAT: Stan/Spec.

The Sporting Gallery

12 Church St. (B. Hulftegger). TADA. Open 10-5. SIZE: Medium. *STOCK: Period and contemporary sporting pictures, engravings, watercolours, oils and associated sporting items.* PARK: Easy. TEL: 01666 504605; e-mail - info@sporting-gallery.com.

Tetbury Gallery

18 Market Place. GL8 8DD. (Jane Maile). FATG. TADA. Open every day. *STOCK: Original and limited edition prints, from Victorian watercolours and oils to contemporary artists including Russell Flint, David Shepherd and Ben Maile.* TEL: 01666 503412.

Tetbury Old Books & Coach House Antiques

4 The Chipping. GL8 8ET. (Tetbury Old Books Ltd). TADA. Open 10-6, Sun. 11-5. *STOCK: Antiquarian and secondhand books and prints.* TEL: 01666 504330; fax - 01666 504458; e-mail - oldbooks@tetbury.co.uk.

Westwood House Antiques and Beehive Antiques

29 Long St. GL8 8AA. (Richard Griffiths and Lynne Petersen). TADA. Resident. Est. 1993. Open 10-5.30 or by appointment. SIZE: Large. *STOCK: Oak, elm and ash country furniture especially dressers, dresser bases and tables, 17th-19th C; occasional French pieces; decorative pottery, pewter and treen.* TEL: 01666 502328; fax - same; mobile - 07774 952909; e-mail - richardgriffiths@tinyworld.co.uk. VAT: Spec.

TEWKESBURY

Berkeley Antiques

132 High St. GL20 5JR. (P.S. Dennis). Open 10-5.30. CL: Thurs. pm. SIZE: Large. *STOCK: Mahogany, oak, walnut, 17th-19th C, £50-£2,000; brass, copper, silver, china and glass.* TEL: 01684 292034; fax - 01684 274264. SER: Restorations. VAT: Stan/Spec.

Gainsborough House Antiques

81 Church St. GL20 5RX. (A. and B. Hilson). Open 9.30-5. *STOCK: Furniture, 18th to early 19th C; glass, porcelain.* TEL: 01684 293072. SER: Restorations; conservation.

Tewkesbury Antiques & Collectables Centre

Tolsey Lane (by The Cross). GL20 5AE. Open 9.30-5.30, Sun. 10.30-5.30. SIZE: 10+ units. *STOCK: Furniture, rugs, porcelain, glass, textiles, pictures, kitchenalia.* LOC: Town centre. TEL: 01684 294091.

THORNBURY, Nr. Bristol

Thornbury Antiques
3A High St. BS35 2AE. (H. Hill). Est. 1993. Open 10-5. SIZE: Small. *STOCK: Victorian pine furniture, china, glass and jewellery.* PARK: Opposite. TEL: 01454 413722. SER: Valuations. VAT: Spec.

TODENHAM, Nr. Moreton-in-Marsh

Geoffrey Stead   BADA
Wyatts Farm. GL56 9NY. Est. 1963. Open by appointment only. *STOCK: English and Continental furniture, decorative works of art and sculpture.* TEL: 01608 650997; fax - 01608 650597; mobile - 07768 460450; e-mail - geoffreystead@geoffreystead.com.

WICKWAR

Bell Passage Antiques
38 High St. GL12 8NP. (Mrs D.V. Brand). LAPADA. Est. 1966. Open 9-5. CL: Thurs.

The Good Templars motto: Faith, Hope and Charity. c.1868. £150-£200.

From an article entitled "A Pottery Celebration of Victorian Temperance" by Arnold Shelton which appeared in the November 2001 issue of **Antique Collecting**. For more details and to subscribe see page 21.

except by appointment. *STOCK: Furniture, glass, porcelain, some pictures.* LOC: On B4060. PARK: Easy. TEL: 01454 294251; fax - same. SER: Restorations; upholstery; caning.

WINCHCOMBE

Campden Country Pine Antiques
Didbrook Fields Farm, Toddington. GL54 5PE. (Jane Kennedy). Est. 1988. Open 7 days by appointment. SIZE: Medium. *STOCK: Antique pine.* PARK: Easy. TEL: 01242 620950; e-mail - thekettle@aol.com. *Trade Only.*

The Clock Shop
11 North St. GL54 5LH. (M. Lovatt). Est. 1994. Open 10-1 and 2-4.30. CL: Mon. SIZE: Small. *STOCK: Antique and period clocks, barometers and gramophones, £100-£3,000.* TEL: 01242 604780; fax - same; website - www.clock-shop-winchcombe.co.uk SER: Valuations; restorations (clocks). VAT: Spec.

Cotswold Antiques. com
Didbrook Fields, Toddington. GL54 5PE. (Frank Kennedy). Est. 1988. Open 7 days mainly by appointment. SIZE: Small. *STOCK: English and Continental furniture, 17th-19th C.* PARK: Own. TEL: 01242 620950; e-mail - thekettle@aol.com.

Government House
St Georges House, High St. GL54 5LJ. Est. 1979. Open by appointment. *STOCK: Antique and pre-war lighting and accessories.* LOC: Village centre. PARK: Own. TEL: 01242 604562; mobile - 07970 430684. SER: Spare parts stocked, restorations (period lighting). FAIRS: Newark, Ardingly, Swinderby. VAT: Spec/Global.

In Period Antiques
Queen Anne House, High St. GL54 5LJ. (John Edgeler). Resident. Est. 1999. Open Thurs.- Sat. 9.30-5, other times by appointment. SIZE: Medium. *STOCK: Furniture, oak, mahogany, 17th -19th C; metalware, glass, ceramics and decorative items.* PARK: Easy. TEL: 01242 602319.

Prichard Antiques
16 High St. GL54 5LJ. (K.H. and D.Y. Prichard). CADA. Est. 1979. Open 9-5.30, Sun. by appointment. SIZE: Large. *STOCK: Period and decorative furniture, £10-£20,000; treen and metalwork, £5-£5,000; interesting and decorative accessories.* LOC: On B4632 Broadway to Cheltenham road. PARK: Easy. TEL: 01242 603566. VAT: Spec.

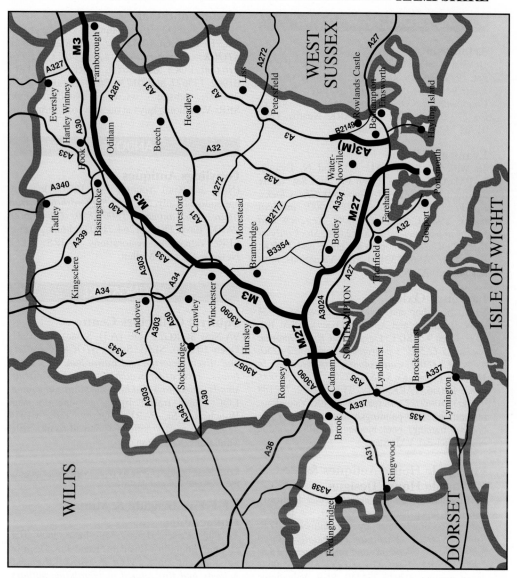

Dealers and Shops in Hampshire

Alresford	6	Fareham	1	Morestead	1
Andover	1	Farnborough	1	Odiham	1
Basingstoke	1	Fordingbridge	2	Petersfield	3
Bedhampton	1	Gosport	3	Portsmouth	5
Beech	1	Hartley Wintney	16	Ringwood	4
Botley	1	Hayling Island	1	Romsey	1
Brambridge	1	Headley	1	Rowlands Castle	1
Brockenhurst	2	Hook	1	Southampton	5
Brook	1	Hursley	2	Stockbridge	8
Cadnam	1	Kingsclere	1	Tadley	1
Crawley	1	Liss	1	Titchfield	2
Emsworth	6	Lymington	6	Waterlooville	1
Eversley	2	Lyndhurst	2	Winchester	12

ALRESFORD, Nr. Winchester

Artemesia
16 West St. SO24 9AT. (D.T.L.Wright). LAPADA. Est. 1972. Open 9.30-5. SIZE: Medium. *STOCK: English and Continental furniture, English, Continental and Oriental porcelain and works of art, £20-£6,000.* LOC: A31. PARK: Nearby. TEL: 01962 732277. SER: Valuations.

Evans and Evans
40 West St. SO24 9AU. (D. and N. Evans). LAPADA. Est. 1953. Open Fri. and Sat. or by appointment. SIZE: Medium. *STOCK: Clocks, watches, 1680-1900, £250-£50,000; musical boxes, 19th C, £500-£12,000; Regency and Victorian barometers, £200-£2,000. Stock only as listed.* LOC: A31. Shop on left going east. PARK: Easy. TEL: 01962 732170. SER: Valuations; buys at auction. VAT: Stan/Spec.

Laurence Oxley
Studio Bookshop and Gallery, 17 Broad St. SO24 9AW. (Laurence and Anthony Oxley). ABA. Est. 1951. Open 9-5. SIZE: Large. *STOCK: Antiquarian books, £5-£2,500; topographical prints, £2-£250; maps, £5-£800; watercolours, (specialising in M.Birket Foster, RWS 1825-1899), £100-£30,000.* LOC: B3046. PARK: Easy. TEL: 01962 732188 (books), 01962 732998 (pictures). SER: Valuations; restorations (oil paintings/watercolours, prints, books); framing; book-binding. FAIRS: London ABA (Chelsea). VAT: Stan.

Pineapple House Antiques & Pineapple House Designs.
49 Broad St. SO24. (Diana and Peter Radford). Est. 1969. Open Thurs. and Fri. 11-4, Sat. 10.30-6, Sun. 11-6, other times by appointment. SIZE: Small. *STOCK: Furniture, especially dining tables, chairs, sideboards and smaller items, 18th-20th C.* PARK: Easy. TEL: 01962 736575; fax - same; mobile - 07973 254749. SER: Valuations; restorations (repairs and cabinet making).

Tudor Antiques & Fine Art Ltd
The Old Exchange, Station Rd. SO24 9JG. Est. 1977. Open 10-4, Sun. by appointment. CL: Wed. SIZE: Medium. *STOCK: 17th-19th C English, Continental and Oriental furniture and works of art; large display of authenticated Chinese furniture; dining tables, £2,000-£25,000; sets of dining chairs, £1,500-£10,000; dining room furniture, £1,000-£20,000.* LOC: Town centre. PARK: Easy and station. TEL: 01962 735345; fax - same; mobile - 07774 908888; e-mail - e&ptudor @tudorantiques.co.uk; website - www.tudor-antiques.co.uk. SER: Valuations; restorations (furniture - structural, veneer and polishing).

Underwood Oak
49 West St. SO24 9AB. (Ann and Dale Egerton). Est. 1995. Open 10-4. CL: Wed. SIZE: Small. *STOCK: Oak furniture, 17th-19th C, £200-£10,000.* LOC: Main street. PARK: Easy. TEL: 01962 735677 and 01730 263972; fax - 01730 267797; website - www.underwoodoak.co.uk. SER: Valuations; buys at auction (oak furniture).

ANDOVER

Graylings Antiques
(Nick and Gail Young). Est. 1968. Open by appointment only. *STOCK: Staffordshire portrait figures and animals, 1800-1890, £50-£2,500.* PARK: Easy. TEL: 01264 710077; home - same. SER: Valuations; restorations. FAIRS: NEC; Newark; Shepton Mallett.

BASINGSTOKE

Squirrel Collectors Centre
9A New St. RG21 1DF. (A.H. Stone). Est. 1981. Open 10-5.30. SIZE: Small. *STOCK: Jewellery and silver, Victorian and Edwardian, £5-£4,500; books, postcards, watches, collectors' items, smalls, china, toys and large furniture showroom.* LOC: Near traffic lights at junction with Winchester St. PARK: Nearby. TEL: 01256 464885; e-mail - antiques@onmail.co.uk. SER: Valuations. VAT: Stan.

BEDHAMPTON

J F F Fire Brigade & Military Collectables
Ye Olde Coach House, Mill Lane. PO9 3JH. (Johnny Franklin). Resident. Est. 1982. Open by appointment only. *STOCK: Brass firemen's helmets and fire related memorabilia; military, police and ambulance items including helmets, cap and collar badges, buttons, uniforms, caps, weapons, equipment, medals and brooches.* PARK: Easy. TEL: 02392 486485; e-mail - jffcollectables@aol.com. SER: Valuations; buys at auction. FAIRS: 999 Memorabilia.

BEECH, Nr. Alton

Jardinique
Old Park Farm, Kings Hill. GU34 4AW. (Edward and Sarah Neish). Resident. Est. 1994. Open 10-5. CL: Sun. and Mon. and Jan. and Feb. except by appointment. SIZE: Very large. *STOCK: Garden ornaments, urns, statuary and furniture, from*

17th C, £10-£5,000. LOC: From Alton on the A339 Basingstoke road, take first left signed Beech, after 1.5 miles premises on left opposite Alton Abbey. PARK: Easy. TEL: 01420 560055; fax - 01420 560050; e-mail - Jardinique@aol. com. SER: Valuations; buys at auction (as stock). VAT: Stan/Spec.

BOTLEY, Nr. Southampton

The Furniture Trading Co
Old Flour Mills. S03 2GB. (L. Davies). Est. 1986. Open 9-5.30, Sun. 12-4. SIZE: Medium. *STOCK: Antique and reproduction furniture, including painted and distressed.* LOC: Off M27, exit 7. PARK: Easy. TEL: 01489 788194; fax - 01489 797337. SER: Valuations; restorations (furniture including upholstery, caning and French polishing); furniture made to order - old and new pine and painted; interior decoration. VAT: Stan.

BRAMBRIDGE, Nr. Eastleigh

Brambridge Antiques
The Barn, Bugle Farm, Highbridge Rd. SO50 6HS. (Desmond and Ann May). Est. 1982. Open 10-5. SIZE: Medium. *STOCK: Furniture, including oak and pine, late Georgian to Edwardian.* PARK: Easy. TEL: 01962 714386; home - 02380 269205. SER: Valuations; restorations (furniture including upholstery and re-leathering).

BROCKENHURST

Antiquiteas
37 Brookley Rd. SO42 7RB. (R. Wolstenholme and S. Hamilton). Resident. Est. 1996. Open 9.30-5, Sun. 10-4. SIZE: Medium. *STOCK: Furniture including pine, £50-£350; china and glass, copper and brass, £10-£100; all 19th-20th C.* LOC: Near watersplash and village post office. PARK: Easy. TEL: 01590 622120. VAT: Stan.

Squirrels
Lyndhurst Rd. SO42 7RL. (Sue Crocket). Est. 1990. Open Wed.-Sun. 10-5, until dusk in winter. *STOCK: Furniture including stripped pine, china especially blue and white, Victoriana, Art Deco, Art Nouveau, kitchenalia and gardenalia, 19th-20th C, to £1,000.* LOC: Opposite Rose and Crown. PARK: Easy. TEL: 01590 622433.

BROOK, Nr. Cadnam

F.E.A. Briggs Ltd
Birchenwood Farm. SO43 7JA. Est. 1968. Open by appointment. SIZE: Large warehouse. *STOCK: Antique and Victorian furniture.* LOC: M27 exit 1. PARK: Easy. TEL: 023 8081 2595; e-mail - feabriggs@aol.com. SER: Restorations; valuations. VAT: Stan/Spec.

CADNAM

C.W. Buckingham
Twin Firs, Southampton Rd. SO40 2NQ. Resident. Open 9-6 or by appointment. CL: Thurs. *STOCK: Mainly pine, some period and Victorian furniture.* TEL: 023 8081 2122.

CRAWLEY, Nr. Winchester

The Pine Barn
Folly Farm. SO21. (S. Baker). Open 9-5, including Sun. *STOCK: Pine and country furniture.* TEL: 01962 776687.

EMSWORTH

Antique Bed Company
32 North St. PO10 7DG. (Ian and Judi Trewick). Est. 1993. Open 9-5.30, Wed. 9-12.30, Sat. 9-5. SIZE: Small. *STOCK: Iron and brass, brass and wooden beds, 19th C, to £1,000.* LOC: From A259 roundabout in Emsworth, turn towards station. PARK: Nearby. TEL: 01243 376074; fax - same; home - 02392 492772. SER: Restorations (beds).

Bookends
7 High St. PO10 7AQ. (Mrs Carol Waldron). Est. 1982. Open 9.30-5, Sun. 10-3. SIZE: Medium. *STOCK: Books, some antiquarian; also sheet music, scores, £2-£100.* PARK: Nearby. TEL: 01243 372154; mobile - 07796 263508; e-mail - cawaldron@tinyworld.co.uk. SER: Valuations; booksearch.

Clockwise
10 South St. PO10 7EH. (D. Judge). AHS. GMC. Est. 1976. Open Tues.-Sat. 10-4. SIZE: Small. *STOCK: Longcase, wall, mantel, bracket and carriage clocks, 18th-19th C, £300-£12,000.* LOC: A259 off A27, head for harbour. PARK: Easy. TEL: 01243 377558; e-mail - judge@clock-wise.fsnet.co.uk; website - www.clock-wise.co.uk. SER: Valuations; restorations.

Dolphin Quay Antique Centre
Queen St. PO10 7BU. (N. and M. Farmer). Est. 1996. Open 10-5, Sun. and Bank Holidays 10-4. SIZE: Large - 30+ dealers. *STOCK: Fine English, French and country furniture, 18th C to 1939, £50-£5,000; marine antiques; clocks - bracket, mantel, longcase, £100-£5,000; wristwatches, fobs, dress watches, vintage pens, sporting apparel, luggage, conservatory and garden antiques, decorative arts, silver, jewellery, china, paintings, watercolours, prints.* PARK: Own and in square. TEL: 01243 379994; fax - 01243 379251; website - www. dolphin-quay-antiques.co.uk.

Mariners Antiques
Dolphin Quay Antiques Centre, Queen St. PO10 7BU. (Derrick W. Humphrey). Est. 1994. Open 10-5, Sun. 10-4. *STOCK: Nautical antiques, marine paintings and prints, ship models, pond yachts, Royal Navy and shipping line memorabilia, books, 19th to mid 20th C, £5-£3,000.* PARK: Easy. TEL: 01420 476718; fax - same; mobile - 07710 330700; e-mail - derrickhumphrey@mariners-antiques.com; website - www.mariners-antiques. com. SER: Valuations. FAIRS: Int. Ship Show, Titanic Society. VAT: Margin.

Tiffins Antiques
12 Queen St. PO10 7BL. (Phyl Hudson). Est. 1987. Open 9.30-5. CL:Mon. and Tues. SIZE: Small. *STOCK: General antiques, oil lamps.* TEL: 01243 372497; home - same.

EVERSLEY, Nr. Wokingham

Eversley Antiques
Church Lane. RG27 0PX. (C. Shaw). Est. 1988. Open Thurs.-Mon. 10.30-5.30. SIZE: Large. *STOCK: Regency, Victorian and Edwardian furniture; glass, ceramics, pictures, mirrors, silver, and collectables.* LOC: 1.5 miles from Blackbush airport. PARK: Easy. TEL: 0118 9328518.

Colin Harris Antiques
at Eversley Antiques Centre, Church Lane. RG27 0PX. Est. 1966. Thurs.-Mon. 10.30-5.30. *STOCK: General antiques, furniture and decorative items.* LOC: 1.5 miles from Blackbush airport. PARK: Easy. TEL: Home - 0118 973 2580. VAT: Spec.

FAREHAM

Elizabethans
58 High St. PO16 7BG. (E.J. Keeble). Est. 1961. Open Mon., Thurs. and Sat. 10-4. *STOCK: Small general antiques including furniture.* PARK: Easy. TEL: 01329 234964 (answerphone).

FARNBOROUGH

Martin and Parke
97 Lynchford Rd. GU14 6ET. (J. Martin). LAPADA. Est. 1971. Open 9-5. SIZE: Large. *STOCK: Furniture, shipping goods and books.* PARK: Easy. TEL: 01252 515311. VAT: Stan.

FORDINGBRIDGE

Mark Collier   BADA
24 High St. SP6 1AX. *STOCK: Period and decorative antiques. Not Stocked: Coins, medals and stamps.* TEL: 01425 652555; fax - 01425 656886.

Quatrefoil
Burgate. SP6 1LX. (C.D. and Mrs I.Aston). Resident. Est. 1972. Always open. SIZE: Large. *STOCK: Early oak furniture, 16th-18th C, £50-£15,000; carvings and sculpture, 13th-17th C, £20-£20,000; antiquities and coins, £50-£10,000.* LOC: On A338, adjacent Tudor Rose Inn. PARK: Easy. TEL: 01425 653309. VAT: Stan/Spec.

GOSPORT

Former Glory
49 Whitworth Rd. PO12 3AH. (Les Brannon). Est. 1987. Open 9.30-5. SIZE: Small. *STOCK: Victorian and Edwardian furniture, £120-£400.* LOC: Near town centre. PARK: Easy. TEL: 02392 504869. SER: Valuations; restorations (furniture repairs, refinishing, repolishing, traditional upholstery)

Peter Pan's Bazaar
87 Forton Rd. PO12 4TG. (S.V. Panormo). Est. 1960. CL: Mon., Tues. and Wed. *STOCK: Vintage cameras, early photographica, images, 1850-1950, £5-£1,500.* LOC: Main road into town. PARK: Easy. TEL: 023 9252 4254. FAIRS: Main south of England.

Peter Pan's of Gosport
87 Forton Rd. PO12 4TG. (J. McClaren). Est. 1965. CL: Mon., Tues. and Wed. *STOCK: Jewellery, dolls, toys and miniatures.* LOC: Main road into town. PARK: Easy. TEL: 023 9252 4254. FAIRS: Main south of England.

HARTLEY WINTNEY

Nicholas Abbott
High St. RG27 8NY. (C.N. Abbott). LAPADA.

Est. 1962. Open 9.30-5.30 or by appointment. SIZE: Medium. *STOCK: Walnut and mahogany English furniture, 18th to early 19th C.* LOC: Village centre. PARK: Easy. TEL: 01252 842365; fax - same; e-mail - nicholasabbott@web-hq.com; website - www.nicholas-abbott.com SER: Valuations. VAT: Stan/Spec.

Andwells Antiques Limited

High St. RG27 8NY. LAPADA. Est. 1967. Open 9-5.30, Sat. 9.30-5.30. SIZE: Large. *STOCK: Georgian and Regency furniture, mainly mahogany.* LOC: Main street. PARK: Easy. TEL: 01252 842305; fax - 01252 845149; e-mail - andwellsantiques@btinternet.com; website - www.andwells-antiques.com. VAT: Stan/Spec.

Antique House

22 High St. RG27 8NY. (R.M. Campbell and David Campbell). Open 10-5.30, Sun. by appointment. *STOCK: Furniture in walnut, mahogany, rosewood, oak and fruitwoods, 1710-1910; inlaid Edwardian furniture, mirrors, oils, watercolours and prints, £50-£5,000.* PARK: Easy. TEL: 01252 844499; fax/answerphone - 01252 845270. SER: Restorations (furniture and porcelain).

Bryan Clisby

ANTIQUE CLOCKS
at
ANDWELLS ANTIQUES,
Hartley Wintney
(North Hampshire)

*Mahogany longcase clock
by Samuel Buxton of Diss*

We specialise in longcase clocks, particularly mahogany, which we restore in our own workshops. The aim of our case restoration is to preserve as much of the acquired patina of age as possible. Dials are cleaned and numerals restored. Movements are overhauled to give a long trouble free working life. We purchase only well proportioned clocks with good colour and figure.

We also keep a range of bracket, wall and mantel clocks and barometers, all displayed amid a very large stock of Georgian furniture. We aim to please our customers with a modest pricing policy. Call in to view our stock of over 50 items, or ring

01252 842305/716436
for more information.
Website:
www.bryanclisby-antiqueclocks.co.uk
E-mail: bryanclisby@cwcom.net

The Antiques Centre
Primrose House, London Rd. RG27 8RJ. (Mrs Shelagh Lister). Open 10-5, Sun. 12-4. SIZE: Large - 15+ dealers. *STOCK: Fine quality antique and country furniture, £250-£10,000; clocks, paintings, brass, copper, silver, 18th-20th C; china, including Art Deco, mirrors, decorative antiques for the home and garden, books, £1-£2,000.* LOC: A30 opposite village hall. PARK: Easy. TEL: 01252 843393; mobile - 07836 734838.

Cedar Antiques Centre Ltd
High St. RG27 8NY. (Derek and Sally Green). Est. 1998. Open 10-5.30, Sun. 11.5. SIZE: Large - 40+ dealers. *STOCK: Quality furniture, glass, porcelain and pottery, paintings, rugs, silver, collectibles from teddy bears to treen; Cornishware museum.* LOC: A30 village centre. PARK: Opposite. TEL: 01252 843222; fax - 01252 842111; website - www.cedar-antiques-com. SER: Restorations (furniture and porcelain). VAT: Stan/Spec.

Cedar Antiques Limited
High St. RG27 8NY. (Derek and Sally Green). Est. 1964. Open 9-5.30, Sat. and Sun. 11-5. SIZE: Large. *STOCK: Fine English oak, walnut and country furniture, 17th-18th C, £50-£10,000; French provincial furniture, 1680-1780, £800-£5,000; steel and brasswork, £30-£1,000.* Not Stocked: China, glass, silver. LOC: A30. PARK: Opposite. TEL: 01252 843252; fax - 01252 842111. SER: Valuations; restorations (period furniture); interior design and furnishing. VAT: Stan/Spec.

Bryan Clisby Antique Clocks
at Andwells Antiques, High St. RG27 8NY. Est. 1976. Open 9.30-5.30. SIZE: Large. *STOCK: Longcase clocks, 1700-1830, £3,000-£20,000; barometers, 1770-1850, £350-£3,000; bracket, wall and mantel clocks.* LOC: A30 village centre. PARK: Easy. TEL: 01252 716436. SER: Valuations; restorations (clocks and barometers). VAT: Spec.

Deva Antiques
High St. RG27 8NY. (A. Gratwick). Est. 1987. Open 9-5.30. SIZE: Large. *STOCK: 18th-19th C English mahogany and walnut furniture.* PARK: Easy. TEL: 01252 843538; 01252 842946; fax - same; e-mail - devaants@aol.com; website - www.deva-antiques.com. VAT: Stan/Spec.

Colin Harris Antiques
at Primrose House Antique Centre. RG27 8NY. Est. 1966. Open 10.30-5.30 including Sun. *STOCK: General antiques, furniture and decorative items.* TEL: Home - 0118 973 2580. VAT: Spec.

Cedar Antiques Centre

Hartley Wintney, Hampshire, RG27 8NY

40 Individual Dealers offer a wide variety of good quality antiques and collectables. Charming Courtyard Café serves delicious Lunches, Cream Teas and also houses The T.G. Green Pottery Museum. Space for Dealers with high quality stock sometimes available.

Open: Mon to Sat. 10am to 5.30pm Sunday 11am to 5pm
Tel: 01252 843222 Fax: 01252 842111
www.cedar-antiques.com e-mail: cac@cedar-ltd.demon.co.uk

Cedar Antiques Ltd

Sally & Derek Green

Oak Potboard Dresser Base. Is it 18th Century or New?
Visit our showrooms to see
Country Furniture with Colour
Alongside Sally Green Designs – our new alternatives
Tel: 01252 843252 Fax: 01252 842111
www.cedar-antiques.com e-mail: ca@cedar-ltd.demon.co.uk

Phoenix Green Antiques

18th and Early 19th Century   English and Continental Furniture

Late 18th Century French Hepplewhite chair.

London Road Phoenix Green Hartley Wintney
Hants RG27 8RT
Tel: Hartley Wintney (01252) 844430 Fax: Hartley Wintney (01252) 844784

David Lazarus Antiques   BADA
High St. RG27 8NS. Resident. Est. 1973. Open 9.30-5.30; some Sundays, other times by appointment. SIZE: Medium. *STOCK: 17th to early 19th C English and Continental furniture; objets d'art.* LOC: Main street. PARK: Own. TEL: 01252 842272. VAT: Stan/Spec.

Old Forge Cottage Antiques
The Green. RG27 8PG. (Sue Carpenter). Open Tues., Thurs., Fri. and Sat. 10-4, other days by appointment. SIZE: Medium. *STOCK: Country and general antiques.* LOC: A30. PARK: Easy. TEL: 01252 842916.

Phoenix Green Antiques
London Rd. RG27 8RT. (John Biles). Open 9-6, Sun. 10-5 or by appointment. SIZE: Large. *STOCK: English and Continental furniture, 17th-19th C.* TEL: 01252 844430; fax - 01252 844784; e-mail - JohnBiles@PhoenixGreenAntiques.com; website - www.PhoenixGreenAntiques.com/Phoenix GreenDesign.com

A.W. Porter and Son
High St. RG27 8NY. (M.A. and S.J. Porter). Est. 1844. Open 9.30-5, Sat. 9.30-4.45. *STOCK: Clocks, silver, jewellery, glass.* LOC: Opposite

Lloyds Bank. TEL: 01252 842676; fax - 01252 842064; e-mail - mark@awporter.fsnet.co.uk. SER: Restorations (clocks). VAT: Stan/Spec.

Roy Precious Antiques & Fine Art
The Antique Shop, London Rd., Phoenix Green. RG27 8RT. Est. 1972. Open 10-5.30 or by appointment. SIZE: Large. *STOCK: Oak, walnut, mahogany and country furniture, 17th-19th C, £200-£15,000; oil paintings, especially portraits, 17th-19th C, £600-£20,000; pottery and prints; textiles, needlework pictures and tapestries, 17th-19th C.* LOC: A30. PARK: Own. TEL: 01252 844422; mobile - 07710 222273; e-mail - roy@ preciousantiques.co.uk: website - www. antiqnet. co.uk/rprecious. SER: VAT: Stan/Spec.

Sheila Revell Antiques
at Deva, High St. RG27 8NY. Est. 1986. Open 9-5.30. *STOCK: 18th-19th C decorative objects, small furniture and collectors' items especially tea caddies and boxes.* PARK: Easy. TEL: 01252 843538.

Gregory Woodcock Antiques
The Old Corner Shop, London Rd., Phoenix Green. RG27 8RT. LAPADA. Est. 1995. Open 9-6, Sun. by appointment. SIZE: Large. *STOCK: English and Continental furniture and objets d'art, early to contemporary.* PARK: Easy. TEL:

01252 845001; fax - same; e-mail - gw@
gregwoodcockantiques.com; website - www.
gregwoodcockantiques.com. SER: Valuations;
restorations; collection and accomodation
arranged; design advice. VAT: Spec.

HAYLING ISLAND

J. Morton Lee   **BADA**
**Cedar House, Bacon Lane. PO11 0DN.
(Commander and Mrs J. Morton Lee). Est.
1984. Open by appointment.** *STOCK: Water-
colours, 18th-20th C, £50-£10,000.* **PARK: Easy.
TEL: 023 9246 4444; mobile - 07860 810938.
SER: Valuations; buys at auction; exhibitions in
June and Dec. FAIRS: West London (Jan);
Petersfield (Feb); BADA (March); Buxton
(May); NEC (Aug); Harrogate (Sept); Olympia
(Nov). VAT: Stan/Spec.**

HEADLEY

Victoria Dreams
The Old Holme School, Village Green, Crabtree
Lane. GU35 8QH. (S. Kay). Est. 1990. Open 9-
5.30, Sun. 10-4. SIZE: Large. *STOCK: Bedsteads, including wooden, brass and iron, brass,
caned and upholstered.* PARK: Easy. TEL: 01428
717000; fax - 01428 717111; e-mail - sales@
victorian-dreams.co.uk; website - www. victorian-
dreams.co.ok. SER: Valuations; restorations (metalwork and woodwork).

HOOK

Csaky's Antiques
RG27 0AT. Open by appointment only. *STOCK:
Early English and Continental furniture;
carvings, works of art; modern art and sculpture,
specialising in Guy Taplin.* TEL: 01256 880111;
fax - 01256 880601; mobile - 0777 3429831; e-
mail - csakyart@btinternet.com.

HURSLEY, Nr. Winchester

The Pine Emporium
The Old Bakery. SO21 2JY. (J. Greatrix). Est.
1993. Open 8.30-6, Sat. 9-5.30, Sun. 11-4. SIZE:
Large. *STOCK: Pine furniture, antique and
reclaimed, from 18th C; oak furniture, from 18th
C.* LOC: 3 miles west of Winchester on A31 to
Romsey. PARK: Easy. TEL: 01962 775449; fax -
01962 775123; website - www.pine-emporium.
com. SER: Valuations; restorations; bespoke
manufacture. VAT: Stan.

J. MORTON LEE
FINE WATERCOLOURS

**Cedar House, Bacon Lane,
Hayling Island, Hants. PO11 0DN**

*By appointment (023) 9246 4444
EMail: j.mortonlee@btinternet.com*

A.V. Copley **FIELDING** p.o.w.s. 1787 - 1855
Off the Entrance to Portsmouth Harbour
Signed and dated 1834. 25.5 x 35.5 cm.

**ALSO EXHIBITING AT MAJOR
ANTIQUE FAIRS**

KINGSCLERE, Nr. Newbury

**Kingsclere Old Bookshop (Wyseby
House Books)**
2A George St. RG20 5NQ. (Dr Tim and Mrs Anne
Oldham). PBFA. Est. 1978. Open 9-5. SIZE:
Medium. *STOCK: Old, unusual and out-of-print
books on fine art, art history, architecture, decorative arts, design, photography, biology, natural
history, science, horticulture and gardening; prints:
all 19th-20th C, £5-£500.* PARK: Nearby. TEL:
01635 297995; fax - 01635 297677; e-mail - info@
wyseby.co.uk; website - www.wyseby.co.uk. SER:
Valuations. FAIRS: PBFA London. VAT: Stan.

LISS

Plestor Barn Antiques
Farnham Rd. GU33 6JQ. Open 10-5, Sat. 10-2.
SIZE: Large. *STOCK: Furniture, including
upholstered, Victorian and Edwardian, shipping
goods, pine; china and glass, copper and brass.*
LOC: A325, 2 mins from A3 roundabout, near
Spread Eagle public house. TEL: 01730 893922;
mobile - 07850 539998.

LYMINGTON

Century Fine Arts
120 High St. SO41 9AQ. Open 9.15-5.30. SIZE: Large. *STOCK: English furniture, porcelain, English School watercolours and oil paintings.* TEL: 01590 673532; fax - 01590 678855. SER: Restorations. VAT: Stan/Spec.

Lymington Antiques Centre
76 High St. SO41 9AL. Open 10-5, Sat. 9-5. SIZE: 30 dealers. *STOCK: General antiques, books, clocks and watches, jewellery, glass.* TEL: 01590 670934.

Barry Papworth
28 St. Thomas St. SO41 9NE. Est. 1960. Open 9-5. SIZE: Small. *STOCK: Diamond jewellery, £50-£4,000; silver, £25-£1,500; both 18th-19th C. Watches, 19th C, £50-£1,000.* LOC: A337 into town, bay window on left. TEL: 01590 676422. SER: Valuations; restorations. VAT: Stan/Spec.

Robert Perera Fine Art
19 St. Thomas St. SO41 9NB. (R.J.D. Perera). Open 10-1 and 2-5, lunch-times and Sun. by appointment. SIZE: Small. *STOCK: British paintings, 19th-20th C, £100-£5,000; occasional ceramics and sculpture, 19th-20th C, £50-£1,500; paintings and etchings by W.L. Wyllie.* LOC: Top (west) end of main shopping area. PARK: Easy. TEL: 01590 678230; website - www.ART-GALLERY.co.uk.

Platt's of Lymington
15 St Thomas St. SO41 9NB. (Mrs Kay Boyd-Platt). Est. 1997. Open Wed.-Sat. 10-5. SIZE: Medium. *STOCK: Porcelain including Worcester, Derby, Coalport, Dresden, Sèvres, Volkstedt, Sitzendorf, Wedgwood, Doulton, Minton, George Jones, Samson, 18th-19th C, £10-£1,000; furniture especially small, 18th-19th C, £50-£5,000; artwork and collectables, 18th-20th C, £5-£2,000.* LOC: Next door to King's Arms, near Waitrose. PARK: Rear of Waitrose. TEL: 01590 688769; home - same. SER: Valuations. VAT: Stan.

Wick Antiques
Fairlea House, 110-112 Marsh Lane. SO41 9EE. (R.W. and Mrs. C. Wallrock). LAPADA. Est. 1985. Open 9-5, Sat. 10-1. SIZE: Medium. *STOCK: French and English furniture, 18th-19th C, £1,000-£15,000; small items, 19th to early 20th C, £100-£1,000.* LOC: Town outskirts. PARK: Own. TEL: 01590 677558; fax - same; home - 01590 672515;

mobile - 07768 877069; e-mail - charles@wick antiques.co.uk; website - www.wick antiques. co.uk. SER: Valuations; restorations (furniture polishing, repairs, upholstery and re-gilding); buys at auction. FAIRS: Olympia (June); LAPADA (Jan., April, Oct). VAT: Spec.

LYNDHURST

Lita Kaye of Lyndhurst
13 High St. SO43 7BB. (S. and S. Ferder). Est. 1947. Open 9.30-1 and 2.15-5. SIZE: Large. *STOCK: Furniture, clocks, 1690-1820; decorative porcelain, 19th C.* LOC: A35. PARK: 100yds. in High St. TEL: 023 8028 2337. VAT: Stan/Spec.

Lyndhurst Antiques Centre
19-21 High St. SO43 7BB. (Robert Sparks). Est. 1997. Open 10-5. SIZE: Medium. *STOCK: Furniture and clocks, 18th to early 20th C, £50-£5,000; ceramics, 18th to mid 20th C, £5-£1,000; collectables, 20th C, £2-£200.* LOC: Main street by traffic lights. PARK: Free public car park nearby. TEL: 023 8028 4000; fax - 023 8028 2424.

MORESTEAD, Nr. Winchester

Burgess Farm Antiques
SO21 1LZ. (N. Spencer-Brayn). Est. 1970. Open 9-5. SIZE: Large. *STOCK: Furniture, especially pine and country, 18th-19th C, £25-£5,000; architectural items - doors, panelling, fire-places.* LOC: 2 miles south of Winchester, off Corehampton road at Jackmans Hill corner. PARK: Easy. TEL: 01962 777546. SER: Stripping; export. VAT: Stan/Spec.

ODIHAM

The Odiham Gallery
78 High St. RG25 1HJ. (I. Walker). LAPADA. Open 10-5, Sat. 10-1. *STOCK: Decorative and Oriental rugs and carpets.* TEL: 01256 703415.

PETERSFIELD

The Barn
North Rd. GU31 4AH. (P. Gadsden). Est. 1956. Open 9-5. *STOCK: Victoriana, bric-a-brac; also large store of trade and shipping goods.* TEL: 01730 262958.

The Folly Antiques Centre
Folly Market, College St. GU31 4AD. (Red Goblet Ltd). Est. 1980. Open 9.30-5. SIZE: Medium. *STOCK: Furniture, 19th-20th C, £20-£1,000; ceramics and silver, 18th-20th C, £5-£100; jewellery, 19th-20th C; pictures, general antiques and collectables.* LOC: Town centre. PARK: Opposite - Festival Hall, Heath Rd. TEL: 01730 269888.

The Petersfield Bookshop
16a Chapel St. GU32 3DS. (F. Westwood). ABA. Est. 1918. Open 9-5.30. SIZE: Large. *STOCK: Books, old and modern, £1-£500; maps and prints, 1600-1859, £1-£200; oils and watercolours, 19th C, £20-£1,000.* LOC: Chapel St. runs from the Square to Station Rd. PARK: Opposite. TEL: 01730 263438; e-mail - sales@petersfieldbookshop.com; website - www. petersfieldbookshop.com. SER: Restorations and rebinding of old leather books; picture-framing and mount-cutting. FAIRS: London ABA. VAT: Stan.

Underwood Oak
Open by appointment only. *STOCK: Oak furniture, 17th-19th C, £200-£10,000.* TEL: 01730 263972 and 01962 735677; fax - 01730 267797; website - www.underwoodoak.co.uk.

PORTSMOUTH

Academy Books
13 Marmion Rd., Southsea. PO5 2AT. (William Robinson). Open 9-12 and 1-5, Fri. 9-12 and 1-3.30, Sat. 9-5.30. SIZE: Medium. *STOCK: Antiquarian books, 17th C, £5-£500; pictures, prints and postcards, £1-£100; some china, £25-£25.* LOC: Near St. Jude's church. PARK: Opposite. TEL: 023 9281 6632; fax/home - same. SER: Valuations; restorations (books).

A. Fleming (Southsea) Ltd
The Clock Tower, Castle Rd., Southsea. PO5 3DE. (A.J. and Mrs C. E. Fleming). Est. 1905. Open 9.30-5.30, Sat. 9.30-1 or by appointment. *STOCK: Furniture, silver, barometers, boxes and general antiques.* PARK: Easy. TEL: 023 9282 2934; fax - 023 9229 3501; e-mail - mail@flemingsantiques. fsnet.co.uk; website - www.flemingsantiques. com. SER: Restorations. FAIRS: Local vetted. VAT: Stan/Spec.

The Gallery
11 and 19 Marmion Rd., Southsea. PO5 2AT. (I. Murphy). Open 10-5. *STOCK: At No.19 - Victorian chairs and chesterfields; at No.11 - furniture, mainly Victorian and Edwardian.* PARK: Nearby. TEL: 023 9282 2016.

Gray's Antique Centre
129-131 Havant Rd., Drayton. PO6 2AA. (Alexandra J. Gray). Est. 1968. Open 10-5, Sun. 12-4. CL: Wed. SIZE: Large - 10 dealers. *STOCK: English and French furniture, 18th-19th C, £200-£5,000; prints and paintings, china, collectables, pine, 18th-20th C, £25-£3,000.* PARK: Easy and side of shop. TEL: 023 9237 6379; mobile - 07811 778601. SER: Restorations (furniture and upholstery).

Oldfield Gallery
76 Elm Grove, Southsea. PO5 1LN. Est. 1970. Open 10-5. CL: Mon. SIZE: Large. *STOCK: Maps and engravings, 16th-19th C, £5-£1,000; decorative prints, 18th-20th C, £5-£1,000.* PARK: Nearby. TEL: 023 9283 8042; fax - 023 9283 8042; e-mail - oldfield_maps@compuserve.com; website - www.oldfield-antiquemaps.co.uk. SER: Valuations; restorations (maps and prints); framing. FAIRS: London Map Bonnington Hotel (monthly). VAT: Stan.

RINGWOOD

Millers of Chelsea Antiques Ltd
Netherbrook House, 86 Christchurch Rd. BH24 1DR. LAPADA. Est. 1897. Open Mon. 9.30-1.30, Tues.-Fri. 9.30-5, Sat. 10-3, other times by appointment. SIZE: Large. *STOCK: Furniture - English and Continental country, mahogany and gilt, military, decorative items, treen, majolica and faïence, 18th-19th C, £25-£5,000.* LOC: On B3347 towards Christchurch. PARK: Own. TEL: 01425 472062; fax - 01425 472727; e-mail - mail @millers-antiques.co.uk; website - www.millers-antiques.co.uk. SER: Restorations. FAIRS: Decorative Antiques; Wilton. VAT: Stan/Spec.

R. Morgan Antiques
90 Christchurch Rd. BH24 1DR. Est. 1984. Open Tues.-Sat. 10-5. SIZE: Small. *STOCK: Militaria and postcards.* LOC: Off A31 into Ringwood, straight over 1st roundabout, left at next roundabout, shop 150yds. on right. PARK: Easy, and at rear. TEL: 01425 479400; fax - same. SER: Valuations; restorations. FAIRS: Yeovil and Woking Postcard. VAT: Stan/Spec.

Smith & Sons
903 Christchurch Rd. BH7 6AX. (D.R., M. and T. Smith). Est. 1978. Open 9.30-5.30. SIZE: Medium. *STOCK: Pine and other woods, 18th-19th C, £30-£1,000; country pottery, collectables.* Not Stocked: LOC: Opposite Pokesdown Station. PARK: Easy. TEL: 01202 429523; e-mail - enquiries@dsmithandsons.demon.co.uk; website

- www.dsmithandsons.demon.co. SER: Makers of cherry and oak replica items and kitchens; restorations. VAT: Stan.

Lorraine Tarrant Antiques
23 Market Place. BH24 1AN. Est. 1991. Open 10-5. CL: Mon. SIZE: Medium. *STOCK: Victorian furniture, to £1,000; china, glass, collectors items, £5-£100.* LOC: Opposite church. PARK: Easy. TEL: 01425 461123.

ROMSEY

Bell Antiques
8 Bell St. SO51 8GA. (M. and B.M. Gay). FGA. Est. 1979. Open 9.30-5.30. CL: Wed. (winter). SIZE: Large. *STOCK: Jewellery and silver, glass, pottery, porcelain, small furniture, prints and maps, mainly 19th-20th C.* LOC: Near market place. PARK: Town centre. TEL: 01794 514719. VAT: Global/Stan/Spec.

ROWLANDS CASTLE, Nr. Portsmouth

Good Day Antiques and Decor
22 The Green. PO9 6AB. (Gillian Day). Est. 1980. 11-5, Sun. 12-4.30. CL: Tues. and Wed. SIZE: Medium. *STOCK: Furniture, 1812-1940, £100-£1,000; porcelain and pottery, 1800-1950, £25-£500; jewellery and silver, 1840-1970, £25-£1,000; collectables, 19th-20th C, £5-£50.* LOC: Off junction 2, A3(M). PARK: Easy. TEL: 02392 412924; home - 02392 413221; e-mail - good dayantiques@aol.com. SER: Restorations (silver plating, gilding, engraving and porcelain).

SOUTHAMPTON

Mr. Alfred's "Old Curiosity Shop" and The Morris and Shirley Galleries
280 Shirley Rd., Shirley. SO15 3HL. Est. 1952. Open 9-6, including Sun. *STOCK: Furniture, 18th-20th C; paintings, porcelain, bronzes, brass, glass, books, silver, jewellery and general antiques.* LOC: On left of main Shirley road, 3/4 mile from Southampton central station. PARK: Own. TEL: 023 8077 4772. SER: Fine art dealer; valuer; auctioneer; curator; restorer; framer.

Amber Antiques
115 Portswood Rd., Portswood. SO17 2FX. (R. Boyle). Est. 1985. Open 10-5, Sat. 9-5, Sun. 11-3. SIZE: Large. *STOCK: Furniture, late Victorian to 1930's, £100-£1,500.* PARK: Easy. TEL: 02380 583645; fax - same. SER: Restorations (repairs, French polishing). VAT: Stan/Spec.

Meg Campbell
10 Church Lane, Highfield. SO17 1SZ. Est. 1967. Open by appointment only. *STOCK: English, Scottish and Irish silver, collectors' pieces, Old Sheffield plate, portrait miniatures.* TEL: 023 8055 7636; fax - 023 8058 1070. SER: Mail order; catalogues available. VAT: Spec.

Cobwebs
78 Northam Rd. SO14 0PB. (P.R. and J.M. Boyd-Smith). Est. 1975. Open 10.30-4. CL: Wed. SIZE: Medium. *STOCK: Ocean liner memorabilia, china, silverplate, ephemera, paintings, furniture, ship fittings, 1840-1990, £5-£5,000.* LOC: Main road into city centre from the east. PARK: 20yds. TEL: 023 8022 7458; fax - same; website - www.cobwebs.uk.com. SER: Valuations. FAIRS: Beaulieu Boat & Auto; Ship Show, Westminster.

The Olympic Gallery
80 Northam Rd. SO14 0PB. Open 10.30-4. CL: Wed. *STOCK: Prints, paintings, posters, artwork from ocean liners; ships furniture and fittings.* PARK: Outside. TEL: 02380 227458; fax - same.

STOCKBRIDGE

Antique Eyes
Brookside, High St. SO20 6EY. (Jane and Julian Benson). Est. 1987. SIZE: Medium. *STOCK: English and Continental furniture and decorative items, china and glass, 18th-19th C, £50-£3,000.* PARK: Easy. TEL: 01264 811137; fax - 01264 710447; mobile - 07747 611025; home - 01264 710389; e-mail - oldreceyes@aol.com. FAIRS: Decorative Antique & Textile, Battersea; Little Chelsea.

T.R. Baker
at Stockbridge Antique Centre, Old London Rd. SO20 6EJ. Est. 1962. Open 10-5. CL: Wed. SIZE: Large. *STOCK: General antiques, country furniture.* LOC: On White Hart roundabout. TEL: 01264 811008; fax - same. SER: Stripping; restorations; repairs.

The Bakhtiyar Carpet Gallery
High St. SO20 6HF. Est. 1992. Open 10-5. SIZE: Medium. *STOCK: Hand-made Persian carpets, runners, kelims, new, old, decorative and antique nomadic, village and fine city pieces.* PARK: Easy. TEL: 01264 811033; fax - 01264 811077; mobile - 07740 333333; e-mail - bakhtiyar@ attglobal.net; website - www.bakhtiyar.com /www. thebakhtiyargallery.com. SER: Valuations; restorations (cleaning, repairs, re-weaving, re-fringing).

The Bakhtiyar Gallery
High St. SO20 6HF. Open 10-5. SIZE: Medium. *STOCK: Fine English and European furniture, decorative antiques, mirrors and clocks.* PARK: Easy. TEL: 01264 811033; fax - 01264 811077; mobile - 07740 333333; e-mail - bakhtiyar @attglobal.net; website - www.bakhtiyar.com/ www.thebakhtiyargallery.com. SER: Valuations; restorations (repairs, veneering, French polishing).

Lane Antiques
High St. SO20 6EU. (Mrs E.K. Lane). Est. 1981. Open 10-5. CL: Mon. SIZE: Small. *STOCK: English and Continental porcelain, 18th-20th C; silver and plate, decorative items, glass, chandeliers, lighting, small furniture, oils and watercolours; boxes, 18th-19th C.* PARK: Easy. TEL: 01264 810435; e-mail - info@lane antiques.fsnet. uk; website - www.stockbridge.org.uk.

Elizabeth Viney Antiques   BADA
Jacob's House, High St. SO20 6HF. Est. 1950. Open by appointment or chance. SIZE: Small. *STOCK: 18th-20th C English furniture, domestic metalware especially brass (not pewter), treen, bygones especially police truncheons, curiosities and unusual items, £30-£3,000.* **PARK: Easy. TEL: 01264 810761; home - same; website - www.stockbridge.org.uk. SER: Advice.**

Fizzy Warren Decorative Antiques
High St. SO20 6EY. Est. 1988. Open 10.30-5. SIZE: Medium. *STOCK: Decorative antique furniture, mirrors, chandeliers, lamps and wall lights, tapestries, small tables, chairs, china and glass, papier mache, brocante, to £2,000.* LOC: Next to Greyhound public house. PARK: Easy. TEL: 01264 811137; home - 01962 867428; mobile - 07762 201076; e-mail - brymerhouse@ aol.com; website - www.stockbridge.org .uk.

The Wykeham Gallery
High St. SO20 6HE. (Mark Jerram and Gerald Dodson). Est. 1986. Open 10-5. SIZE: Medium. *STOCK: Paintings, sculpture, watercolours, 1890-1940 and contemporary, £150-£15,000.* LOC: Main street. PARK: Easy. TEL: 01264 810364; fax - 01264 810182; e-mail - enquiries@ wykehamgallery.co.uk; website - www.wykeham gallery.co.uk. SER: Valuations; restorations (paintings and works on paper); buys at auction (19th-20th C pictures). VAT: Spec.

TADLEY

Gasson Antiques and Interiors
P O Box 7225. RG26 5IY. LAPADA. Open by appointment. *STOCK: Georgian, Victorian and Edwardian furniture, clocks, porcelain and decorative items.* TEL: 01189 813636; mobile - 07860 827651.

TITCHFIELD, Nr. Fareham

Alexanders
13 South St. PO14 4DL. Open Tues.-Sat. 10-5. *STOCK: General antiques including Art Nouveau and Art Deco.* PARK: Easy. TEL: 01329 315962. SER: Restorations (furniture); silver and chrome plating.

Gaylords
75 West St. PO14 4DG. (I. Hebbard). Est. 1970. Open 9.30-5.30. SIZE: Large. *STOCK: Furniture, from 18th C; clocks, £50-£10,000.* LOC: Off junction 9 M27. PARK: Easy. TEL: 01329 843402; home - 01329 847134. SER: Valuations. VAT: Stan/Spec.

WATERLOOVILLE

Goss and Crested China Centre and Goss Museum
62 Murray Rd. PO8 9JL. (L.J. Pine). Est. 1968. Open 9-5. SIZE: Medium. *STOCK: Goss, 1860-1930, £2-£1,000; other heraldic china, Art Deco pottery including Carlton ware, Charlotte Rhead, Chamelion, 1890-1930, £1-£1,000.* PARK: Easy. TEL: 023 9259 7440; fax - 023 9259 1975; e-mail - info@gosschinaclub.demon.co.uk; website - www.gosscrestedchina.co.uk. SER: Valuations; collections purchased. VAT: Stan.

WINCHESTER

Bell Fine Art
67b Parchment St. SO23 8AT. (L.E. Bell). FATG. Est. 1977. Open 9.30-5.30. SIZE: Large. *STOCK: Watercolours, oils and prints, 1750-1950, £5-£10,000.* PARK: 2 spaces. TEL: 01962 860439; fax - same; home - 01962 862947; e-mail - sales@bell-fine-art.demon.co.uk. SER: Valuations; restorations (oils and watercolours); buys at auction. FAIRS: Goodwood House; Petersfield; NEC. VAT: Spec.

Burns and Graham   BADA
27 St. Thomas St. SO23 9HJ. (M. and G. Rollitt). Est. 1971. Open Thurs. and Fri. 9.30-5, Sat. 9.30-1 or by appointment. *STOCK: English furniture, mirrors, period decorative items, 1680-1840.* LOC: Town centre. PARK: At rear. TEL: 01962 853779; fax - same; mobile - 07771 960393. SER: Valuations. FAIRS: Olympia (Feb., June and Nov). VAT: Stan/Spec.

The Clock Workshop (Winchester).
6a Parchment St. SO23 8AT. (P. Ponsford-Jones and K.J. Hurd). BHI. AHS. Est. 1997. Open Mon.-Sat. 9-5. SIZE: *STOCK: Restored longcase, wall, dial, mantel, bracket and carriage clocks, esecially English, 18th-19th C, £300-£18,000; barometers, books and tools.* LOC: Central, off main pedestrian precinct, near W.H.Smiths. PARK: Easy. TEL: 01962 842331; mobiles - 07885 954302 and 07973 736155; e-mail - kjhurd@btopenworld.com; website - www.clock-work-shop.co.uk. SER: Valuations; restorations (clocks and barometers). VAT: Margin.

Peter M. Daly
Rear of Winchester Antiques, 20a Jewry St. SO23 8RZ. PBFA. Est. 1978. Open Wed., Fri. and Sat. 10-4.30. *STOCK: Rare and secondhand books; some pictures and prints, maps.* PARK: Nearby. TEL: Mobile - 07940 335620; home - 01962 867732. SER: Valuations. FAIRS: Russell Hotel (monthly).

Lacewing Fine Art Gallery
28 St Thomas St. SO23 9HJ. (N. James). Open Tues.-Sat. 10-5. *STOCK: Paintings, water-colours, sculpture, Old Master drawings, 16th-20th C.* TEL: 01962 878700; fax - 01962 870583; e-mail - noeljames@lacewing.co.uk; website - www.lacewing.co.uk.

G.E. Marsh Antique Clocks Ltd BADA
32a The Square. SO23 9EX. Est. 1947. Open 9.30-5, Sat. 9.30-1 and 2-5. *STOCK: English clocks, watches and barometers c1680-1880, including longcase, bracket, French and Continental.* LOC: Near Cathedral. PARK: Easy. TEL: 01962 844443; fax - same; e-mail - gem@marshclocks.co.uk; website - www.marshclocks.co.uk. SER: Valuations; restorations; commissions.

The Pine Cellars
39 Jewry St. and 7 Upper Brook St. SO23 8RY. (N. Spencer-Brayn). Est. 1970. Open 10-5. SIZE: Large and warehouses. *STOCK: Pine and country furniture, 18th-19th C, £10-£5,000; painted furniture, architectural items, panelled rooms.* LOC: One way street, a right turn from top of

High St. or St. Georges St., shop 100yds. on right. Brook St. premises - opposite Brooks Shopping Centre. PARK: Nearby. TEL: 01962 867014/ 777546/870102. SER: Stripping and export. VAT: Stan/Spec.

Samuels Spencers Antiques and Decorative Arts Emporium

39 Jewry St. SO23 8RY. (N. Spencer-Brayn). Open 10-5. SIZE: 31 dealers. *STOCK: General antiques.* LOC: One way street, right turn from top of High St. or St. George St., shop 100yds. on right. PARK: Nearby. TEL: 01962 867014/ 777546.

SPCK Bookshops

24 The Square. SO23 9EX. Open 9-5.30. *STOCK: Secondhand theological books.* TEL: 01962 866617.

Todd and Austin Antiques of Winchester

2 Andover Rd. SO23 7BS. (G. Austin). Est. 1964. Open Tues.-Fri. 9.30-5, Sat. 9.30-12.30. SIZE: Medium. *STOCK: 19th C glass, paperweights, silver, tea caddies, boxes, objets d'art and decorative items; late 18th-late 19th C pottery and porcelain, some Oriental porcelain; small furniture; hanging lamps and chandeliers.* LOC: 1 minute from Winchester Station. PARK: Easy. TEL: 01962 869824. SER: Selected range on view at Lainston House Hotel, Sparsholt, Nr Winchester; finder service.

Webb Fine Arts

38 Jewry St. SO23 8RY. (D.H. Webb). Est. 1955. Open 9-5, Sat. 9-1. SIZE: Large - 4 floors. *STOCK: Oil paintings and furniture.* PARK: Own. TEL: 01962 842273; website - www. webbfinearts.co.uk. SER: Valuations; restorations (oil paintings); lining and framing; buys at auction (paintings). VAT: Stan/Spec.

Winchester Antiques

20-20A Jewry St. SO23 8RZ. (D. Letts). Est. 1997. Open 10-5. SIZE: Large. *STOCK: Walnut, mahogany and oak furniture, French and English pine and painted, 17th-19th C; collectables, smalls, brass and copper; memorabilia.* LOC: Town centre, 5 minutes from station. PARK: Adjacent. TEL: 01962 850123. SER: Valuations; restorations (repairs and stripping); buys at auction (furniture).

HEREFORD

Bournville Books
Manor Cottage, Lower Bullingham. HR2 6EG. (Frank Nutt). Est. 1972. Open by appointment only. SIZE: Small. *STOCK: Antique and rare books, leather books for decoration.* TEL: 01432 261263. FAIRS: Newark.

I. and J.L. Brown Ltd
Whitestone Park, Whitestone. HR1 3SE. Open 9-5.30. SIZE: Large. *STOCK: Matched sets of period country chairs, £1,500-£7,500; English country and French provincial furniture, reproduction furniture, decorative items.* LOC: A4103, 4 miles from Hereford towards Worcester. PARK: Easy. TEL: 01432 851991; fax - 01432 851994; e-mail - enquiries@brownantiques.com; website - www.brownantiques.com. SER: Restorations; re-rushing chairs. VAT: Stan/Spec.

Great Brampton House Antiques Ltd
Great Brampton House, Madley. HR2 9NA. (Lady Pidgeon). LAPADA. Est. 1969. Open 9-5, Sat. and Sun. by appointment only. SIZE: Large. *STOCK: English and French furniture and fine art.* TEL: 01981 250244; fax - 01981 251333.

Hereford Antique Centre
128 Widemarsh St. HR4 9HN. (G.P. Smith). Est. 1991. Open 10-5, Sun. 12-5. SIZE: 30 dealers. *STOCK: General antiques and collectables.* PARK: Easy. TEL: 01432 266242. SER: Restorations; shipping.

Warings of Hereford
45-47 St. Owen St. HR1 2JB. Open 9-6 including Sun. *STOCK: Fine 19th C furniture, farmhouse pine; gold and silver.* TEL: 01432 276241.

KINGTON

Castle Hill Books
12 Church St. HR5 3AZ. (Peter Newman). Est. 1988. Open 10.30-1, Sat. 10.30-1 and 2-5. *STOCK: Out of print, secondhand and antiquarian books especially British topography, Herefordshire, Radnorshire, Wales, archaeology.* LOC: Off High St. PARK: Easy. TEL: 01544 231195; fax - 01544 231161; e-mail - sales@castlehillbooks.co.uk; website - www.castlehillbooks.co.uk.

LEDBURY

John Nash Antiques and Interiors
Tudor House, 17c High St. HR8 1DS. (J. Nash and L. Calleja). LAPADA. Est. 1972. Open 10-5.30, Sun. by appointment. SIZE: Medium.

Birmingham 1892, maker's mark of Elkington & Co Ltd. (Bottom) London 1823, maker's mark of William Chawner II. The fork at the top is almost perfect, whilst the one at the bottom is in a very sorry state. The tines are uneven and are considerably shorter than they would originally have been and the original initials or crest has been erased and replaced by a later Victorian monogram. Fiddle and thread pattern is always desirable but this is a single fork, in poor condition, and therefore worth only £15-£20. (Private collection)

From an article entitled "Buying a Set of Old Silver Spoons and Forks" by Jane Ewart which appeared in the May 2002 issue of **Antique Collecting**. For more details and to subscribe see page 21.

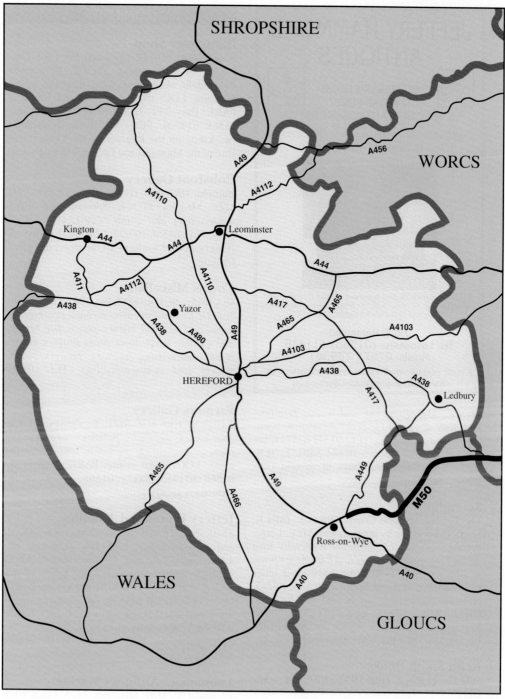

Dealers and Shops in Herefordshire					
Hereford	5	Ledbury	3	Ross-on-Wye	7
Kington	1	Leominster	9	Yazor	1

STOCK: Mahogany, oak and walnut furniture, 18th-20th C, £300-£10,000; decorative items, fabrics and wallpapers. TEL: 01531 635714; fax - 01531 635050; home - 01684 540432. SER: Valuations; restorations; buys at auction (furniture, silver). VAT: Stan/Spec.

Serendipity
The Tythings, Preston Court. HR8 2LL. (Mrs R. Ford). Open 9-5 or by appointment. SIZE: Large. *STOCK: 17th-20th C furniture especially long dining tables, sets of chairs and four-poster beds; general antiques.* LOC: Take A449 for 3 miles from Ledbury, at roundabout turn left on B4215, premises 500yds. on left behind half-timbered house. TEL: 01531 660245/660380. SER: Restorations (furniture); buys at auction. FAIRS: Kensington; Olympia. VAT: Stan/Spec.

Keith Smith Books
78B The Homend. HR8 1BX. PBFA. Est. 1986. Open 10-5. SIZE: Small. *STOCK: Secondhand and old books.* LOC: Main road. PARK: Easy. TEL: 01531 635336; e-mail - keith@ksbooks. demon.co.uk. SER: Valuations. FAIRS: Royal National Book, London; Churchdown Book, Gloucester.

Barometer Shop
New St. HR6 8DP. (R. Cookson). Est. 1965. Open 9-5 or by appointment. *STOCK: Barometers, barographs, clocks, scientific instruments, period furniture.* LOC: Corner of A49 and Broad St. PARK: Easy. TEL: 01568 613652/610200; fax - 01568 610200. SER: Valuations; restorations (workshop on the Register of the Conservation Unit of the Museums and Galleries Commission).

Coltsfoot Gallery
Hatfield. HR6 0SF. (Edwin Collins). Est. 1971. SIZE: Medium. *STOCK: Sporting and wildlife watercolours and prints, £20-£2,000.* PARK: Easy. TEL: 01568 760277. SER: Restoration and conservation of works of art on paper; mounting; framing.

Courts Miscellany
48A Bridge St. HR6 6DZ. Est. 1983. Open 10.30-5. *STOCK: General curios including corkscrews, social and political history, police, fire brigade and sporting items; tools, horse brasses, enamel signs - advertising, military, brewery; studio pottery and commemoratives.* TEL: 01568 612995.

Farmers Gallery
1 High St. HR6 8LZ. SIZE: 6 galleries. *STOCK: 18th-19th C furniture, paintings, prints, maps, frames, needlework, porcelain and decorative items.* LOC: Town centre. PARK: Easy. TEL: 01568 611413; fax - 01568 611141. SER: Exhibition gallery available.

Jeffery Hammond Antiques
Shaftesbury House, 38 Broad St. HR6 8BS. (J. and E. Hammond). LAPADA. Resident. Est. 1970. Open 9-6, Sun. by appointment. SIZE: Medium. *STOCK: Furniture and works of art, 18th to early 19th C.* LOC: Town centre. PARK: Own. TEL: 01568 614876; fax - same; e-mail - enquiries@jefferyhammondantiques.co.uk; website - www.jefferyhammondantiques.co.uk. SER: Valuations; buys at auction (furniture). VAT: Stan/Spec.

Leominster Antiques Market
14 Broad St. HR6 8BS. Est. 1975. Open 10-5. SIZE: 18 units - 3 floors. *STOCK: Mahogany, oak, pine, kitchenalia, collectables, toys, glass, textiles, silver, postcards, Gaudy Welsh, fine china, pictures, jewellery, tools.* PARK: Nearby. TEL: 01568 612189.

Linden House Antiques
1 Draper's Lane. HR6 8ND. (C. Scott-Mayfield).
Est. 1987. Open 11-5. SIZE: Large. *STOCK:
Furniture, 18th C to Edwardian, £100-£10,000,
pictures, 1700's to 1940's, £50-£5,000; silver and
jewellery, porcelain and pottery, carvings, objets
d'art, kitchenalia, textiles, 18th-20th C, £5-
£3,000.* LOC: Town centre. PARK: Easy. TEL:
01568 620350; home - 01568 612127; mobile -
07790 671722; e-mail - busca@lineone.net. SER:
Valuations; restorations (re-upholstery, jewellery
repair). FAIRS: Bingley Hall.

The Old Shoe Box
Church St. HR6. Open 10-5. *STOCK: Furniture,
china, prints, watercolours and smalls.* TEL:
01568 611414. SER: Mount cutting; framing.

T'Morrows Antiques
41 High St. HR6. (J. Connolly, C. Scott-Mayfield
and M. Clayton). Open 9.30-1.30. SIZE: Small.
*STOCK: Furniture, mainly small, Victoriana and
collectables, £5-£550.* PARK: Easy. TEL: Mobile
- 07790 671722; home - 01568 612127 (to 9pm).
FAIRS: Bingley Hall.

ROSS-ON-WYE

Baileys Home & Garden
Station Approach. HR9 7BW. (M. and S.Bailey).
Est. 1978. Open 9-5. SIZE: Medium. *STOCK:
Garden furniture, tools, orchard ladders, junk-
style garden painted furniture, kitchenware,
quilts, Welsh blankets, French and English
lighting, bathrooms (including copper baths,
metal washstands), fireplaces, industrial lamps,
factory trolleys, machinists' stools, shoe lasts,
baskets, bobbins, etc.* LOC: Gloucester side of
Ross, just off A40. TEL: 01989 563015; fax -
01989 768172.

Fritz Fryer Antique Lighting
12 Brookend St. HR9 7EG. (F. Fryer and J.
Graham). Est. 1981. Open 10-5.30, Sun. by appointment. SIZE: Large. *STOCK: Decorative lighting,
original shades, Georgian to Art Deco.* TEL: 01989
567416; fax - 01989 566742; e-mail - ffryer@
wyenet.co.uk; website - www.fritz fryer.co.uk. SER:
Restorations; lighting scheme design.

Robin Lloyd Antiques
23/24 Brookend St. HR9 7EE. Est. 1970. Open
9.30-5.30. SIZE: Large - 5 showrooms. *STOCK:
Country furniture, mainly long tables and early
oak, longcase clocks.* LOC: 100yds. downhill
from Market Hall. PARK: Nearby. TEL: 01989
562123; fax - same. SER: Export (especially to
USA). VAT: Global/Spec.

Merchants House Antiques
36 High St. HR9 5HD. (N. Cockman). Est. 1969.
Open 10-5. SIZE: Large. *STOCK: General
antiques.* LOC: A40. TEL: 01989 563010. SER:
Valuations; restorations; buys at auction. VAT:
Spec.

Ross Old Book and Print Shop
51 and 52 High St. HR9 5HH. Open 10-5. CL:
Mid-Jan. to mid-Feb. *STOCK: Antiquarian and
secondhand books, prints and maps.* TEL: 01989
567458; fax - 01989 567861; e-mail - enquiries
@rossoldbooks.wyenet.co.uk; websites - www.
antiqueprints.com and www.abebooks.com.

Ross-on-Wye Antiques Centre
Gloucester Rd. HR9 5BU. (Michael Aslanian).
Est. 1996. Open 10.30-5, Sun. by appointment.
CL: Bank Holidays. SIZE: Large. *STOCK: Wide
variety of general antiques and collectables, from
BC to 1950's.* LOC: Town centre. TEL: 01989
762290; fax - 01989 762291. SER: Valuations;
buys at auction.

Waterfall Antiques
2 High St. HR9 5HL. (O. McCarthy). Est. 1995.
Open 10-4, Wed. and Fri. 9.30-12. SIZE:
Medium. *STOCK: Country pine furniture,
Victorian and Edwardian; china and general
antiques.* PARK: At rear. TEL: 01989 563103;
mobile - 07932 105542. SER: Valuations.

YAZOR

M. and J. Russell
The Old Vicarage. HR4 7BA. Est. 1969. Usually
open Fri. to Mon. and evenings, other times
appointment advisable. SIZE: Medium. *STOCK:
English period oak and country furniture, some
garden antiques.* LOC: 7 miles west of Hereford
on A480. PARK: Easy. TEL: 01981 590674.
SER: Valuations. VAT: Spec. *Mainly Trade.*

*Two spoons
from the Tek
Sing Cargo
at £48 the
pair. (Robert
McPherson)*

Items salvaged from shipwrecks are evocative,
affordable and find many different types of
buyers. From an article entitled "Shipwreck
Ceramics" by Patricia Hunter which appeared in
the March 2002 issue of **Antique Collecting**. For
more details and to subscribe see page 21.

ABBOTS LANGLEY, Nr. Watford

Dobson's Antiques
53 High St. WD5 0AA. (G.C and F.W. Dobson). Est. 1926. Open 8.30-5.30. CL: Tues. pm. *STOCK: Carved oak, stripped pine, shipping goods, bric-a-brac, £5-£2,000.* LOC: 4 miles north of Watford. TEL: 01923 263186. VAT: Stan/Spec.

BALDOCK

The Attic
20 Whitehorse St. SG7 6QN. (P. Sheppard). Est. 1977. CL: Thurs. SIZE: Small. *STOCK: Small furniture, china, brass and copper, dolls and teddy bears, £5-£100.* LOC: 3 minutes from A1(M). PARK: Easy. TEL: 01462 893880.

Anthony Butt Antiques
7/9 Church St. SG7 5AE. Resident. Est. 1968. Open by appointment. SIZE: Small. *STOCK: English furniture, 17th-19th C, £500-£5,000; works of art and objects of interest.* Not Stocked: Bric-a-brac, shipping goods. PARK: Easy. TEL: 01462 895272. SER: Valuations. VAT: Spec.

Howards
33 Whitehorse St. SG7 6QF. (D.N. Howard). Est. 1970. Open 9.30-5.00. CL: Mon. *STOCK: Clocks, 18th-19th C, £200-£5,000.* PARK: Easy. TEL: 01462 892385. SER: Valuations; restorations and repairs (clocks). VAT: Spec.

Ralph and Bruce Moss
26 Whitehorse St. SG7 6QQ. (R.A. and B.A. Moss). Est. 1973. Open 9-6. SIZE: Large. *STOCK: Furniture, £100-£10,000; general antiques, £5-£5,000.* LOC: A505, in town centre. PARK: Own. TEL: 01462 892751; fax - same. VAT: Stan/Spec.

BARNET

C. Bellinger Antiques
91 Wood St. EN5 4BX. Est. 1974. Open Thurs., Fri. and Sat. 10-4 or by appointment. SIZE: Medium. *STOCK: Furniture, silver and plate, smalls.* LOC: Opposite Ravenscroft Park. PARK: Within 100yds. TEL: 020 8449 3467. VAT: Spec.

Michael Lipitch Ltd
P O Box 3146. EN4 0BP. Est. 1959. By appointment only. *STOCK: 18th to early 19th C English furniture, decoration and works of art.* TEL: 020 8441 43440; mobile - 07730 954347; e-mail - michaellipitch@hotmail.com. SER: Specialist advice. FAIRS: Grosvenor House. VAT: Spec. 020 8441 6050.

BERKHAMSTED

Home and Colonial
134 High St. HP4 3AT. (Alison and Graeme Reid-Davies and Liz and Tony Stanton-Kipping). Est. 1997. Open 10-5.30, Sun. 11-4.30. CL: Wed. SIZE: Large. *STOCK: Period and country furniture, Arts and Crafts, Art Deco, decorative antiques, clocks and barometers, metalware, pictures, porcelain, silver, glass, jewellery, textiles and costume, antiquarian books, radios, gramophones and telephones, toys and teddy bears, fireplaces, garden antiques, and lighting, £10-£10,000.* LOC: M25 junction 20; M1 junction 8. PARK: Easy. TEL: 01442 877007; e-mail - homeandcolonial@bt internet.com; website - www.homeandcolonial. co.uk. SER: Finder; design; prop hire.

BISHOP'S STORTFORD

Christopher Blair Antiques
Ivy House, Gaston Green. CM22 7QS. Open by appointment only. SIZE: Medium. *STOCK: Furniture and decorative items.* TEL: 01279 600566; fax - same.

David Penney
Grooms Cottage, Elsenham Hall, Elsenham. CM22 6DP. BHI. Est. 1973. Strictly no visitors, no stock held on premises. *STOCK: Watches, 18th-19th C, £500-£50,000; watch movements, 18th-19th C, £50-£5,000; horological books and ephemera, 18th-20th C, £5-£15,000.* TEL: 01279 814946; fax - 01279 814962; e-mail - info@ davidpenney.co.uk. SER: Valuations; restorations; specialist research; postal auction catalogue; buys at auction (watches, clocks and all technical horology). VAT: Stan/Spec. *Mail Order Only.*

The Windhill Antiquary
4 High St. CM23 2LT. (G.R. Crozier). Est. 1951. Open 10-1 and 2-4, appointment advisable. CL: Wed. pm. SIZE: Medium. *STOCK: English furniture, 18th C; carved and gilded wall mirrors, 17th-19th C.* Not Stocked: Shipping goods. LOC: Next to George Hotel. PARK: Up hill - first right. TEL: 01279 651587; home - 01920 821316.

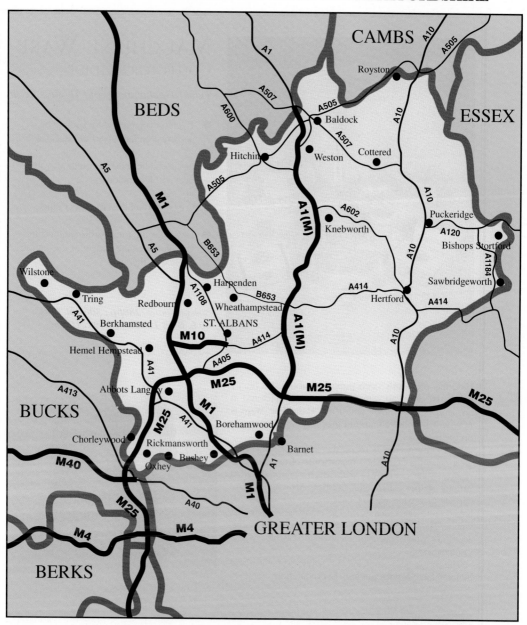

Dealers and Shops in Hertfordshire

Abbots Langley	1	Cottered	1	Redbourn	3
Baldock	4	Harpenden	1	Rickmansworth	1
Barnet	2	Hemel Hempstead	4	Royston	1
Berkhamsted	1	Hertford	5	Sawbridgeworth	3
Bishop's Stortford	3	Hitchin	6	St. Albans	7
Borehamwood	1	Knebworth	1	Tring	4
Bushey	2	Oxhey	1	Weston	1
Chorleywood	1	Puckeridge	1	Wheathampstead	2
				Wilstone	1

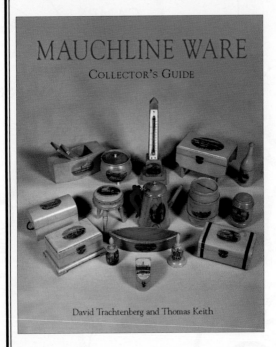

MAUCHLINE WARE
COLLECTOR'S GUIDE

David Trachtenberg and Thomas Keith

● The most comprehensive book to be published on the subject of Mauchline Ware

● Profusely illustrated throughout with over 350 illustrations

● Contains a full list of product ranges

● Describes the process of manufacture and illustrates the variety of decoration applied to the ware

Specifications: **288pp., 306 col. illus., 50 b. & w. 11x8½in./279x216mm.**

£35.00

Little has previously been published about this highly collectable souvenir ware which was manufactured in Scotland between 1840 and 1939. Mauchline Ware is now widely collected around the world and prices are on the increase.

This much needed book on the subject documents in great detail the history and manufacture of the ware and catalogues the vast array of items which were produced in various shapes, sizes and finishes. Mauchline Ware appeals to a wide span of collectors as the articles are linked to activities such as sewing, smoking, reading and writing. The important connection between Robert Burns, Scotland's national poet, and the town of Mauchline is also examined.

The book also contains a chapter on care and maintenance. A price guide is in preparation.

BOREHAMWOOD

Barnet-Cattanach BADA
The Old Marble Works, 18 Glenhaven Ave.
WD6 1BB. LAPADA. Est. 1977. Open by
appointment. *STOCK: 18th to early 19th C
furniture and accessories.* PARK: Easy. TEL:
020 7727 0460/020 8207 6792; fax - 020 8381
5889. SER: Restorations (furniture). FAIRS:
Olympia.

BUSHEY, Nr. Watford

Bushey Antiques Centre
39 High St. WD23 1BD. (Graham Lindsay). Est.
1983. Open 9.30-5.00, Sun. 10-4.00, prior phone
call advisable. SIZE: 14 dealers. *STOCK:
Furniture, 18th-20th C, £50-£500; smalls,
collectables, clocks, dolls and jewellery, £5-£250;
fireplaces and chimney pieces, 18th-19th C,
£160-£800; pictures.* LOC: Between Stanmore,
Harrow and Watford. PARK: At rear. TEL: 020
8950 5040; home - same. SER: Valuations;
restorations (woodwork and furniture); buys at
auction (furniture); framing. VAT: Spec.

Country Life Interiors
33a High St. WD3 1BD. (Peter Myers). Est.
1981. Open 10-6. SIZE: Large. *STOCK:
Victorian and Edwardian, European and
Scandinavian original pine, French country oak;
kitchenalia, watercolours, china and Art Deco.*
PARK: Easy. TEL: 020 8950 8575; fax - 020
8950 6982; e-mail - sales@countrylifeinteriors;
website - www.countrylifeinteriors.com. VAT:
Stan.

CHORLEYWOOD

Pattison's Architectural Antiques incorporating The Architectural Salvage Store
Unit 6, Darvells Works, Common Rd. WD3 5LP.
(Tony Pattison). Est. 1992. Open 9.30-1 and 2-
5.30, Sat. 9-1. SIZE: Large *STOCK: Doors, glass,
18th C to 1930, £5-£1,000; fireplaces, marble
and stone, 18th C to 1920, £500-£3,000; garden
ornaments, 19th C to 1950, £1,000-£2,000.* LOC:
A404 from junction 18, M25. After .75 mile turn
left at lights to town centre, premises 500yds.
on right. PARK: Easy. TEL: 01923 284196;
fax - 01923 282214; e-mail - tony@pattant.com.
SER: Restorations (glass, marble, stone). VAT:
Stan/Spec.

COTTERED

Wareside Antiques
SG9 9PT. (David Broxup). Est. 1983. Open by
appointment only. *STOCK: Victorian dining room
furniture, especially extending dining tables; sets
of 6,8, and 10 Victorian dining chairs, chiffoniers,
buffets etc.* TEL: 01763 281234.

HARPENDEN

Meg Andrews
Est. 1982. Open by appointment. *STOCK:
Worldwide collectable, hangable and wearable
antique costume and textiles including Chinese
embroideries and woven fabrics, robes, shoes,
hats, large hangings, Morris and Arts and Crafts
embroideries and woven cloths, Paisley shawls,
samplers, silkwork pictures; European costumes
and textiles.* TEL: 01582 460107; home - same;
fax - 01582 461112; e-mail - meg.andrews@
clara.co.uk; website - www.meg-andrews.com.
SER: Valuations; advice. FAIRS: Manchester and
Hammersmith Town Hall Costume and Textile.
VAT: Spec.

HEMEL HEMPSTEAD

Abbey Antiques - Fine Jewellery & Silver
97 High St., Old Town. HP1 3AH. (L., E., S. and
C. Eames). Est. 1962. Open 9.30-5.30. SIZE:
Medium. *STOCK: Silver, plate, jewellery, £5-
£5,000.* LOC: M1, junction 8, M25, junction 20,
bypass main shopping centre to old town. PARK:
Easy. TEL: 01442 264667. SER: Valuations;
jewellery design and repair. VAT: Stan/Global.

Cherry Antiques
101-103 High St. HP1 3AH. (A. and R.S. Cullen).
Open 9.30-4.30. CL: Wed. pm. SIZE: Medium.
*STOCK: Victorian, Edwardian, and some period
furniture, pine, general antiques, collectors' and
decorative items, bric-a-brac, needlework tools,
dolls, linens, some silver, plate, jewellery, glass,
pottery, porcelain, brass, copper, some shipping
items.* PARK: Easy. TEL: 01442 264358. VAT:
Stan/Spec.

Off the Wall
52 High St., Old Town. HP1 3AF. (Michelle
Smith). Est. 2001. Open 10-5.30, Sun. 11-4. SIZE:
Small. *STOCK: Antiques and collectables, from
1830; some furniture including pine dressers and
tables.* LOC: Near St. Mary's Church. PARK:
Nearby. TEL: 01442 218300.

The Pine Emporium

Hilliers Garden Centre, Leighton Buzzard Rd., Piccotts End. (J. Greatrix). Open 9-5.30, Sun. 11-4. *STOCK: Pine furniture, antique and reclaimed, from 18th C; oak, from 18th C.* TEL: 01442 244644. SER: Restorations; bespoke manufacture.

Beckwith and Son

St. Nicholas Hall, St. Andrew St. SG14 1HZ. (G.C.M. Gray). Est. 1904. Open 9-1 and 2-5.30. SIZE: Large. *STOCK: General antiques, furniture, silver, pottery, porcelain, prints, weapons, clocks, watches, glass.* Not Stocked: Fabrics. LOC: A414/B158. PARK: Adjacent. TEL: 01992 582079; e-mail - sales@beckwith andsonantiques.co.uk; website - www.beckwith andsonantiques.co.uk. SER: Valuations; restorations (fine porcelain, furniture, upholstery, silver, clocks). VAT: Spec.

Gillmark Gallery

25 Parliament Sq. SG14 1EX. (Mark Pretlove and Gill Woodhouse). Est. 1997. CL: Mon. and Thurs. pm. SIZE: Medium. *STOCK: Maps and prints, 16th-20th C, £10-£5000; secondhand books, 18th-20th C, £1-£5,000.* LOC: 15 yards from roundabout at junction of A414 and B158. PARK: Nearby. TEL: 01992 534444; fax - 01992 554734; e-mail - gillmark@btinternet.com; website - www.gillmark.com. SER: Valuations; restorations (conservation, framing and restoration antique prints and maps). VAT: Stan.

Hertford Antiques

51 St Andrew St. SG14 1HZ. (S.D. Garratt and R.F. Norris). Est. 1994. Open 10-5.30, Sun.11-4.30. SIZE: Large - 50+ dealers. *STOCK: Furniture, jewellery, porcelain, silver, glass, books, £5-£4,000.* LOC: Next to St Andrew's Church. PARK: Easy. TEL: 01992 504504; fax - 01992 589776; e-mail - simonhertfordantiques.fsnet.co.uk; website - www. hertfordantiques.co.uk.

Robert Horton Antiques

13 Castle St. SG14 1ER. BWCMG. Est. 1972. Open 9-5. *STOCK: Clocks, barometers, furniture.* TEL: 01992 587546; fax - same. SER: Repairs and restorations (movements, cases, dials). VAT: Stan/Spec.

Tapestry Antiques

27 St. Andrew St. SG14 1HZ. (D.W. and P. Stokes). Est. 1973. Open 10-1 and 2-5, Sat. 10-5.30, Sun. by appointment. CL: Thurs. SIZE: Medium. *STOCK: Furniture, 18th-19th C, £100-£1,000; porcelain, 19th to early 20th C, £25-£500; brass and copper, 18th-19th C, £50-£300.* LOC: Near railway station. PARK: Easy and behind premises. TEL: 01992 587438. SER: Valuations.

Michael Gander

10-11 Bridge St. SG5 2DE. Est. 1973. Open Mon. 3-6, Wed., Thurs. and Sat. 9-6, or by appointment. *STOCK: Period furniture, metalware, ceramics, glass, pictures.* TEL: 01462 432678; mobile - 07885 728976.

Hanbury Antiques

86 Tilehouse St. SG5 2DU. (Mrs M.D. Hanbury). Est. 1988. CL: Wed afternoons. SIZE: Small. *STOCK: Period furniture, porcelain, silver, jewellery.* LOC: Continuation of Bridge St. PARK: 100 yards. TEL: 01462 420487; home - same. SER: Valuations.

Eric T. Moore

24 Bridge St. SG5 2DF. Open 9.30-5, Sat. 9.30-5.30. SIZE: Large. *STOCK: Secondhand and antiquarian books, maps and prints.* LOC: Bottom of Tilehouse St. TEL: 01462 450497; e-mail - booksales@erictmoore.co.uk; website - www.erictmoore.co.uk. SER: Book binding and search.

Geoffrey Norman

93 Walsworth Rd. SG4 9SX. Open 10-6. SIZE: Small. *STOCK: Collectables, to 1950's; furniture, Georgian to 1930's.* PARK: Easy. TEL: 01462 421138; home - 01462 450783.

Phillips of Hitchin (Antiques) Ltd

BADA
The Manor House. SG5 1JW. (J. and B. Phillips). Est. 1884. Open 9-5.30, Sat. by appointment. SIZE: Small. *STOCK: Mahogany furniture, 18th to early 19th C, £500-£20,000.* LOC: In Bancroft, main street of Hitchin. PARK: Easy. TEL: 01462 432067; fax - 01462 441368. SER: VAT: Spec.

Tom Salusbury Antiques

7 Nutleigh Grove. SG5 2NH. Est. 1963. Open by appointment only. SIZE: Small. *STOCK: Furniture, to 1910, £100-£3,000.* LOC: 3 miles from A1, junction 8. PARK: Easy. TEL: 01462 454274; fax - same; 01462 441520. SER: Valuations; restorations (especially upholstery). VAT: Stan/Spec.

KNEBWORTH

Hamilton Billiards & Games Co.
Park Lane. SG3 6PJ. (H.Hamilton). Est. 1980. Open 9-5, weekends and evenings by appointment. SIZE: Large. *STOCK: Victorian and Edwardian billiard tables, £3,000-£18,000; 19th C convertible billiard/dining tables and accessories, £30-£5,000; indoor and outdoor games.* LOC: Near railway station. PARK: Easy. TEL: 01438 811995. SER: Valuations; restorations (billiard tables and furniture); buys at auction (as stock). VAT: Stan.

PUCKERIDGE

St. Ouen Antiques
Vintage Corner, Old Cambridge Rd. SG11 1SA. (J., J. and S.T. Blake and Mrs P.B. Francis). Est. 1918. Open 10.30-5. SIZE: Large. *STOCK: English and Continental furniture, decorative items, silver, porcelain, pottery, glass, clocks, barometers, paintings.* TEL: 01920 821336. SER: Valuations; restorations.

REDBOURN, Nr. Hemel Hempstead

Bushwood Antiques
Stags End Equestrian Centre, Gaddesden Lane. HP2 6HN. (Anthony Bush). LAPADA. Est. 1967. Open 8.30-4, Sat. 10-4. SIZE: Medium. *STOCK: 18th-19th C furniture, accessories and objects of art.* LOC: Telephone for directions. PARK: Easy. TEL: 01582 794700; fax - 01582 792299; e-mail - antiques@bushwood.co.uk; website - www.bushwood.co.uk.

J.N. Antiques
86 High St. AL3 7BD. (M. and J. Brunning). Est. 1975. Open 9-6. SIZE: Medium. *STOCK: Furniture, 18th-20th C, £5-£3,000; brass and copper, porcelain, 19th C, £5-£100; pictures, 19th-20th C.* PARK: 50 yds. TEL: 01582 793603; e-mail - mbrunning@jnantiques.fsnet.co.uk. SER: Valuations. VAT: Spec.

Tim Wharton Antiques
24 High St. AL3 7LL. LAPADA. Est. 1970. Open 10-5.30, Sat. 10-4. CL: Mon. and usually Thurs. *STOCK: Oak and country furniture, 17th-19th C; some mahogany, 18th to early 19th C; copper, brass, ironware and general small antiques.* LOC: On left entering village from St. Albans on A5183. PARK: Easy. TEL: 01582 794371; mobile - 07850 622880; e-mail - tim@timwhartonantiques.co.uk; website - www.timwhartonantiques.co.uk. VAT: Stan/Spec.

RICKMANSWORTH

Clive A. Burden Ltd
Elmcote House, The Green, Croxley Green. WD3 3HN. (Philip D. Burden). ABA. IMCOS. Est. 1966. Open by appointment only. SIZE: Medium. *STOCK: Maps, 1500-1860, £5-£1,500; natural history, botanical and Vanity Fair prints, 1720-1870, £1-£1,000; antiquarian books, pre-1870, £10-£5,000.* TEL: 01923 778097/772387; fax - 01923 896520. SER: Valuations; buys at auction (as stock). VAT: Stan.

ROYSTON

Philip Dawes Antiques
37-39 Kneesworth St. SG8 5AB. Est. 1997. Open 9.30-5. CL: Mon. SIZE: Medium. *STOCK: Oak, mahogany and pine, 18th to early 20th C, £100-£2,000; garden furniture and ornaments, £50-£500; decorative items, 19th-20th C, £25-£100.* PARK: Easy. TEL: 01763 243039. SER: Valuations; restorations (furniture including caning and upholstery); buys at auction. VAT: Stan.

A tile panel comprising eight 6-inch tiles, c.1900.

From an article entitled "William De Morgan" by Johanna Freidwall" which appeared in the February 2002 issue of **Antique Collecting**. For more details and to subscribe see page 21.

SAWBRIDGEWORTH

Charnwood Antiques and Arcane Antiques Centre

Unit E2 Ground Floor, The Maltings, Station Rd. CM21 9JX. (Nigel Hoy and Nicola Smith). EADA. GMC. Open 10-5, Sat. and Sun. 11-5. CL: Mon. SIZE: Large. *STOCK: Furniture, 18th C to Edwardian, £500-£8,000; porcelain, glass, silver, longcase clocks, 19th C oils and watercolours.* LOC: From Harlow on A1184, turn right at first mini roundabout into Station Rd., over river bridge, first right into maltings. Shop 100 yards on left. PARK: Easy. TEL: 01279 600562; mobile-07957 551899. SER: Restorations (furniture including structural and veneer, French polishing, traditional upholstery, desk re-leathering, brass ware supplied and fitted).

The Herts and Essex Antiques Centre

The Maltings, Station Rd. CM21 9JX. Est. 1982. Open 10-5, Sat. and Sun. 10.30-5.30. SIZE: Large - over 100 dealers. *STOCK: General antiques and collectables, £1-£2,000.* LOC: Opposite B.R. station. PARK: Easy. TEL: 01279 722044.

Riverside Antiques Ltd

The Maltings, Station Rd. CM21 9JX. (Chris Scott and John Maynard). EADA. Est. 1998. Open 10-5 including Sun. SIZE: Large. *STOCK: General antiques, art and collectables.* PARK: Easy. TEL: 01279 600985; fax - 01279 726398. SER: Valuations; restorations.

ST. ALBANS

By George! Antiques Centre

23 George St. AL3 4ER. Open 10-5, Sun. 1-5. SIZE: 20 dealers. *STOCK: A wide range of general antiques, jewellery and collectables.* LOC: 100yds. from Clock Tower. PARK: Internal courtyard (loading) and Christopher Place (NCP) nearby. TEL: 01727 853032. SER: Restorations.

The Clock Shop - Philip Setterfield of St. Albans

161 Victoria St. AL1 3TA.. Est. 1974. Open 11-4. CL: Thurs. *STOCK: Clocks and watches.* LOC: City station bridge. TEL: 01727 856633; fax - same. SER: Restorations; repairs (clocks, watches, barometers). VAT: Stan/Spec.

Forget-me-Knot Antiques

at Over the Moon, 27 High St. AL3 4EH. (Heather Sharp). Est. 1987. Open 9.30-5.30, Sun. by appointment. *STOCK: Mainly Victorian jewellery and collectables, specializing in silver name brooches.* LOC: Opposite The Tudor Tavern. TEL: 01727 848907. SER: Valuations. VAT: Stan.

James of St Albans

11 George St. AL3 4ER. (S.N. and W. James). Est. 1957. Open 10-5, Thurs. 10-4. *STOCK: Furniture including reproduction; smalls, brass and copper; topographical maps and prints of Hertfordshire.* TEL: 01727 856996. VAT: Stan/Spec.

Magic Lanterns

at By George! Antiques Centre, 23 George St. AL3 4ES. (Josie A. Marsden). Est. 1987. Open 10-5, Thurs. 11-5, Sat. 10-5.30, Sun. 1-5. SIZE: Medium. *STOCK: Lighting - candle, gas and early electric, 1800-1950's, £35-£1,000; small furniture, prints, mirrors, china, metalware, fire accessories, 1850-1950, £25-£500.* LOC: Near the abbey. PARK: Multi-storey nearby. TEL: 01727 853032/865680.

Oriental Rug Gallery Ltd

42 Verulam Rd. AL3 4DQ. (R. Mathias and J. Blair). BORDA. Open 10-5.30. *STOCK: Russian, Afghan, Turkish and Persian carpets, rugs and kelims; Oriental objets d'art.* TEL: +44 (0) 1727 841046; fax - same; e-mail - rugs@orinetalruggallery.com; website - www.orientalruggallery.com.

Christopher Wharton Goldsmiths

1 George St. AL3 4ER. FGA DGA. Est. 1967. Open 9-5.30. SIZE: Medium. *STOCK: Silver and plate, 18th-20th C, £20-£2,000; jewellery, mainly modern, £20-£5,000.* LOC: Near clock tower. PARK: Pay and Display at bottom of street or multi-storey, city centre. TEL: 01727 859489; fax - 01727 855474. SER: Registered valuer (jewellery and silver); goldsmithing, gem testing; buys at auction (silver). VAT: Stan.

TRING

John Bly   BADA

The Old Billiards Room, Church Yard. HP23 5AG. Est. 1891. Open Wed.-Sat. 9.30-4.30. SIZE: Large. *STOCK: English furniture.* LOC: Next to church. PARK: Easy. TEL: 01442 890802. SER: Valuations; restorations; consultancy. FAIRS: BADA; Grosvenor House; West Palm Beach.

Country Clocks

3 Pendley Bridge Cottages, Tring Station. HP23 5QU. (T. Cartmell). Resident. Est. 1976. Open daily, prior 'phone call advisable. SIZE: Small. *STOCK: Clocks, 18th-19th C.* LOC: One mile from A41 in village, cottage nearest canal bridge. PARK: Easy. TEL: 01442 825090. SER: Restorations (clocks).

Farrelly Antiques

The Long Barn, 50 High St. HP23 5AG. (P. Farrelly). TVADA. Open 9-4. *STOCK: Furniture.* TEL: 01442 891905. SER: Restorations. VAT: Spec.

New England House Antiques

50 High St. HP23 5AG. (Jennifer and Suj Munjee). Est. 1990. Open 10.30-5. CL: Mon. SIZE: Large - 6 showrooms on 3 floors. *STOCK: Fine Georgian and Victorian furniture, £100-£10,000; paintings, glass, silver, decorative furnishings specialising in antique table lights and hand-made shades.* LOC: A41 towards Aylesbury. PARK: Next to shop. TEL: 01442 827262; home - 01462 431914; website - www.newenglandhouseantiques.co.uk. SER: Valuations; restorations (paintings, metalwork and furniture); searches undertaken. VAT: Stan/Spec.

WATFORD

Thwaites Fine Stringed Instruments

33 Chalk Hill, WD19 4BL. (J.H. and W.J. Pamplin and C.A. Lovell). Est. 1971. Open 9-5, Sat. 9.30-12.30. *STOCK: Stringed instruments, from violins to double basses.* PARK: Own. TEL: 01923 232412; fax - 01923 232463; e-mail - sales@thwaites.com; website - www.thwaites.com. SER: Restorations.

WESTON, Nr. Hitchin

Weston Antiques

Weston Barns, Hitchin Rd. (M.A. Green). Est. 1974. Open Tues.-Sat. 10.30-5.30. SIZE: Small. *STOCK: Period furniture, longcase and mantel clocks, mainly 18th-19th C.* LOC: Off B197, near junction 9 A1(M). PARK: Easy. TEL: 01462 790646; fax - 01462 680304; mobile - 07802 403800; e-mail - greencoantiques@BTinternet.com; website - www.antiques-shop.co.uk. SER: Valuations; restorations (furniture and clocks). VAT: Spec.

Founders: F.G. Collins & C. Collins in 1907

Eighteenth and nineteenth century English furniture

Antiques purchased

Collins Antiques

Wheathampstead

Hertfordshire AL4 8AP England
Telephone: 01582 833111
www.antique-finder.co.uk

Junction 4 on the A1(M) 5 miles

WHEATHAMPSTEAD

Collins Antiques (F.G. and C. Collins Ltd.)

Corner House. AL4 8AP. (S.J. and M.C. Collins). Est. 1907. Open 9-1 and 2-5. SIZE: Medium. *STOCK: Furniture, mahogany, 1730-1920, £100-£8,000; oak, 1600-1800, £50-£5,000; walnut, 1700-1740, £75-£3,000.* Not Stocked: Silver. LOC: London, A1(M) junction 4 to B653. PARK: Easy. TEL: 01582 833111. VAT: Stan/Spec.

The Old Bakery Antiques

3 Station Rd. AL4 8BU. (Maurice Shifrin). Open 10-6, Sun. 11-4. CL: Wed. SIZE: Large. *STOCK: 19th C furniture, £500-£1,000.* PARK: Easy, own. TEL: 01582 831999; fax - 01582 831555. VAT: Stan/Spec.

WILSTONE, Nr. Tring

Michael Armson (Antiques) Ltd

The Old Post Office, 34 Tring Rd. HP23 4PB. Est. 1970. Open 8-2. SIZE: Large. *STOCK: Furniture, 17th-19th C.* PARK: Easy. TEL: 01442 890990; fax - 01442 891167; mobile - 07860 910034; e-mail - armsonantiques@ic24.net; website - www.armsonantiques.com. FAIRS: NEC. VAT: Spec.

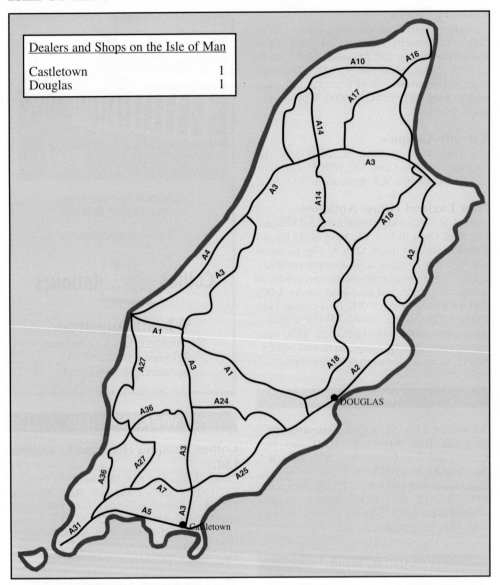

Dealers and Shops on the Isle of Man

Castletown	1
Douglas	1

CASTLETOWN

J. and H. Bell Antiques
22 Arbory St. IM9 1LJ. Est. 1965. Open Wed., Fri. and Sat. 10-5. SIZE: Medium. *STOCK: Jewellery, silver, china, early metalware, furniture, 18th-20th C, £5-£5,000.* TEL: 01624 823132 or 01624 822414. VAT: Stan/Spec.

DOUGLAS

John Corrin Antiques
73 Circular Rd. IM1 1AZ. Est. 1972. Open Sat. 10-4.30 otherwise by appointment. SIZE: Medium. *STOCK: Furniture, 18th-19th C, £100-£6,000; clocks, barometers, 19th C.* LOC: From the promenade, travel up Victoria St., this becomes Prospect Hill and Circular Rd. is on left. PARK: Easy. TEL: 01624 629655; home - 01624 621382.

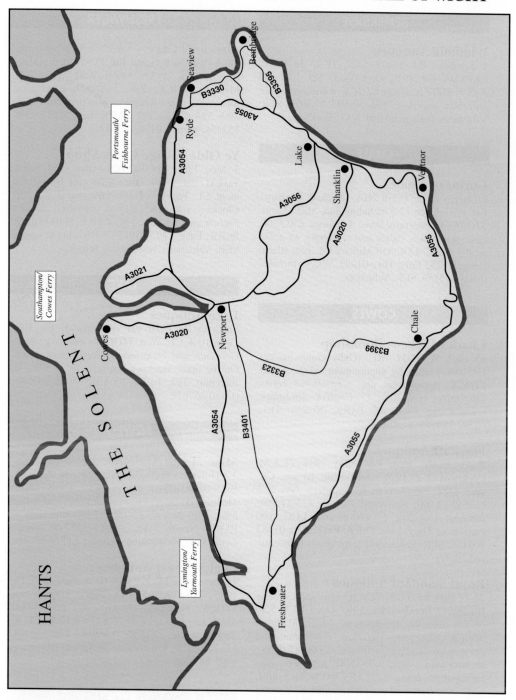

HANTS

THE SOLENT

Portsmouth/
Fishbourne Ferry

Southampton/
Cowes Ferry

Lymington/
Yarmouth Ferry

Bembridge

Seaview

B3330

B3395

A3055

Ryde

A3054

Lake

Shanklin

Ventnor

A3056

A3020

A3055

Cowes

A3021

A3020

Newport

Chale

B3399

B3333

A3054

B3401

A3055

Freshwater

<u>Dealers and Shops on the Isle of Wight</u>

Bembridge	1	Freshwater	2	Ryde	3
Chale	1	Lake	1	Seaview	1
Cowes	3	Newport	2	Shanklin	1
				Ventnor	3

BEMBRIDGE

Windmill Antiques
1 Foreland Rd. PO35 5XN. (E.J. de Kort). LAPADA. Est. 1970. Open Wed.- Sat. 10-1 and 2.15-4. SIZE: Medium. *STOCK: Furniture, silver, porcelain, jewellery.* TEL: 01983 873666. SER: Valuations; buys at auction. VAT: Stan/Spec.

CHALE

Curios of Chale
3 Church Place. PO38 2HA. (Michael Gregory). Est. 1983. Open 12-5 including Sun. SIZE: Large. *STOCK: Architectural items, fireplaces, £50-£500; general antiques, curios and taxidermy, £5-£500; mostly 19th C.* LOC: Off Military Rd., near Black-Gang. PARK: Easy. TEL: 01983 730230; mobile - 07811 835159. SER: Valuations.

COWES

Charles Dickens Bookshop
65 High St. PO31 7RL. (Gaby Goldscheider). Est. 1987. Open by appointment. SIZE: Small. *STOCK: Antiquarian and secondhand books, especially 19th-20th C English literature, nautical and children's.* PARK: Nearby. TEL: 02392 780155. SER: Postal.

Flagstaff Antiques
Tudor House, Bath Rd. PO31 7RH. (T.A.M. Cockram). Est. 1970. Open from 10 am. CL: Wed. SIZE: Small. *STOCK: Jewellery, 19th-20th C, £50-£2,000; porcelain, 19th C, £25-£1,000; pictures, 19th-20th C, £10-£1,000.* LOC: 100 yards from The Parade. PARK: Easy. TEL: 01983 200138. SER: Valuations; restorations (porcelain and silver).

Royal Standard Antiques
70-72 Park Rd. PO31 7LY. (Dennis and Caroline Bradbury). Resident. Est. 1992. Open 10.30-5.30 or any time by appointment. SIZE: Medium. *STOCK: Georgian, Victorian, Edwardian and French provincial furniture, £100-£1,000+; architectural items, £20-£500; pictures, commemoratives, breweriana, £5-£500.* LOC: 5 mins. walk from hydrofoil terminus; corner of Victoria Rd. PARK: Own, behind premises. TEL: 01983 281672; home - same. SER: Restorations; upholstery, caning, stained glass.

FRESHWATER

Aladdin's Cave
147/149 School Green Rd. PO40 9BB. (Mrs J. Dunn). Est. 1984. Open 9.30-4.30. SIZE: Medium. *STOCK: China, collectors' items, glass, linen, old pine, furniture, memorabilia, books, 19th-20th C, £5-£500.* PARK: Easy. TEL: 01983 752934; home - 01983 753846.

Ye Olde Village Clock Shop
3 Moa Place. PO40 9DS. (Ron and Sandra Tayler). Est. 1970. Open 9.30-1 or by appointment. CL: Tues and Thurs. SIZE: Small. *STOCK: Clocks - longcase, Vienna, carriage, bracket, French and novelty, 17th-19th C, £300-£6,000.* PARK: Easy. TEL: 01983 754193; home - same. SER: Valuations; restorations (clocks).

LAKE

Lake Antiques
Sandown Rd. PO36 9JP. (P. Burfield). Est. 1982. Open 10-4. CL: Wed. *STOCK: General antiques, Georgian and Victorian furniture, clocks.* LOC: On the main Sandown-Shanklin Rd. PARK: On forecourt. TEL: 01983 406888/865005; mobile - 07710 067678.

NEWPORT

Mike Heath Antiques
3-4 Holyrood St. PO30 5AU. (M. and B. Heath). Est. 1979. Open 9.30-5. CL: Thurs. SIZE: Medium. *STOCK: General antiques and bric-a-brac, 19th-20th C, £5-£500.* LOC: Off High St. PARK: Nearby. TEL: 01983 525748; home - same. SER: Restorations (copper and brass).

Lugley Street Antiques
13 Lugley St. PO30 5HD. (D.A. Newman). Est. 1986. Open 9.30-5. CL: Thurs. SIZE: Large. *STOCK: Furniture, clocks, china and collectables, late 18th to early 20th C, £5-£2,500.* LOC: Town centre. PARK: Meters. TEL: 01983 523348. SER: Valuations; restorations (furniture). VAT: Margin.

RYDE

Nooks & Crannies
60 High St. PO33 2RS. (David and Sally Burnett). Est. 1985. Open 9.30-1.30 and 2.30-5. CL: Thurs. SIZE: Small. *STOCK: China, glass, collectables, some furniture, gramophones and*

radios, Victorian to 1950's, £1-£750. PARK: Limited. TEL: 01983 568984; home - 01983 868261. FAIRS: Ardingly.

Royal Victoria Arcade
Union St. PO33 2LQ. Open 9-5.30; basement market open Thurs., Fri. and Sat. in summer. TEL: 01983 564661.

Uriah's Heap
9 Royal Victoria Arcade, Union St. PO33 2LQ. (F. Cross). Est. 1975. Open Wed., Fri. and Sat. 10-5. *STOCK: Small antiques, china, silver, collectables, linen, lace, fountain pens, jewellery.* PARK: Easy. TEL: 01983 564661.

SEAVIEW

Seaview Antiques
Regent House, High St. PO34 5EX. Est. 1970. Open 10-1, Sat. 10-5, Sun. (summer only) 12-5, other times by appointment. SIZE: Small. *STOCK: Pine, £100-£1,000; pottery, brass and copper, £10-£300; all 19th C.* LOC: From Ryde towards Seaview, follows signs for Seaview Hotel. PARK: Easy. TEL: 01983 613362; fax - same; home - 01983 760148.

SHANKLIN

The Shanklin Gallery
67 Regent St. PO37 7AE. (Jacqueline and Terry Townsend). FATG. Est. 1992. Open 9-5. SIZE: Medium. *STOCK: Oils, watercolours, engravings, prints, maps, 17th-20th C, £10-£2,000.* LOC: Town centre near railway station. PARK: Easy. TEL: 01983 863113; e-mail - spaltown@ compuserve.com. SER: Valuations; restorations (oils, watercolours and prints); framing.

VENTNOR

Peter Goodall
29 Pier St. PO38 1SX. Est. 1965. Open by appointment only. SIZE: Medium. *STOCK: Engravings, etchings, lithographs and aquatints, 17th-20th C, £5-£1,000.* TEL: 01983 856116. SER: Valuations.

Ultramarine
40B High St. PO38 1LG. (Milly Stevens). Open 10-1, Thurs. and Fri. 10-4, Sat. 10-2. CL: Wed. SIZE: Small. *STOCK: 19th-20th C collectables including jewellery, china, studio pottery, textiles and glass, £5-£500.* LOC: Central. PARK: Nearby. TEL: 01983 854062.

Ventnor Rare Books
19 Pier St. PO38 1ST. (N.C.R. and T.A. Traylen). ABA. PBFA. Est. 1989. Open 10-5, Wed. (school holidays only). *STOCK: Antiquarian and second-hand books, prints.* TEL: 01983 853706; fax - 01983 853357.

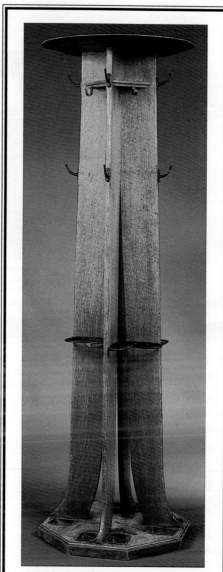

The Charles Rennie Mackintosh hat stand which made £15,500 at Bonhams' Glasgow sale.

From an Auction Report by Christopher Wight on Design 1860 to the Present Day, held by Bonhams at the Glasgow School of Art, on 8th November 2001 which appeared in the December 2001/January 2002 issue of **Antique Collecting**. For more details and to subscribe see page 21.

Roger Kirby Antiques

Caroline Farm, Ridge Row, Acrise Nr. Folkstone, Kent CT18 8JT
Tel: 01303 893230 Fax: 01303 891478

Specialist Dealer & Authority in 16th to late 18th Century English Furniture & Works of Art. Always a fine selection of furniture in stock waiting for a good home. Valuations & probate undertaken. We are always pleased to purchase Furniture & Works of Art of the above period.

A superb & extremely rare pierced & spindled food cupboard on its original stand, date 1660 to 1680. Accompanied by a true pair of Home Counties joint stools of superb colour & patination. Also a 16th century carved & polychromed figure of St Michael, most probably German.

ACRISE, Nr. Folkestone

R. Kirby Antiques
Caroline Farm, Ridge Row. CT18 8JT. Open by appointment 7 days. *STOCK: Early period oak, 16th-18th C, and works of art.* TEL: 01303 893230; fax - 01303 891478; e-mail - rkirby@ antiques8.fsnet.co.uk.

APPLEDORE, Nr. Ashford

Richard Back 2 Wood
The Old Goods Shed, Station Rd. TN26 2DF. Est. 1987. Open 9-5.30, Sat. 9-5, Sun. 10-4. *STOCK: Stripped and finished pine furniture.* LOC: Adjacent to station. PARK: Easy. TEL: 01233 758109; mobile - 07831 655414; home - 01233 860400; e-mail - pine@ back2wood.com; website - www.back2wood.com. VAT: Stan/Margin.

Dealers and Shops in Kent

Acrise	1	Cranbrook	5	Margate	1	Staplehurst	1
Appledore	1	Crayford	1	Newington	1	Stockbury	1
Ash	1	Deal	6	Northfleet	1	Sundridge	1
Ashford	1	East Peckham	1	Otford	3	Sutton Valence	1
Ashurst	1	Edenbridge	2	Petts Wood	1	Tenterden	2
Barham	1	Farningham	3	Ramsgate	2	Teynham	2
Beckenham	2	Faversham	2	Rochester	8	Tonbridge	4
Bilsington	1	Folkestone	2	Rolvenden	3	Tunbridge Wells	27
Birchington	2	Four Elms	2	Sandgate	9	Welling	1
Boughton	1	Goudhurst	1	Sandhurst	1	West Malling	2
Brasted	11	Gravesend	1	Sandwich	4	Westerham	11
Broadstairs	1	Hythe	4	Sevenoaks	4	Whitstable	3
Bromley	2	Lamberhurst	1	Sidcup	2	Wingham	1
Canterbury	15	Littlebourne	1	Snargate	1	Wittersham	1
Chislehurst	2	Maidstone	2	Southborough	2	Wrotham	1

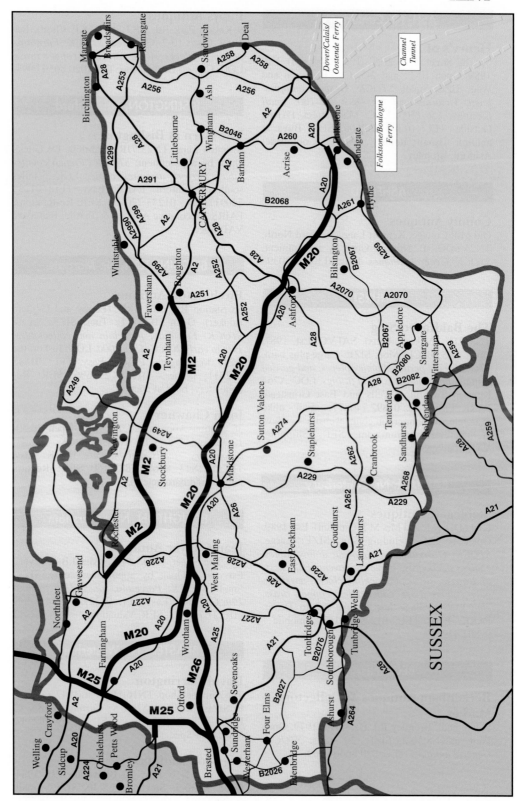

ASH, Nr. Canterbury

Henry's of Ash

51 The Street. CT3 2EN. (P.H. Robinson). Est. 1988. Open 10-12 and 2-5. CL: Tues. pm and Wed. SIZE: Small. *STOCK: General antiques, linen, Victorian and Art Deco, £5-100; small furniture, £50-£500.* LOC: Main street. PARK: Outside. TEL: 01304 812600. SER: Buys at auction (small items). FAIRS: Copthorne; Ashford; Bromley.

ASHFORD

County Antiques

Old Mill Cottage, Kennett Lane, Stanford North. TN25 6DG. (B. Nilson). Open by appointment. *STOCK: General antiques.* TEL: 01303 813039.

ASHURST

The Baldfaced Stag

TN3 9TE. (Mike Roberts). SALVO. Est. 1987. Open 10-5.30. CL: Mon. SIZE: Large plus barn. *STOCK: Fine period chimney pieces, and garden statuary and sculptures, light fittings.* LOC: A264 between Tunbridge Wells and East Grinstead. PARK: Easy. TEL: 01892 740877; e-mail - mike @architecturalemporium.com; website - www. architecturalemporium.com. SER: Shipping. VAT: Stan/Spec.

BARHAM, Nr. Canterbury

Stablegate Antiques

CT4 6QD. (Mr and Mrs M.J. Giuntini). Est. 1989. Open 10-5.30 including Sun. SIZE: Large. *STOCK: Georgian and Victorian dining tables, chairs, sideboards, bureaux, davenports, chests of drawers; silver plate, china, clocks, jewellery, glass, objets d'art, collectables, copper, brass, etc..* LOC: Village just off the A2 to Dover. PARK: Easy. TEL: 01227 831639; mobile - 07802 439777.

BECKENHAM

Beckenham Antiques & Collectors' Market

Public Hall, Bromley Rd. BR3. Est. 1979. Open Wed. only 8.30-2. SIZE: 20 stalls. *STOCK: General antiques.* TEL: 020 8660 1369.

Pepys Antiques

9 Kelsey Park Rd. BR3 2LH. (S.P. Elton). Est. 1969. Open 10-2. CL: Wed. *STOCK: Furniture, paintings, clocks, silver, porcelain, copper, brass.* LOC: Central Beckenham. TEL: 020 8650 0994.

BISLINGTON, Nr. Ashford

The Barn at Bislington

Swanton Lane. TN25 7JR. (Gabrielle De Giles). Open by appointment. *STOCK: French country tables, mirrors, armoires, chairs.* LOC: 5 miles south of Ashford. PARK: Easy. TEL: 01233 720917; fax - 01233 720156. SER: Restorations. FAIRS: Decorative Antique & Textile, Battersea. VAT: Spec.

BIRCHINGTON, Nr. Margate

Birchington Antiques

63 Station Rd. CT7 9RE. (Poppy and Graham Booker). Open 10-5. CL: Tues. SIZE: Small. *STOCK: Furniture, porcelain and collectables, 19th to early 20th C, £5-£1,000.* LOC: Just off the A249 to Margate. PARK: Easy. TEL: 01843 842811; home - 01843 298696. SER: Re-upholstery; buys at auction.

John Chawner

36 Station Approach. CT7 9RD. Open 10.30-12.30 and 2-5. CL: Tues. *STOCK: Clocks, barometers, smalls and bureaux.* PARK: Easy. TEL: 01843 846943/843309. SER: Repairs (clocks and barometers).

BOUGHTON, Nr. Faversham

Jean Collyer Antiques

194 The Street. ME13 9AL. (Mrs J.B. Collyer). Est. 1977. Open by appointment only. SIZE: Small. *STOCK: Porcelain, glass, 18th to mid-19th C.* PARK: Easy. TEL: 01227 751454; home - 01227 752831. SER: Valuations.

BRASTED, Nr. Westerham

David Barrington

The Antique Shop. TN16 1JA. Est. 1947. Open 9-6. SIZE: Medium. *STOCK: Furniture, 18th C.* LOC: A25. PARK: Easy. TEL: 01959 562537. VAT: Stan/Spec.

Bigwood Antiques

High St. TN16 1JA. (S. Bigwood). Est. 1984. Open 10.30-5, Sun. 12.45-4.30. SIZE: Small.

STOCK: Furniture, 19th -20th C, £250-£4,000.
PARK: Easy and rear of shop. TEL: 01959
564458. SER: Restorations. VAT: Stan/Spec.

Cooper Fine Arts Ltd
Swan House, High St. TN16 1JJ. (J. Hill-Reid).
Est. 1976. Open 10-6. SIZE: Medium. STOCK:
Furniture, sculpture, oils and watercolours,
1750-1950, £100-£10,000. PARK: Easy. TEL:
01959 565818. VAT: Stan/Spec.

Courtyard Antiques
High St. TN16 1JE. (H. La Trobe). Open 10-5,
Sun. and Bank Holidays 12.30-4.30. SIZE:
Medium. STOCK: 19th C furniture (including
extending dining tables), silver, jewellery, glass,
ceramics, Tunbridge ware, watercolours, prints
and objets d'art. PARK: Easy. TEL: 01959
564483; fax - 01732 454726. SER: Restorations
(furniture); French polishing; re-leathering.

Keymer Son & Co. Ltd
Swaylands Place, The Green. TN16 1JY. Est.
1977. Open 10-1 and 2.30-5. CL: Sat. SIZE:
Small. STOCK: 18th-19th C furniture, £100-
£3,000. LOC: A25. PARK: Easy. TEL: 01959
564203; fax - 01959 561138.

Roy Massingham Antiques
The Coach House. TN16 1JJ. LAPADA. Est.
1968. Open by appointment. STOCK: 18th-19th
C furniture, pictures and decorative items.
PARK: Easy. TEL: 01959 562408; mobile -
07860 326825.

Old Manor House Antiques
The Green. TN16 1JL. (Jane R. Read). Est. 1983.
Open daily. STOCK: Clocks, barometers, lighting,
copper and brass, mirrors, furniture and general
antiques. PARK: Easy. TEL: 01959 562536.

Southdown House Antiques
High St. TN16 1JE. (Graham Stead). Est. 1982.
Open 10-5. SIZE: 7 showrooms. STOCK:
Furniture, 18th C oak and 19th C mahogany and
walnut; decorative items, metalware, textiles,
porcelain, glass and pictures, £50-£5,000. LOC:
A25. PARK: Own. TEL: 01959 563522. SER:
Restorations (furniture). VAT: Spec.

Dinah Stoodley & Celia Jennings
High St. TN16 1JE. Est. 1965. Open 10-5. SIZE:
Medium. STOCK: Oak and country furniture,
1600-1800; ceramics, 1600-1880; European
woodcarving and sculpture, 1400-1700. LOC:
A25. PARK: Easy. TEL: 01959 563616. FAIRS:
Olympia. VAT: Spec.

Tilings Antiques
High St. TN16 1JA. (Penny Fawcett). Est. 1974.
Open 10-5.30 or by appointment. SIZE: Medium.
STOCK: Furniture, decorative items, 18th-19th
C, £20-£2,000. LOC: Village centre on A25.
PARK: Easy. TEL: 01959 564735; mobile -
07885 103234. VAT: Stan/Spec.

W.W. Warner (Antiques)   BADA
The Green, High St. TN16 1JL. (C.S. Jowitt).
Est. 1957. Open 10-5. STOCK: 18th-19th C
English and Continental pottery, porcelain,
glass, furniture. LOC: A25. PARK: Easy. TEL:
01959 563698. SER: Valuations; restorations.

BROADSTAIRS

Broadstairs Antiques and Collectables
49 Belvedere Rd. CT10 1PF. (P. Edwards). Est.
1980. Open winter 10-4.30, April-end Sept. 10-5.
CL: Wed. STOCK: General antiques, linen, china
and small furniture. LOC: Road opposite Lloyds
TSB. PARK: Easy. TEL: 01843 861965. FAIRS:
Ramada Hotel, Hollingbourne.

BROMLEY

Peter Morris
1 Station Concourse, Bromley North BR Station.
BR1 4EQ. BNTA. OMRS. ANA. IBNS. BDOS.
Open 10-1 and 2-6, Sat. 9-2. CL: Wed. SIZE:
Medium. STOCK: Coins, from 1660's; medals,
from 1790; antiquities, Egyptian, Greek and
Roman; bank notes, from 1800; all 50p to £1,000.
LOC: Inside station. PARK: Easy. TEL: 020 8313
3410; fax - 020 8466 8502. SER: Valuations;
buys at auction. FAIRS: BNTA Coinex; OMRS
Convention; Hong Kong Taiser and various
European. VAT: Stan/Spec.

Past and Present
22 Plaistow Lane. BR1 3DQ. (Mrs. Jan Sibley
and D. Moore). Est. 1992. Open 9-5.30. SIZE:
Small. STOCK: General antiques and collectables including furniture and garden items.
PARK: Nearby. TEL: 020 8466 7056; home - 020
8464 0290. SER: Valuations.

CANTERBURY

Antique and Design
The Old Oast, Hollow Lane. CT1 3SA. (Steve
Couchman). Est. 1988. Open 9-6, Sun. 10-4. SIZE:
Large. STOCK: Pine furniture, decorative items,
1800-1950, £5-£1,500. LOC: M2 from London,
Canterbury exit, straight at first roundabout, right

at second and third roundabouts, left at second pedestrian lights, shop 500 yds. TEL: 01227 762871. SER: Restorations; buys at auction; import and export. VAT: Stan/Spec.

R. J. Baker
16 Palace St. CT1 2DZ. Est. 1979. Open 9.30-5. CL: Mon. SIZE: Small. *STOCK: Silver and jewellery, 18th-19th C, £500-£10,000; handmade modern silverware, modern jewellery.* LOC: 5 minutes from cathedral, opposite The King's School. PARK: Easy. TEL: 01227 463224. SER: Valuations; restorations; gold and silversmiths; manufacturers. VAT: Stan/Spec.

Burgate Antique Centre
10c Burgate. CT1 2HG. (V. Reeves). Est. 1986. Open 10-5. SIZE: 14 dealers. *STOCK: General antiques and collectables.* LOC: City wall overlooking cathedral gardens. TEL: 01227 456500.

Bygones Reclamation
Nackington Rd. CT4 7BA. (Bob and Sue Thorpe). SALVO. Est. 1995. Open 8-5.30, Sat. 8.30-6, Sun. 9-5. *STOCK: Victorian fireplaces, cast-iron radiators, 19th C, £200-£1,500; garden statuary, 18th-20th C, £300-£1,500.* LOC: B2068 Hythe road, 2 miles from city centre. PARK: Own. TEL: 01227 767453; fax - 01227 762153. SER: Valuations; restorations. FAIRS: Newark. VAT: Spec.

The Canterbury Bookshop
37 Northgate. CT1 1BL. (David Miles). ABA. PBFA. Est. 1980. Open 10-5. *STOCK: Antiquarian and secondhand books, children's books, prints.* PARK: Easy. TEL: 01227 464773; fax - 01227 780073. FAIRS: PBFA and major provincial; ABA; Olympia; Chelsea.

Chaucer Bookshop
6-7 Beer Cart Lane. CT1 2NY. (Sir Robert Sherston-Baker, Bt.). ABA. PBFA. Est. 1956. Open 10-5. *STOCK: Books and prints, 18th-20th C, £5-£150; maps, 18th-19th C, £50-£250.* LOC: 5 minutes walk from cathedral, via Mercery Lane and St. Margaret's St. PARK: Castle St. TEL: 01227 453912; fax - 01227 451893; e-mail - chaucerbooks@canterbury.dialnet.com. SER: Valuations; buys at auction (books, maps and prints). VAT: Stan.

Coach House Antiques Centre
2A Duck Lane, St. Radigunds. CT1 2AE. Est. 1975. Open daily. SIZE: Large. *STOCK: General antiques, small furniture, ceramics, glass, linen,* books, collectors' items and bygones. Not Stocked: Jewellery. PARK: Nearby. TEL: 01227 463117.

Conquest House Antiques
17 Palace St. CT1 2DZ. (C.C. Hill and D.A. Magee). Open 10-4. *STOCK: 18th-19th C furniture, chandeliers and decorative items.* TEL: 01227 464587; fax - 01227 451375.

H.S. Greenfield and Son, Gunmakers (Est. 1805)
The Shooting Grounds, Sturry Hill, Sturry. CT2 0NQ. (T.S. Greenfield). Est. 1926. Open 9-5.30. *STOCK: English sporting guns, in pairs and singles; Continental sporting guns, firearms.* PARK: Own. TEL: 01227 713222. SER: Valuations; restorations (antique firearms). VAT: Stan.

Nan Leith's Brocanterbury
Errol House, 68 Stour St. CT1 2NZ. Resident. Open Mon., Wed., Fri. and Sat. 1-6 or by appointment. *STOCK: Art Deco, Victoriana, pressed glass, costume jewellery.* LOC: Close to Heritage Museum. TEL: 01227 454519.

Michael Pearson Antiques
Open by appointment only. *STOCK: 17th-18th C furniture including early oak and country; clocks and wood carvings.* TEL: 01227 459939. SER: Valuations; restorations (clocks and furniture).

Pinetum
25 Oaten Hill. CT1 3HZ. (Alan Pattinson). Est. 1967. Open 9.30-5, Sat. 10-4, Sun. 11-4. SIZE: Medium. *STOCK: 18th-19th C pine and country furniture, £50-£3,000.* LOC: Old Dover road. PARK: Easy. TEL: 01227 780365; home - same. SER: Valuations; restorations (furniture); buys at auction (furniture).

The Saracen's Lantern
8 The Borough. CT1 2DR. (W.J. Christophers). Est. 1970. *STOCK: General antiques, silver, jewellery, clocks, watches, Victorian bottles and pot-lids, Georgian, Victorian and Edwardian furniture.* LOC: Near Cathedral opposite King's School. PARK: At rear, by way of Northgate and St. Radigun's St. TEL: 01227 451968.

Victorian Fireplace
Thanet House, 92 Broad St. CT1 2LU. (J.J. Griffith). Est. 1980. Open 10-5.30. CL: Mon. SIZE: Medium. *STOCK: Georgian to Victorian*

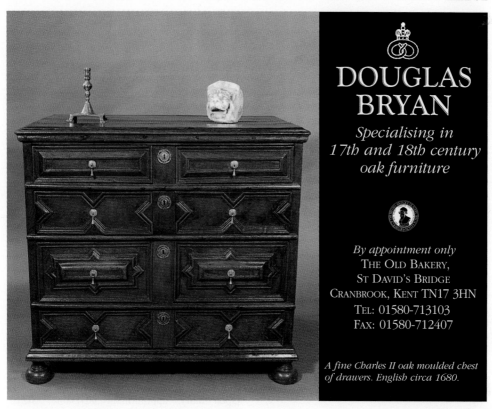

fireplaces. LOC: Town centre. PARK: Nearby. TEL: 01227 767723. SER: Restorations; fitting. VAT: Stan/Spec.

World Coins

35-36 Broad St. CT1 2LR. (David Mason). Est. 1970. CL: Thurs. pm. SIZE: Small. *STOCK: Coins, 3rd C BC to date, £5-£25; banknotes, 1792 to date; medals, 1815-1945.* LOC: Opposite car park by city wall and ring road. PARK: Easy. TEL: 01227 768887. SER: Valuations; identification and advice.

CHISLEHURST

Chislehurst Antiques

7 Royal Parade. BR7 6NR. (Mrs M. Crawley). LAPADA. Est. 1976. Open Mon., Fri., Sat., 10-5, Sun. 11-4. SIZE: Large. *STOCK: Furniture, 1760-1910; lighting - oil, gas, electric, 1850-1910; decorative antiques.* LOC: Half mile from A20, 3 miles from M25. PARK: Easy. TEL: 020 8467 1530; mobile - 07773 345266. VAT: Spec.

Michael Sim

1 Royal Parade. BR7 5PG. Open 9-6 including Sun. SIZE: Medium. *STOCK: English furniture,*

Georgian and Regency, £500-£50,000; clocks, barometers, globes and scientific instruments, £500-£50,000; Oriental works of art, £50-£5,000; portrait miniatures, £300-£5,000; animalier bronzes, £1,000-£10,000. LOC: 50yds. from War Memorial at junction of Bromley Rd. and Centre Common Rd. PARK: Easy. TEL: 020 8467 7040; home - same; fax - 020 8857 1313. SER: Valuations; restorations; buys at auction. VAT: Spec.

CRANBROOK

Antiques at Cranbrook

19 High St. TN17 3EE. Est. 1978. Open 10-5. SIZE: 10 dealers. *STOCK: Small general antiques.* TEL: 01580 712173.

Douglas Bryan   BADA

The Old Bakery, St. David's Bridge. TN17 3HN. (Douglas and Catherine Bryan). LAPADA. Est. 1971. Open by appointment. SIZE: Medium. *STOCK: Mainly English oak and country furniture, 17th-18th C; woodcarvings, some metalware.* LOC: Adjacent Tanyard car park - off road towards Windmill. PARK: Adjacent. TEL: 01580 713103; fax - 01580 712407; mobile - 0774 737303. FAIRS: Olympia (Feb., June, Nov). BADA.

Cranbrook Gallery

21B Stone St. TN17 3HF. (P.J. and N.A. Rodgers). Est. 1978. Open Tues.-Sat. 9.30-5. *STOCK: Watercolours, prints and maps, 18th-19th C.* TEL: 01580 720720; e-mail - cranbrookg@aol.com; website - www.cranbrook gallery.com. SER: Framing; restorations; picture search. VAT: Margin.

Swan Antiques

Stone St. TN17 3HF. (R. White). Est. 1982. Open 10-1 and 2-5 and by appointment. CL: Mon. and Wed. SIZE: Medium. *STOCK: Country furniture, 17th-19th C, from £500+; folk art and nâive paintings.* LOC: Town centre. PARK: Easy. TEL: 01580 712720; home - 01580 291864. SER: Valuations; buys at auction. FAIRS: Olympia; Battersea Decorative and Fine Art. VAT: Spec.

Vestry Antiques

3 Stone St. TN17 3HF. (Mrs Lynn Dawkins). Est. 1992. Open 9.30-5. *STOCK: 18th-19th C oak, mahogany, pine and decorative items.* LOC: Next to church. PARK: Nearby (loading and unloading only outside shop). TEL: 01580 713563. SER: Valuations.

Watling Antiques

139 Crayford Rd. DA1 4AS. Open 10-6.30. *STOCK: General antiques and shipping goods.* TEL: 01322 523620.

J. Clarke-Hall Ltd

75 Middle St. CT14 6HN. (Sally Edgecombe). ABA. Est. 1934. Open by appointment. *STOCK: English literature especially Samuel Johnson and the 18th Century.* PARK: Easy. TEL: 01304 375467. FAIRS: Hilton, Bonnington (June). *Mail Order Only.*

Decors II Ltd

67 Beach St. CT14 6HY. (N. Loftus-Potter). Est. 1973. Open 9.30-7 including Sun; in winter Fri.-Mon. or by appointment. *STOCK: Decorative items, general antiques and fabrics (including modern).* PARK: Easy. TEL: 01304 368030; fax - same; home - same; e-mail - potter@decors antiques.com; website - www.decorsantiques. com. SER: Finder.

Mulbery Antiques

7 St George's Passage. CT14 6TA. (Mrs Nina Spencer). Open Tues., Thurs., Fri. and Sat. 10-4.

SIZE: Medium. *STOCK: General antiques, pre 1930.* LOC: Off High St. PARK: Nearby. TEL: 01304 381800; fax - same.

Pretty Bizarre

170 High St. CT14 6BQ. (Philip Hartley). Open Fri. and Sat. 10-4.30 or by appointment. SIZE: Medium. *STOCK: Art Deco to 1970's ceramics and collectables.* TEL: Mobile - 07973 794537.

Quill Antiques

12 Alfred Sq. CT14 6LR. (A.J. and A.R. Young). Open 9-5.30. *STOCK: General antiques, porcelain, postcards.* TEL: 01304 375958.

Serendipity

125 High St. CT14 6BB. (M. and K. Short). Est. 1976. Open 10-1 and 2-4.30, Sat. 9.30-4.30 or by appointment. SIZE: Medium. *STOCK: Staffordshire figures, ceramics, pictures, furniture.* PARK: Easy. TEL: 01304 369165; home - 01304 366536; e-mail - dipityantiques@aol.com. SER: Valuations; restorations (ceramics, oil paintings).

Desmond and Amanda North

The Orchard, Hale St. TN12 5JB. Est. 1971. Open daily, appointment advisable. SIZE: Medium. *STOCK: Oriental rugs, runners, carpets and cushions, 1800-1939, £60-£3,500.* LOC: On B2015, 400yds south of roundabout at northern end of Hale Street bypass (A228). PARK: Easy. TEL: 01622 871353; home - same; fax - 01622 872998. SER: Valuations; restorations (reweaving, re-edging, patching, cleaning).

Lennox Cato   BADA

1 The Square, Church St. TN8 5BD. (Lennox and Susan Cato). LAPADA. Est. 1975. Open 9.30-5.30, Sat. 10-4. SIZE: Large. STOCK: 18th-19th C English and Continental furniture and related items, including mirrors, lamps, paintings, ceramics. LOC: Town centre (B2026). PARK: Nearby. TEL: 01732 865988; mobile - 07836 233473; e-mail - cato@ lennoxcato.com; website - www.lennoxcato.com. SER: Valuations; restorations. FAIRS: Olympia (Spring, Summer, Winter); BADA (London and Harrogate). VAT: Stan/Spec.

Chevertons of Edenbridge Ltd

Taylour House, 67-73 High St. TN8 5AL. (D. and A. Adam). LAPADA. CINOA. Est. 1961. Open 9-5.30. SIZE: 28 showrooms. *STOCK: Furniture and accessories, £500-£40,000.* LOC: From Westerham, on B2026 to Edenbridge. PARK: Own. TEL: 01732 863196/863358; fax - 01732 864298; e-mail - chevertons@msn.com; website - www.chevertons.com. FAIRS: Olympia (Feb., June, Nov); LAPADA, London and Birmingham. VAT: Stan/Spec.

FARNINGHAM

Adams Arts & Antiques Ltd
The Old Forge, 1 The High St. DA4 0DG. (M. J. Adams and R. K. Dagger). Open 9.30-5 including Sun. CL: Wed. pm. SIZE: Medium. *STOCK: Unusual and distinctive garden and interior statuary.* LOC: Close to junction M25/M20. TEL: 01322 866877; fax - same. FAIRS: Hampton Court; Tatton Park; Chelsea; BBC Gardener's World; CLA Game. VAT: Stan.

P.T. Beasley
Forge Yard, High St. DA4 0DB. (P.T. and R. Beasley). Est. 1964. Open every day, prior telephone call advisable. *STOCK: English furniture, some pewter, brass, Delft, wood-carvings.* LOC: Opposite Social Club. PARK: Easy. TEL: 01322 862453.

Farningham Pine
High St. DA4. (P. and Mrs. T.A. Dzierzek). Est. 1987. Open 10-5. CL: Wed. *STOCK: Pine furniture, from 1830, £25-£5,000.* LOC: 1 mile from M25, junction 3, on A20, first turn off (A225), before Brands Hatch if heading south. PARK: Easy. TEL: 01322 863168/863230; fax - 01322 863168. VAT: Stan/Spec.

Collectors' Corner
East St/Crescent Rd. ME13 8AD. Est. 1952. Open 10-5. CL: Thurs. SIZE: Small. *STOCK: Collectors' items - cigarette and post cards, badges, jewellery, prints, antique and second-hand wood-working and engineering tools.* LOC: Opposite P.O., at only set of traffic lights. PARK: Easy and at rear by arrangement. TEL: 01795 539721; home - 01795 536642. SER: Valuations.

Squires Antiques (Faversham)
3 Jacob Yard, Preston St. ME13 8NY. (A. Squires). Est. 1985. Open 10-5. CL: Wed. and Thurs. *STOCK: General antiques.* TEL: 01795 531503.

Alan Lord Antiques
71 Tontine St. CT20 1JR. (A.G., J.A. and R.G. Lord). Est. 1952. Open 9-5, Sat. pm. and other times by appointment. SIZE: Large. *STOCK: Period and Victorian furniture, china, silver. Rear warehouse - trade and shipping goods.* LOC: Road up from harbour. PARK: Easy. TEL: 01303 253674 anytime. VAT: Stan/Spec.

G. and D.I. Marrin and Sons
149 Sandgate Rd. CT20 2DA. ABA. PBFA. ILABA. Est. 1949. Open 9.30-1 and 2.30-5.30. CL: Mon. SIZE: Large. *STOCK: Maps, early engravings, topographical and sporting prints, paintings, drawings, books, engravings.* TEL: 01303 253016; fax - 01303 850956; e-mail - marrinbook@clara.co.uk; website - www.marrinbook.clara.net. SER: Restorations; framing. VAT: Stan.

Treasures
The Cross Roads. TN8 7NH. (B. Ward-Lee). Est. 1974. Open 10-5. *STOCK: Copper, brass, glass, porcelain, silver, jewellery, linen, books, toys, pine, small furniture and collectables.* PARK: Forecourt. TEL: 01732 700363.

Yew Tree Antiques
The Cross Roads. TN8 7NH. (Mrs. C. Nixon). Est. 1984. Open 10-5. SIZE: Medium. *STOCK: Porcelain and copper, 19th-20th C, £5-£500; glass, jewellery, linen, small furniture and collectables.* LOC: Off A25 - B269. PARK: Easy. TEL: 01732 700215.

Mill House Antiques
High St. Est. 1968. Open 10-5. CL: Wed pm. SIZE: Medium. *STOCK: Oak, pine country and painted furniture and associated items, 18th C to Victorian, £5-£1,000.* LOC: Off A21 on to A262, village about 3 miles. PARK: Easy. TEL: 01580 212476; home - 01580 211703. SER: Valuations.

Manor Antiques
9 Manor Rd. DA12 1AA. (A. Harding). Est. 1992. Open 10-4.30. CL: Wed. SIZE: Small. *STOCK: Collectables, £5-£100.* LOC: Near railway station. PARK: Easy. TEL: 01474 834120. SER: Valuations; buys at auction.

Malthouse Arcade
High St. CT21 5BW. (Mr and Mrs R.M. Maxtone Graham). Est. 1974. Open Fri., Sat. and Bank Holiday Mon. 9.30-5.30. SIZE: Large - 37 stalls. *STOCK: Furniture, jewellery and collectors' items.* LOC: West end of High St. PARK: 50yds. TEL: 01303 260103; home - 01304 613270.

Military History Bookshop
27 High St. CT21 5AD. (I.H. and G.M. Knight). Est. 1975. Open 10-5, Sat. 10-2. SIZE: Medium. *STOCK: Military books.* TEL: 01303 237883; fax - 01303 268149; e-mail - info@militaryhistorybooks.com; website - www.militaryhistorybooks.com. SER: Booksearch.

Owlets
99 High St. CT21 5JH. Open 9-5. *STOCK: Antique and estate jewellery and silver.* TEL: 01303 230333: e-mail - alison@owlets.co.uk; website - www.owlets.co.uk.

Samovar Antiques
158 High St. CT21 5JR. (Mrs F. Rignault). Open 9.30-5, Wed. 9.30-1. *STOCK: 19th C furniture, French provincial furniture, Oriental carpets and rugs and general antiques.* PARK: Own. TEL: 01303 264239.

LAMBERHURST

The China Locker
TN3 8HN. (G. Wilson). Open by appointment
only. SIZE: Small. *STOCK: Prints, 18th-19th C,
£5-£40; pottery and porcelain, 19th C.* TEL:
01892 890555. FAIRS: Local.

LITTLEBOURNE, Nr. Canterbury

Jimmy Warren Antiques
Cedar Lodge, 28 The Hill. CT3 1TA. Est. 1969.
Open 10-5 including Sun. *STOCK: Decorative
antiques and garden ornaments.* LOC: A257. PARK:
Own. TEL: 01227 721510; e-mail - enquiries
@jimmywarren.co.uk; website - www. jimmy
warren.co.uk. SER: Valuations. VAT: Stan/Spec.

MAIDSTONE

Gem Antiques
10 Gabriels Hill. Est. 1969. Open 10-5. SIZE:
Small. *STOCK: Clocks and barometers, £200-
£10,000; jewellery, £5-£10,000.* TEL: 01622
763344. SER: Valuations; restorations; repairs.

Sutton Valence Antiques
Unit 4 Haslemere Estate, Sutton Rd. ME15 9NL.
(T. and N. Mullarkey). Est. 1971. Open 9-5.30,
Sun. 11-4. SIZE: Large warehouse. *STOCK:
Antique and shipping furniture.* LOC: Approx. 3
miles south of Maidstone, just off A274. PARK:
Easy. TEL: 01622 675332; fax - 01622 692593;
e-mail - svantiques@aol.com; website - www.
svantiques.co.uk. SER: Container packing and
shipping; restorations; courier; buys at auction.

MARGATE

Furniture Mart
Grotto Hill. CT9 2BU. (R.G. Scott). Est. 1971.
CL: Wed. SIZE: Large. *STOCK: General
antiques £1-£3,000; shipping goods.* LOC:
Corner of Bath Place. TEL: 01843 220653. SER:
Restorations; restoration materials supplied;
container packing. VAT: Global/Stan.

NEWINGTON, Nr. Sittingbourne

Newington Antiques
58-60 High St. (Georgina McKinnon). LAPADA.
Est. 1979. Open 10-5, Sun. 10-2 or by
appointment. CL: Mon. and Wed. SIZE: Large.
*STOCK: Furniture, late 18th to late 19th C, £500-
£3,000; pre-1930 smalls, pictures, decorative*

items, £50-£4,000. LOC: On the A2 close to A249.
PARK: Own. TEL: 01795 844448; fax - 01795
841448; website - www. antiques kent.co.uk. SER:
Valuations; restorations (furniture including
upholstery, china, metal). FAIRS: Battersea
Antiques & Textiles; NEC; Earls Court.

NORTHFLEET

Northfleet Hill Antiques
36 The Hill. DA11 9EX. (Mrs M. Kilby). Est.
1986. Open Mon., Tues., Fri., some Sats. 10-5
and by appointment. SIZE: Small. *STOCK:
Furniture, 19th to early 20th C, £50-£800;
bygones and collectables, £1-£100.* LOC: A226
near junction with B261 and B2175. PARK: Easy
(behind Ye Olde Coach and Horses Inn). TEL:
01474 321521. FAIRS: Chelsea.

OTFORD

Ellenor Antiques and Tea Shop
11a High St. TN14. (Ellenor Hospice Care). Open
10-5. SIZE: Medium. *STOCK: Furniture,
ceramics, glass, 18th to early 20th C, £5-£1,500.*
LOC: Towards Sevenoaks, 3 miles south of
junction 4, M25. PARK: Nearby. TEL: 01959
524322. SER: Items sold on donation or
commission basis for hospice charity.

Mandarin Gallery - Oriental Art
The Mill Pond, 16 High St. TN14 5PQ. (J. and
M.C. Liu). Est. 1984. Open 10-5. CL: Wed. SIZE:
Medium. *STOCK: Chinese rosewood and lacquer
furniture, 18th-19th C; jade and soap stone, ivory
and wood carvings.* Not Stocked: Non-Oriental
items. LOC: A225. PARK: Easy. TEL: 01959
522778; home - 01732 457399; fax - same. SER:
Restorations (Chinese rosewood furniture).

Otford Antiques & Collectors Centre
26-28 High St. TN15 9DF. (Mr and Mrs David
Lowrie). Est. 1997. Open 10-5, Sun. 11-4. SIZE:
Large. *STOCK: Furniture and collectables, to
£800+.* PARK: Easy. TEL: 01959 522025; fax -
01959 525858/01732 883365; website -
www.@otfordantiques.co.uk. SER: Restorations
(polishing, caning and upholstery).

PETTS WOOD

Beehive
22 Station Sq. BR5 1NA. Est. 1994. Open 9.30-5,
Sat. 9.30-4.30. SIZE: 50 dealers. *STOCK:
Collectables, china, glass, jewellery and fur-
niture, 19th-20th C, £1-£1,000.* PARK: Easy.
TEL: 01689 890675. FAIRS: Bexleyheath.

Granny's Attic
2 Addington St. CT11 9JL. (Penelope J. Warn). Est. 1987. Open 10-5. CL: Thurs. pm. SIZE: Medium. *STOCK: Pre-1940's items, £2-£500.* LOC: Left off harbour approach road or right off Westcliffe Rd. PARK: Easy. TEL: 01843 588955; home - 01843 596288; mobile - 07773 155339. SER: Free local delivery, national and Continental delivery by arrangement.

Thanet Antiques Trading Centre
45 Albert St. CT11 9EX. (Mr and Mrs R. Fomison). Est. 1971. Prior 'phone call advisable. SIZE: Large. *STOCK: Furniture and bric-a-brac, 18th-20th C, £1-£5,000.* LOC: From London Rd. right to seafront. With harbour on right turn first left down Addington St., then last right. PARK: Own. TEL: 01843 597336; home - 01843 597540.

Baggins Book Bazaar - The Largest Secondhand Bookshop in England
19 High St. ME1 1PY. Est. 1986Open 10-6 including Sun. SIZE: Large. *STOCK: Secondhand and antiquarian books.* LOC: Next to the Guildhall Museum. PARK: Nearby. TEL: 01634 811651; fax - 01634 840591; website - www.bagginsbooks.co.uk. SER: Search.

City Antiques Ltd
78 High St. ME1 1JY. (Bryan Ware). Est. 1987. Open 10-5. SIZE: Medium. *STOCK: Clocks - longcase, mantel and bracket, 1760-1930, £300-£4,000; Georgian to Edwardian furniture, £200-£2,500; barometers - banjo, Fitzroy, stick, aneroid and mercury, 1800-1940, £250-£2,000; silver, pocket watches and china.* LOC: Central. PARK: Nearby. TEL: 01634 841278; e-mail - ware clockmad@aol.com. SER: Valuations; restorations (clocks).

Cottage Style Antiques
24 Bill Street Rd. ME2 4RB. (W. Miskimmin). Est. 1981. Open 9.30-5.30. *STOCK: General and architectural antiques.* TEL: 01634 717623.

Field Staff & Woods
93 High St. ME1 1LX. (Jim Field, Jane Staff and John Wood). Open 10-5. SIZE: Large - 3 showrooms. *STOCK: General antiques and collectables.* LOC: Centre of High St. TEL: 01634 846144/840108.

Francis Iles
Rutland House, La Providence, High St. ME1 1LX. (The Family Iles). Est. 1960. Open 9.30-5.30. SIZE: Large. *STOCK: Over 700 works, all mediums including sculpture, mainly 20th C, £50-£10,000.* PARK: 40yds. TEL: 01634 843081; fax - 01634 846681; e-mails - advice@artycat.com; nettie@francis-iles.com; websites - www.francis-iles.com and www.artycat.com. SER: Restorations (cleaning and relining); framing. FAIRS: Affordable Art (Spring). VAT: Stan/Spec.

Kaizen International Ltd
88 High St. ME1 1JT. (Jason Hunt). Est. 1997. Open 9-5.30. SIZE: Medium. *STOCK: General antiques including antique and secondhand jewellery.* PARK: Nearby. TEL: 01634 814132; website - kaizenInternational.com. SER: Valuations; restorations (jewellery).

Langley Galleries
143 High St. ME1 1EL. (K.J. Cook). Est. 1978. Open 9-5. *STOCK: Prints, watercolours, oils, 19th-20th C.* TEL: 01634 811802. SER: Framing.

Memories
128 High St. ME1 1JT. (Mrs V.A. Lhermette). Est. 1985. Open 9-5, Sun. 11-5. SIZE: Medium. *STOCK: Small furniture, £50-£500; china, £5-£75; both 1900-1950; pictures, late Victorian to Edwardian, £20-£70; collectables, bric-a-brac, linen and books.* PARK: Opposite. TEL: 01634 811044.

Falstaff Antiques
63-67 High St. TN17 4LP. (C.M.Booth). Est. 1964. Open 9-6, Sun. by appointment. SIZE: Medium. *STOCK: English furniture, £5-£700; china, metal, glass, silver, £1-£200. Not Stocked: Paintings.* LOC: On A28, 3 miles from Tenterden, 1st shop on left in village. PARK: Easy. TEL: 01580 241234. SER: Valuations. VAT: Stan/Spec.

Harriet Ann Sleigh Beds
Cherry Garden Farm, Hastings Rd. TN17 4PL. (Mrs R. Churchod). Est. 1987. Open by appointment only. SIZE: Medium. *STOCK: Eastern European and Scandinavian sleigh beds; French fruitwood doubles or singles; European pine armoires, chests and cabinets; bedside lights, bedroom decorative accessories especially childrens.* PARK: Easy. TEL: 01580 243005. SER: Mattresses available to order; reproduction beds in certain styles.

FREEMAN & LLOYD

Est. 1968

Member of the British Antique Dealers Association Ltd.

Dealing in only the finest
furniture and associated items
from 1700-1830

44 SANDGATE HIGH STREET
FOLKESTONE, KENT CT20 3AP
TEL: 01303 248986 FAX: 01303 241353

(5 mins. from Channel Tunnel entrance)

A late eighteenth century finely figured inlaid mahogany demi-lune sideboard, original handles. Circa 1790.

J.D. and R.M. Walters
10 Regent St. TN17 4PE. Est. 1977. Open 8-6, Sat. 11-4.30 or by appointment. SIZE: Small. *STOCK: Mahogany furniture, 18th-19th C.* LOC: A28 turn left in village centre onto B2086, shop on left. PARK: Easy. TEL: 01580 241563; home - same. SER: Handmade copies of period furniture including chairs; restorations (GMC). VAT: Stan/Spec.

SANDGATE, Nr. Folkestone

Christopher Buck Antiques BADA
56-60 High St. CT20 3AP. (Christopher and Jane Buck). Est. 1983. Open 10-5. CL: Wed. SIZE: Medium. *STOCK: English furniture, 18th C, £500-£30,000; decorative items, 18th-19th C, £100-£2,000.* LOC: 5 mins. from M20 and Channel Tunnel. PARK: Easy. TEL: 01303 221229; e-mail - chrisbuck@throwley. freeserve.co.uk. SER: Valuations; restorations (furniture); buys at auction. FAIRS: Olympia (June and Nov); BADA(March). VAT: Stan/Spec.

Finch Antiques
40 High St. CT20 3AP. (Robert and Sylvia Finch). Est. 1978. Open 9.30-6, Sun. 11-5. SIZE: Medium. *STOCK: Furniture, 1800-1920, £150-£3,000; silver plate and writing items, £5-£400.* PARK: Easy. TEL: 01303 240725. SER: Restorations (furniture, French polishing).

Michael Fitch Antiques
95-99 High St. CT20 3BY. LAPADA. Est. 1980. Open 10-5.30, Sun. by appointment. SIZE: Large. *STOCK: Georgian, Victorian and Edwardian furniture and clocks.* PARK: Own. TEL: 01303 249600; fax - same. SER: Delivery; shipping advice.

Freeman and Lloyd Antiques BADA
44 High St. CT20 3AP. (K. Freeman and M.R. Lloyd). LAPADA. CINOA. Est. 1968. Open 10-5.30, Mon., Wed. and Fri. by appointment only. SIZE: Medium. *STOCK: Fine Georgian and Regency English furniture; clocks, paintings and other period items.* LOC: On main coast road between Hythe and Folkestone (A259). PARK: Easy. TEL: 01303 248986; fax - 01303 241353; mobile - 07860 100073; e-mail - freeman andlloyd@ukgateway.net. SER: Valuations. FAIRS: Olympia (Feb., June, Nov.); BADA (March). VAT: Spec.

David Gilbert Antiques
30 High St. CT20 3AP. Est. 1975. Open 9-5. SIZE: Medium. *STOCK: Furniture, smalls, glass, 1790-1930, £5-£1,000.* LOC: A259. PARK: Easy. TEL: 01303 850491; home - 01304 812237. SER: Valuations.

Jonathan Greenwall Antiques
61-63 High St. CT20 3AH. LAPADA. Est. 1964. Open 9.30-5. SIZE: Large. *STOCK: Furniture, to 19th C; decorative items, jewellery, oils and watercolours, prints and maps, sculpture and bronzes.* LOC: Folkestone-Brighton road. PARK: Easy. TEL: 01303 248987. SER: Valuations.

David M. Lancefield Antiques
53 High St. CT20 3AH. LAPADA. Est. 1976. Open 10-6, Sun. and Bank Holidays 11-5. SIZE: Large. *STOCK: Furniture, 17th-20th C; silver, metalware, decorative items, ceramics, mainly 18th-20th C.* PARK: Own. TEL: 01303 850149; fax - same; e-mail - david@antiquedirect.freeserve.co.uk; website - www.davidmlancefield.co.uk. SER: Valuations; restorations.

Old English Oak
102 High St. CT20 3BY. (A. Martin). Open 10-6. *STOCK: Oak furniture and interesting items.* TEL: 01303 248560.

Old English Pine
100 High St. CT20 3BY. (A. Martin). Open 10-6. SIZE: 15 showrooms. *STOCK: Pine furniture and interesting items.* TEL: 01303 248560.

Forge Antiques and Restorations
Rye Rd. TN18 5JG. (James Nesfield). Est. 1975. Open 10-1 and 2-5, Sat. 10-5, Sun. and Mon. by appointment. *STOCK: Victorian and Edwardian furniture, £100-£1,200; ceramics, 18th-20th C, £5-£1,000.* LOC: A268. PARK: Own. TEL: 01580 850308; home - 01580 850665. SER: Valuations; restorations (furniture). FAIRS: Penshurst, Ardingly, Maidstone. VAT: Spec.

All Our Yesterdays & Chris Baker Gramophones
3 Cattle Market. CT13 9AE. (Sandie and Chris Baker). Est. 1994. Open 10.30-2.30, Fri. 10.30-2, Sat. 10.30-3.30, Sun. by appointment. CL: Wed. *STOCK: General antiques, gramophones and associated items, £5-£1,000.* PARK: Behind Guildhall. TEL: 01304 614756; e-mail - cbgramophones@aol.com. SER: Repairs (gramophones, phonographs, etc).

James Porter Antiques
5 Potter St. CT13 9DR. Est. 1948. Open 9.30-5.30. CL: Wed. *STOCK: Period furniture, brass and copper.* TEL: 01304 612218.

Sandwich Fine Books
41 Strand St. CT13 9DN. (Nick McConnell). ABA. PBFA. Est. 1987. Open by appointment. SIZE: Medium. *STOCK: Leather bound antiquarian books.* LOC: Central. PARK: Nearby. TEL: 01304 620300; fax - same; mobile - 07977 573766; e-mail - Mcconnellbooks@aol.com; website - www.abebooks.com/home/sandwichfine books. SER: Valuations. FAIRS: ABA - Olympia, Chelsea Town Hall; monthly PBFA Russell Hotel.

Nancy Wilson
Monken Quay, Strand St. CT13 9HP. Est. 1960. Open 11-5, other times by appointment. SIZE: Large. *STOCK: Period furniture, longcase clocks, £100-£5,000.* LOC: 100yds. from King's Arms public house. PARK: Easy. TEL: 01304 612345; home - same.

Neill Robinson Blaxill
21 St. John's Hill. TN13 3NX. FBHI. Open 9-6, appointment preferred. *STOCK: Clocks, barometers, decorative items and furniture, 17th-19th C.* LOC: 1 mile from High St. PARK: Easy. TEL: 01732 454179; website - www.antiques-clocks.co.uk. SER: Valuations; restorations.

Gem Antiques
122 High St. TN13 1XA. Est. 1969. Open 10-5. SIZE: Small. *STOCK: Clocks and furniture, 17th-19th C, £500-£10,000; jewellery, 18th-20th C, £10-£10,000.* LOC: Near Post Office. PARK: Nearby. TEL: 01732 743540. SER: Valuations; restorations (as stock). VAT: Spec.

Time to Remember
18 London Rd., Dunton Green. TN13 2UE. (A. Lyons). Est. 1982. Open Mon. and Tues. 10-5, Thurs.-Sat. 10-6. SIZE: Large. *STOCK: Clocks and watches, period furniture, porcelain, glass, toys, bric-a-brac.* LOC: London road into town, opposite Whitmore's Vauxhall showroom. PARK: Easy. TEL: 01732 454549. SER: Valuations; restorations (clocks and watches, furniture).

Woven Magic
3 Blighs Court, TN13 1DD. (J. Caslake).

LAPADA. Est. 1997. Open 10-6, Sun. by appointment. *STOCK: Oriental carpets and rugs, £250-£10,000; kilim stools, £85-£550; kilim and carpet cushions, £20-£75.* TEL: 01732 469477; fax - 01732 469974. SER: Valuations; restorations; hand-cleaning; kilim stools and cushions made to order. FAIRS: Olympia (June).

SIDCUP

Memory Lane Antiques & Collectables
143 Station Rd. DA15 7AA. (Mrs Lynn Brackley). Est. 1999. Open 10-5.30, Sat. 10-5, Sun. by appointment. CL: Wed. SIZE: Small. *STOCK: Furniture, china, vintage clothes, linen, reproduction lamps, £5-£1,000* LOC: Opposite station. PARK: At rear and station. TEL: 020 8300 0552; home - 020 8304 7066.

Ward Antiques
105 Main Rd. DA14 6ND. (T. and M. Ward). Est. 1981. Open 10-5, Sun. 11-2. SIZE: Large. *STOCK: Fireplaces, Victorian and Edwardian furniture; £50-£1,000.* LOC: Off A20. PARK: Opposite. TEL: 0208 302 2929.

SNARGATE (Romney Marsh)

Judith Peppitt
The Old Rectory. TN29 0EW. Est. 1982. Open by appointment. *STOCK: English watercolours, 19th-20th C.* LOC: 1 mile off A2070, adjoining Snargate Church. PARK: Easy. TEL: 01797 344516; e-mail - judithpeppitt@britishlibrary.net; website - www.artstyle.co.uk.

SOUTHBOROUGH, Nr. Tunbridge Wells

Henry Baines   BADA
14 Church Rd. TN4 0RX. LAPADA. Est. 1968. Open Tues.-Fri. 10-5, Sat. 10-4.30, prior telephone call advisable. SIZE: Medium. *STOCK: Early oak and country furniture especially tables and sets of chairs; French provincial furniture and decorative items.* PARK: Easy. TEL: 01892 532099. VAT: Stan/Spec.

Peter Hoare Antiques
35 London Rd. TN4 0PB. Est. 1985. Open 10-5.30. CL: Mon. SIZE: Medium. *STOCK: British Arts and Crafts furniture, Gothic revival, aesthetic movement, 19th-20th C design, £25-£5,000.* LOC: A26. PARK: At rear. TEL: 01892 524623; fax - 01892 619776. SER: Valuations.

STAPLEHURST, Nr. Tonbridge

Staplehurst Antiques
Crampton House, High St. TN12 0AU. (Mr and Mrs Draper). Est. 1991. Open 10-4.30, Wed. 10-1, Sun. 11-3. SIZE: Medium. *STOCK: Dining furniture including sideboards and cabinets, late Victorian to 1930's, £300-£2,500; collectables, £1-£250.* PARK: Easy. TEL: 01580 890424. SER: Restorations (furniture). VAT: Stan/Spec.

STOCKBURY

Steppes Hill Farm Antiques   BADA
The Hill Farm, South St. ME9 7RB. (W.F.A. Buck). Est. 1965. Always open, appointment advisable. SIZE: Medium. *STOCK: English porcelain, pottery, pot-lids, 18th-20th C, to £30,000; small silver; caddy spoons, wine labels, silver boxes, furniture, 18th-19th C, to £30,000.* LOC: 5 mins. from M2 on A249. Enquire in village for Steppes Hill Antiques. PARK: Easy. TEL: 01795 842205. SER: Valuations; buys at auction. FAIRS: BADA; International Ceramics; Olympia (Nov). VAT: Spec.

SUNDRIDGE, Nr. Sevenoaks

Sundridge Gallery
9 Church Rd. TN14 6DT. (T. and M. Tyrer). Est. 1986. Open 10-5.30. *STOCK: Watercolours and oils, 19th-20th C.* PARK: Easy. TEL: 01959 564104. SER: Restorations. VAT: Spec.

SUTTON VALENCE, Nr. Maidstone

Sutton Valence Antiques
North St. ME17 3AP. (T., N. and J. Mullarkey and O. Marles). LAPADA. CINOA. Est. 1971. Open 9-5, Sat. 10-4. SIZE: Large. *STOCK: Furniture, porcelain, clocks, silver, metalware, 18th-20th C.* LOC: On A274 Maidstone/Tenterden Rd. PARK: Side of shop. TEL: 01622 843333; fax - 01622 843499; e-mail - svantiques@aol.com; website - www.svantiques.co.uk SER: Valuations; restorations; container packing and shipping; courier; buys at auction.

TENTERDEN

Flower House Antiques
90 High St. TN30 6JB. (Barry Rayner and Quentin Johnson). Open 9.30-5.30, Sun. by appointment. SIZE: Medium. *STOCK: English*

and Continental furniture, 16th to early 19th C; Oriental works of art, 16th-19th C; pictures, lighting, mirrors, objets d'art. LOC: A28. PARK: Easy and private. TEL: 01580 763764. SER: Valuations; restorations. VAT: Spec.

Tenterden Antiques and Silver Vaults
66 High St. TN30 6AU. (T.J. Smith). Open 10-5 including Sun. STOCK: Clocks, silver, telephones and general antiques. PARK: Easy. TEL: 01580 765885.

TEYNHAM, Nr. Sittingbourne

Jackson-Grant Antiques
The Old Chapel, 133 London Rd. ME9 9QJ. (D.M. Jackson-Grant). Est. 1966. Open 10-5, Sun. 1-5. SIZE: Large. STOCK: General antiques, French furniture, bookcases and long tables, beds, smalls, 18th C to Art Deco, £5-£3,000. LOC: A2 between Faversham and Sittingbourne. PARK: Easy. TEL: 01795 522027; home - same; mobile - 07831 591881; e-mail - david.jacksongrant@bt.openworld.com; website - www.jackson-grantantiques.co.uk. SER: Customised tester beds available. VAT: Stan/Spec.

Peggottys
The Old Chapel, 133 London Rd. ME9 9QJ. (B. Smith). Est. 1999. Open 10-5, Sun. 1-5. SIZE: Large. STOCK: Beds including wooden, half-testers and four-posters, French, English and Flemish, 1800-1920; Edwardian, Victorian, Georgian, Rococo, Renaissance, Breton and Henri II, £500-£5,000. LOC: A2 Village centre. TEL: 01795 522027; home - same; website - www.peggottysbeds.co.uk.

TONBRIDGE

Barden House Antiques
1-3 Priory St. TN9 2AP. (Mrs B.D. Parsons). Open 10-5. SIZE: 5 dealers. STOCK: General antiques and collectables. TEL: 01732 350142; evenings - 01732 355718.

The New Curiosity Shop
7 Tollgate Buildings, Hadlow Rd. TN9 1NX. (Greta May). Est. 1987. Open Tues., Thurs., Fri. and Sat. 10-5. SIZE: Small. STOCK: General antiques and collectables, from Victorian. LOC: A26 off High St. PARK: Adjacent. TEL: 01732 366730; e-mail - gretamayantiques@hotmail.com. SER: Valuations; restorations (teddy bears). FAIRS: Ramada Hotel.

Derek Roberts Fine Antique Clocks & Barometers BADA
25 Shipbourne Rd. TN10 3DN. Author of several books on clocks. Est. 1968. Open 9.30-5.30 or by appointment. SIZE: Large. STOCK: Fine restored clocks, mostly £2,000-£100,000. LOC: A227. From London A21 take B245 Hildenborough to Tonbridge, left 20 yds before first lights, left again and 50 yds up on right. PARK: Easy. TEL: 01732 358986; fax - 01732 771842; e-mail - drclocks@clara.net; website - www.qualityantiqueclocks.com. SER: Cabinet making. VAT: Spec.

B.V.M. Somerset
Stags Head, 9 Stafford Rd. TN9 1HT. Est. 1948. Open 11-6.30. STOCK: Clocks, £500-£5,000. LOC: Off High Street beside castle. TEL: 01732 352017; fax - 01732 368343. SER: Valuations; restorations (cabinets, gilt and French polishing); buys at auction (longcase and bracket clocks). VAT: Stan.

TUNBRIDGE WELLS

Aaron Antiques
77 St. Johns Rd. TN4 9TT. (R.J. Goodman). Open 9-5. STOCK: Clocks and pocket watches, paintings and prints; period and shipping furniture; English, Continental and Oriental porcelain; antiquarian books, postcards, coins and medals. TEL: 01892 517644. VAT: Stan/Spec.

Amadeus Antiques
32 Mount Ephraim. TN3. (P.A. Davies). Open 10-5, Sun. by appointment. SIZE: Medium. STOCK: Unusual furniture, to Art Deco, £50-£5,000; china and bric-a-brac, £25-£500; chandeliers, £100-£1,000. LOC: Near hospital. PARK: Easy. TEL: 01892 544406; 01892 864884. SER: Valuations.

The Architectural Emporium
55 St John's Rd. TN4 9TP. (Mike Roberts and Nick Bates). SALVO. Est. 1988. Open 10-5.30. SIZE: Medium. STOCK: Fireplaces, garden statuary, lighting, decorative salvage, Georgian to Edwardian. LOC: A26 towards Southborough. PARK: John St. TEL: 01892 540368; website - www.architecturalemporium.com. VAT: Stan/ Spec.

Baskerville Books
13 Nevill St. TN2 5RU. Est. 1982. Open 10-5. SIZE: Small. STOCK: Antiquarian and secondhand books; small collectible antiques and occasional period and shipping furniture. LOC: 50 yards from entrance to Pantiles. PARK: Nearby. TEL: 01892 526776. SER: Valuations.

Beau Nash Antiques
29 Lower Walk, The Pantiles. TN2 5TD. (Nicola
Rowlett and David Wrenn). Est. 1992. Open
Tues., Wed., Thurs. and Sat. 11-5. SIZE: Small.
*STOCK: Furniture, silver, porcelain and glass,
18th-20th C.* LOC: Behind Tourist Information
Centre. PARK: Pantiles. TEL: 01892 537810.

Nicholas Bowlby
9 Castle St. TN1 1XJ. Est. 1981. Open 10-5.30.
CL: Mon. and Wed. SIZE: Medium. *STOCK:
19th-20th C watercolours, contemporary paintings
and sculpture, £200-£20,000.* LOC: Near The
Pantiles. TEL: 01892 540049; e-mail - nicholas
bowlby@hotmail.com: website - www.nicholas
bowlby.co.uk SER: Valuations; restorations; buys
at auction (watercolours and drawings). VAT:
Spec.

Calverley Antiques
30 Crescent Rd. TN1 2LZ. (P. A. Nimmo). Est.
1995. Open 10-5.30 including Sun. *STOCK:
Furniture including European pine, 1920's oak,
decorative painted and garden.* LOC: Near police
station and Assembly Hall. PARK: Multi-storey
next door. TEL: 01892 538254. FAIRS: Ardingly.

Chapel Place Antiques
9 Chapel Place. TN1 1YQ. (J. and A. Clare).
Open 9-6. *STOCK: Silver photo frames, antique
and modern jewellery, old silver plate, claret
jugs, hand-painted Limoge boxes.* TEL: 01892
546561.

Claremont Antiques
48 St John's Rd. TN4 9NY. (Anthony Broad).
Open 10-5.30, other times by appointment. SIZE:
Large. *STOCK: Irish, French, Eastern European,
pine, hardwood and painted country furniture,
18th-19th C; decorative items, all £10-£5,000.*
LOC: On A26 London Road, by St John's church.
PARK: Easy. TEL: 01892 511651; fax - 01892
517360; e-mail - ant@claremontantiques.com;
website - www.claremontantiques.com. VAT:
Stan/Spec.

Corn Exchange Antiques Centre
64 The Pantiles. TN2 5TN. (D. Long). Est. 1999.
Open 10-5. *STOCK: Furniture, silver, mirrors,
pictures, ceramics, glass and collectables.* TEL:
01892 539652; fax - 01892 538454.

Glassdrumman Antiques
7 Union Square, The Pantiles. TN4 8HE.
(Graham and Amanda Dyson Rooke). Open

315

Tues.-Sat. 10-5.30. SIZE: Medium. *STOCK: Silver, jewellery, watches, clocks, furniture, decorative items, 18th-19th C.* PARK: Nearby. TEL: 01892 538615; fax - same.

Pamela Goodwin

11 The Pantiles. TN2 5TD. Est. 1980. Open 9.30-5, Sat. 9.30-5.30. SIZE: Medium. *STOCK: Furniture, longcase and wall clocks, mirrors, oil lamps, ceramics, silver and glass, collectibles and decorative items, 18th-20th C, £50-£5,000.* LOC: Central. PARK: Nearby. TEL: 01892 618200; fax - same; e-mail - pamela.goodwin1@btinternet.com; website - www.goodwinantiques.com.

Hall's Bookshop

20-22 Chapel Place. TN1 1YQ. Est. 1898. Open 9.30-5. *STOCK: Antiquarian and secondhand books.* TEL: 01892 527842.

Kent & Sussex Gold Refiners

7 Vale Rd. (Mr and Mrs A.C. Padley). NAG. Est. 1926. Open 9-5.30. CL: Wed. *STOCK: Antique and modern jewellery, silver and plate, £15-£100,000.* LOC: Around corner from High St. PARK: Nearby. TEL: 01892 526084; fax - 01892 543602. SER: Valuations; restorations (antique silver and jewellery). VAT: Stan/Spec.

Kentdale Antiques

Motts Farm Estate, Forge Rd., Eridge Green. TN3 9LJ. (C. Bigwood and T. Rayfield). Est. 1981. Open 9-5. CL: Sat. SIZE: Warehouse. *STOCK: Mostly mahogany and walnut furniture.* LOC: Telephone for directions. PARK: Easy. TEL: 01892 863840; fax - same; e-mail - kentdale.antiques@ukgateway.net. SER: Restorations (furniture). VAT: Stan/Spec.*Trade only.*

Howard Neville Antiques

21 The Pantiles. TN4. (H.C.C. Neville). Est. 1967. Open by appointment. SIZE: Medium. *STOCK: General antiques, furniture, sculpture and works of art, 16th-18th C.* PARK: Easy. TEL: 01892 511461; home - 01435 882409. SER: Valuations; restorations. VAT: Spec.

Old Colonial

56 St John's Rd., St John's. TN4 9NY. (Dee Martyn and Suzy Rees). Est. 1982. Open 10-5.30. SIZE: Small. *STOCK: English and French country and decorative furniture and associated smalls.* LOC: Approximately 1 mile outside Tunbridge Wells. PARK: Opposite. TEL: 01892 533993; fax - 01892 513281.

The Pantiles Antiques

31 The Pantiles. TN2 5TD. (Mrs E.M. Blackburn). Est. 1979. Open 10-5. SIZE: Medium. *STOCK: Georgian, Victorian and Edwardian furniture; 19th C porcelain, silver.* PARK: Easy. TEL: 01892 531291.

Pantiles Spa Antiques

4/5/6 Union Square, The Pantiles. TN4 8HE. (J.A. Cowpland). Est. 1979. Open 9.30-5, Sat. 9.30-5.30. SIZE: Large. *STOCK: Period and Victorian furniture especially dining tables and chairs, £200-£10,000; pictures, £50-£3,000; clocks, £100-£5,000; porcelain, £50-£2,000; silver, £50-£1,000; all 17th-19th C; dolls, bears and toys.* PARK: Nearby. TEL: 01892 541377; fax - 01435 865660; e-mail - psa.wells@btinternet.com; website - www.antiques-tunwells-kent.co.uk. SER: Restorations (furniture); 30 mile radius free delivery (large items). VAT: Spec.

Phoenix Antiques

51-53 St. John's Rd. TN4 9TP. Est. 1982. Open 10-5.30 or by appointment. SIZE: Large. *STOCK: 18th-19th C French, English, original painted and country furniture, decorative furnishings, original gilt overmantel mirrors, garden statuary.* LOC: On A26 from A21 into town, by St. John's Church. PARK: Easy. TEL: 01892 549099; e-mail - robert.pilbeam@virgin.net. VAT: Spec.

Redleaf Gallery
1 Castle St. TN1 1XJ. (Nick Hills). Open Tues.-Sat. 10.30-5.30. *STOCK: 19th-20th C watercolours and modern British paintings.* LOC: Off High St. PARK: Nearby. TEL: 01892 526695. VAT: Spec.

Ian Relf Antiques
132/134 Camden Rd. TN4. Open 9.30-1.30 and 2.30-5.30. *STOCK: Mainly furniture.* TEL: 01892 538362.

John Thompson
27 The Pantiles. TN2 5TD. Est. 1982. Open 9.30-1 and 2-5. SIZE: Medium. *STOCK: Furniture, late 17th to early 19th C; paintings 17th-20th C; decorative items.* Not Stocked: Jewellery, silver and militaria. PARK: Linden Road or Warwick Park. TEL: 01892 547215. VAT: Spec.

Tunbridge Wells Antiques
12 Union Sq., The Pantiles. TN4 8HE. (N.J. Harding). Est. 1980. Open 10-5. SIZE: Large. *STOCK: Antiques and collectables including silver, jewellery, Georgian, Victorian and Edwardian furniture, soft furnishings, Staffordshire figures, clocks and watches, samplers, collectables, Tunbridgeware, antique-related reference books.* PARK: Nearby. TEL: 01892 533708; e-mail - nick@staffordshirefigures.com; website - www.staffordshirefigures.com. SER: Valuations; buys at auction (Tunbridgeware) shipping. VAT: Stan/Spec.

Up Country
The Old Corn Stores, 68 St. John's Rd. TN4 9PE. (G.J. Price and C.M. Springett). Est. 1988. Open 9-5.30. SIZE: Large. *STOCK: British and European country furniture, £50-£5,000; associated decorative and interesting items, £5-£500; all 18th-19th C.* LOC: On main London Rd. to Southborough and A21 trunk road which joins M25 and M26 at Sevenoaks intersection. PARK: Own at rear. TEL: 01892 523341; fax - 01892 530382; e-mail - mail@upcountryantiques.co.uk; website - www.upcountryantiques.co.uk. VAT: Stan.

Variety Box
16 Chapel Place. TN1 1YQ. Est. 1955. Open 9.45-5. CL: Wed. SIZE: Small. *STOCK: Tunbridge ware and sewing antiques, 19th C, £5-£300; hatpins, 20th C, £5-£100; small collectables, 18th-20th C, £5-£100.* LOC: 2 minutes from Pantiles towards High St. PARK: Limited. TEL: 01892 531868; e-mail - antiques@varietyboxantiques.com. FAIRS: Ardingly, Newark, Alexandra Palace.

The Vintage Watch Co.
The Old Pipe House, 74 High St. TN1 1YB. (F. Lawrence). Open Wed.-Sat. 10-5. *STOCK: Pre-1950's fine wrist watches, pocket watches.* SER: Restorations.

WELLING

The Emporium Antiques, Collectibles & Craft Centre
138-140 Upper Wickham Lane. DA16 3DP. Est. 1999. Open 10-5. SIZE: Medium. *STOCK: Royal Doulton, Wade, Kevin Francis, Sylvac, Beswick, Winstanley cats, Lladro, Wedgwood, £10-£300; Swarovski crystal, furniture, kitchenalia, football memorabilia.* LOC: From Bexleyheath, right at Welling corner on High St. into Upper Wickham Lane. TEL: 020 8855 8308; fax - same; e-mail - info@theemporiumwelling.co.uk; website - www.theemporiumwelling.co.uk.

WEST MALLING

The Old Clock Shop
63 High St. ME19 6NA. (S.L.Luck). Est. 1970. Open 9-5. SIZE: Large. *STOCK: Grandfather clocks, 17th-19th C; carriage, bracket, wall clocks and barometers.* LOC: Half a mile from M20. PARK: Easy. TEL: 01732 843246; website - www.theoldclockshop.co.uk. VAT: Spec.

Rose and Crown Antiques
40 High St.. (Candy and Julian Lovegrove). Est. 1995. Open Tues.-Sat. 9.30-5.30. SIZE: Medium. *STOCK: General antiques including furniture, 18th to early 20th C.* PARK: Free. TEL: 01732 872707; fax - 01732 872810; website - www. antiqueswestmalling.co.uk. SER: Restorations (furniture including French polishing and upholstery)FAIRS: NEC.

WESTERHAM

Apollo Antique Galleries
19 -21 Market Sq. TN16 1AN. (S.M. and R.W. Barr). LAPADA. Est. 1967. Open 9.30-5.30. SIZE: Large. *STOCK: Georgian, Victorian and Edwardian furniture; 19th C oils and watercolours; bronze and marble statuary; clocks, silver.* PARK: Easy. TEL: 01959 562200; fax - 01959 562986; e-mail - enq@apollogalleries. com; website - www.apollogalleries.com. SER: Valuations. FAIRS: Olympia; LAPADA. VAT: Stan/Spec.

Castle Antiques Centre
1 London Rd. TN16 1BB. (Stewart Ward Properties). Est. 1986. Open 10-5, Sun. 11-6. SIZE: Small - 8 dealers. *STOCK: General antiques, books, linen, collectables, retro clothing.* LOC: Just off town centre. PARK: Easy - nearby. TEL: 01959 562492. SER: Valuations; props for stage productions.

Peter Dyke
3 The Green. TN16 1AS. Est. 1977. Open 10-5.30. SIZE: Small. *STOCK: Furniture, 18th-19th C, £500-£10,000; paintings, 19th-20th C, £500-£1,000+; decorative objects, 19th C, £150-£1,000.* TEL: 01959 565020. SER: Valuations; buys at auction. VAT: Spec.

London House Antiques
4 Market Sq. TN16 1AW. Est. 1977. Open 10-5, Sun. by appointment only. SIZE: Medium. *STOCK: Furniture, 18th-19th C, £500-£10,000; paintings, prints and engravings, 19th-20th C, £100-£2,000; English and German teddy bears and dolls, 19th-20th C, £100-£3,000; clocks and bronzes, 19th C, £300-£5,000; silver and porcelain, 19th-20th C, £50-£1,500.* LOC: Off M25, junction 6 on A25 to Westerham. PARK: Easy. TEL: 01959 564479; e-mail - london housedg@netscapeonline.co.uk.

Marks Antiques
5 The Green. TN16 1AS. (Alan and Michael Marks). Est. 1954. Open 9.30-5. SIZE: Medium. *STOCK: Furniture, £500-£30,000; clocks, barometers, porcelain, bronzes and pictures, £200-£3,000: all 18th-19th C.* LOC: A25. PARK: Easy. TEL: 01959 562017; home - 01268 542621. SER: Valuations; restorations (furniture, including upholstery); buys at auction (furniture). VAT: Stan/Spec.

Regal Antiques
2 Market Sq. TN16 1AW. (T. Lawrence). Open Wed.-Sat. 10-5. *STOCK: Antique jewellery, fine paintings, portrait miniatures, porcelain, vintage watches.* TEL: 01959 561778. SER: Picture restorations.

Denys Sargeant
21 The Green. TN16 1AX. Est. 1949. Open 9.30-5.30. *STOCK: Glass especially chandeliers and candelabras, decanters and lustres.* TEL: 01959 562130. SER: Restoration and cleaning (chandeliers, candelabras, lustres); electrification. VAT: Stan/Spec.

Taylor-Smith Antiques
4 The Grange, High St. TN16 1AH. (Alan Taylor-Smith). LAPADA. Open 10-5. CL: Wed. *STOCK: Fine 18th-19th C furniture; paintings, porcelain, glass and decorative items.* PARK: Easy. TEL: 01959 563100; fax - same.

Taylor-Smith Books
2 High St. TN16 1RF. LAPADA. Est. 1972. Open by appointment. *STOCK: Books by Sir Winston Churchill and related items.* TEL: 01959 561561; fax - 01959 561561.

Westerham Antiques Warehouse
The Old Sorting Office, Fullers Hill, London Rd. TN16 1AA. (R.W. Barr). LAPADA. Open 10-5.30. *STOCK: 18th-19th C furniture especially dining tables and sets of chairs.* PARK: Free. TEL: 01959 561622; fax - 01959 562986; e-mail - westhouse.antiques@virgin.net. SER: Valuations; shipping; insurance. FAIRS: NEC; Olympia (LAPADA). VAT: Spec.

Westerham House Antiques
The Old Sorting Office, Fullers Hill, London Rd. TN16 1AA. (R.W. Barr). LAPADA. WKADA. Open 10-5.30. *STOCK: 18th-19th C English furniture, animal and figurative bronzes, oil paintings.* PARK: Easy. TEL: 01959 561622; mobile - 07885 883441; e-mail - westhouse. antiques@virgin.net. SER: Export; valuations. FAIRS: Olympia; NEC; LAPADA. VAT: Spec.

WHITSTABLE

Boulevard Antiques
139 Tankerton Rd. CT5 2HZ. (Mrs J. Baker). Est. 1984. Open 9.30-5. SIZE: Small. *STOCK: China, 18th-20th C, £10-£100; furniture, 19th-20th C, £50-£800; postcards, 20th C, to £30; dolls, books, 19th-20th C, £1-£500.* PARK: Easy. TEL: 01277 273335. SER: Valuations.

Laurens Antiques
2 Harbour St. CT5 1AG. (G. A. Laurens). Est. 1965. Open 9.30-5.30. SIZE: Medium. *STOCK: Furniture, 18th-19th C, £300-£500+.* LOC: Turn off Thanet Way at Whitstable exit, straight down to one-way system in High Street. PARK: Easy. TEL: 01227 261940; home - same. SER: Valuations; restorations (cabinet work); buys at auction.

Tankerton Antiques
136 Tankerton Rd. CT5 2AN. (Mrs. F. Holland). Est. 1985. Open 10-5, Tues. 10-4, Wed. 10-1. CL: Mon. SIZE: Medium. *STOCK: Furniture, Regency to 1930's, £50-£1,500; china, from 18th*

C, to £1,500; glass, Regency to 1930's, to £400; clocks and barometers, from 1800, £30-£2,500; French, English and German costume jewellery, £30-£300. LOC: From A299 Thanet Way take A290/B2205 turn off to Whitstable. Through town and into Tankerton. Shop on right just past roundabout. TEL: 01227 266490; mobile - 07702 244064. SER: Valuations. FAIRS: Ardingly; Brunel Clock & Watch.

WINGHAM, Nr. Canterbury

Silvesters
33 High St. CT3 1AB. (S.N. Hartley and G.M.A.Wallis). LAPADA. Est. 1953. Open 9.30-5 by appointment. *STOCK: Furniture, Georgian and Victorian; decorative items, silver, porcelain, glass.* LOC: At main junction in town. TEL: 01227 720278 and 01843 841524.

WITTERSHAM

Old Corner House Antiques
6 Poplar Rd. TN30 7PG. (G. and F. Shepherd). Open Wed.-Sat. 10-5 or by appointment. *STOCK: General antiques, country furniture, samplers; 18th-19th C English pottery including blue and white and creamware; watercolours, 19th to early 20th C.* PARK: Easy. TEL: 01797 270236.

WROTHAM

Charles International Antiques
The Poplars, London Rd. TN15 7RR. (Mr and Mrs C. Bremner). LAPADA. Est. 1968. Open 9-4.30. *STOCK: Victorian, Edwardian and shipping goods.* LOC: A20. TEL: 01732 823654; e-mail - c.bremner@antiques2.demon.co.uk; website - www.collect.com/charles. SER: Full container and documentation facilities.

Thomas Shotter Boys, The High Street, Shrewsbury, signed and dated 'T Boys/1859', watercolour over pencil heightened with white, 12¾in. x 17in., worth between £15,000 and £20,000. (Sotheby's)

From an article entitled "Thoma Shotter Boys (1803-1874)" by Charles Hind which appeared in the May 2002 issue of **Antique Collecting**. For more details and to subscribe see page 21.

ACCRINGTON

The Coin and Jewellery Shop
129a Blackburn Rd. BB5 0AA. Est. 1977. Open 9.30-5. CL: Wed. *STOCK: Coins, jewellery and small antiques.* TEL: 01254 384757.

ASTLEY BRIDGE, Nr. Bolton

Alpine Antiques
15 Sharples Ave. BL1 7HB. (B. and M. Carney). Est. 1970. Open by appointment. SIZE: Small. *STOCK: Glass, pottery, silver and jewellery, collectables.* LOC: Just off main Blackburn road, turn immediately at Texaco garage. PARK: Own frontage. TEL: 01204 303364; fax - same. SER: Valuations; restorations; buys at auction. FAIRS: Chester monthly; Northgate Arena.

BLACKBURN

Ancient and Modern
17 New Market St. BB1 7DR. (Gail and Zachary Coles). NAG. OMRS. Est. 1943. Open 9-5.30. SIZE: Medium. *STOCK: Jewellery, Georgian to date, up to £30,000; clocks, vintage and modern watches including Rolex, Cartier, Patek; militaria and silver; diamond merchants.* LOC: Town centre, opposite side entrance of Marks & Spencer. PARK: Easy. TEL: 01254 677866/668818; fax - 01254 677866. SER: Valuations; repairs; restorations. FAIRS: Bangkok; Miami; London. VAT: Stan/Margin/Global.

Great Expectations
918 Whalley New Rd., Wilpshire. BB1 9BD. (Mrs Christine Haworth). Est. 1999. Open 6 days 10-5. CL: Tues. SIZE: Small. *STOCK: General antiques including furniture, porcelain, lamps, lustres, clocks, oil lamps, pictures, paintings, late Georgian to Edwardian.* LOC: Outskirts of Blackburn. PARK: Opposite. TEL: 01254 248261; fax - same; mobile - 07951 441649; home - 01254 249974; e-mail - haworth lovejoy@aol.com; website - www.antiqueslancashire.co.uk. SER: Restorations (furniture).

Mitchell's Antiques
76 Bolton Rd. BB2 3PZ. (S. Mitchell). Est. 1972. Open 9-5. *STOCK: General antiques, gold and silver jewellery, wrist watches.* LOC: Main road. PARK: Easy. TEL: 01254 664663.

BLACKPOOL

Ascot Antiques
106 Holmfield Rd. FY2 9RF. (J.C. Winwood). Est. 1987. Open by appointment. SIZE: Small. *STOCK: Furniture and oil paintings, Georgian to Victorian.* PARK: Easy. TEL: 01253 356383; home - same; mobile - 07816 645716. SER: Valuations.

Chard Coins
521 Lytham Rd. FY4 1RJ. Est. 1965. Open 9-5. CL: Sat. SIZE: Large. *STOCK: Paintings and furniture, English and ancient coins, gold bullion coins, jewellery and silver, £50-£20,000+.* LOC: Between Central Promenade south and Blackpool Airport main gates, ¼ mile from airport. PARK: Easy. TEL: 01253 343081. SER: Valuations. VAT: Stan/Spec.

Ann and Peter Christian
400/402 Waterloo Rd., Marton. FY4 4BL. Est. 1978. Open 10-5.30. SIZE: Large. *STOCK: Decorative arts and reproduction lighting.* TEL: 01253 763268; website - www.20da.co.uk.

Nostalgia
95 Coronation St. FY1 4QE. (P. Jackson). Est. 1978. Open 10-4, including Sun. in summer. SIZE: Small. *STOCK: Royal commemoratives, 19th-20th C, £5-£150.* LOC: Town centre, near Winter Gardens. PARK: Easy. TEL: 01253 293251.

BOLTON

Bolton Antique Centre
96 Great Moor St. BL3 6DS. Open 10-4.30. *STOCK: General antiques and collectables.* TEL: 01204 362694.

Drop Dial Antiques
Last Drop Village, Hospital Rd., Bromley Cross. BL7 9PZ. (I.W. and I.E. Roberts). Est. 1975. Open every afternoon except Mon. and Fri. SIZE: Medium. *STOCK: Clocks, mainly English and French, 18th-20th C, £100-£4,000; mercury barometers, 19th-20th C, paintings, silver, furniture and general antiques, £20-£500.* Not Stocked: PARK: Easy. TEL: 01204 307186; home - 01257 480995. SER: Valuations; restorations (clocks and barometers). VAT: Stan/Spec.

Siri Ellis Books
The Last Drop Village, Hospital Rd., Bromley Cross. BL7 9PZ. PBFA. Est. 1998. Open 12-5, Sat. and Sun. 10-5. SIZE: Small. *STOCK: Rare*

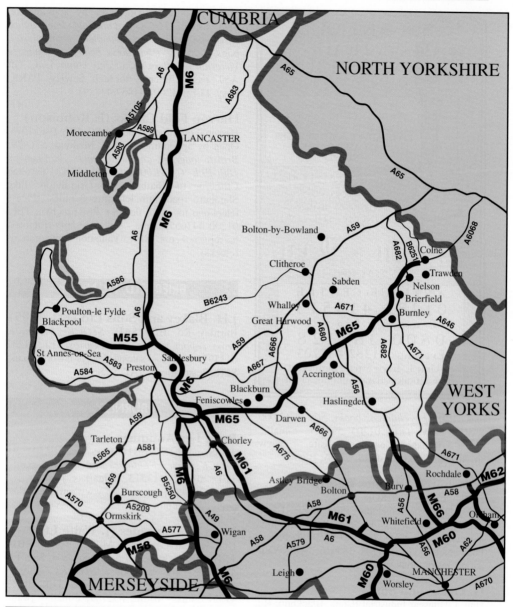

Dealers and Shops in Lancashire

Accrington	1	Burscough	1	Lancaster	5
Astley Bridge	1	Bury	1	Leigh	1
Blackburn	3	Chorley	1	Manchester	21
Blackpool	4	Clitheroe	4	Middleton Village	1
Bolton	2	Colne	1	Morecambe	3
Bolton-by-Bowland		Darwen	3	Nelson	2
	2	Feniscowles	1	Oldham	3
Brierfield	1	Great Harwood	2	Ormskirk	2
Burnley	3	Haslingden	4	Poulton-le-Fylde	1
				Preston	8

Rochdale	3
Sabden	2
Samlesbury	1
St. Annes-on-Sea	1
Tarleton	1
Trawden	1
Whalley	2
Whitefield	1
Wigan	3
Worsley	1

ANTIQUES TRADE WAREHOUSE
(OPEN TO THE PUBLIC)

PEOPLE TRAVEL MILES TO VISIT ONE OF THE LARGEST SELECTIONS OF ANTIQUES & DECORATIVE FURNITURE IN THE LANCASHIRE AREA
EST. 1973

WE ARE A FAMILY RUN BUSINESS HAVING 30 YEARS EXPERIENCE SELLING TO THE TRADE

Brun - Lea

ANTIQUES & FURNISHINGS

ANTIQUE CENTRE
01282 413513
Freephone
0800 387128
Evenings 01282 437703
Unit 1, Travis Street, Burnley
www.antiques-atlas.com/brunlea.htm

and collectable childrens books, 50p to £2,000.
PARK: Easy. TEL: 01204 597511; e-mail - mail@siriellisbooks.co.uk; website - www.siriellisbooks.co.uk. FAIRS: PBFA; Buxton.

Ironchurch Antiques Centre
Blackburn Rd. BL1 8DR. (P.J. Wilkinson). Est. 1975. Open 10-5 including Sun. SIZE: Large. *STOCK: Furniture, china, glass, clocks, books, jewellery, 17th C to date, £1-£10,000.* PARK: Free nearby. TEL: 01204 383616. SER: Valuations; restorations.

G. Oakes and Son
Unit 3, Dunscar Industrial Estate, Blackburn Rd. BL7 9PQ. Est. 1958. Open 9-5 or by appointment. SIZE: Large. *STOCK: Furniture and bric-a-brac.* LOC: Off A666. PARK: Easy. TEL: 01204 309935; e-mail - ycs12@dial.pipex.com. SER: Shipping and packing; buys at auction. VAT: Stan.

BOLTON-BY-BOWLAND, Nr. Clitheroe

Farmhouse Antiques
23 Main St. BB7 4NY. (M. Howard). Est. 1980. Open Sat., Sun. and Bank Holidays 12-4.30

(Sundays only in winter) or by appointment. SIZE: Small. *STOCK: Bed and table linen, quilts, christening robes, lace, samplers, embroideries, bags, buttons, trimmings, beads, costume to Victorian jewellery, Victoriana, china.* LOC: Off A59, past Clitheroe, through Sawley. PARK: Easy. TEL: 01200 441457/447294.

Harrop Fold Clocks (F. Robinson)
Harrop Fold, Lane Ends. BB7 4PJ. Est. 1974. Open by appointment. SIZE: Medium. *STOCK: British longcase and wall clocks, barometers, 18th-19th C, £1,000-£10,000.* LOC: Through Clitheroe to Chatburn and Grindleton. Take Slaidburn road, turn left after 3 miles. (Please telephone for more details). PARK: Own. TEL: 01200 447665; home - same; e-mail - robinson harrop@aol.com. SER: Valuations; restorations (clocks).

BRIERFIELD, Nr. Nelson

J.H. Blakey and Sons Ltd (Est. 1905)
Burnley Rd. BB9 5AD. *STOCK: Furniture, brass, copper, pewter, clocks, curios.* TEL: 01282 613593; e-mail - sales@blakeys.fsworld.co.uk. SER: Restorations. VAT: Stan.

BURNLEY

Brun Lea Antiques
3/5 Standish St. BB11 1AP. Open 9.30-5.30. *STOCK: General antiques and shipping goods.* TEL: 01282 413513; e-mail - jwaite@free netname.co.uk; website - www.antiques-atlas.com/ brunlea/htm.

Brun Lea Antiques (J. Waite Ltd)
Unit 1, Rear Elm Street Mill, Travis St. BB10 1DG. Open 8.30-5.30, Fri. and Sat. 9-4, Sun. 12-4. SIZE: Large warehouse. *STOCK: Georgian furniture to 1930's shipping goods.* TEL: 01282 413513; fax - 01282 832769; e-mail - jwaite @freenetname.co.uk; website - www.antiques-atlas.com/brunlea/htm

King's Mill Antique Centre
Unit 2 King's Mill, Queen St., Harle Syke. (Michael and Linda Heuer). Open 10-5, Thurs. 10-8, Sun. 11-5. SIZE: Large. *STOCK: Furniture and bric-a-brac, Edwardian and Victorian, £5-£1,000.* LOC: From General Hospital, follow brown tourist signs for Queen's Mill. PARK: Easy. TEL: 01282 431953; mobile - 07803 153752. SER: Export.

BURSCOUGH, Nr. Ormskirk

West Lancs. Antique Exports
Victoria Mill, Victoria St. L40 0SN. (W. and B. Griffiths). LAPADA. Est. 1959. Open 9-5.30, Sat. and Sun. 10-5. SIZE: Large. *STOCK: Shipping furniture.* TEL: 01704 894634; fax - 01704 894486. SER: Courier; packing and shipping. VAT: Stan.

BURY

Newtons
151 The Rock. BL9 0ND. (Newtons of Bury). Est. 1931. Open 9-5. SIZE: Small. *STOCK: General antiques, 18th-19th C, £5-£500.* Not Stocked: Continental furniture. LOC: From Manchester through Bury town centre, shop is on left 200yds. before Fire Station. PARK: 50yds. behind shop. TEL: 0161 764 1863. SER: Valuations; restorations (furniture). VAT: Stan.

CHORLEY

Antiques and Crafts Centre
Botany Bay Villages Ltd., Canal Mill, Botany Brow. PR6 9AF. Open daily including Sun. SIZE: Large - 5 floors. *STOCK: Porcelain, china and jewellery; furniture, memorabilia and curios and crafts.* LOC: Opposite junction 8, M61. PARK: Easy. TEL: 01257 261220. VAT: Stan.

Heskin Hall Antiques
Heskin Hall, Wood Lane, Heskin. PR7 5PA. (Harrison Steen Ltd). Est. 1996. Open 10-5.30 seven days. SIZE: Large - 70+ dealers. *STOCK: Wide range of general antiques.* LOC: B5250. PARK: Easy. TEL: 01257 452044; fax - 01257 450690; website - www.heskinhall.com. SER: Valuations; restorations.

CLITHEROE

Brittons - Watches and Antiques
4 King St. BB7 2EP. Est. 1970. CL: Wed. *STOCK: Jewellery and collectors' watches.* LOC: Town centre opposite main Post Office. PARK: Opposite. TEL: 01200 424555; fax - 01200 424200; website - www.brittons-watches.co.uk. SER: Valuations.

Folly Antiques
22 Moor Lane. BB7 1BE. (N.P. Medd). Est. 1967. Open 9-6, Wed. and Sun. by appointment. SIZE: Medium. *STOCK: Decorative and upholstered items, furniture, £100-£2,000; pictures, brass and objects, £5-£2,000; all 19th-20th C; garden furniture, small architectural items, 18th-20th C, £20-£2,000.* LOC: 15 miles from junction 31, M6, via A59. PARK: Opposite. TEL: 01200 429461. VAT: Stan/Spec.

Lee's Antiques
59 Whalley Rd. BB7 1EE. (P.A. Lee). *STOCK: General antiques.* TEL: 01200 424921; home - 01200 425441.

Past & Present
22 Whalley Rd. BB7 1AW. (D. and Mrs K. J. Hollings). Est. 1988. Open Sat. 10.30-5, other times by appointment. SIZE: Small. *STOCK: Victorian and Georgian cast iron fireplaces and ranges, £85-£1,500; Victorian and Edwardian wooden mantels, marble fireplaces, dog grates, coal buckets, brass and cast iron fenders; fireplace accessories, spare parts, brass and copper, small collectables.* LOC: Near town centre. PARK: Easy. TEL: 01200 428678; home - 01200 445373; mobile - 07779 478716. SER: Restorations (repairs, refurbishing, re-tiling cast iron fireplaces).

COLNE

Ingleside Antiques
13 Keighley Rd. BB8 0LP. (J. Fry). Est. 1988. Open 10-5. CL: Tues. and Thurs. SIZE: Medium. *STOCK: General antiques especially longcase, wall and mantel clocks and barometers, 1740-1910, £25-£4,500.* LOC: Just through centre of Colne. PARK: Easy. TEL: 01282 860046; home - same. SER: Valuations; restorations (clocks).

DARWEN

Belgrave Antique Centre
Britannia Mill, 136 Bolton Rd. Est. 1998. Open 9.30-5, Sun. 10-4.30. SIZE: Large - 40 dealers. *STOCK: Porcelain, pottery, glass, furniture, architectural, collectables.* LOC: Opposite India Mill. PARK: At rear. TEL: 01254 777714. SER: Valuations. FAIRS: Newark, Ardingly, Swinderby.

Grove Antiques
Hampden Mill, Springdale. (V. Cooney). Open 10-2.30. *STOCK: General antiques.* TEL: 01254 776644. SER: Valuations.

K.C. Antiques
538 Bolton Rd. BB3 2JR. (K. and J.Anderton). Resident. LAPADA. Open 9-6, Sun. 12-5. *STOCK: Georgian, Victorian and Edwardian*

furniture and decorative items. LOC: A666. PARK: Easy. TEL: 01254 772252. SER: Buys at auction. VAT: Stan/Spec.

FENISCOWLES, Nr. Blackburn

Old Smithy

726 Preston Old Rd. BB2 5EP. (R.C. and I.R. Lynch). Est. 1967. Open 9.30-5. SIZE: Large. *STOCK: Period and Victorian fireplaces, pub and architectural items, violins and musical instruments, pictures and prints, furniture, shipping items, brass, copper.* LOC: Opposite Fieldens Arms. PARK: Own or nearby. TEL: 01254 209943/580874. SER: Valuations; restorations (wooden items); buys at auction. FAIRS: Newark, Lincs.

GREAT HARWOOD, Nr. Blackburn

Benny Charlesworth's Snuff Box

51 Blackburn Rd. BB6 7DF. (N. Walsh). Est. 1984. Open 10-5. SIZE: Small. *STOCK: Furniture, china, linen, costume jewellery, teddies.* LOC: 200yds. from town centre, off A680. PARK: Next to shop. TEL: 01254 888550. FAIRS: Local.

Jean's Military Memories

32 Queen St. BB6 7QQ. (Len and Jean South). Est. 1994. Open 9-5, Sat. 9-4, other times by appointment. SIZE: Medium. *STOCK: Air weaponry, from 1880, £30-£4,000; deactivated weaponry, £100-£2,000; swords, £50-£1,000; knives, £10-£1,200.* LOC: Main road. PARK: Easy. TEL: 01254 877825; fax - same; mobile - 07713 636069; e-mail - jean.south@btinternet.com.

HASLINGDEN

P.J. Brown Antiques

8 Church St. BB4 5QU. Open 10-5, Sat. and Sun. by appointment. SIZE: Medium. *STOCK: Georgian, Victorian and Edwardian furniture, shipping goods, old advertising items, bottles and related items.* LOC: Town centre, off Bury Road/Regent St. PARK: Easy. TEL: 01706 224888. VAT: Stan/Spec.

Fieldings Antiques

176, 178 and 180 Blackburn Rd. BB1 2LG. Est. 1956. Open 9-4.30, Fri. 9-4. CL: Thurs. SIZE: Large. *STOCK: Longcase clocks, £30-£2,000; wall clocks, sets of chairs, pine, period oak, French furniture, glass, shipping goods, toys,*

steam engines, veteran cars, vintage and veteran motor cycles. PARK: Easy. TEL: 01706 214254; mobile - 07973 698961; home - 01254 263358.

Holden Wood Antiques Centre

St Stephen's Church, Grane Rd. BB4 4AT. (Peter and Mary Crossley and John Ainscough). Est. 1996. Open 10-5.30 including Sun. SIZE: 35 dealers. *STOCK: Furniture, 18th-19th C, £200-£2,000; ceramics including figures, glass, 19th C, £50-£2,000.* PARK: Own. TEL: 01706 830803; e-mail - john@holdenwood.co.uk; website - www.holden wood.co.uk. SER: Valuations; restorations.

P.W. Norgrove - Antique Clocks

38 Bury Rd. BB4 5LR. Est. 1978. Open most days, prior 'phone call advisable. *STOCK: Longcase, wall, bracket and mantel clocks.* PARK: Easy. TEL: 01706 211995; mobile - 07788 164621. SER: Repair and restorations (clocks); re-caning Bergere suites and chairs.

LANCASTER

Anything Old & Military Collectables

55 Scotforth Rd. LA1 4SA. (Graham H. Chambers). Est. 1985. Open Wed.-Sat. 1.30-6, Sun. by appointment. SIZE: Medium. *STOCK: WW1 and WW2 British, Imperial German, Third Reich and Commonwealth medals, cap badges, uniforms and head dress, edged weapons and field equipment, £5-£500.* LOC: 1.5 miles south of city centre on A6. PARK: Easy. TEL: 01524 69933; home - same. SER: Valuations; full size and miniature medal mounting.

The Assembly Rooms Market

King St. LA1 1XD. Open Tues.-Sat. 10-4.30. SIZE: Several dealers. *STOCK: General antiques, period and costume jewellery, Victorian to '60's costume and retro fashion, books.* TEL: Market Superintendent - 01524 66627.

G.B. Antiques Ltd

Lancaster Leisure Park, Wyresdale Rd. LA1 3LA. (MrsG.Blackburn). Open 10-5 including Sun. SIZE: Large. 100+ dealers. *STOCK: Porcelain, glass and silver, late 19th to early 20th C; small furniture, Victorian to early 20th C.* LOC: Off M6, junction 33 or 34. PARK: Easy. TEL: 01524 844734; fax - 01524 844735; home - 01772 861593. SER: Valuations; buys at auction. VAT: Stan/Spec.

Lancaster Leisure Park Antiques Centre

Wyresdale Rd. (on site of former Hornsea Pottery Plant). LA1 5LA. Open every day 10-5. SIZE:

140 dealers. *STOCK: Wide range of general antiques and collectables.* LOC: Off M6, junction 33. TEL: 01524 844734.

Lancastrian Antiques & Co
70/72 Penny St. LA1 1XF. (S.P. and H.S. Wilkinson). Open 10-4. CL: Wed. *STOCK: Furniture, lighting, paintings, bric-a-brac.* LOC: City centre. TEL: 01524 847004.

LEIGH

Leigh Jewellery
3 Queens St. (R.Bibby). Open 9.30-5.30, Wed. 9.30-12.30. *STOCK: Jewellery.* TEL: 01942 607947/722509; mobile - 07802 833467.

MANCHESTER

A.S. Antique Galleries
26 Broad St, Salford. M6 5BY. (A. Sternshine). Est. 1975. Open Thurs., Fri. and Sat. 10-5.30 or by appointment. SIZE: Large. *STOCK: Art Nouveau and Art Deco bronzes, bronze and ivory figures, silver, glass, ceramics, furniture, jewellery, lighting and general antiques.* Not Stocked: Weapons. LOC: On A6, one mile north of Manchester city centre, next to Salford University College. PARK: Easy. TEL: 0161 737 5938; mobile - 07836 368230; fax - 0161 737 6626; e-mail - as@sternshine.demon.co.uk. SER: Valuations; restorations; commission purchasing.

Antique Fireplace Warehouse
1090 Stockport Rd, Levenshulme. M19 2SU. (D. McMullan & Son). Open 9-6, Sun. 11-5. *STOCK: Fireplaces and architectural items.* PARK: Easy. TEL: 0161 431 8075; fax - 0161 442 7693.

Antiques Village
The Old Town Hall, 965 Stockport Rd., Levenshulme. M19 3NP. Est. 1978. Open 10-5.30, Sun. 11-4. SIZE: 40+ dealers. *STOCK: Furniture and clocks, reproduction pine, fireplaces, collectables.* LOC: A6 between Manchester and Stockport. PARK: Own. TEL: 0161 256 4644; fax - same; mobile - 07976 985982. SER: Valuations; restorations; pine stripping; picture framing. FAIRS: Newark.

Bus Stop Curios
1 Beech Rd., Chorlton-cum-Hardy. M21 8BX. (John and Jean Higginbotham). Resident. Est. 1989. Open Thurs. 11-5.30, Fri. 11.15-5.45, Sat. 10.30-4.30. SIZE: Medium. *STOCK: Militaria, WW1 & WW2, £1-£100; Victorian and Art Deco pottery and glass and smalls, £1-£100.* PARK: Easy. TEL: 0161 860 6232.

Cathedral Jewellers
38 Thomas St. M4 1ER. Open 9.30-5. *STOCK: Jewellery.* TEL: 0161 832 3042.

Didsbury Antiques
85 School Lane, Didsbury. M20 6WN. (Alan Willis). Est. 1982. Open 10-5. *STOCK: Ceramics, silver and furniture.* LOC: Near village centre. PARK: Easy. TEL: 0161 434 7487; home - 0161 434 6931. SER: Valuations.

Empire Exchange
1 Newton St., Piccadilly. M1 1HW. (David Ireland). Est. 1975. Open every day 9-7.30 except Christmas day. SIZE: Large. *STOCK: General small antiques including silver, pottery, clocks and watches, ephemera, autographs, football memorabilia, records, books and comics, 18th-20th C, £5-£10,000.* PARK: Easy. TEL: 0161 236 4445; fax - 0161 273 5007; home - 0161 256 1140. SER: Valuations. VAT: Stan/Spec.

Family Antiques
405/407 Bury New Rd., Prestwich. M25. (J. and J. Ditondo). Open daily. *STOCK: General antiques.* TEL: 0161 798 0036.

Fernlea Antiques
Failsworth Mill, Ashton Rd West, Failsworth. M35 0FD. (A.J. and Mrs B. McLaughlin). Est. 1983. Open 10-5. SIZE: Large. *STOCK: General antiques and shipping goods.* PARK: Easy. TEL: 0161 682 0589. SER: Container packing (worldwide).

Forest Books of Cheshire
in The Ginnel, 18-22 Lloyd St. M2 5WA. (Mrs E. Mann). Open 9.30-5.30. CL: Bank Holiday weekends and Christmas-New Year. *STOCK: Antiquarian, art, collecting, drama and humanities books and prints.* TEL: 0161 834 0747; 0161 833 9037 (The Ginnel); e-mail - info@fbooks.co.uk; website - www.fbooks.co.uk.

Fulda Gallery Ltd
19 Vine St., Salford. M7 3PG. (M.J. Fulda). Est. 1969. Open by appointment only. *STOCK: Oil paintings, 1500-1950, £500-£30,000; watercolours, 1800-1930, £350-£10,000.* LOC: Near Salford Police Station off Bury New Rd. TEL: 0161 792 1962; mobile - 07836 518313. SER: Valuations; restorations; buys at auction.

Gibb's Bookshop Ltd
10 Charlotte St. M1 4FL. Est. 1926. *STOCK: Books.* TEL: 0161 236 7179.

The Ginnell Gallery Antique Centre

18-22 Lloyd St. M2 5WA. (Mr and Mrs J.K. Mottershead). Est. 1973. Open 9.30-5.30. *STOCK: Art Deco and Art Nouveau, 1950's pottery, furniture, glass, antiquarian and other books.* LOC: Opposite Town Hall. TEL: 0161 833 9037.

In-Situ Manchester

Talbot Mill, 44 Ellesmere St., Hulme. M15 4JY. (Laurence Green). Est. 1983. Open 10-5.30. SIZE: Large. *STOCK: Architectural items including fireplaces, doors, panelling, sanitary ware, radiators, flooring, glass, gardenware, staircasing.* TEL: 0161 839 5525; mobile - 07780 993773; e-mail - enquiries@insitumanchester. com; website - www.insitumanchester.com.

In-Situ Manchester South Architectural Antiques

Unit G4, Longford Rd., Stretford. M32 0HQ. (A. Whyman and S. Newsham). SALVO. Open 9-5.30, Sun. 11-5. *STOCK: Architectural antiques, fireplaces, radiators, flooring, stoves, doors, glass, lighting, sanitaryware.* TEL: 0161 865 2110; fax - same; e-mail - andrew.whyman @virgin.net.

Irving Antique Toys

c/o Ginnel Gallery, 18-22 Lloyd St. M2 5WA. SIZE: Large. *STOCK: Tinplate, trains, Dinkies, teddies and dolls.* LOC: Off Albert Square. TEL: 0161 833 9037; home - 0161 740 9601; mobile - 07703 811715.

Eric J. Morten

Warburton St., Didsbury. M20 6WA. Est. 1959. Open 10-5.30. SIZE: Medium. *STOCK: Antiquarian books, 16th-20th C, £5-£5,000.* LOC: Off Wilmslow Rd., near traffic lights in Didsbury village. A34. PARK: Easy. TEL: 0161 445 7629 and 01265 277959; fax - 0161 448 1323. SER: Valuations; buys at auction (antiquarian books). FAIRS: PBFA.

R.J. O'Brien and Son Antiques Ltd

Failsworth Mill, Ashton Rd. West, Failsworth. M35 0FD. Est. 1970. Open 9-5. CL: Sat. SIZE: Very large. *STOCK: Furniture, Victorian, Edwardian and 1930's; shipping goods, general antiques and pianos.* PARK: Own. TEL: 0161 688 4414; mobile - 07850 485201. SER: Container and courier service.

Secondhand and Rare Books

Corner Church St/High St. M4 1PN. Est. 1970. Open 12-4. *STOCK: Books.* PARK: Nearby. TEL: 0161 834 5964 or 01625 861608. SER: Valuations.

St. James Antiques

STOCK: Jewellery, silver and paintings. TEL: 0161 773 4662; mobile - 07808 521671.

Village Antiques

416 Bury New Rd., Prestwich. M25 1BD. (R. Weidenbaum). Est. 1981. Open 10-5, Wed. 10-1. SIZE: Medium. *STOCK: 19th C pottery and porcelain, £5-£300; 18th C glass; small furniture; Art Deco clocks, figurines and lamps; Art Nouveau figurines.* LOC: Village centre, 2 mins. from M62. PARK: Easy - side and opposite. TEL: 0161 773 3612.

MIDDLETON VILLAGE, Nr. Morecambe

G G Exports

Newfield House, Middleton Rd. LA3 3PP. (G. Goulding). Est. 1970. Always available but prior telephone call essential. SIZE: Large. *STOCK: Shipping goods, £30-£5,000, English and European furniture.* LOC: On main road between Morecambe promenade and Middleton village. PARK: Easy. TEL: 01524 850757; fax - 01524 851565; e-mail - jay@ggantique.wholesalers. com; website - www.ggantique.wholesalers.com. SER: Courier; packing; 40ft containers weekly worldwide. VAT: Stan. *Trade Only.*

MORECAMBE

The Magpies Nest

46 Pedder St. LA4 5EA. (B.Byrne). Est. 1982. Open 10-5. CL: Wed. *STOCK: Bric-a-brac, cutlery, china, glass, militaria.* TEL: 01524 423328.

Tyson's Antiques

Clark St. LA4 5HT. (George, Andrew and Shirley Tyson). Est. 1952. Open Sat. 8-11.30, other times by appointment. SIZE: Large. *STOCK: Georgian, Victorian and Edwardian furniture.* PARK: Easy. TEL: 01524 416763/425235/420098; mobile - 07971 836892; website - www.tysons-antiques. freeserve.co.uk. VAT: Stan/Spec. *Trade Only.*

Luigino Vescovi

135 Balmoral Rd. LA3 1HJ. Est. 1970. Open by appointment every day. SIZE: Warehouse. *STOCK: Georgian and Victorian furniture, inlaid Edwardian and plated ware, £50-£10,000.* PARK: Easy. TEL: 01524 416732; mobile - 07860 784856. VAT: Stan/Spec/Export

NELSON

Colin Blakey Fireplaces
115 Manchester Rd. BB10 2LS. Est. 1906. Open
9.30-5, Sun. 12-3.30. SIZE: Large. *STOCK:
Fireplaces and hearth furniture, paintings and
prints.* LOC: Exit 12, M65. PARK: Opposite.
TEL: 01282 614941; fax - 01282 698511; e-mail
- psc6@underpaid.co.uk; website - www.colin.
blakeyfireplaces.co.uk. SER: Manufacturers and
suppliers of hand-carved marble fireplaces and
hardwood mantels. VAT: Stan.

Brooks Antiques
7 Russell St. BB9 7NL. (D. and S.A. Brooks).
Est. 1987. Open 9-5, Sun. and Tues. by
appointment. SIZE: Medium. *STOCK: Furniture,
£50-£2,000; smalls, £5-£500; both 1750-1930;
postcards, ephemera, early 20th C, to £20.* LOC:
Town centre, 2 mins. from junction 13, M65.
PARK: Easy. TEL: 01282 698148; home - 01282
866234. SER: Valuations.

OLDHAM

Charles Howell Jeweller
2 Lord St. OL1 3EY. (N.G. Howell). NAG. Est.
1870. Open 9.15-5.15. SIZE: Small. *STOCK:
Edwardian and Victorian jewellery, £25-£2,000;
silver, early to mid 20th C, £40-£1,500; watches,
Victorian to mid 20th C, £50-£800.* LOC: Town
centre, off High St. PARK: Limited or by
arrangement. TEL: 0161 624 1479. SER: Valuations; restorations (jewellery and watches); buys at
auction (jewellery and watches). VAT: Stan/Spec.

Marks Jewellers and Antique Dealers
16 Waterloo St. OL1 1SQ. (B.J. and S. Marks).
Est. 1969. Open 9.30-5. SIZE: Medium. *STOCK:
General antiques, Victorian and Edwardian
jewellery, silver and watches.* LOC: Town centre,
off Yorkshire St. PARK: Nearby. TEL: 0161 624
5975; fax - same; e-mail - bmarks46@hotmail.
com. SER: Valuations.

**H.C. Simpson and Sons Jewellers
(Oldham)Ltd**
37 High St. OL3 5AW. Open 9-5.30. *STOCK:
Clocks, jewellery, watches.* TEL: 0161 624 7187.
SER: Restorations (clocks).

ORMSKIRK

Green Lane Antiques
Unit B20 Malthouse Business Centre, 48
Southport Rd. L39 1QR. (J. Swift). Est. 1982.

Open seven days 10-4. SIZE: Large. *STOCK:
Furniture - pine, mahogany and oak; longcase
clocks.* PARK: Easy. TEL: 01695 580731; home -
01704 895444; mobile - 07715 371902. SER:
Restorations (longcase clocks).

Alan Grice Antiques
106 Aughton St. L39 3BS. Open 10-6. *STOCK:
Period furniture.* PARK: Easy. TEL: 01695
572007.

POULTON-LE-FYLDE

Ray Wade Antiques
P O Box 39. FY6 9GA. Est. 1978. Trades at fairs or
by appointment. *STOCK: Decorative items, sculpture, European and Oriental works of art, paintings.*
TEL: 01253 700715; fax - 01253 702342; mobile -
07836 291336; e-mail - antiques@r-wades.demon.
co.uk. SER: Finder; valuations; buys for export.
VAT: Stan/Spec/Global.

PRESTON

The Antique Centre
56 Garstang Rd. PR1 1NA. (Paul Allison). Est.
1966. Open 9-5.30, Sat. 9.30-5.30, Sun. 10.30-
5.30. SIZE: 20 dealers. *STOCK: Furniture,
including French pine, Georgian-Edwardian;
porcelain, silver, clocks, bric-a-brac and pictures.*
PARK: Easy. TEL: 01772 882078; fax - 01772
252842; e-mail - paul@antiquecentre.fsnet.co.uk;
website - www.antiqueweb.co.uk/centre/. SER:
Worldwide shipping; containers.

European Fine Arts and Antiques
10 Cannon St. PR1 3NR. (B. Beck). Est. 1970.
Open 9.30-5.30. SIZE: Medium. *STOCK:
Victorian paintings and furniture, to £2,000.*
LOC: Town centre - Fishergate. PARK: Loading
only and nearby. TEL: 01772 883886; fax - 01772
823888; e-mail - info@european-fine-arts.co.uk;
website - www.european-fine-arts.co.uk. SER:
Valuations; buys at auction. VAT: Stan/Spec.

Hackler's Jewellers
6b Lune St. PR1. (N.E. Oldfield). FBHI. *STOCK:
Antique clocks.* TEL: 01772 258465. VAT: Stan.

Halewood and Sons
37 Friargate. PR1 2AT. Est. 1867. CL: Thurs. pm.
STOCK: Antiquarian books and maps. TEL:
01772 252603.

Nelson's Antiques
113 New Hall Lane. PR1 5PB. (W. and L. Nelson).
Open 10-5 or by appointment. *STOCK: General*

antiques and collectors' items, dolls. LOC: Half mile from junction 31, M6. PARK: Easy. TEL: 01772 794896/862066. SER: Valuations.

Preston Antique Centre
The Mill, New Hall Lane. PR1 5NX. Open 8.30-5.30, Sat.10-4, Sun. 10-5. SIZE: Large - 40+ dealers. *STOCK: General antiques, Georgian-Edwardian; shipping furniture; shipping, Dutch, Italian and French furniture; collectables and longcase clocks.* PARK: Own. TEL: 01772 794498/654531/651548; fax - 01772 651694; e-mail - prestonantiques@talk21.com; websites - www.antiques-atlas.com/preston.htm and www.prestonantiquescentre.com.

Preston Book Co
68 Friargate. PR1 2ED. (M. Halewood). Est. 1950. Open 10-5.30. *STOCK: Antiquarian books.* LOC: Town centre. PARK: Easy. TEL: 01772 252613. SER: Buys at auction.

Priory Collectables
7 Priory Lane, Penwortham. (David Howden). Est. 1988. Open Tues., Thurs., Fri. 1-5, Sat. 10-5, Sun. trade by appointment. SIZE: Small. *STOCK: Cutlery and silver plate, from 1850, £5-£500; collectables including china, glass, clocks, toby jugs, Wade, Sylvac, small furniture.* LOC: Turn right at traffic lights in Penwortham into Priory Lane. PARK: Easy. TEL: 01772 752090.

ROCHDALE

Antiques and Bygones
100 Drake St. OL16 1PQ. (K. and E. Bonn). Est. 1983. Open 10-4, Sat. 10-2. CL: Mon. and Tues. SIZE: Small. *STOCK: Pottery, coins and medals, jewellery, 19th-20th C, £5-£50.* TEL: 01706 648114.

S.C. Falk
LAPADA. Open by appointment only. *STOCK: Fine English period furniture.* TEL: 01706 644946. VAT: Stan/Spec.

Owen Antiques
114 Buersill Avenue. OL16 4TX. (J.G.T. Owen). Est. 1891. Open by appointment. *STOCK: Mainly paintings, clocks, radios; old scarce, rare and unusual books.* TEL: 01706 353270. SER: Valuations.

SABDEN, Nr. Clitheroe

Walter Aspinall Antiques
Pendle Antiques Centre, Union Mill, Watt St. BB7 9ED. Est. 1964. Open 9-5, Sat. and Sun. 11-4 or by appointment. SIZE: Large. *STOCK: Furniture and bric-a-brac.* LOC: On Pendle Hill between Clitheroe and Padiham. PARK: Easy. TEL: 01282 778642; fax - 01282 778643; e-mail - walter.aspinall@btinternet.com. SER: Export; packing; courier; containers; wholesale. VAT: Stan.

Pendle Antiques Centre Ltd
Union Mill, Watt St. BB7 9ED. (B. Seed and J.L. Billington). Est. 1993. Open 10-5, Sun. 11-5 (other times by appointment for Trade). SIZE: 10 dealers. *STOCK: Furniture and bric-a-brac.* LOC: Over Pendle Hill, off the A59 between Clitheroe and Padiham. TEL: 01282 776311; fax - 01282 778643; e-mail - sales@pendleantiquescentre; www - pendleantiquescentre.co.uk.

SAMLESBURY, Nr. Preston

Samlesbury Hall
(Dating from 1325). Preston New Rd. PR5 0UP. (Samlesbury Hall Trust). Est. 1969. Open 11-4.30, but prior telephone call advisable. Admission - adults £2.50, children £1. CL: Mon. SIZE: Large. *STOCK: General collectable antiques.* LOC: Exit 31, M6 on A677 between Preston and Blackburn. PARK: Easy. TEL: 01254 812010/2229

ST. ANNES-ON-SEA

The Victorian Shop
19 Alexandria Drive. FY8 1JF. (G.O. Freeman). Open 10-5. *STOCK: General antiques including furniture, china, silver, watches and clocks.* PARK: Easy. TEL: 01253 725700. FAIRS: Newark.

TARLETON

R.H. Latham Antiques
6 Gorse Lane. PR4 6UJ. Est. 1958. Open by appointment only. SIZE: Medium + warehouse at Old Cornmill Antique Centre, 64 South Road, Bretherton. *STOCK: Antique stripped pine furniture and interesting associated smalls.* TEL: 01772 812900; mobile - 07801 948320. SER: Shipping and courier; pine stripping.

TRAWDEN, Nr. Colne

Jack Moore Antiques and Stained Glass
The Old Rock, Keighley Rd. BB8 8RW. Est. 1976. Open Wed.-Sat. 9-5 or by appointment.

SIZE: Small. *STOCK: Stained glass.* PARK: Easy. TEL: 01282 869478; home - same; fax - 01282 865193; mobile - 07802 331594. SER: Restoration and manufacture of stained glass; container packing; courier. VAT: Stan.

WHALLEY, Nr. Clitheroe

T. Brindle Antiques and Brindle Fine Arts Ltd

41 King St. BB7 9SP. LAPADA. Open 9.30-5.00, Sat. and other times by appointment. *STOCK: English and Continental furniture, fine oil paintings, Japanese works of art, bronzes and porcelain.* TEL: 01254 825200

Edmund Davies & Son Antiques

32 King St. BB7 9SL. (E. and P. Davies). Est. 1960. Open 10-5. SIZE: Medium + trade warehouse. *STOCK: Oak and country furniture, longcase clocks, to £10,000; jewellery, to £500.* Not Stocked: Reproductions. LOC: A59 (11 miles from M6). PARK: Easy. TEL: 01254 823764. SER: Restorations (longcase clocks). VAT: Stan/Spec.

WHITEFIELD, Nr. Manchester

Henry Donn Gallery

138/142 Bury New Rd. M45 6AD. (Henry and Nicholas Donn). FATG. Est. 1954. Open 9.30-5. SIZE: Large. *STOCK: Paintings, 19th-20th C, £20-£100,000.* LOC: Off M60, junction 17 towards Bury. PARK: Own at rear. TEL: 0161 766 8819; fax - same; e-mail - donn@netlineuk.net; website - www.henrydonngallery.com. SER: Valuations; framing; restorations (pictures). VAT: Stan/Spec.

WIGAN

Colin de Rouffignac

57 Wigan Lane. WN1 2LF. BNTA. Est. 1984. Open 10-4.30. CL: Wed. *STOCK: Furniture, jewellery, oils and watercolours.* PARK: Easy. TEL: 01942 237927.

John Robinson Antiques

172-176 Manchester Rd., Higher Ince. WN2 2EA. Est. 1965. Open any time. SIZE: Large. *STOCK: General antiques.* LOC: A577 near Ince Bar. PARK: Easy. TEL: 01942 247773/241671. SER: Export packing. VAT: Stan. *Export and Trade Only.*

Wiend Books & Collectables

8-12 The Wiend. WN1 1PF. (Paul and Roslyn Morris). PBFA. Est. 1997. Open 9.30-5. CL: Tues. SIZE: 7 rooms. *STOCK: Books, £5-£80; ephemera, £1-£20; advertising items, Wade, £5-£50; all mainly 19th-20th C.* LOC: Between Market Place and Millgate. PARK: Millgate. TEL: 01942 820500; fax - same; website - www.wiendbooks.co.uk. SER: Valuations. FAIRS: Bolton Reebok Stadium; Haigh Hall; PBFA; North West Book.

WORSLEY, Nr. Manchester

Northern Clocks

Boothsbank Farm, Leigh Rd. M28 1LL. (R.M. Love and Miss M.A. Love). LAPADA. Est. 1998. Open by appointment. SIZE: Large. *STOCK: Provincial longcase and bracket clocks, 18th C.* LOC: Off junction 13, M60. PARK: Easy. TEL: 0161 790 8414; home - same; fax - 0161 703 7567; e-mail - info@northernclocks.co.uk; website - www.northernclocks.co.uk. SER: Valuations; restorations. VAT: Stan.

A rare composite 1847 Albert pattern helmet of the heavy cavalry. It was fitted with the brass fittings of the Bombay Horse Artillery. The foliage on the helmet's peak is unusual.

From an article entitled "Collecting Antique Helmets – The Prima Donna of Military Antiques" by Robert Attard which appeared in the February 2002 issue of **Antique Collecting**. For more details and to subscribe see page 21.

Affordable Antiques
Old Forge, North St. LE65 1HS. (Jacqueline and Brian Sidwells). Est. 1994. Open 10-5. CL: Wed. SIZE: Small. *STOCK: Victorian pine and period furniture, china especially Bretby and Measham bargeware.* LOC: Just off Market Square. PARK: Opposite. TEL: 01530 413744; fax - same; mobile - 07966 424861; e-mail - j.sidwells@care4free.net; website - www.affordableantiques.co.uk. SER: Restorations (pine stripping). FAIRS: Newark; DMG.

Old Bakehouse Antiques and Gallery
10 Green Rd. LE9 6RA. (S.R. Needham). Open Thurs.-Sat. 10-6, Sun. 2-5. *STOCK: Period furniture.* PARK: Easy. TEL: 01455 282276.

The Book Shop
17 Borough St. DE74 2LP. (Michael and Margaret Fletcher). Est. 1970. Open 9-5, Sat. 9-12. CL: Wed. SIZE: Small. *STOCK: Books - aviation history, military, railway and antiquarian; pictures and prints, die cast toys.* LOC: Opposite village church. PARK: Easy. TEL: 01332 814391. SER: Valuations; restorations (book-binding); framing. FAIRS: Donington; airshows - Duxford, Waddington, Cottesmore, Cosford and Woodford, RIAT, IPMS.

Keystone Antiques
9 Ashby Rd. LE67 3LF. (I. and H. McPherson). LAPADA. FGA. Est. 1979. Open Thurs., Fri. and Sat. 10-5, Mon. and Tues. by appointment. SIZE: Medium. *STOCK: Jewellery, Victorian and Georgian, £25-£1,500; silver, 1700-1920, £20-£500; small collectable items, 18th-19th C, £15-£300; furniture, cranberry, needlework tools, Victorian and Georgian table glass.* LOC: A115, town centre. PARK: At rear. TEL: 01530 835966; e-mail - heathermcp@webleicester.co.uk. SER: Valuations (jewellery); gem testing. VAT: Stan/Spec.

The Glory Hole
69 High St. LE9 7DH. (M. Crowston). Est. 1994. Open 10-5.30, Sun. 10-2. SIZE: Large. *STOCK: Victorian and Edwardian furniture, £100-£1,000; porcelain, 1860-1930's, £5-£50.* PARK: Easy. TEL: 01455 847922; mobile - 07710 101364; e-mail - mark@thegloryhole.co.uk; website - www.thegloryhole.co.uk. SER: Valuations; restorations including door stripping; buys at auction (furniture). FAIRS: Newark and Ardingly.

Ken Smith Antiques Ltd
215-217 Leicester Rd. LE19 2BJ. (K.W. Sansom). LAPADA. Est. 1888. Open Mon.-Fri. 9.30-5. SIZE: Small. *STOCK: Furniture, mainly 1880-1930, £100-£1,000; clocks, smalls and bric-a-brac.* TEL: 0116 286 2341; fax - 0116 286 3230. VAT: Stan/Spec.

Sitting Pretty
45a Main St. LE8 9GH. (Jennifer Jones-Fenleigh). Est. 1979. Open Thurs., Fri. and Sat. 10-5.30, other days by appointment. *STOCK: Upholstered furniture, 18th-20th C, £50-£1,000.* LOC: Off A6. PARK: Easy. TEL: 0116 259 3711; home - same. SER: Valuations; restorations (re-upholstery, French polishing, caning and rushing). VAT: Spec.

Ancient & Oriental Ltd
69 Main St. LE14 3BZ. (A. Szolin). ADA. Open 9-7, or by appointment. SIZE: Medium. *STOCK: Ancient Egyptian, Greek, Roman, Celtic, Saxon, Pre-Columbian, and medieval antiquities.* PARK: Easy. TEL: 01664 812044; fax - 01664 810087; e-mail - alex@antiquities.co.uk; website - www.antiquities.co.uk. SER: Valuations.

House Things Antiques
Trinity Lane, 44 Mansion St. LE10 0AU. (P.W. Robertson). Est. 1976. Open 10-6. SIZE: Small. *STOCK: Stripped pine, satinwood, oak and walnut, mainly Victorian and Edwardian, £50-£600; small collectors' items, 1860-1930s, £5-£100; cast iron fireplaces, brass and iron beds, 1890-1920's, £50-£1,000.* LOC: On inner ring road 200yds. from Leisure Centre. PARK: Easy. TEL: 01455 618518; home - 01455 212797.

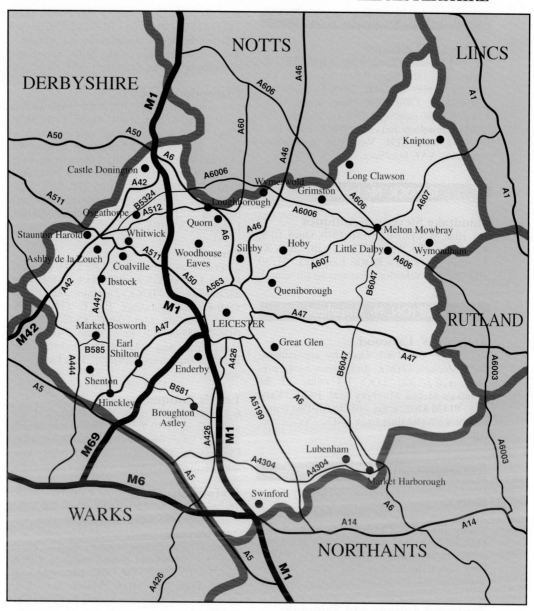

Dealers and Shops in Leicestershire

Ashby de la Zouch	1	Hinckley	1	Lubenham	3	Sileby	1
Broughton Astley	1	Hoby	1	Market Bosworth	4	Staunton Harold	1
Castle Donington	1	Ibstock	1	Market Harborough	3	Swinford	1
Coalville	1	Knipton	1	Melton Mowbray	2	Whitwick	1
Earl Shilton	1	Leicester	10	Osgathorpe	1	Woodhouse Eaves	1
Endby	1	Little Dalby	1	Queniborough	1	Wymeswold	1
Great Glen	1	Long Clawson	1	Quorn	1	Wymondham	1
Grimston	1	Loughborough	1	Shenton	1		

HOBY, Nr. Melton Mowbray

Withers of Leicester

The Old Rutland, Church Lane. LE14 3DU. (S. Frings). Est. 1860. Open 9-5.30. CL: Thurs. pm. and Sat. SIZE: Medium. *STOCK: Furniture, 17th-19th C, £50-£3,000; china, 18th-19th C, £10-£300; oil paintings, 19th C, £5-£500.* Not Stocked: Jewellery and coins. PARK: Easy. TEL: 01664 434803. SER: Valuations; restorations (furniture). VAT: Stan/Spec.

IBSTOCK, Nr. Leicester

Mandrake Stevenson Antiques

101 High St. LE67 6LJ. Est. 1979. Open 10-5, Sat. 10-1. CL: Wed. SIZE: Small. *STOCK: Furniture, pre 1930's.* PARK: Easy. TEL: 01530 260898. SER: Valuations; restorations (furniture).

KNIPTON, Nr. Grantham

Anthony W. Laywood

NG32 1RF. Est. 1967. Open by appointment. SIZE: Medium. *STOCK: Antiquarian books, pre-1850, £20-£8,000.* LOC: 1.5 miles off the Grantham-Melton Mowbray road. PARK: Easy. TEL: 01476 870224; fax - 01476 870198; e-mail - laywood@globalnet.co.uk. SER: Valuations; buys at auction.

LEICESTER

Betty's

9 Knighton Fields Rd. West. LE2 6LH. (A. Smith). Est. 1968. Open 9.30-5. SIZE: Small. *STOCK: Satinwood and pine items, brass and copper, pictures.* LOC: Off Saffron Lane. PARK: Easy. TEL: 0116 2839048. SER: Valuations; buys at auction.

Boulevard Antique and Shipping Centre

63 King Richard's Rd. LE3 5QG. Open Mon.-Fri. 9-6 or anytime by appointment. SIZE: Large. *STOCK: Furniture including oak, mahogany and shipping; general antiques, some smalls.* LOC: A46 from junction 21, M1. PARK: Own. TEL: 0116 233 8828; fax - 0116 233 8823. VAT: Stan.

Britain's Heritage

Shaftesbury Hall, 3 Holy Bones. LE1 4LJ. (Mr and Mrs J. Dennis). Est. 1980. Open 9.30-5.30, Sat. 9.30-5. SIZE: Large. *STOCK: Fireplaces, 18th-20th C, £100-£25,000.* LOC: Off Vaughan Way, 70 yards from Holiday Inn. PARK: Own. TEL: 0116 251 9592; fax - 0116 262 5990; e-mail - britainsheritage@tinyonline.co.uk; website - www.britainsheritage.co.uk. SER: Valuations; restorations (antique fireplaces). VAT: Stan/Spec.

Clarendon Books

144 Clarendon Park Rd. LE2 3AE. (Julian Smith). PBFA. Est. 1984. Open 10-5. SIZE: Small. *STOCK: Antiquarian and second-hand books, £1-£1,000.* LOC: Between London Rd. (A6) and Welford Rd. (A50), 2 miles south of city centre. PARK: Easy. TEL: 0116 270 1856; fax - 0116 270 9020; home - 0116 270 1914. SER: Valuations; restorations (repair and binding); buys at auction (books and maps). FAIRS: London H D; PBFA.

Corry's

24 Francis St., Stoneygate. LE2 2BD. (Mrs E.I. Corry). LAPADA. Est. 1962. Open 10-5. CL: Fri. SIZE: Medium. *STOCK: Furniture, 18th-19th C, £500-£10,000; paintings, 19th C, £100-£8,000; silver, porcelain, 18th-20th C, £5-£5,000.* TEL: 0116 270 3794. SER: Restorations. FAIRS: NEC (Jan., April, Aug.); LAPADA London; Robert Baileys'; Dorchester; Claridges; Park Lane. VAT: Spec.

Letty's Antiques

6 Rutland St. LE1 1RA. (I.H. Dubberley). Est. 1952. Open 9.30-5. CL: Thurs. Jan.-March. *STOCK: Silver, jewellery, china and brass.* LOC: City centre. TEL: 0116 2626435. SER: Valuations (silver and jewellery).

Oxford Street Antique Centre

16-26 Oxford St. LE1 5XU. (Paul and Linda Giles). Est. 1987. Open 10-5.30, Sat. 10-5, Sun. 2-5. SIZE: Large warehouse, 14 showrooms on 4 floors. *STOCK: Period furniture, shipping goods, pine, bric-a-brac and general antiques, 19th to mid-20th C, 50p-£5,000.* LOC: Inner ring road. PARK: Own. TEL: 0116 2553006; fax - 0116 2555863. SER: Container loading facilities. VAT: Stan/Spec.

The Rug Gallery

50 Montague Rd., Clarendon Park. LE2 1TH. (Dr. Roy Short). Est. 1987. Open Fri. and Sat. 10-4 or by appointment. SIZE: Medium. *STOCK: Oriental rugs and kilims, early 19th to 20th C, £100-£2,000; Swat, Afghan, Indian and Chinese furniture, 18th-19th C, £50-£1,000; tribal embroidery and jewellery, 19th-20th C, £10-£1,000.* LOC: From London Rd. A6, take Victoria Park Rd., to Queen's Rd., then Montague Rd. PARK: Easy. TEL: 0116 2700085; home - 0116 2700113.

Hammond Smith (Fine Art)

431 London Rd. LE2 3JW. Est. 1981. Open by appointment. SIZE: Small. *STOCK: British watercolours, 1750-2000, £500-£10,000.* PARK: Easy. TEL: 0116 270 9020; fax - same; mobile - 07973 483231. SER: Valuations; restorations (watercolours and prints cleaned, mounted and framed); buys at auction (watercolours). VAT: Spec.

West End Antiques

1 Lothair Rd., Off Aylestone Rd. LE2 7QE. Est. 1986. Open Tues.-Sat. 10-4.30. SIZE: Small. *STOCK: Furniture, porcelain, silver, 19th C, £25-£1,000.* PARK: Easy. TEL: 0116 244 0086. FAIRS: Castle Donington.

LITTLE DALBY, Nr. Melton Mowbray

Treedale Antiques

Little Dalby Hall, Pickwell Lane. LE14 2XB. (G.K. Warren). GMC. Est. 1972. Open 9-5, Sat. and Sun. by appointment. SIZE: Large. *STOCK: Furniture including walnut, mahogany and oak, from 1680, to £3,000; portraits and paintings, tapestries and chandeliers.* PARK: Own. TEL: 01664 454535; home - same. SER: Valuations; restorations (furniture).

LONG CLAWSON, Nr. Melton Mowbray

Old Hall Farm

Hose Lane. LE14 4NG. Open 8.30-5.30. *STOCK: Pine, French antiques, gas (electric) wall lights and shades, architectural items.* TEL: 01949 860274; fax - 01949 861231. SER: Restorations (oak, mahogany, architectural items, pine stripping); furniture, windows and doors made from reclaimed pine.

LOUGHBOROUGH

Lowe of Loughborough

37-40 Church Gate. LE11 1UE. Est. 1846. CL: Sat. SIZE: Large. *STOCK: Furniture and period upholstery from early oak, 1600 to Edwardian; mahogany, walnut, oak, £20-£8,000; clocks, bracket and longcase, £95-£2,500; porcelain, maps, copper and brass.* Not Stocked: Jewellery. LOC: Opposite parish church. PARK: Own. TEL: 01509 212554/217876. SER: Upholstery; restorations; interior design. VAT: Stan/Spec.

LUBENHAM, Nr. Market Harborough

Leicestershire Sporting Gallery and Brown Jack Bookshop

The Old Granary, 62 Main St. LE16 9DG. (Reg Leete). Est. 1958. Prior 'phone call advisable. SIZE: Large. *STOCK: Oil paintings, prints including Vanity Fair and sporting; engravings, maps, furniture (including mahogany and oak); antiquarian and illustrated books, histories of fox hunts, prints, horse brasses, martingales, swingers, all pre 1930.* LOC: Centre of village. PARK: Rear of village green opposite. TEL: 01858 465787.

Oaktree Antiques

The Draper's House, Main St. LE16 9TF. (Gillian Abraham and John Wright). Open Wed.-Sun. 10-6. SIZE: Medium. *STOCK: Town and country furniture, 17th-19th C; longcase clocks, Georgian to early Victorian; works of art.* PARK: Opposite on village green. TEL: 01858 410041; mobile - 07710 205696; website - www.oaktreeantiques.co.uk. VAT: Spec.

Stevens and Son

61 Main St. LE16 9TF. (M.J. Stevens). Resident. Est. 1977. Open 10-5. *STOCK: General antiques, mainly furniture.* LOC: A427 via junction 20 M1. TEL: 01858 463521. SER: Restorations (furniture).

MARKET BOSWORTH

Bosworth Antiques
10 Main St. CV13 0JW. (John Thorp). Est. 1986. Open 10-1 and 2-5. CL: Tues. *STOCK: General antiques, 19th-20th C.* PARK: Easy. TEL: 01455 292134. SER: Valuations.

Corner Cottage Antiques
7 Market Place, The Square. CV13 0LF. (J. and B. Roberts). Est. 1969. Open 10-5, Mon. and Wed. by appointment. *STOCK: 18th-20th C furniture, silver, paintings; clocks, porcelain, glass, brass and copper, general antiques.* PARK: Easy. TEL: 01455 290344; home - 01455 282583; e-mail - bobandjill@btinternet.com. VAT: Global/Stan/Spec.

Country Pine Antiques
4 Main St. CV13 0JW. (T.W. and L.M. Richardson). Est. 1980. Open 10-5.30, Thurs. 10-3. CL: Mon. SIZE: Medium. *STOCK: Stripped pine, oak and interesting and unusual decorative items.* LOC: Off A447 in Market Place. PARK: Easy. TEL: 01455 291303.

P. Stanworth (Fine Arts)
The Grange, 2 Barton Rd. CV13 0LQ. (Mr and Mrs G. and James Stanworth). Resident. Est. 1965. Open by appointment. SIZE: Medium. *STOCK: Oil paintings and watercolours, 18th to early 20th C.* LOC: Road just off town square. PARK: Easy. TEL: 01455 291023. VAT: Spec.

MARKET HARBOROUGH

Graftons of Market Harborough
92 St Mary's Rd. LE16 7DX. (F. Ingall). Est. 1967. Open Mon., Tues., Fri. and Sat. 10-5.30, other times by appointment. *STOCK: Oils, watercolours, etchings and engravings, 18th-19th C.* PARK: Forecourt. TEL: 01858 433557. FAIRS: Royal Show.

Walter Moores and Son
P O Box 5338. LE16 7WG. (Peter Moores). LAPADA. Est. 1925. Open by appointment only. *STOCK: Georgian furniture; complementary Victorian items.* TEL: 07071 226202; fax - same; mobile - 07710 019045. FAIRS: Most major. VAT: Spec.

J. Stamp and Sons
The Chestnuts, 15 Kettering Rd. LE16 8AN. (M. Stamp). Resident. Est. 1947. Open 8-5.30, Sat. 9-12.30 or by appointment. SIZE: Medium. *STOCK: Mahogany and oak furniture, 18th-19th*

C, £500-£5,000; Victorian furniture, £250-£2,500; Edwardian furniture, £100-£1,000. LOC: A6. PARK: Easy. TEL: 01858 462524; fax - 01858 465643. SER: Valuations (furniture); restorations (furniture). VAT: Stan/Spec.

MELTON MOWBRAY

Flagstones Pine & Interiors
24 Burton St. LE13 1AF. (Julie Adcock and David Kealey). Est. 1986. Open 9.30-5.15, Sun. 10.30-3.30. SIZE: Medium. *STOCK: English and European pine furniture, 18th-20th C; new and reclaimed wood reproductions, including kitchens.* PARK: Easy. TEL: 01664 566438; website - www.flagstonespine.co.uk. SER: Restorations; stripping; waxing. VAT: Stan.

Parkside Antiques
25 Leicester St. LE13 0PP. (Mrs Marilyn Gordon). Open Tues., Fri. and Sat. 9.30-5. SIZE: Small. *STOCK: Furniture, early 19th C to 1920's; silver and jewellery, 19th-20th C; prints, paintings, mirrors.* LOC: Town centre. PARK: Nearby. TEL: 01664 560446; home/fax - same; mobile - 07773 176727. FAIRS: Newark, Ardingly, Birmingham.

OSGATHORPE, Nr. Loughborough

David E. Burrows
Manor House Farm. LE12 9SY. LAPADA. Est. 1973. *STOCK: Pine, oak, mahogany and walnut furniture, clocks, £100-£10,000.* LOC: Junction 23, M1, turn right off Ashby road after 4.5 miles, farm next to church; or A42. PARK: Easy. TEL: 01530 222218; mobile - 07702 059030; fax - 01530 223139; e-mail - david.burrows2@virgin.net. VAT: Stan/Spec.

QUENIBOROUGH, Nr. Leicester

J. Green and Son
1 Coppice Lane. LE7 3DR. (R. Green). Resident. Est. 1932. Appointment advisable. SIZE: Medium. *STOCK: 18th-19th C English and Continental furniture.* LOC: Off A607 Leicester-Melton Mowbray Rd. PARK: Easy. TEL: 0116 2606682. SER: Valuations; buys at auction. VAT: Stan/Spec.

QUORN

Quorn Pine and Decoratives
The New Mills, Leicester Rd. LE12 8ES. (S. Yates and S. Parker). Est. 1982. Open 9-6, Sat.

9.30-5.30. SIZE: Large. *STOCK: Pine and country furniture.* PARK: Own. TEL: 01509 416031; website - www.quorn-pine.co.uk. SER: Stripping and restorations (pine). VAT: Stan/Spec.

SHENTON, Nr. Market Bosworth

Whitemoors Antiques and Fine Art
Mill Lane. CV13 6BZ. (D. Dolby and P. McGowan). Est. 1987. Open Mon.-Fri. 11-4, (until 5 in summer), Sat. and Sun. 11-5. SIZE: Large - 20+ unitholders. *STOCK: Furniture, £25-£2,000; smalls, £5-£200; prints and pictures, Victorian to early 20th C, £40-£400.* LOC: A5 onto A444 towards Burton-on-Trent, first right then second left. PARK: Easy. TEL: 01455 212250; 01455 212981 (ansaphone); fax - 01455 213342.

SILEBY, Nr. Loughborough

R. A. James Antiques
Ammonite Gallery, 15a High St. LE12 7RX. *STOCK: Mainly stripped pine, general antiques.* TEL: 01509 812169; mobile - 07713 132650.

STAUNTON HAROLD

Ropers Hill Antiques
Ropers Hill Farm. LE65 1SE. (S. and R. Southworth). Est. 1974. Open by appointment. SIZE: Small. *STOCK: General antiques, silver and metalware.* LOC: On old A453. PARK: Easy. TEL: 01530 413919. SER: Valuations.

SWINFORD, Nr. Lutterworth

Old Timers
High St. LE17 6BL. (M. S. Harris). Est. 1994. Open every day except Sun., but appointment preferred. SIZE: Small. *STOCK: Clocks and furniture, some brass and copper.* LOC: Village centre, half a mile from junction 19, M1, M6 and A14. PARK: Own. TEL: 01788 860311; fax - same; e-mail - info@old-timers.co.uk; website - www.old-timers.co.uk. SER: Valuations; restorations.

WHITWICK, Nr. Coalville

Charles Antiques
3 Market Place. LE67 5AE. (Brian Haydon). Est. 1970. Open afternoons, Sat. 10-12 and 2-4, Wed. and Sun. by appointment. CL: Mon. SIZE: Small. *STOCK: Clocks, 18th C, £25-£4,000; furniture,*

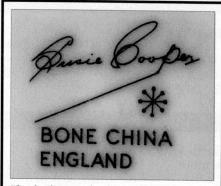

The backstamp for bone china production used from about 1951 to 1966.

From an article entitled "Susie Cooper Bone China 1950-1966" by Ann Eatwell which appeared in the March 2002 issue of **Antique Collecting**. For more details and to subscribe see page 21.

19th C, £50-£1,000; china. LOC: A511. PARK: Easy. TEL: 01530 836932; home - same; mobile - 07831 204406. SER: Buys at auction. VAT: Stan/Spec.

WOODHOUSE EAVES, Nr. Leicester

Paddock Antiques
The Old Smithy, Brand Hill. LE12 8SS. (M., C.A. and T.M. Bray). Open Thurs. - Sat. 10-5.30, other times by appointment. *STOCK: Furniture, 1750-1910, to £5,000; porcelain, 1750-1940's, to £3,500; prints and glass.* PARK: Easy.

WYMESWOLD, Nr. Loughborough

N. Bryan-Peach Antiques
28 Far St. LE12 6TZ. Resident. Open 10-6, Sun. by appointment. SIZE: Medium. *STOCK: Clocks, barometers, 18th-19th C furniture, £50-£5,000.* PARK: Easy. TEL: 01509 880425. SER: Valuations; restorations; buys at auction. VAT: Spec.

WYMONDHAM, Nr. Melton Mowbray

Old Bakery Antiques
Main St. LE14 2AG. (Tina Bryan). Est. 1990. Open 10-5.30. CL: Thurs. SIZE: Medium. *STOCK: Cottage, garden, architectural and reclamation items including pine furniture, kitchenalia, advertising items, chimney pots, stained glass and door hardware; rural and domestic bygones.* PARK: Easy. TEL: 01572 787472; home - same; fax - 01572 787731.

LINCOLNSHIRE

ALFORD

Trade Antiques
5 High St. LN13 9DS. (P.E. Poole). Est. 1961.
CL: Sat. SIZE: Medium. *STOCK: General
shipping goods, clocks and watches.* PARK:
Easy. TEL: 01507 462854. *Trade Only.*

ALLINGTON, Nr. Grantham

Garth Vincent Antique Arms and Armour
The Old Manor House. NG32 2DH. LAPADA.
Est. 1979. Open by appointment. SIZE: Medium.
*STOCK: Militaria including firearms, swords,
rapiers and daggers; armour, 16th-19th C, £50-
£15,000.* LOC: Opposite church. PARK: Easy.
TEL: 01400 281358; home - same; fax - 01400
282658; mobile - 07785 352151; e-mail -
garthvincent@compuserve.com; website - www.
guns.uk.com. SER: Valuations; restorations; buys
at auction. FAIRS: London and major city Arms;
NEC (Aug). VAT: Spec.

AYLESBY, Nr. Grimsby

Robin Fowler (Period Clocks)
Washing Dales, Washing Dales Lane. DN37 7LH.
LAPADA. Open by appointment. SIZE: Large.
STOCK: Clocks and barometers, 17th-18th C.
TEL: 01472 751335. SER: Restorations (clocks,
barometers).

BOSTON

Portobello Row Antique & Collectors' Centre
93-95 High St. PE21. Open 10-4. SIZE: 9 dealers.
*STOCK: Shipping furniture, kitchenalia, blue and
white china, 1940's-70's clothing, bric-a-brac.*
TEL: 01205 368692.

BOURNE

Antique & Secondhand Traders
The Warehouse, 39 West St. (C.A. and A.L.
Thompson). Est. 1962. Open Mon., Tues., Fri. and
Sat. 10-5 or by appointment. SIZE: Warehouse.
*STOCK: Furniture - antique, Victorian, Edwardian,
shipping, oak, reproduction and modern, £50-
£5,000.* LOC: On A15, 8 miles from Stamford A1.
PARK: Own. TEL: 01778 394700; mobiles - Alan -
07885 694299; Clyde - 07958 941728. SER:
Valuations. FAIRS: Newark; Ardingly. VAT:
Spec/Global.

Bourne Antiques & Arts
44 West St. PE10 9NX. (R.A. and Mrs J.M.
Warner). Est. 2000. Open 10-5, Sun. 11-5. CL:
Wed. SIZE: Medium - 30 dealers. *STOCK: Wide
range of general antiques including furniture,
silver, porcelain and glass, maps and prints,
jewellery, clocks, copper and brass, £5-£1,000+.*
LOC: Close to town centre. TEL: 01778 394725;
fax - same; e-mail - baanda@supanet.com;
website - www.bourneantiques.com.

The Complete Automobilist
6 Graham Hill Way. PE10 9PJ. Est. 1967. Open 9-
5. CL: Sat. *STOCK: Hard-to-get parts for older
vehicles.* TEL: 01778 426222; fax - 01778
426333; e-mail - colincrabbe@compauto.co.uk;
website - www.completeautomobilist.com. SER:
Colour catalogue available £2.

CAISTOR

Caistor Antiques
12 High St. LN7 6TX. (Susan Rutter). Est. 1982.
Open by appointment day or night. *STOCK:
Pottery, furniture, jewellery, dolls, linen, silver,
18th-20th C.* LOC: Off A46 between Grimsby
and Market Rasen. PARK: Own. TEL: 01472
851975; home - same. SER: Valuations.

CLEETHORPES

Yesterday's Antiques
86 Grimsby Rd. DN35 7DP. (Jeanette and
Norman Bishop). Resident. Est. 1983. Open 9-5,
Sun. by appointment. SIZE: Large. *STOCK:
Furniture, £50-£2,000; fireplaces, £500-£1,000;
French beds, clocks, £300-£1,200; all 19th C.*
LOC: A180 on right entering town, opposite Esso
garage. PARK: Easy. TEL: 01472 343020/
504093. SER: Valuations; restorations (polishing,
stripping, clock repairs, fireplace renovation).

CONISHOLME, Nr. Louth

A Barn Full of Brass Beds
The Farmhouse, Ashleigh Farm, Main Rd. LN11
7LS. (J.J. Tebbs). Est. 1985. Open by appointment. SIZE: Large. *STOCK: Brass and iron beds,
1860-1910, from £250.* LOC: 10 miles N.E. of
Louth. PARK: Easy. TEL: 01507 358092; e-mail
- brassbeds@clara.co.uk; website - www.brass
andironbeds.co.uk. SER: Restorations. VAT:
Stan.

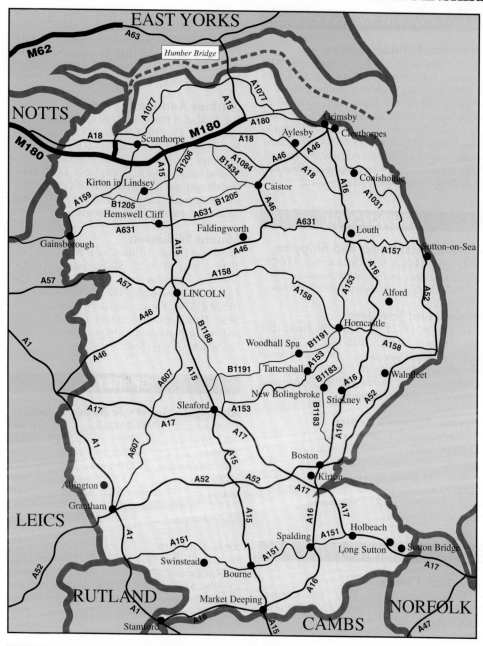

Dealers and Shops in Lincolnshire

				Horncastle	9	Spalding	3
				Kirton	1	Stamford	10
				Kirton in Lindsey	1	Stickney	1
Alford	1	Conisholme	1	Lincoln	11	Sutton Bridge	4
Allington	1	Faldingworth	1	Long Sutton	2	Sutton-on-Sea	1
Aylesby	1	Gainsborough	3	Louth	1	Swinstead	1
Boston	1	Grantham	5	Market Deeping	2	Tattershall	1
Bourne	3	Grimsby	2	New Bolingbroke	1	Wainfleet	1
Caistor	1	Hemswell Cliff	5	Scunthorpe	1	Woodhall Spa	2
Cleethorpes	1	Holbeach	1	Sleaford	2		

Brownlow Antiques Centre

Lincoln Rd. LN8 3SF. (Sylvia and Alex Stephens). Est. 1994. Open Tues.-Sat. 10-5, Sun. 12-5. SIZE: Large. *STOCK: Furniture, 18th C to pre-1940, £50-£3,000; bric-a-brac, collectables, clocks, musical boxes, kitchenalia, from £2.* LOC: A46 towards Grimsby, 10 miles north of Lincoln. PARK: Own. TEL: 01673 885367; home - same; e-mail - brownlowantiquescentre@tinyworld. co.uk; website - www.brownlowantiquescentre. co.uk. SER: Restorations. FAIRS: Local.

GAINSBOROUGH

S. Carrick's Antiques and Shipping

130 Trinity St. DN21 5PD. Open 8.30-5. *STOCK: General antiques and shipping furniture.* TEL: 01427 611393/810409; mobile - 07850 470966.

Stanley Hunt Jewellers

22 Church St. DN21. (S. and R.S. Hunt). Est. 1952. Open 9-5. CL: Wed. SIZE: Medium. *STOCK: Antique jewellery.* LOC: Main street from Market Place. PARK: Easy. TEL: 01427 613051; home - same. SER: Valuations; restorations (gold, silver, clocks).

Pilgrims Antiques Centre

66 Church St. DN21 2JR. Est. 1986. CL: Mon. and Wed. SIZE: Large. *STOCK: Jewellery, miniatures, silver, silhouettes, paintings, textiles, ceramics and books, £5-£1,000; furniture, £50-£1,000.* LOC: Near Old Hall. PARK: Easy. TEL: 01427 810897. SER: Valuations. FAIRS: Newark; Birmingham.

GRANTHAM

Grantham Clocks

30 Lodge Way. NG31 8DD. (R. Conder). Resident. Open by appointment. *STOCK: Clocks.* PARK: Easy. TEL: 01476 561784. SER: Restorations.

Grantham Furniture Emporium

4-6 Wharf Rd. NG31 6BA. (K. and J.E. Hamilton). Est. 1970. Open 10-4, Sun. 11-4. CL: Mon. and Wed. SIZE: Large. *STOCK: Victorian, Edwardian and shipping furniture, £5-£3,000.* LOC: Town centre, near Post Office. PARK: Own at rear. TEL: 01476 562967.

Harlequin Antiques

46 Swinegate. NG31 6RL. (A.R. and Mrs S.B.

Marshall). Est. 1996. Open from 9. SIZE: Medium. *STOCK: Furniture and china, 19th C, £50-£1,000; collectables, 19th-20th C, £20-£200.* LOC: 100 yards from High St., opposite Blue Pig public house. PARK: Easy. TEL: 01476 563346. SER: Valuations.

Notions Antiques Centre

1 & 2a Market Place. NG31 6LQ. (Mr and Mrs L. Checkley). Est. 1984. Open 10-5, Sat. 9.30-5, Sun. 11-4. SIZE: 70+ dealers. *STOCK: Furniture, ceramics, pictures, jewellery, textiles, silver, bygone tooling, clocks, books, toys.* LOC: Down from Angel and Royal Hotel. PARK: Easy. TEL: 01476 563603; mobile - 07736 677978. SER: Valuations; repairs. FAIRS: Newark.

Marcus Wilkinson

The Tyme House, 1 Blue Court. NG31 6NJ. Est. 1935. Open 10-4.30. SIZE: Small. *STOCK: Jewellery, watches and silver, 19th C, £50-£5,000.* PARK: Nearby. TEL: 01476 560400 and 01529 413149; e-mail - marcus@timeshop.co.uk. SER: Valuations; restorations (including clock and watch movements); buys at auction (rings and watches). VAT: Spec.

GRIMSBY

Abbeygate Gallery & Antiques Centre

14 Abbeygate. DN31 1JY. (R.L. Cumming and A.F. Sanders). Est. 1998. Open 10-4. SIZE: Medium. *STOCK: Pottery and glass, militaria, coins and medals, £5-£100; small furniture, £25-£500; all 19th-20th C.* LOC: 2 minutes from train station and Freshney Place Shopping Centre. PARK: Nearby. TEL: 01472 361129; website - www.abbeygate-antiques.co.uk. SER: Valuations.

Bell Antiques

68 Harold St. DN32 7NQ. (V. Hawkey). Est. 1964. Open by appointment, telephone previous evening. SIZE: Large. *STOCK: Antique pine and grandfather clocks. Not Stocked: Reproduction.* PARK: Easy. TEL: 01472 695110; home - same. VAT: Stan/Spec.

Astra House Antiques Centre

RAF Hemswell. DN21 5TL. (M. Frith). Open daily including Sun. 10-5. SIZE: 50 dealers. *STOCK: Wide variety of general antiques and shipping goods, including Victorian, Edwardian and Continental furniture and smalls.* LOC: Near Caenby Corner Roundabout A15/A631. PARK: Easy. TEL: 01427 668312.

Hemswell Antiques Centres

Caenby Corner Estate. DN21 5TJ. (Robert Miller). Est. 1986. Open 10-5 including Sun. SIZE: 270+ dealers. *STOCK: Period furniture, 17th-19th C; watercolours and oils, 19th C; silver and plate, clocks, porcelain, china, jewellery, dolls, toys, books, prints, clothes.* LOC: A15 from Lincoln then A631 towards Gainsborough, 1 mile from roundabout, follow signs. PARK: Easy. TEL: 01427 668389; fax - 01427 668935; e-mail - info@hemswell-antiques.com. SER: Restorations (oak, mahogany and pine; upholstery); delivery.

Kate

Kate House, Caenby Corner Estate. DN21 5TJ. (Mr Shamsa). Open 9-4.30, Sat. 10-1. *STOCK: Pine including reproduction.* TEL: 01427 668724/668904; fax - 01427 668905.

Elaine Lonsdale Bookseller and Bookbinder

Upper Floor, Building 2, Hemswell Antiques Centre, Caenby Corner Estate. DN21 5TJ. (Elaine Lonsdale). PBFA. Est. 1988. Open daily including Sun. SIZE: Small. *STOCK: Antiquarian and second-hand books and ephemera.* PARK: Easy. TEL: 01977 678193; mobile - 07710 480581. SER: Valuations; book-binding. FAIRS: PBFA.

Second Time Around

Hemswell Antique Centre, Caenby Corner Estate, Gainsborough. DN21 5TJ. (G.L. Powis). Open 10-5 including Sun. *STOCK: Longcase and bracket clocks, pre 1830, £1,650-£35,000.* LOC: A15 from Lincoln to Caenby Corner roundabout, left towards Gainsborough for 1 mile (A631). PARK: Easy. TEL: 01427 668389; home - 01522 543167; mobile - 07860 679495. SER: Restorations (clocks).

P.J. Cassidy (Books)

1 Boston Rd. PE12 7LR. Est. 1974. Open 10-6. SIZE: Medium. *STOCK: Books, 19th-20th C, £2-£300; maps, prints and engravings, 17th-19th C, £10-£500.* LOC: ¼ mile from A17. PARK: Nearby. TEL: 01406 426322; fax - same; e-mail - bookscass@aol.com. SER: Valuations; framing and mount cutting. VAT: Stan.

G. Baker Antiques

16 South St. LN9 6DX. Est. 1974. Open 9-5, Wed. 9-1, Sun. by appointment. SIZE: Small. *STOCK: Furniture, 18th-20th C, £10-£10,000.* LOC: A153. PARK: Easy. TEL: 01507 526553; mobile - 07767 216264. SER: Valuations; restorations (furniture). FAIRS: Swinderby and Newark. VAT: Stan/Spec.

Clare Boam

22-38 North St. LN9 5DX. Est. 1977. Open 9-5, Sun 2-4.30. SIZE: Large. *STOCK: Furniture and bric-a-brac, 19th-20th C, to £1,000.* LOC: Louth/Grimsby road out of town. PARK: Easy. TEL: 01507 522381; home - same; e-mail - clareboam@btconnect.com. VAT: Global.

Great Expectations

37-43 East St. LN9. (Clare Boam). Est. 1977. Open 9-5, Sun. and Bank Holidays 1-4.30. SIZE: Large. *STOCK: Wide variety of general antiques including pine, oak, mahogany, kitchenalia, luggage, books, china, glass, collectables, 50p to £1,000.* LOC: A158, 100 yards from traffic lights. PARK: At rear or in Trinity Centre. TEL: 01507 524202; home - 01507 522381.

Le Strange Emporium

25 Bull Ring, LN9 5HU. Open 9-5.30, Sun. 11-5. *STOCK: Antiques and collectables.* TEL: 01507 524260; fax - same.

Lindsey Court Architectural Antiques

Lindsey Court. LN9 5DH. (Lindsay White). Est. 1989. Open 10-4, Sun. by appointment. SIZE: Medium. *STOCK: Architectural antiques, English, French and Spanish reclamations, York stone flagging and garden statuary, £50-£10,000.* LOC: Behind the library. PARK: Own. TEL: 01507 527794; fax - 01507 526670; mobile - 07768 396117; e-mail - lndsy150@netscape online.co.uk; sales@1starchitectural.co.uk; website - www.1starchitectural.co.uk. SER: Container and shipping. FAIRS: Newark. VAT: Stan/Global.

North Street Antiques & Interiors

48 North St. LN9 5DX. (Mrs Vivien Hallberg and Miss Nikki Barnard). Est. 1985. Open 10-4, Sun. and evenings by appointment. SIZE: Small. *STOCK: Smalls, pre 1900, £100-£3,000; portrait miniatures, 18th-19th C, £250-£1,000; small furniture, 18th-19th C, £200-£2,000; silver, ceramics, 18th-19th C glass, objets de vertu; jewellery, vintage and earlier costume.* LOC: Left off Lincoln Rd. into town centre, premises on left opposite the Admiral Rodney Hotel. PARK: Easy. TEL: 07796 577757/1612705. SER: Valuations; buys at auction. FAIRS: Swinderby, Newark, Lincoln, Uppingham, Louth, Barnsdale Country Club.

Alan Read - Period Furniture
60 & 62 West St. LN9 5AD. Est. 1981. Open 10-4.30. CL: Mon. and Wed. except by appointment. SIZE: Large. *STOCK: 17th-19th C furniture, early oak, walnut and decorative items.* LOC: A158 Lincoln to Skegness road, at junction with B1191 Woodhall Spa road. PARK: Easy. TEL: 01507 524324; fax - 01507 525548; e-mail - alanpread@lineone.net. SER: Valuations; bespoke copies; interior design. VAT: Stan/Spec.

Seaview Antiques
Stanhope Rd. LN9 5DG. (M. Chalk and Tracey Collins). Open 9-5. SIZE: Large + warehouse. *STOCK: Victorian, Edwardian and decorative furniture; smalls, brassware, silver and plate, lamps, boxes.* LOC: A158. PARK: Easy. TEL: 01507 524524.

Laurence Shaw Antiques
77 East St. LN9 6AA. (L.D. and C.R. Shaw). Est. 1971. Open 8.30-5. SIZE: Medium. *STOCK: Furniture, china, glass, metalware, books, collectables, general antiques, 17th-20th C.* LOC: Opposite Trinity Church. TEL: 01507 527638/526272; e-mail - lmidwinter@aol.com. SER: Consultant; valuations. VAT: Global/Spec.

KIRTON

Kirton Antiques
3 High St. PE20 1DR. (A.R. Marshall). LAPADA. Est. 1973. Open 8.30-5, Sat. 8.30-12 or by appointment. SIZE: Large - warehouse. *STOCK: Furniture, all periods; painted pine, chairs, decorative items, glass, metal, pottery, china, picture frames.* PARK: Own. TEL: 01205 722595; evenings - 01205 722134; fax - 01205 722895; e-mail - alan.marshall@modcomp.net. SER: Valuations. VAT: Stan.

KIRTON IN LINDSEY

Mr Van Hefflin
12 High St. DN21 4LU. Est. 1820. Open 10-5. *STOCK: Jewellery, curios, silver, paintings.* PARK: Easy. TEL: 01652 648044. SER: Guide.

LINCOLN

Annette Antiques
77 Bailgate. LN1 3AR. (Mrs A. Bhalla). Est. 1972. Open Tues.-Sat. 2-6. SIZE: Small. *STOCK: Porcelain, glass and small silver, 19th-20th C; clocks, silver flatware, watercolours, prints and drawings, 18th-20th C, £10-£500; collectables,* *including dolls houses, furniture and accessories.* LOC: 2 minutes from castle and cathedral. PARK: Nearby. TEL: 01522 546838; home - 01205 260219. SER: Restorations (furniture). FAIRS: Alexandra Palace.

Rebecca Calvert Antiques
6 & 7 Castle Hill. LN1 3AA. Est. 1992. Open 10-1 and 2.15-5. *STOCK: Oak and country furniture, 17th-18th C; textiles (mainly cushions and drapes), 18th-19th C; painted and garden furniture, 19th C; needlework pictures, treen.* LOC: Cathedral quarter. PARK: Opposite. TEL: Mobile - 07770 978501; fax - 01522 530044. SER: Valuations; restorations. FAIRS: Decorative Antiques & Textile, London; Olympia.

C. and K.E. Dring
111 High St. LN5 7PY. Open 10-5.30. CL: Wed. *STOCK: Victorian and Edwardian inlaid furniture; shipping goods, porcelain, clocks, musical boxes, tin-plated toys, trains and Dinkys.* TEL: 01522 540733/792794.

Golden Goose Books
20 and 21 Steep Hill. LN2 1LT. (R.West-Skinn and Mrs A. Cockram). PBFA. Est. 1983. Open 10-5.30. SIZE: Large. *STOCK: Antiquarian and secondhand books, maps and prints.* PARK: Nearby. TEL: 01522 522589; home - 01673 878622.

David J. Hansord & Son   BADA
6 & 7 Castle Hill. LN1 3AA. (David, John and Anne Hansord). Est. 1972. Open 10-1 and 2-5. SIZE: Large. *STOCK: Furniture, clocks, barometers, works of art, 18th C, £50-£25,000.* LOC: In square between cathedral and castle. PARK: Castle Hill. TEL: 01522 530044; fax - same; home - 01522 731088. SER: Valuations; restorations (furniture, barometers and clocks); buys at auction. FAIRS: Olympia (June and Nov). VAT: Spec.

Harlequin Gallery and Golden Goose Globe Restorers
22 Steep Hill. LN2 1LT. (R. West-Skinn). PBFA. Est. 1962. Open 10-5.30. SIZE: Large. *STOCK: Antiquarian and secondhand books, antique maps and prints.* TEL: 01522 522589; home - 01673 858294. SER: Restoration (globes and philosophical instruments).

Dorrian Lambert Antiques Centre
64, 65 Steep Hill. LN1 1YN. (R. Lambert). Est. 1981. Open 10-5, Sun. in summer. SIZE: Medium, 15 dealers. *STOCK: Small furniture, clocks, chairs, pottery, porcelain, jewellery,*

books, sporting antiques, books and collectables, 18th to early 20th C. PARK: Loading only or nearby. TEL: 01522 545916; home - 01427 848686. SER: Valuations; restorations (clocks).

Mansions
5a Eastgate. LN2 1QA. (R.E. & J.A. Mance). Est. 1989. Open 10-5. *STOCK: General antiques, decorative items, period lighting.* TEL: 01522 513631/560271.

Rowletts of Lincoln
338 High St. LN5 7DQ. (A.H. Rowlett). Est. 1965. Open 9-5. *STOCK: Antique and second-hand jewellery.* TEL: 01522 524139.

Timepiece Repairs
43 Steep Hill. LN2 1LU. (R. Ellis). FBHI. Est. 1978. Open 10-5, Sat. 10-4.30 prior telephone call advisable. CL: Mon. and Wed. SIZE: Small. *STOCK: Clocks and watches, 18th-20th C, £10-£8,000; barometers, 19th-20th C, £100-£1,500.* LOC: Near cathedral. PARK: 100 metres. TEL: 01522 525831; home - 01522 881790. SER: Valuations; restorations (movements, dials and cases); buys at auction (horological). VAT: Stan/Spec.

James Usher and Son Ltd
incorporating John Smith & Son, 26 & 27 Guildhall St. LN1 1TR. Open 9-5.30. *STOCK: Silver, jewellery.* TEL: 01522 527547/523120.

LONG SUTTON

The Chapel Emporium Antique Centre
London Rd. PE12. (J.A. Beck and B. Hill). Est. 1984. Open 10-5 including Sun. SIZE: Large. *STOCK: Furniture, 18th-19th C, £100-£5,000; collectables, 19th-20th C, 50p-£300; ephemera, 19th C, 50p-£25.* LOC: Opposite playing fields. PARK: Free opposite. TEL: 01406 364808.

J.W. Talton
15-19 Market St. PE12 9DD. (J., W. and J.J. Talton). Resident. Est. 1952. Open 9-5, Wed. 9-12. SIZE: Small. *STOCK: General antiques.* LOC: On old A17. PARK: Easy. TEL: 01406 362147; home - same. SER: Restorations (furniture and cabinet making).

LOUTH

Old Maltings Antique Centre
38 Aswell St. LN11 9HP. (Norman and Margaret Coffey). Est. 1980. Open 10-4.30, Sat. 10-5. SIZE: Large - over 40 cabinets. *STOCK:*

Furniture including Victorian and Edwardian, collectables, ceramics, glass, jewellery. LOC: 2 minutes walk from town centre. PARK: Easy. TEL: 01507 600366. SER: Valuations; restorations; pine stripping.

MARKET DEEPING

Market Deeping Antiques & Craft Centre
50-56 High St. PE6. (J. Strutt and C. Stubbins). Resident. Est. 1995. SIZE: Large. *STOCK: General antiques, bric-a-brac and craft items.* LOC: A15. PARK: Easy. TEL: 01778 380238.

Portland House Antiques
23 Church St. PE6 8AN. (G.W. Cree and V.E. Bass). Est. 1987. Open Mon.-Sat. or by appointment. SIZE: Medium. *STOCK: Porcelain, glass, furniture, 18th-19th C, £100-£10,000.* PARK: Easy. TEL: 01778 347129; home - same. SER: Buys at auction. VAT: Stan/Spec.

NEW BOLINGBROKE, Nr. Boston

Junktion
The Old Railway Station. (J. Rundle). Est. 1981. Open Wed., Thurs. and Sat. SIZE: Large. *STOCK: Early advertising, decorative and architectural items; toys, automobilia, mechanical antiques and bygones; early slot machines, wireless, telephones, bakelite, 20th C collectables.* Not Stocked: Porcelain and jewellery. LOC: B1183 Boston to Horncastle. PARK: Easy. TEL: 01205 480087/ 480068.

SCUNTHORPE

Antiques & Collectables & Gun Shop
Rear of 251 Ashby High St. DN16 2SQ. (J.A. Bowden). Open 9-5. *STOCK: Clocks, furniture, arms and collectables.* TEL: 01724 865445/ 720606. SER: Restorations and repairs (clocks and guns).

SLEAFORD

Mill Antiques
19A Northgate. NG34 7BH. (John Noble and A. Crabtree). Est. 1988. Open 9-5. SIZE: Medium. *STOCK: General antiques including furniture, porcelain and pictures, 18th-20th C, £5-£2,500.* LOC: 100 yds. from Market Square. PARK: Loading only. TEL: 01529 413342; home - 01529 415101. SER: Valuations; restorations (furniture and porcelain).

Marcus Wilkinson

The Little Tyme House, 13 Southgate. NG34 7SU. (M. and P. Wilkinson). Est. 1935. Open 10-4.30. SIZE: Small. *STOCK: Jewellery, watches and silver, £50-£5,000.* LOC: High St. near river Slea. PARK: Nearby. TEL: 01529 413149 and 01476 560400; e-mail - marcus@timeshop. freeserve.co.uk. SER: Valuations; restorations (including clock and watch movements); buys at auction (rings and watches). VAT: Stan.

SPALDING

Dean's Antiques

"The Walnuts", Weston St. Mary's. PE12 6JB. (Mrs B. Dean). Est. 1969. Open daily. SIZE: Medium. *STOCK: General antiques, farm and country bygones, £2-£200.* LOC: On Spalding to Holbeach main road A151. PARK: Easy. TEL: 01406 370429.

Penman Clockcare

Unit 4 & 5 Pied Calf Yard, Sheepmarket. PE11 1BE. (Michael Strutt). BWCMG. Est. 1998. Open 9-5 Sat. 9-4. *STOCK: Clocks 18th-20th C; watches, 19th-20th C; jewellery.* LOC: In yard behind Pied Calf public house, opposite PO. PARK: Nearby. TEL: 01755 714900; 01755 840955 (ansaphone); website - www.penmanc lockcare.co.uk. SER: Valuations; restorations (clocks and watches).

Spalding Antiques

1 Abbey Path, The Crescent. PE11 1AY. (John Mumford). Est. 1980. Open 10-5, Thurs. 10-12 and 1.30-5, Sat. 10-4. SIZE: Medium. *STOCK: Clocks, furniture and smalls, 19th C, £10-£3,000.* LOC: Opposite Sessions House. PARK: Victoria St. TEL: 01775 713185. SER: Valuations.

STAMFORD

Norman Blackburn

Old Print Shop, 7 Red Lion Sq. PE9 2AJ. Est. 1974. Open 10-5, Tues. by appointment; CL: Mon. SIZE: Large. *STOCK: Prints - decorative, stipple and mezzotints, botanical, sporting, marine, portraits and views, pre-1860.* PARK: On riverside. TEL: 01780 489151; fax - same; mobile - 07714 721846; e-mail - oldprints @normanblackburn.com; website - www.norman blackburn.com. SER: Valuations.

Dawson of Stamford Ltd

6 Red Lion Sq. PE9 2AJ. (J. Dawson). Open 9-5.30. *STOCK: Fine antique furniture, jewellery and silver.* LOC: Town centre between St. John's church and All Saint's church. TEL: 01780 754166. VAT: Stan/Spec.

Hunters Antiques & Interior Design

9a St. Mary's Hill. PE9 2DP. (Jill Hunter). Est. 2000. Open 9.30-5.30. SIZE: Medium. *STOCK: Period mahogany and country furniture, decorative items.* LOC: Just over town bridge, on the left. PARK: George Hotel. TEL: 01780 757946; fax - same; mobile - 07976 796969. SER: Restorations (furniture, clocks and barometers). VAT: Stan/Spec.

Graham Pickett Antiques

7 High St., St Martins. PE9 2LF. (G.R. Pickett). Est. 1990. Open 10-5.30. SIZE: Medium. *STOCK: Furniture - country, 1650-1900, French provincial, 1700-1900, both £50-£2,000; French and English beds, 1750-1900, £350-£2,000.* LOC: From A1 north into town, on right by 1st lights opposite George Hotel. PARK: Easy. TEL: 01780 481064; home - 01780 764502; mobile - 07710 936948; e-mail - graham@pickett antiques.demon.co.uk. FAIRS: Newark IACF. VAT: Stan/Spec.

Sinclair's

11/12 St. Mary's St. PE9. (J.S. Sinclair). Est. 1970. Open 9-5.30. SIZE: Large. *STOCK: Oak country furniture, 18th C, £200-£3,000; Victorian mahogany furniture, £100-£1,000; Edwardian furniture.* LOC: Near A1. PARK: George Hotel. TEL: 01780 765421. VAT: Stan/Spec.

St. George's Antiques

1 St. George's Sq. PE9 2BN. (G.H. Burns). Est. 1974. Open 9-1 and 2-4.30. CL: Sat. SIZE: Shop + trade only warehouse. *STOCK: Period and Victorian furniture, some small items.* TEL: 01780 754117; home - 01780 460456. VAT: Stan/Spec.

St. Martins Antiques Centre

23a High St., St. Martin's. PE9 2LF. (P. B. Light). Est. 1993. Open every day 10-5. SIZE: 60 dealers. *STOCK: Georgian, Victorian and Edwardian furniture, country pine, Art Deco and Arts and Crafts furniture, porcelain, glass, copper, brass, clocks and watches, silver, jewellery, military books, leather and willow, paintings, prints, textiles, fireplaces, surrounds and grates, 20th C lighting and other artefacts, collectables and ephemera.* LOC: Approx.1 mile from first exit for Stamford on A1. PARK: At rear. TEL: 01780 481158; fax - same; e-mail - peter@st-martins-antiques.co.uk; website - www.st-martins-antiques.co.uk.

Staniland (Booksellers)
4/5 St. George's St. PE9 2BJ. (V.A. and B.J. Valentine-Ketchum). PBFA. Est. 1973. Open 10-5. CL: Thurs. SIZE: Large. *STOCK: Books, mainly 19th-20th C, £1-£2,000.* LOC: High St. PARK: St. Leonard's St. TEL: 01780 755800; e-mail - stanilandbooksellers@btinternet.com.

Andrew Thomas
Old Granary, 10 North St. PE9 2YN. Est. 1970. Open 9-6. SIZE: Large. *STOCK: Pine and country furniture in original paint; ironware.* LOC: From south take old A1 through Stamford. Turn right at second set of traffic lights, warehouse on right. PARK: Opposite. TEL: 01780 762236; home - 01780 410627. VAT: Stan.

Vaughan Antiques
45 Broad St. PE9 1PX.. (Barry and Lindy Vaughan). LAPADA. Est. 1993. Open 10-5, Fri. 10-3. SIZE: Large. *STOCK: 18th-19th C furniture, decorative items, clocks, paintings, metalware, mirrors.* PARK: Easy. TEL: 01780 765888. FAIRS: NEC. VAT: Spec.

STICKNEY, Nr. Boston

B and B Antiques
Main Rd. PE22 8AD. (B.J. Whittaker and J. Shooter). Open by appointment. *STOCK: General antiques.* PARK: Easy. TEL: 01205 480204.

SUTTON BRIDGE

The Antique Shop
100 Bridge Rd. PE12 9SA. (R. Gittins). Est. 1973. Open 9-5.30, Sun. 11-5. SIZE: Large - 8 showrooms. *STOCK: Victorian furniture, glass, china, oil lamps and clocks.* Not Stocked: Pine. LOC: On old A17 opposite church. PARK: Easy. TEL: 01406 350535. VAT: Spec.

Bridge Antiques
30-32 Bridge Rd. PE12 9UA. Open 8-5. CL: Sat. SIZE: Large. *STOCK: Shipping furniture - barleytwist, linenfold, pineapple, Jacobean styles.* LOC: Old A17. PARK: Easy. TEL: 01406 350704/351669.

Old Barn Antiques & Furnishings
48-50 Bridge Rd. PE12 9UA. (S. and Mrs T.J. Jackson). Est. 1984. Open 9-5, Sat. 10-5, Sun. 11-4. SIZE: Large + trade warehouse. *STOCK: 19th-20th C furniture - oak, mahogany, walnut, pine and upholstered.* LOC: Village centre, 200 yds from swing-bridge. PARK: Easy. TEL: 01406 359123; fax - 01406 359158; mobile - 07956 677282. SER: Shipping; storage and packing. VAT: Spec.

Old Barn Antiques Warehouse
220 New Rd. PE12 9QE. (S. and Mrs T. Jackson). Est. 1984. Open Mon.-Fri. 9-5.30 or by appointment. SIZE: Large. *STOCK: 18th-20th C furniture - shipping goods, oak - carved, pineapple, Jacobean, distressed, barley twist; mahogany, walnut and pine original, unrestored and reclaimed timber copies.* LOC: 1 mile out of village, following new road past golf course. PARK: Own. TEL: 01406 350435; fax - 01406 359158; mobile - 07956 677228; e-mail - oldbarnanti@aol.com. SER: Storage; container and export facilities. VAT: Stan/Spec. *Trade & Export Only.*

SUTTON-ON-SEA

Knicks Knacks Emporium
41 High St. LN12 2EY. (Mr and Mrs R.A. Nicholson). Est. 1983. Open 10.30-1 and 2-5, including Sun. CL: Mon. SIZE: Medium + small warehouse. *STOCK: Victorian gas lights, lights and lamps, brass and iron beds, cast-iron fireplaces, bygones, curios, tools, collectables, pottery, porcelain, Art Deco, Art Nouveau,*

advertising items, furniture and shipping goods, £1-£1,000. LOC: A52. PARK: Easy. TEL: 01507 441916; fax - same; home - 01507 441657; mobile - 07977 547199; e-mail - robin@knicks knacks.com; website - www.knicksknacks.com. FAIRS: Newark.

SWINSTEAD

Robin Shield Antiques   BADA
Tyton House, 11 Park Rd. NG33 4PH. LAPADA. Est. 1974. Open by appointment anytime. SIZE: Medium. *STOCK: Furniture and paintings, £200-£20,000; works of art, £100-£5,000; all 17th-19th C.* **PARK: Easy. TEL: 01476 550892; mobile - 07860 520391; e-mail - robinshield@fsmail.net. SER: Valuations; buys at auction. FAIRS: Olympia (June). VAT: Stan/Spec.**

TATTERSHALL

Wayside Antiques
Market Place. LN4 4LQ. (G. Ball). Est. 1969. Open anytime by appointment. *STOCK: General antiques.* LOC: A158. PARK: Easy. TEL: 01526 342436.

WAINFLEET, Nr. Skegness

Haven Antiques
Bank House, 36 High St. PE24 4BJ. (Colin and Julie Crowson). Est. 1980. Open daily except Thurs., Sun. by appointment. SIZE: Small. *STOCK: General antiques, jewellery, porcelain and collectibles.* LOC: A52. PARK: Easy and opposite. TEL: 01754 880661; home - same. SER: Valuations.

WOODHALL SPA

Underwoodhall Antiques
5 The Broadway. LN10 6ST. Est. 1987. Open 10-5, Sun. 1-4.30, prior telephone advisable. SIZE: Medium. *STOCK: Furniture, £10-£1,000; porcelain and china, £5-£500; general antiques, £1-£500; pictures, £5-£500, all 1750 to date.* LOC: B1191. PARK: Easy. TEL: 01526 353815; e-mail - underwoodhall@supanet.com. FAIRS: Newark.

V.O.C. Antiques
27 Witham Rd. LN10 6RW. (D.J. and C.J. Leyland). LAPADA. Resident. Est. 1970. Open 9.30-5.30, Sun. 2-5. SIZE: Medium. *STOCK: 17th-19th C furniture, to £5,000; period brass and copper, pottery, porcelain and pictures.* LOC: B1191. PARK: Easy. TEL: 01526 352753; fax - same; home - same. SER: Valuations.

The Four Seasons, 1840s, 9½in. high. Note the characteristic sandy base.

From an article entitled "Dudson – A Family of Potters since 1800" by Audrey Dudson which appeared in the May 2002 issue of **Antique Collecting**. For more details and to subscribe see page 21.

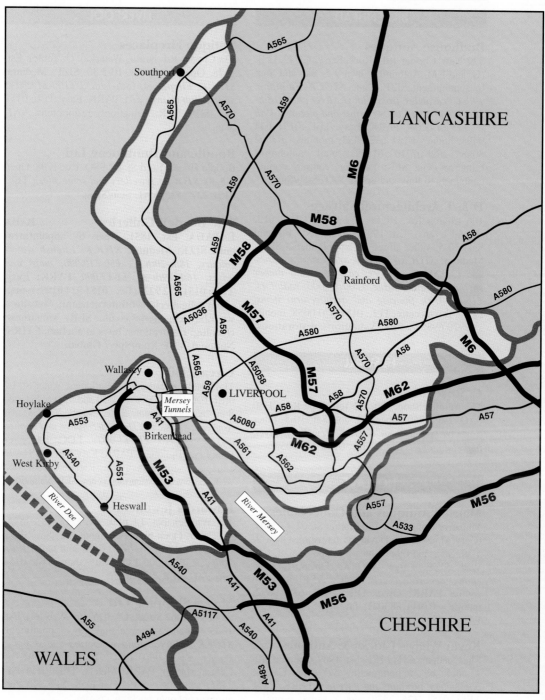

Dealers and Shops on Merseyside

Birkenhead	2	Liverpool	10	Wallasey	3
Heswall	1	Rainford	1	West Kirby	1
Hoylake	2	Southport	11		

BIRKENHEAD

Bodhouse Antiques
379 New Chester Rd., Rock Ferry. CH42 1LB. (G. and F.M. Antonini). Open 9-5, Sat. and Sun. by appointment. SIZE: Large. *STOCK: Furniture, 19th C; ceramics, from 19th C; silver plate, 18th-20th C; all £5-£1,000+; prints and pictures, 19th C, £25-£1,000+.* PARK: Easy. TEL: 0151 644 9494; home - 0151 652 6433; mobiles - 07802 608357 and 07710 561199; e-mail - antonini@ btinternet.com. SER: Packing; courier; regular containers to Italy and Spain. VAT: Stan/Spec.

D & T Architectural Salvage
106 Church Rd., Higher Tranmere. CH42 0LJ. (David Lyons). Est. 1998. Open Wed., Fri. and Sat. 10-5, other times by appointment. SIZE: Medium. *STOCK: Interior and exterior doors, £35-£3,000; fire places, cast iron and timber surrounds, slate marble, £200-£5,000; radiators, £150-£1,000; flooring and architectural items.* LOC: Town centre. TEL: 0151 670 0058; mobile - 07970 698518. SER: Valuations; restorations.

HESWALL

C. Rosenberg
The Antique Shop, 120-122 Telegraph Rd. CH60 0AQ. Est. 1960. Open Fri. and Sat. 10-5, other times by appointment. *STOCK: Jewellery, silver, porcelain, objets d'art.* TEL: 0151 342 1053.

HOYLAKE

Mansell Antiques and Collectables
Mulberry House, 128-130 Market St. CH47 3BH. (Gary Mansell and David Williamson). Open 9-5.30, Sun. and other times by appointment. CL: Wed. SIZE: Large. *STOCK: Furniture, pine, china, decorative arts.* LOC: A540 in town centre. PARK: Own. TEL: 0151 632 0892; mobile - 07944 883021; fax - 0151 632 6137. FAIRS: Chester Art Deco.

Kevin Whay's Clocks & Antiques
The Quadrant. CH47 2EE. Est. 1969. Open Fri. 10-4 and by appointment. *STOCK: Clocks, barometers, furniture and jewellery.* PARK: Easy. TEL: 0151 336 3432; fax - same; e-mail - kevin@lots. uk.com. SER: Restorations (clocks, barometers, dials and cases).

LIVERPOOL

Antique Fireplaces
43a Crosby Rd. North, Waterloo. (J. Toole). Est. 1978. Open 10-5, Sat. 10-5.30. SIZE: Medium. *STOCK: Fireplaces, 18th-19th C, £100-£1,000+; doors, 19th C, from £35.* PARK: Easy. TEL: 0151 949 0819. SER: Valuations; restorations. VAT: Stan.

Boodle and Dunthorne Ltd
Boodle House, Lord St. L2 9SQ. Est. 1798. Open 9-5.30. *STOCK: Jewellery and some silver.* TEL: 0151 227 2525. VAT: Stan/Spec.

The Boydell Galleries   BADA
LAPADA. Est. 1851. Open by appointment only. SIZE: Medium. *STOCK: English water-colours, 18th-20th C, £50-£10,000; maps and prints, 16th-19th C, £1-£2,000.* PARK: Easy. TEL: 0151 932 9220; fax - 0151 924 0199; e-mail - boydellgalleries@btinternet.com; website - www.boydellgalleries.co.uk. SER: Valuations; cleaning; restorations; buys at auction. FAIRS: National. VAT: Stan/Spec/ Global.

Circa 1900
11-13 Holts Arcade, India Buildings, Water St. L2 0RR. Est. 1989. Open 10-2.30 and 3.30-6, Sat. and Sun. by appointment. SIZE: Small. *STOCK: Art Nouveau, classic Art Deco, decorative and applied arts, 1860-1940, £10-£1,000+.* LOC: 100 yards from Liver Buildings. PARK: Easy. TEL: 0151 236 1282; fax - same; e-mail - classicart deco@aol.com; website - www.classicartdeco.com. SER: Valuations.

Edward's Jewellers
45a Whitechapel. LI 6DJ. (R.A. Lewis). FGA. Est. 1967. Open by appointment. CL: Sat. SIZE: Small. *STOCK: Jewellery, silver and plate, 19th-20th C, £50-£1,000.* LOC: City centre. TEL: 0151 236 2909. SER: Valuations.

Maggs Shipping Ltd
66-68 St Anne Street. L3 3DY. (G. Webster). Est. 1965. Open 9-5, weekends by appointment. *STOCK: General antiques, period and shipping smalls, £1-£1,000.* LOC: In town centre by Central station. PARK: Meters. TEL: 0151 207 2555; evenings - 01928 564958. SER: Restorations; container packing, courier.

Pryors of Liverpool
110 London Rd. L3 5NL. (Mr Wilding). Est. 1876. Open 8-4. CL: Wed. *STOCK: General antiques, jewellery, Georgian and Victorian silver, pottery, porcelain, coins and medals,*

clocks, paintings, ivory and carvings. LOC: 400 yards from St. Georges Hall, Walker Art Gallery. PARK: Nearby. TEL: 0151 709 1361; pawilding @aol.com. VAT: Stan.

Ryan-Wood Antiques
102 Seel St. L1 4BL. Est. 1972. Open 10-5. CL: Some Bank Holiday weekends. SIZE: Large. *STOCK: Furniture, paintings, china, silver, curios, bric-a-brac, Victoriana, Edwardiana, Art Deco, architectural.* LOC: City centre, close to Anglican Cathedral. PARK: Easy. TEL: 0151 709 7776; home/fax - 0151 709 3203; mobile - 07050 094779; e-mail - pdw@ryan-wood.freeserve.co. uk; website - www.ryan-wood.freeserve.co.uk. SER: Restorations; valuations. VAT: Stan/Spec.

Stefani Antiques
497 Smithdown Rd. L15 5AE. (T. Stefani). Est. 1969. Open 10-5. CL: Wed. SIZE: Medium. *STOCK: Furniture, to 1910, £200-£2,000; jewellery, £25-£2,000; pottery, silver, old Sheffield plate, porcelain, bronzes.* LOC: On main road, near Penny Lane. PARK: Easy. TEL: 0151 734 1933; home - 0151 733 4836. SER: Valuations; restorations (furniture including French polishing and upholstery).

Swainbanks Ltd
50-56 Fox St. L3 3BQ. Open 9-5 or by appointment. CL: Sat. SIZE: Large. *STOCK: Shipping goods and general antiques.* TEL: 0151 207 9466; fax - 0151 260 9130. SER: Containers. VAT: Stan.

RAINFORD, Nr. St. Helens

Colin Stock   BADA
8 Mossborough Rd. WA11 8QN. Est. 1895. Open by appointment. STOCK: Furniture, 18th-19th C. TEL: 0174 488 2246.

SOUTHPORT

Birkdale Antiques
119a Upper Aughton Rd., Birkdale. PR8 5EX. (John Napp). Est. 1996. CL: Mon. SIZE: Small. *STOCK: English and Continental furniture, £200-£2,000.* LOC: From Lord St. West into Lulworth Rd., first left into Aughton Rd., over railway crossing into Upper Aughton Rd. PARK: Easy. TEL: 01704 550117; home - 01704 567680. SER: Valuations; restorations (furniture including polishing); buys at auction. FAIRS: Stafford, Newark, Swinderby.

C.K. Broadhurst and Co Ltd
5-7 Market St. PR8 1HD. (Laurens R. Hardman). ABA. LLAB. PBFA. Est. 1926. Open 9-5.30. SIZE: 4 floors. *STOCK: Rare books, first editions, art and architecture, collecting.* LOC: Town centre, off Lord St. by Victorian bandstand. TEL: 01704 532064/534110; fax - 01704 542009; e-mail - litereria@aol.com; website - www.ckbroadhurst.com. SER: Book search; valuations; restorations; rebinding. FAIRS: Olympia; Chelsea; some provincial.

Molloy's Furnishers Ltd
6-8 St. James St. PR8 5AE. (P. Molloy). Est. 1955. Open daily. SIZE: Large. *STOCK: Mahogany and oak, shipping and Edwardian furniture.* LOC: Off A570 Scarisbrick New Road. PARK: Easy. TEL: 01704 535204; fax - 01704 548101. VAT: Stan.

John Nolan - King Street Antiques
29 King St. PR8 1LH. Open Mon.-Sat. *STOCK: Furniture and decorative items.* TEL: 01704 540808; mobile - 07714 322252; home - 01704 841065. SER: Courier; packing and shipping.

The Original British American Antiques
Kings House, 27 King St. PR8 1LH. (John Nolan). Open 10-5; evenings by appointment. SIZE: Medium. *STOCK: Export items, especially for US decorator market.* LOC: Town centre. TEL: 01704 540808; mobile - 07714 322252. SER: Courier; packing and shipping. VAT: Stan/Spec. *Trade only.*

Osiris Antiques
104 Shakespeare St. and The Royal Arcade, 131A Lord St. PR8. (C. and P. Wood). Est. 1983. Open 10.45-4.45, Sat. 11-5.15, Sun. by appointment; Royal Arcade - 11-5.30 including Sun. CL: Tues. SIZE: Small. *STOCK: Art Nouveau and Art Deco, Arts and Crafts, £10-£1,000; period clothing and accessories, 1850-1950, £5-£200; jewellery, 1880-1960, to £150.* LOC: Just out of town, off main road leading to motorway. PARK: Easy. TEL: 01704 500991; mobile - 07802 818500; home - 01704 560418. SER: Valuations; buys at auction (Art Nouveau, Art Deco); lectures given on Decorative Arts 1895-1930.

David M. Regan
25 Hoghton St. PR9 0NS. Est. 1983. Open Mon., Wed., Fri. and Sat. 10-5. SIZE: Small. *STOCK: Roman and English coins, £3-£300; post and cigarette cards, small collectables.* TEL: 01704 531266. SER: Valuations.

The Southport Antiques Centre
27/29 King St. PR8 1LH. (J. Nolan). Open 10-5. TEL: 01704 540808; mobile - 07714 322252. Below are listed the dealers at this centre.

Antiques and Interiors

British-American Antiques
Shipping goods.

Halsall Hall Antiques
Country furniture.

King St. Antiques
General antiques.

John Nolan
Period furniture.

Pine Country Antiques
Country pine furniture.

S.M. Collectors Items
Doulton and pressed glass.

The Spinning Wheel Antiques
1 Liverpool Rd., Birkdale. PR8 4AR. (Roy and Pat Bell). Est. 1966. Open 10.30-5. CL: Tues. SIZE: Small. *STOCK: Antiques and collectables, old golf items, £5-£5,000+.* TEL: 01704 568245/567613; fax - same; e-mail - roypat@patroy.fsnet.co.uk.

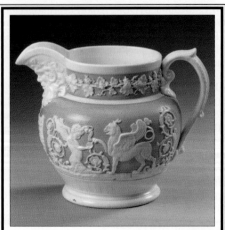

A moulded Job Ridgway jug with Regency motifs that could have come from bronze mounts from furniture. The blue ground is painted on and simulates Wedgwood. Many factories produced similar wares but Ridgway is arguably the best. 6¼in., unmarked, 1815-20, £250-£300.

From an article entitled "Factory Fact File" by David Battie which appeared in the March 2002 issue of **Antique Collecting**. For more details and to subscribe see page 21.

Tony and Anne Sutcliffe Antiques
130 Cemetery Rd. and warehouse - 37A Linaker St. PR8. Est. 1969. Open 8.30-5 including Sun. or by appointment. SIZE: Large. *STOCK: Shipping goods, Victorian and period furniture.* LOC: Town centre. TEL: 01704 537068; home - 01704 533465; mobile - 07860 949816/480376. SER: Containers; courier. VAT: Stan/Spec.

Weldons Jewellery and Antiques
567 Lord St. PR9 0BB. (H.W. and N.C. Weldon). Est. 1914. Open 9.30-5.30. SIZE: Medium. *STOCK: Furniture, clocks, watches, jewellery, silver, coins.* Not Stocked: Militaria. PARK: Easy. TEL: 01704 532191; fax - 01704 500091; e-mail - weldongemsuk@aol.com. SER: Valuations; restorations. VAT: Stan/Spec.

WALLASEY

Arbiter
10 Atherton St., New Brighton. CH45 2NY. (W.D.L. Scobie and P.D. Ferrett). Resident. Est. 1983. Open Wed.-Sat. 1-5 or by appointment. *STOCK: Decorative arts, 1850-1980; base metal and treen, £20-£2,000; Oriental, ethnographic and antiquities, £40-£1,500; original prints and drawings, £80-£500.* LOC: Opposite New Brighton station. PARK: Easy. TEL: 0151 639 1159. SER: Valuations; buys at auction; consultant.

Decade Antiques & Interiors
62 Grove Rd. CH45 3HW. (A.M. Duffy). Est. 1980. Open 10-5. SIZE: Medium. *STOCK: General antiques, textiles, decorative items, Continental furniture.* LOC: From junction 1, M53 take A554 to Wallasey/New Brighton, turn right into Harrison Drive then left into Grove Rd. PARK: Easy. TEL: 0151 638 0433/639 6905; fax - 0151 638 9995. FAIRS: Antique Textile (Manchester).

Victoria Antiques/City Strippers
155-157 Brighton St. CH44 8DU. (J.M. Colyer). Est. 1978. Open 9.30-5.30. SIZE: Large. *STOCK: Furniture.* PARK: Easy. TEL: 0151 639 0080. SER: Restorations.

WEST KIRBY

Helen Horswill Antiques and Decorative Arts
62 Grange Rd. CH48 4EG. Open 10-5 or by appointment. SIZE: Medium. *STOCK: Furniture, 17th-19th C; decorative items.* LOC: A540. PARK: Easy. TEL: 0151 625 2803/8660.

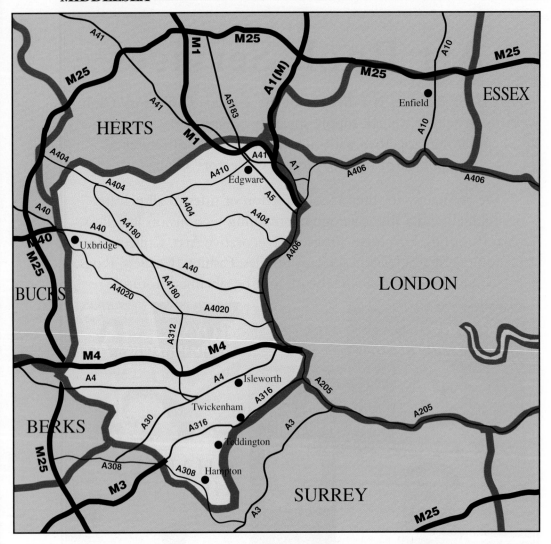

EDGWARE

Edgware Antiques
19 Whitchurch Lane. HA8 7JZ. (E. Schloss). Est. 1972. Open Thurs.- Sat. 10-5 or by appointment. SIZE: Medium. *STOCK: Furniture, pictures, silver and plate, brass and copper, clocks, bric-a-brac, porcelain and shipping goods.* PARK: Easy. TEL: 020 8952 1606; home - 020 8952 5924.

ENFIELD

Gallerie Veronique
66 Chase Side. EN2 6NJ. (Veronica Aslangul). Est. 1993. Open 10-3, Sat. 10-5. CL: Sun (except by appointment) and Wed. SIZE: Medium. *STOCK: Furniture including decorative, 1820-1920, £100-£1,000.* LOC: Near junction A10 and M25. PARK: Easy. TEL: 020 8342 1005; fax - 020 8342 1005; mobile - 07770 410041. SER: Restorations (French polishing and upholstery).

Period Style Lighting
8-9 Antiques Village, East Lodge Lane, Botany Bay. EN2 8AS. (Gillian and Geoff Day). Est. 1992. Open 10-5 including Sun. CL: Mon. SIZE: Medium. *STOCK: Lighting - period, Victorian and Edwardian, French and Italian chandeliers, £150-£1,000; period style wall and centre lights, Tiffany lamps, glass shades.* PARK: Easy. TEL: 020 8363 9789; fax - 020 8363 2369. SER: Lighting design for cottages and country houses; restorations and repairs.

HAMPTON

Hunter's of Hampton
76 Station Rd. TW12 2AX. (Robin and Julia Hunter). Est. 1990. Open Mon. 10-5.30, Fri. and Sat. 10-6, other times by appointment. *STOCK: Victorian and Edwardian furniture, mirrors, etc, £50-£1,500.* LOC: Off High St. PARK: Easy. TEL: 020 8979 5624; fax - same.

Peco
72 Station Rd. TW12 2BT. (C.D. Taylor). Est. 1969. Open 8.15-5.15. SIZE: Large. *STOCK: Doors, 18th-20th C, £75-£250; fireplaces including French and marble, 18th-19th C, £495-£5,500; stoves.* LOC: 1.5 miles from Hampton Court. Turning off Hampton Court/Sunbury Rd. PARK: Own. TEL: 020 8979 8310. SER: Restorations (marble, stained glass, cast iron fireplaces, doors); stained glass made to order. VAT: Stan.

Ian Sheridan's Bookshop
Thames Villa, 34 Thames St. TW12 2DX. Est. 1960. Open 10.30-5 including Sun. SIZE: Large. *STOCK: Antiquarian and secondhand books.* LOC: 1 mile from Hampton Court Palace. PARK: Riverside. TEL: 020 8979 1704.

TEDDINGTON

Chris Hollingshead
10 Linden Grove. TW11 8LT. Resident. Est. 1994. Open 9-6 by appointment only. SIZE: Small. *STOCK: Antiquarian, scarce and out-of-print books, specialising in botany, horticulture, landscape architecture and plant hunting, £10-£500.* PARK: Easy. TEL: 020 8255 4774; e-mail - c.hollingshead@btinternet.com.

TWICKENHAM

Ailsa Gallery
32 Crown Rd. (C.A. Wiltshire). Open Thurs., Fri. and Sat. 10-5, other times by appointment. SIZE:

Small. *STOCK: Paintings, 19th-20th C, £200-£3,000; bronze, decorative arts, small furniture, silver and glass.* LOC: Off St. Margarets Rd., near station. PARK: Easy. TEL: 020 8891 2345; home - 020 8892 0188.

Antique Interiors
93 Crown Rd., St. Margaret's. TW1 3EX. (A. Mundy). Est. 1996. Open 10.30-5.30, Sun. by appointment. CL: Mon. SIZE: Medium. *STOCK: English and French pine, painted, country and mahogany furniture and doors, 19th C and earlier; French garden seating and tables.* LOC: Close to BR station. PARK: Easy. TEL: 020 8607 9853; e-mail - andrewmundy@netscapeonline. co.uk. SER: Valuations; restorations.

Anthony C. Hall
30 Staines Rd. TW2 5AH. Est. 1966. Open Mon., Tues., Thurs. and Fri. 10-5. SIZE: Medium. *STOCK: Antiquarian books.* PARK: Easy. TEL: 020 8898 2638; fax - 020 8893 8855; website - www.hallbooks.co.uk.

John Ives Bookseller
5 Normanhurst Drive, St. Margarets. TW1 1NA. PBFA. Resident. Est. 1977. Open by appointment at any time. SIZE: Medium. *STOCK: Scarce and out of print books on antiques and collecting, £1-£500.* LOC: Off St. Margarets Rd. near its junction with Chertsey Rd. PARK: Easy. TEL: 020 8892 6265; fax - 020 8744 3944; e-mail - jives@btconnect.com; website - www.ukbookworld.com/members/john ives. SER: Valuations (as stock).

Tobias Jellinek Antiques
20 Park Road. TW1 2PX. (Mrs D.L. and T.P. Jellinek). Est. 1963. By appointment only. SIZE: Small. *STOCK: Fine early furniture and objects, 16th-17th C or earlier, £500-£5,000+.* LOC: Near Richmond Bridge. PARK: Easy. TEL: 020 8892 6892; home - same; fax - 020 8744 9298; e-mail - toby@jellinek.com. SER: Valuations; buys at auction (as stock). VAT: Stan/Spec.

Marble Hill Gallery
70/72 Richmond Rd. TW1 3BE. (D. and L. Newson). Est. 1974. Open 10-5.30. *STOCK: English and French marble and natural stone, pine and white Adam-style mantels.* PARK: Easy. TEL: 020 8892 1488; website - www.marble hill.co.uk. VAT: Stan/Spec.

David Morley Antiques
371 Richmond Rd. TW1 2EF. Est. 1968. Open 10-1 and 2-5. CL: Wed. SIZE: Medium. *STOCK: General antiques, collectors' items, old toys.* Not Stocked: Large furniture. LOC: Approx. 200yds. from Richmond Bridge. PARK: In side road (adjacent to shop). TEL: 020 8892 2986.

Phelps Antiques

133-135 St. Margarets Rd. TW1 1RG. (R.C. Phelps). LAPADA. Est. 1870. Open 10-5.30, Sat. 9.30-5.30, Sun. 12-4. SIZE: Large - several dealers. *STOCK: Furniture and small collectables, 1800-1920's.* LOC: Adjacent St. Margaret's station. PARK: Easy, at rear of shop. TEL: 020 8892 1778/7129; fax - 020 8892 3661; website - www.phelps.co.uk; e-mail - antiques@phelps.co.uk. SER: Restorations. VAT: Stan/Spec.

Rita Shenton

142 Percy Rd. TW2 6JG. Est. 1973. Open by appointment only. SIZE: Medium. *STOCK: Clocks, watches, barometers, sundials, scientific instruments, automata and ornamental turning books, £1-£1,000.* LOC: Continuation of Whitton High St. PARK: Easy. TEL: 020 8894 6888; fax - 020 8893 8766; e-mail - rita@shentonbooks.demon.co.uk; website - www.shentonbooks.demon.co.uk. SER: Valuations; buys at auction (horological books); catalogues available. FAIRS: Midland and Brunel Clock and Watch. *International postal service.*

Twickenham Antiques Warehouse

80 Colne Rd. TW2 6QE. (A. Clubb and E. Robinson). Est. 1985. Open 9.30-1 and 2-5, Sat. 10-4, Sun. 10-2. SIZE: Medium. *STOCK: European furniture, 1700-1920, £50-£2,000.* LOC: Off London Rd. PARK: Easy. TEL: 020 8894 5555; mobile - 07973 132847; e-mail - andclubb@aol.com. SER: Valuations; restorations (French polishing, cabinet work, carving). VAT: Spec.

UXBRIDGE

Antiques Warehouse (Uxbridge)

34-35 Rockingham Rd. UB8 2TZ. (Mike, Sue and Ben Allenby and Simon Phillips). Est. 1977. Open 10-6. SIZE: Large. *STOCK: General antiques, shipping items, £1-£4,000.* PARK: Easy. TEL: 01895 256963/271012; fax - 01895 252157; e-mail - info@uxbridgeantiques.co.uk; website - www.uxbridgeantiques.co.uk. SER: Restorations; French polishing; re-upholstery; VAT: Stan/Global.

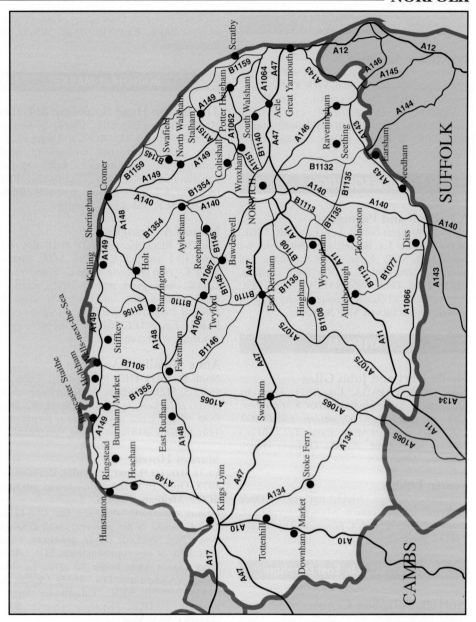

Dealers and Shops in Norfolk

Acle	1	East Dereham	1	Needham	1	South Walsham	1
Attleborough	1	East Rudham	1	North Walsham	2	Stalham	1
Aylsham	2	Fakenham	3	Norwich	26	Stiffkey	2
Bawdeswell	1	Great Yarmouth	7	Potter Heigham	1	Stoke Ferry	1
Brancaster Staithe	1	Heacham	1	Raveningham	1	Swaffham	2
Burnham Market	4	Hingham	2	Reepham	1	Swafield	1
Coltishall	4	Holkham	1	Ringstead	1	Tacolneston	1
Cromer	3	Holt	11	Scratby	1	Tottenhill	1
Diss	2	Hunstanton	4	Seething	1	Twyford	1
Downham Market	1	Kelling	1	Sharrington	1	Wells-next-the-Sea	2
Earsham	1	King's Lynn	5	Sheringham	4	Wymondham	4

ACLE, Nr. Norwich

Ivy House Antiques
Ivy House, The Street. NR13 3BH. (N. Pratt). Est. 1970. Open 9-5. SIZE: Small. *STOCK: Furniture, porcelain, pottery, glass, metalware, 18th-20th C, £25-£2,000; pictures, £50-£500.* LOC: Village centre. PARK: Easy. TEL: 01493 750682; home - same. SER: Valuations. FAIRS: Norwich. VAT: Stan/Spec.

ATTLEBOROUGH

A.E. Bush and Partners
Vineyards Antiques Gallery, Leys Lane. NR17 1NE. (A.G., M.S. and J.A. Becker). Est. 1940. Open 9-1 and 2-5.30. SIZE: Large. *STOCK: Walnut and mahogany, 18th-19th C.* LOC: Town outskirts. PARK: Easy. TEL: 01953 454239/452175. SER: Restorations; wholesale antiques and export; storage; buys at auction. VAT: Stan/Spec.

AYLSHAM

Sheila Hart and John Giles
NR11 7QQ. LAPADA. Est. 1971. Open by appointment. SIZE: Medium. *STOCK: Furniture, 18th-19th C, £200-£5,000; objects, £50-£1,000.* LOC: Off A140. PARK: Easy. TEL: 01263 768216; fax - same. FAIRS: Olympia (June); Battersea. *Trade Only.*

Pearse Lukies
The Old Vicarage. NR11. Est. 1975. Open preferably by appointment. *STOCK: Period oak, sculpture, objects, 18th C furniture.* TEL: 01263 734137. *Trade Only.*

BAWDESWELL, Nr. East Dereham

Norfolk Polyphon Centre
Wood Farm. NR20 4RX. (N.B. Vince). Open weekends, week days preferably by appointment. *STOCK: Mechanical music - polyphons, cylinder musical boxes, organs, orchestrions, automata.* LOC: On B1145, 1 mile east of Bawdeswell village and junction with A1067. TEL: 01362 688230. VAT: Stan/Spec.

BRANCASTER STAITHE, Nr. King's Lynn

Staithe Antiques
Coast Rd. PE31 8BJ. (Anne and Tony Webb). Est. 1994. Open Tues.-Sun. SIZE: Small. *STOCK: 18th-19th C furniture, china, glass and pictures.* PARK: Easy. TEL: 01485 210600. SER: Restorations.

BURNHAM MARKET

The Brazen Head Bookshop & Gallery
Market Place. PE31 8HD. (David S. Kenyon). Est. 1997. Open 9.30-5.30. SIZE: Large. *STOCK: Rare, out-of-print and secondhand books; paintings, prints and ceramics.* LOC: On green, opposite PO. PARK: Easy. TEL: 01328 730700; fax - 01328 730929; e-mail - brazenheadbook@aol.com. SER: Valuations; framing.

M. and A. Cringle
The Old Black Horse. PE31 8HD. Est. 1965. Open 10-1 and 2-5. CL: Wed. SIZE: Medium. *STOCK: 18th to early 19th C furniture, £50-£2,000; china, glass, pottery, prints, maps, £10-£500; modern china and decorative items.* Not Stocked: Large furniture. LOC: In village centre. PARK: Easy. TEL: 01328 738456; e-mail - pmcringle@aol.com.

Anne Hamilton Antiques
North St. PE31 8HG. (A. Hudson). Open 10-1 and 2-5. SIZE: Medium. *STOCK: Georgian furniture; porcelain, decorative items.* LOC: 20yds. from village green towards coast. PARK: Easy. TEL: 01328 738187; fax - same. VAT: Stan/Spec.

Market House　　　　　　　　　BADA
PE31 8HF. (D.H. and J. Maufe). Resident. Est. 1978. Open 10-6, but appointment advisable. SIZE: Medium. STOCK: English furniture - walnut, mahogany, rosewood, late 17th to mid-19th C; works of art, mirrors, small decorative items. Not Stocked: Silver, jewellery, clocks, porcelain, or any reproductions. LOC: B1355, large Queen Anne house on green in village centre. PARK: Easy. TEL: 01328 738475; fax - 01328 730750. SER: Valuations; buys at auction. FAIRS: Olympia (Nov); BADA (March). VAT: Spec.

COLTISHALL

Roger Bradbury Antiques
Church St. NR12 7DJ. Est. 1967. Open by appointment. *STOCK: Cargoes - Tek Sing, Nanking, Vung Tao, Diana.* PARK: Easy. TEL: 01603 737444. SER: Valuations. VAT: Stan.

Coltishall Antiques Centre
High St. NR3 7AA. (I. Ford). Est. 1980. Open 10-4.30. SIZE: Several specialists. *STOCK: A wide*

variety of items including 19th C porcelain and pottery, silver and silver plate, copper, brass, jewellery, collectors' items, militaria, glass, bijouterie. LOC: B1150 on corner of main street. PARK: Easy. TEL: 01603 738306.

Gwendoline Golder Antiques
Point House, 5 High St. NR12 7AA. Est. 1974. Open 10-4.30. CL: Sun. except by appointment. *STOCK: General antiques and collectors' items.* PARK: Easy. TEL: 01603 738099.

Village Clocks
9 High St. NR12 7AA. (Mike Darley). Open Mon.-Sat. *STOCK: Clocks - 18th-19th C longcase and bracket, regulators, wood and marble.* LOC: Main Norwich to North Walsham road. PARK: Easy. TEL: 01603 736047; fax - same; mobile - 07050 229758; e-mail - mdarley1@excite.co.uk; website - www.village-clocks.co.uk. SER: Valuations; restorations (cases and movements).

CROMER

Bond Street Antiques
6 Bond St. and 38 Church St. NR27 9DA. (M.R.T. and J.A. Jones). NAG, FGA. Est. 1970. Open 9-1 and 2-5. SIZE: Medium. *STOCK: Jewellery, silver, porcelain, china, glass, small furniture, 18th-20th C, £50-£5,000.* LOC: From Church St. bear right to Post Office, shop on opposite side on street further along. PARK: Easy. TEL: 01263 513134; home - same. SER: Valuations; repairs (jewellery); gem testing. VAT: Stan.

Books Etc.
15A Church St. NR27 9ES. (Kevin and Christine Reynor). UACC. Est. 1996. Open Easter to end Oct, 10-4 including Sun., Nov.-Easter Thurs.-Sat. 10-3.30 or by appointment. SIZE: Medium. *STOCK: Books, football programmes, memorabilia and autographs.* LOC: Town centre. PARK: Nearby. TEL: 01263 515501; e-mail - bookskcr@aol.com. SER: Valuations.

Collectors World
6 New Parade, Church St. NR27 9EP. (John and Irene Nockels). Est. 1988. Open 10-1 and 2-4, Sat. 10-1 and 2-5, Sun. 2.30-5. CL: Mon. SIZE: Small. *STOCK: Collectables, 19th-20th C, £5-£100.* LOC: Near traffic lights on Norwich road. PARK: Limited at rear. TEL: 01263 515330; home - 01263 514174. FAIRS: Norfolk Showground and Swinderby.

DISS

The Antiques & Collectors Centre (Diss)
3 Cobbs Yard, St Nicholas St. IP22 4LB. (Dean Cockaday and Chris Beecham). Est. 1997. Open 9.30-5. SIZE: Large. *STOCK: Royal commemoratives, 19th-20th C; Victorian to 1930's porcelain, £50-£100; modern collectables, 1930's-70's, £25-£50; rustic bygones, £20-£200; jewellery, £10-£300.* LOC: Next to Diss Ironworks, off St. Nicholas St. PARK: Easy. TEL: 01379 644472. VAT: Spec.

Diss Antiques & Interiors
2 & 3 Market Place. IP22 4JT. LAPADA. Open 9-5. SIZE: Large. *STOCK: Furniture, barometers, clocks, jewellery, porcelain, copper, brass.* PARK: Nearby. TEL: 01379 642213; e-mail - sales@dissantiques.co.uk. SER: Repairs (furniture, jewellery, china). VAT: Stan/Spec.

DOWNHAM MARKET

Antiques & Gifts
47 Bridge St. PE38 9DW. (B. and T. Addrison). Est. 1980. Usually open 10-5. SIZE: Medium. *STOCK: Furniture - pine, oak, mahogany; brass and iron beds, bric-a-brac and smalls, Victorian to 1930.* PARK: Free nearby. TEL: 01366 387700 Janbo.

EARSHAM, Nr. Bungay

Earsham Hall Pine
Earsham Hall. NR35 2AN. (R. Derham). Est. 1976. Open 9-5, Sun. 10.30-5. SIZE: Large. *STOCK: Pine furniture.* LOC: On Earsham to Hedenham Rd. PARK: Easy. TEL: 01986 893423; fax - 01986 895656; website - www. earshamhallpine.co.uk. SER: Containers.

EAST DEREHAM

Village Books
20A High St. NR19 1DR. (J.A.R. and J.W. James). Est. 1996. Open 9.30-4.30, Wed. 9.30-1, Sat. 9.30-5. SIZE: Medium. *STOCK: Books, 19th-20th C, £1-£150.* LOC: Just off Market Place. PARK: Nearby. TEL: 01362 853066; fax - same; e-mail - villagebooksdereham@ukonline. co.uk. SER: Book binding. VAT: Stan.

EAST RUDHAM, Nr. King's Lynn

Old Grain Store Antiques
The Square. PE31 8RB. (Margaret Goodwin). Est. 1987. Open every day except Wed. SIZE: Large. *STOCK: Georgian and Victorian furniture; porcelain including 19th C Sitzendorf, Moorcroft, Clarice Cliff, Shelley; bronze figures, glass.* TEL: 01485 529410; fax - same; home - 01366 501070.

FAKENHAM

Colbrook Antiques
Fakenham Antiques Centre, Old Congregational Church, 14 Norwich Rd. NR21 8AZ. (Brian Weeks). Est. 1989. Open 10-4.30. SIZE: Medium. *STOCK: Furniture, 18th to early 20th C, £100-£2,000; clocks, 18th-19th C, £150-£2,000; pictures and prints, china, glass, 19th to early 20th C, £50-£500.* LOC: Turn off A148 at roundabout towards town, right at traffic lights, left at next roundabout, centre is 50 yards on right. TEL: 01328 862941; home - 01485 576138; mobile - 07776 041826. SER: Valuations; restorations (furniture); buys at auction.

Fakenham Antique Centre
Old Congregational Church, 14 Norwich Rd. NR21 8AZ. (Julie Hunt and Mandy Allen). Est. 1984. Open 10-4.30, Sun. and Bank Holidays 10-4. SIZE: 27 dealers. *STOCK: Furniture, glass, ceramics, books, pens, oil lamps, kitchenalia, memorabilia, curtains, Americana and clocks.* LOC: Turn off A148 at roundabout to town, at traffic lights turn up Queens Rd., left at second mini-roundabout, centre 50yds. on right opposite Godfrey DIY. PARK: Easy. TEL: 01328 862941; home - 01328 830225. SER: Restorations (furniture); polishing; replacement handles; cane and rush seating repairs.

Sue Rivett Antiques and Bygones
6 Norwich Rd. NR21. (Mrs S. Rivett). Est. 1969. Open 10-1. *STOCK: General antiques and bygones.* LOC: On Norwich Rd. into Fakenham. TEL: 01328 862924; home - 01263 860462.

GT. YARMOUTH

Barry's Antiques
35 King St. NR30 2PN. Open 9.30-5. SIZE: Large. *STOCK: Jewellery, porcelain, clocks, glass, pictures.* LOC: In main shopping street. PARK: Opposite. TEL: 01493 842713. VAT: Stan/Spec.

David Ferrow
77 Howard St. South. NR30 1LN. ABA. PBFA. Est. 1940. Open 10-5. CL: Thurs. SIZE: Large. *STOCK: Books, some antiquarian maps, local prints, manuscripts.* LOC: From London, sign before river bridge to The Docks, keep to nearside, turn left and then right to car park. PARK: Easy. TEL: 01493 843800; home - 01493 662247. SER: Valuations; restorations (books and prints). VAT: Stan.

Folkes Antiques and Jewellers
74 Victoria Arcade. NR30 2NU. (Mrs J. Baldry). Est. 1946. Open 10-4. *STOCK: General antiques especially jewellery and collectables.* LOC: From A47 into town centre, shop on right of Victoria Arcade, opposite Regent Rd. to seafront. PARK: Easy. TEL: 01493 851354. SER: Valuations; repairs. FAIRS: Local collectors.

Gold and Silver Exchange
Theatre Plain. NR30 2BE. (C. Birch). Open 9.30-5.15. *STOCK: Coins, medals and secondhand jewellery.* TEL: 01493 859430.

Peter Howkins Antiques
132 King St. NR30 2PQ. Est. 1946. Open 9.30-4. *STOCK: Furniture, silver, pottery, glass, bronzes, Georgian-Edwardian.* LOC: From Norwich through town one-way system to road signposted Lowestoft which intersects King St. PARK: Easy. TEL: 01493 851180. SER: Valuations; restorations.

Peter Howkins Jewellers
135 King St. NR30 2PQ. (Peter and Valerie Howkins). NAG. Est. 1945. Open 9-5. SIZE: Medium. *STOCK: Jewellery, silver, crystal, porcelain, pottery, Georgian to present day.* LOC: South of Market Place. PARK: Limited and nearby. TEL: 01493 844639; fax - 01493 844857. SER: Valuations; restorations; repairs. VAT: Spec.

Wheatleys
16 Northgate St., White Horse Plain and Fullers Hill. NR30 1BA. Est. 1971. Open 9.30-5, Thurs. 9.30-1. SIZE: Large. *STOCK: Jewellery and general antiques.* LOC: 2 minutes walk from Market Place. PARK: Easy. TEL: 01493 857219. VAT: Stan.

HEACHAM, Nr. King's Lynn

Peter Robinson
Pear Tree House, 7 Lynn Rd. PE31 7HU. Est. 1880. Appointment advisable. SIZE: Small. *STOCK: Furniture, 1600-1900, £10-£5,000; china, 1750-1900, metalwork, 1700-1870; both £2-£1,000.* LOC: Shop on left on entry to village. PARK: Easy. TEL: 01485 570228. SER: Valuations; buys at auction. VAT: Stan/Spec.

HINGHAM, Nr. Norwich

Mongers
15 Market Place. NR9 4AF. (Sam and Trudie Coster). Est. 1997. Open 9.30-5.30. SIZE: Large. *STOCK: Fireplaces, 1700-1930, £400-£900; sanitaryware, 1870-1950, £250-£1,000; Victorian and Edwardian garden antiques, £50-£500.* LOC: B1108. PARK: Easy. TEL: 01953 851868; fax - 01953 851870; e-mail - trudie@mongersofhingham.co.uk; website - www.mongersofhingham.co.uk. SER: Restorations (pine stripping, bath re-surfacing, fireplaces). VAT: Stan/Spec.

Past & Present
16a The Fairland. NR9 4HN. (C. George). Est. 1970. Open Tues.-Sun. 10-5. SIZE: Medium. *STOCK: Furniture, £25-£1,500; smalls, 18th-19th C, £10-£500.* LOC: B1108. PARK: Easy. TEL: 01953 851471; home - 01953 851400; website - www.pastandpresentantiques.co.uk. SER: Valuations. FAIRS: Swinderby, Newark, Staffordshire. VAT: Stan.

HOLKHAM, Nr. Wells-next-the-Sea

The Potting Shed
Main Rd. (Bill Jellings). Est. 1993. Open Sun. afternoons only, trade mid-week by appointment. SIZE: Medium. *STOCK: English and French gardenalia.* LOC: On north Norfolk coast road (A149) by entrance to Holkham Hall. PARK: Easy. TEL: 01692 402424; home - same.

HOLT

Baron Art
9 &17 Chapel Yard, Albert St. NR25 6HG. (Anthony R. Baron and Michael J. Bellis). Est. 1992. Open 9.30-5.30 including Sun. SIZE: Medium. *STOCK: Paintings, 19th-20th C, £50-£5,000; prints and lithographs, 19th-20th C, £5-£500; collectables, 1830-1940, £5-£500; books and Art Deco.* PARK: Easy. TEL: 01263 713906; home - 01263 713430. SER: Valuations; buys at auction (paintings); framing. VAT: Stan/Spec.

Cottage Collectables
8 Fish Hill and 3 Chapel Yard. NR25 6BD. (Philip & Linda Morris). Est. 1984. Open 10-5, Sun. 11-5. SIZE: Medium. *STOCK: Collectables, 18th-20th C, £5-£250; furniture, 18th-20th C, £50-£300; jewellery, from Victorian, £5-£50; linen.* PARK: Easy. TEL: 01263 711707/712920; e-mail - cottcoll@aol.com. SER: Valuations; restorations (furniture and ceramics); buys at auction (furniture and collectables). FAIRS: Swinderby, Peterborough, Newark and others.

Anthony Fell
Chester House, 47 Bull St. NR25 6HP. (A.J. and C.R. Austin-Fell). LAPADA. CINOA. Est. 1996. Open 9.30-1 and 2-5, prior telephone call advisable if travelling long distance. SIZE: Medium. *STOCK: English and Continental furniture, 16th-18th C, £1,000-£50,000; works of art, 16th C to contemporary, £1,000-£20,000.* LOC: Near Post Office. PARK: Easy. TEL: 01263 712712; fax - same. SER: Valuations; restorations. FAIRS: Olympia (June, Nov). VAT: Spec.

Simon Gough Books
5 Fish Hill. NR25 6BD. Est. 1976. Open 10-5. *STOCK: Antiquarian and secondhand books; bindings.* TEL: 01263 712650.

Heathfield Antiques & Country Pine
The Warehouse, 39 Hempstead Rd. NR25 6DL. (J.E., H.B. and S.M. Heathfield). Est. 1990. Open 8-5. SIZE: Large. *STOCK: Pine furniture, £50-£1,500.* LOC: Follow signs to Hempstead. PARK: Own. TEL: 01263 711122/711609; website - www.antique-pine.net. VAT: Stan/Global.

Judy Hines of Holt - The Gallery
3 Fish Hill. NR25 6BD. Est. 1973. Open 11-5, Thurs. 11-1. CL: Mon. *STOCK: Modern British paintings; sculptures.* TEL: 01263 713000; fax - same; e-mail - judyhinesgallery@hotmail.com. SER: Framing; viewing by card index.

Holt Antique Centre
Albert Hall, Albert St. NR25. (David Attfield). Est. 1980. Open 10-5, Sat. 10-5.30 (Sun. Easter-October). SIZE: Large. *STOCK: Pine and country furniture, china, glass, lighting, silver plate and kitchenalia, jewellery, clothes, soft furnishings, 18th-20th C, £1-£1,500.* LOC: Turn right from Chapel Yard car park, 100 yards. PARK: Easy. TEL: 01263 712097; home - 01263 860347.

Mews Antique Emporium
17B High St. Est. 1998. Open 10-5. SIZE: Large - 12 dealers. *STOCK: 18th-20th C furniture, collectables, £1-£1,000.* PARK: Nearby. TEL: 01263 713224.

Past Caring
6 Chapel Yard. NR25 6HG. (L. Mossman). Est. 1988. Open 11-5. CL: Thurs. SIZE: Medium. *STOCK: Period clothes, linen and textiles, Victorian to 1950, £5-£100; jewellery and accessories, Victorian to 1960, £2-£75.* PARK: Easy. TEL: 01263 713771; home - 01362 683363; e-mail - pstcaring@aol.com. SER: Valuations; restorations (christening gowns and some beadwork). FAIRS: Alexandra Palace, Stand W60.

CHESTNEY HOUSE

ANTIQUES & COLLECTORS GALLERY

WESTGATE
HUNSTANTON
NORFOLK PE36 5AL

*Trade Space Available
for Rent*

Tel: 01485 532563
Mobile: 07790 959315
e-mail:
G.M.@berto.fsnet.co.uk

Proprietor: Gordon M. Burton

Richard Scott Antiques
30 High St. NR25 6BH. Est. 1967. Open 10-5. CL: Thurs. SIZE: Large. *STOCK: Pottery, porcelain, glass, furniture, contemporary ceramics, oil lamps and spares, general antiques.* LOC: On A148. PARK: Easy. TEL: 01263 712479. SER: Valuations; conservation advice.

HUNSTANTON

Chestney House Antiques & Collectors Gallery
Westgate, PE36 5AL. (Gordon M. Burton). Open 10-5. SIZE: Medium. *STOCK: Mainly smalls, some furniture, pictures, mirrors, clocks.* LOC: Opposite library. TEL: 01485 532563; mobile - 07790 959315; e-mail - G.M.@berto.fsnet.co.uk. SER: Valuations.

Delawood Antiques
10 Westgate. PE36 5AL. (R.C. Woodhouse). Resident. Est. 1975. Open Mon., Wed., Fri., Sat. 10-5 and most Sun. afternoons, other times by chance or appointment. SIZE: Small. *STOCK: General antiques, furniture, jewellery, collectors' items, books, £1-£1,000.* LOC: Near town centre and bus station. PARK: Easy. TEL: 01485 532903; home and fax - same. SER: Valuations; commission sales.

Le Strange Old Barns Antiques, Arts & Craft Centre
Golf Course Rd., Old Hunstanton. PE36 6JG. (E. Maloney and R.M. Welier). Est. 1994. Open 10-6, (10-5 winter), including Sun. SIZE: Large. *STOCK: General antiques, collectables, arts and crafts.* PARK: Easy. TEL: 01485 533402.

R.C. Woodhouse (Antiquarian Horologist)
10 Westgate. PE36 5AL. MBHI. BWCG. Resident. Est. 1975. Open Mon., Wed., Fri, Sat. and usually Sun. afternoons, other times by chance or appointment. SIZE: Small. *STOCK: Georgian, Victorian and Edwardian longcase, dial, wall and mantel clocks; some watches and barometers.* LOC: Near town centre and bus station. PARK: Easy. TEL: 01485 532903; home and fax - same. SER: Valuations; restorations (longcase, bracket, chiming, carriage, French, wall clocks, dials, barometers); small locks repaired and lost keys made - postal service if required.

KELLING, Nr. Holt

The Old Reading Room Gallery and Tea Room
NR25 7EL. (B.R. Taylor). Est. 1994. Open 9.30-4.30 including Sun. SIZE: Large. *STOCK: Paintings and prints, wood carvings, books, postcards and collectables.* LOC: A149 coast road between Weybourne and Cley, at war memorial in village. PARK: Easy. TEL: 01263 588227; home - 01263 588435. SER: Restorations; framing. VAT: Stan/Spec.

KING'S LYNN

Tim Clayton Jewellery & Antiques
21-23 Chapel St. PE30 1EG. (Tim and Sue Clayton). NAG. Est. 1975. Open 9-5. SIZE: Small. *STOCK: Silver, jewellery, clocks, furniture, china and pictures.* LOC: Town centre. PARK: Nearby. TEL: 01553 772329; fax - 01553 776583; e-mail - tpcjewellery@netscapeonline.co.uk. SER: Bespoke jewellery; repairs; picture framing. VAT: Global/ Margin.

James K. Lee
Nicholson House, 29 Church St. PE30. (A.J. and J.K. Lee). Est. 1950. Open 9-6 including Sun. SIZE: Small. *STOCK: Furniture including desks, chests of drawers and tables, 18th-19th C, £800-£4,500.* LOC: In old town, through Southgates, by mini roundabout. PARK: Easy and NCP opposite. TEL: 01553 810681; fax - 01553

760128; home - 01553 811522. SER: Valuations; restorations including polishing; buys at auction (furniture).

Norfolk Galleries
Railway Rd. PE30 1PF. (B. Houchen and G.R. Cumbley). Open 8.30-5.30, Sat. 8.30-12.30. *STOCK: Victorian and Edwardian furniture.* PARK: Nearby. TEL: 01553 765060.

Old Curiosity Shop
25 St. James St. PE30 5DA. (Mrs R.S. Wright). Est. 1980. Open 10.30-5, Sat. 9.30-6. SIZE: Small. *STOCK: General collectable smalls, glass, clothing, linen, jewellery, lighting, Art Deco and Art Nouveau, furniture, prints, stripped pine and paintings, pre 1930, £1-£500.* LOC: Off Saturday market place towards London Rd. PARK: At rear or nearby. TEL: 01553 766591. SER: Restorations (teddy bears); repairs (clocks). FAIRS: Alexandra Palace, Newark and local.

The Old Granary Antiques and Collectors Centre
King Staithe Lane, Off Queen St. PE30 1LZ. Open 10-5. *STOCK: China, glass, books, silver, jewellery, brass, copper, postcards, linen, some furniture and general antiques.* PARK: Easy. TEL: 01553 775509.

NEEDHAM, Nr. Harleston

Jennifer and Raymond Norman Antiques
Henstead Lodge. IP20 9LA. Resident. Est. 1974. Open by appointment. *STOCK: Clocks, 1780-1900, £100-£5,000; longcase, 1720-1830, £1,000-£8,000.* LOC: A143 Harleston by-pass. At Harleston/Needham roundabout turn towards Harleston. Entrance to Henstead Lodge immediately on right. PARK: Easy. TEL: 01379 855124; fax - 01379 855134; mobile - 07774 887045; e-mail - rjn@longcase.co.uk. SER: Valuations; restorations (longcase clocks - cases and movements); buys at auction (clocks). VAT: Stan/Spec.

NORTH WALSHAM

The Angel Bookshop
4 Aylsham Rd. NR28 0BH. (O.D., M.E. and W.T.E. Green). PBFA. ABA. Est. 1980. Open 9.30-5, Sat. 9.30-3.30. CL: Wed. SIZE: Medium. *STOCK: Books, 1700 to date, £3-£500.* LOC: Short walk from town centre. PARK: Nearby. TEL: 01692 404054; e-mail - angelbooks@ onetel.net.uk. SER: Valuations; buys at auction. FAIRS: East Anglia PBFA.

Eric Bates and Sons Ltd.
Melbourne House, Bacton Rd. NR28 0RA. Est. 1973. Open 8-5. SIZE: Large. *STOCK: Victorian and Edwardian furniture.* TEL: 01692 403221; fax - 01692 404388. SER: Restorations (furniture); manufacturer of period-style furniture; upholstery; shipping and container packing. VAT: Stan/Spec.

NORWICH

Albrow and Sons Family Jewellers
10 All Saints Green. NR1 3NA. (R. Albrow). NAG Registered Valuer. Open 9.30-4.30. *STOCK: Jewellery, silver, plate, china, glass, furniture.* LOC: Opposite John Lewis'. PARK: Behind John Lewis'. TEL: 01603 622569; fax - 01603 766158. SER: Valuations; repairs.

Liz Allport-Lomax
t/a Corner Antiques. *STOCK: Porcelain, glass, silver, objects de vertue, sewing accessories, small furniture and collectors items - card cases, lace bobbins, snuff boxes, scent bottles.* TEL: 01603 737631; mobile - 07747 843074: website - www.lomaxantiques.fairs.co.uk. FAIRS: Organiser of Lomax Antiques Fairs at Langley School (May and Oct.); North Norfolk, Burnham Market (Easter); Norwich (Feb.)

Antiques & Interiors
31-35 Elm Hill. NR3 1HG. Est. 1976. Open 10-5. *STOCK: Furniture including Arts and Crafts, Victorian, £5-£5,000.* PARK: Nearby. TEL: 01603 622695; home and fax - 01603 632446. SER: Restorations.

The Bank House Gallery
Newmarket Rd. NR2 2HW. (R.S. Mitchell). LAPADA. Resident. Est. 1979. Open by appointment. *STOCK: English oil paintings especially Norwich and Suffolk schools, 19th C, £1,000-£50,000.* LOC: On A11 between city centre and ring road. PARK: Own. TEL: 01603 633380; fax - 01603 633387. SER: Valuations; restorations. VAT: Stan/Spec.

JAMES BRETT

Dealers in Antique Furniture

42 St. Giles Street, NORWICH, NR2 1LW
Telephone: 01603 628171
Fax: 01603 630245

Open Mon.-Fri. 9.30-1.00 & 2.00-5.00

18th Century Pearwood Lowboy c.1720.

James Brett
BADA
42 St. Giles St. NR2 1LW. Est. 1870. Open 9.30-1 and 2-5. CL: Sat. except by appointment. SIZE: Large. STOCK: Antique furniture, mahogany, walnut and oak; sculpture and metalwork. LOC: Near City Hall. PARK: Easy. TEL: 01603 628171; fax - 01603 630245. FAIRS: Olympia. VAT: Stan/Spec.

J & D Clarke Book and Print Dealers
St Michael at Plea Church, Redwell St. NR2 4SN. PBFA. Est. 1988. Open 9.30-5. SIZE: Medium. *STOCK: Books, prints and ephemera, £1-£1,000.* LOC: Twixt Elm Hill and city centre. PARK: 30mins. on street, multi-storey nearby. TEL: 01603 617700/619226. SER: Valuations; print colouring and mounting. FAIRS: PBFA (Norwich).

Cloisters Antique & Collectors Fair
St. Andrew's and Blackfriars Hall, St. Andrew's Plain. NR3 1AU. (Norwich City Council). Est. 1976. Open Wed. only 9-3.30. SIZE: 21 dealers. *STOCK: Wide range of antiques and collectables.* LOC: City centre. PARK: Easy. TEL: 01603 628477; fax - 01603 762182; bookings - 01493 750981.

Country and Eastern Ltd.
Old Skating Rink Gallery, 34-36 Bethal St. NR2 1NR. (J. Millward). Est. 1978. Open 10-5. SIZE: Large. *STOCK: Oriental rugs, kelims and textiles; Indian and S.E. Asian antiques - furniture, objects, ceramics and metalwork.* LOC: Near the Forum, and next to the Fire Station. PARK: Easy. TEL: 01603 663890; website - www.countryand eastern.co.uk. VAT: Stan.

Crome Gallery and Frame Shop
34 Elm Hill. NR3 1HG. (J. Willis). UKIC. Est. 1971. Open 9.30-5. SIZE: Large. *STOCK: Watercolours, oils and prints, mainly 20th C, some 19th C; wood carvings and sculpture.* LOC: Near cathedral. PARK: Easy. TEL: 01603 622827; e-mail - elmhillgallery@netscape.net. SER: Crome Gallery Conservation (oils, watercolours, prints, frames); framing.

Clive Dennett Coins
66 St. Benedicts St. NR2 4AR. BNTA. Est. 1970. CL: Thurs. and lunchtime. SIZE: Small. *STOCK: Coins and medals, ancient Greek to date, £5-£5,000; jewellery, 19th-20th C; banknotes, 20th C; both £5-£1,000.* PARK: Easy. TEL: 01603 624315. SER: Valuations; buys at auction (as stock). FAIRS: London Coin; International Banknote, London and Maastricht.

The Fairhurst Gallery
Bedford St. NR2 1AR. Est. 1951. Open 9-5. CL: Sat. pm. SIZE: Medium. *STOCK: Oil paintings, £5-£5,000; watercolours, £5-£2,000, both 19th-20th C; frames, 18th-20th C; furniture, £500-£10,000.* LOC: Behind Travel Centre. TEL: 01603 614214. SER: Valuations; restorations; cleaning; framemakers. VAT: Spec.

Nicholas Fowle Antiques
BADA
Websdale Court, Bedford St. NR2 1AR. Est. 1965. Open 9-5, Sat. 9-1. SIZE: Medium. STOCK: Furniture, £500-£10,000; works of art, £5-£1,000; both 17th-19th C. LOC: City centre pedestrian area (limited access for loading and unloading). PARK: St Andrews multi-storey. TEL: 01603 219964; fax - 01692 630378; e-mail - nfowleantiques@aol.com. SER: Valuations; restorations (furniture). VAT: Stan/Spec.

Peter J. Hadley Bookseller
29 Surrey St. NR1 3NX. ABA. Est. 1982. Open by appointment. SIZE: Small. *STOCK: Books - architecture, literature, art reference and illustrated.* LOC: City centre. TEL: 01603 663411; home - same; fax - 01603 613113; e-mail - books @hadley.co.uk; website - www.hadley.co.uk.

John Howkins Antiques Ltd
1 Dereham Rd. NR2 4HX. (J.G. Howkins). Est.

1973. Open 10-5, prior telephone call advisable. SIZE: Large. *STOCK: Furniture and smalls, 18th to early 20th C, £25-£15,000.* LOC: Inner ring road, junction of Dereham Road and Grapes Hill. PARK: Own at rear. TEL: 01603 627832; fax - 01603 666626; e-mail - howkinsantiques@clara.co.uk; website - www.antiques-antiques.co.uk. SER: Valuations; restorations (furniture, clocks, upholstery); buys at auction. VAT: Stan/Spec.

Leona Levine Silver Specialist BADA
35 St. Giles St. NR2 1JN. Est. 1865. Open 9.30-5. CL: Thurs. *STOCK: Silver and Sheffield plate.* LOC: 100 yds. from City Hall. PARK: Multi-storey. TEL: 01603 628709; fax - same. SER: Valuations; engraving; restorations. VAT: Stan/Spec.

Maddermarket Antiques
18c Lower Goat Lane. NR2 1EL. Est. 1955. Open 9.30-4.30. *STOCK: Jewellery, silverware.* TEL: 01603 620610. SER: Part exchange.

Mandell's Gallery BADA
Elm Hill. NR3 1HN. (Geoffrey and Pauline Allen). Est. 1964. Open 9-5.30. SIZE: Large. *STOCK: Oils and watercolours, especially English and Continental works and Norwich and Suffolk painters, 19th-20th C.* LOC: Near shopping centre, close to cathedral. PARK: Easy. TEL: 01603 626892/629180; fax - 01603 767471. SER: Conservation; framing. FAIRS: Snape. VAT: Spec.

The Movie Shop
Antiquarian and Nostalgia Centre, 11 St. Gregory's Alley. NR2 1ER. Open 11-5. SIZE: Large. *STOCK: Books, magazines and movie ephemera; telephones, pre-1940 clothes and textiles, collectables and general antiques.* TEL: 01603 615239; e-mail - petecossey@thenorwichmovieshop.com; website - www.thenorwichmovieshop.com.

Norwich Collectors Toyshop
St Michael at Plea Antiques Centre, Bank Plain. NR2 4SN. (S. Marshall). Est. 1985. Open 9.30-5. SIZE: Small. *STOCK: Dinky and Corgi toys, 1940-1990, £5-£150; trains and soldiers, 1910-1980, £5-£500; teddies and tin toys, 1920-1980, £5-£200.* PARK: Meters and multi-storey nearby. TEL: 01603 457761. SER: Valuations. FAIRS: Sandown Park, NEC, Donington Park, Doncaster Racecourse, Norfolk Showground.

Oswald Sebley
20 Lower Goat Lane. NR2 1EL. (P.H. Knights). Est. 1895. Open 9-5.15. CL: Thurs. SIZE: Small. *STOCK: Silver, 18th-20th C, £15-£2,000; jewel-lery, Victorian, £10-£4,000.* LOC: 150yds. to right of City Hall, down paved street. PARK: Nearby. TEL: 01603 626504. SER: Valuations; restorations (silver and gold jewellery). VAT: Stan/Spec.

St. Michael at Plea Antiques and Book Centre
Bank Plain. NR2 4SN. (Joy and David Clarke). PBFA. Est. 1984. Open 9.30-5. SIZE: Medium - 30 dealers. *STOCK: General antiques and collectables, pre-1960, £1-£1,000; antiquarian prints.* LOC: Between Elm Hill and city centre. PARK: 30 minutes roadside, multi-storey nearby. TEL: 01603 618989. SER: Valuations; restorations.

Stiffkey Bathrooms
89 Upper St. Giles St. NR2 1AB. *STOCK: Victorian, Edwardian and French bathroom fittings.* PARK: Easy. TEL: 01603 627850; fax - 01603 619775. SER: Mail order period bathroom accessories.

Tombland Antiques Centre
Augustine Steward House, 14 Tombland. NR3 1HF. (Mrs Betty Godsafe). Est. 1974. Open 10-5, Sun. 11-3. SIZE: Large. *STOCK: Furniture, 18th-20th C, £50-£1,000; china, porcelain, antiquities, dolls, Art Deco, Art Nouveau, collectables, curios, militaria, clocks and watches, pens, silver, pictures, postcards, jewellery, cranberry and other glass.* LOC: City centre, opposite cathedral. PARK: Elm Hill. TEL: 01603 619129. SER: Valuations.

The Tombland Bookshop
8 Tombland. NR3 1HF. (J.G. and A.H. Freeman). Open 9.30-5. *STOCK: Antiquarian and second-hand books.* TEL: 01603 490000; fax - 01603 760610; e-mail - tombland.bookshop@virgin.net.

Tombland Jewellers & Silversmiths
12/13 Tombland. NR3 1HF. NAG. Est. 1972. Open 9-5, Sat. 9-4. *STOCK: English silver, flatware and jewellery, from 17th C; mustard pots, collectors' items, barometers, barographs, from 18th C.* LOC: Opposite Erpingham Gate, Norwich Cathedral and Maid's Head Hotel. TEL: 01603 624914; fax - 01603 764310. SER: Valuations; restorations; export facilities. VAT: Stan/Spec.

Malcolm Turner
15 St. Giles St. NR2 1JL. Open 9-5. CL: Thurs. SIZE: Small. *STOCK: Bronzeware, coins, Oriental ceramics, silver, Staffordshire, Imari, mostly 19th C, £50-£1,000.* PARK: Nearby. TEL: 01603 627007. SER: Valuations. VAT: Stan.

POTTER HEIGHAM

Times Past Antiques
Station Rd. NR29 5AD. (P. Dellar). Open Tues - Sun. 10-5 in summer. CL: Mon. (and Tues. in winter). *STOCK: Barometers, clocks, furniture including reproduction, china, pictures, glass, collectables, bric-a-brac.* LOC: A149 village centre. PARK: Easy. TEL: 01692 670898.

RAVENINGHAM

M.D. Cannell Antiques
Castell Farm, Beccles Rd. NR14 6NU. Resident. Est. 1982. Open Fri., Sat., Sun. and Mon. 10-6 or by appointment. SIZE: Large. *STOCK: Oriental rugs, carpets, kilims, furniture, metalwork and decorative items.* LOC: On B1140. PARK: Easy. TEL: 01508 548441. VAT: Stan/Spec.

REEPHAM

Echo Antiques
Church Hill. NR10 4JW. (M. Stiefel and N. Bundock). Est. 1986. Open 10-5. CL: Thurs. SIZE: Medium. *STOCK: Furniture, 1650-1900,* £10-£2,000; pine, 1800-1900, £50-£1,000; small items, 1650-1900, £10-£1,000. Not Stocked: Jewellery. PARK: Market Sq. TEL: 01603 873291; home - 01603 872068. SER: Valuations; restorations (furniture); buys at auction.

RINGSTEAD, Nr. Hunstanton

Ringstead Village Antique Centre
41 High St. PE36 5JU. (Tim and Cathy Roberts). Est. 1997. Open 8-5.30 including Sun; Tues., Wed. and Sat. 8-1. SIZE: Small. *STOCK: Furniture including pine, Edwardian and period,* £50-£2,000; porcelain, curios, kitchenalia, books and magazines, paintings and prints. PARK: Easy. TEL: 01485 525270.

SCRATBY, Nr. Gt. Yarmouth

Keith Lawson Antique Clocks
Scratby Garden Centre, Beach Rd. NR29 3AJ. LBHI. Est. 1979. Open seven days 2-6. SIZE: Large. *STOCK: Clocks and barometers.* LOC: B1159. PARK: Easy. TEL: 01493 730950; website - www.antiqueclocks.co.uk. SER: Valuations; restorations. VAT: Stan/Spec.

SEETHING, Nr. Brooke

Country House Antiques
NR15 1AL. Est. 1979. Open by appointment. SIZE: Large trade warehouses. *STOCK: Mahogany, oak, walnut furniture, 17th-19th C; interesting china and porcelain.* LOC: Village centre. PARK: Easy. TEL: 01508 558144; mobile - 07860 595658. *Trade only.*

SHARRINGTON, Nr. Holt

Sharrington Antiques
NR24 2PQ. (P. Coke). Est. 1944. Open by chance 9.30-5.00 or by appointment. CL: Jan.-Mar. SIZE: Medium. *STOCK: Small and interesting items, £5-£1,500; china, pictures, embroideries, treen, papier mâché.* LOC: 3 miles west of Holt. PARK: Easy. TEL: 01263 861411; home - 01263 860719.

SHERINGHAM

R.L. Cook
12 Sycamore Grove. NR26 8PG. Est. 1950. Open by appointment. SIZE: Small. *STOCK: Second-hand and antiquarian books.* TEL: 01263 822050.

Dorothy's Antiques
23 Waterbank Rd. NR26 8RB. (Mrs D.E. Collier). Est. 1975. Open 11.15-4. *STOCK: Cranberry glass, Royal Worcester, Royal Dux, commemorative and other china; small furniture.* PARK: Easy. TEL: 01263 822319; home - 01263 823018.

Parriss
20 Station Rd. NR26 8RE. (J.H. Parriss). Est. 1947. Open 9-5.30. CL: Wed. SIZE: Medium. *STOCK: Jewellery, £30-£2,500; silver, £40-£2,000; clocks, £100-£3,000.* LOC: A1082, in main street. PARK: Within 150yds. TEL: 01263 822661. SER: Valuations; restorations (jewellery, silver, clocks). VAT: Stan.

The Westcliffe Gallery
2-8 Augusta St. NR26 8LA. (Richard and Sheila Parks). Resident. Est. 1979. Open 9.30-1 and 2-5.30, Sat. 9.30-5.30, Sun. 10-4. SIZE: Medium. *STOCK: Oils, watercolours and drawings, 19th-20th C, £100-£15,000; furniture.* LOC: Town centre. PARK: Easy. TEL: 01263 824320; e-mail - sheila@westcliffe.swinternet.co.uk. SER: Valuations; restorations (oils, watercolours, prints); gilding. VAT: Stan/Spec.

SOUTH WALSHAM

Leo Pratt and Son
Old Curiosity Shop. NR13 6EA. (R. and E.D. Pratt). LAPADA. Est. 1890. Open 9-5.30 or by appointment. SIZE: Large. *STOCK: Furniture, from 1700; porcelain, glass, pottery, 1830; shipping furniture, metalware.* PARK: Easy. TEL: 01603 270204. SER: Restorations (furniture); buys at auction. FAIRS: Norwich; Langley; Luton; NEC. VAT: Stan/Spec.

STALHAM

Stalham Antique Gallery
29 High St. NR12 9AH. (Mike Hicks). LAPADA. CINOA. Est. 1970. Open 9-1 and 2-5. CL: Sat pm. SIZE: Medium. *STOCK: Furniture, 17th C to 19th C; pictures, china, glass, brass.* Not Stocked: Reproductions. PARK: Easy. TEL: 01692 580636; e-mail - mbhickslink@talk21.com. SER: Valuations; restorations. FAIRS: Langley (Oct). VAT: Spec.

Close-up view of part of a Duplex movement, showing the kink in the outer coil of the balance-spring and the pin in the arm of the balance with which it acts if the arc of the balance gets too large.

From an article entitled "Nicole Nielsen and Co" by David Penney which appeared in the April 2002 issue of **Antique Collecting**. For more details and to subscribe see page 21.

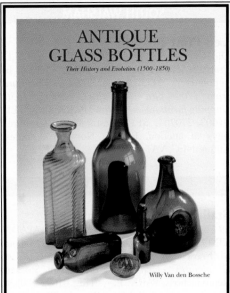

ANTIQUE GLASS BOTTLES
Their History and Evolution (1500-1850)

Willy Van den Bossche

This major work is the first of its kind. It comprehensively charts the history and evolution of antique glass utility bottles between 1500 and 1850. This unmatched book is destined to become *the* indispensable reference work on the subject. An incredible visual history of the evolution of the glass bottle over a period of 350 years is presented here. The thorough text is accompanied by 368 remarkable original colour photographs of 773 bottles and seals.

Willy Van den Bossche's achievement is staggering. He has succeeded in producing an accurate study of each and every main region of Europe that has produced glass utility bottles. The inter-relationships and influences are observed and a comparative guide covering almost all of the bottle-producing world has been created. In addition to this, the book boasts the most comprehensive bibliography on glass bottles ever produced, listing 1,150 titles. Almost all of the bottles illustrated in this volume have been carefully chosen from a variety of private collections.

ISBN 1 85149 337 9
439pp., 368 col., 26 b.&w. line drawings
£50.00

Available from the
ANTIQUE COLLECTORS' CLUB
Sandy Lane, Old Martlesham,
Woodbridge, Suffolk IP12 4SD, UK.
For your free copy of the catalogue:
Tel: **01394 389950** or Fax: **01394 389999**
Email: sales@antique-acc.com
Website: www.antique-acc.com

STIFFKEY

Stiffkey Antiques
The Old Methodist Chapel. NR23 1AJ. Est. 1976. Open 10-5 including Sun. *STOCK: Door furniture, window fittings, fireplaces and accessories, 1800-1920; carpets, bric-a-brac, bronze garden statuary and water features.* PARK: Easy. TEL: 01328 830099; door and window fittings - 01328 830690; fax - 01328 830005.

The Stiffkey Lamp Shop
Townshend Arms. NR23 1AJ. (R. Belsten and D. Mann). Est. 1976. Open 10-5 including Sun. SIZE: Medium. *STOCK: Lamps including rare, hanging, wall and table and fittings, electric, converted gas and oil, 1800-1920, £25-£2,000.* LOC: Coast road near Wells-next-the-Sea. PARK: Easy. TEL: 01328 830460; fax - 01328 830005. VAT: Stan.

STOKE FERRY, Nr. King's Lynn

Farmhouse Antiques
White's Farmhouse, Barker's Drove. PE33 9TA. (P. Philpot). Resident. Est. 1969. Open by appointment. *STOCK: General antiques.* PARK: Easy. TEL: 01366 500588. SER: Restorations; furniture made to order in old timber.

SWAFFHAM

Cranglegate Antiques
Market Place. PE37 7LE. (Mrs R.D. Buckie). Resident. Est. 1965. Open Tues., Thurs. and Sat. 10-1 and 2-5.30. SIZE: Small. *STOCK: Small furniture, general antiques and collectors items, 17th-20th C.* LOC: A47. PARK: In square opposite or in passage at rear. TEL: Home - 01760 721052; e-mail - rbuckie@buckie-antiques.com; website - www.buckie-antiques.com.

Swaffham Antiques Supplies
66/68 London St. PE37. (M. and R. Cross). Est. 1959. Open Thurs.-Sat. 10-4 (warehouse by appointment only). SIZE: Large + warehouse at The Old Cold Store Buildings, 7 Cley Road. *STOCK: General antiques, 18th-19th C; shipping furniture, £100-£5,000.* LOC: Off Market Place. PARK: Easy. TEL: 01760 721697/725418; home - 01760 721697.

SWAFIELD, Nr. North Walsham

Staithe Lodge Gallery
Staithe Lodge. NR28 0RQ. (M.C.A. Foster). Resident. Est. 1976. Open 9-5, Sun. by appoint-

ment. CL: Wed. pm. SIZE: Large. *STOCK: Watercolours, paintings and prints, 1800-1950, £50-£500; furniture including reproduction.* LOC: On B1145 at the Mundesley end of the North Walsham by-pass. PARK: Easy. TEL: 01692 402669. SER: Restorations; framing; buys at auction (mainly watercolours).

TACOLNESTON, Nr. Norwich

Freya Antiques
St. Mary's Farm, Cheneys Lane. NR16 1DB. Usually open but appointment advisable; evenings by appointment. SIZE: Large. *STOCK: General antiques, especially pine and country furniture; upholstery.* PARK: Own. TEL: 01508 489252; mobile - 07799 401067; e-mail - freyaantiques@ic24.net; websites - www.freyaantiques.co.uk and www.antiquesbarn.co.uk. SER: Valuations; restorations; re-upholstery.

TOTTENHILL, Nr. King's Lynn

Jubilee Antiques
Coach House, Whin Common Rd. PE33 0RS. (Mr and Mrs A.J. Lee). Est. 1953. Open daily including Sun. SIZE: Medium. *STOCK: Furniture especially Victorian chairs, £50-£4,000; interesting items.* LOC: Between King's Lynn and Downham Market, adjacent to A10. PARK: Easy. TEL: 01553 810681; home - same. SER: Valuations; restorations (furniture).

TWYFORD, Nr. Fakenham

Norton Antiques
NR20 5LY. (T. and N. Hepburn). Est. 1966. Open by appointment only. *STOCK: Furniture 1680-1900, £25-£3,500; oils and watercolours, 19th to early 20th C, £25-£2,500; clocks, 18th-19th C, £40-£3,500; woodworking and craftsman's hand tools.* PARK: Easy. TEL: 01362 683331. SER: Valuations.

WELLS-NEXT-THE-SEA

Church Street Antiques
2 Church St. NR23 1JA. (Paula Ford and Lesley Ann Irons). Open 10-4 including Sun. (winter - Thurs.-Sun.), Mon. by appointment. SIZE: Small. *STOCK: Textiles, lace, costume jewellery, hat pins, kitchenalia, ephemera, collectables, £1-£500.* LOC: A149 main coast road, opposite church. PARK: Easy. TEL: 01328 711698.

Wells Antique Centre
The Old Mill, Maryland. NR23 1LY. Open 10-5 (10-4 winter) including Sun. SIZE: 15 dealers. *STOCK: General antiques and collectables.* PARK: Easy. TEL: 01328 711433.

WROXHAM

T.C.S. Brooke   BADA
incorporating The Ruth Lowe Gallery of Contemporary Art, The Grange. NR12 8RX. (S.T. Brooke). Est. 1952. Open 9.30-1 and 2.15-5.30. CL: Mon. *STOCK: English porcelain, 18th C; furniture, mainly Georgian; silver, glass, works of art, Oriental rugs.* LOC: On main Norwich road. PARK: Easy. TEL: 01603 782644. SER: Valuations. VAT: Spec.

WYMONDHAM

Antique and Collectors Fair
Central Hall. (Gabrielle Thornhill). 1st Friday monthly 9-3.30. SIZE: 25 stalls. *STOCK: General antiques and collectables.* TEL: 01493 750981.

King
Market Place. NR18 0AX. (M. King). Est. 1969. Open 9-4. CL: Mon., Tues. and Wed., except by appointment. SIZE: 5 Rooms. *STOCK: General antiques, furniture, copper, brass, silver, jewellery, porcelain.* PARK: Easy. TEL: 01953 604758; evenings - 01953 602427. FAIRS: Lomax.

Turret House
27 Middleton St. NR18 0AB. (Dr and Mrs D.H. Morgan). PBFA. Resident. Est. 1972. SIZE: Small. *STOCK: Antiquarian books especially science and medical; occasional scientific instruments.* LOC: Corner of Vicar St., adjacent to War Memorial. TEL: 01953 603462. SER: Buys at auction. FAIRS: London Scientific & Medical Instrument Fairs; PBFA. VAT: Stan/Spec.

Wymondham Antique and Collectors Centre
3 Town Green. NR18 0PN. (Charles White). Est. 1987. Open 10-5 including Sun. SIZE: Large. *STOCK: China including crested, Victorian to 1960's; jewellery, postcards, books, glass, toys, furniture, clocks.* PARK: Easy. TEL: 01953 604817; fax - 01603 811112; home - same; mobile - 07771 970112. SER: Valuations. FAIRS: Norwich; Swinderby; Crystal Palace; Newark; Peterborough.

A period roomset at our showroom.

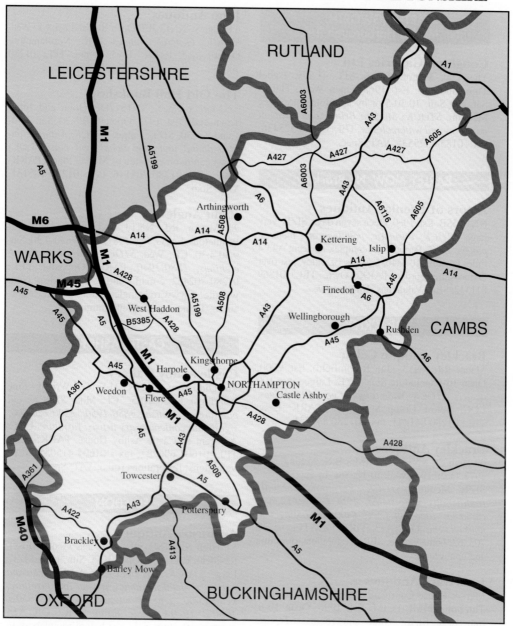

Dealers and Shops in Northamptonshire

			Northampton	4
			Potterspury	2
Arthingworth	1	Flore	2	Rushden	2
Barley Mow	1	Harpole	1	Towcester	3
Brackley	7	Islip	1	Weedon	4
Castle Ashby	1	Kettering	1	Wellingborough	3
Finedon	6	Kingsthorpe	2	West Haddon	4

NORTHAMPTONSHIRE

ARTHINGWORTH, Nr. Market Harborough (Leics)

Coughton Galleries Ltd
The Old Manor. LE16 8JT. (Lady Isabel Throckmorton). Est. 1968. Open Wed., Thurs., Sat. and Sun. 10.30-5 or by appointment. SIZE: Medium. STOCK: Modern British and Irish oil paintings and watercolours. TEL: 01858 525436; fax - 01858 525535. VAT: Spec.

BARLEY MOW, Nr. Brackley

Amors of Evenley Antiques
NN13 5SB. Est. 1960. Open seven days. SIZE: Very large. STOCK: Furniture, paintings and pictures, pottery. LOC: Period barn complex adjacent A43 4 miles junction 10 M40, towards Brackley, just over Oxfordshire border. PARK: Own. TEL: 01869 811342. SER: Valuations. Mainly trade.

BRACKLEY

Brackley Antique Cellar
Manor Rd. NN13. (Jim Broomfield). Est. 2000. Open 10-5 including Sun. SIZE: Large, over 100 dealers. STOCK: Wide range of general antiques. LOC: Below Co-op Superstore. PARK: Easy. TEL: 01280 841841; fax - 01280 841851.

Brackley Antiques
69 High St. NN13 7BW. (Mrs B.H. Nutting). Est. 1977. Open 10-6, Wed. 10-12, Sun. by appointment. SIZE: Medium. STOCK: Furniture especially traditionally upholstered, 19th C, £50-£2,000; ceramics, 18th-20th C, £2-£400; interesting and unusual items. LOC: A43. PARK: Easy. TEL: 01280 703362; home - same. SER: Restorations (furniture and upholstery).

Courtyard Antiques
Market House Courtyard. NN13 7AB. (Peter G. Titterton). FIMI, FCIM. Est. 1996. Open 10-6, Sat. 10-5. SIZE: Three showrooms. STOCK: 17th-20th C furniture and effects including Oriental. LOC: Close to Town Hall. PARK: Easy. TEL: 01280 703631; fax/home - same. SER: Valuations; restorations (furniture).

Peter Jackson Antiques
3 Market Place. NN13 7AB. Open 10.30-1 and 2-5. STOCK: English and Continental porcelain and pottery, 18th-19th C; furniture, paintings, silver, jewellery, glass, watercolours and prints. TEL: Mobile - 07702 230074. SER: Valuations; restorations.

Juno Antiques
4 Bridge St. NN13 7EP. Open 10-1 and 2-5. CL: Wed. STOCK: General antiques. LOC: Northampton/Oxford road. PARK: Town centre. TEL: 01280 700639.

The Old Hall Bookshop
32 Market Place. NN13 7DP. (John and Juliet Townsend). Est. 1977. Open 9.30-5.30, Sat. 9.30-1 and 2-5.30. SIZE: Large. STOCK: Antiquarian, secondhand and new books and maps. LOC: Town centre on east side of Market Place. PARK: Easy. TEL: 01280 704146; fax - 01280 705131. VAT: Stan.

Right Angle
24 Manor Rd. NN13 6AJ. (Chris and Val Pendleton). FATG. Est. 1981. Open 9.30-5.30, Sat. 9.30-4.30. CL: Wed. STOCK: Drawings, British etchings, 1880-1940. PARK: Opposite. TEL: 01280 702462; e-mail - chris@rightangleart.com; website - www.rightangleart.com. SER: Restorations (frames); gilding and framing.

CASTLE ASHBY

Castle Ashby Gallery
The Old Farmyard. NN7 1LF. (G.S.Wright - Fine Paintings). Open 10-5. CL: Mon. STOCK: Oil paintings - British, 1850-1950, £200-£20,000; significant contemporary artists; furniture. LOC: Adjacent to Castle Ashby House. PARK: Easy. TEL: 01604 696787; fax - 01604 415055. SER: Valuations; restorations (oils). VAT: Spec.

FINEDON

Aspidistra Antiques
51 High St. NN9 5JN. (Pat and Geoff Moss). Resident. Est. 1993. Open 10-5, Sun. 11-5. SIZE: Large. STOCK: Arts and Crafts, Art Nouveau and Art Deco metal, ceramics, plaster and furniture, £25-£1,000; general antiques, £1-£500; 1950's, 1960's, 1970's memorabilia. LOC: Off A14 junction 10 - turn right just before roundabout in village centre. From junction 11, turn right at roundabout and immediate left. PARK: Easy. TEL: 01933 680196; mobile - 07768 071948. SER: Valuations; restorations (furniture); buys at auction. FAIRS: NEC; Earls Court; Newark; Alexandra Palace.

Simon Banks Antiques
28 Church St. NN9 5NA. Est. 1984. Every day including Sun. SIZE: Large. STOCK: 17th-20th C furniture, £50-£5,000; glass, silver, ceramics, prints, copper, decorative and collectable items,

clocks including longcase, wall and mantel. LOC: Near church. PARK: Easy. TEL: 01933 680371; mobile - 07976 787539. SER: Valuations; search; nationwide deliveries. VAT: Stan/Spec.

M.C. Chapman

11-25 Bell Hill. NN9 5ND. LAPADA. Est. 1967. Open 9-5.30, Sun. 11-5. SIZE: Large. *STOCK: Furniture, clocks, decorative items, 18th-20th C, £100-£4,000.* LOC: 400 yds. off A510. PARK: Easy. TEL: 01933 681260; fax - 01933 681779. SER: Container facilities. VAT: Stan/Spec/ Global.

Robert Cheney Antiques

11-13 High St. NN9 5JN. Est. 1992. Open 9-5.30, Sun. 11-4. SIZE: Medium. *STOCK: 18th-20th C furniture, china and glass, £5-£5,000.* LOC: A6. PARK: Easy. TEL: 01933 681048; home - 01933 680085. SER: Valuations.

E.K. Antiques

37 High St. NN9 5NB. (Edward Kubacki). Est. 1967. Open 9.30-5, Sun. 11-4. SIZE: Medium-several dealers. *STOCK: Furniture, china, silver, glass, pictures, needlework, clocks and decorative items, 1680-1950, £5-£8,000.* PARK: Easy. TEL: 01933 681882; home - 01933 410245. SER: Restorations (furniture); French polishing; valuations. FAIRS: Huntingdon; Kimbolton Castle.

Finedon Antiques (Centre)

11-25 Bell Hill. NN9 5ND. Est. 1973. Open 9-5.30, Sun. 11-5. SIZE: Large - 35 dealers. *STOCK: Furniture, decorative items, collectables, silver, ceramics, soft furnishings, 18th to mid-20th C.* LOC: 400 yds. off A510. PARK: Easy. TEL: 01933 681260/682210; fax - 01933 681779; e-mail - sales @finedonantiques.com; website - www.finedon antiques.com. SER: Search service; export facilities; nationwide delivery. VAT: Stan/Spec/Global.

FLORE, Nr. Weedon

Huntershield Antiques and Granary Antiques

The Huntershields. NN7 4LZ. (Mrs. C. Madeira and Richard Sear). Est. 1968. Open 9-6, Sun. and other times by appointment. SIZE: Large. *STOCK: Furniture, 17th-19th C, £50-£5,000; early metalware specialist; decorative and period items, 19th C, £50-£2,000.* LOC: Off M1, junction 16, into Flore, last turning on left at bollard, premises on right. PARK: Easy. TEL: 01327 340718; home - same; fax - 01327 349263. FAIRS: Newark.

Christopher Jones Antiques

Flore House, The Avenue. NN7 4LZ. Est. 1977. Open 10-5, Sat. 11-4.30, Sun. by appointment. SIZE: Large. *STOCK: Period and decorative furniture, lighting, porcelain, glass and objects, 18th-20th C.* PARK: Easy. TEL: 01327 342165; e-mail - florehouse@msn.com. SER: Interior decor advice. FAIRS: Olympia. VAT: Spec.

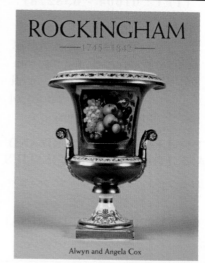

HARPOLE

Inglenook Antiques
23 High St. NN7 4DH. (T. and P. Havard). Est. 1971. Open 9-7. SIZE: Small. *STOCK: General antiques, £1-£500.* LOC: In main street. PARK: Easy. TEL: 01604 830007.

ISLIP, Nr. Thrapston

John Roe Antiques
The Furnace Site, Kettering Rd. NN14 3JW. Est. 1968. Open 9-5.30, Sat. 10-4. *STOCK: General antiques; Continental and American shipping goods.* TEL: 01832 732937. VAT: Stan.

KETTERNG

Dragon Antiques
85 Rockingham Rd. NN16 8LA. Open 10-4. CL: Thurs. *STOCK: Pictures, Oriental items, militaria and general antiques.* TEL: 01536 517017. SER: Framing.

KINGSTHORPE, Nr. Northampton

Laila Gray Antiques
25 Welford Rd. NN2 8AQ. Open 9-5.30. *STOCK: Pine.* TEL: 01604 715277. SER: Waxing; stripping.

The Old Brigade
10a Harborough Rd. NN2 7AZ. (S.C. Wilson). Est. 1978. Open by appointment. SIZE: Medium. *STOCK: Military items, especially German Third Reich, 1850's to 1945, £5-£5,000.* LOC: Junction 15, M1. PARK: Easy. TEL: 01604 719389; fax - 01604 712489; website - www.theoldbrigade. co.uk. SER: Valuations; illus. catalogue (£5 + SAE). VAT: Stan/Spec.

NORTHAMPTON

F. and C.H. Cave
111 Kettering Rd. NN1 4BA. Est. 1879. Open 9-5.30. CL: Thurs. SIZE: Large. *STOCK: Furniture - Georgian, Victorian and decorative; general antiques.* LOC: Near town centre, quarter mile outside pedestrianised area. PARK: Adjoining side streets. TEL: 01604 638278. VAT: Spec.

Michael Jones Jeweller
1 Gold St. NN1 1SA. Est. 1919. *STOCK: Silver, gold and gem jewellery, French carriage clocks.* TEL: 01604 632548; fax - 01604 233813; website - www.michaeljonesjeweller.co.uk. VAT: Margin.

Occultique
30 St Michael's Avenue. NN1 4JQ. (M.J. Lovett). Est. 1973. SIZE: Small. *STOCK: Books and artifacts, 50p-£500.* TEL: 01604 627727; fax - 01604 603860; e-mail - enquiries@occultique.co.uk; website - www.occultique.co.uk. SER: Catalogue available. VAT: Stan. *Mail Order only.*

Penny's Antiques
83 Kettering Rd. NN1 4AW. (Mrs P. Mawby). Est. 1976. Open Mon., Wed., Fri. and Sat. 11-4. SIZE: Small. *STOCK: Shipping goods, kitchen chairs, pictures, army badges, furniture, china, smalls, glass and brass, Victorian to 1940, £5-£100.* LOC: On A43 near town centre. PARK: Easy. TEL: 01604 632429.

POTTERSPURY, Nr. Towcester

Reindeer Antiques Ltd   BADA
43 Watling St. NN12 7QD. (John Butterworth and Nicholas Fuller). LAPADA. Est. 1959. Open 9-6, Sat. 10-5, Sun. by appointment. SIZE: Large. *STOCK: Fine English furniture,*

17th-19th C; caddies, clocks, smalls, paintings. LOC: A5. PARK: Own. TEL: 01908 542407/ 542200; fax - 01908 542121. FAIRS: BADA. LAPADA. VAT: Stan/Spec.

Tillmans Antiques
Wakefield Country Courtyard, Wakefield Farm. (N.L. Tillman). Est. 1999. Open 10-5, Sat. 10-5.30, Sun. and Bank Holiday Mon. 10-4. CL: Mon. and Tues. SIZE: Small. STOCK: Porcelain and glass including cranberry, vaseline and decorative, 19th C; silver, 18th to early 20th C; pictures and furniture. LOC: Off A5. PARK: Easy. TEL: 01327 811882; home - 01327 342524; e-mail - nick_tillman@lineone.net. FAIRS: NEC; Silsoe; Milton Keynes; Wavendon.

RUSHDEN

Magpies
1 East Grove. NN10 0AP. (Jim and Janet Ward). Est. 1993. Open 10-5, Nov.-Feb. 10-4, Sun. 12-4. SIZE: Large. STOCK: Furniture, £20-£1,000; china, glass, kitchenalia and bric-a-brac, postcards, clocks, 78 records, £1-£100, all 19th-20th C. LOC: A6 south on one-way system, first left after passing old station. PARK: Easy. TEL: 01933 411404.

D.W. Sherwood Antiques Ltd
59 Little St. NN10 0LS. Est. 1960. Open Tues., Wed., Fri. and Sat. 11-5. STOCK: General antiques. TEL: 01933 353265.

TOWCESTER

Clark Galleries
215 Watling St. NN12 6BX. (A. Clark). FABPR. Est. 1964. Open 9-5, Sat. 9-4. SIZE: Medium. STOCK: Landscape paintings, 18th-19th C, £500-£15,000; portraits, 17th-18th C, £500-£5,000. LOC: M1, junction 15A, on A5. PARK: Easy and at rear. TEL: 01327 352957; website - www.clarkgalleries.com. SER: Valuations; restorations and re-lining (oil paintings); picture hire. VAT: Stan/Spec.

Ron Green
227-239 Watling St. West. NN12 6DD. (Michael, Nicholas and Christopher Green). Est. 1952. Open 9-6, Sun. by appointment. SIZE: Large. STOCK: English and Continental furniture, paintings and decorative items, £30-£30,000. PARK: Easy. TEL: 01327 350387/350615; fax - 01327 350615; e-mail - ron@green227.freeserve.co.uk; website - www.rongreenantiques.com. SER: Valuations; restorations.

R. and M. Nicholas
161 Watling St. NN12 6BX. Open 9.30-5. SIZE: Small. STOCK: 18th-19th C porcelain, silver and glass. TEL: 01327 350639.

WEEDON

Helios & Co (Antiques)
25/27 High St. NN7 4QD. (J. Skiba and B. Walters). Est. 1976. Open 9.30-5.30, Sat. and Sun. 10-5. CL: Mon. SIZE: 20 showrooms. STOCK: English and Continental furniture especially dining tables; decorative accessories, longcase clocks and pianos. PARK: Easy. TEL: 01327 340264; fax - 01327 342235. SER: Suppliers and restorers to H. M. Govt. VAT: Spec.

Rococo Antiques, Architectural Goods and Furnishings
5 New St., Lower Weedon. NN7 4QS. (N.K. Griffiths). Resident. Usually available. STOCK: Architectural goods and furnishings. LOC: 3 miles junction 16, M1, quarter mile off A5. PARK: Easy. TEL: 01327 341288; mobile - 07721 836302. VAT: Stan/Spec.

The Village Antique Market
62 High St. NN7 4QD. (E.A. and J.M. Saunders). Est. 1967. Open 10.30-5.15 including Sun. and Bank Holidays. SIZE: Large - 40 dealers. STOCK: General antiques and interesting items. LOC: Off junction 16, M1. PARK: In front yard. TEL: 01327 342015.

Weedon Antiques
23 High St. NN7 4QDN. (N.L. Tillman). Est. 1985. Open 10-5, Sun. and Bank Holidays 10.30-4.30. CL: Mon. and Tues. SIZE: Medium. STOCK: Porcelain including Royal Worcester, Coalport, Derby, Noritake, George Jones, Aynsley and Limoges; silver including Georgian, all £15-£1,000; glass including cranberry, vaseline, rummers, 17th-20th C, £15-£500; pictures, £50-£1,000; furniture, £200-£3,000. PARK: Easy. TEL: 01327 349777; home - 01327 342524; e-mail - nick_tillman@lineone.net. SER: Valuations. FAIRS: NEC; Milton Keynes; Wavendon.

WELLINGBOROUGH

Antiques and Bric-a-Brac Market
Market Sq. NN8 1AF. Open Tues. 9-4. SIZE: 135 stalls. STOCK: General antiques and collectables. LOC: Town Centre.

Park Gallery & Bookshop

16 Cannon St. NN8 5DJ. (Mrs J.A. Foster). Est. 1979. Open 10-5.30. SIZE: Medium. *STOCK: Books, maps and prints, 18th-19th C, £2-£300.* LOC: Continuation of A510 into town. PARK: Easy. TEL: 01933 222592; e-mail - judy@parkbookshop. freeserve.co.uk. SER: Framing; booksearch.

Bryan Perkins Antiques

Finedon Rd. NN8 4DJ. (J., B.H. and S.C. Perkins). Est. 1971. Open 9-5. CL: Sat. pm. SIZE: Large. *STOCK: Furniture and paintings, 19th C, £200-£5,000; small items.* PARK: Easy. TEL: 01933 228812; home - 01536 790259. SER: Valuations; restorations (furniture). VAT: Spec. *Trade Only.*

WEST HADDON

Barber Antiques

8 High St. NN6 7AP. (Miss Alison Barber). Est. 1994. Open by appointment. SIZE: Medium. *STOCK: Furniture, 18th-19th C, £100-£5,000; Staffordshire animals and blue and white, 19th-20th C, £50-£2,000.* LOC: A428. PARK: Easy. TEL: 01788 510315; e-mail - ali@barberantiques. freeserve.co.uk; website - www.barberantiques. co.uk.

The Country Pine Shop

The Romney Building, Northampton Rd. NN6 7AS. (Ryan and Dodd). Est. 1985. Open 8-5. SIZE: Large. *STOCK: English and Continental stripped pine, £30-£1,200.* LOC: A428. TEL: 01788 510430.

Paul Hopwell Antiques   BADA

30 High St. NN6 7AP. LAPADA. Est. 1974. Open 10-6, Sun.by appointment. SIZE: Large. *STOCK: 17th-18th C oak and walnut country furniture, longcase clocks, metalware: oil paintings and prints, mainly sporting and country pursuits.* LOC: A428. PARK: Easy. TEL: 01788 510636; fax - 01788 510044; e-mail - PaulHopwell@ antiqueoak.co.uk; website - www.antiqueoak. co.uk. SER: Valuations; restorations (furniture and metalware); buys at auction. VAT: Spec.

Mark Seabrook Antiques

9 West End. NN6 7AY. Est. 1996. Open 10.30-5.30, Tues. 1-5.30. SIZE: Medium. *STOCK: Early oak and country furniture, period metalware, brass and copper, treen and other domestic items.* LOC: A428. PARK: Easy. TEL: 01788 510772; mobile - 07770 721931. FAIRS: Chelsea; Kensington; NEC.

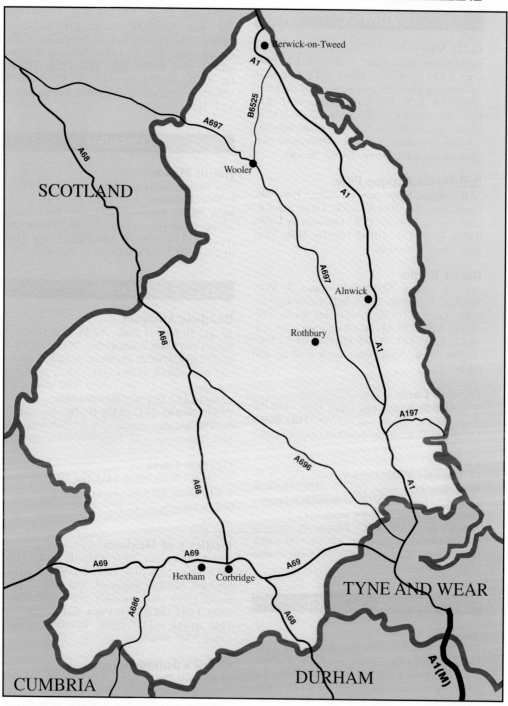

Dealers and Shops in Northumberland					
Alnwick	5	Corbridge	1	Rothbury	1
Berwick-on-Tweed	2	Hexham	7	Wooler	2

G.M. Athey
Castle Corner, Narrowgate. NE66 0NP. Est. 1980. Open 8.30-4.30. SIZE: 3 floors. *STOCK: English oak and mahogany furniture, glass, china and brass, 18th-19th C.* LOC: Part of Alnwick Castle. PARK: Easy. TEL: 01665 604229; mobile - 07836 718350; e-mail - gmatheyantiques51@fsnet.co.uk; website - www.atheysantiques.com. SER: Restorations (furniture including upholstery). FAIRS: Newark.

Bailiffgate Antique Pine
22 Bailiffgate. NE66 1LX. (S. Aston). Est. 1994. Open Thurs.-Sat. 10-4.30. SIZE: Large. *STOCK: Country pine furniture.* LOC: Opposite the castle. PARK: Easy. TEL: 01665 603616. SER: Valuations; buys at auction.

Barter Books
Alnwick Station. NE66 2NP. (Stuart & Mary Manley). Est. 1990. Open daily including Sun. SIZE: Large. *STOCK: Antiquarian books, £10-£5,000.* LOC: Off A1, on left on town approach. PARK: Easy. TEL: 01665 604888; fax - 01665 604444. SER: Valuations; book-binding and repair.

Gordon Caris
30 Fenkle St. NE66 1HR. Open Thurs. and Fri. 10-4. *STOCK: Clocks and watches.* TEL: 01665 510820. SER: Restorations (clocks and watches).

Tamblyn
12 Bondgate Without. NE66 1PP. (Mrs S.M. Hirst). Est. 1981. Open 10-4.30. SIZE: Medium. *STOCK: General antiques including country furniture, pottery, pictures; antiquities, glass, to 20th C, £5-£1,500.* LOC: Diagonally opposite war memorial at southern entrance to town. PARK: Easy. TEL: 01665 603024; home - same. SER: Valuations.

Treasure Chest
53 West St. TD15 2DX. (Y. Scott). Est. 1988. Open 11-4. CL: Tues. and Thurs. SIZE: Medium. *STOCK: China, jewellery, glass, silver plate and small furniture, from 1860, £1-£400.* LOC: Approximately 1 mile from A1. PARK: Easy. TEL: Home - 01289 307736. SER: Restorations (china). FAIRS: Local.

Woodside Reclamation (Architectural Antiques)
Woodside, Scremerston. TD15 2SY. (Keith Allan and Lynne Gray). SALVO. Est. 1990. Open Tues.-Sat. 9-5. SIZE: Large. *STOCK: Architectural salvage including fireplaces, baths, kitchen pine, 19th C.* LOC: Adjacent A1, just south of town. PARK: Easy. TEL: 01289 331211; fax - 01289 330274; home - 01289 302658. SER: Valuations; restorations (stripping and finishing). VAT: Stan.

Judith Michael
20A Watling St. NE45 5AH. (Judith Troldahl and Gillian Anderson). Est. 1970. Open 10-5. CL: Mon. SIZE: Medium. *STOCK: China, glass, silver, furniture, mirrors, light fittings and jewellery.* LOC: Just off A69. PARK: Easy. TEL: 01434 633165; fax - same. SER: Valuations.

Boadens Antiques
29 and 30 Market Place. NE46 3PB. (Richard, Sandra and Chris Boaden). Est. 1948. Open 9-5. SIZE: Large. *STOCK: Furniture - antique, Victorian and secondhand, £100-£3,000; silver, paintings, jewellery, £50-£1,500; china and glass, £5-£2,000.* LOC: Opposite Hexham Abbey, off A69. PARK: Nearby. TEL: 01434 603187; fax - 01434 603474; e-mail - antiques@boadens.fsnet.co.uk. SER: Valuations. VAT: Stan/Spec.

Gordon Caris
16 Market Place. NE46 1XQ. Est. 1972. Open 9-5. CL: Thurs. *STOCK: Clocks and watches.* TEL: 01434 602106. SER: Restorations (clocks and watches).

Hedley's of Hexham
3 St. Mary's Chare. NE46 1NQ. (P. Torday). Est. 1819. Open Mon.10-4, Tues.-Sat. 9.30-5. SIZE: Medium. *STOCK: Furniture, 18th-20th C; porcelain, silver, glass, jewellery, prints and collectables.* LOC: Off Market Place. PARK: 200 yds. TEL: 01434 602317. SER: Valuations; restorations. VAT: Stan/Spec.

ONeil's Antiques
45 Hallstile Bank. NE46 3PQ. (Neil Perry). Est. 1987. Open 10-5. SIZE: Large. *STOCK: Georgian, Victorian and Edwardian furniture; reproduction pine.* PARK: Easy. TEL: 01434 600510.

Priest Popple Books
9B Priest Popple. NE46 1PF. (John B Patterson). Est. 1997. Open 9-5. SIZE: Medium. *STOCK: Books - second-hand non-fiction, first editions,*

antiquarian, £5-£1,500. LOC: From A69 to town centre, premises top of bus station. PARK: Easy. TEL: 01434 607773. SER: Valuations; bookbinding.

Renney Antiques
6 Rear Battle Hill. NE46 1BB. Est. 1987. Open 10-5. SIZE: Large. *STOCK: Decorative lighting, English and French furniture, garden, architectural and decorative items, textiles, china and glass.* LOC: Main shopping street, opposite NatWest Bank. PARK: 400 metres. TEL: 01434 607964; e-mail - renney@btconnect.com. SER: Valuations; buys at auction.

The Violin Shop
27 Hencotes. NE46 2EQ. (D. Mann). Est. 1970. Open 10-5 or by appointment. *STOCK: Violins, violas, cellos, basses and bows.* TEL: 01434 607897; e-mail - davehexviolins@aol.com; website - www.hexham-violins.co.uk. SER: Repairs; restorations; bow re-hairing; new instruments made.

ROTHBURY, Nr. Morpeth

Golfark International
5 Tollgate Crescent. NE65 7RE. (Michael Arkle).

Est. 1997. *STOCK: Golf clubs and bags.* LOC: 2 mins. from centre. PARK: Easy. TEL: 01669 620487; fax/home - same; mobile - 07710 693860; e-mail - michael@golfark.freeserve. co.uk.

WOOLER

Hamish Dunn Antiques
17 High St. NE71 6BU. Est. 1986. Open 9.30-12 and 1-4.30, Thurs. 9.30-12. SIZE: Medium. *STOCK: Curios and collectables, 19th-20th C, £5-£500; antiquarian and secondhand books, 18th-20th C, £1-£200; small furniture, 19th-20th C, £15-£1,000.* LOC: Off A697. PARK: Easy. TEL: 01668 281341; home - 01668 282013. VAT: Stan/Spec.

James Miller Antiques
1-5 Church St. NE71 6BZ. LAPADA. Est. 1947. Open Mon.-Fri. 9.30-5. SIZE: Large and warehouses. *STOCK: Georgian-Edwardian furniture and clocks.* LOC: A697. PARK: Nearby. TEL: 01668 281500; fax - 01668 282383; home - 01668 217281; website - www.millersantiques ofwooler.com. VAT: Stan/Spec.

BEESTON

S. & E.M. Turner Violins
1-5 Lily Grove. NG9 1QL. (Steve and Liz Turner). Est. 1987. Open 9-6, Sat. 9-5. *STOCK: 18th-20th C violins, violas, cellos, basses, bows; old flutes, clarinets, concertinas, guitars, harps, oboes and saxophones.* PARK: Easy. TEL: 0115 943 0333; fax - 0115 943 0444; mobile - 07831 265272; e-mail - turnerviolins@compuserv.com. SER: Valuations; restorations.

DARLTON

A.J. O'Sullivan Antiques
Whimpton House, Dunham Rd. NG22 0TA. Resident. Est. 1977. Open 9-5, Sat. 9-1. SIZE: Medium. *STOCK: Furniture, 18th-19th C, £200-£4,000: decorative items.* LOC: From A1 take A57 (Lincoln road) at Markham Moor roundabout through Darlton, premises ¼ mile on left. PARK: Easy. TEL: 01777 228626; fax - same; e-mail - tonyos@talk21.com. SER: Valuations; restorations (furniture). FAIRS: Newark. VAT: Stan/Spec/Global.

DUNHAM-ON-TRENT

R. G. Antiques
Main St. NG22 0TY. (R.G. and D.C. Barnett). Est. 1975. Open 10-6 including Sun. SIZE: Small. *STOCK: Arms, armour and militaria, general antiques, 18th-20th C, £5-£1,000.* PARK: Easy. TEL: 01777 228312. SER: Buys at auction (arms and armour). FAIRS: Newark.

LANGFORD, Nr. Newark

T. Baker
Langford House Farm. NG23 7RR. Est. 1966. CL: Sun. except by appointment and Sat. SIZE: Medium. *STOCK: Victoriana, period furniture and oak.* LOC: A1133. PARK: Own. TEL: 01636 704026. *Trade Only.*

MANSFIELD

Fair Deal Antiques
138 Chesterfield Rd. North. NG19 7JD. (D. Lowe). Est. 1972. Open 9.30-5.30. CL: Sat. pm. and Sun. except by appointment. SIZE: Large. *STOCK: Shipping goods, £50-£100; furniture, mainly mahogany, Victorian, £100-£1,000; period furniture, metalware and small items.* PARK: Easy. TEL: 01623 653768/512419. VAT: Stan. *Trade Only.*

NEWARK

Castle Gate Antiques Centre
55 Castle Gate. NG24 1BE. Est. 1985. Open 9.30-5. SIZE: Large. LOC: A46 through town, 250yds. from castle. PARK: Easy. TEL: 01636 700076. SER: Restorations. Below are listed the dealers at this centre.

& Barrington
Fine antique and modern silver. TEL: Mobile - 07850 577724.

John Dench
Period furniture.

Dukeries Antiques
Period furniture.

Vivienne Flint
Town and country furniture.

Sinclair Antiques
Furniture, pottery, decorative items.

Peter Straw
Furniture.

Village Antiques
Period furniture.

David Walsh
Early pottery.

R.R. Limb Antiques
31-35 Northgate. NG24 1HD. Open 9-6. *STOCK: General antiques and pianos.* TEL: 01636 674546.

Lombard Antiques
35 Lombard St. NG24 1XG. (Bernard J. McGrath and Ann Mason). Est. 1980. Open 10-5. CL: Tues. and Sun. except Newark Fair times. SIZE: Medium. *STOCK: Collectables, 18th-19th C; longcase clocks, 18th-19th C, £2,000-£15,000; furniture, 17th to early 20th C, £50-£10,000.* LOC: Corner of Castlegate. PARK: Own. TEL: Mobile - 07866 756337; e-mail - mcgrathbl@aol.com; website - www.quality-antique-clocks.com. SER: Valuations; restorations (clock movements, dials, cases; porcelain repairs); buys at auction. FAIRS: Newark. VAT: Spec.

M B G Antiques, Fine Art & Jewellery
41B Castlegate. NG24 1BE. (Margaret Begley-Gray DGA). Est. 1982. Open 11-4. CL: Mon. and Tues. SIZE: Small. *STOCK: Jewellery, paintings, miniatures, 19th to early 20th C, to £4,000.* PARK: Nearby. TEL: 01636 650790; fax - 01636 679586; mobile - 07702 209808; e-mail - mbgantiques@mail.com. SER: Valuations; restorations (jewellery and paintings). FAIRS: NEC; Robert Bailey.

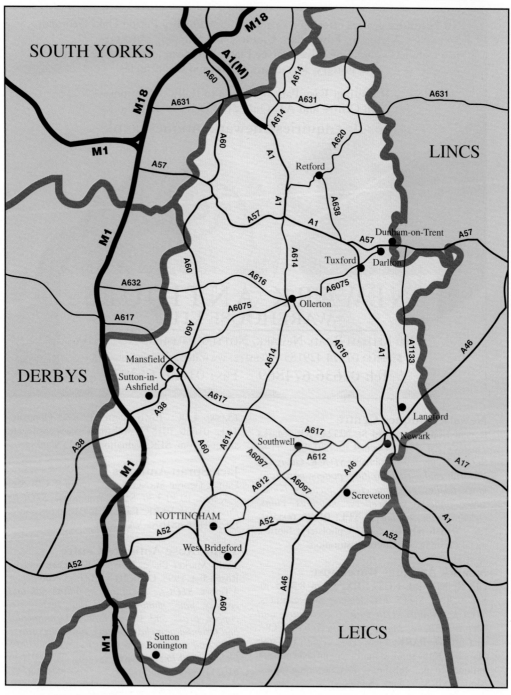

Dealers and Shops in Nottinghamshire

Darlton	1	Newark	9	Screveton	1	Tuxford	1
Dunham-on-Trent	1	Nottingham	20	Southwell	2	West Bridgford	3
Langford	1	Ollerton	1	Sutton Bonington	1		
Mansfield	1	Retford	2	Sutton-in-Ashfield	1		

Newark Antiques Centre
Regent House, Lombard St. NG24 1XP. (Marks Tinsley). Est. 1986. Open 9.30-4.30, Sun. 11-4. SIZE: 55 units and 58 cabinets. *STOCK: Georgian, Victorian and period furniture, pottery, porcelain, glass, textiles, militaria, clocks, pictures, books, silver, antiquities, jewellery, paintings, coins, Oriental, pine, oil lamps.* TEL: 01636 605504; fax - 01636 605101. SER: Upholstery, fabrics, metal cleaning, valuations, restorations.

Newark Antiques Warehouse
Old Kelham Rd. NG24 1BX. Open 8.30-5.30, Sat. 9.30-4. SIZE: 30+ dealers, 80+ cabinets. *STOCK: Mainly 17th-20th C furniture and decorative items, smalls and collectables.* LOC: Just off A1. PARK: Easy. TEL: 01636 674869; fax - 01636 612933; e-mail - enquiries@newark antiques.co.uk; website - www.newarkantiques. co.uk. FAIRS: Newark (Sundays).

No. 1 Castlegate Antiques
1-3 Castlegate. NG24 1AZ. (Christine Kavanagh). Est. 1998. Open 9.30-5, Sat. 9.30-5.30. SIZE: Large - 12 dealers. *STOCK: 18th-19th C English mahogany furniture; 17th-19th C English oak furniture and decorative objects; all £100-*£5,000. LOC: Town centre. PARK: Opposite. TEL: 01636 701877; website - www.castlegate antiques.com. SER: Valuations. VAT: Stan/Spec.

Jack Spratt Antiques
Unit 5, George St. NG24 1LU. Open 8-5.30, Sat. 8-4, Sun. 10.30-3.30. SIZE: Warehouse. *STOCK: Pine and oak.* PARK: Easy. TEL: 01636 681666/7; fax - 01636 681670. VAT: Stan.

Tudor Rose Antiques Centre
12-13 Market Place. NG24 1DU. (D.H. and C. Rose). Est. 1995. Open 10-5. SIZE: 35 cabinets + 4 floors. *STOCK: Furniture, including oak and country, pine, mahogany and fine; metalware, copper, brass and silver; English, Continental and Oriental porcelain, pottery, glass, decorative items and soft furnishings; treen, toys, jewellery, pictures and linen.* PARK: Nearby. TEL: 01636 610311. VAT: Stan/Spec.

NOTTINGHAM

Acanthus Antiques & Collectables
140 Derby Rd., Off Canning Circus. NG7 1LR. (Trak E. and Mrs Smith). Est. 1980. Open Tues., Wed. and Thurs. 10-3. SIZE: Small. *STOCK:*

Ceramics and glass, 19th-20th C, £5-£1,000; collectors' items, mainly 20th C, £5-£800; period furniture, 18th-19th C, £200-£1,500. LOC: Derby Rd. exit from Queens Medical Centre traffic island, continue for 1 mile, shop on left. PARK: Nearby. TEL: 0115 924 3226; e-mail - trak.e. smith@btinternet.com; website - www.acanthus antiques.co.uk. SER: Valuations; restorations (furniture and ceramics); buys at auction. FAIRS: Newark, Swinderby, Donington.

Antiques across the World
James Alexander Building, BR Goods Yard, London Rd./Manvers St. NG2 3AE. (A.R. Rimes). LAPADA. Est. 1993. Open 9-5, Sat. 10-2. SIZE: Large. *STOCK: Furniture, 18th C to Edwardian, £300-£5,000.* PARK: Easy. TEL: 0115 979 9199; fax - 0116 239 3134; home - 0116 239 3119; e-mail - tonyrimes@btinternet.com. SER: Valuations; buys at auction (furniture); finder; courier. FAIRS: Newark. VAT: Stan/Spec.

Dave Buckley Antique Exports
Nottingham Antique Centre, London Rd. NG2 3AE. Open by appointment. SIZE: Warehouse. *STOCK: Shipping furniture for USA, European and Japanese markets.* LOC: Old British Rail goods yard, off London Road, by Hooters restaurant. PARK: Easy. TEL: 0115 9504504; mobile - 07713 254549; e-mail - dave@notts antiques.fsnet.co.uk. SER: Container packing; export facilities. *Trade Only.*

Castle Antiques
78 Derby Rd. NG1 5FD. Open 9.30-5. *STOCK: Maps, prints and general antiques.* TEL: 0115 947 3913.

Collectors World
188 Wollaton Rd., Wollaton. NG8 1MJ. (M. T. Ray). Est. 1975. Open 10.30-5. CL: Mon. SIZE: Small. *STOCK: Ancient and modern coins and banknotes, 20th C cigarette and postcards, 19th C medals and accessories, all £1-£100.* LOC: Ring road at A609 Crown Island/Raleigh Island. PARK: Easy. TEL: 0115 928 0347; fax - same. SER: Valuations; buys at auction (coins and banknotes). FAIRS: Newark, Birmingham MSCF and various specialist.

The Golden Cage
99 Derby Rd., Canning Circus. NG1 5BB. (J. Pearson). Open 10-5. *STOCK: Formal wear and period clothing, from Victorian to 1970's; costume jewellery.* TEL: 0115 9411600/9476478. SER: Hire (including 20's-40's and period costume); clothes copied to order.

Granny's Attic
308 Carlton Hill, Carlton. NG4 1GD. (Mrs A. Pembleton). Open Tues., Thurs., Fri. and Sat. 9-5. *STOCK: Dolls, miniatures, general antiques and furniture.* TEL: 0115 9265204.

Harlequin Antiques
79-81 Mansfield Rd., Daybrook. NG5 6BE. (P.R. Hinchley). Est. 1992. Open 9.30-5. SIZE: Large. *STOCK: 18th-19th C pine furniture, £300-£1,200.* LOC: A60 Mansfield road, north from Nottingham. PARK: Easy. TEL: 01159 674590. SER: Valuations; restorations (oak and mahogany). VAT: Global.

D.D. and A. Ingle
380 Carlton Hill. NG4 1JA. Est. 1968. Open 9-5. SIZE: Small. *STOCK: Coins and medals, from Roman, £50-£100; jewellery and watches, £50-£1,000.* PARK: Nearby. TEL: 0115 987 3325; e-mail - ddaingle@talk21.com. SER: Valuations; restorations.

Ivory Gate Antiques
106 Derby Rd. NG1 5FB. (B. Orridge). Est. 1975. Open 9.45-4.45. SIZE: Medium. *STOCK: Furniture, 18th-19th C, £500-£4,000; clocks, 19th C, £200-£2,000; porcelain and glass, 18th-20th C, £10-£1,500.* LOC: A52 near city centre. PARK: Easy. TEL: 0115 947 3054; home - 0115 963 2734; mobile - 07799 533272. SER: Restorations (furniture including upholstery). FAIRS: Keddleston Hall, Lamport; Derby University.

Melville Kemp Ltd
79-81 Derby Rd. NG1 5BA. LAPADA. Est. 1900. Open 9-5.30. CL: Thurs. SIZE: Small. *STOCK: Jewellery, Victorian; silver, Georgian and Victorian, both £5-£10,000; ornate English and Continental porcelain, Sheffield plate.* LOC: From Nottingham on main Derby Rd. PARK: Easy. TEL: 0115 941 7055; fax - 0115 941 3075. SER: Valuations; restorations (silver, china, jewellery); buys at auction. VAT: Stan/Spec.

Lights, Camera, Action UK Ltd.
6 Western Gardens, Western Boulevard, Aspley. NG8 5GP. UACC. Est. 1996. Open by appointment. SIZE: Small. *STOCK: Autographs - film, television, sport, historical; Titanic memorabilia.* LOC: Off Nutall Rd. PARK: Easy. TEL: 0115 913 1116; mobile - 0797 0342363; e-mail - nickstraw @lca.ntl-midlands.com; website - www.lca-autographs.co.uk. SER: Valuations; buys at auction. FAIRS: NEC and local.

Michael D. Long
96-98 Derby Rd. NG1 5FB. Est. 1970. Open 9.30-5, Sat. 10-4. SIZE: Large. *STOCK: Arms and armour of all ages and nations.* LOC: From city

centre take main Derby Rd., shop on right. PARK: Easy. TEL: 0115 9474137; fax - 0115 9414199; e-mail - sales@michaeldlong.com; website - www. michaeldlong.com. VAT: Stan/ Spec.

Luna
23 George St. NG1 3BH. (Paul Rose). Est. 1994. Open 10-5.30. SIZE: Small. *STOCK: Design items - glass, ceramics, furniture, telephones, 1940's-1970's, from £5.* LOC: Near Market Sq. Hockley. PARK: Easy. TEL: 0115 924 3267; website - www.luna-online.co.uk.

Anthony Mitchell Fine Paintings
Sunnymede House, 11 Albemarle Rd., Woodthorpe. NG5 4FE. (M. Mitchell). Est. 1965. Open by appointment. *STOCK: Oil paintings, £2,000-£100,000; watercolours, £500-£30,000.* LOC: North on Nottingham ring road to junction with Mansfield road, turn right, then 3rd left. PARK: Easy. TEL: 0115 9623865; fax - same. SER: Valuations; restorations. VAT: Spec.

NSE Medal Dept.
97 Derby Rd. NG1 5BB. (Dennis Henson). Est. 1983. Open 8.30-3.30. SIZE: Medium. *STOCK: Medals, badges and coins, £5-£1,000+.* PARK: Easy. TEL: 0115 950 1882. SER: Valuations; medal mounting and framing.

S. Pembleton
306-308 Carlton Hill, Carlton. NG4 1JB. Open Tues., Thurs. and Fri. 9-5, Sat. 10-5. *STOCK: General antiques.* TEL: 0115 9265204.

David and Carole Potter Antiques
76 Derby Rd. NG1 5FD. LAPADA. Est. 1966. Open by appointment only. SIZE: Medium. *STOCK: Clocks, 18th-19th C, £50-£8,000; period furniture, 17th-19th C, £500-£20,000; pottery, porcelain and glass, 18th-19th C, £20-£10,000; trade goods.* LOC: From Nottingham centre, take main Derby Rd., shop on right. PARK: Easy. TEL: 0115 9417911; mobile - 07973 689962. VAT: Stan/Spec.

Top Hat Antiques Centre
62 Derby Rd. NG1 5FD. (Top Hat Exhibitions). Est. 1978. Open 10-5. SIZE: 3 floors. *STOCK: Furniture, Georgian to Edwardian; metalware, silver, porcelain, prints, watercolours, oil paintings, glass and collectables.* LOC: A51 town centre. PARK: Meters. TEL: 0115 941 9143; website - www.tophat-antiques.co.uk. VAT: Stan/Spec.

Vintage Wireless Shop
The Hewarths, Sandiacre. NG10 5NQ. (Mr Yates). Est. 1977. Open by appointment. *STOCK: Early wireless and pre-war televisions, crystal sets, horn speakers, valves, books and magazines.* PARK: Easy. TEL: 0115 9393139; fax - 0115 9490180; mobile - 07989 102976; e-mail - vintagewireless @aol.com. SER: Valuations; repairs; finder.

OLLERTON

Hamlyn Lodge
Station Rd. NG22 9BN. (N., J.S. and M.J. Barrows). Open Tues.-Sat. 10-5. SIZE: Small. *STOCK: General antiques, 18th-19th C, £100-£3,000.* LOC: Off A614. PARK: Easy. TEL: 01623 823600; website - www.hamlynlodge.co. uk. SER: Restorations (furniture).

RETFORD

Stanley Hunt Jewellers
19 Exchange St. *STOCK: Antique jewellery.* TEL: 01777 703144.

Ranby Hall
Barnby Moor. DN22 8JQ. (Paul Wyatt). LAPADA. Est. 1980. Open Sat. and Sun. 10-7, other days by appointment. SIZE: Large. *STOCK: Furniture, 18th-20th C, £300-£25,000; mirrors, 19th C to 1930, £500-£15,000; oil paintings, 17th-20th C, £1,500-£10,000; garden urns and furniture, from 19th C, £500-£8,000.* LOC: Take Barnby Moor turning off A1, travel 1/4 mile - drive to house on right. PARK: Easy. TEL: 01777 860696; fax - 01777 701317; e-mail - paul.wyatt4 @virgin.net. SER: Buys at auction (furniture and oils). FAIRS: DMG Newark, LAPADA; Bailey, Tatton Park; RDS Dublin. VAT: Stan/Spec.

SCREVETON

Red Lodge Antiques
Fosseway. (L. Bradford). Resident. Est. 1999. Open 9-5 or by appointment, Sat. and Sun. appointment only. SIZE: Large. *STOCK: Shipping furniture, 1900-1930s, £25-£1,000.* LOC: A46 approx. 10 miles from Nottingham and 5 miles from Newark. PARK: Own. TEL: 01949 20244; home - same; e-mail - redlodgeantiques@trade export.fsnet.co.uk. SER: Container facilites available. *Trade & Export Only.*

SOUTHWELL

Strouds (of Southwell Antiques)
3-7 Church St. NG25 0HQ. (V.N. and J. Stroud). Est. 1972. Open 9.30-5 or by appointment. SIZE: Large. *STOCK: Furniture, clocks, metalware and*

decorative items, 17th-19th C, £10-£50,000. LOC: Town centre. PARK: Easy. TEL: 01636 815001. VAT: Stan/Spec.

Westhorpe Antiques

Old Grapes Inn, Westhorpe. (Ralph Downing). Est. 1974. Open 10-5.30, Sun. until 4 - ring bell to gain admittance. SIZE: Small. *STOCK: Furniture, mainly oak, 17th to mid 19th C, £50-£500; brass, copper and pewter, 17th to late 19th C, £10-£200; vintage fishing tackle including reels and rods, stuffed fish, sporting items, £10-£300.* LOC: 15 minutes from Newark. PARK: Easy. TEL: 01636 814095; home - same. SER: Valuations; restorations (furniture); buys at auction. FAIRS: Newark.

SUTTON BONINGTON

Goodacre Engraving

The Dial House, 120 Main St. LE12 5PF. Est. 1948. *STOCK: Longcase and bracket clock movements, parts and castings.* TEL: 01509 673082, fax - same. SER: Hand engraving, movement repairs, silvering and dial repainting. VAT: Stan.

SUTTON-IN-ASHFIELD

Yesterday and Today

82 Station Rd. NG17 5HB. (John and Chris Turner). Resident. Est. 1990. Open 9-5, Sat. 9-4, other times by appointment. SIZE: Small. *STOCK: Furniture, 1920's-1930's oak and walnut, £50-£500; clocks, 19th C, £100-£2,000.* LOC: Junction 28, M1, take A38 towards Mansfield. PARK: Easy. TEL: 01623 442215; mobile - 07957 552753. FAIRS: Swinderby.

TUXFORD

Sally Mitchell's Gallery

9 Eldon St. NG22 0LB. FATG. Est. 1976. Open Tues.-Sat. 10-5, Sun. and Mon. by appointment. SIZE: Medium. *STOCK: Contemporary sporting and animal paintings, £200-£5,000; limited edition sporting and animal prints, 20th C, £20-£350.* LOC: 1 minute from A1, 14 miles north of Newark. PARK: Easy. TEL: 01777 838 234/655; e-mail - info@sallymitchell.com; website - www.sallymitchell.com. FAIRS: CLA Game and Burghley Horse Trials. VAT: Stan/Spec.

WEST BRIDGFORD

Bridgford Antiques

2A Rushworth Ave. NG2 7LF. Est. 1986. Open 10.30-5. SIZE: Small. *STOCK: General antiques, collectables, pictures, books and postcards.* LOC: Opposite County Hall. PARK: Easy. TEL: 0115 9821835; home - 0115 9817161.

Joan Cotton (Antiques)

5 Davies Rd. NG2 5JE. Est. 1969. Open 9-4.30. CL: Wed. *STOCK: General antiques, Victoriana, jewellery, silver, china, glass and bygones.* LOC: ½ mile along Bridgford Rd. from Trent Bridge, in town centre. PARK: On forecourt. TEL: 0115 9813043.

Portland Antiques & Curios

5 Portland Rd. NG2 6DN. (Brendan and Carole Sprakes). Est. 2000. Open Wed.-Sat. 10-5, other days by appointment. SIZE: Small. *STOCK: Furniture, £150-£300; china, £20-£40; jewellery, £30-£60; all 19th-20th C.* LOC: Off Melton Rd. PARK: Easy. TEL: 0115 914 2123; fax - same; home - 0115 914 8614. VAT: Stan.

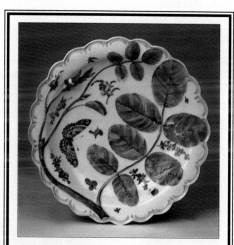

Plate from the so-called 'Blind Earl' service, Worcester c.1765. The rose and branch pattern is moulded in relief. The name refers to the 18th century Earl of Coventry who ordered a pattern he could feel. As the earliest 'Blind Earl' pieces pre-date the accident which blinded him, the name became attached to an already existing design.

From an article entitled "Country Collections" by Lars Tharp which appeared in the October 2001 issue of **Antique Collecting**. For more details and to subscribe see page 21.

ASCOTT-UNDER-WYCHWOOD

William Antiques

Manor Farm. OX7 6AL. (Robert Gripper). Est. 1982. Open Mon.-Fri. 9-5. SIZE: Medium. *STOCK: Victorian and Georgian furniture, mainly mahogany.* LOC: Left turn off A361 from Chipping Norton, turn left between river bridge and level crossing. PARK: Easy. TEL: 01993 831960; home - same; fax - 01993 830395; e-mail - robgripper@aol.com. SER: Valuations; restorations. VAT: Margin.

ASTON TIRROLD, Nr. Didcot

John Harrison Fine Art

Skirmers, Aston St. OX11 9DQ. (J.M.C. Harrison). TVADA. Strictly by appointment. *STOCK: Drawings and watercolours, 18th-19th C.* TEL: 01235 850260. SER: Commissions undertaken.

BICESTER

R.A. Barnes

PO Box 82. OX25 1RA. LAPADA. Open by appointment only. *STOCK: English, Oriental and* Continental porcelain, antiques and collectables; Wedgwood, ironstone, china, glass, copper, 19th C; Bohemian and art glass, Regency, Victorian and some 18th C small furniture, primitive paintings. TEL: 01844 237388. VAT: Stan/Spec.

BLADON, Nr. Woodstock

Park House Tearoom & Antiques

26 Park St. OX20 1RW. (H.R. and T. Thomas). Resident. Est. 1996. Open daily. SIZE: Small. *STOCK: Small furniture and decorative smalls.* LOC: On A4095 Woodstock to Witney road. PARK: Own. TEL: 01993 812817; fax - 01993 812912; e-mail - hughthomas@htshipping.com; website - www.htshipping.com. SER: Valuations; restorations; buys at auction; monthly shipping service to USA (check website for rate details).

BLEWBURY

Blewbury Antiques

London Rd. OX11 9NX. (S. and E. Richardson). Est. 1971. Open 10-6 including weekends. CL: Tues. *STOCK: General antiques, books, bric-a-brac, country and garden items, oil lamps and oil lamp parts.* PARK: Easy. TEL: 01235 850366.

Mother-of-pearl egg with gilt metal fittings, mounted on a stand of gilt brass grapes and leaves and standing on an alabaster foot. A press on the top reveals a gilt metal tray supporting six miniature sewing tools: scissors, thimble, bodkin, needle case, ribbon-threader and perfume bottle. France, c.1860-80. 8¾in. high. £500-£800.

From an article entitled "Novelty Sewing Sets" by Kay Sullivan which appeared in the February 2002 issue of **Antique Collecting**. For more details and to subscribe see page 21.

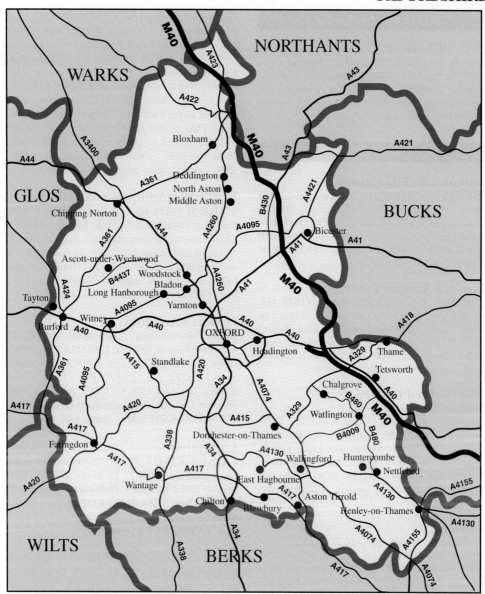

Dealers and Shops in Oxfordshire

Ascott-under-Wychwood	1	Dorchester-on-Thames	2	Standlake	1
Aston Tirrold	1	East Hagbourne	2	Taynton	1
Bicester	1	Faringdon	2	Tetsworth	2
Bladon	1	Headington	1	Thame	1
Blewbury	1	Henley-on-Thames	10	Wallingford	9
Bloxham	1	Huntercombe	1	Wantage	1
Burford	17	Long Hanborough	1	Watlington	2
Chalgrove	1	Middle Aston	1	Witney	6
Chilton	1	Nettlebed	1	Woodstock	7
Chipping Norton	9	North Aston	1	Yarnton	1
Deddington	2	Oxford	15		

BLOXHAM, Nr. Banbury

H.C. Dickins
High St. OX15 4LT. (P. and H.R. Dickins). Open 10-5.30, Sat. 10-1. *STOCK: 19th-20th C British sporting and landscape paintings, watercolours, drawings and prints.* TEL: 01295 721949; website - www.hcdickins.co.uk.

BURFORD

Antiques @ The George
104 High St. OX18 4QJ. (C. Oswald). Est. 1992. Open 10-5, Sun. 12-5. SIZE: Large. *STOCK: General antiques including china, furniture, textiles, silver, plate, books, glass, pictures, early 18th C to 1930's.* LOC: Main road. PARK: Around corner. TEL: 01993 823319.

Burford Antique Centre
Cheltenham Rd., At the Roundabout. OX18 4JA. (G. Viventi). Est. 1979. Open 10-6 including Sun. SIZE: Large. *STOCK: Furniture, 18th-19th C, £100-£5,000; china and pictures.* LOC: A40. PARK: Easy. TEL: 01993 823227. SER: Restorations (furniture including re-leathering).

The Burford Gallery
Classica House, High St. OX18 4QA. (B. Etheridge). Est. 1976. Open 9.30-5.30. SIZE: Medium. *STOCK: British and Continental watercolours, 18th-20th C, £40-£6,000.* LOC: 400yds. from A40 roundabout. PARK: Easy. TEL: 01993 822305; fax - 01993 824148. SER: Valuations; framing and mounting; buys at auction (watercolours). VAT: Spec.

Bygones
29 High St. OX18 4RN. (C.B. Jenkins). Est. 1986. Open 10-1 and 2-5, Sat. 10-5, Sun. 12-5. SIZE:Small. *STOCK: Prints and pictures, 1900's, £5-£50; china and glass, curios, 1880-1950, £5-£250.* LOC: A40. PARK: Easy. TEL: 01993 823588; fax - 01993 704338.

Jonathan Fyson Antiques
50 High St. OX18 4QF. (J.R. Fyson). CADA. Est. 1970. Open 9.30-1 and 2-5.30. SIZE: Medium. *STOCK: English and Continental furniture, decorative brass and steel including lighting and fireplace accessories; club fenders, mirrors, porcelain, glass, jewellery.* LOC: At junction of A40/A361 between Oxford and Cheltenham. PARK: Easy. TEL: 01993 823204; fax - same; home - 01367 860223; e-mail - j@fyson.co.uk. SER: Valuations. VAT: Spec.

Gateway Antiques
Cheltenham Rd., Burford Roundabout. OX18 4JA.. (M.C. Ford and P. Brown). CADA. Est. 1986. Open 10-5.30 and Sun. 2-5. SIZE: Large. *STOCK: English and Continental furniture, 18th to early 20th C; decorative accessories.* LOC: On roundabout (A40) Oxford/Cheltenham road, adjacent to the Cotswold Gateway Hotel. PARK: Easy. TEL: 01993 823678/822624; fax - 01993 823857; e-mail - enquiries@gatewayantiques. co.uk; website - www.gatewayantiques.co.uk. SER: Courier (multi-lingual). VAT: Stan/Spec.

Horseshoe Antiques and Gallery
97 High St. OX18 4QA. (B. Evans). Open 9-5.30, Sun. by appointment only. SIZE: Medium. *STOCK: Clocks including longcase (all fully restored); early oak and country furniture; oil paintings and watercolours; copper and brass, horse brasses.* LOC: East side of High St. PARK: Easy. TEL: 01993 823244; fax - 01993 822429. VAT: Spec.

Hubert's Antiques
Burford Roundabout, Cheltenham Rd. OX18 4JA. (Michael R. Hinds). LAPADA. Est. 1987. Open 10-5.30. SIZE: Large. *STOCK: Furniture, £150-£10,000; oils, £50-£5,000; clocks, £250-£5,000; all 17th-19th C.* LOC: A40 half way between Oxford and Cheltenham. PARK: Easy. TEL: 01993 822151; fax - same. VAT: Spec.

Lucy Johnson   BADA
LAPADA. CINOA. Est. 1982. Showroom open by appointment. SIZE: Medium. *STOCK: 17th to early 18th C furniture, Delftware and interiors.* PARK: Easy. TEL: 01993 823726; fax - 01993 824799; e-mail - lucy-johnson@lucy-johnson. com. FAIRS: BADA; Olympia.

Anthony Nielsen Antiques
80 High St. OX18 4QF. Est. 1977. Open 9.30-1 and 2-5.30. SIZE: Large. *STOCK: Furniture, mahogany, walnut, rosewood, oak, William and Mary to Edwardian, £200-£20,000; copper, brass, £20-£500.* PARK: Easy. TEL: 01993 822014; fax - same; after hours - 01451 821710.

David Pickup   BADA
115 High St. OX18 4RG. CADA. Est. 1977. Open 9.30-1 and 2-5.30, Sat. 10-1 and 2-4. SIZE: Medium. *STOCK: Fine furniture, works of art, from £500+; decorative objects, from £100+; all late 17th to mid 20th C, specialising in Arts and Crafts.* PARK: Easy. TEL: 01993 822555. FAIRS: Olympia. VAT: Spec.

Richard Purdon Antique Carpets

BADA
158 The Hill. OX18 4QY. CADA. Open 10-5.
SIZE: Medium. *STOCK: Antique Eastern and European carpets, village and tribal rugs, needlework, textiles and related items.* TEL: **01993 823777**; fax - 01993 823719; e-mail - rp@richard purdon.demon.co.uk; website - www.purdon. com. SER: Valuations; restorations. FAIRS: Hali (Olympia). VAT: Stan/Spec.

Manfred Schotten Antiques

109 High St. OX18 4RG. CADA. Est. 1974. Open 9.30-5.30 or by appointment. *STOCK: Sporting antiques and library furniture.* TEL: 01993 822302; fax - 01993 822055; e-mail - antiques@schotten.com; website - www.schotten. com. SER: Restorations. FAIRS: Olympia (Sprng, Summer and Winter). VAT: Stan/Margin.

Brian Sinfield Gallery

150 High St. OX18 4QU. CADA. Est. 1972. Open 10-5.30, Mon. by appointment. *STOCK: Mainly contemporary and late 20th C paintings, watercolours and sculpture; contemporary Indian miniatures.* TEL: 01993 824464; fax - 01993 824525; e-mail - gallery@briansinfield.com; website - www. briansinfield.com. SER: 8 exhibitions annually.

The Stone Gallery

93 High St. OX18 4QA. (Mrs Phyllis M. and Simon Marshall). Est. 1918. Open 9.15-6. SIZE: Medium. *STOCK: Pre-Raphaelite and modern British pictures, 1840-1980, £120-£30,000; paperweights, from 1845, £50-£15,000; enamel boxes, from 1760, £50-£1,000.* LOC: Halfway down High St. PARK: Easy. TEL: 01993 823302; fax/home - same; e-mail - mail@stonegallery.co. uk; website - www.stonegallery.co.uk. SER: Valuations (paperweights); buys at auction (pictures and paperweights). VAT: Stan/Spec.

Swan Gallery

High St. OX18 4RE. (D. Pratt). CADA. Est. 1966. Open 10-5.30. SIZE: Large. *STOCK: Country furniture in oak, yew, walnut and fruitwood, 17th-19th C, £300-£12,000; Staffordshire figures and small decorative items, 18th-20th C, £50-£800.* PARK: Easy. TEL: 01993 822244. VAT: Mainly Spec.

Wren Gallery

34 Lower High St. OX18 4RR. (S. Hall and G. Mitchell). Est. 1986. Open 10-5.30. SIZE: Medium. *STOCK: 19th-20th C watercolours and drawings.* TEL: 01993 823495. SER: Valuations; restorations (watercolours); buys at auction (watercolours). VAT: Spec.

CHALGROVE, Nr. Oxford

Rupert Hitchcox Antiques
Warpsgrove Lane. OX44 7RW. (P. and R. Hitchcox). Est. 1957. Open Mon.-Sat. 10-5 (Trade), Sun. 2-5 (Trade and public). SIZE: Large - 6 barns. *STOCK: Georgian, Victorian, Edwardian and 1920's furniture.* LOC: Halfway between Oxford and Henley, just off the B480, 6 miles from junction 6 M40. PARK: Easy. TEL: 01865 890241; fax - same; e-mail - rupertsantiques@aol.com. VAT: Stan/Spec.

CHILTON, Nr. Didcot

Country Markets Antiques and Collectables
at Country Gardens Garden Centre, Newbury Rd. OX11 0QN. (G.W. Vaughan). Est. 1991. Open 10-5.30, Mon. 10.30-5.30, Sun. 10.30-4.30. SIZE: Large - 30 dealers. *STOCK: Wide variety of general antiques including furniture, books, jewellery, porcelain, militaria, cased fish and fishing tackle, £5-£5,000.* LOC: Off A34 near Harwell, 10 mins. from junction 13, M4, 20 mins. from Oxford. PARK: Easy. TEL: 01235 835125; fax - 01235 833068; e-mail - country.markets.antiques@breathe mail.net; website - www.countrymarkets.co.uk. SER: Restorations (furniture and ceramics).

CHIPPING NORTON

Antique English Windsor Chairs BADA
at Bugle Antiques 9 Horse Fair. OX7 5AL. CINOA. CADA. Est. 1971. Open 10-5 (prior telephone call advisable). CL: Mon. and Tues. except by appointment. *STOCK: 18th-19th C Windsor chairs, including sets.* TEL: 01608 643322; fax - 01608 644322; e-mail - michael@antique-english-windsor-chairs.com; website - www.antique-english-windsor-chairs.com. FAIRS: BADA; Olympia (June, Nov). VAT: Stan/Spec.

Chipping Norton Antique Centre
Ivy House, 1 Market Place and 21/44 West St. OX7 5NH. (G. Wissinger). Open 10-5.30 including Sun. SIZE: 20 dealers. *STOCK: A wide variety of smalls and furniture.* PARK: Own. TEL: 01608 644212.

Georgian House Antiques
21 West St. OX7 5EU. LAPADA. Open 9-6. *STOCK: 17th-19th C furniture and paintings.* TEL: 01608 641369.

Jonathan Howard
21 Market Place. OX7 5NA. (J.G. Howard). Est.

1979. Open by appointment or ring bell. SIZE: Small. *STOCK: Clocks - longcase, wall and carriage, 18th-19th C.* PARK: Easy. TEL: 01608 643065. SER: Valuations; restorations (movement, dials and cases).

Key Antiques
11 Horse Fair. OX7 5AL. (J. Riley). LAPADA, CADA. Open 10-5.30 or by appointment. CL: Mon. and Tues. SIZE: Medium. *STOCK: English period oak and country furniture, 17th-19th C; domestic metalware, pottery and associated items.* LOC: On main road. PARK: Easy. TEL: 01608 644992. VAT: Spec.

The Quiet Woman Antiques Centre
Southcombe. OX7 5QH. (David Belcher and Ann Marriott). Est. 1998. Open 10-7, Sat. 10-5.30, Sun. 11-4. SIZE: Large - several dealers. *STOCK: Wide variety of general antiques.* PARK: Own. TEL: 01608 646262; fax - same.

Station Mill Antiques Centre
Station Mill, Station Rd. OX7 5HX. (M.T. Langer). Est. 1994. Open 10-5 including Sun. SIZE: Large. *STOCK: Furniture, fine art, bric-a-brac and collectables, 17th-20th C, £2-£2,000.* LOC: Just out of town off A44 towards Moreton in Marsh. PARK: Easy. TEL: 01608 644563; fax - 01327 860952; e-mail - info@stationmill.com; website - www.stationmill.com. SER: Valuations; restorations.

TRADA
21 High St. OX7 5AD. Open 9-5. *STOCK: Antiquarian maps and engravings, 1600-1900.* TEL: 01608 644325. SER: Print renovation; colouring; picture frame making.

Peter Wiggins
Raffles Farm, Southcombe. OX7 5QH. Est. 1969. Usually available. *STOCK: Barometers.* LOC: 1 mile from Chipping Norton on A34. TEL: 01608 642652; home - same. SER: Valuations; restorations (barometers, clocks, automata); clock repairs; buys at auction.

DEDDINGTON

Castle Antiques Ltd
Manor Farm, Clifton. OX15 0PA. (J. and J. Vaughan). LAPADA. Est. 1968. Open 10-5, Sun. 10-4. SIZE: Large. *STOCK: Furniture, £25-£3,000; silver, metalware, £10-£1,000; pottery, porcelain, £10-£2,000; kitchenalia.* LOC: B4031, 6 miles from junction 10, M40. PARK: Own. TEL: 01869 338688. VAT: Stan/Spec.

Deddington Antiques Centre
Laurel House, Bull Ring, Market Sq. OX15 0TT. (Mrs B. J. Haller). TVADA. Est. 1972. Open 10-5, including Sun. SIZE: 27 dealers. *STOCK: Furniture, Georgian to 1930's, £100-£4,000; porcelain, silver, pictures, jewellery, 1700-1930, £5-£5,000; collectables, £10-£200.* LOC: Off A4260 Oxford-Banbury road at Deddington traffic lights. PARK: Easy, free. TEL: 01869 338968; fax - 01869 338916. SER: Valuations. FAIRS: TVADA.

DORCHESTER-ON-THAMES

Dorchester Antiques
The Barn, 3 High St. OX10 7HH. (J. and S. Hearnden). LAPADA. TVADA. Est. 1992. Open Tues.-Sat. 10-5. SIZE: Medium. *STOCK: Furniture including chairs and decorative country pieces, 18th-19th C.* LOC: Opposite Abbey. PARK: Easy. TEL: 01865 341373. SER: Restorations; finder. FAIRS: TVADA.

Hallidays (Fine Antiques) Ltd
The Old College, High St. OX10 7HL. LAPADA. TVADA. CINOA. Est. 1950. Open 9-5, Sat. 10-1 and 2-4. SIZE: Large. *STOCK: Furniture, 17th-*19th C, £100-£70,000; paintings, 18th-19th C, £100-£20,000; decorative and small items, pine and marble mantelpieces, firegrates, fenders, 18th-20th C; room panelling.* LOC: 8 miles south-east of Oxford. PARK: At rear. TEL: 01865 340028; fax - 01865 341149. FAIRS: Olympia. VAT: Stan/Spec.

EAST HAGBOURNE

Craig Barfoot
Tudor House. OX11 9LR. (I.C. Barfoot). Est. 1993. Open any time by appointment. SIZE: Medium. *STOCK: Longcase clocks, £2,000-£12,000; bracket and lantern clocks.* LOC: Just off A34 halfway between Oxford and Newbury. PARK: Easy. TEL: 01235 818968; home - same; mobile - 07710 858158; e-mail - craigbarfootclocks@tinyworld. co.uk. SER: Restorations (clocks); buys at auction (clocks, English oak furniture). VAT: Spec.

E.M. Lawson and Co
Kingsholm. OX11 9LN. (W.J. and K.M. Lawson). Est. 1921. Usually open 10-5 but appointment preferred. CL: Sat. *STOCK: Antiquarian and rare books, 1500-1900.* PARK: Easy. TEL: 01235 812033. VAT: Stan.

FARINGDON

Aston Pine Antiques
16-18 London St. SN7 7AA. (P. O'Gara). Est. 1982. Open Tues.-Sat. 9-5. *STOCK: Victorian and Continental pine; Victorian fireplaces, doors and bathrooms.* TEL: 01367 243840.

Oxford Architectural Antiques
16-18 London St. SN7 7AA. (M. O'Gara). Open Tues.-Sat. 9-5. *STOCK: Fireplaces, fixtures and fittings, doors.* TEL: 01367 242268; mobile - 07973 922393. SER: Packaging and container. VAT: Margin.

HEADINGTON, Nr. Oxford

Barclay Antiques
107 Windmill Rd. OX3 7BT. (C. Barclay). Est. 1979. Open 10-5.30. CL: Wed. SIZE: Small. *STOCK: Porcelain, silver and jewellery, 18th-19th C, £50-£100; period lamps, 20th C, £50-£500.* PARK: Easy. TEL: 01865 769551. SER: Valuations.

HENLEY-ON-THAMES

Easystrip
Old Manor Farm, Bix. RG9 6BX. (R.J. Cain). Est. 1973. Open by apointment only. *STOCK: Victorian doors.* LOC: A4130 right at top of dual carriageway. PARK: Easy. TEL: 01491 577289; mobile - 07785 938580. SER: Restorations (stripping).

Friday Street Antique Centre (The Ferret)
4 Friday St. RG9 1AH. Open 10-5.30, Sun. 12-5. SIZE: 6 dealers. *STOCK: Furniture, china, silver, books, pictures, musical instruments, unusual items.* LOC: First left after Henley bridge, then first right, business on left. PARK: Easy. TEL: 01491 574104.

Jackdaw Antiques Centres
5 Reading Rd. RG9 0AS. (Mr. and Mrs. Mayle). Est. 1998. Open 10-5.30, Sun. 12-5. *STOCK: Furniture, from Regency, £100-£2,500; china, from Victorian, £2-£200; limited edition books, £2-£50; silver, from Victorian, £15-£500.* TEL: 01491 572289; office - 01491 680954. SER: Restorations (furniture and china).

Jonkers Rare Books
24 Hart St. RG9 2AU. (Christian Jonkers). Est. 1990. SIZE: Medium. *STOCK: Fine and rare books, 1800-1950, £50-£50,000.* LOC: Main road. PARK: Easy. TEL: 01491 576427; fax - 01491 573805; e-mail - info@jonkers.co.uk; website - www.jonkers.co.uk. SER: Valuations; buys at auction (rare books). FAIRS: Olympia.

The Barry Keene Gallery
12 Thameside. RG9 1BH. (B.M. and J.S. Keene). FATG. Est. 1971. Open 9.30-5.30 and by appointment. *STOCK: Antique and modern art, paintings, watercolours, drawings, etchings, prints and sculpture.* LOC: Junction 8/9 M4, over Henley bridge, left along riverside, 5th building on right. TEL: 01491 577119; e-mail - barrykeene@fsbdial.co.uk; website - www.barrykeenegallery.com. SER: Restorations; framing, cleaning, relining, gilding, export. VAT: Stan/Spec.

Richard J. Kingston   BADA
95 Bell St. RG9 2BD. Open 9.30-5 or by appointment. SIZE: Medium. *STOCK: Furniture, 17th to early 19th C; silver, porcelain, glass, paintings, antiquarian and secondhand books.* PARK: Easy. TEL: 01491 574535; home - 01491 573133. SER: Restorations. FAIRS: Surrey, Buxton. VAT: Stan/Spec.

The Old French Mirror Company Ltd
Nightingales, Rotherfield Greys. RG9 4QQ. (Roger and Bridget Johnson). Resident. Est. 1999. Open by appointment only. *STOCK: French mirrors, 19th to early 20th C.* LOC: 3 miles from Henley-on-Thames. PARK: Easy. TEL: 01491 628080; fax - same; e-mail - bridget@frenchmirrors.com; website - www.oldfrenchmirrors.com. SER: Restorations; gilding. FAIRS: Daily Telegraph House and Garden; Olympia (June). VAT: Spec.

Thames Oriental Rug Co
Thames Carpet Cleaners Ltd, 48/56 Reading Rd. RG9 1AG. (B. and Mrs A. Javadi-Babreh). Resident. Est. 1955. Open 9-12.30 and 1.30-5, Sat. 9-12.30. SIZE: Large. *STOCK: Oriental rugs, mid-19th C to modern.* PARK: Easy. TEL: 01491 574676. SER: Valuations; restorations and cleaning (carpets). VAT: Stan.

Tudor House Antiques
49 Duke St. (David and Linda Potter). Open 10-5 including Sun. *STOCK: Furniture, garden ornaments, architectural items, brass, copper, tools, glass, china, silver and plate, 1750's to 1950's.* LOC: Town centre. PARK: Nearby. TEL: 01491 573680; home - 01189 471858. SER: Valuations.

Richard Way Bookseller
54 Friday St. RG9 1AH. (Diana Cook and Richard Way). ABA. Est. 1977. Open 10-5.30. SIZE: Small. *STOCK: Rare and secondhand*

books, 1600-1999, £5-£1,000. LOC: Over Henley bridge, turn immediately left behind Angel public house, follow river, turn right, shop past Anchor public house. PARK: Easy. TEL: 01491 576663; fax - 01491 576663. SER: Valuations; restorations. VAT: Stan.

HUNTERCOMBE

The Country Seat
Huntercombe Manor Barn. RG9 5RY. (Harvey Ferry and William Clegg). LAPADA. TVADA. Est. 1965. Open 9-5.30, Sun. by appointment. SIZE: Large. *STOCK: Furniture - signed and designed, 1700-1970; garden and architectural/ panelling; art pottery and metalwork, lighting and Whitefriars glass.* LOC: 200 yds down right-hand turn off A4130 Nettlebed-Wallingford. PARK: Easy. TEL: 01491 641349; fax - 01491 641533; e-mail - ferry&clegg@thecountryseat. com; websites - www.thecountryseat.com and www.whitefriarsglass.com. SER: Restorations. VAT: Spec.

LONG HANBOROUGH

Hanborough Antiques
125A-127 Main Rd. OX29 8JX. Open 10.30-5. CL: Mon. and Tues. SIZE: Medium. *STOCK: Furniture, country and period; pottery, porcelain, Victoriana, rural and domestic bygones, brass and copper, collectors' items.* LOC: Going north from Oxford on A34 turn left before Woodstock on to A4095 near Witney. PARK: Easy. TEL: 01993 882767.

MIDDLE ASTON, Nr. Bicester

Cotswold Pine & Associates
The Old Poultry Farm. OX25 5QL. (R.J. Prancks). Est. 1980. Open 9-6, Sun. 10-4.30. SIZE: Large. *STOCK: Furniture, 18th-20th C.* LOC: Off A4260, 15 mins. from M40. PARK: Easy. TEL: 01869 340963. SER: Restorations (stripping, polishing and repairs). VAT: Stan/Spec.

NETTLEBED, Nr. Henley-on-Thames

Willow Antiques and the Nettlebed Antique Merchants
The Barns, 1 High St. RG9 5DA. (Willow Bicknell, Michael Plummer and Laurie Brunton). TVADA. Est. 1984. Open 10-5.30, Sun. 11-4, other times by appointment. SIZE: Large. *STOCK: Decorative, fine and unusual furniture,*

objects and decorations, including architectural and garden items, 17th C to 1970s, including Gothic, Aesthetic, Arts and Crafts and Art Deco. LOC: Between Wallingford and Henley on A4074. PARK: Easy. TEL: 01491 642062/ 628811; mobile - 07770 554559. SER: Finder; copy and design; advice on period design for house and garden. FAIRS: TVADA. VAT: Spec.

NORTH ASTON

Elizabeth Harvey-Lee
1 West Cottages, Middle Aston Lane. OX25 5QB. Est. 1986. Open by appointment. *STOCK: Original prints, 15th-20th C; artists' etchings, engravings, lithographs, £100-£6,000.* LOC: 6 miles from junction 10, M40, 15 miles north of Oxford. TEL: 01869 347164. SER: Illustrated catalogue available twice yearly (£20 p.a.). FAIRS: London Original Print, Royal Academy; Olympia (June and Nov); Art on Paper, Royal College of Art. VAT: Spec.

OXFORD

Antiques on High Ltd
85 High St. OX1 4BG. (Paul Lipson and Sally Young). TVADA. Est. 1982. Open 10-5, Sun. and Bank Holidays 11-5. SIZE: Large - 35 dealers. *STOCK: Small antiques and collectables including jewellery, silver and plate, ceramics, glass, antiquities, watches, books and coins, 17th-20th C.* LOC: Opposite Queen's Lane. PARK: St Clements, Westgate, Seacourt/Thornhill Park and Ride. TEL: 01865 251075. SER: Valuations; restorations (jewellery, silver including replating). FAIRS: TVADA.

Blackwell's Rare Books
48-51 Broad St. OX1 3BQ. Est. 1879. Open 9-6, Tues. 9.30-6. *STOCK: Antiquarian and rare modern books.* PARK: Easy. TEL: 01865 333555; fax - 01865 794143; e-mail - rarebooks@blackwellsbookshops. co.uk; website - www.rarebooks.blackwell.co.uk/. SER: Buys at auction. FAIRS: ABA (Olympia). VAT: Stan/Spec.

The Corner Shop
29 Walton St. OX2 6AA. (P. Hitchcox and D. Florey). Est. 1978. Open 10-5. *STOCK: Pictures, china, glass, silver, small furniture and general items.* LOC: Central north Oxford. TEL: 01865 553364.

Reginald Davis Ltd   BADA
34 High St. OX1 4AN. Est. 1941. Open Tues.-Sat. 9-5. *STOCK: Silver, English and Continental, 17th to early 19th C; jewellery, Sheffield*

plate, Georgian and Victorian. Not Stocked: Glass, china, pewter. LOC: On A40. PARK: Nearby. TEL: 01865 248347. SER: Valuations; restorations (silver, jewellery). VAT: Stan/Spec.

Jeremy's (Oxford Stamp Centre)

98 Cowley Rd. OX4 1JE. Open 10-12.30 and 2-5. *STOCK: Stamps, postcards and cigarette cards.* TEL: 01865 241011; website - www.postcard. co.uk/jeremys.

Jericho Books

48 Walton St. OX2 6AD. (Frank Stringer). PBFA. Est. 1980. Open 10.30-6, Sun. 12-5. SIZE: Medium. *STOCK: Secondhand and antiquarian books.* PARK: Easy. TEL: 01865 511992; e-mail - shop@jerichobooks.com; website - www.jericho books.com. SER: Valuations; buys at auction (antiquarian books). FAIRS: Royal National Hotel. VAT: Stan.

Christopher Legge Oriental Carpets

25 Oakthorpe Rd., Summertown. OX2 7BD. (C.T. Legge). Est. 1970. Open 9.30-5. SIZE: Medium. *STOCK: Rugs, various sizes, 19th to early 20th C, £300-£15,000.* LOC: Near shopping parade. PARK: Easy. TEL: 01865 557572; fax - 01865 554877. SER: Valuations; restorations; re-weaving; handcleaning. VAT: Stan/Margin.

Laurie Leigh Antiques

36 High St. OX1 4AN. (L. and D. Leigh). LAPADA. Est. 1963. Open 10.30-5.30. CL: Thurs. *STOCK: Glass and keyboard musical instruments.* TEL: 01865 244197; e-mail - laurieleigh@hotmail.com; website - www.laurieleighantiques.com. SER: Restorations (keyboards). VAT: Stan/Spec.

Magna Gallery

41 High St. OX1 4AP. (Martin J. Blant). Est. 1969. Open 10.30-6. SIZE: Medium. *STOCK: Maps especially English counties, general topography especially Oxford, prints including botanical, caricatures, 1550-1895.* TEL: 01865 245805; e-mail - info@magna-gallery.com; website - www. magna-gallery.com. SER: Valuations; framing. VAT: Stan.

Oriental Rug Gallery Ltd

15 Woodstock Rd. OX2 6HA. (Richard Mathias and Julian Blair). BORDA. *STOCK: Russian, Afghan, Turkish and Persian carpets, rugs and kelims; Oriental objets d'art.* TEL: +44 (0) 1865 316333; fax - same; e-mail - rugs@orientalrug gallery.com; website - www.orientalruggallery. com.

Payne and Son (Goldsmiths) Ltd BADA

131 High St. OX1 4DH. (E.P., G.N. and J.D.Payne, P.J. Coppock, A. Salmon and D. Thornton). Est. 1790. Open weekdays 9-5. SIZE: Medium. *STOCK: British silver, antique, modern and secondhand; jewellery, all £50-£10,000+.* LOC: Town centre near Carfax traffic lights. PARK: 800yds. TEL: 01865 243787; fax - 01865 793241; e-mail - silver@ payneandson.co.uk; website - www.payneand son.co.uk. SER: Restorations (English silver). FAIRS: BADA; Chelsea (Spring); Olympia (Autumn). VAT: Stan/Spec.

Sanders of Oxford Ltd

Salutation House, 104 High St. OX1 4BW. Open 10-6. SIZE: Large. *STOCK: Prints, especially Oxford; maps and Japanese woodcuts.* TEL: 01865 242590; fax - 01865 721748; e-mail - info @sanders-oxford.co.uk; website - www.oxlink. co.uk/antiques/sanders.html. SER: Restorations (framing). FAIRS: PBFA (Russell Hotel London); London Original Print. VAT: Stan/Spec.

St. Clements Antiques

93 St. Clements St. OX4 1AR. (Giles Power). Est. 1998. Open 10.30-5. SIZE: Medium. *STOCK: Oak and country items, 18th-19th C, £50-£5,000; interesting curios, 18th-20th C, £5-£500.* LOC: Close to city centre, next to Magdalen Bridge. PARK: Easy, opposite. TEL: 01865 727010; home - 01865 200359. SER: Valuations. VAT: Stan/Spec.

Thorntons of Oxford Ltd

11 Broad St. OX1 3AR. ABA. ILAB. Est. 1835. Open 9-6. SIZE: Large. *STOCK: Antiquarian books, prints and cards.* TEL: 01865 242939; fax - 01865 204021; e-mail - Thorntons@booknews. demon.co.uk; website - www.thorntonsbooks.co. uk. SER: Binding.

Waterfield's

52 High St. OX1 4AS. ABA. PBFA. Est. 1973. Open 9.45-5.45. *STOCK: Antiquarian and second-hand books, all subjects, especially academic in the humanities; literature, history, philosophy, 17th-18th C English books.* TEL: 01865 721809.

STANDLAKE, Nr. Witney

Manor Farm Antiques

Manor Farm. OX29 7RL. (C.W. Leveson-Gower). Est. 1964. Open daily, Sun. by appointment. SIZE: Large. *STOCK: Victorian brass and iron beds.* PARK: Easy, in farmyard. TEL: 01865 300303.

TAYNTON, Nr. Burford

Wychwood Antiques
Upper Farm Cottage. OX18 4UH. Open by appointment only. *STOCK: English country furniture, Mason's Ironstone, treen, metalware and decorative items.* TEL: 01993 822860. VAT: Spec.

TETSWORTH, Nr. Thame

Quillon Antiques of Tetsworth
The Old Stores, 42a High St. OX9 7AS. Open Tues.-Thurs. 10-5, Sat. 10-6, Sun. 12-5. SIZE: Medium. *STOCK: 17th-19th C oak and country furniture, refectory tables and coffers; armour, 15th-19th C; muskets, pistols, armourial items; big game, taxidermy and large bore folding guns.* LOC: A40 between exits 6 and 7, M40. PARK: Easy. TEL: 01844 281636. SER: Valuations; restorations.

The Swan at Tetsworth
High St. OX9 7AB. TVADA. Est. 1995. Open 7 days 10-6. SIZE: 40+ rooms. LOC: A40, 5 minutes from junctions 6 and 8, M40. PARK: Own large. TEL: 01844 281777; fax - 01844 281770; website - www.theswan.co.uk; e-mail - antiques@theswan. co.uk. SER: Restorations (clocks, cabinet work and gilding). Below are listed the dealers at this centre.

Deborah Abbot
Jewellery and objets d'art.

Jason Abbot
Sporting guns.

Acanthus Design
Arts & Crafts and Art Nouveau furniture and accessories.

S.J. Allison
Decorative ceramics, small furniture and silver.

Beagle Antiques
Fine watercolours and oils

David Binns
Books.

Peter Bond
Prints, watercolours. SER: Gilding.

S. Bond & Sons
Fine period furniture.

Ann Casey
Antique textiles, ceramics, fashion accessories and small furniture.

Caversham Antiques
Furniture and collectables.

John Chaffer
Framed antiquarian prints and maps.

Perry Clayton
Furniture and decorative items.

Polly Clewer Antiques
LAPADA. *Small furniture and decorative items.*

Audrey Cooper
Kitchenalia and country items.

Jenny Corkhill-Callin
Textiles including cushions, curtains, braids and quilts.

S. and K. Cullup
Linens and textiles.

Jacqueline Ding
Oriental antiques.

Dorchester Antiques
Fine period furniture and decorative items.

Richard and Deby Earls
Textiles, cushions, small decorative French furniture.

Farrelly Antiques
TVADA. *18th-19th C furniture.*

Sally Forster
Costume jewellery and antique accessories.

Mavis Foster-Abbott
20th C glass, specialising in Latticinio.

Framed Antiques
Collectable framed cigarette cards.

Gillian Gould
Maritime antiques.

Grate Expectations
Fireplaces, Cornish ranges, tiles, garden items and architectural salvage.

Griffin Fine Art & Antiques
Fine bronze sculptures, furniture and decorative antiques.

Le Grenier
Fine quality French mirrors.

Hen's Teeth Antiques
(Martin Murray). TVADA. *Period furniture and decorative items.*

Patricia Heppell
Jewellery, silver and accessories.

John Howkins Antiques
Late 18th to early 20th C furniture and decorative items.

Martin Isenberg
Period, decorative furniture, treen and ceramics.

Nigel Johnston
Furniture and clocks.

Rupert Landen Antiques
Georgian and Regency mahogany furniture.

Susan Ling
Small furniture, brass and copper.

Shelagh Lister
Fine English and decorative furniture.

J. MacNaughton-Smith
TVADA. *Mainly 18th-19th C English furniture including desks, writing tables, chiffoniers, chests of drawers; small decorative items, 19th C watercolours.*

Marquetry Antiques
Chinese antiques and objets d'art.

Eddie McCourt
Period furniture and decorative items.

Millroyal Antiques
Fine furniture and smalls.

Nicholas Mitchell
Unusual period furniture and smalls.

Nazaré Antiques
Antique funiture and collectables.

Old Chair Company
Upholstered furniture.

Orient Carpets
Persian rugs, kelims and textiles.

Peter Phillips
Ceramics, especially blue & white transferware; small period furniture.

T.H.A. & F.M. Sharland
Frames, prints and watercolours.

Michael Soule
Fine period furniture.

Gail Spence Antiques
Small decorative, collectables and gift antiques.

Lorraine Spooner
Antique furniture and decorative items.

E. Stone Associates
Antique and secondhand jewellery. SER: Restorations.

Sunrising Antiques
Furniture and decorative items.

Tartan Antiques
Objets d'art, pictures and toys.

393

Geoff and Coral Taylor-Robinson
French provincial furniture and decorative accessories.

Paul Templeton
Silver, jewellery and objets d'art.

Touchwood Antiques
English country furniture, specialising in oak.

Paul Treadaway   BADA
Framed prints.

Anthony Vingoe
Glass, sporting, leather and metalware items, porcelain.

Jinny Wright
French country furniture including garden and kitchen.

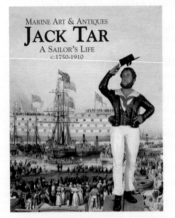
Wright Associates
Jewellery, glass, silver, boxes and small furniture.

Caroline Wyatt
Fine English oak furniture, pine and silver collectables.

THAME

Rosemary and Time
42 Park St. OX9 3HR. Open 9-6. CL: Mon. *STOCK: Clocks and barometers.* TEL: 01844 216923. SER: Valuations; restorations; old spare parts. VAT: Stan/Spec.

WALLINGFORD

de Albuquerque Antiques
12 High St. OX10 0BP. Est. 1982. Open 10-5. SIZE: Medium. *STOCK: Furniture and objects, 18th-19th C.* PARK: At rear. TEL: 01491 832322; fax - same; e-mail - janedea@lineone.net. SER: Framing; gilding. VAT: Spec.

Toby English
10 St Mary's St. OX10 0EL. PBFA. Est. 1980. Open 9.30-5. SIZE: Medium. *STOCK: Books including art and antiques reference, 19th-20th C, £5-£500; prints, 19th-20th C, £20-£200; maps, 19th C, £30-£500.* LOC: Town centre. PARK: Cattle Market. TEL: 01491 836389; fax - same; e-mail - toby@tobyenglish.com; website - www. tobyenglish.com. SER: Valuations; restorations; buys at auction; catalogues issued. FAIRS: PBFA London.

The Lamb Arcade
83 High St. OX10 0BX. TVADA. Open 10-5, Sat. 10-5.30. *STOCK: As below plus books, crafts and ephemera.* TEL: 01491 835166. SER: Restorations (furniture). Below are listed some of the dealers at this centre.

Alicia Antiques
(A. Collins). *China, silver and collectors' items.* TEL: 01491 33737.

Anne Brewer Antiques
Furniture, china, jewellery and objets d'art. TEL: 01491 38486.

Bright Art and Framing
Pictures.

Goodwood Antiques
Furniture.

Pat Hayward
Furniture, light fittings and decorative items.

Highway Pictures
Pictures.

OTT
Tin toys, motoring and aviation memorabilia, pictures. TEL: 01491 832023.

Phoenix Antiques
Victorian furniture, Continental and English pine, lighting.

Precious Antiques
Art Nouveau and Arts & Crafts furniture, china and glass, specialising in Noritake.

Stag Antiques & Gallery
Jewellery, furniture, pictures, Staffordshire figures, Clarice Cliff and Belleek. TEL: 01491 834516.

Gretel Stone
Small furniture, porcelain, silver, pictures and objets d'art.

Tags
(T. and A. Green). *Collectors' items, curios, dolls' house furniture, jewellery, militaria, scientific instruments and furniture.* TEL: 01491 35048; home - 01491 872962.

MGJ Jewellers Ltd.
1A St. Martins St. OX10 0AQ. (Mrs M. Jane). Est. 1971. Open 10-4.30, Sat. 10-5. SIZE: Small.

STOCK: Jewellery, Victorian and secondhand, £100-£2,500. LOC: Town centre. PARK: Nearby. TEL: 01491 834336. VAT: Stan/Spec.

Chris and Lin O'Donnell Antiques
26 High St. OX10 0BU. Est. 1974. Open 9.30-1 and 2-5, Sat. 9.30-5.30. SIZE: Large. *STOCK: Furniture, 18th C to Edwardian, to £3,000; rugs, to £500; unusual objects, Oriental antiques, taxidermy.* LOC: Into town over Wallingford Bridge, 150yds. along High St. on left-hand side. PARK: Thames St. TEL: 01491 839332. VAT: Spec.

Otter Antiques
20 High St. OX10 0BP. (P. and B. Otter). Open 9.30-5, Sun. 10.30-5. SIZE: Medium. *STOCK: Furniture, writing boxes, tea caddies, jewellery boxes, humidors.* PARK: Easy, rear of shop. TEL: 01491 825544; website - www.otterantiques. co.uk. SER: Restorations (boxes). VAT: Stan/Spec.

Mike Ottrey Antiques
16 High St. OX10 0BP. (M.J. Ottrey). Est. 1955. Open 9.30-5.30. CL: Sat. SIZE: Large. *STOCK: Furniture, 17th-19th C; oil paintings, copper and brass, decorative and unusual items.* LOC: A429. PARK: At rear. TEL: 01491 836429. VAT: Spec.

Summers Davis Antiques Ltd
Calleva House, 6 High St. OX10 0BP. (Graham Wells). LAPADA. CINOA. TVADA. Est. 1917. Open 9-5.30, Sat. 9-5, Sun. 11-5. SIZE: Large. *STOCK: English and Continental furniture, decorative items and objects.* Not Stocked: Silver, shipping goods. LOC: From London, shop is on left, 50yds. from Thames Bridge. PARK: Opposite, behind castellated gates. TEL: 01491 836284; fax - 01491 833443; e-mail - antiques@summers davis.co.uk; website - www.summers-davisantiques. co.uk. VAT: Spec.

Tooley Adams & Co
P O Box 174. OX10 0YT. (S. Luck). ABA. IMCOS. Est. 1979. *STOCK: Antiquarian maps and atlases; travel and map related reference books.* TEL: 01491 838298; fax - 01491 834616; e-mail - steve@tooleys.co.uk; website - www. tooleys.co.uk. SER: Valuations; restorations. FAIRS: Worldwide; London (Bonnington Hotel); IMCOS (June); Miami (Feb).

WANTAGE

The Arbery Centre
Market Place. OX12 8AB. (Cedarstar Ltd.).

TVADA. Est. 2000. Open 9.30-5, Sun. 11.30-5. SIZE: Large. *STOCK: Wide range of general antiques and collectables including 20th C paintings, costumes, pine and country furniture, silver, gramophones, maps, books on French furniture.* TEL: 01235 769325; fax - 01235 765242.

WATLINGTON, Nr. Oxford

Cross Antiques
37 High St. OX9 5PZ. (R.A. and I.D. Crawley). Est. 1986. Open 10-6, Sun. and Wed. by appointment. SIZE: Small. *STOCK: Furniture, £100-£5,000; decorative smalls, clocks and garden items, £50-£2,000; all 1600-1900.* LOC: Off B4009 in village centre. PARK: Easy and at rear. TEL: 01491 612324; home - same.

Stephen Orton Antiques
The Antiques Warehouse, Shirburn Rd. OX49 5BZ. TVADA. Open Mon.-Fri. 9-5, other times by appointment. SIZE: Warehouse. *STOCK: 18th-19th C furniture, some decorative items.* LOC: 2 mins. from exit 6, M40. TEL: 01491 613752; e-mail - Orton.Antiques@virgin.net. SER: Supply and pack containers; valuations; restorations; buying agent. VAT: Stan/Spec.

W. R. Harvey & Co (Antiques) Ltd.

FINE ANTIQUE FURNITURE
& WORKS OF ART,
CONSERVATION &
CONSULTANCY

86 Corn Street, Witney,
Oxfordshire OX28 6BU.

Tel: 01993 706501
Fax: 01993 706601

Web Site:
www.wrharvey.co.uk

e-mail:
antiques@wrharvey.co.uk

A fine, small and rare George III period Satinwood, Mahogany and Rosewood Crossbanded Cylinder Kneehole Bureau. C.1785. Height: 44" (112cm), Width: 33" (84cm), Depth: 18" (46cm).

WITNEY

The Clock Work Shop

79 Corn St. OX28 6AS. (Steve Fletcher). Est. 1973. Open Tues.-Fri. 9-12 and 1-5, Sat. 9-4. CL: Mon. SIZE: Small. *STOCK: Clocks, furniture, £30-£10,000; treen, £30-£150; all 18th-19th C.* PARK: Easy. TEL: 01993 772123. SER: Valuations; restorations (clock movements, furniture). VAT: Stan/Spec.

Colin Greenway Antiques

90 Corn St. OX28 6BU. CADA Resident. Est. 1975. Open 9.30-5, Sat. 10-4, Sun. by appointment. SIZE: Large. *STOCK: Furniture, 17th-20th C; metalware, decorative and unusual items.* LOC: Along High St. to town centre, turn right, shop 400yds. on right. PARK: Easy. TEL: 01993 705026; mobile - 07831 585014. VAT: Stan/Spec.

W.R. Harvey & Co (Antiques) Ltd   BADA

86 Corn St. OX28 6BU. CADA. GMC. Open 9.30-5.30, and by appointment. SIZE: Large. *STOCK: Fine English furniture, £500-£50,000; clocks, mirrors, objets d'art, £250-£20,000; all 1680-1830.* LOC: 300 yds. from Market Place.

PARK: Easy. TEL: 01993 706501; fax - 01993 706601; e-mail - antiques@wrharvey.co.uk; website - www.wrharvey.co.uk. SER: Valuations; restorations; consultancy. FAIRS: BADA; Chelsea (March & Sept.); Olympia (June). VAT: Stan/Spec.

Barbara Radman

Westfield House 2G Westfield Rd. OX28 1JG. OMRS. Est. 1976. Open by appointment only. SIZE: Medium. *STOCK: Orders, medals, badges, decorations, specialist in miniature orders, medals and decorations of the world; military books, police and fire brigade memorabilia, postal history, paper money, maps and books.* PARK: Easy and nearby. TEL: 01993 772705; fax - same; e-mail - radman@tinyonline.co.uk. SER: Valuations; buys at auction.

Joan Wilkins Antiques

158 Corn St. OX28 6BY. (Mrs J. Wilkins). Est. 1973. Open 10-5. *STOCK: Furniture, 18th-19th C, £250-£3,500; 19th C glass, metalware, £10-£1,500.* LOC: Town centre. PARK: Easy. TEL: 01993 704749. VAT: Spec.

Witney Antiques

LSA & CJ JARRETT AND RR SCOTT
96-100 CORN STREET, WITNEY,
OXON OX28 6BU, ENGLAND.

TEL: 01993 703902. FAX: 01993 779852.
E-mail: witneyantiques@community.co.uk
Website: www.witneyantiques.com

*An example from our large stock of fine British
embroideries and samplers.*

ANTIQUE FURNITURE,
CLOCKS & TEXTILES.

Witney Antiques   **BADA**
**96/100 Corn St. OX28 6BU. (L.S.A. and C.J.
Jarrett and R.R. Jarrett-Scott). LAPADA,
CADA. Est. 1962. Open 10-5, Mon. and Tues.
by appointment. SIZE: Large.** *STOCK: English
furniture, 17th-18th C; bracket and longcase
clocks, mahogany, oak and walnut, needleworks
and works of art.* **LOC: From Oxford on old
A40 through Witney via High St., turn right at
T-junction, 400yds. on right. PARK: Easy.
TEL: 01993 703902/703887; fax - 01993
779852; e-mail - witneyantiques@community.
co.uk; website - www.witneyantiques.com.
SER: Restorations. FAIRS: BADA; Grosvenor
House. VAT: Spec.**

Antiques of Woodstock

18/20 Market Place. OX20 1TA. (Allan James and
Andrew Hennell). Est. 1975. Open 10.30-5.30, Sun.
10.30-5. SIZE: Large. *STOCK: Fine Georgian and
Regency dining room furniture, long sets of period
chairs, early 17th to 19th C oak and country furniture, Roman to medieval antiquities.* LOC:
Opposite The Bear Hotel. PARK: Easy. TEL: 01993
811818; fax - 01993 811831. SER: Valuations;
restorations; consultations; interior decor advice;
buys at auction; search; commission sales. VAT:
Stan.

Chris Baylis Country Chairs

16 Oxford St. OX20 1TS. TVADA. Open 10.30-
5.30, Sun. 11-5, appointment advisable to view
stock. *STOCK: English country chairs, from
1780; sets of rush seated chairs including ladder
and spindle backs, Windsors and kitchen chairs.*
TEL: 01993 813887; fax - 01993 812379; e-mail
- info@realwoodfurniture.co.uk; website - www.
realwoodfurniture.co.uk.

Bees Antiques

30 High St. OX20 1TG. (Jo and Jim Bateman).
TVADA. Est. 1991. Open 10-1 and 1.30-5, Sun.
11-5. CL: Tues. SIZE: Small. *STOCK: Pottery,
porcelain and glass, 18th-20th C, £30-£1,500;
small furniture, 19th to early 20th C, £50-£2,000;
metalware, 19th C, £30-£200; jewellery, 19th-
20th C, £30-£1,000.* LOC: Just off A3440
Oxford/Stratford-on-Avon road, in town centre.
PARK: Opposite. TEL: 01993 811062; home -
01993 771593; mobile - 07702 603419. SER:
Valuations; buys at auction (as stock).

The Chair Set - Antiques

18-20 Market Place. OX20. (Allan James). Est.
1982. Open 10.30-5.30, including Sun. SIZE:
Large. *STOCK: Sets of chairs, £1,000-£20,000;
single and pairs of chairs, £200-£3,000; dining
tables and accessories, £800-£15,000; all early*

*A basket and stand made by Andrew Stevenson, potting in
Staffordshire 1816-30.*

From an article entitled "Green Glaze" by Barbara Tomkins which
appeared in the October 2001 issue of **Antique Collecting**. For more
details and to subscribe see page 21.

18th to late 19th C. LOC: Opposite Bear Hotel. PARK: Easy. TEL: 01993 811818; fax - 01428 707435. SER: Valuations; restorations (woodwork and upholstery); buys at auction (sets of chairs). VAT: Spec.

John Howard
BADA
19 High St. OX20 1TE. LAPADA. TVADA. CADA. Open 10-5.30. SIZE: Small. *STOCK: 18th-19th C British pottery especially rare Staffordshire animal figures, bocage figures, lustre, 18th C creamware and unusual items.* PARK: Easy. TEL: 0870 4440678; fax - same; mobile - 07831 850544; e-mail - john@johnhoward.co.uk; website - www.antiquepottery.co.uk and www.Staffordshires.com. SER: Packing; insurance service to USA. FAIRS: Olympia; BADA. VAT: Spec.

Robin Sanders and Sons
11 Market St. OX20 1SU. LAPADA. CINOA. *STOCK: English and some French furniture, 17th-19th C; Staffordshire and Masons ironstone pottery, brass, treen and English glass pictures.* TEL: 01993 813930.

Span Antiques
6 Market Place. OX20 1TA. TVADA. Est. 1978. Open 10-1 and 2-5, Sun 1-5. SIZE: Medium.

LOC: Near Town Hall. PARK: Easy. Below are listed some of the dealers selling from these premises. TEL: 01993 811332.

Doreen Caudwell
Textiles and porcelain.

Diana Clark
Old and interesting books.

Francoise Daniel
Boxes, porcelain and collectables.

Liz Hall-Bakker
Art Nouveau and Deco.

Jasper Antiques
Silver and decorative items.

Rebecca Stuart-Mobey
Furniture and glass.

YARNTON

Yarnton Antiques Centre
Yarnton Nurseries Garden Centre, Sandy Lane. OX5 1PA. Open 10-4.30 including Sun. SIZE: 50 dealers. *STOCK: General antiques.* PARK: Easy. TEL: 01865 379600.

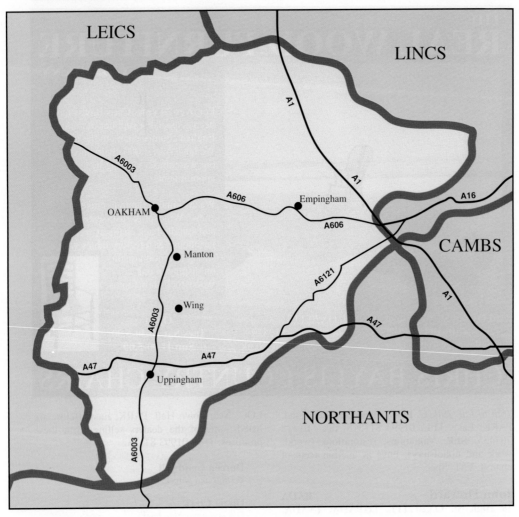

Dealers and Shops in Rutland

Empingham	1	Oakham	4	Wing	1
Manton	1	Uppingham	9		

EMPINGHAM, Nr. Oakham

Churchgate Antiques
13 Church St. LE15 8PN. (R. Wheatley). Open
Wed., Fri., Sat. and Sun. 12-6, other times by
appointment. SIZE: Medium. *STOCK: Furniture,
mainly 18th-19th C, £50-£4,000; paintings and
prints, £25-£1,000; plate, 19th-20th C, £5-£300;
ceramics, £5-£250; collectables, £5-£100.* LOC:
Opposite church, off A606. PARK: Easy. TEL:
01780 460528.

MANTON

David Smith Antiques
Old Cottage, 20 St. Mary's Rd. LE15 8SU. Est.
1953. Open 9-5. CL: Sun., except by appointment. *STOCK: Furniture, glass, silver.* PARK:
Easy. TEL: 01572 737244/737607.

JOHN GARNER

51-53 High Street East, Uppingham,
Rutland, LE15 9PY

Fine 18th & 19th Century Furniture,
Paintings, Clocks, Bronzes, Garden Statuary
Some 20th Century Furniture.

Very large selection of period prints

Tel: **01572 823607** Fax: **01572 821654**
Website: **www.johngarnerantiques.com**

OAKHAM

Fine Art of Oakham BADA
**4 High St. LE15 6AL. (Dr A.J. Smith). LAPADA.
Open 10-5. CL: Mon.** *STOCK: Continental oils
and watercolours, Victorian and 19th C.* **TEL:
01572 755221; fax - 01572 770047.**

The Old House Gallery
13-15 Market Place. LE15 6DT. (R.A. Clarke).
Est. 1979. Open 10-1 and 2-5. CL: Thurs. SIZE:
Medium. *STOCK: Oil paintings, £50-£3,500; art
studio pottery, 1850-1990, £5-£500; watercolours, £25-£2,000; prints and objets d'art, £5-
£500; antiquarian county maps, £15-£250;
contemporary paintings, sculpture and three-
dimensional works.* PARK: Easy. TEL: 01572
755538. SER: Valuations; restorations (oils, watercolours, prints, frames); framing.

C. Reynolds Antiques
The East Lodge, Burley Mansion House, Burley-
on-the-Hill. LE15 7TE. Est. 1972. Resident.
Usually available but telephone call advisable.
SIZE: Large. *STOCK: Early verge watches,
repeater and other unusual clocks and watches.*
TEL: 01572 771551.

Swans
17 Mill St. LE15 6EA. (P.W. Jones). Est. 1988.
Open 9.30-5.30, Sun. 2-5. SIZE: Large. *STOCK:
French and English beds and associated furniture;
18th-19th C antiques, mainly decorative and
upholstered.* LOC: 150yds. from High St. PARK:
Easy. TEL: 01572 724364; fax - 01572 755094;
e-mail - info@swansofoakham.co.uk; website -
www.swansofoakham.co.uk. SER: Manufactures
new bases and mattresses; valuations; restorations;
deliveries to and from France. VAT: Stan/Spec.

UPPINGHAM

Clutter
14 Orange St. LE15 9SQ. (M.C. Sumner). Est.
1982. Open 10-5. *STOCK: Victorian linen and
lace; textiles including Durham quilts, chenilles;
interesting silver, porcelain, glass, small furniture, kitchenalia, 10p-£1,000.* LOC: Take old
A47 from by-pass, shop 25yds. from traffic
lights. PARK: Nearby. TEL: 01572 823745;
home - 01572 717243. SER: Valuations; restorations (furniture, brass, copper, silver, bronze,
ivory, lacquer, shibayama and associated materials,
ceramics); hire (christening gowns and Victorian
wedding dress and accessories).

John Garner
51-53 High St. East. LE15 9PY. LAPADA.
FATG. Est. 1966. Open 9-5.30, Sun. 2-5, prior
telephone call advisable. SIZE: 12 showrooms +
warehouse. *STOCK: 18th-19th C furniture,
paintings, prints, clocks, bronzes, mirrors, garden
statuary, some 20th C furniture.* LOC: Just off
A47, 80 yards from market place. PARK: Easy.
TEL: 01572 823607; fax - 01572 821654; mobile
- 07850 596556; e-mail - johngarner@aol.com;
website - www.johngarnerantiques.com. SER:
Valuations; restorations (furniture, paintings,
prints); framing (trade); courier; export. FAIRS:
Newark; Miami. VAT: Stan/Spec.

Gilberts of Uppingham
8 Ayston Rd. LE15 9RL. (M. Gilbert). Open 9.30-
5, Mon. and Tues. 9.30-1 and 2-5. *STOCK:
General antiques.* TEL: 01572 823486.

Goldmark Books
14 Orange St. LE15 9SQ. (Mike Goldmark).
Open 9.30-5.30 and Sunday afternoons. *STOCK:
Antiquarian and secondhand books.* LOC:
Between Market Sq. and traffic lights. PARK:
Nearby. TEL: 01572 822694.

Marc Oxley Fine Art

10 Orange St. LE15 9SQ. Resident. Est. 1981. Open 9.30-5.30, Sat. 10-6, Sun. by appointment. *STOCK: Original watercolours and drawings, 1700-1950, £5-£850; oils, 19th-20th C, £100-£1,500; prints, mainly 19th C, £5-£50; maps, 17th-19th C, £10-£850.* LOC: From A47 on main road into town, just before Market Sq. PARK: Market Sq. TEL: 01572 822334; home - same; e-mail - marc@19thCwatercolours.com. SER: Valuations; restorations (oils).

T.J. Roberts

39/41 High St. East. LE15 9PY. Resident. Open 9.30-5.30. *STOCK: Furniture, porcelain and pottery, 18th-19th C; Staffordshire figures, general antiques.* PARK: Easy. TEL: 01572 821493. VAT: Stan/Spec.

Rutland Antiques Centre

Crown Passage. LE15. (Wendy Foster Grindley). Est. 1987. Open 10-5.30, Sun. 11-5. SIZE: Large. *STOCK: Wide range of general antiques, £5-£3,000.* LOC: Behind Crown Hotel, High St. PARK: Easy. TEL: 01572 824011; fax - same.

Tattersall's

14b Orange St. LE15 9SQ. (J. Tattersall). Est. 1985. Open 9.30-5. CL: Mon. SIZE: Small. *STOCK: Persian rugs, 19th-20th C.* PARK: Easy, 200yds. TEL: 01572 821171; e-mail - persian rugs@tattersall.go-plus.net. SER: Restorations (rugs, carpets).

Woodman's House Antiques

35 High St. East. LE15 9PY. (Mr. and Mrs. James Collie). Est. 1991. SIZE: Small. *STOCK: Furniture, 17th-18th C.* PARK: Easy. TEL: 01572 821799; fax - same; website - www.rutnet.co.uk/woodmans. SER: Valuations; restorations; buys at auction.

WING, Nr. Oakham

Robert Bingley Antiques

Home Farm, Church St. LE15 8RS. Open Wed.-Sat. 10-5, Sun.-Tues. by appointment. SIZE: Large. *STOCK: Furniture, 17th-19th C, £50-£5,000; glass, clocks, silver and plate, pictures and porcelain.* LOC: Next to church. PARK: Own. TEL: 01572 737725; mobile - 07909 585285. SER: Valuations; restorations. VAT: Spec.

Piper returned to Norfolk's church towers time and again throughout his career, and his 1980s screenprints of these subjects proved the most popular at Christie's. Long Sutton took £2,800.

From an article entitled "The Titian Gallery" which appeared in the October 2001 issue of **Antique Collecting**. For more details and to subscribe see page 21.

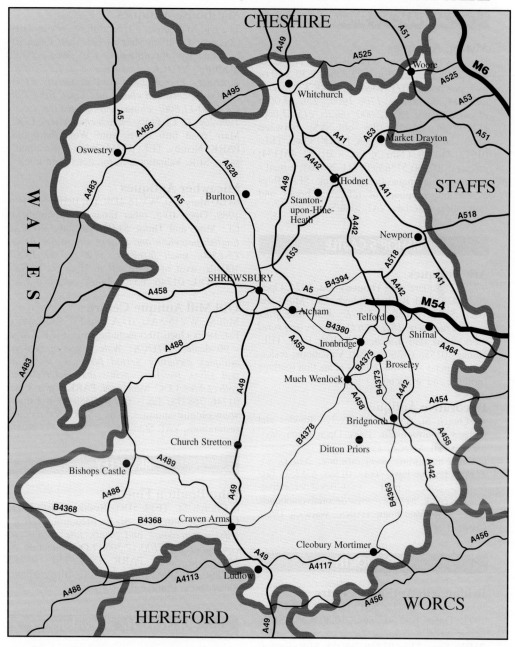

Dealers and Shops in Shropshire

				Newport	1
Atcham	1	Craven Arms	1	Oswestry	1
Bishop's Castle	2	Ditton Priors	1	Shifnal	1
Bridgnorth	5	Hodnet	1	Shrewsbury	15
Broseley	1	Ironbridge	1	Stanton upon Hine Heath	1
Burlton	1	Ludlow	12	Telford	2
Church Stretton	3	Market Drayton	2	Whitchurch	2
Cleobury Mortimer	2	Much Wenlock	4	Woore	1

ATCHAM, Nr. Shrewsbury

Mytton Antiques

Norton Cross Roads. SY4 4UH. (M.A., E.A., J.M. and S. Nares). Est. 1972. Open 9.30-5.30 or by appointment. SIZE: Medium. *STOCK: General antiques, furniture, 1700-1900, £50-£4,000; clocks, all types, £35-£2,000; smalls, £15-£1,000.* LOC: On B5061 (the old A5) between Shrewsbury and Wellington. PARK: Own. TEL: 01952 740229 (24hrs.); fax - 01952 461154; mobiles - 07860 575639/07711 205503; e-mail - nares@myttonantiques.freeserve.co.uk. SER: Buys at auction; suppliers of reference books and restoration materials. VAT: Stan/Spec.

BISHOP'S CASTLE

Ark Antiques

9 Market Square. (Jill Thomas). Est. 1974. Open 10.30-4.30 and Bank Holidays. CL: Mon. and Wed. SIZE: Small. *STOCK: Oak and pine country furniture, 18th-19th C; country and rural tools, brass and iron beds.* PARK: Easy. TEL: Home - 01588 638608. SER: Valuations; restorations (metal and wood); buys at auction (cottage furniture and artifacts).

Decorative Antiques

47 Church St. SY9 5AD. (Evelyn Bowles and Richard Moulson). Est. 1996. Open seven days. SIZE: Small. *STOCK: Ceramics and glass, jewellery and metalware, small furniture, 20th C, £5-£1,000.* PARK: Easy. TEL: 01588 638851; fax/home - same; e-mail - enquiries@decorative-antiques.co.uk; website - www.decorative-antiques.co.uk. SER: Valuations. FAIRS: Warwick Deco; Chester Deco.

BRIDGNORTH

Bridgnorth Antiques Centre

Whitburn St. WV16 4QT. (R.G. Lewis). Est. 1992. Open 10-5.30, Sun. 10.30-4.30. SIZE: Large. *STOCK: Clocks, furniture, collectables.* PARK: Easy. TEL: 01746 768055. SER: Restorations (clocks).

English Heritage

2 Whitburn St., High Town. WV16 4QN. (P.J. Wainwright). Est. 1988. Open 10-5. CL: Thurs. SIZE: Medium. *STOCK: Jewellery, silverware and general antiques, militaria, coins, collectibles.* LOC: Just off High St. PARK: High St. TEL: 01746 762097. VAT: Stan/Spec.

Malthouse Antiques

The Old Malthouse, 6 Underhill St. WV16 4BB. (Susan and William Mantle). Est. 1980. Open 10-6, Sun. by appointment. CL: Wed. SIZE: Medium. *STOCK: Victorian and Edwardian furniture, French beds and armoires, £100-£1,500; upholstered chairs and sofas, from 19th C, £300-£1,800; china and decorative items, 19th-20th C, £5-£150; French chandeliers.* LOC: Main road into town from Wolverhampton. PARK: Nearby. TEL: 01746 763054; fax/home - same. SER: Valuations; restorations (furniture).

Micawber Antiques

64 St. Mary's St. WV16 4DR. (N. Berthoud). Est. 1989. Open 10-5, other times by appointment. CL: Mon. and Thurs. SIZE: Medium. *STOCK: English porcelain and pottery, decorative items, £5-£500; small furniture, £100-£1,000.* LOC: 100yds. west of town hall in High St. PARK: Easy. TEL: 01746 763254; home - same.

Old Mill Antique Centre

Mill St. WV15 5AG. (D.A. and J.R. Ridgeway). Est. 1996. Open 10-5 including Sun. SIZE: Large - 90 dealers. *STOCK: Wide range of general antiques including period furniture, porcelain and silver, jewellery, prints and watercolours, collectables.* LOC: Main road. PARK: Own. TEL: 01746 768778; fax - 01746 768944; website - www.oldmill-antiques.co.uk. SER: Valuations; restorations. VAT: Stan.

BROSELEY

John Boulton Fine Art

6 Church St. TF12 5DG. Resident. Est. 1983. Open 9-5, Sun. 2-5. SIZE: Medium. *STOCK: Oils, watercolours and prints, late 19th C to contemporary, £100-£2,500.* LOC: Junction 4, M54, take A442. PARK: Easy. TEL: 01952 882860. FAIRS: Buxton; NEC Birmingham; Shrewsbury; Edinburgh.

BURLTON, Nr. Shrewsbury

North Shropshire Reclamation

Wackley Lodge Farm. SY4 5TD. (A. and J. Powell). SALVO. Est. 1997. Open 7 days 9-5. SIZE: Large. *STOCK: Wide range of reclaimed materials.* LOC: A528. PARK: Easy. TEL: 01939 270719; home/fax - 01939 270895.

CHURCH STRETTON

Cardingmill Antiques
1 Burway Rd. SY6 6DL. (Mrs P. A. Benton). NHBS. Est. 1976. Open Thurs., Fri. and Sat. 11-5 or by appointment. SIZE: Medium. *STOCK: 18th-19th C longcase and wall clocks, furniture, £250-£2,000; Measham teapots, £90-£450; original horsebrasses and martingales (NHBS); Victorian oil lamps with original shades, £200-£650; 18th-19th C metalware.* LOC: A49. PARK: Easy. TEL: 01694 724555; home - 01584 877880; mobile - 07802 194253; website - www.churchstretton.co.uk.

Church Stretton Books
48 High St. SY6 6BX. (Roger Toon). PBFA. Est. 1992. Open 10-5, Wed. 10-1. SIZE: Small. *STOCK: Books - mainly secondhand, some antiquarian.* LOC: Off A49 at traffic lights, after 300 yards turn left at bank, shop 150 yards on right. PARK: Nearby. TEL: 01694 724337; fax - same; e-mail - csbooks@btinternet.com. SER: Valuations. FAIRS: PBFA, Birmingham; Haydock Park; Bristol.

Stretton Antiques Market
36 Sandford Ave. SY6 6BH. (T. and L. Elvins). Est. 1986. Open 9.30-5.30, Sun. and Bank Holidays 10.30-4.30. SIZE: Large - 55 dealers. *STOCK: General antiques, shipping items and collectables.* LOC: Town centre. PARK: Easy. TEL: 01694 723718.

CLEOBURY MORTIMER, Nr. Kidderminster

Antique Centre
Childe Rd. DY14 8PA. Open 10-5, Sun. by appointment. SIZE: Large. *STOCK: Georgian, Victorian, Edwardian, old pine and French furniture, period beds, garden statuary and architectural items.* PARK: Own. TEL: 01299 270513; fax - 01299 270513; e-mail - antiquecentre@supanet.com.

M. and M. Baldwin
24 High St. DY14 8BY. Est. 1978. Open mainly by appointment. SIZE: Medium. *STOCK: 19th-20th C books, to £500.* LOC: A4117. PARK: Easy. TEL: 01299 270110; fax/home - same; e-mail - books@mbaldwin.free-online.co.uk. SER: Valuations; buys at auction (books). FAIRS: Crick Boat Show; IWA National Festival. VAT: Stan.

CRAVEN ARMS

Portcullis Furniture
Ludlow Rd. SY7 9QL. (Sally Allen and John Cox). Est. 1980. Open 10-5.30, Sun. 10.30-4.30. SIZE: Large. *STOCK: Victorian, Edwardian, shipping and reproduction furniture, £5-£2,000.* LOC: A49. PARK: Easy. TEL: 01588 672263; fax - 01588 673321; home - 01588 673007. SER: Buys at auction (furniture). FAIRS: Newark; Swinderby. VAT: Stan/Spec.

DITTON PRIORS

Priors ReclamationUnit
2A Ditton Priors Industrial Estate. WV16 6SS. (Vicki Bale and Martin Foley). SALVO. Est. 1996. Open by appointment. *STOCK: Reclaimed flooring and period doors.* PARK: Easy. TEL: 01746 712450; home - same; e-mail - vicki@priorsrec.co.uk; website - www.priorsrec.co.uk. FAIRS: Burwarton.

HODNET, Nr. Market Drayton

Hodnet Antiques
13a Shrewsbury St. TF9 3NP. (Mrs J. Scott). Est. 1976. Open Tues.-Thurs. 2-5.30, other times by appointment. SIZE: Small. *STOCK: General antiques - china, glass, silver, jewellery, pictures, brass and copper, collectables and unusual decorative items, £5-£1,000; 18th-20th C furniture, £100-£5,000.* LOC: A53, Newcastle-under-Lyme to Shrewsbury road. PARK: Outside shop. TEL: Home - 01630 638591; e-mail - janescott@btopenworld.com. SER: Valuations; buys at auction.

IRONBRIDGE

Tudor House Antiques
11 Tontine Hill. TF8 7AL. (Peter Whitelaw). Est. 1963. Open 10-5. *STOCK: General antiques, especially porcelain including Coalport and Caughley.* LOC: Opposite bridge. TEL: 01952 433783; e-mail - tudoriron@aol.com; website - www.tudorhouseantiques.com.

LUDLOW

Bayliss Antiques
22-24 Old St. SY8 1NP. (D., A.B. and N. Bayliss). Resident. Est. 1966. Open 10-6 or by appointment. *STOCK: 18th-19th C furniture.* TEL: 01584 873634. SER: Valuations.

John Clegg Antiques

12 Old Street
Ludlow
Shropshire SY8 1NP

Telephone
01584 873176

R.G. Cave and Sons Ltd **BADA**
17 Broad St. SY8 1NG. LAPADA. Resident.
Est. 1962. Open 9.30-5.30. SIZE: Medium.
*STOCK: Furniture, 1630-1830; clocks, barometers,
metalwork, fine art and collectors' items.* LOC:
Old town. PARK: Easy. TEL: 01584 873568;
fax - 01584 875050. SER: Valuations. VAT:
Spec.

Claymore Antiques
18 Broad St. SY8 1NG. Est. 1995. Open 10-5,
Fri. and Sat. 10-5.30, Sun. by appointment.
*STOCK: English furniture, 18th-19th C, £200-
£10,000; English giltwood mirrors, 18th-19th C.*
PARK: Easy. TEL: 01584 875851; fax - 01885
400278; mobile - 07801 627235. SER: Valuations; buys at auction.

John Clegg
12 Old St. SY8 1NP. Resident. Est. 1960. Open
8.30-5. *STOCK: Country and other period furniture, metalware and decorative items.* TEL:
01584 873176.

Garrard Antiques
139a Corve St. SY8 2PG. (Caroline Garrard). Est.
1985. Open 10-1 and 2-5, Sat. 10-5. SIZE:
Medium. *STOCK: Pine and country furniture,*

*18th-19th C, to £3,000; French provincial
furniture, 19th to early 20th C, to £900; books,
linen, textiles, silver and treen, porcelain.* LOC:
200 yards below Feathers Hotel. PARK: Opposite.
TEL: 01584 876727. SER: Valuations. VAT: Spec.

G. & D. Ginger Antiques
5 Corve St. SY8 1DA. Resident. Open 9-5. SIZE:
Large. *STOCK: Oak dressers and farmhouse
tables, Welsh cupboards and presses, country and
mahogany furniture; decorative and associated
items.* TEL: 01584 876939; fax - 01584 876456;
mobile - 07970 666437; e-mail - gdginger@
ntiques-5.fsnet.co.uk.

**Mackenzie & Smith Furniture
Restoration**
4 Bull Ring. SY8 1AD. (Tim Smith). UKIC.
Resident. Est. 1998. Open 9-5, Sat. 10-1. SIZE:
Small. *STOCK: Oak, country and some mahogany
furniture, to £1,000; smalls including door locks
and fittings.* PARK: Loading and nearby. TEL:
01584 877133. SER: Restorations (17th-19th C
mahogany, walnut, oak, rosewood).

Robert Miller
The Angel, Broad St. SY8 1NG. Est. 1996. Open
9.30-5.30, Sun. by appointment. SIZE: Large.

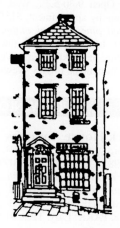
STOCK: English and Continental furniture, 1680-1940; paintings and drawings, 17th-20th C; ceramics, silver, works of art; all £50-£25,000. PARK: Easy. TEL: 01584 877788; home - 01584 831221. SER: Valuations; restorations (furniture and oil paintings); buys at auction. FAIRS: Olympia. VAT: Spec.

Mitre House Antiques
Corve Bridge. SY8 1DY. (L. Jones). Open 9-5.30. SIZE: Shop + trade warehouse. *STOCK: Clocks, pine and general antiques. Warehouse - unstripped pine and shipping goods.* TEL: 01584 872138.

M. & R. Taylor Antiques and Sarah Taylor Interiors
1 Pepper Lane. SY8 1PX. (M. Taylor). Est. 1977. Open 10-4. SIZE: Medium. *STOCK: Furniture, mahogany, oak and walnut, brass and copper, 17th-19th C.* PARK: Nearby. TEL: 01584 874169; home - 01299 832352. VAT: Stan/Spec.

Teme Valley Antiques
1 The Bull Ring. SY8 1AD. (C.S. Harvey). NAG. Est. 1979. Usually open 10-5.30, Sun. by appointment. SIZE: Medium. *STOCK: English and Continental porcelain, 18th to early 20th C, £25-£2,500; furniture, oil and watercolour paintings,* *£50-£2,500; jewellery, silver, plate, metalware and glass, £10-£3,500; both 17th to early 20th C.* Not Stocked: Militaria, coins and carpets. LOC: Town centre opposite Lunn Poly. PARK: Easy. TEL: 01584 874686. SER: Valuations; buys at auction (porcelain). VAT: Stan/Spec.

Valentyne Dawes Gallery
Church St. SY8 1AP. (B.S. McCreddie). Open 10-5.30. SIZE: Medium. *STOCK: Paintings, 19th to early 20th C, £200-£40,000; furniture, 17th-19th C, £50-£4,000; porcelain, 19th C, £5-£500.* LOC: Town centre near Buttercross. PARK: Nearby. TEL: 01584 874160; fax - 01384 455576; e-mail - sales@gallery.wyenet.co.uk; website - www.starmark.co.uk/valentyne-dawes/. SER: Valuations; restorations (oil paintings, watercolours, furniture). VAT: Spec.

MARKET DRAYTON

Arty Faherty
Honeypots Farm, Rosehill. (McNulty Wholesalers). Est. 1983. Open 11-5. *STOCK: Painted pine, mahogany; small interesting items.* PARK: Easy. TEL: 01630 639562. VAT: Stan.

Deppner Antiques
The Towers Lawn. TF9 3EB. (J. Deppner). Est. 1985. Open 9.30-5.30, Wed. 9.30-3.30, Thurs. and Sun. by appointment. SIZE: Small. *STOCK: Stripped pine, general antiques, 19th C, £20-£1,000.* LOC: From A53 towards town centre (Cheshire St.). PARK: Easy. TEL: 01630 654111. SER: Valuations. FAIRS: Newark, Ardingly.

MUCH WENLOCK

Cruck House Antiques
23 Barrow St. TF13 6EN. (B. Roderick Smith). Est. 1985. Open 9.30-5.30. SIZE: Small. *STOCK: Silver and watercolours, 19th-20th C, £25-£300; furniture, 19th C, £50-£500; general antiques.* Not Stocked: Weapons and gold. LOC: Near Square. PARK: Easy. TEL: 01952 727165.

Myra's Antiques
5 High St. TF13 6AA. (M. Mullard). Open Wed.-Sat. 10-4. *STOCK: Collectables, small antiques and furniture, Carltonware.* TEL: 01952 727596. SER: Clock repairs; polishing; restorations.

Raynalds Mansion
BADA
Raynalds Mansion. TF13 6AE. (John King). Resident. Est. 1970. Open Mon., Tues. and Fri. 10-2, prior 'phone call advisable. SIZE: Medium. STOCK: Period furniture and associated items, £500-£45,000. PARK: Easy. TEL: 01952 727456; fax/home - same. FAIRS: Olympia (June). VAT: Spec.

Wenlock Fine Art
3 The Square. TF13 6LX. (P. Cotterill). Est. 1990. Open Wed.-Sat. 10-5. SIZE: Medium. *STOCK: Modern British paintings, mainly 20th C, some late 19th C.* PARK: Nearby. TEL: 01952 728232; home - 01952 252376. SER: Valuations; restorations (cleaning); mounting; framing; buys at auction (as stock). VAT: Spec.

NEWPORT

Amanda's Secondhand Hypermarket
Salter's Lane, TF10 7LB . (Amanda Sutton). Est. 1992. Open 10-4, Sun. 12-4. SIZE: Large. *STOCK: General antiques.* PARK: 50 yds. TEL: 01952 820030.

OSWESTRY

Arcadia
6 Upper Brook St. SY10 2TB. (Joyce & Rod Whitehead). Est. 1980. Open 9.30-5. *STOCK:* *Fine art, 18th C to contemporary applied artists, £5-£1,000; contemporary pottery, glass and country furniture.* LOC: Near parish church. PARK: Easy. TEL: 01691 655622. SER: Buys at auction.

SHIFNAL

Corner Farm Antiques
Weston Heath, Sheriffhales. TF11 8RY. (Tim Dams). Est. 1994. Open 10-5 including Sun. SIZE: Large. *STOCK: Georgian to Edwardian furniture, especially extending tables and sets of chairs; £100-£4,000; longcase and wall clocks, barometers; Victorian fireplaces, £350-£750; collectables, £5-£500.* LOC: A41 between Tong and Newport. PARK: Own large. TEL: 01952 691543; home/fax - same; website - www. antiques.uk.ws. SER: Valuations; restorations (furniture and clocks); buys at auction. VAT: Stan.

SHREWSBURY

Candle Lane Books
28-29 Princess St. SY1 1LW. (J. Thornhill). Open 9.30-4.30. SIZE: Large. *STOCK: Antiquarian and secondhand books.* LOC: Town centre. PARK: Nearby. TEL: 01743 365301.

Juliet Chilton Antiques and Interiors
69 Wyle Cop. SY1 1UX. Open 9.30-6. SIZE: Large. *STOCK: Furniture and smalls, mainly 1700's-1920's and some reproduction.* TEL: 01743 358699/366553; fax - 01743 366563. SER: Shipping and packing.

Collectors' Place
29a Princess St., The Square. SY1 1LW. (Keith Jones). Open Wed-Sat. 9.30-5. *STOCK: Collectables especially Prattware potlids and bottles, 1700-1900; ceramics including Wade, Beswick, Carltonware, early 20th C; Art Deco, eyebaths.* LOC: Town centre opposite Shrewsbury Antique Centre. TEL: 01743 246150; e-mail - glanbrogan. hall@virgin.net.

Deja Vu Antiques
48 High St. SY1 1ST. (I. and Mrs A. S. Jones). Open 9.30-5. SIZE: Small. *STOCK: 1920's to 1950's telephones, £50-£500; Victorian pine and walnut furniture, general antiques and reproduction items, £5-£500.* PARK: Nearby. TEL: 01743 362251; website - www.antiquephones. co.uk. SER: Restorations (telephones). FAIRS: Art Deco - Loughborough, Chester, Leeds, Warwick Hilton.

Adrian Donnelly Antique Clocks

7 The Parade, St Mary's Place. SY1 1DL. BHI. BWCG. Est. 1985. Open 10-5, Sat. 10-1. SIZE: Medium. *STOCK: Longcase and bracket clocks and barometers, 17th-19th C, £250-£12,000.* LOC: Town centre. PARK: Easy. TEL: 01743 361388; fax - same. SER: Restorations (clocks and barometers). VAT: Stan/Spec.

Expressions

17 Princess St. SY1 1LP. Open 10.30-4.30. *STOCK: Art Deco originals, ceramics, furniture, jewellery, lighting, mirrors, prints.* TEL: 01743 351731.

Hutton Antiques

18 Princess St. SY1 1LP. (Mrs C. Brookfield). Est. 1978. Open 9.30-12.30 and 1.30-4. CL: Mon. SIZE: Medium. *STOCK: Silver, porcelain and glass, 18th-19th C, £25-£500; small furniture, £100-£2,000; Victorian jewellery.* LOC: Off square, near Music Hall. PARK: Easy. TEL: 01743 245810. SER: Valuations.

The Little Gem

18 St. Mary's St. SY1 1ED. (M.A. Bowdler). Est. 1969. Open 9-5.30. CL: Thurs. (except Dec.). SIZE: Medium. *STOCK: Georgian and Victorian jewellery; unusual gem stones, watches; hand-made jewellery.* Not Stocked: Weapons, coins, medals, furniture. LOC: Opposite St. Mary's Church along from G.P.O. PARK: In side road (St. Mary's Place) opposite shop. TEL: 01743 352085; e-mail - mbowdler@littlegem. freeserve. co.uk; website - www.thelittlegem.co.uk. SER: Repairs; valuations.

Mansers Antiques

Coleham Head. SY3 7BJ. LAPADA. Est. 1944. Open 9-5. SIZE: Large. *STOCK: Furniture, 18th-20th C, £250-£50,000; silver, porcelain, glass, mirrors, decorative items, £50-£10,000.* Not Stocked: Coins, books. LOC: 150yds. from English bridge away from town centre. PARK: Own. TEL: 01743 351120/245730; fax - 01743 271047; e-mail - mansers@theantiquedealers.com; website - www. theantiquedealers.com. SER: Valuations; restorations. VAT: Stan/Spec.

Princess Antique Centre

14a The Square. SY1. (J. Langford). Open 9.30-5. SIZE: 35 dealers. *STOCK: General antiques and collectables.* PARK: Nearby. TEL: 01743 343701.

Minton and Coalport trompe l'oeil *dishes look magnificent on a side table, but would never survive regular dusting. A display cabinet free of dust is the only practical way to display very delicate porcelain.*

From an article entitled "Displaying and Caring for your Porcelain Collection" by John Sandon which appeared in the March 2002 issue of **Antique Collecting**. For more details and to subscribe see page 21.

SHROPSHIRE

Quayside Antiques
9 Frankwell. (Jean and Chris Winter). Open Tues. and Wed. 10-4, Fri. and Sat. 10-5. SIZE: Large. *STOCK: Victorian and Edwardian furniture, especially dining tables and sets of chairs, desks, bookcases, wardrobes.* LOC: Near Halls Saleroom. PARK: Own. TEL: 01743 360490; workshop - 01948 665838; home - 01948 830363. SER: Restorations (furniture).

Raleigh Antiques of Hanwood Hall
Hanwood. SY5 8LY. (Ruth and Greville Handbury-Madin). Open 6 days. *STOCK: Furniture, small antiques and collectables.* TEL: 01743 860489.

Shrewsbury Antique Centre
15 Princess House, The Square. SY1 1JZ. (J. Langford). Est. 1978. Open 9.30-5.30. SIZE: Large - 50 dealers. *STOCK: General antiques and collectables.* LOC: Town centre just off the Square. PARK: Nearby. TEL: 01743 247704.

Shrewsbury Antique Market
Frankwell Quay Warehouse. SY3 8LG. (J. Langford). Open 9.30-5. SIZE: Large - 45 units. *STOCK: General antiques and collectors' items, £1-£2,000.* LOC: Alongside Frankwell Quay car park. PARK: Easy. TEL: 01743 350916.

Tiffany Antiques
Shrewsbury Antique Centre, 15 Princess House, The Square. SY1 1JZ. (A. Wilcox). Est. 1988. Open 9.30-5.30. *STOCK: Metalware, collectables, curios, china and glass.* LOC: Town centre. PARK: Multi-storey. TEL: Home - 01270 257425; mobile - 07970 419263. SER: Buys at auction

Marcus Moore Antiques
Booley House, Booley. SY4 4LY. (M.G.J. and M.P. Moore). Est. 1980. Usually open but prior telephone call advisable. SIZE: Large. *STOCK: Oak and country furniture, late 17th to 18th C; Georgian mahogany furniture, 18th to early 19th C; all £50-£7,000; some Victorian furniture; associated items.* LOC: Half a mile north of Stanton on right. PARK: Easy. TEL: 01939 200333; website - www.marcusmoore-antiques. com. SER: Restorations (furniture); polishing; search; shipping. VAT: Stan/Spec.

Haygate Gallery
40 Haygate Rd., Wellington. TF1 1QT. (Mrs M. Kuznierz). Open 9-5, Sat. 9-1. CL: Wed. *STOCK: Chandeliers, lighting and decorative antiques.* LOC: One mile from junction 7, M54. PARK: Easy. TEL: 01952 248553. SER: Framing.

Brian James Antiques
Old Maltings, The Lawns, Wellington. TF1 3AF. Est. 1985. Open 9-6, Sat. 9.30-12.30, Sun. by appointment. SIZE: Large. *STOCK: Chests of drawers, Georgian to Victorian, £50-£1,500.* LOC: Off M54, junction 6. Follow signs for Telford Hospital then Wellington Centre, turn right at Red Lion. PARK: Easy. TEL: 01952 256592/243906; e-mail - bjames45@hotmail. com. SER: Restorations and conversions; linen presses, sideboards, cabinets and chests made to order. VAT: Stan.

Age of Elegance
54 High St. SY13 1BB. (Mike and Janet Proudlove). Est. 1988. Open 10-4. CL: Wed. SIZE: Small. *STOCK: Collectables including china and glass; Victorian and Edwardian furniture.* LOC: Midway between Shrewsbury and Chester. PARK: Easy. TEL: 01948 666145; fax - same.

Dodington Antiques
7 Sherrymill Hill. SY13 1BN. (G. MacGillivray). Resident. Est. 1978. By appointment. SIZE: Large. *STOCK: Oak, fruitwood, walnut country and 18th to early 19th C mahogany furniture, longcase clocks, barometers, £10-£6,000.* LOC: On fringe of town centre. PARK: Easy. TEL: 01948 663399. SER: Buys at auction. VAT: Stan/Spec.

The Mount
12 Nantwich Rd. CW3 9SA. Est. 1978. Open most afternoons and weekends (prior telephone call advisable). *STOCK: Watercolours, oils and drawings, Victorian to 20th C; maps, prints and topographical items, from 17th C; all £2-£500.* LOC: Junction of A51 and A525. PARK: Easy. TEL: 01630 647274; home - same. SER: Framing; finder (maps and topography).

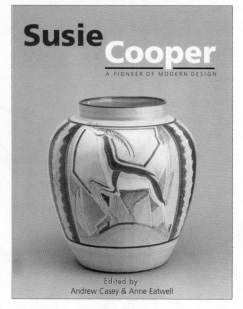

SUSIE COOPER
A PIONEER OF MODERN DESIGN

Andrew Casey & Anne Eatwell

As a woman in an industry run by men, it was her ability to anticipate the mood of the day and understand market trends that enabled Susie Cooper to keep ahead of her competitors. Cooper made her name through designing for and managing her own company. This was not, however, the only way in which she was unique; she produced modern pots at affordable prices and provided customers who possessed exceptional taste, but little money, with well-designed practical and attractive pottery. Cooper's pots became symbolic of the new domestic life enjoyed by the suburban middle classes. Her career spanned seven decades and a staggering four thousand patterns ranging from the jazz modern colours of the Art Deco period to the Pop Art of the swinging sixties.

This centenary book outlines and discusses Susie Cooper's major achievements throughout her prolific career. The focus of the book is on new information and original research to add to the understanding of one of our greatest ceramic designers. Essays incorporated in this book include 'Women Designers in Context', 'Unknown Susie Cooper', 'The Susie Cooper Style', 'Royal Connections', 'Pottery Patronage' and 'Susie Cooper and Wedgwood'.

Specifications: 224pp., 154 col. illus. 90 b.&w. illus., 11x8½in./279x216mm.
£45.00

Available from the
ANTIQUE COLLECTORS' CLUB
Sandy Lane, Old Martlesham, Woodbridge, Suffolk IP12 4SD, UK.
For your free copy of the catalogue:
Tel: **01394 389950** or Fax: **01394 389999**
Email: sales@antique-acc.com   Website: www.antique-acc.com

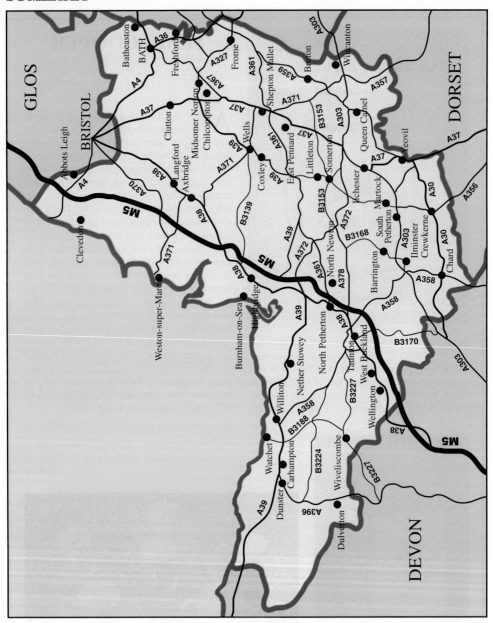

Dealers and Shops in Somerset

Abbots Leigh	1	Chilcompton	1	Frome	2	North Newton	1	Wells	3
Axbridge	1	Clevedon	3	Highbridge	2	North Petherton	1	West Buckland	1
Barrington	1	Clutton	1	Ilchester	1	Queen Camel	1	Weston-Super-	
Bath	51	Coxley	2	Ilminster	1	Shepton Mallet	1	Mare	3
Batheaston	1	Crewkerne	5	Langford	1	Somerton	3	Williton	2
Bruton	3	Dulverton	4	Littleton	1	South Petherton	1	Wincanton	1
Burnham-on-Sea	4	Dunster	1	Martock	1	Taunton	5	Wiveliscombe	3
Carhampton	1	East Pennard	1	Midsomer Norton	1	Watchet	2	Yeovil	2
Chard	2	Freshford	2	Nether Stowey	2	Wellington	1		

ABBOTS LEIGH, Nr. Bristol

David and Sally March Antiques

Oak Wood Lodge, Stoke Leigh Woods. BS8 3QB. (D. and S. March). LAPADA. Est. 1981. Open by appointment. *STOCK: 18th to early 19th C English porcelain especially figures and Bristol.* PARK: Easy. TEL: 01275 372422; fax - same; mobile - 07774 838376. SER: Valuations; buys at auction (as stock). FAIRS: Olympia; LAPADA; NEC. VAT: Spec.

AXBRIDGE

The Old Post House

Weare, Bridgewater Rd. BS26 2JF. (Ray and Mollie Seaman). *STOCK: General antiques and country furniture.* TEL: 01934 732372.

BARRINGTON, Nr. Ilminster

Stuart Interiors Ltd

Barrington Court. TA19 0NG. LAPADA. Open 9-5, Sat. 10-5. SIZE: Large. *STOCK: Oak furniture, £100-£10,000; accessories, £50-£2,500; both pre-1720.* Not Stocked: 18th C mahogany. LOC: Between A303 and M5, 5 miles north-east of Ilminster. House is National Trust property, signposted in area. PARK: Easy. TEL: 01460 240349. SER: Valuations; buys at auction (early oak furniture and accessories, interior design and architectural items including oak panelling). VAT: Spec.

BATH

A J Antiques

13 Broad St. BA1 5LJ. (Patrick Anketell-Jones). BABAADA. Open 10-5.30 or by appointment. *STOCK: Furniture, Georgian to Art Deco.* LOC: City centre. PARK: Nearby. TEL: 01225 447765.

Abbey Galleries

9 Abbey Churchyard. BA1 1LY. (R. Dickson). Est. 1930. Open 10.30-5.30. *STOCK: Jewellery, Oriental items, 18th-19th C; silver, 18th C.* Not Stocked: Furniture. LOC: Next to the Roman Baths. TEL: 01225 460565. SER: Valuations; restorations (jewellery and clocks); buys at auction. VAT: Stan.

Adam Gallery

13 John St. BA1 2JL. (P. and P. Dye). Open 9.30-5.30 or by appointment. *STOCK: 20th C and contemporary paintings, especially St Ives, Nicholson, Piper, Lanyon, Moore, Picasso,* *Braque, Hitchens, Hilton, Heron and Scott, £500-£30,000.* TEL: 01225 480406; fax - same. SER: Contemporary exhibitions.

Alderson   BADA

2 Princes Buildings, George St. BA1 2ED. (C.J.R. Alderson). BABAADA. Est. 1976. Open 9.30-1 and 2-5.30, Sat 9.30-3 or by appointment. *STOCK: Furniture and accessories, 17th-18th C.* **LOC: Central. PARK: Nearby. TEL: 01225 421652; fax - same; e-mail - kit.alderson@ amserve.net. SER: Valuations. FAIRS: BADA; Olympia. VAT: Spec.**

Antique Linens and Lace

11 Pulteney Bridge. BA2 4AY. (Mrs R. Mellor). BABAADA. Est. 1971. Open 10-5.30. SIZE: Small. *STOCK: Quality linens and lace, bedspreads, sheets, tablecloths, pillow cases, christening gowns, baby bonnets, beaded bags, veils, shawls, quilts and textiles, 1850-1920, £10-£600.* LOC: City centre. PARK: Great Pulteney St.- 100 yards. TEL: 01225 465782; fax - 01225 867551. VAT: Stan/Spec.

Antique Textiles & Lighting

34 Belvedere, Lansdown Rd. BA1 5BN. (Joanna Proops). BABAADA. Open Tues.-Fri. 10-5 or by appointment. *STOCK: Chandeliers, wall lights, tapestries, paisleys, beadwork, fans, samplers, bellpulls, linen and lace, tapes, ties.* TEL: 01225 310795.

Antiques of Bath

12 Margarets Buildings, Brock St. BA1 2LP. BABAADA. Open 10.30-5.30 including Sun. or by appointment. SIZE: Medium. *STOCK: 19th-20th C furniture, paintings, silver and decorative items.* LOC: Off Brock St. between The Circus and Royal Crescent. PARK: Nearby. TEL: 01225 448432; e-mail - sales@antiques-of-bath.co.uk; website - www.antiques-of-bath.co.uk.

The Antiques Warehouse

57 Walcot St. BA1 5BN. BABAADA. Est. 1991. Open 10.30-5.30. SIZE: Medium. *STOCK: 19th C mahogany furniture, £300-£5,000; decorative objects, £20-£500.* LOC: From junction 18, M4 along A46 then A4, at first mini-roundabout veer left into Walcot St. Shop 300yds on right. PARK: Easy. TEL: 01225 444201; mobile - 07990 690240. VAT: Stan/Spec.

Arkea Antiques

10A Monmouth Place. BA1 2AX. (G. Harmandian). Est. 1969. *STOCK: Furniture and china.* TEL: 01225 429413/835382. SER: Repairs (antiques); traditional French polishing; desk leathering.

Assembly Antiques Centre

5/8 Saville Row. BA1 2QP. BABAADA. Open 10-5, Wed. 7-5. *STOCK: 18th-19th C furniture, scent*

bottles and jewellery, Art Deco items, tea caddies, boxes, pictures, lighting, furniture, decorative effects. LOC: Rear of the Assembly Rooms. TEL: 01225 426288; fax - 01225 429661; e-mail - lyndabrine@ yahoo.co.uk; website - www.assemblyeantique centre.co.uk.

Bartlett Street Antiques Centre
5-10 Bartlett St. BA1 2QZ. BABAADA. Open 9.30-5, Wed. 8-5. SIZE: 50+ dealers and 150 display cases. *STOCK: Wide range of general antiques.* TEL: 01225 466689; stallholders - 01225 310457/446322; fax - 01225 444146; e-mail - info@antiques-centre.co.uk; website - www.antiques-centre.co.uk.

Bath Galleries
33 Broad St. BA1 5LP. (J. Griffiths). BABAADA. Open 9.30-5. SIZE: Medium. *STOCK: Clocks, furniture, paintings, porcelain, barometers, silver.* LOC: 50yds. from Central Post Office. PARK: Walcot St. multi-storey, 30yds. TEL: 01225 462946. SER: Valuations; restorations; buys at auction. VAT: Stan/Spec.

Bath Saturday Antiques Market
Walcot St. BA1 5B. (J. Whittingham). Est. 1978. Open Sat. 7-5. SIZE: 100 stalls. *STOCK: Wide variety of general antiques, £1-£4,000.* LOC: Close to Hilton Hotel. PARK: Multi-storey. TEL: Mobile - 07836 534893.

Bath Stamp and Coin Shop
Pulteney Bridge. BA2 4AY. (H. and A. Swindells). Est. 1946. Open 9.30-5.30. *STOCK: Coins - Roman, hammered, early milled, G.B. gold, silver and copper, some foreign; literature and accessories; banknotes, medals, stamps and postal history.* PARK: Laura Place; Walcot multi-storey. TEL: 01225 463073; e-mail - m.swindells @virgin.net. SER: Valuations. VAT: Stan.

George Bayntun
Manvers St. BA1 1JW. (E.W.G. Bayntun-Coward). BABAADA. Est. 1894. Open 9-1 and 2-5.30, Sat. 9.30-1. SIZE: Large. *STOCK: Rare*

books. First or fine editions of English literature, standard sets, illustrated and sporting books, poetry, biography and travel, mainly in new leather bindings; antiquarian books in original bindings. LOC: By railway and bus stations. PARK: 50 yds. by station. TEL: 01225 466000; fax - 01225 482122; e-mail - ebc@george bayntun.com; website - www.georgebayntun. com. SER: Restorations (rare books). VAT: Stan.

Bedsteads
2 Walcot Buildings, London Rd. BA1 6AD. (Mark and Nikki Ashton). BABAADA. Est. 1991. Open Tues.-Sat. 10-5.30. *STOCK: Brass, iron and wooden bedsteads, 1840-1920, £500-£4,500; bedroom suites, 1880-1920, £2,000-£5,500.* LOC: 200 yds. before traffic lights, end of London Road. TEL: 01225 339182; fax - same; home - 01275 464114. SER: Valuations; restorations (bedsteads). VAT: Stan/Spec.

Bladud House Antiques
8 Bladud Buildings. BA1 5LS. (Mrs E. Radosenska). Open 9.30-1 and 2-4.30. CL: Mon. and Thurs. *STOCK: Jewellery and small items.* Not Stocked: Furniture. TEL: 01225 462929.

Lawrence Brass
Apple Studio, Ashley. BA1 3SD. BAFRA. UKIC. Est. 1973. Open by appointment. SIZE: Small. *STOCK: Furniture, 16th-19th C, £50-£5,000.* Not Stocked: Ceramics, silver, glass. LOC: A4 towards Chippenham. PARK: Easy. TEL: 01225 852222; fax - 01225 851050. SER: Restorations (furniture, clocks and barometers). VAT: Stan/Spec.

Geoffrey Breeze
6 George St. BA1 2EH. LAPADA. BABAADA. Open 10-5. SIZE: Large. *STOCK: Furniture, 18th-20th C.* LOC: City centre. TEL: 01225 466499; e-mail - gebreeze@aol.com.

David Bridgwater
Heather Cottage, Lansdown. BA1 9BL. Open by appointment. *STOCK: Architectural and garden sculpture, decorative and practical items for the period garden.* TEL: 01225 463435.

Bryers Antiques

Entrance to the Guildhall Market, High St. BA1 1JQ. (S. Bryers). Est. 1940. *STOCK: Furniture, decorative items, porcelain, glass, silver and Victorian plate.* TEL: 01225 466352/460535.

Camden Books

146 Walcot St. BA1 5BL. (Victor and Elizabeth Suchar). PBFA. Est. 1984. Open 10-5. *STOCK: Books - architecture, philosophy, economics, science, 18th-20th C; general, 19th-20th C.* LOC: From east on to London Rd., then Walcot St. PARK: Easy. TEL: 01225 461606; fax - same; website - www.camdenbooks.com. SER: Valuations; buys at auction. FAIRS: Bath PBFA; London PBFA.

Brian and Caroline Craik Ltd

8 Margaret's Buildings. BA1 2LP. Est. 1963. Open 10-4. *STOCK: Decorative items, mainly 19th C; metalwork, treen, glass and pewter.* PARK: Nearby. TEL: 01225 337161.

Mary Cruz

5 Broad St. BA1 5LJ. LAPADA. BABAADA. CINOA. Est. 1974. Open 10-6.30, Sun. by appointment. SIZE: Medium. *STOCK: 18th-19th C furniture and decorative items; 19th-20th C paintings and sculpture.* PARK: Easy. TEL: 01225 334174; fax - 01225 423300. SER: Valuations; restorations; finder (Latin American Art). VAT: Stan/Spec.

Andrew Dando   BADA

4 Wood St., Queen Sq. BA1 2JQ. (A.P. and J.M. Dando). LAPADA. BABAADA. Est. 1915. Open 10-5.30, Sat. 10-1. CL: Some Mon. SIZE: Large. *STOCK: English, Continental, Oriental porcelain and pottery, including Staffordshire, 17th to mid-19th C; local topographical and decorative antique prints.* **LOC: 200yds. from bottom of Milsom St. towards Queen Sq. TEL: 01225 422702; website - www.andrewdando. co.uk. SER: Valuations. VAT: Stan/Spec.**

D. and B. Dickinson   BADA

22 New Bond St. BA1 1BA. (S.G., D. and N.W. Dickinson). BABAADA. Est. 1917. Open 9.30-1 and 2-5. SIZE: Small. *STOCK: Jewellery, 1770-1900, £20-£2,000; silver, 1750-1900, £25-£3,000; Sheffield plate, 1770-1845, £50-£1,000.* **LOC: Next to Post Office. PARK: 100yds. at bottom of street, turn left then right for multi-storey. TEL: 01225 466502; website - www. dickinsonsilver.co.uk. VAT: Stan/Spec.**

Frank Dux Antiques

33 Belvedere, Lansdown Rd. BA1 5HR. (F. Dux and M. Hopkins). Resident. BABAADA. Est. 1988. Open Tues.-Sat. 10-6. SIZE: Medium. *STOCK: Mainly glass, 18th-19th C English drinking glasses and decanters and later Venetian; some furniture, unusual decorative items including glass paintings.* LOC: From Broad St. up Lansdown Hill, on right 100yds. past Guinea Lane. PARK: Easy. TEL: 01225 312367; fax - same; e-mail - antique.glass @which.net; website - www.antique-glass.co.uk.

George Gregory

Manvers St. BA1 1JW. (C.A.W. Bayntun-Coward). Est. 1845. Open 9-1 and 2-5.30, Sat. 9.30-1. SIZE: Large. *STOCK: Secondhand books, engraved views and portraits.* LOC: By rail station. PARK: By rail station. TEL: 01225 466000; fax - 01225 482122; e-mail - ebc@ georgebayntun.com.

Haliden Oriental Rug Shop

98 Walcot St. BA1 5BG. (Andrew Lloyd, Craig Bale and Owen Parry). Est. 1963. Open 10-5. SIZE: Medium. *STOCK: Caucasian, Turkish, Persian, Chinese, Afghan, Turcoman and tribal rugs and carpets, 19th C, £50-£3,000; some Oriental textiles - coats, embroideries, wall hangings, 19th C, £50-£750.* LOC: Off main London road, into town by Walcot Reclamation. PARK: Walcot St. or multi-storey. TEL: 01225 469240. SER: Valuations; cleaning; restorations (as stock); buys at auction (as stock).

Anthony Hepworth Fine Art Dealers

1 Margarets Buildings, Brock St. BA1 2LP. Open during exhibitions Wed.-Sat. 11-5 other times by appointment. *STOCK: Mainly 20th C British paintings and sculpture; African tribal art.* LOC: Off Brock St. between Royal Crescent and Circus. PARK: Brock St. TEL: 01225 447480/ 442917; fax - 01225 442917; mobile - 07970 480650 (during fairs only). SER: Exhibitions Bath and London. FAIRS: Olympia; 20th/21st C British Art.

Helena Hood and Co

3 Margarets Buildings, Brock St. BA1 2LP. (Mrs L.M. Hood). BABAADA. Est. 1973. Open 9.30-1 and 2.15-5.30, Sat. 10.30-1. CL: Mon. SIZE: Medium. *STOCK: Decorative items - furniture, prints, paintings and porcelain, 18th-19th C, £50-£2,500.* LOC: Pedestrian walkway running north from Brock St. PARK: Easy. TEL: 01225 424438; fax - 01225 336363. SER: Restorations. VAT: Stan/Spec.

Jadis Ltd

14 and 15 Walcot Buildings, London Rd., BA1 6AD. (S.H. Creese-Parsons and N.A. Mackay). BABAADA. Est. 1970. Open 9.30-6, Sun. by appointment. SIZE: Medium. *STOCK: English and European furniture, 18th-19th C; decorative items.* LOC: On left hand side of A4 London Rd., entering Bath. PARK: At rear. TEL: 01225 338797; fax - same; 01225 333130; mobiles - 07768 232133/07879 692371; e-mail - Jadpalad

@aol.com and scp.Jadis@aol.com; website - www.Jadis-Ltd.com. SER: Design service, murals and trompe l'oeil. VAT: Stan/Spec.

Kembery Antique Clocks (inc. K. & D. Antique Clocks)
Bartlett Street Antique Centre, 5 Bartlett St. BA1 2QZ. (E. Kembery). BABAADA. BWCMG. Est. 1993. Open 10-5. *STOCK: Longcase, bracket, mantel, wall and carriage clocks and barometers, 18th-19th C, £200-£10,000.* TEL: 0117 956 5281; website - www.kdclocks.co.uk. SER: Valuations; restorations. VAT: Spec.

Ann King
38 Belvedere, Lansdown Rd. BA1 5HR. Est. 1977. Open 10-5. SIZE: Small. *STOCK: Period clothes, 19th C to 1960; baby clothes, shawls, bead dresses, linen, lace, curtains, cushions, quilts and textiles.* LOC: Around corner from Guinea Lane Antique Market. PARK: Easy. TEL: 01225 336245.

Nick Kuhn
4 Miles Buildings, Off George St. BA1 2QS. Est. 1992. Always open Sat. 10-5, other times by appointment. SIZE: Small. *STOCK: 20th C modern furniture and design, British fine art, naïve art, hooked rugs, £30-£3,000.* LOC: City centre, near Bartlett Street Antiques Centre.

PARK: Nearby. TEL: 01225 425486. FAIRS: BABAADA.

Lansdown Antiques
23 Belvedere, Lansdown Rd. BA1 5ED. (Chris and Ann Kemp). BABAADA. Open 9.30-5.30, Sun. by appointment. *STOCK: Painted pine and country furniture, 17th-19th C; metalware, unusual and decorative items.* LOC: From A4/A46 roundabout across 2 sets of traffic lights, right at mini roundabout, right at next traffic lights, shop 350yds. on left. PARK: Easy. TEL: 01225 313417; home - same; mobile - 07801 013663; e-mail - lansdown-antiques@lineone.net. VAT: Stan/Spec.

Looking Glass of Bath
94-96 Walcot St. BA1 5BG. (Anthony Reed). Est. 1972. Open 9-6. SIZE: Small. *STOCK: Large mirrors and picture frames, 18th-19th C, £50-£5,000; decorative prints, 18th-20th C.* PARK: Easy. TEL: 01225 461969; fax - 01225 316191; home - 01275 333595; website - www. lookinglassofbath.co.uk. SER: Valuations; restorations (re-gilding, gesso and compo work, re-silvering and bevelling glass); manufactures arched top overmantel, pier, convex and triptych mirrors; old mirror plates supplied; simulated mercury silvered mirror glass; buys at auction (mirrors and pictures). VAT: Stan/Spec.

Lopburi Art & Antiques
5 Saville Row. BA1 2QP. (Simon and Mee Ling Roper). BABAADA. Est. 1998. Open 10-5. SIZE: Medium. *STOCK: 12th-19th C Buddhist art from Thailand, Cambodia and Burma, in bronze, stone and wood, £500-£35,000; 17th-19th C Tibetan painted wooden chests, £900-£7,000; Chinese furniture, carpets and Nepalese contemporary paintings.* LOC: City centre. PARK: Meters. TEL: 01225 322947; fax - same; e-mail - mail@lopburi.co.uk; website - www.lopburi.co.uk. SER: Valuations.

E.P. Mallory and Son Ltd   BADA
1-4 Bridge St. and 5 Old Bond St. BA2 4AP. BABAADA. Est. 1898. Open 10-5. *STOCK: Period silver and Sheffield plate, jewellery, objets de vertu, £50-£5,000.* **TEL: 01225 788800; fax - 01225 442210; e-mail - mail@mallory-jewellers. com; website - www. mallory-jewellers.com. VAT: Stan/Spec.**

Montague Antiques
16 Walcot Buildings, London Rd. BA1 6AD. (A. R. Schlesinger and D.K. Moore). BABAADA. Resident. Est. 1986. Open 10-6, Sun.11-4. CL: Thurs. SIZE: Medium. *STOCK: Furniture, 17th C to 1920, £50-£1,000; collectables, Oriental rugs, ceramics, glass, £1-£500; glass light shades and fittings, to 1939, £5-£1,500.* Not Stocked: Weapons and jewellery. LOC: A4. Shop 100m west of Safeway supermarket. PARK: Own at rear, via Bedford St. TEL: 01225 469282; home - same. SER: Valuations.

Paragon Antiques and Collectors Market
3 Bladud Buildings, The Paragon. BA1 5LS. (T.J. Clifford and Son Ltd). BABAADA. Est. 1978. Open Wed. 6.30-3. SIZE: Large. LOC: Milsom St./Broad St. PARK: 50yds. TEL: 01225 463715.

Patterson Liddle
10 Margaret's Buildings, Brock St. BA1 2LP. ABA. PBFA. ILAB. Open 10-5.30. *STOCK: Antiquarian books and prints especially art and architecture, illustrated and transport history, travel, English literature, maps.* PARK: Nearby. TEL: 01225 426722; fax - same; e-mail - mail@pattersonliddle.com; website - www.pattersonliddle.com. SER: Transport History catalogues issued.

Quiet Street Antiques
3 Quiet St. and 14/15 John St. BA1 2JS. (K. Hastings-Spital). BABAADA. Est. 1985. Open 10-6. SIZE: Large - 8 showrooms. *STOCK: Furniture especially English mahogany, 1750-1870, £250-£8,000; objects including bronzes, caddies, boxes, mirrors, £50-£2,000; Royal Worcester porcelain, £30-£2,000; clocks including longcase, wall, bracket and carriage, 1750-1900, £150-£6,000.* LOC: 25yds. from Milsom St. PARK: Nearby. TEL: 01225 315727; fax - 01225 448300; e-mail - kerry@quietstreetantiques.co.uk; website - www.quietstreetantiques.co.uk. SER: Buys at auction (furniture and clocks); upholstery; free delivery service 100 mile radius of Bath, and weekly delivery to London. Export facilities. VAT: Spec.

Sarah Russell Antiquarian Prints
5 Margaret's Buildings, Brock St. BA1 2LP. ABA. Open 10-5. *STOCK: Unusual antiquarian prints - architecture, flowers, portraits, landscapes and Bath views, many in original frames.* TEL: 01225 466335; fax - same; e-mail - bathprint@aol.com.

Michael and Jo Saffell
3 Walcot Buildings, London Rd. BA1 6AD. BABAADA. Est. 1975. Open 9.30-5, Sat. by appointment. SIZE: Small. *STOCK: British tins and other advertising material including showcards and enamels, 1870-1939; decorative items; all £5-£5,000.* LOC: A4 - main road into city from M4. PARK: Side streets opposite. TEL: 01225 315857; fax - same; home - same; mobile - 07941 158049; e-mail - michael.saffell@virgin.net. FAIRS: Newark.

Tim Snell Antiques
5 & 6 Cleveland Terrace, London Rd. BA1 5DF. BABAADA. Open 10-6 including Sun. *STOCK: Fully restored golden oak, mahogany and walnut furniture, late 19th to early 20th C.* TEL: 01225 423045.

Source
93-95 Walcot St. BA1 3SD. (Roderick I. Donaldson). Open Tues.-Sat. 10-5. *STOCK: Period architectural materials, church and bar fittings, mirrors, lighting, decorative items, metalware, ironwork and garden furniture, 20th C metal fitted kitchens.* PARK: Nearby and limited. TEL: 01225 4692000; website - www.source-antiques.co.uk. SER: Worldwide search and supply.

Susannah
25 Broad St. BA1 5LW. (Sue Holley). BABAADA. Est. 1985. Open 10-5. *STOCK: Decorative textiles and antiques.* PARK: Opposite. TEL: 01225 445069; fax - 01225 339004. FAIRS: Bath Decorative (March).

James Townshend Antiques

1 Saville Row. BA1 2QP. BABAADA. Est. 1977. Open 10-5. SIZE: Large. *STOCK: Trade furniture, china, unusual decorative items and clocks.* LOC: City centre. PARK: Easy. TEL: 01225 332290; website - www.jtownshendantiques.co.uk. SER: Deliveries arranged. VAT: Spec/Global.

Trimbridge Galleries

2 Trimbridge. BA1 1HE. (Mr and Mrs A. Anderson). BABAADA. Est. 1973. SIZE: Medium. *STOCK: Watercolours and drawings, £50-£3,000; prints and oil paintings; all 18th to early 20th C.* LOC: Just off lower end of Milsom St. PARK: Easy. TEL: 01225 466390.

Walcot Reclamation

108 Walcot St. BA1 5BG. BABAADA. Est. 1977. Open 8.30-5.30, Sat. 9-5. SIZE: Large. *STOCK: Architectural items - chimney pieces, ironwork, doors, fireplaces, garden statuary, period baths and fittings and traditional building materials.* PARK: Own and multi-storey nearby. TEL: 01225 444404/335532; e-mail - rick@walcot.com and jane@reproshop.com; websites - www.walcot.com and www.reproshop.com. SER: Valuations; restorations. VAT: Stan.

BATHEASTON, Nr. Bath

Piccadilly Antiques

280 High St. BA1 7RA. BABAADA. Est. 1990. Open 9.30-5.30, Sun. 10.30-4.30 or by appointment. SIZE: Large. *STOCK: Country furniture, decorative accessories, £100-£5,000.* LOC: 1 mile east of Bath on old A4. PARK: Easy. TEL: 01225 851494; fax - 01225 851120; e-mail - piccadillyantiques@ukonline.co.uk. SER: Restorations (country furniture). FAIRS: VAT: Stan/Spec. Below are listed the dealers trading from these premises.

Robin Coleman Antiques

BABAADA. *Interesting and decorative items.* VAT: Stan/Spec.

John Davies

18th-19th C furniture especially country and Gothic oak, and decorative smalls. TEL: Home - 01225 852103.

Gene Foster (Antiques)

BABAADA. *Decorative and unusual items, 17th-19th C; Continental and English painted furniture, paintings, needlework, prints and metalware, £25-£2,500.* VAT: Stan/Spec.

Mike Holt

BABAADA. *19th C decorative metalware.*

BRUTON

The Antique Shop
5 High St. BA10 0AB. (D.L. Gwilliam and M.J. Wren). Est. 1976. Open Thurs.-Sat. 10-5.30 or by appointment. SIZE: Medium. *STOCK: Furniture, jewellery, silver, china, copper, brass, general collectables, decorative art and antiques, Georgian to Art Deco, £5-£4,000.* PARK: Easy. TEL: 01749 813264. SER: Repairs (clock, watch, jewellery); re-stringing pearls and beads.

Michael Lewis Gallery - Antiquarian Maps & Prints
17 High St. BA10 0AB. Est. 1980. Open 9.30-5.30 or by appointment. CL: Thurs. pm. SIZE: Large. *STOCK: Prints and maps, 18th-19th C.* LOC: A359. PARK: Nearby. TEL: 01749 813557; home - same. SER: Picture framing.

M.G.R. Exports
Station Rd. BA10 0EH. BABAADA. Est. 1980. Open Mon.-Fri. 8.30-5.30 or by appointment. SIZE: Large. *STOCK: Georgian, Victorian, Edwardian and decorative items, carved oak, barley twist and shipping goods, Continental furniture.* PARK: Easy. TEL: 01749 812460; fax - 01749 812882; e-mail - antiques@mgr.exports. co.uk. SER: Packing and shipping.

BURNHAM-ON-SEA

Burnham Model & Collectors Shop
3 College Court, College St., TA8 1AR. (W.I. Loudon). Est. 1994. Open 9.30-5, some Sun. SIZE: Medium. *STOCK: Postcards, pre-1945, 50p-£100; models, Corgi, trackside, old trains.* LOC: Seafront, opposite Pavilion Amusements. PARK: Limited. TEL: 01278 780066; fax - same. SER: Valuations. FAIRS: Yeovil (Feb.)

Castle Antiques
(T.C. Germain). Open by appointment. *STOCK: Jewellery, silver, 18th-19th C furniture, porcelain, clocks.* TEL: 01278 785031; website - www. castleantiquesjewellery.com.

John Dyte Antiques
Vicarage Chambers, Victoria St. TA8 1AW. *STOCK: Longcase clocks, 18th-20th C, furniture.* TEL: 01278 788603; fax - 01278 788604.

Heape's Antiques
39 Victoria St. TA8 1AN. (Mrs M.M. Heap). Open 10-1 and 2.30-4.30. *STOCK: Small furniture, fine arts, porcelain, glass, memorabilia.* LOC: Town centre. PARK: Easy. TEL: 01278 782131. SER: Picture framing.

CARHAMPTON, Nr. Minehead

Chris's Crackers
Townsend Garage. Est. 1995. Open 11-5.30 including Sun. SIZE: Large warehouses. *STOCK: Mainly 18th-19th C furniture, stripped pine, architectural antiques, iron and stonework, general building reclamation materials and country artefacts.* LOC: A39 coast road. PARK: Easy. TEL: 01643 821873. SER: Pine-stripping.

CHARD

Chard Antique Centre
23 High St. TA20 1QFA.(W.E. and Mrs J. Smith). Est. 1994. Open 10-5. SIZE: Medium. *STOCK: Furniture, 19th C to Edwardian; pine, decorative items, pictures and collectables.* PARK: Nearby. TEL: 01460 63517.

Chez Chalon
Field Bars House, Shepherds Lane. TA20 1QX. (Jake and Nick Chalon). Est. 1973. Open 9-6, Sun. by appointment. *STOCK: French and English country furniture, £100-£10,000.* LOC: A30. PARK: Easy. TEL: 01460 68679; fax - 01460 239005; e-mail - info@chezchalon.com; website - www.chezchalon.com. SER: Restorations (trade only). VAT: Stan.

CHILCOMPTON, Nr. Bath

Billiard Room Antiques
The Old School, Church Lane. BA3 4HP. (Mrs J. McKeivor). LAPADA. BABAADA. Est. 1992. Open by appointment. SIZE: Medium. *STOCK: Billiard, snooker and pool tables and accessories, 19th C, £100-£40,000.* PARK: Easy. TEL: 01761 232839; home and fax - same. SER: Valuations; restorations; buys at auction; search.

CLEVEDON

Beach Antiques
Adelaide House, 13 The Beach. BS21 7QU. (D.A. Coles). Open 2-5, Sat. and Sun. 11-5. CL: Mon. and Fri. *STOCK: Jewellery, silver frames, china, brass, glass, mainly small items.* PARK: Easy. TEL: 01275 876881.

The Collector
14 The Beach. BS21 7QU. (Mrs Tina Simmonds). Est. 1993. Open 10-5, Sun. 12-5. CL: Thurs. (Jan.-Feb. open weekends only). SIZE: Small. *STOCK: Small items and collectables, from 1880,*

£5-£200; postcards and ephemera, 1900-1960, £1-£30; Beatrix Potter and Bunnykins figures, from 1960, £16-£300. LOC: On sea front, near pier. PARK: Easy. TEL: 01275 875066; home - same. FAIRS: Malvern 3 Counties; Temple Meads, Brunel, Bristol.

Nostalgia
65a Hill Rd. BS21 7PD. (Mrs Wendy Moore). Est. 1985. Open Wed.-Fri. 10-1 and 2-5, Tues. 10-1 and 2-4.30, Sat. 10-1 and 2-5.30. SIZE: Medium. *STOCK: Furniture, Victorian, £200-£600; china and linen, 1930's and earlier, £3-£100.* PARK: Easy. TEL: 01275 342587.

CLUTTON

Ian McCarthy
Arcadian Cottage, 112 Station Rd. BS39 5RA. Resident. Est. 1958. Open by appointment. SIZE: Medium. *STOCK: Lamps - oil, gas, electric for domestic, industrial, shipping and transport usage; unusual candle lamps; copper and brassware, 17th C to 1920, £5-£2,000.* PARK: Easy and opposite. TEL: 01761 453188; fax - same. SER: Valuations; restorations (metalware); cleaning; spares and lamp-shades.

COXLEY, Nr. Wells

Courtyard Antiques
Main Rd. BA5 1QZ. (Mr and Mrs M. J. Mitchell). Est. 1985. Open 9-5, Sun by appointment. SIZE: Medium. *STOCK: Furniture, £100-£300; smalls, £10-£50; both 19th-20th C.* TEL: 01749 679533. SER: Valuations; restorations (upholstery, cane and rush work, china and furniture).

Wells Reclamation Company
BA5 1RQ. (H. Davies). Est. 1984. Open 9-5.30. SIZE: Large. *STOCK: Architectural items, 18th-19th C.* LOC: A39 towards Glastonbury from Wells. PARK: Easy. TEL: 01749 677087. SER: Valuations. VAT: Stan.

CREWKERNE

Antiques and Country Pine
14 East St. TA18 7AG. (M.J. Wheeler). Est. 1980. Open Tues.-Sat. 10-5 or by appointment. *STOCK: Country pine and decorative items.* PARK: Own. TEL: 01460 75623.

Julian Armytage
TA18 8QG. Open by appointment only. *STOCK: Fine sporting, marine and decorative prints, 18th-19th C.* TEL: 01460 73449; fax - same.

Crewkerne Antique Centre
16 Market St. TA18 7LA. (F. Martin). Est. 1987. Open 9.30-4.30. CL: Mon. SIZE: Large. *STOCK: Furniture, £25-£3,000; collectables, £5-£1,000; pictures, £5-£2,000; all 18th-20th C.* LOC: A303 westward, A359 to Crewkerne, Chard road through town. PARK: Easy. TEL: 01460 77111. SER: Valuations; restorations.

Gresham Books
31 Market St. TA18 7JU. (J. and A. Hine). ABA. PBFA. Est. 1972. Open 10-5. SIZE: Medium. *STOCK: Books, 50p to £1,000.* LOC: A30. PARK: Nearby. TEL: 01460 77726; fax - 01460 52479; e-mail - jameshine@gresham-books.demon.co.uk; website - www.greshambooks.co.uk. SER: Valuations.

Hennessy
42 East St. TA18 7AG. (Carl Hennessy). Est. 1977. Open 10-5. SIZE: Large. *STOCK: Furniture - pine, country, painted and French provincial; related decorative items.* LOC: A30 from Yeovil. PARK: Easy. TEL: 01460 78600; fax - same; workshop - 01460 78060; mobile - 07768 286455; e-mail - carl@veryold.co.uk; website - www.veryold.co.uk. VAT: Stan/Spec.

A rosewood music Canterbury, c.1840, of a design illustrated by J.C. Loudon in 1833. Sotheby's South sold two in January, at £1,610 and £1,265 respectively.

From an article entitled "19th Century English Furniture" by John Andrews which appeared in the July/August 2001 issue of **Antique Collecting**. For more details and to subscribe see page 21.

DULVERTON

Acorn Antiques
39 High St. TA22 9DW. (P. Hounslow). Est. 1988. Open 9.30-5.30. SIZE: Medium. *STOCK: Decorative antique furniture, period and reproduction upholstery, sofas, fine art, textiles, country furniture.* LOC: Town centre. PARK: Nearby. TEL: 01398 323286; home - same. SER: Interior design.

Guy Dennler Antiques
The White Hart, 23 High St. TA22 9HB. Open 10-1 and 2-5. CL: Thurs pm. *STOCK: Fine 18th to early 19th C English furniture and decorative objects.* TEL: 01398 324300; fax - 01398 324301; e-mail - guydennler@btconnect.com.

Rothwell and Dunworth
2 Bridge St. TA22 9HJ. (Mrs C. Rothwell and M. Rothwell). ABA. Est. 1975. Open 10.30-1 and 2.15-5, including Sun. (excluding Nov-Feb). SIZE: Medium. *STOCK: Antiquarian and secondhand books especially on hunting, horses and military history.* LOC: 1st shop in village over River Barle. PARK: 100yds. TEL: 01398 323169; fax - 01398 331161; e-mail - rothwellm @aol.com. SER: Valuations.

Anthony Sampson Antiques
Holland House, Bridge St. TA22 9HJ. Open 9.30-5.30, Sun. by appointment. SIZE: Medium. *STOCK: Town and country furniture, 17th to early 19th C, £500-£10,000+; porcelain, pottery, silver, glass, pictures and garden ornaments.* LOC: Main road, prominent position near bridge. PARK: Nearby. TEL: 01398 324247; fax - 01398 324027; e-mail - anthony.sampson@virgin.net. SER: Valuations. VAT: Spec.

DUNSTER

The Crooked Window
7 High St. TA24 6SF. (Robert Ricketts). Est. 1984. SIZE: Small. *STOCK: Chinese ceramics and jade, 3000BC-19th C, £50-£50,000; English furniture, 16th-18th C, £500-£50,000; maps and prints, 16th-18th C, £50-£2,000.* PARK: Easy. TEL: 01643 821606; home - same; mobile - 07764 175627; e-mail - enquiries@antiquities. uk.com; website - www.antiquities.uk.com. SER: Valuations; restorations (walnut and mahogany 'problem' surface); buys at auction; lectures. FAIRS: Wilton House.

EAST PENNARD, Nr. Shepton Mallet

Pennard House Antiques
BA4 6TP. (Martin Dearden). Resident. BABAADA. Est. 1979. Open 9.30-5.30 or by appointment. SIZE: Large. *STOCK: French and English country furniture, £300-£5,000.* LOC: From Shepton Mallet, 4 miles south off A37. One hour from Bath. PARK: Easy. TEL: 01749 860731; home - 01749 860266; fax - 01749 860732. SER: Valuations; restorations; export. VAT: Stan/Spec.

FRESHFORD, Nr. Bath

Janet Clarke
3 Woodside Cottages. BA2 7WJ. Open by appointment. *STOCK: Antiquarian books on gastronomy, cookery and wine.* TEL: 01225 723186; fax - 01225 722063. SER: Catalogue issued.

Freshfords
High St. BA2 7WF. LAPADA. CINOA. Est. 1973. Open 10-5, Sat. and Sun. by appointment. SIZE: Large. *STOCK: English Regency furniture, 18th-19th C, £2,000-£50,000; Victorian oil paintings, £2,000-£12,000; decorative accessories, 18th-19th C, £2,000-£5,000.* LOC: 4 miles from Bath towards Warminster, just off A36. PARK: Easy. TEL: 01225 722111; fax - 01225 722991; mobile - 07720 838877. SER: Valuations; restorations; buys at auction. FAIRS: Olympia; Chelsea. VAT: Spec.

FROME

Antiques & Country Living
43-44 Vallis Way, Badcox. BA11 3BA. (Mrs D.M. Williams). Open 9.30-5.30 including Sun. SIZE: Medium. *STOCK: Furniture including country, 19th-20th C, £15-£1,000; porcelain, 18th-19th C, £5-£500; books; lighting.* LOC: A362 Frome to Radstock road. PARK: Free opposite. TEL: 01373 463015; mobile - 07808 933076.

Frome Reclamation
Station Approach. BA11 1RE. (S.J., K.R., R.L. and J.B. Horler). Est. 1987. Open 8-5. SIZE: Large + yard. *STOCK: Architectural reclamation.* LOC: From A361 follow signs for railway station. PARK: Easy. TEL: 01373 463919/ 453122; fax - 01373 453122. SER: Valuations. VAT: Stan.

PENNARD HOUSE ANTIQUES

Martin and Susie Dearden
with five guest dealers

Major source of English and French country
furniture and decorative accessories
Set in splendid country house forty-five
minutes south of Bath off A37

Open 6 days a week or by appointment
Shipping and restoration services on site
Courier services and accommodation arranged

Established 25 years
LAPADA and BABAADA member

Pennard House Antiques
East Pennard, Shepton Mallet, Somerset, BA4 6TP
Telephone: **(01749) 860731**
Fax: **(01749) 860732**
Mobile: **(07802) 243569**
Email: **pennardantiques@ukonline.co.uk**

HIGHBRIDGE

C.W.E. Dyte
The Old Bacon Factory, Huntspill Rd. TA9 3DE.
Est. 1950. Open 8-6 or by appointment. SIZE:
Large - 3 dealers. *STOCK: 18th-20th C shipping
goods.* PARK: Easy. TEL: 01278 788590. SER:
Packing; transport; documentation.

T.M. Dyte Antiques
9 Gass Close, Isleport Business Park. TA9 4JT.
Open 8.30-5.30. CL: Sat. *STOCK: Shipping goods.*
TEL: 01278 786495; e-mail - 106611.1232@
compuserve.com.

ILCHESTER

Gilbert & Dale
The Old Chapel, Church St. BA22 8LN. (Roy
Gilbert and Joan Dale). Est. 1965. Open 9-5.30 or
by appointment. SIZE: Large. *STOCK: English
and French country furniture and accessories.*
LOC: Centre of village on A37. PARK: Easy.
TEL: 01935 840464; fax - 01935 841599; e-mail
- roy@roygilbert.com.

ILMINSTER

County Antiques
Rear of 21 West St. TA19 0DU. (Mrs J.P.
Barnard). Resident. Est. 1981. Open by appointment only. SIZE: 6 dealers. *STOCK: 18th-19th C
pottery, porcelain, metalwork, furniture and
decorative antiques.* TEL: 01460 54151; home -
01460 52269; mobile - 07803 362327. SER:
Upholstery.

LANGFORD, Nr. Bristol

Richard Essex Antiques
BS40 5BP. (B.R. and C.L. Essex). Est. 1969.
STOCK: General antiques from mid-18th C.
TEL: 01934 863302.

LITTLETON, Nr. Somerton

Westville House Antiques
TA11 6NP. (D. and M. Stacey). Est. 1986. Open
daily, Sun. by appointment. SIZE: Large.
*STOCK: 18th-19th C pine, mahogany and oak
furniture;* LOC: B3151 approximately 1.5 miles
north of Somerton. PARK: Own. TEL: 01458

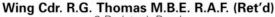

273376; fax - same; e-mail - antique@westville. co.uk; website - www.westville.co.uk. SER: Valuations; buys at auction. VAT: Stan/Spec.

MARTOCK

Castle Reclamation
Parrett Works. TA12 6AE. (T.A.B. Dance and A.J. Wills). Est. 1986. Open daily, Sat. 10-1. SIZE: Large. *STOCK: Architectural antiques.* LOC: 2 miles off A303 between Martock and South Petherton. PARK: Easy. TEL: 01935 826483; fax - 01935 826791; website - www. castlereclamation.com. SER: Restorations (stone). FAIRS: Bath and West. VAT: Stan.

MIDSOMER NORTON

Somervale Antiques   BADA
6 Radstock Rd. BA3 2AJ. (Wing Cdr. R.G. Thomas). BABAADA. LAPADA. CINOA. Resident. Open by appointment only. *STOCK: English drinking glasses, decanters, cut and coloured; "Bristol" and "Nailsea" glass; bijouterie; glass scent bottles, 18th to early 19th C.* LOC: On A362. PARK: Forecourt. TEL: 01761

412686 (24hrs); fax - same; mobile - 07885 088022; e-mail - ronthomas@somervale antiquesglass.co.uk; website - www.somervale antiquesglass.co.uk. SER: Valuations; buys at auction; trains to Bath met by arrangement. VAT: Stan/Spec.

NETHER STOWEY, Nr. Bridgwater

The Court Gallery
2 Lime St. TA5 1NG. (John Wilcox). Est. 1990. Open during exhibitions or by appointment. SIZE: Medium. *STOCK: British paintings, 1880-1939, especially Newlyn, St Ives and London Group, £50-£15,000.* LOC: Bridgwater turn off M5, then A39 towards Minehead. PARK: Easy. TEL: 01278 732539; home - same. SER: Valuations; restorations; buys at auction.

House of Antiquity
St. Mary St. TA5 1LJ. (M.S. Todd). Est. 1967. Open 10-5 or by appointment. SIZE: Medium. *STOCK: Philatelic literature, world topo-graphical, maps, handbooks, postcards, ephemera, postal history.* LOC: A39. PARK: Easy. TEL: 01278 732426; fax - same; e-mail - mstodd @lineone.net. SER: Valuations; buys at auction. VAT: Stan.

NORTH NEWTON

Asianart.co.uk.Ltd.
Bigbere Farm, Cox Hill, TA7 0BT. (James Yarrow). Open by appointment. SIZE: Large. *STOCK: Architectural features, Chinese furniture.* LOC: Off junction 24, M5. PARK: Own. TEL: 01278 662535; website - www.asianart. co.uk. *Trade Only.*

NORTH PETHERTON

Jay's Antiques and Collectables
121A Fore St. TA6 6SA. (Mr. and Mrs. Jose Alba). Est. 1982. Open 10-4.30, Mon. 10-1. CL: Wed. *STOCK: Clocks including Victorian, mantel and wall, £50-£400; pressed and coloured glass, £15-£45; china, £10-£85.* LOC: Main st. PARK: Easy. TEL: Home - 01278 662508; mobile - 07815 734965. SER: Repairs (clocks). FAIRS: Talisman.

QUEEN CAMEL, Nr. Yeovil

Steven Ferdinando
The Old Vicarage. BA22 7NG. PBFA. Est. 1978. Open by appointment. *STOCK: Antiquarian and secondhand books.* TEL: 01935 850210; e-mail - stevenferdinando@onetel.net.uk. FAIRS: Shepton Mallet.

SHEPTON MALLET

Edward Marnier Antiques
Old Bowlish House, Forum Lane, Bowlish. BA4 5JA. (E.F. Marnier). Resident. BABAADA. Est. 1989. Open 7 days, prior telephone call advisable. *STOCK: English and Continental furniture, pictures, rugs, carpets and interesting decorative objects, 17th-20th C, £5-£10,000.* LOC: Quarter mile from Shepton Mallet on A371 Wells Road, turn right into Forum Lane. PARK: Easy. TEL: 01749 343340; mobile - 07785 110122; e-mail - emarnier@ukonline.co.uk. SER: Valuations; buys at auction. VAT: Spec.

SOMERTON

John Gardiner Antiques
Monteclefe House. TA11 7NL. Appointment advisable. *STOCK: General antiques; decorative Edwardian, Georgian and quality old reproduction furnishings.* LOC: A303, close to M5. TEL: 01458 272238; fax/answerphone - 01458 274329; mobile - 07831 274427.

The London Cigarette Card Co. Ltd

West St. TA11 6NB. (I.A. and E.K. Laker, F.C. Doggett and Y. Berktay). Est. 1927. Open daily. SIZE: Medium. *STOCK: Cigarette and trade cards, 1885 to date; sets from £1.50; other cards, from 15p; frames for mounting cards and special albums.* PARK: Easy. TEL: 01458 273452; e-mail - cards@londoncigcard.co.uk; website - www. londoncigcard.co.uk. SER: Publishers of catalogues, reference books and monthly magazine; mail order.

Somerton Antiques Centre

Market Place. TA11 7NB. Est. 1998. Open 10-5, Sun. by appointment. SIZE: Large - 40 dealers. *STOCK: General antiques, £5-£1,200.* PARK: Own. TEL: 01458 274423. SER: Valuations; repair and restoration (furniture). FAIRS: Shepton Mallet.

SOUTH PETHERTON

Rostrum Antiques

The Old Flaxmill, Flaxdrayton Farm, Drayton. TA13 5LR. Open by appointment. *STOCK: 18th-19th C English and Continental furniture, objets d'art, £100-£20,000.* TEL: 01460 249249. SER: Valuations; gilding; French polishing; restorations (antique furniture and musical instruments only); replica dining tables and other furniture designed and hand-made to order; interior decoration. VAT: Spec.

TAUNTON

T J Atkins

East Criddles Farm, Tolland, Lydeard St. Lawrence. TA4 3PW. Est. 1958. Open by appointment only. SIZE: Medium. *STOCK: Porcelain and pottery including Prattware, 18th-19th C.* TEL: 01984 667310.

Lords Antiques

8 East Reach. TA1 3EN. (J.R. and A.A. Lord). Open 10-4. SIZE: Medium. *STOCK: Furniture and metalware, 18th-19th C, £50-£1,000.* PARK: Easy. TEL: 01823 275641. VAT: Global.

Selwoods

Queen Anne Cottage, Mary St. TA1 3PE. Est. 1927. Open 9.30-5. SIZE: Large. *STOCK: Furniture, including Victorian and Edwardian.* TEL: 01823 272780.

Taunton Antiques Market - Silver Street

25/29 Silver St. TA1 3DH. (Bath Antiques Market Ltd). Est. 1978. Open Mon. 9-4 including Bank Holidays. SIZE: 100+ dealers. *STOCK: General antiques and collectables, including specialists in most fields.* LOC: 2 miles from M5, junction 25, to town centre, 100yds. from Sainsburys car park across lights. PARK: Easy - Sainsburys (town centre branch). TEL: 01823 289327; fax - same; enquiries - 020 7969 1500. SER: Valuations.

M.G. Welch Jeweller

1 Corporation St. TA1 4AJ. (Mark and Liz Welch). NAG. Est. 1978. Open 9.30-5. SIZE: Medium. *STOCK: Antique and secondhand jewellery, £100-£10,000; antique and secondhand silver, £100-£1,000; early 20th C masters including Cartier, Tiffany, Georg Jensen, Chaumet.* LOC: Town centre, corner of High St. PARK: Nearby. TEL: 01823 270456; fax - same; e-mail - sales@mg welch.com. SER: Valuations; restorations (jewellery). VAT: Stan/Spec.

WATCHET

Clarence House Antiques

41 Swain St. TA23 0AE. Est. 1970. Open 10.30-5.30. CL: Sun. in winter. SIZE: Medium. *STOCK: General antiques, pine, brass, copper, bric-a-brac, collectables and books (including specialist and antiquarian).* PARK: Nearby. TEL: 01984 631389. VAT: Stan.

Nick Cotton Fine Art

Beachstone House, 46/47 Swain St. TA23 0AG. (Nick and Lynda Cotton). Est. 1970. Open 10-6. SIZE: Large. *STOCK: Paintings, 1850-2000; some period furniture.* PARK: Adjacent. TEL: 01984 631814; website - www.thelyndacotton gallery.co.uk. SER: Restorations; conservation; research. VAT: Spec.

WELLINGTON

Michael and Amanda Lewis Oriental Carpets and Rugs

8 North St. TA21 8LT. LAPADA. UKIC. Est. 1982. Open 10-1 and 2-5.30, Mon. and weekends by appointment. SIZE: Medium. *STOCK: Oriental carpets and rugs, mainly 19th-20th C, £25-£25,000.* PARK: 100yds. TEL: 01823 667430. SER: Valuations; restorations; repairs and cleaning; tapestry restoration and conservation.

WELLS

Bernard G. House
Market Place. BA5 2RF. Est. 1963. Open 9.30-5.30. SIZE: Medium. *STOCK: Barometers and scientific instruments, barographs, telescopes, tripod and hand held; furniture including miniatures and apprentice pieces, 18th-19th C; longcase and bracket clocks, metalware, decorative and architectural items.* PARK: Opposite shop. TEL: 01749 672607. SER: Repairs; restorations. VAT: Stan/Spec.

Edward A. Nowell   BADA
12 Market Place. BA5 2RB. BABAADA. Est. 1952. Open 9.15-5. SIZE: Large. *STOCK: Furniture, clocks, barometers, 17th to early 19th C; jewellery, silver, porcelain, English and Continental, all prices.* Not Stocked: Victoriana, bric-a-brac, curios, weapons, books. LOC: From any direction, turn left into Market Place (one-way system). PARK: 20yds. facing shop. TEL: 01749 672415; fax - 01749 673519; e-mail - antiques@ eanowell.demon.co.uk. SER: Valuations; restorations (furniture, silver, clocks and jewellery); re-upholstery. VAT: Stan/Spec.

Sadler Street Gallery,
7a Sadler St. BA5 2RR. (Jill Swale). Est. 1993. Open 10-5. CL: Mon. *STOCK: 18th to early 20th C watercolours, oils and etchings and contemporary watercolours and oils, mainly by West Country artists.* LOC: City centre. TEL: 01749 670220.

WEST BUCKLAND, Nr. Taunton

Everett Fine Art Ltd
Budleigh Studios, Budleigh. (Tim and Karen Everett). Open by appointment. *STOCK: Fine paintings and furniture, £1,000-£10,000+.* LOC: 3 miles from junction 26, M5. PARK: Easy. TEL: 01823 421710; e-mail - info@everett-art.co.uk; website - www.everett-art.co.uk. SER: Restorations; conservation (paintings and frames); framemakers. VAT: Stan/Spec.

WESTON-SUPER-MARE

D.M. Restorations
3 Laburnum Rd. BS23 3LL. (D. Pike). Open 9-5. *STOCK: Small mahogany furniture.* PARK: Easy. TEL: 01934 811120.

Sterling Books
43A Locking Rd. BS23 3DG. ABA. PBFA. ILAB. Est. 1966. Open 10-5.30. CL: Mon. and Thurs. p.m. *STOCK: Books, antiquarian and secondhand, some new; ephemera and prints.* TEL: 01934 625056; e-mail - sterling.books@ talk21.com. SER: Bookbinding and picture framing.

Winter's Antiques
62 Severn Rd. BS23 1DT. (R.N. and E.P. Winters). LAPADA. Open 9-12 and 2-3.30. CL: Sat. pm. and Thurs. SIZE: Large. *STOCK: Furniture, clocks, smalls and fine art, all periods.* Not Stocked: Coins, stamps. LOC: Off sea front. PARK: Easy. TEL: 01934 620118/814610.

WILLITON

Courtyard Antiques
Home Farm Holiday Centre, St. Audries. TA4 4DP. (Nick Wass and Liz Cain). Est. 1997. Open 9-4, Sat. 9-1, Sun. 10-4. CL: Wed. SIZE: Medium. *STOCK: English vernacular furniture - oak, elm and pine, upholstered chairs, mostly 18th-20th C, £100-£2,000.* LOC: Off the A39 at West Quantoxhead. PARK: Easy. TEL: 01984 633701; home - 01984 640314; e-mail - sales@ courtyardantiques.net; website - www.courtyard antiques.net. VAT: Stan/Spec.

Edward Venn
Unit 3, 52 Long St. TA4 4QU. Est. 1979. Open 10-5. *STOCK: Furniture, clocks.* TEL: 01984 632631. SER: Restorations (furniture, barometers and clocks).

WINCANTON

Green Dragon Antiques Centre
24 High St. BA9 9JF. (Mrs Sally Denning). Est. 1991. Open 10-5 including Sun. SIZE: 112 dealers. *STOCK: Wide variety of general antiques and collectables, £1-£1,000.* PARK: Own. TEL: 01963 34111/34702; fax - 01963 34111; website - www.greendragonantiques.com.SER: Valuations.

WIVELISCOMBE

J.C. Giddings
TA4 2SN. Est. 1969. Open by appointment only. SIZE: Large warehouses. *STOCK: Mostly 18th-19th C furniture, iron-work and reclamation timber.* PARK: Easy. TEL: 01984 623703. VAT: Stan. *Mainly Trade.*

Heads 'n' Tails
Bournes House, 41 Church St. TA4 2LT. (D. McKinley). Resident. Open by appointment. *STOCK: Taxidermy including Victorian cased and uncased birds, mammals and fish, £5-£2,000; decorative items, glass domes.* LOC: Opposite church. PARK: Easy. TEL: 01984 623097; fax - 01984 624445. SER: Taxidermy; restorations; commissions; hire. VAT: Spec.

Yew Tree Antiques Warehouse
Old Brewery, Golden Hill. TA4 2NA. (Nigel and Sheila Nation). Est. 1997. Open Tues.-Fri. 10-4.30, Sat. 10-5. SIZE: Large. *STOCK: English and French furniture, mainly Victorian and Edwardian, some Georgian including French beds, armoires, buffets, chairs, tables, mirrors, pot cupboards, wash stands, over mantels, desks, piano stools £25-£750; china, glass and pictures,* £3-£100. PARK: Easy. TEL: 01984 623950; home - 01984 623914; mobile - 07714 266667; website - www.yewtreeantiques.co.uk.

YEOVIL

John Hamblin
Unit 6, 15 Oxford Rd., Penn Mill Trading Estate. BA21 5HR. (J. and M. A. Hamblin). Est. 1980. Open 8.30-5. CL: Sat. SIZE: Small. *STOCK: Furniture, 1750-1900, £300-£3,000.* PARK: Easy. TEL: 01935 471154; home - 01935 476673. SER: Restorations (furniture); cabinet work. VAT: Stan.

Alan & Kathy Stacey Tea Caddies & Fine Boxes
BAFRA. LAPADA. Resident. Est. 1989. Open any time by appointment. SIZE: Medium. *STOCK: Tea caddies and boxes, tortoishell, ivory, MOP, shagreen, horn, bone and exotic timber, 1770-1930.* LOC: 2 miles from A303. PARK: Own. TEL: 01963 441333; home - same; fax - 01963 441330; website - www.antiqueboxes. uk.com. SER: Valuations; restorations; conservation; consultancy; search; worldwide collection and delivery. FAIRS: LAPADA. VAT: Stan/Spec.

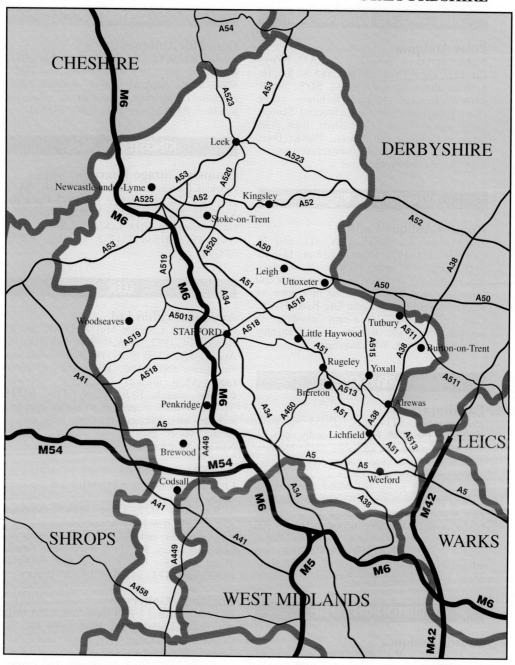

Dealers and Shops in Staffordshire

Alrewas	1	Leigh	1	Stoke-on-Trent	4
Brereton	1	Lichfield	6	Tutbury	3
Brewood	1	Little Haywood	1	Uttoxeter	1
Burton-on-Trent	2	Newcastle-under-Lyme	3	Weeford	1
Codsall	1	Penkridge	1	Woodseaves	1
Kingsley	1	Rugeley	1	Yoxall	1
Leek	13	Stafford	2		

ALRESWAS, Nr. Burton-on-Trent

Poley Antiques
5 Main St. DE13 7AA. (D.T. and A.G. Poley).
Est. 1977. Open Thurs. and Fri. 10-5.30, Sat. 10-5, other times by appointment. SIZE: Small.
STOCK: General antiques, furniture, silver, china, glass, copper, brass. Not Stocked: Stamps, coins and militaria. LOC: 20yds. from A38, between Lichfield and Burton. PARK: Own. TEL: 01283 791151; home - same; fax - same; e-mail - dennis.poley@which.net.

BRERETON, Nr. Rugeley

Rugeley Antique Centre
161/3 Main Rd. WS15 1DX. (D. and N. Edwards). Est. 1979. Open 9-5, Sun. 12-4.30. SIZE: Large - 40 units. *STOCK: China, glass, pottery, pictures, furniture, pine, treen, linen and shipping goods.* LOC: A51, one mile south of Rugeley town, opposite Cedar Tree Hotel. PARK: Own. TEL: 01889 577166; e-mail - info@rugeley antiquecentre.co.uk; website - www.rugeley antiquecentre.co.uk. VAT: Stan/Spec.

BREWOOD

Passiflora
25 Stafford St. ST19 9DX. (David and Paula Whitfield). Est. 1988. Flexible - usually open 10-4ish, prior 'phone call advisable. SIZE: Medium. *STOCK: General antiques, collectables and curios, copper and brass, Victorian to 1950's, £1-£300; early children's books and Mabel Lucie Attwell corner; garden statuary.* LOC: Off A5 and A449 near Gailey roundabout, village on Shropshire Union canal. PARK: Free opposite. TEL: 01902 851557 (answerphone); mobile - 07711 682216; e-mails - paula.whitfield@ukonline.co.uk and whitfield@passiflora25.fsnet.co.uk. SER: Valuations. FAIRS: Bingley Hall; Stafford.

BURTON-ON-TRENT

Burton Antiques
1-2 Horninglow Rd. DE14 2PR. (C.H. Armett). Est. 1977. Open 10-5 every day. SIZE: Large. *STOCK: Shipping and pine furniture.* LOC: A511. PARK: Nearby. TEL: 01283 542331. SER: Valuations; pine stripping; buys at auction.

Justin Pinewood Ltd
The Maltings, Wharf Rd. DE14 1PZ. (S. Silvester). Open 9-5.30, including Sun. *STOCK: Stripped pine furniture and decorative accessories.* TEL: 01283 510860.

CODSALL

Dam Mill Antiques
Birches Rd. WV8 2JR. (H. Bassett). Est. 1977. Open 10-1 and 2.30-5.30. CL: Tues. and Thurs. SIZE: Small. *STOCK: General antiques, small furniture, china, glass, copper, brass, silver and jewellery.* PARK: Easy. TEL: 01902 843780.

KINGSLEY, Nr. Leek

Country Cottage Interiors
Newhall Farmhouse, Hazels Crossroads. ST10 2AY. (L. Salmon). Resident. Est. 1972. Open 10-5. SIZE: Medium. *STOCK: Pine, £5-£500; kitchenalia, 25p-£100.* LOC: Off A52. PARK: Own. TEL: 01538 754762; mobile - 07855 584790.

LEEK

Antiques Within Ltd
Ground Floor, Compton Mill. ST13. (R. and K. Hicks). Est. 1992. Open 10-5.30. Sun. (Oct. to April) 1-5.30. SIZE: Stan. *STOCK: Pine, oak and mahogany, £50-£3,000; bric-a-brac, £5-£500.* LOC: A520 towards Cheddleton, opposite Catholic church. PARK: Easy. TEL: 01538 387848; e-mail - antiques.within@virgin.net; website - www.antiques-within.com. SER: Restorations; courier, packing and shipping. FAIRS: Newark; Swinderby. VAT: Stan.

Anvil Antiques Ltd
Cross Mills, Cross St. ST13 6BL. (J.S. Spooner and N.M. Sullivan). Est. 1975. Open 9-5, Sat. 10-5, Sun. 12-4. SIZE: Large. *STOCK: Stripped pine, old and reproduction; oak, mahogany, bric-a-brac and decorative items, architectural items.* LOC: Ashbourne Rd., from town centre roundabout, turn first left, Victorian mill on right. PARK: Easy. TEL: 01538 371657. VAT: Stan.

England's Gallery
Ball Haye House, 1 Ball Haye Terr. ST13 6AP. (F.J. and S. England). Est. 1968. Open 10-5.30. CL: Mon. SIZE: Large. *STOCK: Oils and water-colours, 18th-19th C, £500-£10,000; etchings, engravings, lithographs, mezzotints, £50-£4,000.* LOC: Towards Ball Haye Green from A523 turn at lights. PARK: Nearby. TEL: 01538 373451. SER: Valuations; restorations (cleaning, relining, regilding); framing, mount cutting; buys at auction (paintings). VAT: Stan.

Gemini Trading
Limes Mill, Abbotts Rd. ST13 6EY. (T.J. Lancaster and Mrs Y.A. Goldstraw). Est. 1981.

Open Mon.-Fri. 9-5, other times by appointment. SIZE: Large. *STOCK: Antique pine, £25-£1,000; decorative items, £10-£75.* LOC: Turn off A53 along Abbotts Rd. before town centre. PARK: Easy. TEL: 01538 387834; fax - 01538 399819; e-mail - geminitrading@lineone.net. VAT: Stan.

Gilligans Antiques
59 St. Edward St. ST13 5DN. (M.T. Gilligan). Est. 1977. *STOCK: Victorian and Edwardian furniture.* TEL: 01538 384174.

Roger Haynes - Antiques Finder
31 Compton. ST13 5NJ. Open by appointment. *STOCK: Pine, smalls and decorative items.* TEL: 01538 385161.

Jewel Antiques
'Whitegates', 63 Basford Bridge Lane, Cheddleton. ST13 7EQ. (B. and D. Jeacott-Smith). Est. 1967. Open by appointment. *STOCK: Paintings, prints, jewellery, oil lamps, small furniture and clocks, 18th-19th C, £25-£2,000.* PARK: Easy. TEL: 01538 360744; fax - same.

Johnson's
120 Mill St. ST13 8HA. Est. 1976. Open 8-5, Sat. and Sun. by appointment. SIZE: Large. *STOCK: 18th-19th C English, Irish and French country furniture, £50-£2,000; decorative accessories, £10-£500.* PARK: At rear and side. TEL: 01538 386745; fax - same.

The Leek Antiques Centre (Barclay House)
4-6 Brook St. ST13 5JE. Est. 1977. Open 10-5, Sun. by appointment. SIZE: 3 floors - 13 showrooms. *STOCK: Extending dining tables, sets of chairs, chests of drawers, bedroom furniture, pine, pottery, watercolours and oils, upholstered furniture.* TEL: 01538 398475. SER: Valuations; restorations (furniture). FAIRS: Bowman's and West Midland, Staffordshire Showground. VAT: Stan/Spec.

Molland Antique Mirrors
2 Duke St. ST13 5LG. (John Molland). Est. 1980. Open 8-5. SIZE: Medium. *STOCK: Mirrors - gilt, painted and wooden, 19th C, £350-£4,000.* LOC: On A53 from Stoke-on-Trent, right at 1st traffic lights, shop 200 yards on left. PARK: Easy. TEL: 01538 372553; fax - 01538 387072; e-mail - sales@mollandmirrors.co.uk; website - www. mollandmirrors.co.uk. SER: Export packing. FAIRS: NEC. VAT: Stan/Spec. *Mainly Trade.*

Odeon Antiques
76-78 St. Edward St. ST13 5DL. (Steve Ford). Open 10-5. *STOCK: Lighting, beds, pine and general antiques.* TEL: 01538 387188; fax - same. SER: Restorations (lighting).

Page Antiques
Ground Floor, Compton Mill. ST13 5NJ. (Denis and Alma Page). Est. 1974. Open 10-5.30, Sun. 1-5 (winter only). SIZE: Medium. *STOCK: Georgian to Edwardian furniture, stripped pine and decorative items.* LOC: Town centre. PARK: Easy. TEL: Mobile - 07966 154993. SER: Courier. FAIRS: Newark; Swinderby; Buxton; Stockport. VAT: Stan/Spec.

Period Features
60B St Edward St. ST13 5DL. (Lucie Storrs). Est. 2001. Open 10-5. SIZE: Small. *STOCK: Antique hardware and ironmongery; Farrow and Ball paints and papers.* PARK: Limited. TEL: 01538 372202; e-mail - periodfeatures@btopenworld. com.

LEIGH, Nr. Stoke-on-Trent

John Nicholls
Open by appointment only. *STOCK: Oak furniture and related items, 17th-18th C.* LOC: 2 miles from Uttoxeter, just off A50 towards Stoke-on-Trent. TEL: 01889 502351; mobile - 07836 244024.

LICHFIELD

Mike Abrahams Books
9 Burton Old Rd., Streethay. WS13 8LJ. Est. 1975. Open by appointment. SIZE: Large. *STOCK: Books and ephemera especially Midlands topography, sport, transport, children's, illustrated, military and antiquarian, 17th C to date, £2-£1,000.* LOC: Last but one right turn A5127 Lichfield to Burton-on-Trent before road joins A38 by-pass, house on left near corner. PARK: Easy. TEL: 01543 256200; home - same. SER: Valuations. FAIRS: Stafford, Bingley Hall and Pavillion; Midland Antiquarian Book (organiser).

Cordelia and Perdy's Antique Junk Shop
53 Tamworth St. WS13 6JW. (C.R.J. and P.J. Mellor). Est. 2000. Open Wed., Fri., Sat., 10.30-4, other times by appointment. SIZE: 2 rooms. *STOCK: General antiques and trade shipping goods.* PARK: Nearby. TEL: 01543 263223.

James A. Jordan
7 The Corn Exchange. WS13. CMBHI. Open 9-5. *STOCK: Clocks, longcase, barometers, jewellery and small furniture.* LOC: Market Sq. city centre. PARK: Nearby. TEL: 01543 416221. SER: Restorations (clocks and chronometers).

Milestone Antiques

5 Main St., Whittington. WS14 9JU. (H. and E. Crawshaw). LAPADA. Resident. Est. 1988. Open Thurs.-Sat. 10-6, Sun. 11-3, other times by appointment. *STOCK: British furniture, porcelain, pottery, pictures, copper, mirrors, Georgian and Victorian.* LOC: A51 Lichfield/Tamworth road, turn north at Whittington Barracks, shop 50yds. past crossroads in village. PARK: Outside. TEL: 01543 432248. VAT: Stan/Spec.

L. Royden Smith

Church View, Farewell Lane, Burntwood. WS7 9DP. Est. 1972. Open Sat. and Sun. 10-4 or by appointment. *STOCK: Secondhand books, general antiques, bric-a-brac.* TEL: 01543 682217.

Brett Wilkins Ltd

Cranebrook Farm, Cranebrook Lane, Hilton. WS14 0EY. Est. 1983. Open by appointment only. SIZE: Large. *STOCK: Shipping, export and French furniture.* PARK: Easy. TEL: 01543 483662; mobile - 07860 541260. FAIRS: Newark. VAT: Stan. *Export Only.*

LITTLE HAYWOOD, Nr. Stafford

Jalna Antiques

Coley Lane. ST18 0UP. Resident. Est. 1974. Open most times. *STOCK: Furniture, pre-1900.* Not Stocked: Shipping goods. LOC: 1/2 mile off A51, 12 miles north of Lichfield. TEL: 01889 881381. SER: Restorations; re-upholstery. VAT: Spec.

NEWCASTLE-UNDER-LYME

Antique Forum

The Stones. ST5 2AG. Every Tues. 8-3. SIZE: 70 tables. *STOCK: General antiques.* TEL: 01278 595805.

Winder's Fine Art and Antiques

31 Bridge St. ST5 2RY. (S. Winder). Est. 1996. Open 10-5, Thurs. by appointment. SIZE: Medium. *STOCK: Furniture, oak, walnut, mahogany, 17th-19th C, £50-£10,000; longcase, mantel and wall clocks, £150-£4,000; paintings, £35-£3,000, both 18th-19th C; ceramics, especially Doulton Lambeth, and watercolours, 19th C, £15-£1,500; silver, £50-£2,000.* Not Stocked: Pine and ephemera. LOC: Close to Sainsburys and the Magistrates Courts. TEL: 01782 712483; mobile - 07881 652425. SER: Valuations; restorations (gilding, clock repair). VAT: Spec.

Windsor House Antiques

5a King St. ST5 1EH. (Paul Barker and Shelagh Teahan). Est. 1990. Open 10-5. SIZE: Large.

STOCK: Furniture, 18th-20th C, £50-£2,000; silver, paintings, ceramics and glass, 19th-20th C, £20-£500. LOC: A53 Hanley road, 200 yards out of Newcastle. PARK: Easy. TEL: 01782 633111; mobile - 07946 761081. SER: Valuations; buys at auction. FAIRS: Bingley Hall, Stafford; Prestwood Centre, Stafford. VAT: Margin.

PENKRIDGE, Nr. Stafford

Golden Oldies

1 and 5 Crown Bridge. ST19 5AA. (W.A. and M.A. Knowles). Est. 1980. Open 9.30-5.30, Mon. 9.30-1.30. *STOCK: Victorian, Edwardian and later furniture; paintings, decorative items.* LOC: 2 miles south junction 13, M6. PARK: Easy. TEL: 01785 714722. FAIRS: Newark. VAT: Global.

RUGELEY

Eveline Winter

1 Wolseley Rd. WS15 2QH. (Mrs E. Winter). Est. 1962. Open Thurs.-Sat. 10.30-5 appointment advisable. SIZE: Small. *STOCK: Staffordshire figures, pre-Victorian, from £90; Victorian, £30-£500; copper, brass, glass and general antiques.* Not Stocked: Coins and weapons. LOC: Coming from Lichfield or Stafford stay on A51 and avoid town by-pass. PARK: Easy and at side of shop. TEL: 01889 583259.

STAFFORD

Browse

127 Lichfield Rd. ST17 4LF. (H. Barnes). Est. 1981. Open 10-5, Sun. 12-4. CL: Wed. SIZE: Large. *STOCK: Furniture, 1860-1940 and repro-duction.* LOC: Outskirts of town. PARK: Easy. TEL: 01785 241097; home - 01785 660336. SER: Valuations; restorations. VAT: Stan.

Windmill Antiques

9 Castle Hill, Broadeye. ST16 2QB. Est. 1990. Open 10-5. SIZE: Medium - several dealers. *STOCK: General antiques and decorative items.* LOC: Opposite Sainsbury's. PARK: Easy. TEL: 01785 228505. SER: Valuations; restorations (ceramics).

STOKE-ON-TRENT

Ann's Antiques

26 Leek Rd., Stockton Brook. ST9 9MN. Open 10-5. CL: Wed. and Thurs. *STOCK: Victorian furniture, brass, copper, jewellery, paintings, pottery and unusual items.* TEL: 01782 503991. VAT: Stan.

The Potteries Antique Centre Ltd
271 Waterloo Rd., Cobridge. ST6 3HR. (W. Buckley). Est. 1972. Open 9-5.30, Sun. 10-4. SIZE: Large + trade and export warehouse. *STOCK: Pottery and porcelain including Doulton, Moorcroft, Beswick, Wedgwood, Coalport, Shelley, 19th and especially 20th C British; collectors' items, silver plate, clocks, brass, jewellery, pictures, furniture, 18th-20th C, £1-£5,000.* LOC: Off M6, junction 15 or 16 on to A500, follow signs for Festival Park or Potteries Shopping Centre. PARK: Easy. TEL: 01782 201455; fax - 01782 201518; auctions - 01782 286622; e-mail - info@potteriesantiquecentre. com; website - www. potteriesantiquecentre.com. SER: Valuations; export facilities - supply and packing; buys at auction (pottery and collectors' items); pottery auctions held on site. VAT: Stan/Spec.

The Pottery Buying Centre
535 Etruria Road, Basford. ST4 6HT. (Paul Hume). Est. 1989. Open 10-4. SIZE: 2 floors. *STOCK: Pottery and porcelain, 19th-20th C; collectables, 20th C; furniture, 18th-20th C; all £10-£1,000.* PARK: Easy. TEL: 01782 635453; home - same. SER: Valuations; restorations.

Top of the Hill (Ceramic Search)
12/14/14a Nile St., Burslem. ST6 2AF. (A. and J. Phillips). Est. 1980. Open 9.30-5, Sun. by appointment. SIZE: Large. *STOCK: Ceramics, antique and collectable, £50-£100; curios, antique and reproduction furniture, £50-£1,000.* LOC: Follow Royal Doulton signs from A500, premises opposite factory shop. PARK: Easy. TEL: 01782 834506; fax - same. SER: Valuations; restorations (ceramics); buys at auction (ceramics).

TUTBURY, Nr. Burton-on-Trent

R.A. James - The Clock Shop
1 High St. DE13 9LP. (Rob and Alison James). MBHI. Est. 1988. Open 10-5. SIZE: Medium. *STOCK: Longcase, bracket and wall clocks, £500-£10,000.* LOC: 2 miles from A38/A50 junction. PARK: Easy. TEL: 01283 814596; fax - 01283 814594; website - www.antique-clocks-watches.co.uk. SER: Valuations; restorations (clocks). VAT: Stan/Spec.

Old Chapel Antique & Collectables Centre
High St. DE13 9LP. (Roger Clarke). Est. 1996. Open 10-5 including Sun., other times by appointment. SIZE: Large. *STOCK: China, glass, furniture.* PARK: Easy. TEL: 01283 815255; mobile - 07774 238775; e-mail - rocla@supanet.com. SER: Mail order. FAIRS: Swinderby.

Tutbury Mill Antiques Centre
Tutbury Mill Mews, Lower High St. DE13 9LU. Open 10.30-5.30, Sun. 12-5. SIZE: Large. *STOCK: General antiques including collectables, china and pine, from 18th C, £10-£2,500.* PARK: Easy. TEL: 01283 520074. SER: Valuations. VAT: Stan/Spec.

UTTOXETER

White House Antiques
50-52 Bridge St. ST14 8AP. (Christopher White). Est. 1983. Open 10-4.30. CL: Mon. SIZE: Medium. *STOCK: Victorian and Edwardian furniture, £100-£500; Beswick pottery, £10-£700; Beatrix Potter figures, £15-£450.* LOC: Next to Wheatsheaf public house, on Market Sq. PARK: Nearby. TEL: 01889 569344; home/fax - 01889 500380. SER: Valuations; restorations (pottery); buys at auction (Beswick, furniture). FAIRS: Castle Donington.

WEEFORD, Nr. Lichfield

Blackbrook Antiques Village
London Rd. WS14 0PS. Open Tues.-Sun. 10-5.30. SIZE: 6 large showrooms. *STOCK: Architectural antiques including fireplaces, lighting, garden statuary, stained glass, furniture.* LOC: A38. PARK: Own. TEL: 01543 481450; fax - same. SER: Delivery and installation. VAT: Margin

WOODSEAVES

AD Antiques
P O Box 1623. ST20 0SF. (Alison Davey). Open by appointment. *STOCK: British Art pottery, Arts and Crafts, Art Nouveau, Art Deco, £50-£2,000.* TEL: 01785 284815; mobile - 07939 508171; e-mail - alison@adantiques.freeserve.co.uk; website - www.adantiques.com. SER: Valuations; buys at auction; mail order through website. FAIRS: NEC; Bingley Hall; Gaydon; Penmans Chester/Kensington; GMEX; SECC.

YOXALL, Nr. Burton-on-Trent

H.W. Heron and Son Ltd
The Antique Shop, 1 King St. DE13 8NF. (H.N.M., J. and P.D. Heron). LAPADA. Est. 1949. Open 9-6, Sat. 9-5.30, Sun. 2-6, Bank Holidays 10.30-5.30. SIZE: Medium. *STOCK: 18th-19th C furniture, ceramics and decorative items.* LOC: A515 village centre, opposite church. PARK: Easy. TEL: 01543 472266; home - same; fax - 01543 473800. SER: Valuations. VAT: Spec.

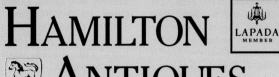

HAMILTON ANTIQUES

LAPADA MEMBER

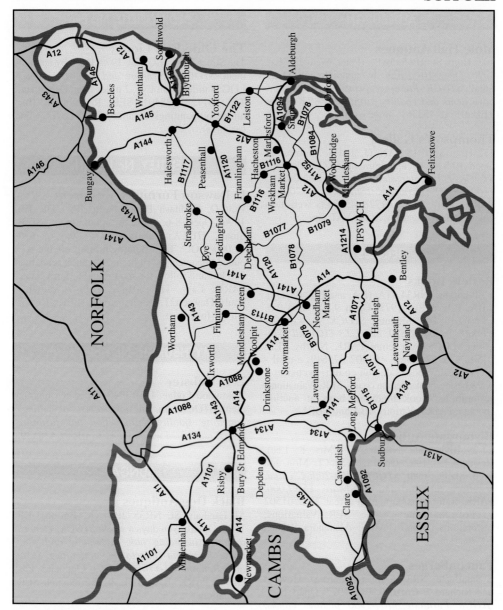

Dealers and Shops in Suffolk

				Peasenhall	1
				Risby	1
Aldeburgh	2	Drinkstone	1	Leavenheath	1	Snape	1
Beccles	4	Eye	3	Leiston	2	Southwold	5
Bedingfield	1	Felixstowe	1	Long Melford	15	Stowmarket	1
Bentley	1	Finningham	1	Marlesford	1	Stradbroke	1
Blythburgh	1	Framlingham	5	Martlesham	2	Sudbury	5
Bungay	4	Hacheston	1	Mendlesham Green	1	Wickham Market	2
Bury St. Edmunds	6	Hadleigh	1	Mildenhall	1	Woodbridge	11
Cavendish	1	Halesworth	1	Nayland	1	Woolpit	1
Clare	4	Ipswich	8	Needham Market	3	Wortham	1
Debenham	5	Ixworth	1	Newmarket	2	Wrentham	3
Depden	1	Lavenham	4	Orford	1	Yoxford	2

ALDEBURGH

Mole Hall Antiques
102 High St. IP15 5AB. (Peter Weaver). Est. 1976. Open 10-5, Sun. by appointment. SIZE: Small. *STOCK: Paintings, prints, unusual decorative items and country furniture.* PARK: Easy. TEL: 01728 452361; home - same.

Thompson's Gallery
175 High St. IP15 5AN. (J. and S. Thompson). Open 10-5 or by appointment. SIZE: Medium. *STOCK: Oils, watercolours, pastels, 19th-20th C, £300-£20,000; furniture, 18th to early 20th C.* PARK: Easy. TEL: 01728 453743; website - www.thompsonsgallery.co.uk. VAT: Spec.

BECCLES

Besleys Books
4 Blyburgate. NR34 9TA. (P.A. and P. F. Besley). ABA. PBFA. Est. 1978. Open 9.30-1 and 2-5. CL: Wed. SIZE: Medium. *STOCK: Books, 50p-£1,000; prints, £7-£50; maps, £3-£100; all 17th-20th C.* LOC: Town centre. PARK: Nearby. TEL: 01502 715762; home - 01502 675649; e-mail - piers@besleysbooks.demon.co.uk; website - www.besleysbooks.demon.co.uk. SER: Valuations; restorations (book binding); buys at auction (books). FAIRS: Various ABA and PBFA.

Blyburgate Antiques
27-29 Blyburgate. NR34 9TB. (Mrs. K. Lee). Resident. Est. 1997. Open 10-4.30. CL: Mon. and Wed. SIZE: Small. *STOCK: 19th-20th C china, jewellery, furniture and metalware, £5-£1,000.* PARK: Rainbow supermarket at rear. TEL: 01502 711174; fax/home - same. SER: Valuations; restorations (china). FAIRS: Alexandra Palace; Newmarket.

Fauconberges
8 Smallgate. NR34 9AD. (Richard D. Howard and Richard J. Crozier). Est. 1977. Open 10-5. *STOCK: Furniture, 1700-1900; pictures, clocks, glass, porcelain, silver.* LOC: Town centre. PARK: Easy. TEL: 01502 716147. SER: Valuations; deliveries arranged. FAIRS: Lomax (Langley and Norwich).

Saltgate Antiques
11 Saltgate. NR34 9AN. (A.M. Ratcliffe). Resident. Est. 1971. Open 10-5. CL: Wed. pm. SIZE: Medium. *STOCK: Furniture, 17th-19th C, £100-£4,500; clocks, collectors' items, brass, copper, Staffordshire figures, paintings and prints, 19th C bric-a-brac, £5-£300.* LOC: Town centre opposite bus station. PARK: Easy. TEL: 01502 712776.

BEDINGFIELD, Nr. Eye

The Olde Red Lion
The Street. IP23 7LQ. Est. 1973. Open by appointment. *STOCK: Furniture and general antiques.* LOC: 3 miles from Eye, 2 miles from Debenham. TEL: 01728 628491. SER: Restorations (furniture, oil paintings, ceramics, snuff boxes, wood carvings).

BENTLEY, Nr. Ipswich

P. Dawson Furniture Restorers
Unit O, Dodnash Priory Farm. IP9 2DF. Est. 1996. Open 8-6, Sun. by appointment. SIZE: Small. *STOCK: Furniture, 17th-20th C, £50-£3,000.* LOC: Take Bentley turning off the A12 outside Ipswich, 1st right into Bergholt road, then 2nd left and follow the road round to farm estate. PARK: Easy. TEL: 01473 311947; e-mail - Paul@Dawson21.freeserve.co.uk. SER: Restorations (furniture).

BLYTHBURGH, Nr. Halesworth

E.T. Webster
Westwood Lodge. IP19 9NB. Open by appointment. *STOCK: Ancient oak beams, oak ceilings, panelling, quality reproduction oak furniture, doors, mullioned windows.* TEL: 01502 478539.

BUNGAY

Black Dog Antiques
51 Earsham St. NR35 2PB. (K. Button). Est. 1986. Open seven days a week. *STOCK: General antiques including oak, mahogany and pine, china, linen and collectables; antiquities, Saxon and Roman, £1-£1000.* LOC: Opposite Post Office. PARK: Easy. TEL: 01986 895554. SER: Valuations.

Cork Brick Antiques
6 Earsham St. NR35 1AG. (G. and K. Skipper). Open 10.30-5.30. CL: Mon. *STOCK: Country and decorative antiques; architectural decoration.* PARK: Easy. TEL: 01986 894873; home - 01502 712646.

Friend or Faux
28 Earsham St. NR35 1AQ. (Kim Sisson and Jane Cudlipp). Resident. Est. 1993. Open Fri. and Sat. 10-5.30 (prior phone call advisable on Fri.), other days by appointment. *STOCK: Porcelain, 1800-1900, £50-£100; lighting, late 1800's to 1950,*

£100-£500; Victorian watercolours, £100-£200.
PARK: Nearby. TEL: 01986 896170; fax - 01502
714246. SER: Restorations (painted furniture,
gilded pieces, porcelain).

One Step Back
4a Earsham St. NR35 1AQ. (Ian and Diane
Wells). Est. 1970. Open 10-5. CL: Wed. SIZE:
Medium. *STOCK: Furniture, from 17th C; por-*
celain and rugs, from 18th C; both £50-£1,000.
TEL: 01986 896626; home - 01508 550988. SER:
Valuations; restorations. FAIRS: Halesworth,
Bungay, Norwich.

BURY ST. EDMUNDS

The Antique Shop
22/23 St. John's St. IP33 1SJ. (Mr. and Mrs.
Hodgson). Est. 1997. Open 6 days. SIZE: Small.
STOCK: Furniture, collectables, porcelain, crested
ware, jewellery and pictures, 19th C. LOC: Just off
town centre. PARK: Easy. TEL: 01284 747077.

The Enchanted Aviary
Lapwings, Rushbrooke Lane. IP33 2RS. (C.C.
Frost). Est. 1970. Open by appointment only.
STOCK: Cased and uncased mounted birds, animals
and fish, mostly late Victorian, £15-£800. PARK:
Easy. TEL: 01284 725430. SER: Restorations.

Guildhall Street Antiques
27 Guildhall St. IP33 1QD. (Mrs T. Cutting). Est.
1965. Open 9-5. CL: Thurs. SIZE: Medium.
STOCK: General antiques, bric-a-brac and
books, £25-£5,000. LOC: From town centre down
Guildhall St. to below Churchgate St. junction.
TEL: 01284 703060/735278.

Peppers Period Pieces
23 Churchgate St. IP33 1RG. (M.E. Pepper). Est.
1975. Open 10-5, Mon. and Thurs. by appointment. *STOCK: Furniture, oak, elm, yew, fruit-*
wood, mahogany, 16th-19th C; English domestic
implements in brass, copper, lead, tin, iron,
pewter and treen, 16th to early 20th C; some
pottery and porcelain, bygones and collectables,
late 19th to early 20th C. Not Stocked: Reproductions. LOC: Town centre. PARK: Easy. TEL:
01284 768786; home - 01359 250606. SER:
Valuations; repairs and polishing.

Talisman 2
18 Out Westgate. IP33 3NZ. (Shirley and David
McNaught). Est. 1980. Open 10-1 and 2-5, Sat. 10-
3, Thurs. by appointment. CL: Tues. SIZE: Small.
STOCK: Small antiques and decorative collect-
ables, some period furniture, 18th-20th C, £5-
£1,500. LOC: Just outside town centre on A143

Haverhill road. PARK: Nearby. TEL: 01284
725712; fax - 01284 724660; website - www.
talisman2.co.uk. SER: Valuations; restorations
(ceramics, furniture, metalwork); upholstery.

Winston Mac (Silversmith)
65 St. John's St. IP33 1SJ. (E.W. McKnight). Est.
1978. Open 9-5. CL: Sun. except by appointment
and Sat. SIZE: Small. *STOCK: Silver tea services,*
creamers, salts, sugar casters, candlesticks,
flatware. PARK: Easy. TEL: 01284 767910. SER:
Restorations (silver and plating). VAT: Stan/Spec.

CAVENDISH

Cavendish Rose Antiques
High St. CO10 8AF. (T. Patterson). Est. 1972.
Open 10.30-5. SIZE: Large. *STOCK: Furniture,*
18th-19th C mahogany, £150-£5,000. PARK:
Easy. TEL: 01787 282133. VAT: Spec.

CLARE

Robin Butler
The Old Bank House, Market Hill. CO10 8NN.
Est. 1963. Open by appointment. SIZE: Large.
STOCK: Furniture, 18th-19th C, £200-£20,000;
silver, 18th C, £80-£8,000; glass, 18th C, £20-
£5,000; wine associated antiques, 17th-20th C,
£50-£5,000. LOC: Town centre. PARK: Easy.
TEL: 01787 279111; e-mail - robin.butler@
btinternet.com. SER: Valuations. VAT: Spec.

Clare Antique Warehouse
The Mill, Malting Lane. CO10 8NW. Est. 1989.
Open 9.30-5, Sun. 1-5. SIZE: Large - over 80
dealers. *STOCK: 17th-20th C furniture, textiles,*
pictures, porcelain, glass, silver, decorative items.
LOC: 100yds. from High St. Follow signs for
Clare Castle, Country Park. PARK: Easy. TEL:
01787 278449. SER: Valuations; restorations.
VAT: Stan/Spec.

F.D. Salter Antiques
1-2 Church St. CO10 8NN. Est. 1959. Open 9-5.
CL: Wed. pm. SIZE: Medium. *STOCK: 18th to*
early 19th C English furniture, porcelain and
glass. LOC: A1092. PARK: Easy. TEL: 01787
277693. SER: Valuations; restorations (furniture).
FAIRS: West London. VAT: Stan/Spec.

Trinders' Fine Tools
Malting Lane. CO10 8NW. (P. and R. Trinder).
PBFA. Est. 1975. Open 10-1 and 2-5, Wed. and
Sat. 10-12 prior 'phone call advisable. SIZE:
Medium. *STOCK: Hand tools for craftsmen,*
engineers and collectors, woodworking and metal-

working books including furniture reference and clocks, other art and antiques reference books. PARK: Easy. TEL: 01787 277130; home - same; fax - 01787 277677; e-mail - peter@trinders finetools.co.uk; website - www.trindersfinetools. co.uk/.

DEBENHAM

Edward Bigden Antiques
48 High St. IP14 6QW. (Edward and Christopher Bigden). Est. 2001. Open Sat. 10-5.30 or by appointment. SIZE: Small. *STOCK: Furniture, architectural items, objets d'art, 17th-19th C; drawings and paintings, 17th-20th C; all £300-£20,000.* LOC: Opposite church. PARK: Easy. TEL: 01728 862065; home - same; fax - 01728 862066; mobile - 07876 745228; e-mail - edwardbigden. antiques@virgin.net. FAIRS: Snape.

Debenham Antiques
73 High St. IP14 6QS. Est. 1969. Open 9.15-5.30. SIZE: Large. *STOCK: 17th-19th C furniture and paintings, £50-£10,000.* PARK: Easy. TEL: 01728 860707; fax - 01728 860333. VAT: Stan/Spec.

Josh Antiques
2a Chancery Lane. IP14. (John W. Etheridge). Est. 1990. Usually open seven days 9.30-3, some days until 4.30. SIZE: Small. *STOCK: Oil lamps, Victorian to 1950's, £20-£200; pictures, £5-£150; metalware, china, glass, £2-100; cigarette and phone cards.* LOC: Just off High St. PARK: Easy. TEL: 01728 861680; home - same; e-mail - josh antiques@bushinternet.com. SER: Valuations.

Quercus
4 High St. IP14 6QH. (Peter Horsman and Bill Bristow-Jones). Resident. Est. 1972. Open by appointment. SIZE: Medium. *STOCK: Oak furniture, 17th-18th C, £1,000-£5,000.* PARK: Easy. TEL: 01728 860262; home - same. SER: Valuations; restorations (17th C oak furniture). VAT: Spec.

The Suffolk Table Company
21 High St. IP14. (D. and Mrs A. Bew). Est. 1992. Open 10-6. SIZE: Medium. *STOCK: Furniture especially country tables, 18th to date, £250-£3,500.* PARK: Easy. TEL: 01728 861102; home - same; fax - 01728 861689; mobile - 07961 977070; e-mail - jbew220@aol.com. SER: Restorations (furniture). FAIRS: Newark; Ardingly.

DEPDEN, Nr. Bury St. Edmunds

Coblands Farm Antiques
Bury Rd. IP29 4BT. (Mrs Janet Harding). Open

10-5.30, Sun. 2-5. SIZE: Large. *STOCK: Antique pine and other furniture, especially wing chairs and sofas, £5-£2,000.* LOC: A143 between Haverhill and Bury St. Edmunds. PARK: Easy. TEL: 01440 820007; home - same; fax - 01440 821165. SER: Restorations (upholstery).

DRINKSTONE, Nr. Bury St. Edmunds

Denzil Grant Antiques   BADA
Drinkstone House. IP30 9TG. LAPADA. Est. 1979. Open anytime by appointment. *STOCK: Furniture, 16th to early 19th C; speciality French farm tables.* LOC: Off A14 between Bury St. Edmunds and Ipswich. PARK: Easy. TEL: 01449 736576; fax - 01449 737679; e-mail - denzil@denzilgrant.com; website - www.denzil grant.com.

EYE

Bramley Antiques
4 Broad St. IP23 7AF. (C. Grater). Open Wed.-Sat. 9.30-5, other times by appointment. SIZE: Medium. *STOCK: Furniture, £20-£5,000; glass, £5-£500; boxes, pictures, general antiques, all 18th to early 20th C.* PARK: Easy. TEL: 01379 871386. SER: Valuations; restorations.

English and Continental Antiques
1 Broad St. IP23. (Steve Harmer). Est. 1977. Open 10-5.15. CL: Mon. SIZE: Medium. *STOCK: Furniture, 17th-19th C, £50-£5,000.* PARK: Easy. TEL: 01379 871199; e-mail - stevenECA@ aol.com.

Laburnum Cottage Antiques
Laburnum Cottage, 2 Broad St. IP23 7AF. (S. Grater). Resident. Est. 1978. Open Wed.-Sun. 9.30-5, other times by appointment. SIZE: Small. *STOCK: Porcelain and glass, £5-£250; silver and plate, £30-£100; linen, jewellery, £2.50-£100; all 18th-20th C.* PARK: Easy. TEL: 01379 871386. SER: Valuations.

FELIXSTOWE

John McCulloch Antiques
1a Hamilton Rd. IP11 7HN. Open 10-4.30. CL: Wed. *STOCK: Furniture, copper, brass, pictures, clocks and bric-a-brac.* LOC: Main street, sea front end at top of Bent Hill. PARK: Around corner. TEL: 01394 283126.

FINNINGHAM

Abington Books

Primrose Cottage, Westhorpe Rd. IP14 4TW. (J. Haldane). Est. 1971. By appointment only. SIZE: Small. *STOCK: Books on Oriental rugs, from 1877, £1-£5,000; books on classical tapestries, from 17th C, £1-£3,000.* LOC: At bottom of private drive, about 150m. west of intersection with B1113. PARK: Easy. TEL: 01449 780303; fax - 01449 780202. SER: Valuations; book binding.

FRAMLINGHAM

Bed Bazaar

The Old Station, Station Rd. IP13 9EE. (B.J. Goodbrey). GMC. Est. 1980. Open 10-5, Sun. and Bank Holidays, 11-4. SIZE: Large. *STOCK: Wooden and metal bedsteads.* PARK: Own. TEL: 01728 723756; fax - 01728 724626; e-mail - bedbazaar@aol.com. SER: Restorations (beds); mattresses and bases made-to-measure. VAT: Stan/Spec.

Dix-Sept

17 Station Rd. IP13. (S. Goodbrey and M. Cluzan). Est. 1996. Open Sat. 10-1 and 2-5, other times by appointment. *STOCK: French furniture and decoration, pottery, garden furniture, mirrors and textiles.* LOC: On approach road from A12. PARK: Easy. TEL: 01728 621505; fax - 01728 724884. FAIRS: Newark. VAT: Global.

Goodbreys

29 Double St. IP13 9BN. (R. and M. Goodbrey). Est. 1965. Open Sat. 9-5.30, other times by appointment. SIZE: Large. *STOCK: Decorative items including sleighbeds, upholstery, Biedermeier, simulated bamboo, painted cupboards, garden furniture, country pieces; pottery, glass, textiles, mirrors, bric-a-brac.* LOC: Up Church St. towards Framlingham Castle. Opposite church gates turn right into Double St. PARK: Easy.

TEL: 01728 621191; fax - 01728 724626. SER: Restorations. FAIRS: Newark. VAT: Mainly Spec. *Mainly Trade.*

Grannies

8 and 8a Market Hill. IP13 9AN. (K.C. Weston). Est. 1999. Open summer 7 days 9.30-5; winter - closed Sun. and Wed pm. SIZE: Small. *STOCK: China, glass, treen, jewellery and silver, pictures, small furniture, textiles, brass and copper, toys.* PARK: Easy. TEL: 01728 724987; home - 01473 735540. SER: Valuations.

The Theatre Antiques Centre

10 Church St. IP13 9BH. (J.G. Mulligan). Est. 1988. Open 9.30-5.30. SIZE: Large. *STOCK: Furniture, 18th C, £500-£1,000; French country, 18th-19th C, £500-£1,000; country pine, 19th C, £100-£500; objets d'art, £50-£100.* TEL: 01728 621069; home - 01986 784553. SER: Valuations; restorations. VAT: Spec.

HACHESTON, Nr. Wickham Market

Joyce Hardy Pine and Country Furniture

IP13 0DS. Resident. Open 9.30-5.30, Sun. 10-12. *STOCK: Pine - dressers, corner cupboards, butcher's blocks, old French farmhouse tables.* LOC: B1116, Framlingham Rd. PARK: Easy. TEL: 01728 746485. SER: Hand-made furniture from old pine.

HADLEIGH, Nr. Ipswich

Tara's Hall

Victoria House, Market Place. IP7 5DL. (B. O'Keefe). Est. 1977. Open by appointment. SIZE: Medium. *STOCK: Textiles and linen, jewellery, Art Nouveau and Art Deco, small items.* PARK: Easy. TEL: 01473 824031; mobile - 07899 516670. SER: Valuations; buys at auction (jewellery, Art Nouveau objects).

A fine pair of George II cast salts made by (arguably the finest silversmith of the 18th century) Paul de Lamerie, London 1731. Sold for £9,645 last September. (Woolley & Wallis)

From an article entitled "Silver" by Alexis Butcher which appeared in the July/August 2001 issue of **Antique Collecting**. For more details and to subscribe see page 21.

P & R Antiques Ltd.

Large selection of 17th, 18th and 19th century furniture in mahogany, oak, walnut & rosewood

Fairstead Farm Buildings, Spexhall, Halesworth, Suffolk, IP19 0RF

Tel: **01986 873232** Fax: **01986 874682**
www.prantiques.com email: pauline@prantiques.com

HALESWORTH

P & R Antiques Ltd
Fairstead Farm Buildings, Wash Lane, Spexhall. IP19 0RF. (Pauline and Robert Lewis). Est. 1997. Open by appointment. SIZE: Large. *STOCK: Chests of drawers, £900-£3,000; dining and drawing room furniture, £500-£4,000; all 18th-19th C.* LOC: From A12, take Halesworth turning, through town, turn left into Wissett Road, then right after half mile into Wash Lane, farm is half mile on right. PARK: Easy. TEL: 01986 873232; home - same; fax - 01986 874682; e-mail - pauline@ prantiques.com; website - www.prantiques.com. SER: Worldwide deliveries. FAIRS: Snape. VAT: Spec.

IPSWICH

A. Abbott Antiques
757 Woodbridge Rd. IP4 4NE. (C. Lillistone). Est. 1965. Open 10.30-5. CL: Wed. SIZE: Medium. *STOCK: Small items, especially clocks and jewellery; Victorian, Edwardian and shipping furniture, £5-£5,000.* PARK: Easy. TEL: 01473 728900; fax - same; mobile - 07771 533413; e-mail - abbott_antiques@hotmail.com. FAIRS: Newark; Ardingly. VAT: Global.

Tony Adams Wireless & Bygones Shop
175 Spring Rd. IP4 5NG. Open Fri. and Sat., 9.30-12.30. *STOCK: Bygones, especially wireless sets; toy trains, cameras.*

Bridge Collectables
425 Norwich Rd. IP1 5DN. (A.A. and S.J. Creasey). Est. 1988. Open 10-5. SIZE: Small. *STOCK: Mechanical bygones, 19th-20th C, £10-£100; cameras, bakelite, postcards, 20th C, £1-£150.* PARK: Easy. TEL: 01473 421316.

Claude Cox at College Gateway Bookshop
3 Silent St. IP1 1TF. (Anthony Cox). ABA. PBFA. Est. 1944. Open Wed.-Sat. 10-5. SIZE: Medium. *STOCK: Books, from 1470; some local maps and prints.* LOC: Leave inner ring road at Novotel double roundabout, turn into St. Peters St. PARK: Cromwell Square and Buttermarket Centre. TEL: 01473 254776; fax - same; e-mail - books@claudecox.co.uk; website - www.claude cox.co.uk. SER: Valuations; restorations (rebinding); buys at auction; catalogue available.

The Edwardian Shop
556 Spring Rd. IP4 4NT. Est. 1979. Open 9-5. *STOCK: Victorian, Edwardian and 1920's shipping goods, £10-£400.* LOC: Half-mile from hospital. PARK: Own. TEL: 01473 716576.

Hubbard Antiques
16-18 St. Margarets Green. IP4 2BS. Est. 1964. Open 9.30-5.30 and by appointment. SIZE: Large. *STOCK: Furniture and decorative items, 18th-19th C.* PARK: Easy. TEL: 01473 226033/ 233034; fax - 01473 253639. SER: Valuations; restorations. VAT: Stan/Spec. *Trade & Export.*

Orwell Furniture For Life
Halifax Mill, 427 Wherstead Rd. IP2 8LH. (M. Weiner). Open 8.30-5.30, Sat. 8.30-4. *STOCK: Pine.* TEL: 01473 680091. SER: Restorations; stripping; pine furniture and kitchens made to order from old wood.

Thompson's
418 Norwich Rd. IP1 5DX. (D. Thompson). Est. 1977. Open 9-5. CL: Sun. except by appointment. SIZE: Medium. *STOCK: Furniture, mainly late Victorian and shipping, 1870 to date, £10-£1,000.* LOC: 1 mile from town centre, on corner at traffic lights next to railway bridge. PARK: Own, at side of premises. TEL: 01473 747793; fax - same; e-mail - sales@thompsons-furniture.com. SER: Valuations; buys at auction (shipping items). VAT: Stan/Spec.

IXWORTH, Nr. Bury St. Edmunds

E.W. Cousins and Son
27 High St. and The Old School. IP31 2HJ. (E.J.A., J.E. and R.W. Cousins). LAPADA. Est. 1920. CL: Sat. pm. SIZE: Large and warehouse. *STOCK: General antiques, 18th-19th C, £50-£6,000; shipping items.* LOC: A143. PARK: Easy. TEL: 01359 230254; fax - 01359 232370; e-mail - john@ewcousins.co.uk; website - www. ewcousins.co.uk. SER: Valuations; restorations. VAT: Stan/Spec.

LAVENHAM, Nr. Sudbury

R.G. Archer (Books)
7 Water St. CO10 9RW. Est. 1970. Open 10-5 including Sun. CL: Wed. *STOCK: Antiquarian and secondhand books.* TEL: 01787 247229.

J. and J. Baker
12-14 Water St. and 3a High St. CO10 9RW. (C.J. and Mrs B.A.J. Baker). Est. 1960. Open 10-1 and 2-5.30. SIZE: Medium. *STOCK: Oak and mahogany furniture, 1680-1900, £100-£10,000; oils and watercolours, 19th C, £150-£5,000; English porcelain and metalware, 18th-19th C, £20-£1,000; collectors' items, £20-£1,000.* LOC:

Below Swan Hotel at T junction of A1141 and B1071. PARK: Easy. TEL: 01787 247610. VAT: Stan/Spec.

One Bell
46 High St. CO10 9PY. (J.F. and M.A. Tinworth). Open 11-4.30, Sat. 10.30-5, Sun. 11-5. CL: Wed. and Thurs. SIZE: Small. *STOCK: Militaria and collectables.* LOC: A134. PARK: Easy. TEL: 01787 248206; home - same.

The Timbers Antique & Collectables Centre
High St. CO1 9PY. (B.A. Preece and A.M. Trodd). Resident. Est. 1996. CL: Wed. SIZE: Medium. *STOCK: Smalls and furniture, £5-£500.* PARK: Easy. TEL: 01787 247218; home - same.

LEAVENHEATH

Clock House
Locks Lane. CO6 4PF. (A.G. Smeeth). Est. 1983. Open by appointment. SIZE: Small. *STOCK: English clocks, 17th to early 19th C, £1,500-£6,000; French and English clocks, Victorian and Edwardian, £300-£2,000.* PARK: Easy. TEL: 01206 262187; home - same. SER: Valuations; restorations (clocks and furniture); buys at auction (clocks and furniture).

Long Melford Antiques Centre

Large selection of quality antique furniture, silver, pictures, clocks, objets d'art, and decorator accessories.

Open Mon-Sat 9.30am-5.30pm

Chapel Maltings, Long Melford

Suffolk. Phone: SUDBURY 01787 379287

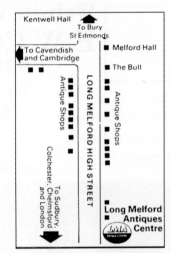

At the **SUDBURY** end of the town.

LEISTON

Leiston Trading Post
13a High St. IP16 4EL. (L.K. Smith). Est. 1967. Open 10-1 and 2-5, other times by appointment. CL: Wed. pm. SIZE: Large. *STOCK: Bric-a-brac, Victoriana, Victorian and Edwardian furniture, collectables.* LOC: 4 miles from Aldeburgh, Snape and Saxmundham. PARK: Easy. TEL: 01728 830081; home - 01728 831488; e-mail - lisa@renaultsuffolk.co.uk; website - www.leiston tradingpost.co.uk. SER: Valuations. VAT: Stan.

Warrens Antiques Warehouse
High St. IP16 4EL. (J.R. Warren). Est. 1980. CL: Wed. and Sat. pm. except by appointment. SIZE: Medium. *STOCK: Furniture, Georgian, Victorian, Edwardian and shipping oak, £20-£2,000.* LOC: Off High St., driveway beside Geaters Florists. PARK: Easy. TEL: 01728 831414; home - same; mobile - 07989 865598. SER: Valuations; restorations (furniture). FAIRS: Newark; Ardingly. VAT: Stan/Spec.

LONG MELFORD

Sandy Cooke Antiques
Hall St. CO10 9JQ. Est. 1982. Open Fri., Sat. and Mon. 10-5. SIZE: Large. *STOCK: Furniture, 17th to early 19th C, £500-£40,000.* Not Stocked: Silver and glass. LOC: A134. PARK: Easy. TEL: 01787 378265; fax - 01284 830935; mobile - 07860 206787; e-mail - sandycooke@englishfurn iture.co.uk; website - www.englishfurniture. co.uk. SER: Valuations; restorations; buys at auction (furniture). VAT: Stan/Spec.

Country Antiques
10 Westgate St. CO10 9DS. (Mr and Mrs G. Pink). Est. 1984. Open 11-5. CL: Mon. and Thurs. SIZE: Small. *STOCK: Objects, jewellery; metalware and small furniture, £50-£2,000; unusual objects, £50-£500.* LOC: Outskirts of village, on Clare road. PARK: Easy. TEL: 01787 310617; fax - same; e-mail - countrypink@supanet.com.

Long Melford Antiques Centre
Chapel Maltings. CO10 9HX. (Baroness V.von Dahlen). Est. 1984. Open 9.30-5.30 or by appointment. SIZE: Large - 42 dealers. *STOCK: Furniture - oak, Georgian, Edwardian and Victorian; silver, china, glass, clocks and decorators' items.* LOC: A134, Sudbury end of village. TEL: 01787 379287. SER: Packing and shipping. VAT: Stan/Spec.

Alexander Lyall Antiques
Belmont House, Hall St. CO10 9JF. (A.J. Lyall).

Est. 1977. Open 10-5.30. SIZE: Medium. *STOCK: Furniture, 18th-19th C.* LOC: A134 opposite Crown Hotel. PARK: Easy. TEL: 01787 375434; home - same; website - www.lyallant iques.com. SER: Restorations (furniture); buys at auction (English furniture). VAT: Stan/Spec.

Magpie Antiques
Hall St. CO10 9JT. (Mrs P. Coll). Est. 1985. Open 10.30-1 and 2.15-5, Sat. 11-5. CL: Mon. and Wed. SIZE: Small. *STOCK: Smalls including hand-painted china; furniture, Victorian and stripped pine.* LOC: Main street. PARK: Easy. TEL: 01787 310581; home - same.

Patrick Marney
The Gate House, Melford Hall. CO10 9AA. Est. 1964. Open by appointment. SIZE: Small. *STOCK: Fine barometers, 18th-19th C, £1,000-£5,000; pocket aneroids, 19th C, £150-£1,000; scientific instruments, 18th-19th C, £250-£2,000; all fully restored.* LOC: A134. PARK: Easy. TEL: 01787 880533; e-mail - patrick.marney@virgin. net. SER: Valuations; restorations (mercury barometers). VAT: Stan.

Melford Antique Warehouse
Hall St. CO10 9JG. (D. Edwards and J. Tanner). Open 9.30-5, Sun. 1-5. SIZE: 150 dealers exhibiting. *STOCK: 18th-20th C furniture and decorative items.* PARK: Easy. TEL: 01787 379638; e-mail - patrick @worldwideantiques.co.uk; website - www. antiques-access-agency. com.

Noel Mercer Antiques
Aurora House, Hall St. CO10 9RJ. Est. 1990. Open 10-5. SIZE: Large. *STOCK: Early oak, walnut and country furniture, including refectory and gateleg tables, sets of chairs and dressers; works of art, £500-£30,000.* LOC: Centre of Hall St. PARK: Easy. TEL: 01787 311882. SER: Valuations; restorations. VAT: Stan/Spec.

The Persian Carpet Studio
The Old White Hart. CO10 9HX. (Sara Barber). Est. 1990. Open 10-5.30. SIZE: Medium. *STOCK: Antique and decorative Oriental carpets and rugs, from 1860, from £50.* LOC: Sudbury end of Long Melford. PARK: Own. TEL: 01787 882214; fax - 01787 882213; e-mail - sarabarber@ persian-carpet-studio.net; website - www. persian-carpet-studio.net. SER: Valuations; repairs and hand-cleaning (Oriental rugs); buys at auction (Oriental carpets, rugs and textiles). Exhibitions held. VAT: Stan/Spec.

Seabrook Antiques
Hall St. CO10 9JG. (J. Tanner). Est. 1965. Open 9.30-5.30, Sun. 1-5. SIZE: Large - 10 showroms. *STOCK: Furniture, £500-£15,000; objects, £100-*

£2,000; both 17th-18th C. LOC: A134 near Bull Hotel. TEL: 01787 375787; fax - same; home - 01787 311788. SER: Valuations; restorations (17th-18th C furniture); buys at auction (17th-18th C furniture). FAIRS: International.

Suthburgh Antiques
Red House, Hall St. CO10 9JQ. (R.P. Alston). Est. 1977. Open by appointment. SIZE: Medium. *STOCK: Furniture, 17th C oak, 18th C walnut and mahogany, £500-£5,000; portraits, 17th-19th C, £2,000-£10,000; Georgian barometers and clocks, £400-£15,000; small collectors' items, boxes, glass, brass, copper, oak carvings and panels, £50-£600; English county maps and prints, £40-£500. Not Stocked: Victorian furniture and later items.* LOC: Opposite Bull Hotel. PARK: Easy. TEL: 01787 374818; fax - same; home - same. SER: Valuations; restorations (furniture, barometers); buys at auction. VAT: Stan/Spec.

Trident Antiques
2 Foundry House, Hall St. CO10 9JR. (Thomas McGlynn). LAPADA. Est. 1989. Open 10-5.30, Sat. 10-6, Sun. by appointment. SIZE: Medium. *STOCK: Oak furniture, 17th C, £250-£10,000; barometers, 19th C, £450-£2,500; paintings, 17th-18th C, £2,000-£6,000; objects including bottles, spoons and carvings, 17th-18th C, £100-£600.* LOC: Next to Cock and Bell Inn. PARK: Easy. TEL: 01787 883388; fax - 01787 378850; home - 01787 371867; e-mail - tridentoak@aol. com; website - www.earlyoak.com. SER: Valuations; restorations (early English oak); buys at auction (oak furniture). FAIRS: LAPADA (NEC and London). VAT: Spec.

Tudor Antiques
Little St. Marys. CO10 9HY. (S.J. Denton-Ford). Est. 1974. Open 10-5, Sun. 2-4.30 (usually). CL: Sat. (except during Fairs). SIZE: Large + art gallery. *STOCK: General antiques, £5-£5,000; curios, silver, objets d'art, furniture, bygones, books on antiques, wine and dine items.* LOC: Sudbury end of Long Melford, shop with yellow blind. PARK: Easy. TEL: 01787 375950; mobile - 07968 201654; e-mail - sford@antiqueandsilver. demon.co.uk. SER: Valuations; metal polishing; repairs (metal, silver, china, barometers). VAT: Stan/Spec.

Village Clocks
Little St. Mary's. CO10 9LQ. (J.C. Massey). Est. 1975. Open 10-5, Sat. 9.30-5. CL: Wed. SIZE: Small. *STOCK: Clocks - longcase, bracket, wall and mantel, 18th-19th C, £500-£5,000+; carriage, 19th C, £500-£2,000+.* PARK: Easy. TEL: 01787 375896. SER: Valuations; restorations (as stock); buys at auction (clocks). FAIRS: Uxbridge Horological, Brunel University.

Vintage Pine
Hall St. CO10 9JL. (Nikki Hamilton and Irene Fielding). Est. 1999. Open 10-5. CL: Mon. SIZE: Medium. *STOCK: Victorian stripped pine, brass and copper, china and country implements.* PARK: Easy. TEL: 01787 377523; home - 01787 247771.

Antiques Warehouse (incorporating The Woodbridge Trading Co.)
The Old Mill, Main Rd. IP13 0AG. (John M. Ball). Est. 1979. Open 8-4.30, Sat. 10-4.30, Sun. 11-4. SIZE: Large. *STOCK: Furniture including fine country, 18th-20th C, £50-£5,000; mirrors and decorative items, 18th-20th C, £10-£2,000.* LOC: A12 7 miles north of Woodbridge. PARK: Easy. TEL: 01728 747438; fax - 01728 747627; home - 01394 382426. SER: Valuations; buys at auction.

Martlesham Antiques
The Thatched Roadhouse. IP12 4RJ. (R.F. Frost). Est. 1973. Open Mon.-Fri., Sat. and Sun. by appointment. SIZE: Large. *STOCK: Furniture and decorative items, 17th-20th C, £25-£3,000.* LOC: A1214 opposite Red Lion public house. PARK: Own. TEL: 01394 386732; fax - 01394 382959.

John Read
29 Lark Rise, Martlesham Heath. IP5 3SA. Est. 1992. By appointment. *STOCK: Pre 1840 Staffordshire figures, animals and English pottery, including Delft, salt glaze, creamware and pearlware, coloured glazed, underglazed (Pratt) and enamel decoration, 1750-1840, £100-£8,000.* LOC: A12 Ipswich bypass, opposite B.T. tower. PARK: Easy. TEL: 01473 624897; home - same. SER: Valuations; restorations (as stock). FAIRS: Chelsea; NEC.

Frank Collins Antiques
Green Farm. IP14 5RE. Open by appointment only. *STOCK: Furniture, mainly mahogany and oak, 17th-18th C; decorative works of art.* TEL: 01449 766135; mobile - 07802 492153.

Mildenhall Antiques
10 North Terrace. IP28 7AA. (Carl Hunt and Gary Bunker). Est. 1979. Open Tues.-Sat. 11-5. SIZE: Large. *STOCK: Restored antique pine, Victorian and 1920's oak furniture, bric-a-brac.* LOC: Near fire station. PARK: Own at rear. TEL: 01638 718025; e-mail - moc1oak@aol.com.

Maria Cass Interiors
15 High St. CO6 4JF. (Mrs B. M. Stevens). Resident. Est. 1998. Open Tues.-Fri. 10-3, Sat. 9-1, Sun. by appointment. SIZE: Small. *STOCK: 18th-19th C furniture; clocks and pocket watches; mirrors, glass, china and porcelain; rare and out of print books; picture gallery.* LOC: Village centre, on A134 towards Sudbury. PARK: Easy. TEL: 01206 263929; fax - same. SER: Restorations including upholstery. FAIRS: Newark.

Roy Arnold
77 High St. IP6 8AN. Est. 1974. Open 10-5.30, appointment advisable, Sun. by appointment. SIZE: Medium. *STOCK: Woodworkers' and craftsmen's tools; scientific instruments; books - new, secondhand and antiquarian - on tools and trades; all £10-£5,000.* LOC: A14, centre of High St. PARK: Easy. TEL: 01449 720110; fax - 01449 722498; e-mail - ra@royarnold.com. VAT: Stan.

The Old Town Hall Antique Centre
High St. IP6 8AL. (S. and R. Abbott). Est. 1980. Open 10-5. SIZE: Several dealers. *STOCK: General antiques and collectables.* PARK: Easy. TEL: 01449 720773.

The Tool Shop
78 High St. IP6 8AW. (Tony Murland and Mike Hancock). LAPADA. Est. 1988. Open 10-5. SIZE: Small. *STOCK: Antique and usable woodworking tools, from 19th C.* PARK: Easy. TEL: 01449 722992; fax - 01449 722683; e-mail - tony@antiquetools.com; website - www.antiquetools.com. SER: Valuations; buys at auction; tool auctions held. FAIRS: All major Woodworking Shows, Woodmex, Axminster, Harrogate. VAT: Stan.

NEWMARKET

Jemima Godfrey
5 Rous Rd. CB8 8DH. (Miss A. Lanham). Est. 1968. Open Thurs. and Fri. 10-1 and 2-4.30. SIZE: Small. *STOCK: Small antiques, jewellery and linen, 19th C.* LOC: Just off High St., near clock tower. PARK: Easy. TEL: 01638 663584.

R.E. and G.B. Way
Brettons, Burrough Green. CB8 9NA. ABA. PBFA. Est. 1964. Open 8.30-5 appointment advisable. *STOCK: Antiquarian and secondhand books on shooting, fishing, horses, racing and hunting and small general section.* TEL: 01638 507217; fax - 01638 508058; e-mail - waybks@ msn.com.

ORFORD

Castle Antiques
Market Sq. IP12 2LH. (S. Simpkin). Est. 1969. Open daily including Sun. 11-4.30. SIZE: Medium. *STOCK: Furniture, general small antiques, bric-a-brac, glass, china, clocks.* PARK: Easy. TEL: 01394 450100; website - www.castle-antiques.co.uk.

PEASENHALL, Nr. Saxmundham

Peasenhall Art and Antiques Gallery
The Street. IP17 2HJ. (A. and M. Wickins). Resident. Est. 1972. Open every day. *STOCK: 19th to early 20th C watercolours and oils; some furniture; walking sticks.* PARK: Easy. TEL: 01728 660224; home - same. SER: Restorations (oils, watercolours, furniture).

RISBY, Nr. Bury St. Edmunds

The Risby Barn
IP28 6QU. (R. and S. Martin). Open 9-5.30, Sun. and Bank Holidays 10-5. SIZE: 24 dealers. *STOCK: Furniture, porcelain, metalware, tools, pine, Art Deco, oil lamps.* LOC: Just off A14 west of Bury St. Edmunds. PARK: Own. TEL: 01284 811126; fax - 01284 810783; website - www.risby barn.co.uk.

SNAPE

Snape Antiques and Collectors Centre
Snape Maltings. IP17 1SR. Est. 1992. Open 7 days 10-5 or until dusk in winter. SIZE: 40

A multigem bandeau of platinum set with carved emeralds, rubies and sapphires to represent leaves and fruit on the branches of a tree. Each branch is set with brilliant diamonds. This jewel was made by Cartier in October 1928 and purchased by Countess Mountbatten a month later for £900. The stones were probably carved in India, and were especially appropriate for Lady Mountbatten when her husband became Viceroy in March 1947. The bandeau has two hinged 'claws' in the front that can be lowered to secure the jewel to the brow. It comes apart to form two bracelets. (Private Collection)

From an article entitled "Art Deco Tiaras" by Geoffrey C. Munn which appeared in the May 2002 issue of **Antique Collecting**. For more details and to subscribe see page 21.

dealers. *STOCK: Antiques and collectables, especially smalls - cutlery, pens, sewing, silver, jewellery, ceramics from 18th C, Doulton, Deco, Studio, glass, maps, prints, paintings, textiles, country, decorative and useful furniture, stamps, costume jewellery, autographs.* LOC: Next to the Concert Hall. PARK: Easy. TEL: 01728 688038.

SOUTHWOLD

Cannonbury
Bridgefoot Corner, Reydon. IP18 6NF. (D. Brinsmead). Est. 1975. Open 10-5, Sun. 11-4. SIZE: Medium. *STOCK: General antiques and furniture, 1800-1950's, £5-£500+.* LOC: A1095 to Southwold from A12. PARK: Easy. TEL: 01502 722133. SER: Valuations; restorations; buys at auction. FAIRS: Newark; Stoneleigh.

Farleigh House Antiques
Basement, 39 High St. IP18 6AB. (Sharon Munday). Est. 1996. Open 10-5, Sun. by appointment. CL: Wed. SIZE: Small. *STOCK: Porcelain - Lowestoft, Worcester, etc; glass and silver, jewellery, coins, medals, militaria, brass, copper and antiquities, decorative furniture.* PARK: Easy. TEL: 01502 722630.

Puritan Values at the Dome
The Dome Art and Antiques Centre, Southwold Business Centre, St. Edmunds Rd. IP18 6BZ. (A.F. Geering). Resident. Est. 1984. Open 10-6, Sun. 11-5. SIZE: Large. *STOCK: Arts and Crafts, Gothic Revival, Aesthetic, decorative arts and Art Nouveau, £50-£20,000.* PARK: Easy. TEL: 01502 722211; mobile - 07966 371676; e-mail - sales@puritanvalues.com; website - www.puritanvalues.com. SER: Valuations; restorations. FAIRS: Earls Court; Newark; NEC; Scottish Exhibition Centre. VAT: Stan/Spec.

T. Schotte Antiques
The Old Bakehouse, Black Mill Rd. IP18 6AQ. (T. and J. Schotte). Open 10-1 and 2-4. CL: Wed. SIZE: Small. *STOCK: Small furniture, £25-£500; decorative objects, £5-£250; both 18th-19th C. Unusual collectables, £5-£100.* LOC: Turn right at the King's Head, then first left. TEL: 01502 722083. FAIRS: Long Melford monthly; Adams, Horticultural Hall, London.

S. J. Webster-Speakman   BADA
Open by appointment only. *STOCK: English furniture, clocks, Staffordshire pottery, general antiques.* TEL: 01502 722252. SER: Valuations; restorations (clocks, furniture, ceramics). FAIRS: Various.

STOWMARKET

Trench Puzzles
Three Cow Green, Bacton. IP14 4HJ. (Kevin Holmes). Est. 1984. Open by appointment. *STOCK: Antique, old jigsaw and mechanical puzzles.* PARK: Limited. TEL: 01449 781178. SER: Mail order; search.

STRADBROKE, Nr. Eye

Mary Palmer Antiques
The Cottage Farm, New St. IP21 5JG. (Mrs M. Palmer Stones). Resident. Est. 1980. Open 9-5, Sun. by appointment. SIZE: Small. *STOCK: English glass, 1750-1850; furniture, 1700-1900.* LOC: B1117. PARK: Easy. TEL: 01379 388100.

SUDBURY

Antique Clocks by Simon Charles
The Limes, 72 Melford Rd. CO10 1LT. BWCG. Est. 1970. Open by appointment only. SIZE: Medium. *STOCK: Interesting clocks especially English longcase, bracket, lantern, unusual skeleton, and French, 17th-19th C.* PARK: Easy. TEL: 01787 375931; fax - same; 01787 880040; e-mail - simon.charles@virgin.net; website - www.go.to/antiqueclocks. SER: Valuations; free estimates; restorations; repairs.

Gainsborough Antiques
36 Cross St. CO10 2DR. (William Robison-Smith). Est. 1984. Open Thurs., Fri. and Sat. 10.30-5 or by appointment. SIZE: Medium. *STOCK: Furniture, 18th-19th C, £150-£3,500.* LOC: A131 towards Chelmsford, on left before bridge. PARK: Nearby. TEL: 01787 315800; fax - same; website - www.gainsboroughantiques.co. uk. SER: Valuations; restorations (furniture); buys at auction. VAT: Spec.

Napier House Antiques
Church St. CO10 6BJ. (Veronica McGregor). Est. 1977. Open 10-4.30 and by appointment. SIZE: Large. *STOCK: 18th-19th C mahogany furniture, especially larger items - linen presses, wardrobes, desks, bureaux, bookcases, dining tables, sideboards, wing chairs, £350-£5,000.* PARK: Easy. TEL: 01787 375280; fax - 01787 478757. SER: Free delivery (UK).

Neate Militaria & Antiques
P O Box 3794, Preston St Mary. CO10 9PX. (Gary C. Neate). OMRS, OMSA, MMSSA. MCCofC. Open Mon.-Fri. 9-6. *STOCK: Orders,* decorations and medals of the world, £5-£15,000. TEL: 01787 248168; fax - 01787 248363; e-mail - gary@neatemedals.co.uk; website - www. neatemedals.co.uk. SER: Valuations; 4 catalogues p.a. FAIRS: Brittania Medal; Aldershot Medal & Militaria; OMRS Convention. VAT: Spec. *Mail order only.*

Sitting Pretty Antiques
16 Friars St. CO10 2AA. (Mrs Susan Fletcher). Est. 1982. Open 9.30-12.45 and 1.45-5 or by appointment. SIZE: Large. *STOCK: Re-upholstered period furniture, small tables and mirrors, 18th C to 1930, £50-£2,000.* LOC: Through Market Square, branch left at bottom fork. PARK: Further down street. TEL: 01787 880908. SER: Valuations; restorations; re-upholstery; buys at auction.

WICKHAM MARKET

Ashe Antiques Warehouse
The Old Engine Shed, Station Rd., Campsea Ashe. IP13. (Graham Laffling). Est. 1986. Open 10-5 including Sun. SIZE: Large. *STOCK:*

Band of Hope flat-back, c.1850. £250.

From an article entitled "A Pottery Celebration of Victorian Temperance" by Arnold Shelton which appeared in the November 2001 issue of **Antique Collecting**. For more details and to subscribe see page 21.

Furniture, 18th-20th C, £100-£5,000; collectables, pictures and prints, 19th C, £50-£500. LOC: 1.5 miles from A12 Wickham Market bypass, signposted Orford and Tunstall. PARK: Easy. TEL: 01473 747255; 01394 460490. SER: Valuations; restorations (ceramics, furniture repairs, re-polishing, upholstery); buys at auction. FAIRS: Newark.

Roy Webb
179 & 181 High St. IP13 0RQ. Open Mon., Thurs. and Sat. 10-6 or by appointment. *STOCK: Furniture, 18th-19th C; clocks.* TEL: 01728 746077; home - 01394 382697. VAT: Stan.

WOODBRIDGE

Antiques & Desirables
20 Market Hill. IP12 4LX. (C.L. and J.B.L. Buckley). Open 10-5, Wed. 10-1. SIZE: Medium. *STOCK: General antiques, 18th-20th C, £25-£1,000.* LOC: Within the market square. PARK: 200 yds. TEL: 01394 389500; fax - same; mobile - 07881 628514.

Church Street Centre
6E Church St. IP12 1DH. (M. Brown). Est. 1994. Open 10-5, Sat. 10-5.30. SIZE: Medium. *STOCK:*

18th-19th C general antiques; 20th C collectables, jewellery, silver, pictures and linen. LOC: Town centre, just off Thoroughfare, next to Barclays Bank. PARK: Nearby. TEL: 01394 388887.

David Gibbins Antiques   BADA
The White House, 14 Market Hill. IP12 4LU. Est. 1964. Open by appointment only. *STOCK: English furniture, late 16th to early 19th C, £300-£40,000; English pottery and porcelain, metalwork.* PARK: Own in Theatre St. TEL: 01394 383531; fax - same; home - 01394 382685; mobile - 07702 306914. SER: Valuations; buys at auction. FAIRS: BADA; Harrogate (Spring & Autumn). VAT: Spec.

Hamilton Antiques
5 Church St. IP12 1DH. (H.T. and R.E. Ferguson). LAPADA. Est. 1976. Open 8.30-5, Sat. 10-5. *STOCK: Furniture - mahogany and walnut, especially inlaid, rosewood and some oak; prints.* TEL: 01394 387222; fax - 01394 383832; e-mail - hamiltonantiques@fsmail.net. SER: Restorations; polishing. VAT: Stan/Spec.

Anthony Hurst Antiques
13 Church St. IP12 1DS. (C.G.B. Hurst). Est. 1957. Open 9.30-1 and 2-5.30. CL: Wed. and Sat. pm. SIZE: Large. *STOCK: English furniture, oak,*

Andras Kaldor

The importance of Berlin has changed from being on the front line between the opposing armies of NATO and the Warsaw Pact, to becoming once again the capital city of reunited Germany.

Most of the City's buildings are now either new or restored after the war. In the last ten years entire new districts have grown up on the site of the now disappeared Berlin Wall. The illustrations include the Reichstag with its new glass dome, museums and churches around the Unter den Linden and on Museum Island, the restored old districts just north and east of the centre, government buildings and the gleaming new development around Potsdamer Platz. All these make Berlin an exciting and changing city for those interested in architecture. The book illustrates some forty of these buildings, with a short description accompanying each including details of its architect and dates of construction and reconstruction.

ISBN 1 85149 362 X. 96pp., 90 col. illus
9¾ x 7⅜in./247 x 196mm. **£9.50**

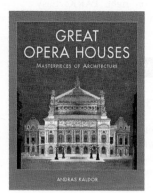

Although he trained as an architect, Andras Kaldor's love of the opera has proved the stronger influence and he has spent the last twelve years painting major opera houses around the world.

The façade of each opera house is illustrated in all its splendour. Each opera house has been personally visited by the artist. The drawings are first done in pen and ink in architectural style, with scrupulous attention to detail. They are then painted in gouache. The effect is stunning and allows the viewer to fully experience the complexity and exuberance of these flamboyant 18th, 19th and 20th century buildings. In addition to the façades Andras Kaldor has also added many detailed drawings of particular aspects of both the exteriors and interiors of the buildings. Anecdotal text accompanying the opera houses is written by well-known personalities who have a personal association with the individual house. Background details of the history, architecture, composers, operas, and singers are also given.

ISBN 1 85149 363 8. 129pp., colour throughout
9¾ x 7⅜in./247 x 196mm. **£9.50**

In this work Andras Kaldor crosses the Atlantic to survey the splendid buildings of New York, concentrating mainly on those designed and constructed at the end of the 19th century and the early 20th century. Most of the buildings featured are included in the New York City Preservation Commission's list. Kaldor features the main façades as well as finer architectural details of some fifty historic New York landmarks ranging from the US Custom House and the Woolworth Building in Lower Manhattan, through the Flatiron Building, the Empire State Building, Grand Central Station and St Patrick's Cathedral in Midtown and the Metropolitan Museum, the Dakota Appartments and the Frick Collection uptown.

ISBN 1 85149 398 0. 96pp., colour throughout
9¾ x 7⅜in./247 x 196mm. **£9.50**

Available from the
ANTIQUE COLLECTORS' CLUB
Sandy Lane, Old Martlesham, Woodbridge, Suffolk IP12 4SD, UK.
For your free copy of the catalogue:
Tel: **01394 389950** or Fax: **01394 389999**
Email: sales@antique-acc.com Website: www.antique-acc.com

walnut and mahogany, 1600-1900, £100-£5,000. PARK: Easy. TEL: 01394 382500. SER: Valuations; restorations (furniture); buys at auction. VAT: Stan/Spec.

R.A and S.M. Lambert and Son
The Bull Ride, 70A New St. IP12 1DX. Open 9.30-1 and 2-5. SIZE: Large. *STOCK: 19th-20th C furniture.* TEL: 01394 382380.

Edward Manson (Clocks)
8 Market Hill. IP12 4LU. Open 10-5.30, Wed. 10-1. *STOCK: Clocks.* TEL: 01394 380235; e-mail - edwardmanson@hotmail.com. SER: Restorations (clocks); dial painting.

Melton Antiques
Kingdom Hall, Melton Rd., Melton. IP12 1NZ. (A. Harvey-Jones). Est. 1975. Open 9.30-5. CL: Wed. pm. SIZE: Small. *STOCK: Silver, collector's items, £5-£500; decorative items and furniture, £15-£500; both 18th-19th C; Victoriana and general antiques, 19th C, £5-£500; sewing items.* LOC: On right handside coming from Woodbridge. PARK: Outside shop. TEL: 01394 386232. FAIRS: Sandown Park.

Sarah Meysey-Thompson Antiques
10 Church St. IP12 1DH. Est. 1962. Open 10-5 some days, by appointment any time. SIZE: Medium. *STOCK: Small furniture, late 18th to early 20th C; china, glass, and decorative items.* PARK: Easy. TEL: 01394 382144. FAIRS: Decorative Antiques and Textiles, London. VAT: Spec.

Isobel Rhodes
10-12 Market Hill. IP12 4LU. *STOCK: Furniture, oak, country, mahogany; brassware.* PARK: Easy. TEL: 01394 382763. VAT: Spec.

Woodbridge Pine & Collectables
6 Market Hill. IP12. (S. Tallowin). Est. 1996. Open 10-5. SIZE: Small. *STOCK: Small items, collectables, £5-£100.* PARK: Easy. TEL: 01394 383831. SER: Valuations.

WOOLPIT, Nr. Bury St. Edmunds

J.C. Heather
The Old Crown. IP30 9SA. Est. 1946. Open every day 9-8. SIZE: Large. *STOCK: Furniture, 18th-19th C, £20-£1,000.* Not Stocked: China. LOC: Near centre of village on right. PARK: Easy. TEL: 01359 240297; e-mail - oldcrown@lineone.net. VAT: Stan/Spec.

WORTHAM, Nr. Eye

The Falcon Gallery
Honeypot Farm. IP22 1PW. (N. Smith). Est. 1974. By appointment only. SIZE: Small. *STOCK: Watercolours and oils especially animal paintings and primitives, 19th C.* LOC: South side of A143 in village centre, overlooking village green, 4 miles west of Diss. PARK: Easy.

The lacquer on this drawer front is unblemished after more than three centuries, a testament to the extraordinary durability of high quality lacquer. The loop handle with double fixings was employed in Japan decades before it became fashionable in England.

From an article entitled "The Trade in Oriental Lacquerware" by Adam Bowett which appeared in the April 2002 issue of **Antique Collecting**. For more details and to subscribe see page 21.

TEL: 01379 783312; fax - same; e-mail - falcongallery@talk21.com. SER: Valuations; restorations (oils, watercolours); framing.

WRENTHAM, Nr. Beccles

Bly Valley Antiques
The Old Reading Rooms, 7 High St. NR34 7HD. Open 11-5, including Sun. SIZE: *STOCK: 18th-19th C furniture, ceramics, silver and plate, pictures, objets d'art.* TEL: 01502 675376.

Wren House Antiques
1 High St. NR34 7HD. (Valerie and Tony Kemp). Open Thurs.-Sat. 10.30-5, Sun. 11-4 or by appointment. SIZE: Medium. *STOCK: Furniture, china and collectables.* LOC: A12 village centre, Fiveways junction. TEL: 01502 675276.

Wrentham Antiques
40-44 High St. NR34 7HB. (B. Spearing). Open Mon.-Sat. SIZE: Large. *STOCK: Victorian, Georgian, Edwardian and decorative furniture.* LOC: A12. PARK: Easy. TEL: 01502 675583; fax - 01502 675707; home - 01502 562495; e-mail - wrentham.antiques@netcom.co.uk. SER: Buys at auction. VAT: Stan/Spec.

YOXFORD

Red House Antiques
The Red House, Old High Rd. IP17 3HW. (J. and Mrs M. Trotter). Est. 1987. Open Fri. and Sat. 9.30-5, other times by appointment. *STOCK: 18th and early 19th C ceramics, £20-£1,000.* Not Stocked: Stamps, arms, silver and clocks. LOC: Off either A1120 or A12, opposite churchyard. PARK: Easy. TEL: 01728 668615. SER: Valuations. FAIRS: Snape.

Suffolk House Antiques   BADA
High St. IP17 3EP. (A. Singleton). Est. 1990. Open 10-1 and 2.15-5.15. CL: Wed. SIZE: Large. *STOCK: 17th-18th C oak and country furniture, works of art, paintings, clocks, delftware and metalware.* LOC: A1120, just off A12. PARK: Easy. TEL: 01728 668122; fax - same; mobile - 07860 521583; e-mail - andrew. singleton@suffolk-house-antiques.co.uk; website - www.suffolk-house-antiques.co.uk. FAIRS: BADA; Snape.

ABINGER HAMMER

Abinger Bazaar
Guildford Rd. RH5 6SA. Est. 1978. Open Wed.-Sun. 12-5. SIZE: Medium. *STOCK: Antiques, collectables, books and bric-a-brac.* LOC: A25 next to Drake's on the Pond Restaurant. PARK: By shop or nearby. TEL: 01306 730756.

Stirling Antiques
Aberdeen House. RH5 6RY. (V.S. Burrell). Est. 1968. Open 9.30-6.30. CL: Thurs. *STOCK: Stained glass, furniture, copper, brass, jewellery, silver, curios, dolls.* PARK: Easy. TEL: 01306 730706; fax - 01306 731575. VAT: Stan.

ASH VALE, Nr. Aldershot (Hants)

House of Christian
5-7 Vale Rd. GU12 5HH. (A. Bail). Est. 1978. Open 10-4, Sat. 12-3. SIZE: Medium. *STOCK: Pine, 19th-20th C, £30-£1,500; some mahogany, oak, 19th-20th C.* LOC: On B3411 between Ash and Ash Vale. From Ash Wharf over canal bridge, shop (bright green) on left on hill. PARK: Easy - opposite. TEL: 01252 314478. SER: Valuations; restorations (including waxing and staining); stockists of Briwax and Liberon products.

ASHTEAD

Bumbles
90 The Street. KT21 1AW. (Barbara Kay). Est. 1992. Open 10.30-5.30. *STOCK: Coins and cigarette cards.* PARK: Easy. TEL: 01372 276219. SER: Restorations (furniture including upholstery); oil lamp spare parts.

Temptations
88 The Street. KT21 1AW. (Pauline Watson). FGA, NAG. Open 10-5. *STOCK: Jewellery and silver.* LOC: Main street. PARK: Easy. TEL: 01372 277713. SER: NAG registered valuer; security photography; lecturer. VAT: Stan/Spec.

BAGSHOT

Country Antiques
Pantiles, 20 London Rd. GU19 5HN. (S. Sommers and C. Martin). Est. 1990. Open 10-5 including Sun. SIZE: Large. *STOCK: Victorian and Edwardian, some Georgian, furniture, £50-£3,000; china and glass, collectables including lace and prints, Victorian to 1930's, £2-£100.* LOC: A30. PARK: Easy. TEL: 01276 489499.

BETCHWORTH, Nr. Dorking

Stoneycroft Farm
Chalkpit Lane, Reigate Rd. RH3 7EY. (J.G. Elias). LAPADA. Est. 1970. Open Mon.-Fri. 8-5.30, evenings and weekends by appointment. SIZE: Large. *STOCK: Large oak and country furniture, library bookcases, dining tables and chairs, special writing furniture.* LOC: North of A25. PARK: Own, TEL: 01737 845215; e-mail - dorking desks@aol.com; website - www.desk.uk.com. SER: Search; shipping.

BLETCHINGLEY

Cider House Galleries Ltd
Norfolk House, 80 High St. RH1 4PA. (T. Roberts). LAPADA. Est. 1967. Open 10-5.30. CL: Sat. pm. and Sun. except by appointment. SIZE: Large. *STOCK: Paintings, 17th-20th C, from £450.* LOC: A25, behind Lawrence Auctioneers. PARK: Own. TEL: 01883 742198; fax - 01883 744014; e-mail - tony.roberts@virgin.net; website - www.ciderhousegalleries.com. SER: Valuations. FAIRS: Olympia. VAT: Stan/ Spec.

John Anthony Antiques
71 High St. RH1 4LJ. (J.A. and N. Hart). Resident. Est. 1973. Open by appointment only. *STOCK: 18th to early 19th C furniture.* TEL: 01883 743197; fax - 01883 742108.

Post House Antiques
32 High St. RH1 4PE. (P. and V. Bradley). Open daily, Sun. by appointment. *STOCK: Antique lighting, fenders, mirrors.* LOC: A25. PARK: Easy. TEL: 01883 743317; website - www.antiquelightinguk.co.uk. VAT: Stan/Spec.

Quill Antiques
86 High St. RH1 4PA. (Mrs J. Davis). Est. 1971. Open 10-1 and 2-5.30, other times by appointment. *STOCK: Farm and agricultural bygones and cottage antiques including copper, brass, china, kitchenalia, linen and lace.* LOC: A25. PARK: Easy. TEL: 01883 743755; home - same. SER: Valuations. FAIRS: Dorking Halls monthly.

BRAMLEY, Nr. Guildford

Memories
High St. GU5 0HB. (P. Kelsey). Est. 1984. Open 10-5. SIZE: Small - 7 dealers. *STOCK: Victorian and Edwardian furniture, china and glass, silver, linen and lace, collectables and bygones, kitchenalia, stripped pine furniture, Art Deco.* LOC: South of Guildford on A281. PARK: Easy. TEL: 01483 892205.

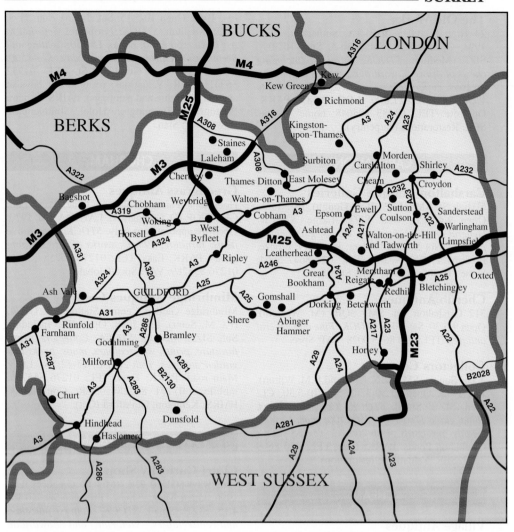

Dealers and Shops in Surrey

Abinger Hammer	2	Dorking	23	Kew Green	1	Sanderstead	1
Ash Vale	1	Dunsfold	1	Kingston-upon-		Shere	2
Ashtead	2	East Molesey	6	Thames	3	Shirley	1
Bagshot	1	Epsom	1	Laleham	1	Staines	2
Betchworth	1	Ewell	2	Leatherhead	1	Surbiton	4
Bletchingley	4	Farnham	8	Limpsfield	1	Sutton	1
Bramley	2	Godalming	3	Merstham	2	Thames Ditton	1
Carshalton	3	Gomshall	2	Milford	2	Walton-on-Thames	2
Cheam	1	Great Bookham	2	Morden	1	Walton-on-the-Hill	
Chertsey	2	Guildford	5	Oxted	2	and Tadworth	1
Chobham	2	Haslemere	4	Redhill	1	Warlingham	1
Churt	1	Hindhead	3	Reigate	5	West Byfleet	1
Cobham	2	Horley	1	Richmond	12	Weybridge	9
Coulsdon	2	Horsell	1	Ripley	7	Woking	2
Croydon	3	Kew	1	Runfold	1		

The Old Works
24 High St. GU5 0HB. (A. Sutherland). Est. 1994. Open 9-5.30, Sat. 9.30-5, Sun. 10.30-4. SIZE: Medium. *STOCK: Furniture including chests of drawers, wardrobes, tables, cupboards, dressers, coffers, chairs, bookcases, Georgian to Victorian, £100-£1,000.* LOC: A281. PARK: Opposite. TEL: 01483 894648; home - same. SER: Restorations (carpentry).

CARSHALTON

Carshalton Antique Galleries
5 High St. SM5 3AP. (B.A. Gough). Est. 1968. Open 9-4. CL: Wed. SIZE: Large. *STOCK: General antiques, furniture, clocks, glass, china, pictures.* Not Stocked: Silver, jewellery, bronze, firearms. PARK: Nearby. TEL: 020 8647 5664; home - 01306 887187. VAT: Stan/Spec.

Cherub Antiques
312 Carshalton Rd. SM5 3QB. (M. Wisdom). Open 9-5.30, Sat. 10-6. *STOCK: Pine and general antiques.* TEL: 020 8643 0028. VAT: Spec.

Collectors Corner
3 The Square. SM5 3BN. (A.J. and B.M. Wilton). Est. 1975. Open 11.30-3.30, Sat. 10-5.30. CL: Wed. SIZE: Small. *STOCK: Collectors items, china, glass, 1780-1980, £50-£100; stamps, coins, medals, postcards, 19th-20th C, £5-£25.* LOC: Carshalton Ponds. PARK: Easy. TEL: 020 8669 7377. SER: Valuations; restorations.

CHEAM

Village Antiques
16 Malden Rd. SM3 8QF. (Rebecca Fownes and Sandy Jenner). Resident. Est. 1986. Open 11-5. CL: Thurs. SIZE: Medium. *STOCK: General antiques including furniture, lighting and smalls, 19th-20th C, £5-£1,000.* LOC: 10 mins. off A3 towards Worcester Park. PARK: Easy. TEL: 020 8644 8567. FAIRS: Kempton Racecourse.

CHERTSEY

Chertsey Antiques
10 Windsor St. KT16 8AS. Open 8-5, Sun 11-4. SIZE: Medium. *STOCK: Furniture, jewellery, glass, pottery and porcelain, silver, silver plate, pictures, kitchenalia, memorabilia, books, linen, clocks.* TEL: 01932 563313; fax - 01753 682082.

D'Eyncourt
21 Windsor St. KT16 8AY. (Mr and Mrs Davies).

Est. 1968. Open 10-5.15, Sat. 7-5.30, Sun. 11-5. SIZE: Medium. *STOCK: Furniture, Victorian to Art Deco, £50-£500; china, £5-£50; lighting and fireplaces, Victorian to present day, £25-£500.* PARK: Easy and Guildford St. TEL: 01932 563411. SER: Valuations; restorations; buys at auction (furniture and paintings). FAIRS: London Photograph (Bonnington Hotel, Southampton Row). VAT: Stan.

CHOBHAM

Greengrass Antiques
Hookstone Farm, Hookstone Lane, West End. GU24 9QP. (D. Greengrass). LAPADA. Est. 1970. Open by appointment only. *STOCK: Decorative items; furniture, 19th C; works of art; shipping goods.* PARK: Easy. TEL: 01276 857582; fax - 01276 855289. VAT: Spec/Global.

Mimbridge Antiques Centre
Mimbridge Garden Centre, Station Rd. GU24. (F.C.M. Scott). Est. 1998. Open 10-5 including Sun. SIZE: Medium. *STOCK: Collectors' items, furniture, prints, watercolours, maps, books and garden antiques, 18th-20th C, £5-£2,500.* LOC: Main road. PARK: Easy. TEL: 01276 855736; mobile - 07771 862284. SER: Consultants. FAIRS: Kempton; Guildford (Oct).

CHURT, Nr. Farnham

Churt Curiosity Shop
Crossways. GU10 2JE. (Mrs G. Gregory). Est. 1996. Open Tues., Thurs., Fri. and Sat. 10.15-4.15. SIZE: Small. *STOCK: Pottery, porcelain and collectables, Victorian and Edwardian furniture.* LOC: A287 Farnham to Hindhead road. PARK: Easy. TEL: 01428 714096.

COBHAM

Cobham Galleries
65 Portsmouth Rd. KT11 1JQ. (Mrs Jerry Burkard). LAPADA. Open Mon. by appointment, Tues.-Sat. 10-5, Sun. 11-5. SIZE: Medium. *STOCK: Period and country furniture, 19th to early 20th C oils and watercolours.* LOC: South off A3, on second roundabout. 5 minutes from M25. PARK: Driveway beside shop. TEL: 01932 867909; mobile - 07850 651743. SER: Buys at auction; searches.

Village Antiques
38 Portsmouth Rd. KT11 1HZ. (N. Tsangari & Son). Resident. Est. 1965. Open 10-6, Sat. and

Sun. by appointment. SIZE: Small. *STOCK: Oil paintings, watercolours, chairs, brass, wood, mainly 19th C.* LOC: Just off A3. PARK: Easy. TEL: 01932 589841. SER: Restorations (oil paintings). VAT: Stan.

COULSDON

Decodream
233 Chipstead Valley Rd. CR5 3BY. Open by appointment only. *STOCK: Pottery - Clarice Cliff, Shorter, Shelley, Foley, F. and C. Rhead and Carlton ware.* LOC: Off junction 7, M25. PARK: Free. TEL: 020 8668 5534.

D. Potashnick Antiques
7 Stoats Nest Parade, 73 Stoats Nest Rd. CR5 2JJ. Open 9-5.30, Sat. 9-12 or by appointment. *STOCK: General antiques.* TEL: 020 8660 8403. SER: Restorations (furniture).

CROYDON

Oscar Dahling Antiques
87 Cherry Orchard Rd. CR0 6BE. (Oscar Dahling and Liz Lancaster). Est. 1988. Open Tues., Wed., Thurs. 10.30-6, Sat. 10.30-4.30, other times by appointment. SIZE: Medium. *STOCK: Furniture, £50-£2,500; ceramics, £10-£250; jewellery and costume, £10-£500; all 18th-20th C.* LOC: Ist left after leaving East Croydon B.R. station. shop 300 yards, near Grouse and Claret public house. PARK: Easy. TEL: 020 8681 8090; home - same; e-mail - oscar.dahling@virgin.net. SER: Valuations; restorations.

G.E. Griffin
43a Brighton Rd., South Croydon. CR2 6EB. (E.H. Robinson). Est. 1896. Open 10-4. SIZE: Medium. *STOCK: General antiques.* PARK: Easy. TEL: 020 8688 3130 and 01883 349147; e-mail - ted@gegriffin.freeserve.co.uk; website - www.griffinantiques.co.uk. SER: Restorations; upholstery.

The Whitgift Galleries
77 South End. CR0 1BF. FATG. Est. 1945. *STOCK: 20th C paintings.* TEL: 020 8688 0990; fax - 020 8760 0522; e-mail - info@whitgift galleries.co.uk; website - www.whitgiftgalleries. co.uk. SER: Restorations; conservation, framing. VAT: Spec.

DORKING

Antique Clocks by Patrick Thomas
62A West St. RH4 1BS. Est. 1992. Open 9.30-

5.30, Sun. 11-4. SIZE: Medium. *STOCK: Clocks, 18th-19th C, £50-£5,000; optical antiques, 19th-20th C, £50-£3,000; sporting memorabilia, 19th-20th C, £50-£1,000.* PARK: Easy. TEL: 01306 743661; fax - same; website - www.antiqueclock shop.co.uk. SER: Valuations; restorations (clock and furniture). VAT: Spec.

G. D. Blay Antiques   **BADA**
56 West St. RH4 1BS. Open 10-5 and by appointment. CL: Mon. SIZE: Medium. *STOCK: Fine 18th to early 19th C furniture, £500-£50,000.* TEL: 01306 743398; mobile - 07785 767718. FAIRS: Olympia (summer, winter); BADA Chelsea (spring). VAT: Spec.

J. and M. Coombes
44 West St. RH4 1BU. Est. 1965. Open 9-5, Sun. 11-4. *STOCK: General antiques.* TEL: 01306 885479. VAT: Stan.

Dolphin Square Antiques
42 West St. RH4 1BU. (Mr and Mrs N. James). Est. 1995. Open 10-5.30. *STOCK: Furniture, clocks, china and glass, bronzes, Staffordshire, 17th to early 20th C, £50-£15,000.* LOC: Western end of High St. PARK: Nearby. TEL: 01306 887901. SER: Valuations; shipping.

Dorking Desk Shop
41 West St. RH4 1BU. (J.G. Elias). LAPADA. Est. 1969. Open 8-1 and 2-5.30, Sat. 10.30-1 and 2-5. SIZE: Large. *STOCK: Desks, especially partners, cylinder bureaux, davenports, kneehole and pedestal, 18th to mid-20th C, £100-£60,000.* PARK: Nearby. TEL: 01306 883327; fax - 01306 875363; e-mail - dorkingdesks@aol.com; website - wwwdesk.uk.com. VAT: Stan/Spec.

Dorking House Antiques
17/18 West St. RH4 1BS. (Mrs G.D. Emburey). Est. 1989. Open 10-5. SIZE: 30 dealers. *STOCK: Period and pine furniture, silver, porcelain, longcase, wall and table clocks, jewellery, copper and brass, pictures and prints, decorative and collectors' items.* LOC: Continuation of High St. into one-way system. PARK: Opposite. TEL: 01306 740915. SER: Restorations.

Gallery Eleven
11 West St. RH4 1BL. (Janet Denise). LAPADA. Open 10-5, Sun. 11.30-4 Oct.-April. SIZE: Large. *STOCK: Furniture, 1650-1920; smalls.* PARK: Opposite. TEL: 01306 887771; fax - same. SER: Valuations. VAT: Spec.

Hampshires of Dorking
50-52 West St. RH4 1BU. LAPADA. CINOA. Open 9.30-5.30, Sun. 10-4. SIZE: 10 rooms.

STOCK: Fine English walnut, mahogany, rose-wood and satinwood furniture, 18th-19th C, £500-£70,000; fine art, silver, glass, porcelain, rugs, carpets and jewellery. PARK: Own. TEL: 01306 887076; fax/ansaphone - 01306 881029; e-mail - victor@hampshires.co.uk; website - www.hampshires.co.uk. VAT: Spec.

Harman's Antiques
19 West St. RH4 1QH. (Paul and Nicholas Harman). LAPADA. Est. 1956. Open 10-5. SIZE: Large. *STOCK: Country oak and cherry furniture including tables and chairs, linen presses, side-boards, bookcases, 18th-19th C, £100-£15,000; Moorcroft and lamps.* PARK: Nearby. TEL: 01306 743330; home - same; fax - 01306 742593; e-mail - antiques@harmans-antiques.co.uk; website - www.harmans-antiques.co.uk. SER: Restorations (polishing and repairs); upholstery; valuations. VAT: Stan/Spec.

Holmwood Antiques
Norfolk Rd., South Holmwood. RH5 4LA. (R. Dewdney). Open 9-6.30, evenings and weekends by appointment. *STOCK: Georgian and Victorian furniture.* TEL: 01306 888174/888468.

King's Court Galleries
54 West St. RH4 1BS. (Mrs J. Joel). Open 9.30-5.30. *STOCK: Antique maps, engravings, decorative and sporting prints.* TEL: 01306 881757; website - www.kingscourtgalleries.co.uk. SER: Framing.

Malthouse Antiques
49 West St. RH4 1BU. (Ross Dodsworth and Colin Waters). Open 10-5, Sat. 10-5.30. SIZE: Large. *STOCK: 18th-19th C mahogany, rose-wood and walnut, 17th-19th C oak and country, £100-£15,000; giltwood mirrors, 18th-19th C, £300-£5,000.* PARK: Pay and display behind shop. TEL: 01306 886169. VAT: Spec.

Mayfair Antiques
43 West St. RH4 1BU. Est. 1963. Open 9-1 and 2-5. SIZE: Large. *STOCK: Furniture, mainly 18th-19th C, to £500+.* LOC: Opposite Junction Rd. PARK: Nearby. TEL: 01306 885007. VAT: Spec.

Norfolk House Galleries
48 West St. RH4 1BU. Open 10-5. *STOCK: 18th-19th C furniture, especially dining tables and sets of chairs.* TEL: 01306 881028.

The Olde Bakehouse Antiques
1A West St. RH4 1BL. (D. and S. Kenny). Est. 1982. Open Tues.-Sat. 10-5. SIZE: Medium. *STOCK: 18th-19th C oak, walnut and mahogany furniture; decorative items, ceramics, Art Deco.* LOC: A25. PARK: Nearby. TEL: 01306 876646. VAT: Margin.

Pilgrims Antique Centre
7 West St. RH4 1BL. Est. 1974. Open 10-5.30. SIZE: 10 dealers. *STOCK: Furniture, 18th to early 20th C, glass, books, barometers, Art Deco and Nouveau, paintings, smalls, copper and brass, silver.* LOC: A25 through town, just off High St. PARK: Easy. TEL: 01306 875028.

Elaine Saunderson Antiques   BADA
18/18a Church St. RH4 1DW. (Mrs E.C. Saunderson). Est. 1988. Open 10-1 and 2-5.30, Sat. 9.30-6, other times by appointment. SIZE: Medium. *STOCK: Furniture, late 18th to early 19th C, £1,000-£25,000; decorative items.* Not Stocked: Silver and jewellery. LOC: Turn left into North St. at end of West St. one-way. 100yds. up North St., opposite junction with Church St. PARK: Easy. TEL: 01306 881231; fax - 01306 502120; mobile - 07836 597485. SER: Valuations; restorations (furniture). VAT: Spec.

Scotts of Dorking
70 High St. RH4 1AY. Open 9-5.15. SIZE: Medium. *STOCK: Jewellery.* LOC: Opposite Boots chemist. PARK: Behind shop. TEL: 01306 880790.

Temptations, Antique Jewellery & Silver
4 Old King's Head Court. RH4 1AR. FGA, NAG. Est. 1960. Open 9.30-5. SIZE: Small. *STOCK: Jewellery and silver especially Victorian.* LOC: Off 11 High Street at the top of West Street. PARK: Behind shop in North St. TEL: 01306 885452. SER: NAG registered valuer; lecturer; photographer. VAT: Stan/Spec.

Victoria and Edward Antiques Centre
61 West St. RH4 1BS. Est. 1972. Open 9.30-5.30. SIZE: Medium - 28 dealers. *STOCK: General antiques.* PARK: Nearby. TEL: 01306 889645.

The Vinery
55 West St. RH4 1BS. (Pauline Schwarz and Cindy King). Resident. Est. 1980. Open 10.30-5, Mon. and Sun. by appointment. SIZE: Medium. *STOCK: Mahogany and walnut furniture, 18th-19th C, £500-£10,000; small Edwardian inlaid furniture and display cabinets, £300-£3,000; French furniture, late 19th to early 20th C, £500-£2,500.* LOC: Town centre. PARK: West St. TEL: 01306 743440; fax - same. SER: Valuations; restorations (polishing and repairs). VAT: Margin.

West Street Antiques
63 West St. RH4 1BS. (J.G. Spooner, R.A. Ratner and P.J. Spooner). Est. 1980. Open 9.30-1 and 2.15-5.30. SIZE: Medium. *STOCK: Furniture, 17th to*

early 20th C, £500-£15,000; arms and armour, 17th-19th C, £500-£30,000; brass and copper, ceramics, paintings and collectors' items. Not Stocked: Jewellery and carpets. LOC: A25, one-way system. PARK: Nearby. TEL: 01306 883487; fax - same; home - 01306 730182 or 01372 452877; e-mail - weststant@aol.com; website - www.antiquearms andarmour.com. VAT: Spec.

The Westcott Gallery
4 Guildford Rd., Westcott. RH4 3NR. (Anthony Wakefield). Open 9-5, Sat. 10-5 (exhibitions only). *STOCK: Specialist in contemporary paintings and ceramics by Surrey artists.* TEL: 01306 876261; fax - 01306 740770; e-mail - westcott gallery@cs. com; website - www.westcottgallery.co.uk.

DUNSFOLD, Nr. Godalming

Antique Buildings Ltd
GU8 4NP. (Peter Barker). Resident. Est. 1975. Open daily, Sat. and Sun. by appointment. SIZE: Large. *STOCK: Oak timbers, 17th C, £25-£1,000; architectural items, 15th-18th C, £25-£500; barn frames, 17th C, £2,000-£50,000.* LOC: From Sun public house 500 yards down Alfold road, row of white posts on left hand side, premises up tarmac drive between last two. PARK: Easy. TEL: 01483 200477; fax - 01483 200752. SER: Valuations; restorations (ancient oak framed buildings); buys at auction (buildings and architectural items). VAT: Stan.

EAST MOLESEY

Elizabeth R. Antiques
39 Bridge Rd., Hampton Court. KT8 9ER. Est. 1988. Open 10-4.30, Sun. 11-3.30. SIZE: Medium. *STOCK: Furniture, 19th C, £500-£2,000; silver, 18th-20th C, £75-£300; toys, 20th C, £35-£600; jewellery, 19th-20th C, £40-£700.* PARK: Easy. TEL: 020 8979 4004; fax - same. SER: Valuations; restorations (French polishing, waxing; clock, glass and china repairs). FAIRS: Sandown; Alexandra Palace.

Hampton Court Emporium
52-54 Bridge Rd., Hampton Court. KT8 9HA. Open 10-5.30, Sun 11-5.30. SIZE: Medium. *STOCK: Furniture, paintings, silver, jewellery, mirrors, books, clocks, brass and copper, objets d'art, lamps, china and porcelain, collector's cameras, Art Deco.* PARK: Palace Rd. station. TEL: 020 8941 8876. SER: Valuations; restorations. VAT: Stan/Spec.

Hampton Court Palace Antiques
16 Bridge Rd., Hampton Court. KT8 9HA. Est. 1969. Open 10-6 including Sun. SIZE: Medium. *STOCK: Decorative furniture, oils, watercolours, prints, 18th-19th C, £35-£6,000.* PARK: Easy. TEL: 020 8941 2212. SER: Export facilities; valuations; restorations (furniture and art).

Journeyman Antiques Centre
77 Bridge Rd., Hampton Court. KT8 9HH. (Stuart James). Open 10.30-5.30. SIZE: 10 dealers. *STOCK: 18th to early 20th C furniture, silver, ceramics, glass, prints, jewellery and decorative antiques.* LOC: Turn down Creek Rd., opposite Hampton Court station, into Bridge Rd. TEL: 020 8979 7954; e-mail - journeymanac@ aol.co.uk.

The Nostradamus Centre
30-32 Bridge Rd., Hampton Court. KT8 9HA. (Heather Ferri). Est. 1998. Open 10-5.30, Sun. 11-6. CL: Mon. SIZE: Medium. *STOCK: Furniture, 18th-19th C; Art Deco, £25-£1,000; Victorian jewellery and silver, £100-£1,000; brass, lighting, cameras.* LOC: 5 mins. walk from Hampton Court railway station, 10 mins from the Palace. PARK: Easy. TEL: 020 8979 6766. SER: Valuations; restorations. VAT: Stan.

Nostradamus II
53 Bridge Rd., Hampton Court. KT8 9HA. (Heather Ferri). Est. 1998. Open 10-5.30, Sun. 11-6. CL: Mon. SIZE: Medium. *STOCK: Furniture, 18th-19th C; Art Deco, £25-£1,000; Victorian jewellery and silver, £100-£1,000; brass, lighting, cameras.* LOC: 5 mins walk from Hampton Court railway station, 10 mins from the Palace. PARK: Easy. TEL: 020 8783 0595. SER: Valuations; restorations. VAT: Stan.

EPSOM

Vandeleur Antiquarian Books
6 Seaforth Gdns. KT19 0NR. (E.H. Bryant). By appointment only. *STOCK: Antiquarian and secondhand books on all subjects; prints including rowing, and maps.* TEL: 020 8393 7752; fax - same. SER: Valuations; subject lists on request. FAIRS: Various book. VAT: Stan.

EWELL

A. E. Booth & Son
9 High St. KT17 1SG. (David J. and Mrs Ann Booth). BAFRA. Assn. Master Upholsterers. Est. 1934. Open 9.30-4.30. SIZE: Large. *STOCK: Furniture, 1700-1900, £200-£2,000; porcelain,*

from 1800, £20-£200. LOC: A24 to Ewell village. PARK: Own - through gates beside shop. TEL: 020 8393 5245; fax - same. SER: Restorations (furniture including polishing, repairs and upholstery). VAT: Stan/Spec.

J.W. McKenzie
12 Stoneleigh Park Rd. KT19 0QT. Est. 1971. Appointment advisable. *STOCK: Old and new books on cricket.* TEL: 020 8393 7700; e-mail - jwmck@netcomuk.co.uk; website - www.mckenzie-cricket.co.uk.

FARNHAM

Annie's Antiques
1 Ridgway Parade, Frensham Rd. GU9 8UZ. Est. 1982. Open 9.30-5.30, Fri. 10.30-5.30, Sun. by appointment. SIZE: Medium. *STOCK: Furniture, bric-a-brac, jewellery, 19th to early 20th C, £5-£1,000; general antiques.* LOC: 1 mile out of Farnham on A287 towards Hindhead. PARK: Easy. TEL: 01252 713447; home - 01252 723217.

The Antiques Warehouse
Badshot Farm, St George's Rd., Runfold. GU9 9HR. (Hilary Burroughs). Est. 1995. Open 10-5.30, including Sun. SIZE: Large - 2 barns, 30 dealers. *STOCK: Furniture, 18th C to 1940's, £75-£2,000; china, glass, silver, jewellery, paintings, prints and interesting collectables, 18th C to 1960's, £5-£500.* LOC: A31 from Farnham towards Guildford, 1st exit (signed Runfold), left at end of slip road towards Badshot Lea, premises 200 yds on left. PARK: Own. TEL: 01252 317590; fax - 01252 879751; website - www.w3b-ink.com/antiqueswarehouse. SER: Restorations (woodwork including dipping, veneering, caning).

Bourne Mill Antiques
39-43 Guildford Rd. GU9 9PY. Est. 1960. Open 10-5.30 every day. SIZE: Large - 83 dealers. *STOCK: Antique and reproduction furniture in oak, walnut, mahogany, yew and pine; china, glass, pictures, jewellery, fireplaces, beds, kitchenalia, bespoke furniture, collectors' items, books, bric-a-brac; garden ornaments, furniture and buildings.* PARK: Own. TEL: 01252 716663.

Casque and Gauntlet Militaria
55/59 Badshot Lea Rd., Badshot Lea. GU9 9LP. (R. Colt). Est. 1957. Open 11-5. SIZE: Large. *STOCK: Militaria, arms, armour.* LOC: A324 Aldershot to Farnham road. PARK: Easy. TEL: 01252 320745; fax - same. SER: Restorations (metals); re-gilding.

Christopher's Antiques
Sandford Lodge, 39a West St. GU9 7DX. (Mr and Mrs C.M. Booth). Resident. Est. 1972. Open 8-1 and 2-5.30, weekends by appointment. SIZE: Large. *STOCK: Fruitwood country and mahogany furniture, 18th-19th C; walnut furniture, 17th-18th C.* LOC: From Guildford on the A31, turn right at second roundabout. PARK: Easy. TEL: 01252 713794; fax - 01252 713266; e-mail - cbooth7956@aol.com. SER: Valuations; restorations (furniture). VAT: Stan/Spec.

Heytesbury Antiques   BADA
P.O. Box 222. GU10 5HN. (Ivor and Sally Ingall). LAPADA. Est. 1974. Open by appointment only. SIZE: Medium. *STOCK: 18th-19th C Continental and English furniture, statuary, bronzes and decorative items, £1,000-£15,000.* TEL: 01252 850893; mobile - 07836 675727; fax - 01252 850828. FAIRS: Olympia; Decorative Antiques & Textiles. VAT: Spec.

Maltings Monthly Market
Bridge Sq. GU9 7QR. (Farnham Maltings). Est. 1969. First Sat. monthly. SIZE: 200+ stalls. *STOCK: 60% of the dealers sell a wide variety of antiques, postcards, bric-a-brac and collectables.* LOC: Follow signs to Wagon Yard car park, Maltings over footbridge. TEL: Stalls - 01252 717434; fax - 01252 718177; e-mail - FarnMalt@aol.com; website - www.farnhammaltings.com.

Karel Weijand Fine Oriental Carpets
                                          BADA
Lion and Lamb Courtyard. GU9 7LL. LAPADA. Est. 1975. Open 9.30-5.30. SIZE: Large. *STOCK: Fine antique and contemporary Oriental rugs and carpets, from £150.* LOC: Off West St. PARK: Easy. TEL: 01252 726215; e-mail - carpets@karelweijand.com. SER: Valuations; restorations; cleaning. FAIRS: BADA; LAPADA. VAT: Stan/Spec.

GODALMING

The Antique Shop
72 Ockford Rd. GU7 1RF. (G. Jones). Open 10.30-4.30, Sat. 11-5. SIZE: 6 dealers. *STOCK: General antiques including furniture, light fittings.* PARK: Opposite. TEL: 01483 414428. FAIRS: Clandon.

Heath-Bullocks   BADA
8 Meadrow. GU7 3HN. (Roger, Mary and Charlotte Heath-Bullock). Est. 1926. Open Fri. and Sat. 10-4.30 and by appointment. SIZE: Large. *STOCK: English and Continental*

furniture. LOC: A3100. From Guildford on the left side approaching Godalming. PARK: Own. TEL: 01483 422562; fax - 01483 426077; e-mail - rogrheathbullock@aol.com; website - www.heath-bullocks.com. SER: Valuations; restorations. FAIRS: BADA; Buxton; Surrey.

Priory Antiques
29 Church St. GU7 1EL. (P. Rotchell). Open 10-4. CL: Wed. *STOCK: General antiques*. TEL: 01483 421804.

The Coach House Antiques
60 Station Rd. GU5 9NP. (P.W. and L. Reeves). Resident. Est. 1985. Open 9-5.30, Sun. 11-5. SIZE: Small. *STOCK: Longcase clocks, 1780 to 19th C, £4,000-£20,000; furniture, 1790 to late 19th C, £1,000-£20,000*. LOC: Between Guildford and Dorking on the Shere by-pass. PARK: Easy. TEL: 01483 203838; fax - 01483 202999; e-mail - coach_house.antiques@virgin.net; website - www.coachhouseantiques.com. SER: Valuations; restorations (clocks and furniture); buys at auction (as stock). FAIRS: Guildford; Buxton. VAT: Spec.

The Studio
Station Rd. GU5 9LQ. (Mrs M. Ellenger). Est. 1985. Open 12-5, Sat. and Sun. 10.30-5. SIZE: Small. *STOCK: General antiques*. LOC: A25 midway between Guildford and Dorking. PARK: Easy. TEL: 01483 202449. SER: Valuations. VAT: Stan.

Roger A. Davis Antiquarian Horologist
19 Dorking Rd. KT23 4PU. Est. 1971. Open Tues., Thurs. and Sat. 9.30-12.30 and 2-5, other times by appointment. SIZE: Small. *STOCK: Clocks, 18th-19th C, £150-£5,000*. LOC: From Leatherhead A246 to centre of village, turn left at sign for Polesden Lacey, shop ¼ mile along Dorking Rd. PARK: Easy. TEL: 01372 457655; home - 01372 453167. SER: Valuations; restorations (mechanical and case work).

Memory Lane Antiques
30 Church Rd. KT23 3PW. (J.Westwood). Est. 1984. Open 10-5. CL: Wed. *STOCK: Toys and general antiques, pre-1920, £5-£1,000*. PARK: Easy. TEL: 01372 459908.

Motoring magazines from the 1960s. £2-£5 each.

From an article entitled "Periodically Valuable" by Adrian Greenwood which appeared in the December 2001/January 2002 issue of **Antique Collecting**. For more details and to subscribe see page 21.

GUILDFORD

Cry for the Moon
17 Tunsgate. GU1 3QT. (J.L. Ackroyd). Est. 1977. Open 9.30-5.30. SIZE: Medium. *STOCK: Mainly jewellery and certificated diamonds, £30-£50,000; silver and objets d'art.* TEL: 01483 306600; fax - 01483 306300. SER: Valuations; repairs; jewellery commissions undertaken. VAT: Stan/Margin.

Denning Antiques
1 Chapel St. GU1 3UA. Est. 1986. Open 10-5. *STOCK: Silver, jewellery, lace, linen, and collectors' items.* LOC: Off High St. PARK: Nearby. TEL: 01483 539595.

Horological Workshops   BADA
204 Worplesdon Rd. GU2 9UY. (M.D.Tooke). Est. 1968. Open Tues.-Fri. 8.30-5.30, Sat. 9-12.30 or by appointment. SIZE: Large. *STOCK: Clocks, watches, barometers.* **PARK: Easy. TEL: 01483 576496; fax - 01483 452212; e-mail - enquiries@horologicalworkshops.com. SER: Restorations; collection and delivery.**

Oriental Rug Gallery
230 Upper High St. GU1 3JD. (R. Mathias and J. Blair). *STOCK: Russian, Afghan, Turkish and Persian carpets, rugs and kelims; Oriental objets d'art.* TEL: + 4 (0) 1483 457600; fax - same; e-mail - rugs@orientalruggallery.com; website - www.orientalruggallery.com.

Thomas Thorp Bookseller
170 High St. GU1 3HP. Est. 1883. Open 9-5. SIZE: Large. *STOCK: Books including antiquarian and out-of-print.* LOC: At traffic lights at top of High St. PARK: Road running parallel High St. 200yds. away. TEL: 01483 562770. SER: Buys at auction (antiquarian books); private collections bought.

Charles W. Traylen
Castle House, 49/50 Quarry St. GU1 3UA. Est. 1945. Open 9-5. CL: Mon. SIZE: Large. *STOCK: Fine books and manuscripts, 13th C to date.* PARK: 200yds. TEL: 01483 572424; fax - 01483 450048. SER: Valuations; restorations (bindings); catalogues issued. FAIRS: Olympia. VAT: Stan.

HASLEMERE

Haslemere Antique Market
1A Causewayside, High St. GU27 2JZ. Est. 1990. Open 9.30-5. SIZE: Large. *STOCK: Wide variety of general antiques.* LOC: Off High St. (A286). PARK: Easy. TEL: 01428 643959. SER: Valuations; restorations; buys at auction.

Serendipity Antiques & Crafts
7 Petworth Rd. GU27 2JB. (E.J. Moore). Est. 1995. Open 10-5, Sun. 10.30-4. SIZE: Medium. *STOCK: Furniture, £400-£2,000, books, £20-£100, both 19th C; china, late 19th to early 20th C, glass, silver, metalware, clocks, £5-£1,000.* LOC: East at base of High Street, 100 yds on right. PARK: High St. TEL: 01428 642682. SER: Restorations (clocks).

Surrey Clock Centre
3 Lower St. GU27 2NY. (J.P. Ingrams and S. Haw). Est. 1962. Open 9-1 and 2-5. SIZE: Large. *STOCK: Clocks and barometers.* PARK: Easy. TEL: 01428 651313. SER: Restorations; handmade parts; shipping orders; clocks made to order. VAT: Stan/Spec.

Wood's Wharf Antiques Bazaar
56 High St. GU27 2LA. (C.M. Lunnon). SIZE: 12 dealers. *STOCK: A wide selection of antiques.* TEL: 01428 642125; fax - same.

HINDHEAD

Albany Antiques Ltd
8-10 London Rd. GU26 6AF. (T. Winstanley). Est. 1965. Open 9-6. CL: Sun. except by appointment. *STOCK: Furniture, 17th-18th C, £20-£400; china including Chinese, £5-£400; metalware, £7-£50; both 18th-19th C.* Not Stocked: Silver. LOC: A3. PARK: Easy. TEL: 01428 605528. VAT: Stan/Spec.

M. J. Bowdery   BADA
12 London Rd. GU26 6AF. Est. 1970. Always available, prior telephone call advisable. SIZE: Medium. *STOCK: Furniture, 18th-19th C.* LOC: A3. PARK: Own. TEL: 01428 606376; mobile - 07774 821444. SER: Valuations. FAIRS: Buxton; Guildford. VAT: Spec.

Drummonds Architectural Antiques
The Kirkpatrick Buildings, 25 London Rd. GU26 6AB. SALVO. Est. 1988. Open 9-6 including Sun. SIZE: Large. *STOCK: Architectural and decorative antiques, garden statuary and furniture, period bathrooms.* LOC: West side of A3, 50 yards north of traffic lights. PARK: Own. TEL: 01428 609444; fax - 01428 609445; website - www.drummonds-arch.co.uk. SER: Restorations (stonework and gates); handmade cast iron baths and fittings, cast iron conservatories; vitreous re-enamelling of baths. VAT: Stan/Spec.

HORLEY

Surrey Antiques
3 Central Parade, Massetts Rd. RH6 7PP. (Michael Bradnum). Est. 1990. Open 10-5, Sat. 10-4. SIZE: Small. *STOCK: China, pottery and glass, furniture, pictures, mirrors, collectables, 19th-20th C.* LOC: On left by traffic lights. PARK: Public behind shop. TEL: 01293 775522. FAIRS: Ardingly; Copthorne; Effingham Park Hotel.

HORSELL, Nr. Woking

Philip Gilbert
77 High St. GU21 4UA. Est. 1974. Open 10-5. SIZE: Small. *STOCK: Brown furniture, 18th-19th C, £100-£3,000.* LOC: From A322 along Knaphill High St. At roundabout turn right into Horsell High St. PARK: High St. TEL: 01483 756807. SER: Restorations (French polishing, cabinet work, upholstery); buys at auction (furniture). VAT: Spec.

KEW

Lloyds of Kew
9 Mortlake Terrace. TW9 3DT. (C. Patterson). Open 10.30-6. *STOCK: Out-of-print and antiquarian books including gardening, film, childrens.* LOC: Junction of Kew and Mortlake Roads, 10 mins walk from Kew Gardens Station (District line). PARK: Easy. TEL: 020 8940 2512; fax - same; mobile - 07941 592141; e-mail - books@lloydsofkew.co.uk; website - www.loydsofkew.co.uk. SER: Quarterly catalogues.

KEW GREEN

Andrew Davis
6 Mortlake Terrace. TW9 3DT. Resident. Est. 1969. *STOCK: Decorative and functional items of all periods, including furniture, ceramics, glass, pictures, clocks, garden and architectural items.* PARK: Easy. TEL: 020 8948 4911. SER: Valuations.

KINGSTON-UPON-THAMES

Glencorse Antiques
321 Richmond Rd., Ham Parade, Ham Common. KT2 5QU. (M. Igel and B.S. Prydal). LAPADA. Est. 1983. Open 10-5.30. *STOCK: 18th-19th C furniture; traditional modern British art, oils and watercolours, 20th-21st C.* PARK: Own. TEL: 020 8541 0871 and 020 7229 6770.

Glydon and Guess Ltd
14 Apple Market. KT1 1JE. NAG; GMC. Est. 1940. Open 9.30-5. *STOCK: Jewellery, small silver, £100-£5,000.* LOC: Town centre. TEL: 020 8546 3758. SER: Valuations; restorations.

Kingston Antique Market
29-31 Old London Rd. KT2 6ND. Est. 1995. Open 9.30-6, Thurs. 9.30-7, Sun. 10-6. SIZE: 100 dealers. *STOCK: General antiques including period furniture, porcelain, collectables and jewellery.* LOC: Off Clarence St. PARK: Easy. TEL: 020 8549 2004; e-mail - webmaster@ antiquesmarket.co.uk; website - www.antique market.co. uk.

LALEHAM, Nr. Staines

Laleham Antiques
23 Shepperton Rd. TW18 1SE. (E. Potter). Est. 1970. Open 10.30-5. SIZE: Medium. *STOCK: Furniture, porcelain, mirrors, antique lighting, silver, general and trade antiques.* LOC: B376. PARK: Easy. TEL: 01784 450353.

LEATHERHEAD

Alan's Antiques
1-3 Church St. KT22 8DN. (Michael Laikin). Est. 1960. Open 9-5.30. SIZE: Medium. *STOCK: Furniture, £200+, porcelain, £100-£300, silver, £100+, all late 19th to early 20th C.* LOC: Town centre. PARK: Opposite. TEL: 01372 360646; e-mail - michael.laikin@virgin.net. SER: Valuations; restorations (porcelain). FAIRS: Sandown Park. VAT: Stan/Spec.

LIMPSFIELD

Limpsfield Watercolours
High St. RH8 0DT. (Mrs C. Reason). FATG. Est. 1985. Open Tues.-Fri. 10.30-5, Sat. 9.30-4. SIZE: Small. *STOCK: Watercolours, £15-£5,000; prints and etchings, £5-£200; all 1850-1940 and contemporary.* Not Stocked: Oils. LOC: From junction 6 M25 follow A25 towards Westerham, village is left on B269. PARK: Easy. TEL: 01883 717010; website - www.limpsfieldwatercolours. com. SER: Valuations; restoration and cleaning of watercolours, prints and oils; framing including conservation. VAT: Spec.

MERSTHAM

Elm House Antiques
3 High St. RH1 3BA. (Robert Black). Est. 1995. Open 10.30-5.30. SIZE: Medium. *STOCK: Georgian to Edwardian town and country furniture, mahogany, oak and decorative items, £50-£5,000; country furniture, pine, kitchenalia, decorative items, textiles, £5-£500; brass and copper, £5-£100; period cabinet fittings.* LOC: A23 just past beginning of M23. PARK: Own. TEL: 01737 643983. SER: Valuations; restorations (textiles, boxes, inlay, gesso work, furniture including French polishing, upholstery).

Geoffrey Van-Hay Antiques
The Old Smithy, 7 High St. RH1 3BA. Open 9-5. SIZE: Medium. *STOCK: 18th-19th C furniture, £500-£1,000.* PARK: Easy. TEL: 01737 645131; fax - same. SER: Valuations; restorations. VAT: Spec.

MILFORD, Nr. Godalming

Michael Andrews Antiques
Portsmouth Rd. GU8 5AU. Est. 1974. Open daily, Thurs. and Sun. by appointment. SIZE: Medium. *STOCK: Furniture, 18th-19th C.* LOC: Corner of Cherry Tree Rd. (on traffic lights, from A3 slip road to Petworth). PARK: Own. TEL: 01483 420765; home - same.

E. Bailey
Portsmouth Rd. GU8 5DR. (Eric Bailey). Est. 1979. Open 9-5. CL: Thurs. SIZE: Small. *STOCK: Furniture and tools, from Victorian, £5-£100; china, £5-£25.* LOC: Main road. PARK: Easy. TEL: 01483 422943.

MORDEN

A. Burton-Garbett
35 The Green. SM4 4HJ. Est. 1959. By appointment only. Prospective clients met (at either Morden or Wimbledon tube station) by car. *STOCK: Books on Latin American and Caribbean travel, arts and antiquities.* TEL: 020 8540 2367; fax - 020 8540 4594. SER: Buys at auction (books, pictures, fine arts, ethnographica). VAT: Stan.

OXTED

Secondhand Bookshop
56 Station Rd. West. RH8 9EU. (David Neal). Est. 1985. Open 10-5. SIZE: Small. *STOCK: Books, 18th C to present day, £1-£500.* LOC: Adjacent to station. PARK: Safeway immediately behind shop. TEL: 01883 715755; home - 01883 723131. SER: Valuations; buys at auction (books). FAIRS: Book - in south-east. VAT: Stan.

Wagstaffs
Books in the Basement, 80-84 Station Rd. East. RH8 0PG. (David Neal). Est. 1985. Open 9.30-5.30. SIZE: Medium. *STOCK: 20th C books, £1-£100.* LOC: Opposite Station Parade. PARK: Nearby. TEL: 01883 717183; home - 01883 723131. SER: Valuations; buys at auction. VAT: Stan.

REDHILL

F.G. Lawrence and Sons
89 Brighton Rd. RH1 6PS. (Chris Lawrence). Est. 1891. Open 9-5, Sat. 9-1. SIZE: Large. *STOCK: 1920's, Edwardian, Victorian and Georgian furniture.* LOC: On A23. PARK: Own. TEL: 01737 764196; e-mail - catherine.lawrence@btinternet. com. SER: Valuations. VAT: Stan.

REIGATE

Bourne Gallery Ltd
31/33 Lesbourne Rd. RH2 7JS. (J. Robertson and Ian and Linda Read). LAPADA. Est. 1970. Open 10-1 and 2-5. CL: Mon. SIZE: Large. *STOCK: 19th-20th C oils and watercolours, £250-£25,000; contemporary works, £250-£2,500.* PARK: Easy. TEL: 01737 241614; e-mail - bournegallery@aol. com; website- www.bournegallery.com. FAIRS: Olympia; Chelsea. VAT: Spec.

The Gallery
3/5 Church St. RH2 0AA. (Jeffrey S. Cohen). LAPADA. Open 10-6. SIZE: Medium. *STOCK: 19th-20th C oil paintings and watercolours, especially Modern British artists post 1850, £250-£15,000; 18th-19th C furniture and mirrors, especially small decorative pieces, £500-£10,000.* LOC: Town centre. PARK: Easy and opposite. TEL: 01737 242813; fax - 01737 362819; e-mail - the.gallery@virgin.net; website - www.thegallery.uk.com. SER: Valuations; restorations (paintings and furniture). VAT: Stan/Spec.

Bertram Noller (Reigate)
14a London Rd. RH2 9HY. (A.M. Noller). Est. 1970. Open Tues., Thurs., Sat. 9.30-1 and 2-5.30. SIZE: Small. *STOCK: Collectors' items, furniture, grates, fenders, mantels, copper, brass, glass, pewter, £1-£500.* LOC: West side of one-way traffic system. Opposite Upper West St. car park. PARK: Opposite. TEL: 01737 242548. SER: Valuations; restorations (furniture, clocks, bronzes, brass and copper, marble).

Reigate Galleries
45a Bell St. RH2 7AQ. (J.S. Morrish). PBFA. Est. 1958. Open 9-5.30, Wed. 9-1. SIZE: Large. *STOCK: Old prints, engravings, antiquarian books.* PARK: Opposite. TEL: 01737 246055. SER: Picture framing. VAT: Stan.

M. & M. White Antique & Reproduction Centre
57 High St. RH2 9AE. Est. 1993. Open 10-5.30. SIZE: Medium. *STOCK: Mahogany, £100-£2,500, pine, £60-£1,500, both 18th C; reproduction, 1920-1970, £40-£1,000.* PARK: Easy. TEL: 01737 222331; fax - 01737 215702. FAIRS: Newark; Ardingly; Kempton Park. VAT: Spec.

RICHMOND

Antique Mart
72-74 Hill Rise. TW10 6UB. (G. Katz). Open Thurs., Fri., Sat. and Sun. 2-6, otherwise by appointment. SIZE: *STOCK: Furniture, 18th-19th C; French and English oils and watercolours, 19th-20th C.* TEL: 020 8940 6942; fax - 020 8715 4668; mobile - 07775 626423; e-mail - georgekatz@blueyonder.co.uk. SER: Buys at auction. VAT: Stan/Spec.

The Gooday Gallery
14 Richmond Hill. TW10 6QX. (Debbie Gooday). Est. 1971. Open Thurs.-Sat. 11-5. SIZE: Medium. *STOCK: Decorative and applied design, 1880-1980, Arts and Crafts, Art Nouveau, Art Deco, furniture, pictures, ceramics, metalwork, jewellery; African and oceanic tribal artefacts; 1950's and 1960's designer items, all £100-£5,000.* LOC: 100yds. from Richmond Bridge. PARK: Easy. TEL: 020 8940 8652; mobile - 07710 124540; e-mail - Goodaygallery@aol.com. SER: Valuations; buys at auction.

Roland Goslett Gallery
139 Kew Rd. TW9 2PN. Est. 1974. Open Thurs. and Fri. 10-6, Sat. 10-2 or by appointment. SIZE: Medium. *STOCK: English watercolours and oil paintings, 19th to early 20th C, £100-£5,000.* PARK: Meters. TEL: 020 8940 4009. SER: Valuations; restorations (oils, watercolours and frames); framing. VAT: Spec.

Hill Rise Antiques

26 Hill Rise. TW10 6UA. (P. Hinde and D. Milewski). LAPADA. Est. 1978. Open 10.30-5.30, Sun. 2.30-5.30. CL: Wed. SIZE: Large. *STOCK: 18th-19th C walnut and mahogany furniture, £100-£10,000; silver and plate, mirrors, boxes and glassware.* LOC: 1 mile from A316 (M3). PARK: At rear by arrangement. TEL: 020 8332 2941; home - same; e-mail - antiques@hillrisehouse.com. VAT: Stan/Spec.

Horton

2 Paved Court, The Green. TW9 1LZ. (D. Horton). LAPADA. FGA. *STOCK: Jewellery and silver, 18th-20th C, £500-£5,000.* TEL: 020 8332 1775; fax - 020 8332 1994; website - www.horton london.co.uk.

Lionel Jacobs

12-14 Brewers Lane. TW9 1HH. Est. 1982. Open 9-5. *STOCK: Silver and jewellery.* TEL: 020 8940 8069.

Robin Kennedy

P.O Box 265. TW9 1UB. Est. 1971. Open by appointment. *STOCK: Japanese prints, £50-£5,000.* TEL: 020 8940 5346; fax - same; e-mail - robin@japaneseprints.co.uk; website - www.japaneseprints.co.uk. FAIRS: Arts of Pacific Asia (New York, San Francisco, Santa Monica).

F. and T. Lawson Antiques

13 Hill Rise. TW10 6UQ. Resident. Est. 1965. Open 10-5.30, Sat. 10-5. CL: Wed. and Sun. am. SIZE: Medium. *STOCK: Furniture, 1680-1870; paintings and watercolours; both £30-£1,500; clocks, 1650-1930, £50-£2,000; bric-a-brac, £5-£300.* LOC: Near Richmond Bridge at bottom of Hill Rise on the river side, overlooking river. PARK: Limited and further up Hill Rise. TEL: 020 8940 0461. SER: Valuations; buys at auction.

Marryat

88 Sheen Rd. TW9 1AJ. (Marryat (Richmond) Ltd). LAPADA. Est. 1990. Open 10-5.30. SIZE: Large. *STOCK: English and Continental furniture, watercolours and oils, £150-£5,000; porcelain, pottery, glass, silver, objets and decorative antiques, £10-£1,000; all 18th-19th C.* LOC: Follow M3/A316 towards Richmond, first left into Church Rd. then left again. Close to underground station. PARK: Easy. TEL: 020 8332 0262. SER: Restorations. VAT: Stan/Spec.

Palmer Galleries

10 Paved Court. TW9 1LZ. (C.D. and V.J. Palmer). Est. 1984. Open 10-5. SIZE: Medium. *STOCK: Prints, watercolours and engravings, 19th-20th C, £50-£1,000.* PARK: Richmond Green. TEL: 020 8948 2668; website - www.palmergalleries.co.uk. VAT: Stan.

Piano Nobile Fine Paintings

26 Richmond Hill. TW10 6QX. (Dr. Robert A. Travers). SLAD. Est. 1986. Open Tues.-Sat. 10-5.30. SIZE: Medium. *STOCK: Fine 19th C Impressionist and 20th C Post-Impressionist and Modernist British and Continental oil paintings and sculpture, especially Les Petit Maitres of the Paris Schools, £500-£100,000.* PARK: Easy. TEL: 020 8940 2435; fax - same; e-mail - art@pianonobile.freeserve.co.uk; website - www.piano-nobile.com. SER: Valuations; restorations (paintings and sculpture); framing; buys at auction (19th-20th C oil paintings). FAIRS: Grosvenor; 20th C British Art & London Contemporary; BADA; Olympia; Art London. VAT: Stan/Spec.

Town & Country Decorative

24 Hill Rise. TW10 6UA. Open 10.30-5.30, Sun. 2-5. CL: Wed. *STOCK: Decorative antiques.* TEL: 020 8948 4638.

RIPLEY

Cedar House Gallery

High St. GU23 6AE. Resident. Est. 1987. Open 9-6, Sun. 2-5. *STOCK: Watercolours and oils, 19th to early 20th C, £500-£10,000; general antiques.* LOC: ½ mile M25/A3 junction. PARK: Easy. TEL: 01483 211221; e-mail - johnrgspeed@aol.com. SER: Restorations.

J. Hartley Antiques Ltd

186 High St. GU23 6BB. LAPADA. Est. 1949. Open 8.45-5.45, Sat. 9.45-4.45. *STOCK: Queen Anne, Georgian and Edwardian furniture.* TEL: 01483 224318. VAT: Stan.

Ripley Antiques

67 High St. GU23 6AN. (H. Denham). LAPADA. Est. 1960. Open 9.30-5.30, Sun. by appointment. SIZE: Large. *STOCK: Furniture, English and French, 18th-19th C; decorative items - mirrors and chandeliers.* LOC: 2 mins. from junction 10 at M25/A3 interchange. Between Heathrow and Gatwick Airports. PARK: Easy. TEL: 01483 224981; fax - 01483 224333. SER: Valuations; restorations. VAT: Stan/Spec.

Sage Antiques and Interiors

High St. GU23 6BB. (H. and C. Sage). LAPADA. GMC. Est. 1971. Open 9.30-5.30. SIZE: Large. *STOCK: Furniture, mahogany, oak, walnut, 1600-1900, £150-£8,000; oil paintings, £100-£5,000; watercolours, £50-£1,000, china, £2-£500, all 18th-19th C; silver, Sheffield plate, brass, pewter, decorative items, 18th-19th C, £50-£1,000.* LOC: Village centre, on main road. PARK: Easy. TEL: 01483 224396; fax - 01483 211996. SER: Restorations (furniture, pictures); interior furnishing. VAT: Stan.

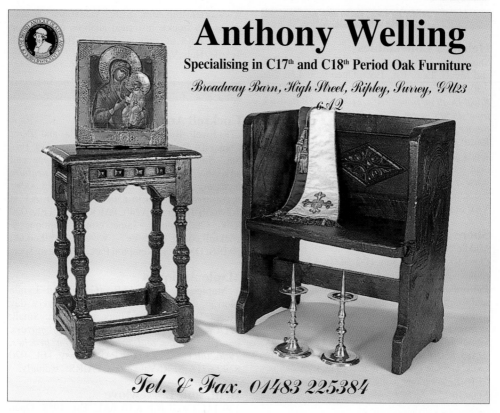

Anthony Welling
Specialising in C17th and C18th Period Oak Furniture
Broadway Barn, High Street, Ripley, Surrey, GU23 6AJ

Tel. & Fax. 01483 225384

Sweerts de Landas
BADA
Dunsborough Park, Newark Lane. GU23 6AL. (A.J.H. and A.C. Sweerts de Landas). SALCO. Est. 1979. Open by appointment only. SIZE: Large. *STOCK: Garden ornaments and statuary, 17th-20th C, £500-£250,000.* LOC: From High St. turn into Newark Lane (between estate agent and Suzuki garage), continue 400 yds, go through archway on right, follow drive to gate. PARK: Easy. TEL: 01483 225366; home - same. SER: Valuations; restorations (stone, lead, cast iron, marble); buys at auction (as stock). FAIRS: Olympia; Grosvenor House. VAT: Stan/Spec.

Talbot Walk Antique Centre
The Talbot Hotel, High St. GU23 6BB. (P. Skellett). Est. 1999. Open 10-5, Sun. 11-4. SIZE: Large. *STOCK: English furniture, 1750-1920, £100-£5,000+; glass and ceramics, 1800-1940, £10-£3,000+; lighting, 1850-1940, £50-£2,000+; general antiques, 1850-1920, £10-£1,000+.* LOC: 1 mile south of A3/M25, junction 10, take the B2215 to Ripley, 400yds on left after entering village. PARK: Own at rear of premises. TEL: 01483 211724; fax - 01483 211724. VAT: Stan/Spec.

Anthony Welling Antiques
BADA
Broadway Barn, High St. GU23 6AQ. Est.

1970. Open 9.30-1 and 2-5. Sun. and evenings by appointment. SIZE: Large. *STOCK: English oak, 17th-18th C, £250-£8,000; country furniture, 18th C, £200-£6,000; brass, copper, pewter, 18th C, £100-£750.* Not Stocked: Glass, china, silver. LOC: Turn off A3 at Ripley, shop in village centre on service road. PARK: Easy. TEL: 01483 225384; fax - same. SER: Restoration (furniture). VAT: Spec.

RUNFOLD, Nr. Farnham

The Packhouse
Hewetts Kilns, Tongham Rd. GU10 1PQ. (P. Hewett). Est. 1991. Open 10.30-5.30 including Sun. SIZE: Large. *STOCK: Furniture including period, 1930's and country pine; garden statuary, architectural items.* LOC: Off A31 (Hogs Back). PARK: Easy. TEL: 01252 781010; fax - 01252 783876.

SANDERSTEAD

Raymond Slack FRSA & Shirley Warren
CR2 9DQ. *STOCK: Reference books on glass collecting.* TEL: 020 8657 1751. FAIRS: Birmingham Glass. *Mail Order.*

465

SHERE, Nr. Guildford

Helena's Collectables

Shops 1 and 2, Middle St. GU5 9HF. (Mrs. K. White and Mrs.H. Lee). Est. 1995. Open 9.30-4.30, Sat. 9.30-5, Sun. 10.30-4.30. SIZE: Medium. *STOCK: Royal Doulton, from 1930's, £100-£2,500; Beswick, from 1950's, from £50+; Walt Disney classics, Border Fine Art, Bunnykins and Beatrix Potter, Royal Crown Derby.*LOC: A24. PARK: Behind sports ground. TEL: 01483 203039; fax - same; e-mail - helen@collectables.demon.co.uk; website - www.collectables.demon.co.uk. SER: Valuations; restorations; search; buys at auction. FAIRS: DMG. VAT: Stan.

Shere Antiques Centre

Middle St. GU5 9HL. (Jean Watson). Est. 1986. Open 10-5, Sat. and Sun. 11-5. SIZE: 4 large show-rooms. *STOCK: Mid-Georgian, Victorian and Edwardian clocks, silver, copper, brass, English and Continental porcelain, maps and prints, pens, watches; Victorian garden tools and associated items.* LOC: A25 - between Dorking and Guildford. PARK: Easy. TEL: 01483 202846; fax - 01483 830761; e-mail - jean.watson@glenturret. co.uk; website - www.glenturret.co.uk.shereantiques. SER: Restorations; collection and delivery. VAT: Stan/Spec.

SHIRLEY

Norman Witham

217 Wickham Rd. CR0 8TG. Est. 1959. Open Mon.-Sat. *STOCK: Porcelain, glass, small furniture, mainly Victorian, £5-£500.* TEL: 020 8655 4445; evenings - 020 8650 4651. SER: Valuations.

STAINES

K.W. Dunster Antiques

23 Church St. TW18 4EN. Est. 1972. Open 9-4.30. CL: Thurs. SIZE: Medium. *STOCK: Clocks, furniture, general antiques, interior decor, jewellery, nautical items.* PARK: Easy. TEL: 01784 453297; fax - 01784 483146; e-mail - kdunsterantiques@ aol.com. SER: Valuations. VAT: Stan/Spec.

Clive Rogers Oriental Rugs

PO Box 234. TVADA. PADA. Est. 1974. Open by appointment. SIZE: Medium. *STOCK: Oriental rugs, carpets, textiles; Oriental and Islamic works of art.* LOC: On B376, 10 minutes from Heathrow Airport. PARK: Own. TEL: 01784 481177/ 481100; fax - 01784 481144; mobile - 07747 114757; e-mail - info@orient-rug.com; website - www.orient-rug.com. SER: Valuations; restorations (as stock); historical analysis commission agents; buys at auction. FAIRS: Hammersmith Textile; Hali. VAT: Stan/Spec.

SURBITON

Cockrell Antiques

278 Ewell Rd. KT6 7AG. (Sheila and Peter Cockrell). Resident. Est. 1982. Open most Fri., Sat., Sun. and evenings - prior telephone call advisable. SIZE: Medium. *STOCK: Furniture including Art Deco, from 18th C, £50-£3,000+; decorative items, £50-£500.* LOC: Off A3 at Tolworth Tower on A240. PARK: Easy. TEL: 020 8390 8290; home - same; e-mail - antiques@ cockrell.co.uk; website - www.cockrell.co.uk. FAIRS: DMG and Kempton Park. VAT: Stan/Spec.

Maple Antiques

4 Maple Rd. KT6 4AB. (Geoff and Lynda Morris). Resident. Est. 1965. Open every day except Tues. am and Thurs. am. SIZE: Small. *STOCK: Pine, oak, mahogany, lights and mirrors, garden statuary and urns, cast iron benches, 19th-20th C, £25-£1,000.* PARK: Easy. TEL: 020 8399 6718. SER: Valuations. FAIRS: Ardingly.

B. M. and E. Newlove

139-141 Ewell Rd. KT6 6AL. Est. 1958. Open 9.30-5.30, Sat. by appointment. CL: Wed. SIZE: Medium and store. *STOCK: Furniture especially early oak and Georgian mahogany, 17th-19th C, £500-£10,000; china, 18th-19th C, £75-£200; paintings, all periods, £50-£2,000; longcase clocks, Georgian barometers.* Not Stocked: Pot-lids, fairings. LOC: Down Kingston by-pass at Tolworth underpass, turn right into Tolworth Broadway, then into Ewell Rd. Shop one mile on. PARK: Easy. TEL: 020 8399 8857. SER: Gilding. VAT: Stan/Spec.

Laurence Tauber Antiques

131 Ewell Rd. KT6 6AL. Open 10-5. CL: Wed. pm. *STOCK: General antiques, especially for Trade.* PARK: Easy. TEL: 020 8390 0020. VAT: Stan/Spec.

SUTTON

S. Warrender and Co

4 and 6 Cheam Rd. SM1 1SR. (F.R. Warrender). Est. 1953. Open 9-5.30. CL: Wed. SIZE: Medium. *STOCK: Jewellery, 1790 to date, £10-£1,500; silver, 1762 to date, £10-£1,000; carriage clocks, 1860-1900, £115-£800.* TEL: 020 8643 4381. SER: Valuations; restorations (jewellery, silver, quality clocks). VAT: Stan.

THAMES DITTON

Clifford and Roger Dade
Boldre House, Weston Green. KT7 0JP. LAPADA. Resident. Est. 1937. Open 9.30-6. SIZE: Large. *STOCK: Mahogany furniture, 18th to early 19th C, £500-£5,000.* LOC: A309 between Esher and Hampton Court, near Sandown Park Racecourse. PARK: Outside shop. TEL: 020 8398 6293; fax - same; mobile - 07702 014222. VAT: Spec.

WALTON-ON-THAMES

Antique Church Furnishings
Rivernook Farm, Sunnyside. KT12 2ET. (L. Skilling and S. Williams). Est. 1989. Open Mon.-Fri. 10-6. SIZE: Large. *STOCK: Church chairs and pews, £10-£750; altar tables and screens, pulpits, lecterns, reredos, pine and architectural items, £20-£2,000; all late 19th C to early 20th C.* LOC: Between A3050 and River Thames. PARK: Easy. TEL: 01932 252736; fax - same. SER: Valuations; buys at auction (church fixtures and furnishings, stained glass). FAIRS: Newark. VAT: Stan/Spec.

Susan Becker
P O Box 160. KT12 3HJ. (S. Becker Fleming). LAPADA. Est. 1959. Open by appointment only. *STOCK: English (especially Royal Worcester), and Continental porcelain, 18th-20th C, £200-£25,000; glass and fine objects.* LOC: 10 minutes A3, M25, M4. PARK: Easy. TEL: 01932 227820. SER: Valuations. VAT: Spec.

WALTON-ON-THE-HILL AND TADWORTH

Ian Caldwell
9a Tadworth Green, Dorking Rd. KT20 5SQ. LAPADA. Est. 1978. Open 10-5. CL: Wed. SIZE: Medium. *STOCK: Oak, walnut and mahogany furniture especially Georgian.* LOC: 2 miles from M25, ¼ mile from A217 on B2032 in Dorking direction. PARK: Easy. TEL: 01737 813969; e-mail - caldwell.antiques@virgin.net; website - www.freespace.virgin.net/caldwell.antiques. SER: Valuations; restorations. VAT: Stan/Spec.

WARLINGHAM

Trengove
397 Limpsfield Rd, The Green. CR6 9LA. (Brian Trengrove). Est. 1890. Open by appointment. SIZE: Small. *STOCK: General antiques, pictures.* PARK: Easy. TEL: 01883 624422.

WEST BYFLEET

Academy Billiard Company
5 Camphill Industrial Estate. KT14 6EW. (R.W.Donnachie). Est. 1975. Open anytime by appointment. SIZE: Large warehouse and showroom. *STOCK: Period and antique billiard/snooker tables, all sizes, 1830-1920; combined billiard/dining tables, period accessories including other games-room equipment and lighting.* LOC: On A245, 2 miles from M25/A3 junction. PARK: Easy. TEL: 01932 352067; mobile - 07860 523757; fax - 01932 353904; e-mail - academy games@fsbdial.co.uk; website - www.games-room.com. SER: Valuations; restorations; removals; structural advice. VAT: Stan/Spec.

WEYBRIDGE

Ariel
89 Queens Rd. KT13 9UQ. (Mrs. P. Harvey and Mrs. G. Rees). Est. 1993. Open 10-5. SIZE: Small. *STOCK: Furniture, Georgian-Edwardian, £50-£1,500; clocks, jewellery and silver, 19th C, £100-£500.* PARK: Easy. TEL: 01932 850135. SER: Valuations; restorations (including re-upholstery); clock repairs; shipping.

Brocante
120 Oatlands Drive, Oatlands Village. KT13 9HL. (Barry Dean and Ray Gwilliams). Est. 1988. Open 10-5.30, Sun. 10-5. CL: Mon. and Wed. SIZE: Small. *STOCK: Furniture, 19th C, £300-£1,500; porcelain, 19th C, £10-£250; Sheffield plate, 18th-19th C, £10-£300.* PARK: Easy. TEL: 01932 857807; home - 01932 345524. SER: Valuations. FAIRS: Oatlands Park Hotel; Seven Hills Hilton, Cobham.

Church House Antiques
42 Church St. KT13 8DP. (M.I. Foster). Est. 1886. Open Thurs., Fri., Sat. 10-5.30. SIZE: Medium. *STOCK: Furniture, 18th-19th C, £95-£7,000; jewellery, 18th-19th C, some modern, £30-£5,000; pictures, silver, plate, decorative items.* Not Stocked: Coins and stamps. PARK: Behind library. TEL: 01932 842190. VAT: Stan/Spec.

The Clock Shop Weybridge
64 Church St. KT13 8DL. Est. 1970. Open 10-6. CL: Wed. SIZE: Medium. *STOCK: Clocks, 1685-1900, from £500; French carriage clocks, from £300.* LOC: Opposite HSBC bank on corner. PARK: Easy. TEL: 01932 840407/855503. SER: Valuations; restorations (clocks). VAT: Stan/Spec.

Edward Cross - Fine Paintings

128 Oatlands Drive. KT13 9HL. Est. 1973. Open Fri. 10-3, Sat. 10-12.30. SIZE: Medium. *STOCK: Fine paintings and bronzes, 19th-20th C, £500-£30,000.* LOC: A3050. PARK: Opposite. TEL: 01932 851093. SER: Valuations; restorations (watercolours and oil paintings); buys at auction (pictures). VAT: Spec.

Not Just Silver

16 York Rd. KT13 9DT. (Mrs S. Hughes). BJA. Est. 1969. Open 9.30-5.30, Sun. by appointment. *STOCK: Silver, Georgian to modern.* LOC: Opposite car park, just off Queens Rd. PARK: Opposite. TEL: 01932 842468; fax - 01932 830054; mobile - 07774 298151; e-mail - info@not-just-silver.com. SER: Valuations; repairs; silver plating.

Village Antiques

39 St Mary's Rd., Oatlands Village. KT13 9PT. (B. Mulvany). Est. 1976. Open 10-4.30. CL: Wed. SIZE: Small. *STOCK: Furniture, small silver and china, 19th-20th C, £50-£1,000.* LOC: Off Oatlands Drive. PARK: Easy. TEL: 01932 846554. SER: Valuations; restorations (French polishing, small furniture repairs). FAIRS: Ardingly.

Weybridge Antiques

43 Church St., The Quadrant. KT13 8XD. (P. Pocock). Est. 1974. Open 10-5.30. SIZE: Large. *STOCK: Furniture, 18th-19th C; paintings, objects.* LOC: From M25 into town, Church St. is first right.

PARK: Opposite in Mayfield Road. TEL: 01932 852503. SER: Restorations (oil paintings, porcelain, furniture, leathering). VAT: Spec.

Willow Gallery   BADA

75 Queens Rd. KT13 9UQ. (Andrew and Jean Stevens and Alick Forrester). LAPADA. Est. 1987. Open 10-6, Sun. by appointment. SIZE: Large. *STOCK: British and European oil paintings, 19th C, £3,000-£200,000.* **LOC: Near town centre. PARK: Easy and nearby. TEL: 01932 846095/6; e-mail - enquiries@thewillowgallery.com; website - www.thewillowgallery.com. SER: Valuations; restorations; conservation; framing; catalogue available. FAIRS: BADA; LAPADA; New York; Olympia. VAT: Spec.**

WOKING

Aspidistra Antiques

Wych Hill. GU22 0EU. (Mrs P. Caswell). Open 10-4.30, Sun. 11-4. SIZE: Medium. *STOCK: Furniture, 19th C to Art Deco, £100-£3,000; china and glass, 18th C to Art Deco, £50-£1,000; silver and jewellery, 19th C to Art Deco, £50-£1,500.* LOC: Just off A320. PARK: Easy. TEL: 01483 771117; fax - same. SER: Restorations.

Keith Baker

42 Arnold Rd. GU21 5JU. (K.R. Baker). Open Wed.-Sat. 9-4.30. *STOCK: General antiques.* PARK: Easy. TEL: 01483 767425.

A Robin Day for Hille desk, c.1960. Sold for £1,035 at Phillips Bayswater.

From an article entitled "20th Century Decorative Arts" by Christopher Parker which appeared in the July/August 2001 issue of **Antique Collecting**. For more details and to subscribe see page 21.

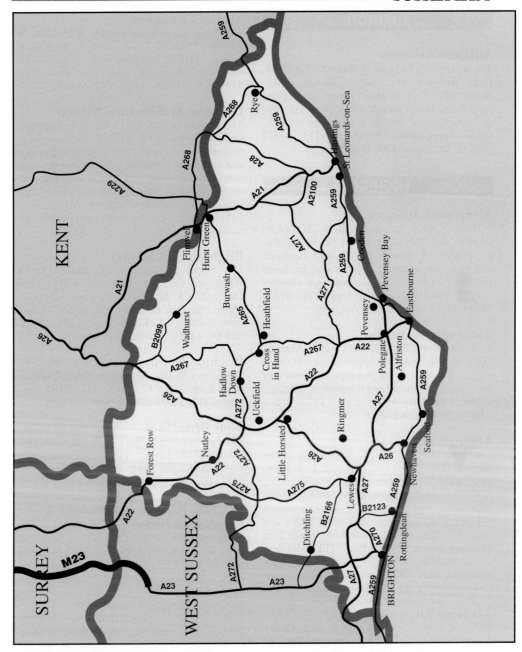

Dealers and Shops in East Sussex

Alfriston	1	Flimwell	1	Little Horsted	1	Rottingdean	1
Brighton	45	Forest Row	1	Newhaven	1	Rye	6
Burwash	1	Hadlow Down	1	Nutley	1	Seaford	3
Cooden	1	Hastings	6	Pevensey	1	St. Leonards-on-	
Cross in Hand	1	Heathfield	1	Pevensey Bay	1	Sea	7
Ditchling	1	Hurst Green	3	Polegate	2	Uckfield	1
Eastbourne	14	Lewes	11	Ringmer	1	Wadhurst	1

ALFRISTON

Alfriston Antiques
The Square. BN26 5UD. (J. Tourell). Est. 1967. Open Wed.-Sat. 11-5, Sun. 2.30-4.30. SIZE: Small. *STOCK: Collectors' items, vinaigrettes, snuff boxes, caddy spoons, silver, plate, carriage and other clocks, jewellery, paintings, pot-lids, copper, brass, books.* PARK: Easy. TEL: 01323 870498; fax - same. VAT: Stan/Spec.

BRIGHTON

Alexandria Antiques
3 Hanover Place, Lewes Rd. BN2 2SD. (A.H. Ahmed). Est. 1978. Open 9.30-6, Sat. by appointment. SIZE: 9 showrooms. *STOCK: Georgian and Victorian furniture; Oriental and European porcelain; oil and watercolour paintings; Oriental carpets, objets d'art.* PARK: Own. TEL: 01273 688793; fax - same. FAIRS: Ardingly.

Alexandria Antiques
33 Upper North St. BN1 3FG. (A.H. Ahmed). Open 9.30-6, Sat. by appointment. *STOCK: Georgian and Victorian furniture, Oriental and European porcelain; oil and watercolour paintings; Oriental carpets, objets d'art.* TEL: 01273 328072. FAIRS: Ardingly.

Antiques et cetera
190 Portland Rd., Hove. BN3 5QN. (Ken Bomzer). Est. 1994. Open 10-4, Sat. 10-1. SIZE: Small. *STOCK: Porcelain, £20-£1,000; glassware, £10-£500; small furniture, £50-£2,000; costume, silver and gold jewellery, £5-£8,000; watercolours, prints and oils, £20-£500; silver and plate, £10-£500; 19th C to date.* LOC: 1 mile from Portslade station. PARK: Easy. TEL: Mobile - 07747 666343; e-mail - antiques.etcetera@ btinternet.com. SER: Valuations; restorations (porcelain, jewellery). FAIRS: Ardingly.

Art Deco Etc.
73 Upper Gloucester Rd. BN1 3LQ. (John Clark). Est. 1979. Open 12-5.30, Sun. and other times by appointment. SIZE: Medium. *STOCK: Pottery, especially Poole; Scandinavian ceramics and glass; glass, lighting, mirrors, pictures and collectors' items, Art Deco, Art Nouveau, Arts and Crafts, 1950's, £5-£2,000.* LOC: From Brighton station down Queens Rd., first on right. PARK: Easy. TEL: 01273 329268; mobile - 07971 268302; e-mail - johnclark@artdecoetc.co.uk. SER: Valuations. FAIRS: Art Deco, Battersea; Alexandra Palace; Ardingly and Newark.

Ashton's Antiques
1-3 Clyde Rd., Preston Circus. BN1 4NN. (R. Ashton). Open 10-4. CL: Wed. SIZE: 4 showrooms. *STOCK: Victorian and Edwardian furniture, upholstery and decorative items.* TEL: 01273 605253; fax - same. VAT: Stan/Spec.

Brighton Architectural Salvage
33-34 Gloucester Rd. BN1 4AQ. (R.L. Legendre). Open Tues.-Sat. 10-5. *STOCK: Restored architectural items including pine furniture; fireplaces and surrounds - marble, pine, mahogany, cast-iron, Victorian tiled and cast inserts and overmantels; doors, stained glass, panelling; cast-iron balcony and street railings, gas coal fires, light fittings; garden seats and ornaments, reclaimed flooring.* TEL: 01273 681656.

Brighton Flea Market
31A Upper St. James's St. BN2 1JN. (A. Wilkinson). Est. 1990. Open seven days. SIZE: Large. *STOCK: Bric-a-brac, furniture and collectables, 19th-20th C, £5-£1,000.* LOC: 50 yards from coast road, Kemp Town. TEL: 01273 624006; e-mail - arwilkinsn@aol.com.

Brighton Retro
24A Sydney St. BN1 3EN. Open 10-6 and Sun. pm. SIZE: Large. *STOCK: 20th C items.* PARK: NCP nearby. TEL: 01273 628444. SER: Valuations.

Tony Broadfoot
39 Upper Gardner St. BN1 4AN. Est. 1985. Open 9-5.30. SIZE: Large. *STOCK: Furniture, from 17th C.* LOC: Off North Rd. PARK: Easy. TEL: 01273 695457. SER: Restorations.

C.A.R.S. (Classic Automobilia & Regalia Specialists)
4-4a Chapel Terrace Mews, Kemp Town. BN2 1HU. (G.G. Weiner). Est. 1976. Open 10-6 by appointment only. *STOCK: Collectors' car badges, mascots and associated automobilia and related motoring memorabilia; children's pedal cars, electric cars, collectors' veteran and vintage pedal cars, 1930's-1970's.* PARK: Easy. TEL: 01273 622722 (office hours); 01273 601960; fax - same; e-mail - cars@kemptown-brighton.freeserve.co.uk; website - www.carsofbrighton.co.uk; website for The Pedal Car Collectors' Club - www.eurosurf.co. uk and www. brmmbrmm.com/pedalcars. SER: Catalogue/ price list on receipt of SAE. FAIRS: NEC; Alexandra Palace; Ardingly; Brighton Classic Car.

Campbell Wilson
1 Brunswick Sq., Hove.BN3 1EG. (Neil Wilson). Est. 1996. Open by appointment. *STOCK: Paintings especially Pre-Raphaelite and Romantic British, 1845-1903; modern British, to 1945.* LOC: On

seafront. TEL: 01273 777087; website - www. campbell-wilson.demon.co.uk. SER: Buys at auction (Victorian and Modern British paintings). FAIRS: Olympia; Watercolours and Drawings; Antiques for Everyone (Glasgow).

Harry Diamond and Son
9 Union St., The Lanes. BN1 1HA. (R. and H. Diamond). Est. 1937. Open 9-5. *STOCK: Diamond jewellery, antique silver, £50-£20,000.* Not Stocked: Coins, furniture. TEL: 01273 329696. VAT: Stan.

James Doyle Antiques
10 Union St., The Lanes. BN1 1HA. (J.R. Doyle). Est. 1975. Open 9.30-6. *STOCK: Jewellery, silver.* TEL: 01273 323694; fax - 01273 324330.

Faques Gallery
32 Upper St James's St., BN2 1JN. Est. 1962. Open 10-5.30. SIZE: Large. *STOCK: Repro-duction oil paintings.* LOC: Kemp Town area. PARK: Side roads. TEL: 01273 624432; fax - 01273 683692. VAT: Stan.

Paul Goble Jewellers
44 Meeting House Lane, The Lanes. BN1 1HB. NAG. Est. 1965. Open 9-5.30, Sat. 9-6, Sun. 10-6. *STOCK: Jewellery, watches, silver, pictures and prints, teddy bears and dolls.* TEL: 01273 202801; fax - 01273 202736. SER: Trade/export; valuations. FAIRS: KM Antiques; Sandown Park. VAT: Stan/Spec.

Douglas Hall Ltd
23 Meeting House Lane. BN1 1HB. (K.J. Longthorne). Est. 1968. Open 9.30-5. *STOCK: Silver, jewellery.* TEL: 01273 325323. VAT: Stan.

Hallmark Jewellers
4 Union St., The Lanes. BN1 1HA. (J. Hersheson). Est. 1966. Open 9-5. SIZE: Small. *STOCK: Diamond and gem set jewellery; antique and modern silver.* TEL: 01273 725477; fax - same. VAT: Stan/Spec.

Mark and David Hawkins The Lanes Armoury
26 Meeting House Lane, The Lanes. BN1 1HB. Open 10-5.15. *STOCK: Militaria, arms, armour and books, from 500BC to WWII.* TEL: 01273 321357; website - www.thelanesarmoury.co.uk.

Heritage Antiques   BADA
P O Box 2974. BN1 3QG. (Anjula Daniel). LAPADA. CINOA. Est. 1975. Open by appointment. SIZE: Large. *STOCK: Metal-ware, £50-£5,000; interesting and decorative *items.* **PARK: Easy. TEL: 01273 326850; fax - same; e-mail - ahd@heritage-antiques-uk.com. FAIRS: Olympia. VAT: Stan/Spec.**

Dudley Hume
46 Upper North St. BN1 3FH. LAPADA. Est. 1973. CL: Sat. pm. and Sun., except by appoint-ment. SIZE: Medium. *STOCK: Period and Victorian furniture, metal, light fittings, decor-ative items.* LOC: Parallel to the Western Rd., one block to the north. TEL: 01273 323461; fax - 01273 240422; e-mail - dudley@dudleyhume. co.uk. FAIRS: Olympia (June); LAPADA (Oct.). VAT: Stan/Spec.

Jezebel
14 Prince Albert St. BN1 1HE. (Amanda Davis). Est. 1989. Open 11-5.30, Sun. by appointment. SIZE: Medium. *STOCK: Art Deco ceramics, fur-niture, lighting, chrome, collectables including Bakelite jewellery, £20-£2,000.* LOC: Just off Ship Street, near the Lanes. PARK: Easy. TEL: 01273 206091; fax - same; home - 01273 675616. SER: Valuations; restorations; buys at auction (Art Deco/Nouveau). FAIRS: Newark.

Leoframes
70 North Rd. BN1 1YD. (S. Round). Open 9-5.30. *STOCK: Prints and maps.* TEL: 01273 695862. SER: Restorations; framing.

Harry Mason
P O Box 687, Hove. BN3 6JY. Est. 1954. Open by appointment. *STOCK: Silver and plate, 18th-20th C; jewellery, 19th-20th C.* TEL: 01273 500330; fax - 01273 553300; e-mail - mason@fastnet. co.uk. SER: Valuations; restorations (silver and jewellery); buys at auction (as stock); buyers of scrap silver and gold. FAIRS: Sunday London Hotel. VAT: Stan/Spec.

PATRICK MOORHEAD ANTIQUES
THE SOUTH OF ENGLAND'S LARGEST
QUALITY ANTIQUE WAREHOUSE 30,000 SQ FT

50 Minutes mainline from London Victoria
2 minutes from Brighton Station
20 Minutes London Gatwick Airport
(collection service available)

Extensive stock of quality 18th, 19th & 20th Century English and Continental Antiques

Open Monday to Friday
9.30 to 5.30 or by appointment

76 Church Street,
corner of Spring Gardens Brighton
BN1 1RL

Tel: 01273 779696
E.Mail:
patrick.moorhead@virgin.net

Patrick Moorhead Antiques
Spring Gardens, 76 Church St. BN1 1RL. (Patrick and Heather Moorhead). Est. 1984. Open 9.30-5.30 or by appointment. SIZE: Large trade warehouse - showrooms at 15b Prince Albert St. *STOCK: Victorian, Georgian and Continental furniture; Oriental, Continental and English porcelain, clocks, pictures, decorative objects and bronzes.* PARK: Easy. TEL: 01273 779696; fax - 01273 220196; e-mail - patrick.moorhead@virgin.net.

Michael Norman Antiques Ltd BADA
Palmeira House, 82 Western Rd., Hove. BN3 1JB. (Michael P. Keehan). Est. 1965. Open 9-1 and 2-5.30, other times by appointment. *STOCK: English furniture.* **PARK: Easy. TEL: 01273 329253 or 01273 326712; fax - 01273 206556; e-mail - antiques@michaelnorman.com; website - www.michaelnorman.com. VAT: Stan/Spec.**

TheNorth Laine Antiques Market, incorporating Alan Fitchett Antiques
5-5A Upper Gardner St. BN1 4AN. Est. 1969. Open 10-5.30, Sat. 9-5.30, Sun. 10-4. SIZE: Large. *STOCK: Furniture, 18th-20th C, £50-£10,000; works of art, silver, ceramics, books,* *jewellery, paintings, prints, collectables.* LOC: North Laines (Station area). PARK: Easy. TEL: 01273 600894; fax - same. SER: Valuations; restorations.

Oasis Antiques
39 Kensington Gdns. BN1 4AL. (I. and A. Stevenson). Est. 1970. Open 10-5.30, Mon. 11-5, Sat. 8-5.30. SIZE: Medium. *STOCK: Lighting and furniture, to 1970, £1-£5,000; European and Oriental items including bronzes, art glass, period clothes, linen and lace, gramophones, radios, telephones, collectable modern design, Art Nouveau, Art Deco.* LOC: Off North Road from railway station, centre of North Laines. PARK: Nearby. TEL: 01273 683885. SER: Restorations (radios, telephones, furniture, metals); polishing.

Odin Antiques
43 Preston St. BN1 2HP. (Audun Sjovold). Resident. Est. 1981. Open 10.30-5.30. SIZE: Medium. *STOCK: Furniture, 18th-19th C; telescopes, scientific instruments, 19th-20th C, £500-£1,500; maritime instruments, 19th-20th C, £500-£1,000.* LOC: Off Kings Rd. (seafront) near West Pier. PARK: Regency Sq. TEL: 01273 732738; home - same. VAT: Stan/Spec.

Colin Page Antiquarian Books

36 Duke St. BN1 1AG. (John Loska). Est. 1971. Open 9.30-5.30. *STOCK: Antiquarian and second-hand books, especially topography, travel, natural history, illustrated and leather bindings, 16th-20th C, £1-£5,000.* LOC: Town centre. PARK: Multi-storey nearby. TEL: 01273 325954; fax - 01273 746246; e-mail - cpage@pavilion.co.uk.

Brian Page Antiques

18 Regent Arcade, East St. BN1 1HR. Open 10-5.30. *STOCK: Oriental antiques, 3000 BC to 20th C.* LOC: Adjacent to Town Hall. TEL: 01273 723956; fax - 01273 719228; e-mail - brianpage antiques@btinternet.com; website - www. trocadero. com/paha. VAT: Spec.

Dermot and Jill Palmer Antiques

7-8 Union St., The Lanes. BN1 1HA. Resident. Est. 1968. Open 9-6, Sun. by appointment. SIZE: Large + warehouse. *STOCK: French and English furniture, objects, pictures, mirrors, screens, garden furniture and ornamental pieces, textiles, £50-£5,000.* PARK: NCP. TEL: 01273 328669 (2 lines); fax - 01273 777641; e-mail - info@ martinkidman.com. FAIRS: Olympia; Decorative Antique & Textile. VAT: Stan/Spec.

Sue Pearson

13 1/2 Prince Albert St. BN1 1HE. Open 10-5. SIZE: Small. *STOCK: Antique dolls, teddy bears, dolls' house miniatures.* LOC: Lanes area. PARK: NCP. TEL: 01273 329247. SER: Valuations; restorations; buys at auction (dolls and bears). FAIRS: Major London Doll and Bear. VAT: Stan/Spec.

Ben Ponting Antiques

53 Upper North St. BN1 3FH. Open 9.30-5.30. CL: Sat. *STOCK: Furniture, 18th-19th C.* TEL: 01273 329409. VAT: Spec.

Recollections

1a Sydney St. BN1 4EN. (B. Bagley). Est. 1973. Open Tues., Thurs., Fri. and Sat. 10.30-4.30. SIZE: Small. *STOCK: Antique and reproduction firebaskets, firebacks, fenders, scuttles, firetools in sets or loose, spark guards, architectural salvage items, décor pieces.* LOC: From railway station down Trafalgar St., last turning on right. PARK: Opposite in Belmont St. TEL: 01273 681517. SER: Metal polishing; repairs.

Savery Antiques

257 Ditchling Rd., (Fiveways). BN1 6JH. (A. and M. Savery). Resident. Est. 1968. Open Mon. 10.30-5, Thurs.-Sat. 9.30-5. *STOCK: China, glass, metalware and collectables.* LOC: Near HSBC Bank. TEL: 01273 564899. FAIRS: Ardingly; Sandown Park.

Shirley Ann's Antiques - International Interiors

69 New Church Rd., Hove. BN3 2BB. (Shirley Ann Downes). Est. 1985. Open 10-5.30. SIZE: Medium. *STOCK: General antiques, Victorian, Georgian, French reproduction, especially mirrors.* PARK: Easy. TEL: 01273 770045. SER: Valuations; restorations (polishing, upholstery, silver and brass repair). VAT: Stan.

S.L. Simmons

22 Meeting House Lane, The Lanes. BN1 1HB. NAG. Est. 1948. Open 9.30-5.30. *STOCK: Jewellery and silver, 19th C.* TEL: 01273 327949. VAT: Stan.

Sleeping Beauty Antique Beds

212 Church Rd., Hove. BN3 2DT. (Mr and Mrs Roberts). Est. 1975. Open 10-5 including Sun. SIZE: Medium. *STOCK: Brass, iron and French wooden beds, 19th C, £500-£3,500.* LOC: Continuation of Western Rd. PARK: Nearby. TEL: 01273 205115; home - same; e-mail - info@antiquebeds.com; website - www.antique beds.com. SER: Valuations; restorations; buys at auction (beds).

Wardrobe

51 Upper North St. BN1 3FH. (Clive Parks and Philip Parfitt). Est. 1984. Open Wed.-Sat. 10-5, other times by appointment. SIZE: Medium. *STOCK: Vintage clothing, '20's to '30's, £300-£1,200; Art Deco plastics/Bakelite, 20's-40's, £20-£100; Art Deco furniture, £400-£800.* PARK: On street - vouchers. TEL: 01273 202201; fax - same. FAIRS: Alexandra Palace; Sandown Park; Royal Horticultural Hall, Vincent Square.

Graham Webb

59A Ship St. BN1 1AE. Est. 1961. Open 10-5, prior telephone call advisable. SIZE: Small. *STOCK: Cylinder and disc musical boxes, all mechanical musical instruments, £650-£45,000.* LOC: Close to the Lanes. PARK: Middle St. TEL: 01273 321803; fax - same; home - 01273 772154. VAT: Stan/Spec.

E. and B. White

43 & 47 Upper North St. BN1 3FH. Est. 1962. Open 9.30-5. CL: Sat. pm. SIZE: Medium. *STOCK: Country furniture and decorative items, £50-£2,000.* LOC: Upper North St. runs parallel to and north of Western Rd. (main shopping street). TEL: 01273 328706; fax - 01273 207035. VAT: Spec.

Wilkinsons

11 Church St. BN1 1US. (Rosalind and Alan Wilkinson). Est. 1985. Open Mon.-Sat. SIZE:

Small. *STOCK: Furniture, lighting, decorative accessories and collectables, 18th-20th C, £10-£5,000.* LOC: 200 metres north of Brighton Pavilion. PARK: NCP adjacent. TEL: 01273 328665; fax - same; e-mail - arwilkinsn.@aol.com.

The Witch Ball
48 Meeting House Lane. BN1 1HB. (Mrs Gina Daniels). Est. 1967. Open 10.30-6. *STOCK: 18th-19th C topographical and decorative engravings; 16th-19th C maps.* PARK: Nearby. TEL: 01273 326618. SER: Finder; framing. VAT: Stan/Spec.

Yellow Lantern Antiques Ltd
34 Holland Rd., Hove. BN3 1JL. (B.R. and E.A. Higgins). LAPADA. Est. 1950. Open 10-1 and 2.15-5.30, Sat. 10-4. SIZE: Medium. *STOCK: Mainly English furniture, £50-£3,000; French and English clocks; both to 1850; bronzes, 19th C, £100-£1,500; Continental porcelain, 1820-1860, £50-£1,000.* Not Stocked: Pottery, oak, 18th C porcelain. LOC: From Brighton seafront to Hove, turn right after parade of Regency houses, shop 100yds. on left past traffic lights, opposite Michael Norman Antiques. PARK: Easy. TEL: 01273 771572; mobile - 07860 342976; home - 01273 455476. SER: Valuations; restorations; buys at auction. FAIRS: Buxton; Harrogate; NEC; Olympia; Guildford; Kensington; Chester. VAT: Spec.

BURWASH, Nr. Etchingham

Chateaubriand Antiques Centre
High St. TN19 7ES. Open 10-5.30, Sun. 12-5.30. SIZE: 8 dealers. *STOCK: Linen, furniture, country oak, glass, paintings, smalls.* LOC: A265. PARK: Nearby. TEL: 01435 882535; e-mail - chateauframe@hotmail.com. SER: Shipping; picture framing.

COODEN

Annies
4 Bixlea Parade, Little Common Rd. TN39 4SD. (P.A. Rose). Est. 1990. Open 10-5, Wed. and Sun. by appointment. SIZE: Small. *STOCK: China, glass, porcelain and linen, 1800-1930, £5-£500; furniture, from 1880, £50-£750; silver plate, kitchenalia, copper, brass and clocks, from 1800, £5-£150.* LOC: A259 between Bexhill and Eastbourne by Little Common roundabout. PARK: Easy. TEL: 01424 846966. SER: Valuations; buys at auction. FAIRS: De La Warr, Bexhill. VAT: Stan/Spec.

CROSS IN HAND, Nr. Heathfield

Colonial Times
Lewes Rd. TN21 0TA. (A.P. Skinner). Est. 1979. Open 10-5. SIZE: Medium + 3 barns. *STOCK: Colonial furniture, Victorian and Edwardian, £50-£2,500; china, including Staffordshire, £20-£300; clocks, Edwardian, £40-£125.* LOC: A267 from Tunbridge Wells to Eastbourne, opposite Esso garage. PARK: Easy. TEL: 01435 866442; fax and home - 01435 862962; e-mail - enquiries@colonial-times.com; website - www.colonial-times.com. FAIRS: Newark. VAT: Stan.

DITCHLING

Dycheling Antiques
34 High St. BN6 8TA. (E.A. Hudson). Est. 1977. Open 10.30-5.30. CL: Mon. and Wed. SIZE: Large - shop and showroom. *STOCK: Georgian, Victorian and Edwardian furniture, especially dining and armchairs, £25-£5,000.* LOC: Off A23 on A273-B2112 north of Brighton. PARK: Easy. TEL: 01273 842929; home - same; fax - 01273 841929; mobile - 07885 456341; website - www.antiquechairmatching.com. VAT: Spec

---

EASTBOURNE

W. Bruford
11/13 Cornfield Rd. BN21 3NA. Est. 1883. Open 9.30-5.15. SIZE: Medium. *STOCK: Jewellery, Victorian, late Georgian; some silver, clocks (bracket, carriage).* Not Stocked: China, glass, brass, pewter, furniture. TEL: 01323 725452. SER: Valuations; restorations (clocks and silver). VAT: Stan/Spec.

Camilla's Bookshop
57 Grove Rd. BN21 4TX. (C. Francombe and S. Broad). Est. 1976. Open 10-5.30. SIZE: Medium. *STOCK: Books including antiquarian and on art, antiques and collectables, and especially naval, military, aviation, technical, needlework, broadcasting.* LOC: Next to police station, 5 minutes from railway station. PARK: Nearby. TEL: 01323 736001; e-mail - c@millasbooks.fsnet.co.uk. SER: Valuations; postal service; own book tokens.

John Cowderoy Antiques
The Clock and Musical Box Centre, 42 South St. BN21 4XB. (D.J. and R.A.Cowderoy). LAPADA. GMC. Est. 1973. Open 8.30-5. CL: Wed. pm. SIZE: Large. *STOCK: Clocks, musical boxes, furniture, porcelain, silver and plate, jewellery, copper, brass.* LOC: 150yds. from town hall.

PARK: Easy. TEL: 01323 720058; website - www.cowderoyantiques.co.uk SER: Restorations (clocks, barometers, music boxes and furniture). VAT: Stan/Margin.

Crest Collectables
54 Grove Rd. BN21 4UD. (C. Powell). Open 10-6. *STOCK: General antiques and collectables.* TEL: 01323 721185.

John Day of Eastbourne Fine Art
9 Meads St. BN20 7QY. Est. 1964. Open during exhibitions 9.30-1 and 2-5, otherwise by appointment. SIZE: Medium. *STOCK: English, especially East Anglian, and Continental paintings and watercolours, 19th C.* LOC: Meads village, west end of Eastbourne. PARK: Easy. TEL: 01323 725634; fax - same; mobile - 07960 274139; e-mail - eastbournefineart@hotmail.com. SER: Restorations; framing (oils and watercolours).

Roderick Dew
10 Furness Rd. BN21 4EZ. Est. 1971. *STOCK: Antiquarian books, especially on art and antiques.* TEL: 01323 720239. *Postal Only.*

Eastbourne Antiques Market
80 Seaside. BN22 7QP. Est. 1969. Open 10-5.30, Sat. 10-5. SIZE: Large - 30+ stalls. *STOCK: A wide selection of general antiques and collectables.* PARK: Easy. TEL: 01323 642233.

Elliott and Scholz Antiques
12 Willingdon Rd. BN21 1TH. (C.R. Elliott and K.V. Scholz). Est. 1981. Open 9.30-4.30, Wed. and Sat. 9.30-1. SIZE: Small. *STOCK: Small furniture, £100-£500; clocks, £20-£300; bric-a-brac, £10-£100; all 19th-20th C.* LOC: A22. PARK: Easy. TEL: 01323 732200. SER: Valuations.

Enterprise Collectors Market
The Enterprise Centre, Station Parade. BN21 1BE. Est. 1989. Open 9.30-5. SIZE: Medium. *STOCK: Wide range of general antiques and collectables.* LOC: Next to railway station. PARK: Easy. TEL: 01323 732690. SER: Valuations.

A. & T. Gibbard
30 South St. BN21 4XB. PBFA. Est. 1993. Open 9.30-5.30. SIZE: Large. *STOCK: Secondhand and antiquarian books, 16th-20th C, £1-£1,000.* LOC: 200yds. east of Town Hall. TEL: 01323 734128. SER: Valuations. VAT: Stan.

The Old Town Antiques Centre
52 Ocklynge Rd. BN21 1PR. (V. Franklin). Est. 1990. Open 10-5. SIZE: Medium. *STOCK: General antiques.* LOC: East Dean coast road. PARK: Easy. TEL: 01323 416016. FAIRS: Ardingly.

Timothy Partridge Antiques
46 Ocklynge Rd. BN21 1PP. Open 10-1. *STOCK: Victorian, Edwardian and 1920's furniture.* LOC: In old town, near St. Mary's Church. PARK: Easy. TEL: 01323 638731.

Pharoahs Antiques
28 South St. Little Chelsea. BN21 4XB. (W. and J. Pharoah). Est. 1973. Open 10-5. SIZE: Medium. 14 stallholders. *STOCK: A wide range of antiques including jewellery, pine, kitchenalia, china, curios, lace, linen, Victorian furniture, original light fittings and lamps.* LOC: Near Town Hall. PARK: Easy. TEL: 01323 738655; e-mail - williampharoah@hotmail.com. FAIRS: Ardingly.

Stewart Gallery
25 Grove Rd. BN21 4TT. (Gallery Laraine Ltd.). Est. 1970. Open 9-5.30. SIZE: Large. *STOCK: Paintings and ceramics, 19th-20th C, £5-£25,000.* LOC: Next to library, 150yds. from station. PARK: Easy. TEL: 01323 729588; fax - 01424 772828; e-mail - stewart.gallery@virgin.net. SER: Valuations; restorations (paintings and frames). VAT: Stan/Spec.

FLIMWELL

Graham Lower
Stonecrouch Farmhouse. TN5 7QB. (Graham and Penny Lower). Est. 1972. Open by appointment. SIZE: Small. *STOCK: English and Continental 17th-18th C oak furniture.* LOC: A21. PARK: Own. TEL: 01580 879535. SER: Valuations. VAT: Spec.

FOREST ROW

J. Markies Ltd - Antiques
16 Hartfield Rd. RH18 5DN. (Trudy and Jeroen Markies). Est. 1980. Open 9.30-5.30. *STOCK: Fine 18th-19th C furniture, £500-£8,000; silver, European and Oriental ceramics, £20-£2,000.* LOC: 3 miles south of East Grinstead on A22, left at roundabout down Hartfield Rd. PARK: Behind shop. TEL: 01342 824980; fax - 01342 823677; e-mail - sales@markies.co.uk; website - www.markies.co.uk.

HADLOW DOWN, Nr. Uckfield

Hadlow Down Antiques
Hastingford Farm, School Lane. TN22 4DY. (Adrian Butler). Est. 1989. Open 10-5, Sun. 2-5, Wed. by appointment. SIZE: Large. *STOCK: General antiques, country and formal furniture,*

17th-20th C, £25-£2,500; decorative accessories, £5-£500. LOC: 2 mins. down School Lane from A272 in village. PARK: Easy. TEL: 01825 830707; home - same; e-mail - hdantiques@talk21.com. SER: Valuations; restorations (furniture); courier.

HASTINGS

Coach House Antiques
42 George St. TN34 3EA. (R.J. Luck). Est. 1972. Open 10-5 including Sun. SIZE: Medium. *STOCK: Longcase clocks, 18th-19th C, £1,000+; furniture, 19th C, £100+; collectables including Dinky toys, trains, dolls houses.* PARK: Nearby. TEL: 01424 461849. SER: Valuations; restorations (clocks and furniture); buys at auction (clocks and furniture). VAT: Spec.

George Street Antiques Centre
47 George St. TN34 3EA. (F. Stanley and H. Stallybrass). Est. 1969. Open 10-5, Sun. and winter 11-4. SIZE: Medium - 10 dealers. *STOCK: Small items, 19th-20th C, £5-£500.* LOC: In old town, parallel to seafront. PARK: Seafront. TEL: 01424 429339; home - 01424 813526/428105.

Howes Bookshop
Trinity Hall, Braybrooke Terrace. TN34 1HQ. ABA. PBFA. Est. 1920. Open 9.30-5. *STOCK: Antiquarian and academic books in literature, history, arts, bibliography.* PARK: Nearby. TEL: 01424 423437; fax - 01424 460620; e-mail - rarebooks@howes.co.uk. FAIRS: ABA.

Nakota Curios
12 Courthouse St. TN35 3AU. (D.H. Brant). Est. 1964. Open 10.30-1 and 2-5. SIZE: Medium. *STOCK: General trade items, decorative china, Victoriana, jewellery, pictures, lighting.* Not Stocked: Coins, medals. PARK: Easy. TEL: 01424 438900.

J. Radcliffe
5 Claremont. TN34 1HA. Open 10-1 and 2-5. CL: Wed. pm. *STOCK: General antiques, trade goods.* TEL: 01424 426361.

Spice
Samphire House, 75 High St., Old Town. TN34 3EL. (S. Dix). Open by appointment. *STOCK: Early furniture and decorative items.* TEL: Mobile - 07710 209556.

HEATHFIELD

Forty One Antiques
41 High st. Open 9.30-4.30. *STOCK: General antiques.* TEL: 01435 863656/813553.

HURST GREEN

Delmar Antiques
77 London Rd. TN19 7PN. (Harry and Sara Nicol). Est. 1973. Open 10-6, Sun. by appointment. CL: Mon. SIZE: *STOCK: Fine furniture, paintings and antiquarian books, 17th-18th C.* LOC: A21 between Tunbridge Wells and Hastings. PARK: Own. TEL: 01580 860345; fax - 01580 860099.

Lawson Antiques Limited
Silver Hill Farm, Silver Hill. TN19 7PU. (M.P. Baldwin). Est. 1735. Open 10-5 including Sun. SIZE: Large. *STOCK: Furniture, pictures, collectables, £5-£5,000.* LOC: North end of High St. PARK: Public at rear. TEL: 01580 860177.

Libra Antiques
81 London Rd. TN19 7PN. (Janice Hebert). Resident. Est. 1976. Open 9.30-6, Sun. and Mon. by appointment. SIZE: Medium. *STOCK: Lighting, 19th to early 20th C, £100-£500; pine furniture, £50-£500; decorative items, £10-£200; both 18th-19th C.* LOC: A21. PARK: Easy. TEL: 01580 860569; home - same.

LEWES

Bow Windows Book Shop
175 High St. BN7 1YE. (A. and J. Shelley). ABA. PBFA. Est. 1964. Open 9.30-5. SIZE: Large. *STOCK: Books including natural history, English literature, travel, topography.* LOC: Off A27. TEL: 01273 480780; fax - 01273 486686; e-mail - rarebooks@bowwindows.com. FAIRS: Antiquarian Book.

Castle Antiques
163a High St. BN7 1XU. (C. J. Harris). Est. 1984. Open 10-5, Sun. 12-5. SIZE: Medium. *STOCK: Pine furniture, late 19th C, £80-£300; kitchenalia, late 19th C, £5-£25; bric-a-brac, late 19th to early 20th C, £5-£25.* LOC: Top part of High St., down a twitten, opposite Lloyds Bank. TEL: 01273 475176.

Church-Hill Antiques Centre
6 Station St. BN7 2DA. (S. Miller and S. Ramm). Est. 1970. Open 9.30-5. SIZE: 60 stalls and cabinets. *STOCK: Wide range of general antiques including furniture, china, silver, jewellery, clocks, lighting, paintings and decorative items.* LOC: From railway station, in town centre. PARK: Easy, own. TEL: 01273 474842; fax - 01273 846797. VAT: Stan.

Cliffe Antiques Centre
47 Cliffe High St. BN7 2AN. Est. 1984. Open 9.30-5. SIZE: Medium - 16 dealers. *STOCK: General antiques, £5-£1,000.* LOC: Follow town centre signs, turning left 200 yds. past Safeways. PARK: Easy. TEL: 01273 473266.

A. & Y. Cumming
84 High St. BN7 1XN. ABA. Est. 1976. Open 10-5, Sat. 10-5.30. *STOCK: Antiquarian and out of print books.* TEL: 01273 472319; e-mail - a.y.cumming@ukgateway.net. SER: Buys at auction. FAIRS: Chelsea; Olympia.

The Emporium Antique Centre
42 Cliffe High St. BN7 2AN. (Doyle and Madigan). Open 9.30-5, Sun. (Easter-Christmas) 11-4. SIZE: 48 dealers. *STOCK: Furniture, pictures, clocks, collectables, books, jewellery, Art Nouveau and Deco, decorative arts, vintage and collector's toys, Royal Winton.* TEL: 01273 486866.

The Fifteenth Century Bookshop
99/100 High St. BN7 1XH. (Mrs. S. Mirabaud). PBFA. Est. 1938. Open 10-5.30. Sun. 10.30-4. *STOCK: Antiquarian and general secondhand books, especially children's and illustrated; prints, teddies and china.* PARK: Opposite. TEL: 01273 474160; e-mail - 15thcenturybookshop. co.uk.

Lewes Antique Centre
20 Cliffe High St. BN7 2AH. (Jamie Pettit). Est. 1968. Open 9.30-5. SIZE: Large - 75 stallholders. *STOCK: Furniture, china, copper and metalware, glass, clocks, architectural salvage.* LOC: A27 from Brighton, 2nd roundabout into Lewes, end of tunnel turn left, then next left, next right into Phoenix car park. 100m. walk to Cliffe High Street. PARK: Easy. TEL: 01273 476148/472173. SER: Shipping; stripping; restorations; valuations.

Lewes Flea Market
14a Market St. BN7 2NB. Est. 1995. Open daily including Sun. SIZE: Large. *STOCK: Bric-a-brac, furniture, collectables, 18th-20th C, £5-£1,000.* LOC: 50 metres north of monument. TEL: 01273 480328.

Pastorale Antiques
15 Malling St. BN7 2RA. (O. Soucek). Est. 1984. Open 9.30-6 or by appointment. SIZE: Large. *STOCK: Pine and European country furniture, Georgian and Victorian mahogany and decorative items and garden items.* TEL: 01273 473259; home - 01435 863044; fax - 01273 473259; e-mail - pastorale@btinternet.com; website - www.pastorale. cz. SER: Deliveries (Europe).

Southdown Antiques
48 Cliffe High St. BN7 2AN. (Miss P. I. and Mr K.A.Foster). Est. 1969. Open by appointment. SIZE: Medium. *STOCK: Small antiques, especially 18th-19th C English, Continental and Oriental porcelain, objets d'art, works of art, glass, papier mâché trays, silver plate, £50-£350,000; reproduction and interior decor items.* LOC: A27. One-way street north. PARK: Easy. TEL: 01273 472439. VAT: Stan/Spec.

LITTLE HORSTED, Nr. Uckfield

Pianos Galore
Worth Farm. TN22 5TT. Est. 1922. Open 9-5, Sun. 10-12. SIZE: Large. *STOCK: Pianos, upright and grands especially Steinway and Bechstein grands, £250-£20,000; also piano stools.* LOC: From A22 Uckfield by-pass take A26 at Little Horsted roundabout. After 1 mile, opposite Wicklands Residential Home, turn right (opposite piano sign), down lane. PARK: Easy. TEL: 01825 750567; fax - 01825 750566. SER: Valuations; restorations (piano repolishing and reconditioning); buys at auction (pianos). VAT: Margin/Stan.

NEWHAVEN

Newhaven Flea Market
28 South Way. BN9 9LA. (J. Mayne). Est. 1971. Open every day 10-5.30 except 25th Dec. *STOCK: Victoriana, Edwardian, bric-a-brac.* TEL: 01273 517207/516065.

NUTLEY

Nutley Antiques
Libra House, High St. TN22 3NF. (Liza Hall and Anne-Marie Dickinson). Open 10-5, Sun. and Bank Holidays 1.30-5. SIZE: Small. *STOCK: Country and cottage furniture, £10-£1,000; decorative items, £1-£400; prints, oils, watercolours, £5-£500; all 19th C to 1930.* LOC: A22 between East Grinstead and Uckfield. PARK: Easy. TEL: 01825 713220. VAT: Stan.

The Old Mint House Antiques
(Est 1903)

ANTIQUE WHOLESALERS & RETAILERS
52 Showrooms of constantly changing stock
10,000 items of furniture, clocks, porcelain & decorative accessories from 18th, 19th and early 20th C

To experience our very special service to the antiques trade, please contact us with your enquiries

HIGH STREET, PEVENSEY, EAST SUSSEX, BN24 5LF, ENGLAND
TEL/FAX: +44 1323 762337 AFTER HOURS: +44 1323 870608
Email: antiques@minthouse.co.uk Website: www.minthouse.co.uk

OPEN TO TRADE AND GENERAL PUBLIC

PEVENSEY

The Old Mint House
High St. BN24 5LF. (J.C. and A.J. Nicholson). Est. 1903. Open 9-5.30, Sat. 10.30-4.30, otherwise by appointment. SIZE: Large + export warehouse. *STOCK: Furniture - Georgian, Victorian, Edwardian; porcelain, clocks, barometers and decorative items, 18th C-1920's, £50-£10,000.* LOC: A27, 1 mile from Eastbourne. PARK: Easy. TEL: 01323 762337; fax - same; e-mail - antiques @minthouse.co.uk; website - www.minthouse. co.uk. SER: London trains met at local station (Polegate). VAT: Stan/Spec.

PEVENSEY BAY

Murray Brown
The Studio, Norman Rd. BN24 6JE. (G. Murray-Brown). Open by appointment only. *STOCK: Paintings and prints.* TEL: 01323 764298. SER: Valuations; restorations; cleaning; conservation.

POLEGATE

Graham Price Antiques Ltd
Applestore, Chaucer Industrial Estate. BN26 6JF.

Est. 1979. Open 9-5. SIZE: Large. *STOCK: Mainly furniture - country, decorative, French, Irish, painted, some formal and shipping.* LOC: Between Hastings and Brighton on A27. TEL: 01323 487167; fax - 01323 483904; website - www.grahampriceantiques.co.uk. SER: Export, packing, shipping and courier; restorations.

E. Stacy-Marks Limited   BADA
The Flint Rooms, P O Box 808. BN26 5ST. Est. 1889. SIZE: Large. *STOCK: Paintings, English, Dutch and Continental schools, 18th-20th C.* TEL: 01323 482156; fax - 01323 482513. VAT: Stan.

RINGMER, Nr. Lewes

Bob Hoare - Pine Antiques
Averys Nursery, Uckfield Rd. BN8 5RU. Open 9-5, Sun. 10-4. *STOCK: Country furniture.* LOC: A26. TEL: 01273 814181; fax - 01273 814714; e-mail - bob@antiquebob.demon.co.uk; website - www.antiquebob.demon.co.uk.

ROTTINGDEAN

Trade Wind
15A Little Crescent. BN2 7GF. (R. Morley

ANN LINGARD

Rope Walk Antiques, Rye, Sussex
Telephone: Rye (01797) 223486
Fax: (01797) 224700
Email: annlingard@ropewalkantiques.freeserve.co.uk

Large selection of hand finished Antique
English Pine furniture. Complementary
Accessories and Garden tools etc.
Separate Kitchen Shop.

SHIPPERS WELCOME

Smith). Est. 1974. Open by appointment only. *STOCK: Caddy and sifter spoons, wine labels and other interesting items, including coloured glass, Bristol blue, green and amethyst; early 18th-19th C white glass including folded foot and engraved items, 1710-1830.* TEL: 01273,301177.

RYE

Bragge and Sons
Landgate House. TN31 7LH. (J.R. Bragge). Est. 1840. Open 9-5. CL: Tues. and Sat. pm. *STOCK: 18th C furniture and works of art.* LOC: Entrance to town - Landgate. TEL: 01797 223358. SER: Valuations; restorations.

Chapter & Verse Booksellers
105 High St. TN31 7JE. (Spencer J. Rogers). Open Tues. to Sun. 10-5. SIZE: Medium. *STOCK: Rare and antiquarian books - single items to large collections, £50-£25,000.* PARK: Loading only or nearby. TEL: 01797 222692; mobile - 07970 386905; e-mail - chapterandverse@ btconnect.com. SER: Valuations; book search.

East Street Antiques
Apothecary House, 1 East St. TN31 7JY. (Mr and Mrs Bloomfield). Est. 1988. Open 10.30-5 including Sun. SIZE: Medium. *STOCK: Furniture, 18th-19th C, £500-£1,000.* LOC: Just off High St. PARK: Easy. TEL: 01797 229266; home - same. SER: Buys at auction. FAIRS: Newark and Ardingly.

Herbert Gordon Gasson
The Lion Galleries, Lion St. TN31 7LB. (T.J. Booth). Est. 1909. Open 10-5, Tues. and Sun. by appointment. SIZE: Large. *STOCK: 17th-19th C oak, walnut and mahogany furniture; decorative items.* Not Stocked: Silver and glass. PARK: Easy. TEL: 01797 222208; fax - same; e-mail - hggassonantiques@hotmail.com. SER: Restorations. VAT: Spec.

Ann Lingard - Rope Walk Antiques
18-22 Rope Walk. TN31 7NA. LAPADA. Est. 1972. Open 9-5.30, sometimes closed for lunch. SIZE: Large. *STOCK: English antique pine furniture and accessories; kitchen shop; garden tools and accessories, some architectural items.* Not Stocked: Jewellery, silver and plate. PARK: Own, and public next door. TEL: 01797 223486; fax - 01797 224700; e-mail - ann-lingard@ropewalk antiques.freeserve.co.uk. FAIRS: Ardingly. VAT: Stan/Global.

Wish Barn Antiques
Wish St. TN31 7DA. (Joe Dearden and Robert Wheeler). Est. 1993. Open 10-5 including Sun. SIZE: Medium. *STOCK: 19th C furniture including oak, mahogany and pine, £50-£1,500; silver plate.* LOC: Just off A259. PARK: Easy. TEL: 01797 226797; home - 01580 881485.

SEAFORD

The Courtyard Antiques Market
15 High St. BN25 1PD. (Mrs V.E. Finch). Open 9-5, Wed. 9-1. SIZE: Medium - 13 dealers. *STOCK: General antiques and collectables.* TEL: 01323 892091.

The Old House
15/17 High St. BN25 1PD. (S.M. Barrett). Est. 1928. Open 9-5, Wed. 9-1. SIZE: Large. *STOCK: 18th-20th C furniture, china and glass, £5-£5,000.* LOC: Near railway station. PARK: Opposite in Pelham Yard. TEL: 01323 892091/893795. SER: Valuations; restorations (furniture); shippers. VAT: Stan/Spec.

Seaford's "Barn Collectors' Market" and Studio Bookshop
The Barn, Church Lane. BN25 1HL. Est. 1967. Open 9.30-5. SIZE: Several dealers. *STOCK: Collectables, ephemera, books, post and cigarette cards.* LOC: Off High St. TEL: 01323 890010.

ST. LEONARDS-ON-SEA

Aarquebus Antiques
37 & 46 Norman Rd. TN38 0EJ. (Mr and Mrs G. Jukes). Resident. Est. 1957. Open 9.30-5, Sat. 9.30-1. SIZE: Medium. *STOCK: Furniture, 18th C, £500-£1,000; shipping goods, Victorian to 1930, £5-£500; glass, gold and silver, 18th-19th C, £5-£1,000.* LOC: Take A2100 to St. Leonards-on-Sea, turn right after main P.O. PARK: Easy. TEL: 01424 433267. SER: Valuations.

Bexhill Antiques
78 Norman Rd. TN38. Open 10-5. SIZE: *STOCK: General antiques.* TEL: Mobile - 07702 006982.

The Book Jungle
24 North St. TN38 0EX. (M. Gowen). Est. 1988. Open 10-5. CL: Wed. SIZE: Medium. *STOCK: Secondhand books.* LOC: Just off seafront. PARK: Nearby. TEL: 01424 421187.

Gensing Antiques
70 Norman Rd.TN38 0EJ. (Peter Cawson). Open normal shop hours and by appointment. *STOCK: General antiques especially early Chinese furniture and other Oriental items.* TEL: 01424 424145/714981.

The Hastings Antique Centre
59-61 Norman Rd. TN38 0EG. (R.J. Amstad). Open 10-5.30, Sun. by appointment. SIZE: Large. TEL: 01424 428561. Below are listed some of the dealers at this centre.

R.J. Amstad
Furniture.

Fred Bourne
French decorative antiques.

Pascal Bourne
French furniture.

Jenny Brown
Decorative wares.

Bruno Antiques
French furniture.

Dee's Antiques
Decorative items.

P. Few
Decorative French items.

P. Grant
French furniture, decorative items and pine.

K. Gumbrell
Decorative items.

Bridget Howett
Decorative items.

Clare Kinloch
Dolls.

G. Mennis
Sporting, leather goods.

Mick Neale
Oak.

Robert Paul Antiques
Furniture and shipping goods.

Pat Robbins
Furniture.

Monarch Antiques
19 Grand Parade. TN38 0DD. (J.H. King). Est. 1983. Open Mon.-Fri. 8.30-5 or by appointment. SIZE: Large + warehouse (371 Bexhill Road). *STOCK: General furniture, especially 1930's oak furniture for the Japanese, Korean, American and European markets.* LOC: A259. PARK: Own. TEL: 01424 204141; fax - 01424 204142; home - 01424 214158/720821; mobiles - 07802 217842/213081 and 07809 027930; e-mail - monarch.antiques@virgin.net. SER: Shipping and packing; courier; restorations. FAIRS: Newark.

John H. Yorke Antiques
Filsham Farmhouse, 111 Harley Shute Rd. TN38 8BY. Est. 40 years. Open 9-5.30. *STOCK: Furniture for trade, export and shipping.* TEL: 01424 433109; fax - 01424 461061; e-mail - filsham farmhouse@talk21.com. website - www.filsham farmhouse.co.uk. VAT: Stan.

UCKFIELD

Ringles Cross Antiques
Ringles Cross. TN22 1HF. (J. Dunford). Resident. Est. 1965. Open 10-5 or by appointment. *STOCK: English furniture, mainly oak and country, 17th-18th C; accessories.* LOC: 1 mile north of Uckfield. PARK: Own. TEL: 01825 762909.

WADHURST

Park View Antiques
High St., Durgates. TN5 6DE. (B. Ross). Est. 1985. Open 10-4. CL: Mon. SIZE: Medium. *STOCK: Pine, oak and country furniture, 17th-19th C, £100-£1,500; decorative items, 1930's, £25-£150; iron and metalware, 17th-19th C, £25-£250.* LOC: On B2099 Frant-Hurst Green road. PARK: Easy. TEL: 01892 783630; fax - 01892 740264; home - 01892 740264; website - www.parkviewantiques.co.uk. SER: Valuations; restorations (furniture).

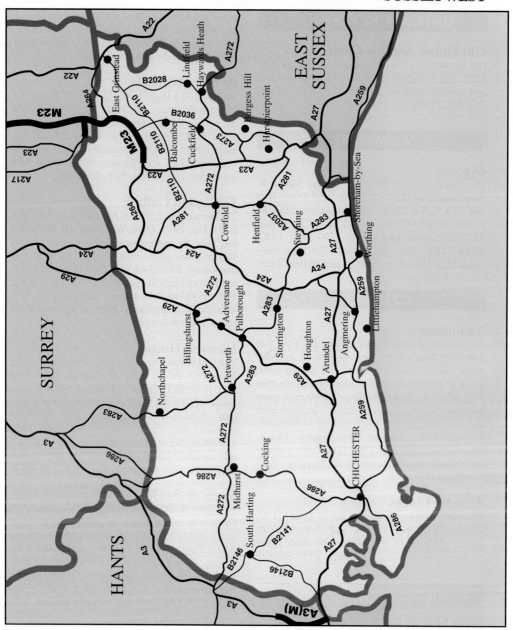

Dealers and Shops in West Sussex

Adversane	1	Cocking	1	Hurstpierpoint	2	Shoreham-by-Sea	1
Angmering	1	Cowfold	1	Lindfield	3	South Harting	1
Arundel	7	Cuckfield	2	Littlehampton	2	Steyning	1
Balcombe	1	East Grinstead	1	Midhurst	2	Storrington	1
Billingshurst	4	Haywards Heath	1	Northchapel	1	Worthing	5
Burgess Hill	2	Henfield	2	Petworth	24		
Chichester	13	Houghton	1	Pulborough	2		

Old House Antique Centre
Old House. RH14 9JJ. Open daily including Sun. SIZE: 30+ stallholders. *STOCK: General antiques and collectors' items.* PARK: Easy. TEL: 01403 782186/783594.

Bygones
The Square. BN16 4EQ. (R.A. and Mrs L.R. Whittaker). Est. 1965. Open Tues. and Thurs. 10-1 and 2.15-5, Sat. 10-12. SIZE: Medium. *STOCK: Furniture, £50-£2,500; china, £5-£750; silver, £10-£250; linen, £5-£75; all 1790-1940.* LOC: A280. PARK: Easy. TEL: 01903 786152; home - same. SER: Valuations; buys at auction (furniture).

Antiquities
5/7 Tarrant St. BN18 9DG. (Ian and Christina Fenwick). Est. 1990. Open 10-5 or by appointment. SIZE: Large + displayed warehouses. *STOCK: Decorative and unusual - including 19th C English and French furniture, some mahogany and fruitwood, painted items, Staffordshire, majolica, metalware, French mirrors, pond yachts, luggage.* LOC: Just off town square. PARK: Nearby. TEL: 01903 884355; fax - same; e-mail - antiquities@btconnect.com. SER: Shipping. VAT: Stan/Spec.

Arundel Clocks
Lasseters Corner, High St. BN18 9AB. (F.M. Henderson). Open 9.30-1 and 2-5. *STOCK: Clocks - longcase, £1,500-£6,000; dial, £300-£4,000; mantel and bracket, £250-£5,000;*

carriage, *£200-£2,000.* LOC: Corner of High St. and Mill Lane. PARK: Easy. TEL: 01903 884525; fax - same. SER: Valuations; restorations (dials, movements and cases). VAT: Spec.

Baynton-Williams
1st Floor, 37A High St. BN18 9AG. (R.H. and S.C. Baynton-Williams). Est. 1946. Open 10-6. *STOCK: Maps, views, sporting, marine and decorative prints.* PARK: Nearby. TEL: 01903 883588; fax - same; e-mail - gallery@baynton-williams.freeserve. co.uk; website - www.baynton-williams.com. SER: Valuations; cataloguing. VAT: Stan/Spec.

Faringdon Gallery
27 Tarrant St. BN18 9DG. (Mr and Mrs G.E. Lott). Est. 1970. Open Wed.-Sun. 10.30-5, Mon. and Tues. by appointment. SIZE: Small. *STOCK: Watercolours and etchings, late 19th C to contemporary, £150-£4,000.* LOC: From A27, first right down High St. hill. PARK: 100 yards at rear. TEL: 01903 882047; home - 01243 554572. SER: Valuations; restorations; buys at auction (watercolours and etchings).

Nineveh House
The Old Chapel Antiques and Collector's Centre, Tarrant St. BN18 9DG. (P. Jarrett). Open 10-5, Sun. 11-5. SIZE: Large - 12 dealers. *STOCK: Wide range of general antiques including Edwardian and Victorian, country and pine furniture, jewellery and silver, paintings and prints, china and glass, luggage and Oriental rugs.* LOC: Off A27 and A29 into town then second left off High St. PARK: Own forecourt. TEL: 01903 884307.

Spencer Swaffer
30 High St. BN18 9AB. LAPADA. Est. 1974. Open 9-6, other times by appointment. SIZE: Large. *STOCK: Quirky decorative and traditional items, English, French, brown and painted furniture, dinner services, chandeliers, lighting, marble tables, iron low tables, bamboo, shop fittings, majolica, garden furniture.* PARK: Easy. TEL: 01903 882132; fax - 01903 884564. VAT: Stan/Spec.

The Walking Stick Shop
8/9 The Old Printing Works, Tarrant St. BN18 9JH. (S. Thompson). Est. 1981. Open 8.30-5.30, Wed. 8.30-1, Sun. pm. by appointment. SIZE: Large. *STOCK: Walking sticks and canes, 1620 to date, £10-£2,000.* LOC: Off High St. PARK: Easy. TEL: 01903 883796; home - 01903 882713; fax - 01903 884491; e-mail - stuart.walkingsticks@ btinternet.com; websites - www.walkingsticks. uk.com and www.walkingstickshop.co.uk. SER: Valuations; buys at auction (canes). VAT: Stan.

BALCOMBE

Woodall and Emery Ltd

Haywards Heath Rd. RH17 6PG. Est. 1884. Open 10-5. *STOCK: Chandeliers, wall brackets, table lights.* PARK: Easy. TEL: 01444 811608. SER: Restorations (including re-wiring). VAT: Stan.

BILLINGSHURST

Great Grooms Antique Centre

Great Grooms, Parbrook. RH14 9EU. Est. 1983. Open Mon.-Sat. 9.30-5.30, Sun. 10-6. SIZE: 50 dealers. *STOCK: Wide variety of specialist dealers in 18th-19th C English and Continental town and country furniture, pottery and porcelain, silver (including Scottish) and plate, tortoiseshell, works of art, metalware, glass, clocks, Oriental, oils and watercolours, prints, books, clocks and watches.* LOC: Old A29 south of Billingshurst. PARK: Easy. TEL: 01403 786202; fax - 01403 786224. SER: Valuations; restorations (furniture, pictures, silver and jewellery). VAT: Spec.

Lannards Gallery

Okehurst Lane. RH14 9HR. (Mr and Mrs Derek Sims). Open by appointment; open every day during exhibitions. *STOCK: Watercolours, oils and furniture, from 1850.* TEL: 01403 782692. SER: Exhibitions held, please telephone for details.

The portrayal of working class folk was a recurring theme for many 19th century artists with some continuing the genre well into the 20th century. Typical of these is Arthur Trevor Haddon (1864-1941) whose passé and romanticised compositions of young Italian flower sellers were exhibited not only at the major London venues such as the Royal Society of British Artists, of which he was a member, but also at the Victoria Art Gallery, Bath; Rochdale Art Gallery & Museum; Brighton Art Gallery and the Royal Hibernian Academy, Dublin. Despite winning a medal for life drawing while at the Slade and working with the great figurative painter Sir Hubert von Herkomer (1849-1914), Haddon's figures frequently give the impression of being 'stage set' and look stiff and lifeless. These characteristics are certainly evident in 'The Venetian Flower Stall', a 22in. x 30in. oil on canvas, which sold at Bonhams for the top estimate of £3,500.

From an article entitled "19th Century Paintings" by Anthony J. Lester which appeared in the June 2002 issue of **Antique Collecting**. For more details and to subscribe see page 21.

Nicholas Shaw Antiques

A rare George III Coffee Pot made in Edinburgh 1761-62 by Alexander Gairdner. The body engraved with a family coat-of-arms. Wt: 30.97ozs Ht: 9¼ ins.

Gt. Grooms Antiques Centre, Parbrook, Billingshurst, Sussex RH14 9EU

Tel/Fax: 01403 786656

Nicholas Shaw Antiques BADA
Gt. Grooms Antique Centre, Parbrook. RH14 9EU. LAPADA. CINOA. Est. 1990. Open 9.30-5.30, Sun. 10-4. SIZE: Small. *STOCK: Fine and rare English, Scottish and Irish silver, 16th to mid 20th C, £30-£30,000.* LOC: A29 south of Billingshurst. PARK: Easy. TEL: 01403 786656; fax - same; mobile - 07885 643000; e-mail - silver @nicholas-shaw.com; website - www.nicholas-shaw.com. SER: Valuations; restorations.

Michael Wakelin and Helen Linfield
BADA
P.O Box 48. RH14 0YZ. LAPADA. Est. 1968. Open any time by appointment only. *STOCK: Fine English and Continental formal and country furniture - walnut, fruitwoods, faded mahogany and other exotic woods; early brass, bronze, iron and steel; wood carvings, treen, needlework, naïve pictures and lighting.* PARK: Easy. TEL: 01403 700004; fax - 01403 701173; e-mail - wakelin_linfield@lineone.net. SER: Shipping; valuations. FAIRS: Olympia; BADA; LAPADA; Chelsea. VAT: Stan/Spec.

BURGESS HILL

British Antique Replicas
School Close, Queen Elizabeth Ave. RH15 9RX. LAPADA. Est. 1963. Open 9-5.30. SIZE: Large. *STOCK: Furniture, £100-£20,000.* LOC: 3 miles west A23. PARK: Easy. TEL: 01444 245577. SER: Bespoke furniture. VAT: Stan.

Recollect Dolls Hospital
17 Junction Rd. RH15 0HR. (P. Jago). Est. 1970. Open 10-4. CL: Mon. and Sat. *STOCK: Dolls, dolls house miniatures, doll restoration materials.* TEL: 01444 871052. SER: Restorations (dolls); catalogues available (£2.75 cash/stamps).

CHICHESTER

Almshouses Arcade
19 The Hornet. PO19 4JL. (Mrs V. Barnet). Est. 1983. Open 9.30-4.30. LOC: 200yds. from Cattle Market at eastern end of city. On one-way system (A286) just before traffic lights at Market Ave. PARK: Easy. Below are listed the dealers at these premises. TEL: 01243 528089.

Antics
(P. German). *General antiques and collectables.*

Autodrome
Motoring, tin plate and ephemera. TEL: 01243 778126.

R .K. Barnett
Antiques and collectables, furniture. TEL: 01243 528089.

Collectors Corner
Small collectables and antiques. TEL: 01243 778126

Decographic
Toys, wirelesses, cameras, gramaphones. TEL: 01243 787391.

East Side Records
Records. TEL: 01243 782786.

Yesteryears
(J.A. Cook). *Lighting (oil), general antiques and collectables.* TEL: 01243 771994.

Antiques & Bygones
24 The Old Butter Market, North St. PO19 1LO. (Mrs Maureen Haydon). Est. 1975. Open Tues.-Sat. 9.30-4. SIZE: Small. *STOCK: General collector's items, mainly porcelain and glass, Doulton, Beswick, small pieces of furniture.* LOC: City centre precinct opposite Woolworth's. TEL: 01243 788071. SER: Valuations.

Canon Gate Bookshop
28 South St. PO19 1EL. (Philip and Wendy Pegler). PBFA. Est. 1980. Open 10.30-5. SIZE: Small. *STOCK: Books, mainly 19th-20th C, £1-£1,000.* LOC: Town centre. PARK: Nearby. TEL: 01243 778477; e-mail - philip@canongate.fsbusiness.co.uk. SER: Valuations.

Chichester Antiques Centre
46-48 The Hornet. PO19 4JG. (Mike Carter). Est. 1994. Open 10-5, Sun. 11-5. SIZE: 50 stalls. *STOCK: General antiques and collectables, 50p to £10,000.* LOC: M27 onto A27 to town. PARK: Loading only and nearby. TEL: 01243 530100; website - www.antiqueschichester.com. SER: Clock restoration on premises.

Chichester Gallery
8 The Hornet. PO19 4JG. (Tom McHale). Est. 1988. Open Tues., Wed. and Fri. 10-4. SIZE: 5 rooms. *STOCK: Victorian oils, watercolours, etchings and engravings, £250-£2,500.* PARK: Nearby. TEL: 01243 779821. SER: Cleaning and restorations; commission sales.

The Delightful Muddle
82 Fishbourne Rd. West. PO19 3JL. Open Wed.-Sat. 11-4. *STOCK: China, glass, objets d'art, Victorian and Edwardian, £1-£100; lace £1-£50; linen, general antiques and bric-a-brac, £3-£65.* LOC: 1 mile west of Chichester on A259, opposite Fishbourne P.O & Stores. PARK: Easy.

Frensham House Antiques
Hunston. PO20 6NX. (J. and M. Riley). Est. 1966. Open 9-6. *STOCK: English furniture, 1700-1830, £500-£6,000; clocks, paintings, copper.* LOC: One mile south of Chichester by-pass on B2145. PARK: Easy. TEL: 01243 782660.

Gems Antiques
39 West St. PO19 1RP. Open 10-1 and 2.30-5.30. CL: Mon. *STOCK: Period furniture, Staffordshire and porcelain figures, glass and pictures.* PARK: Easy. TEL: 01243 786173.

Peter Hancock Antiques
40-41 West St. PO19 1RP. Articles on coins. Est. 1950. Open 10.30-1 and 2.30-5.30. CL: Mon. SIZE: Medium. *STOCK: Silver, jewellery, porcelain, furniture, £20-£2,000; pictures, glass, clocks, books, £5-£500; all 18th-19th C; enthnographica, Art Nouveau, Art Deco, 19th-20th C, £5-£500.* LOC: From Chichester Cross, 17 doors past Cathedral. PARK: Easy. TEL: 01243 786173. SER: Valuations; repairs. VAT: Stan/Spec.

Heritage Antiques
84 St. Pancras. PO19 4NL. (D.R. Grover). Est. 1987. Open 9.30-5. *STOCK: Furniture and decorative items.* TEL: 01243 783796.

Rathbone Law
59 North St. PO19 1NB. (Mr and Mrs R. Law). NAG. Est. 1902. Open 9.30-5. CL: Some Mon. *STOCK: Victorian and Edwardian fine jewellery, silver, designer pieces in gold and silver, objets d'art, fine gems.* PARK: Nearby. TEL: 01243 787881; e-mail - info@rathbonelaw.com; website - www.rathbonelaw.com. SER: Valuations.

W.D. Priddy Antiques
Unit 6 Terminus Mill, Terminus Rd. PO19 2UN. Open 10-5, Sun. 11-4, or by appointment. SIZE: Large. *STOCK: Oak, mahogany, walnut and pine furniture, mid-19th C to pre-war and shipping, £20-£3,000.* LOC: Runs off A27 Chichester bypass. PARK: Easy. TEL: 01243 783960; fax - same; e-mail - bill@priddyantiques.fsnet.co.uk; website - www.priddyantiques.co.uk. VAT: Stan./Spec.

St. Pancras Antiques
150 St. Pancras. PO19 1SH. (R.F. and M. Willatt). Est. 1980. Open 9.30-1 and 2-5. CL: Thurs. pm. SIZE: Small. *STOCK: Arms and armour, militaria, medals, documents, uniforms and maps, 1600-1914, £5-£3,000; china, pottery and ceramics, 1800-1930, £2-£500; small furniture, 17th-19th C, £20-£1,000; coins, ancient to date.* Not Stocked: Silver and carpets. TEL: 01243 787645. SER: Valuations; restorations (arms and armour); buys at auction (militaria).

COCKING, Nr. Midhurst

The Victorian Brass Bedstead Company
Hoe Copse. GU29 0HL. (David Woolley). Resident. Est. 1970. Open by appointment. SIZE: Large. *STOCK: Victorian and Edwardian brass and iron bedsteads, bases and mattresses, 19th-20th C, £300-£3,500.* LOC: Right behind village Post Office, ¾ mile left turning to Hoe Copse. PARK: Easy. TEL: 01730 812287. SER: Valuations; restorations (brass and iron bedsteads). VAT: Stan.

COWFOLD

Squire's Pantry Pine and Antiques
Station Rd. RH13 8DA. (B. Holmes and B. Hart). Est. 1981. Open 10-1 and 2-5. *STOCK: Pine furniture including reproduction.* TEL: 01403 864869; fax - 01403 864869; e-mail - jos.holmes@virgin.net. SER: Furniture made from reclaimed timber. VAT: Stan/Spec.

CUCKFIELD

David Foord-Brown Antiques   BADA
High St. RH17 5JU. (David Foord-Brown and Sean Barry). LAPADA. Est. 1988. Open 10-5.30. SIZE: Medium. *STOCK: Furniture, 1750-1880, £500-£25,000; decorative objects.* Not Stocked: Country furniture. LOC: A272. PARK: Easy. TEL: 01444 414418.

Richard Usher Antiques
23 South St. RH17 5LB. Est. 1978. Open 10-5 and at other times by appointment. CL: Wed. pm. and Sat. pm. SIZE: Medium. *STOCK: Furniture, 17th-19th C, £50-£3,000; decorative items.* LOC: A272. PARK: Easy. TEL: 01444 451699. SER: Valuations; restorations.

EAST GRINSTEAD

The Antique Print Shop
11 Middle Row. RH19 3AX. (A.A.W. Daszewski and Mrs A.C. Keddie). Est. 1988. Open 9.30-5. CL: Mon. and Tues. SIZE: Small. *STOCK: Prints, pre-1880, £10-£200; maps, especially British county, 1500-1870, £20-£5,000.* LOC: On island in middle High St., opposite St. Swithins church. PARK: Lewes Rd. TEL: 01342 410501; fax - 01342 410795. SER: Restorations; framing. FAIRS: Park Lane Hotel, London (Sundays); West London Antiques (Penman). VAT: Stan.

HAYWARDS HEATH

Roundabout Antiques Centre
7 Commercial Sq. RH16 1DW. (Angie Craik). Est. 1993. Open 10-5. CL: Mon. SIZE: Medium. *STOCK: Ceramics, glass and silver, jewellery, £50-£1,000; furniture, £50-£2,000; all 19th-20th C. Musical instruments, 20th C, £50-£2,000.* LOC: Across roundabout from railway station. PARK: On forecourt. TEL: 01273 835926/01444 417654.

HENFIELD

Alexander Antiques
Post House, Small Dole. BN5 9XE. (Mrs J.A. Goodinge). Est. 1971. CL: Sun. except by appointment. SIZE: Medium. *STOCK: Country furniture, brass, copper, pewter, samplers, small collectors' and decorative items, treen.* LOC: A2037. PARK: Easy. TEL: 01273 493121; home - same. VAT: Stan/Spec.

Ashcombe Coach House   BADA
P O Box 2527. CINOA. LAPADA. Est. 1954. Open strictly by appointment only. *STOCK: Furniture and objects, 17th to early 19th C.* TEL: 01273 491630; fax - same; mobile - 07803 180098. FAIRS: Olympia; BADA.

HOUGHTON, Nr. Arundel

Stable Antiques at Houghton
The Old Church, Main Rd. BN18 9LW. (Ian. J. Wadey). Open Tues.-Sat. 11-4. *STOCK: General antiques and furniture, £20-£1,000.* LOC: On B2139 5 miles between Storrington and Arundel. PARK: Own. TEL: 01798 839555; fax - same; website - www.stableantiques.co.uk.

HURSTPIERPOINT

The Clock Shop
34-36 High St. BN6 9RG. LAPADA. Open 9-6 including Sun., or by appointment. *STOCK: 18th-19th longcase, table and wall clocks.* PARK: Easy. TEL: 01273 832081; mobile - 07860 230888. SER: Restorations (clocks and furniture).

Julian Antiques
124 High St. BN6 9PX. (Julian and Carol Ingram). Est. 1964. Open by appointment only. *STOCK: French 19th C mirrors, fireplaces, fenders, furniture.* PARK: Easy. TEL: 01273 832145. FAIRS: Olympia (June).

LINDFIELD

Lindfield Galleries - David Adam
BADA
62 High St. RH16 2HL. Est. 1972. Open 9.30-5.00. CL: Mon. STOCK: Oriental carpets. PARK: Easy. TEL: 01444 483817; e-mail - david@ orientalandantiquerugs.com. SER: Restorations; cleaning. VAT: Stan/Spec.

Spongs Antiques Centre
102 High St. RH16 2HS. (Ashley and Karen Richardson). Est. 1999. Open 10-5, Sun. 2-5. SIZE: Medium. *STOCK: Porcelain and pottery, 18th-20th C, £10-£2000; oak, pine and mahogany furniture, 17th-20th C, £50-£1,000; silver, 17th-20th C, £30-£500.* PARK: Nearby. TEL: 01444 487566; e-mail - spongs80@hotmail.com; website - www.spongs antiquescentre.co.uk. SER: Valuations.

Stable Antiques
98A High St. RH16 2HP. (Adrian Hoyle). Est. 1987. Open 10-5.30. Sun. 12.30-5.30. SIZE: Large. *STOCK: Regency, and mahogany Victorian furniture, including extending tables, bookcases, and chests of drawers; pine and country furniture.* LOC: Off A272 on B2028, 2 miles south of Ardingly. PARK: Easy and free. TEL: 01444 483662; mobile - 07768 900331; e-mail - a.hoyle @cwcom.net. SER: Valuations. VAT: Spec.

LITTLEHAMPTON

Joan's Antiques
1 New Rd. BN17 5AX. (J. Walkden and M. Hill). Est. 1976. Open Thurs.-Sat. 10.30-4.30. SIZE: Small. *STOCK: China and collectables, Victorian to 1930's, £5-£100.* LOC: From Woolworths, Surrey St, keep left and turn into New Road. PARK: Easy. TEL: 01903 722422; home - 01903 784495. FAIRS: Goodwood.

Magic of Quimper
Faux Cottage, 4A Selborne Rd. BN17 5NN. (John Haynes and Kay Meader). Usually available but prior telephone call advisable. *STOCK: Over 200 pieces of Quimper faience, Desvres and other French faience.* PARK: Easy. TEL: 01903 714261; e-mail - magic.quimper@virgin.net.

Churchill Clocks
Rumbolds Hill. GU29 9BZ. (W.P. and Dr. E. Tyrrell). Open 9-5, Wed. 9-1. *STOCK: Clocks and furniture.* LOC: Main street. TEL: 01730 81389; website - www.churchillclocks.co.uk. SER: Clock restoration.

The Old Town Hall Antique Centre
Market Square. GU29 9NJ. (P. B. Baker). Open 10-5. SIZE: Medium. *STOCK: Furniture, porcelain, decorative items.* PARK: Easy. TEL: 01730 817166.

NORTHCHAPEL, Nr. Petworth

Callingham Antiques
GU28 9HL. Est. 1979. Open 9.30-5.30. CL: Wed. SIZE: Medium. *STOCK: Furniture, 1700-1900, £10-£10,000.* LOC: London Road 5 miles north of Petworth. PARK: Easy. TEL: 01428 707379; e-mail - antiques@callinghamfreeserve.co.uk. SER: Valuations; restorations.

PETWORTH

Angel Antiques
Church St. GU28 0AD. (Nick and Barbara Swanson). PAADA. Open 10-5.30, Sun. by appointment. SIZE: Medium. *STOCK: English and French 17th-19th C country furniture, ceramics and decorative items, £80-£15,000.* LOC: Opposite Petworth House and war memorial. TEL: 01798 343306; fax - 01798 342665; e-mail - swan189@aol.com; website - www.angel-antiques.co.uk. VAT: Spec.

Antiquated
10 New St. GU28 0AS. (Vicki Emery). PAADA. Open 10-5.30 or by appointment. *STOCK: 18th-19th C original painted furniture, decorative items, garden furniture; 19th C rocking horses.* TEL: 01798 344011; fax - same.

Bacchus Gallery
Lombard St. GU28 0AG. (R. and A. Gillett). Est. 1988. Open 10-1 and 2.30-5. SIZE: Small. *STOCK: Wine related items.* LOC: Cobbled street leading off town square. PARK: Town square. TEL: 01798 342844; fax - 01798 342634. SER: Buys at auction (as stock). VAT: Stan/Spec.

Baskerville Antiques   BADA
Saddlers House, Saddlers Row. GU28 0AN. (A. and B. Baskerville). Est. 1978. Open Tues.-Sat. 10-6, or by appointment. SIZE: Medium. *STOCK: English clocks, barometers and furniture, £1,000-£40,000; decorative items and instruments, £500-£10,000; all 17th-19th C.* LOC: Town centre. PARK: Public, adjoining shop. TEL: 01798 342067; home - same; fax - 01798 343956; e-mail - brianbaskerville@ aol.com. VAT: Spec.

One of a pair of French bombé *commodes in the Louis XV style, mounted in ormolu and with* vernis Martin *decoration, c.1890. Estimated at £7,000-£10,000 for the pair at the end of last year. (Christie's King Street)*

From an article entitled "How the Chest Developed" by Peter Philp which appeared in the February 2001 issue of **Antique Collecting**. For more details and to subscribe see page 21.

PETWORTH

WEST SUSSEX

*Antiques
Centre of the
South*

**For Brochure –
Tel: (01798) 343411**

John Bird
High St. GU28 0AU. Open 10-5.15. SIZE: Medium. *STOCK: Furniture - country, pine, oak, fruitwood, mahogany, painted, architectural, garden and upholstered.* PARK: Easy. TEL: 01798 343250; mobile - 07970 683949; e-mail - bird.puttnam@virgin.net. VAT: Spec.

Bradley's Past & Present
21 High St. GU28 0AU. (M. and A. Bradley). Est. 1975. CL: Mon. SIZE: Small. *STOCK: Furniture, 19th-20th C, £50-£500; china and decorative items, £5-£100; metalware, phonographs, gramophones and records.* PARK: Nearby. TEL: 01798 343533. SER: Restorations; repairs.

The Canon Gallery   BADA
New St. GU28 0AS. (Jeremy Green and James Fergusson). LAPADA. PAADA. Est. 1987. Open 10-1 and 2-5.30. SIZE: Medium. *STOCK: Oils and watercolours, 18th-20th C, £500-£100,000.* LOC: Main road. PARK: Easy. TEL: 01798 344422; e-mail - canongallery@btinternet.com. SER: Valuations; restorations. FAIRS: World of Watercolours; NEC; Harrogate; Olympia; New York; BADA. VAT: Spec.

Ronald G. Chambers Fine Antiques
Market Sq. GU28 0AH. (Ronald G. Chambers and Jacqueline F. Tudor). LAPADA. CINOA. PAADA. Est. 1985. Open 10-5.30 including Sun. SIZE: 5 showrooms. *STOCK: Fine 18th-19th C furniture and objets d'art.* PARK: Free. TEL: 01798 342305; fax - 01798 342724; mobile - 07932 161968; website - www.ronaldchambers.com; e-mail - Jackie@ronaldchambers.com. SER: Search; valuations; shipping; storage.

J. Du Cros Antiques
1 Pound St. GU28 0DX. (J. and P. Du Cros). PAADA. Est. 1982. Open 10-5.30, sometimes closed Wed. pm. SIZE: Medium. *STOCK: English furniture, 1660-1900, £100-£5,000; treen, metalware, some glass.* LOC: Corner of Sadlers Row. PARK: Nearby. TEL: 01798 342071. VAT: Stan/Spec.

Elliott's
East St. GU28 0AB. PAADA. Open Wed., Fri. and Sat. 10-5. *STOCK: 18th-20th C furniture, fine art and decorative items.* TEL: 01798 343408.

Richard Gardner Antiques
Swan House, Market Sq. GU28 0AN. (Richard and Janice Gardner). LAPADA. PAADA. Resident. Est. 1992. Open 10-5.30 including Sun. SIZE: Large. *STOCK: Fine period furniture and works of art, up to £75,000; English and Continental porcelain, Victorian Staffordshire figures, bronzes, silver, paintings, 17th-19th C; associated items.* PARK: 50 yards. TEL: 01798 343411/344463; website - www.richardgardnerantiques.co.uk. VAT: Spec.

William Hockley Antiques
East St. GU28 0AB. (D. and V. Thrower). LAPADA. PAADA. Est. 1974. Open 10-5.30. *STOCK: Fine 18th to early 19th C furniture and decorative items, fabrics, carpets and related items.* PARK: Easy. TEL: 01798 343172; 01403 701917. SER: Interior design. VAT: Stan/Spec.

The Madison Gallery
Swan House, Market Sq. GU28 0AH. (G.W. Mott). PAADA. Est. 1991. Open 10-5 including Sun. SIZE: Large. *STOCK: Furniture - oak, country, formal and decorative; pictures, silver, porcelain and accessories.* PARK: Easy. TEL: 01798 343638. SER: Restorations; upholstery. VAT: Spec.

Octavia Antiques
East St. GU28 0AB. (Aline Bell). PAADA. Est. 1973. Open 10.30-5.30. CL: Fri. SIZE: Small. *STOCK: Decorative items - blue and white china, lamps, mirrors, chairs, small sofas, mainly 19th C.* PARK: Easy. TEL: 01798 342771.

Old Bank House Antiques
Market Sq. GU28 0AH. (Bruce Wheeler and Anthony Graham). Open 10-5. *STOCK: English and Continental furniture and objects, 1800-1940.* TEL: 01798 344176; mobile - 07970 616434.

Oliver Charles Antiques
Lombard St. GU28 0AG. (Allan and Deborah Gardner). PAADA. Est. 1987. Open 10-5.30 (including Sun. from April to Sept) or by appointment. SIZE: Medium. *STOCK: Georgian, Regency and selected French furniture, 1700-1850, £1,000-£25,000; Victorian paintings, £750-£100,000.* LOC: Opposite church. PARK: Easy. TEL: 01798 344443; fax - 01798 343916; e-mail - olivercharles1@aol.com; website - www.olivercharles.co.uk. SER: Valuations.

Persian Carpet Gallery of Petworth
Church St. GU28 0AD. (Dr. Ali Mandegaran). LAPADA. Est. 1974. Open 9.30-5. *STOCK: Old and new Oriental rugs and carpets.* LOC: A272. PARK: Nearby. TEL: 01798 343344; fax - 01798 342673. SER: Valuations; restorations; hand cleaning; insurance claims.

OLIVER CHARLES

Charles Sillem Lidderdale RBA   Canvas size 125cms x 82cms

English Period Furniture & Fine 19th Century Paintings

Lombard Street, Petworth, West Sussex, GU28 0AG

Tel +44 (0) 1798 344443 Fax +44 (0) 1798 343916

www.olivercharles.co.uk   e-mail olivercharles1@aol.com

Petworth Antique Market
East St. GU28 0AB. (D.M. Rayment). PAADA. Est. 1968. Open 10-5.30. SIZE: Large - 36 dealers. *STOCK: General antiques, books, furniture, brass, copper, pictures, textiles.* LOC: Near church. PARK: Adjoining. TEL: 01798 342073. VAT: Stan/Spec.

Annette Puttnam
2 Leppards High St. GU28 0AU. Open 10-5.15. *STOCK: Furniture - country, pine, oak, fruitwood, mahogany, painted, architectural, garden and upholstery.* TEL: 01798 343933; mobile - 07973 421070; e-mail - bird.puttnam@virgin.net. Spec.

Red Lion Antiques
New St. GU28 0AS. (R. Wilson and D. Swanson). PAADA. LAPADA. Est. 1981. Open 10-5.30. SIZE: Large. *STOCK: Antiques for the country home, oak, walnut and pine furniture, 17th-19th C, £100-£20,000.* LOC: Town centre. PARK: Easy. TEL: 01798 344485; fax - 01798 342367; e-mail - rod@redlion-antiques.com; website - www.redlion-antiques.com. VAT: Spec.

Riverbank
High St. GU28 0AU. (Linda Burke-White). PAADA. Open 10-5.30. *STOCK: Antiques for the house and garden.* TEL: 01798 344401; fax - 01798 343135.

Ruddy Antiques
10A New St. GU28 0AS. (Robin and Paula Ruddy). Est. 1994. Open 10.30-5 or by appointment. SIZE: Medium. *STOCK: Eclectic Continental and English furniture, 18th-19th C.* TEL: 01798 344622.

Stewart Antiques
High St. GU28 0AU. (John and Sandra Moore). Est. 1984. Open 10-5.30, Sun. by appointment. SIZE: Medium. *STOCK: Victorian stripped pine and fruitwood, £30-£3,000; kitchenalia and Continental decorative items.* LOC: Town centre. PARK: Easy. TEL: 01798 342136. SER: Valuations. VAT: Spec.

J.C. Tutt Antiques
Angel St. GU28 0BQ. Open 10-5. CL: Some Mon. SIZE: Large. *STOCK: Mahogany and country furniture and accessories.* PARK: Nearby. TEL: 01798 343221.

Georgia Antiques
The Barn, Broomershill Farm. RH20 2HZ. (Georgia Hicks). LAPADA. CINOA. Est. 1979. Open by appointment. SIZE: Medium. *STOCK: English furniture, pictures and fine art, 18th-19th C; decorative lighting, 19th C.* TEL: 01798 872348; fax - 01798 875200; e-mail - georgia@georgiaantiques.com; website - www.georgia-antiques.com. VAT: Spec.

Thakeham Furniture
Marehill Rd. RH20 2DY. (T. and B. Chavasse). Est. 1988. Open Mon.-Fri. 9-5. SIZE: Medium. *STOCK: 18th-19th C English furniture, £100-£8,000; clocks.* LOC: 1 mile east of Pulborough next to White Horse Inn on A283. PARK: Easy. TEL: 01798 872006. SER: Restorations (furniture). VAT: Spec.

Rodney Arthur Classics
Unit 6 Riverbank Business Centre, Old Shoreham Rd. BN43 5FL. (Rodney Oliver). Est. 1979. Open 9.30-5, Sat. and Sun. by appointment. SIZE: Large. *STOCK: Furniture, 1800-1920, £100-£2,500.* LOC: From A27 take A283 exit near Shoreham Airport, then south towards sea, shop opposite Swiss Cottage pub. TEL: 01273 441606; fax - 01273 441977. SER: Restorations; French polishing. VAT: Stan/Spec.

Julia Holmes Antique Maps and Prints
South Gardens Cottage. GU31 5QJ. FATG. Est. 1961. By appointment only. SIZE: Medium. *STOCK: Maps, mainly British Isles, 1600-1850, £25-£2,000; prints, especially sporting, to £500.* LOC: End of main street, on the Chichester road. PARK: Opposite. TEL: 01730 825040; e-mail - juliaandroger@beeb.net; website - www. juliamaps. co.uk. SER: Valuations; restorations (cleaning and colouring maps and prints); framing; buys at auction; catalogues. FAIRS: Local and major sporting events.

David R. Fileman
Squirrels, Bayards. BN44 3AA. Open daily. *STOCK: Table glass, £20-£1,000; chandeliers, candelabra, £500-£20,000; all 18th-19th C. Collectors' items, 17th-19th C, £25-£2,000; paperweights, 19th C, £50-£5,000.* LOC: A283 to

One of the largest selections of

Antique Country Furniture

in the South of England

displayed in superb period setting

RED LION ANTIQUES

Rod Wilson – David Swanson

New Street, Petworth, West Sussex

Tel: (01798) 344485 Fax: (01798) 342367

Website: www.redlion-antiques.com
E-mail: rod@redlion-antiques.com

north of Steyning village. TEL: 01903 813229. SER: Valuations; restorations (chandeliers and candelabra). VAT: Stan/Spec.

STORRINGTON

Stable Antiques
46 West St. RH20 4EE. (Ian J.Wadey). Est. 1993. Open 10-6 including Sun. SIZE: Large. *STOCK: General antiques, furniture and bric-a-brac, £1-£1,000*. LOC: A283 west of A24 towards Pulborough, just before Amberley turn. PARK: Easy. TEL: 01903 740555; fax - 01903 740441; website - www.stableantiques.co.uk.

WORTHING

Acorn Antiques
91 Rowlands Rd. BN11 3JX. (Henry Nicholls). Est. 1992. Open 9-5.30, Mon. and Wed. 9-4. SIZE: Small. *STOCK: Furniture, china and porcelain, 18th-20th C*. LOC: Off Heene Road near seafront. PARK: Easy. TEL: 01903 216926. SER: Restorations; polishing. FAIRS: Ardingly; Goodwood.

Chloe Antiques
61 Brighton Rd. BN11 3EE. (Mrs D. Peters). Est. 1960. Open 10-12.30 and 1.30-4.30. CL: Wed. SIZE: Small. *STOCK: General antiques, furniture, jewellery, china, glass, bric-a-brac*. LOC: From Brighton, on main rd. just past Beach House Park on corner. PARK: Opposite. TEL: 01903 202697.

Corner Antiques
9/10 Havercroft Buildings, North St. BN11 1DY. (R.A. Mihok). Est. 1992. Open 10-5. SIZE: Small. *STOCK: Pine and country furniture, 19th C, £200-£500; objets d'art, 50p-£150, furniture, £100-£1,000; all 19th-20th C*. LOC: Top end of High Street, turn right at the roundabout. PARK: Loading only, otherwise Connaught NCP. TEL: 01903 537669; fax - 01903 206881. SER: Restorations (furniture including French polishing, upholstering and repairs); buys at auction.

Robert Warner Antiques Ltd
1-13 South Farm Rd. BN14 7AB. Est. 1940. CL: Wed. pm. SIZE: Large. *STOCK: Furniture*. TEL: 01903 232710; fax - 01903 217515; website - www.rewarner.co.uk. VAT: Stan.

Wilsons Antiques
45-47 New Broadway, Tarring Rd. BN11 4HS. (F. and K.P. Wilson). LAPADA. Est. 1936. Open 10-5, Sat. 10-1. SIZE: Large. *STOCK: Period furniture, 18th-19th C, £100-£10,000; Edwardian furniture, £50-£4,000; decorative items, 19th C, £10-£750; watercolours and oil paintings, 19th-20th C*. Not Stocked: Pine. PARK: Easy. TEL: 01903 202059; fax - 01903 206300; mobile - 07778 813395; e-mail - Frank@Wilsons-Antiques.com; website - www.wilsons-antiques.com. SER: Valuations. FAIRS: Olympia (June); Goodwood House; NEC. VAT: Stan/Spec/Global.

Thomas Shotter Boys, Paris from the Seine, watercolour over traces of pencil, heightened with bodycolour and with scratching out, 9¼in. x 22¼in., worth between £50,000 and £60,000. (Sotheby's)

From an article entitled "Thomas Shotter Boys" by Charles Hind which appeared in the May 2002 issue of **Antique Collecting**. For more details and to subscribe see page 21.

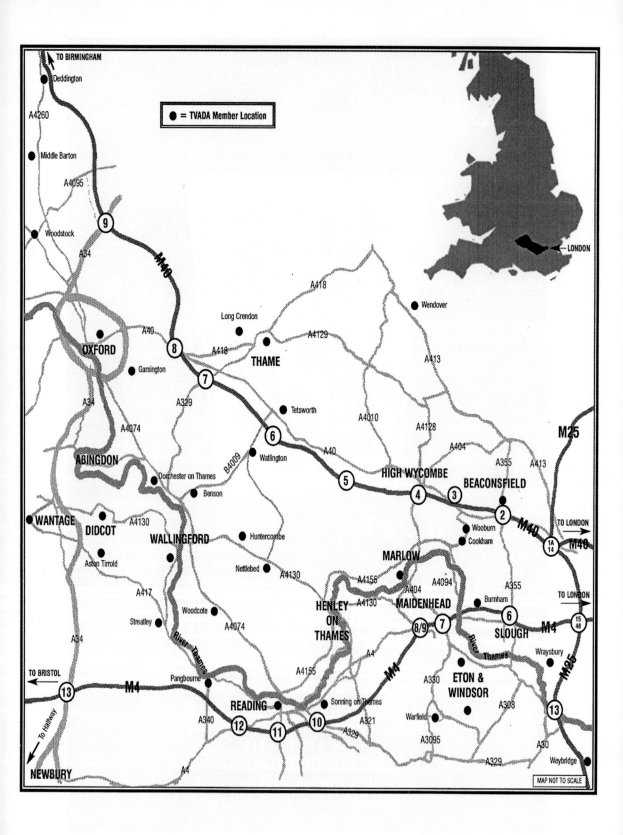

THAMES VALLEY
ANTIQUE DEALERS ASSOCIATION

Representing some 250 member dealers

In this historic and beautiful area of the Thames Valley you will find a wide variety of antiques and decorative items – appealing to the connoisseur, collector, decorator and homemaker.

Medieval and Georgian buildings are host to many of the antique dealers' shops and centres, so why not combine your search for antiques with an historical tour.

Look out for the black & gold TVADA Logo sign (Tamesis, the Roman God of the Thames), hanging in the window or on the door, you can always be sure of a warm welcome inside and often refreshments too!

Our Associate Members can help you with restoration, conservation and decorating advice. Our members are experienced in dealing with customers worldwide and will help with advice on packing, shipping, and insurance.

T.V.A.D.A.

Twice a year – in the Spring and Autumn we hold award winning Fairs and provide an opportunity to sample the quality and range of items available from TVADA members.

The Thames Valley is conveniently situated, from central London most TVADA members can be reached within one hour by road. Trains and buses serve the area well. Heathrow airport is only 8 miles from our nearest dealer, and the M4, M25 and M40 motorways provide easy accessibility. We are pleased to offer a courier service to guide you round the area.

Visit our Website **www.tvada.co.uk** for information, e-mail **antiques@tvada.co.uk** or telephone the TVADA office for more information.

The Secretary, TVADA, The Old College, Queen Street
Dorchester on Thames, Oxon OX10 7HL. Tel/Fax: 01865 341639

ASTON TIRROLD, Nr. Didcot

John Harrison Fine Art
Skirmers, Aston St. OX11 9DQ. (J.M.C. Harrison). TVADA. Strictly by appointment. *STOCK: Drawings and watercolours, 18th-19th C.* TEL: 01235 850260. SER: Commissions undertaken.

BEACONSFIELD

Period Furniture Showrooms
49 London End. HP9 2HW. (R.E.W. Hearne and N.J. Hearne). TVADA. Est. 1965. Open Mon.-Sat. 9-5.30. SIZE: Large. *STOCK: Furniture, 1700-1900, £50-£5,000.* LOC: A40 Beaconsfield Old Town. PARK: Own. TEL: 01494 674112; fax - 01494 681046; e-mail - sales@periodfurniture. net; website - www.periodfurniture.net. SER: Restorations (furniture). VAT: Stan/Spec.

CAVERSHAM, Nr. Reading

The Clock Workshop
17 Prospect St. RG4 8JB. (J. M. Yealland FBHI). LAPADA. TVADA. CINOA. Est. 1980. Open 9.30-5.30, Sat. 10-1. SIZE: Small. *STOCK: Clocks, late 17th to late 19th C, £350-£60,000; barometers, 18th-19th C, £500-£12,000.* LOC: Prospect St. is the beginning of main Reading to Henley road. PARK: Behind shop in North St. TEL: 0118 9470741; e-mail - theclockworkshop @supanet.com. SER: Valuations; restorations (clocks, barometers, chronometers, barographs); buys at auction. FAIRS: TVADA; LAPADA; Olympia. VAT: Stan/Spec.

COOKHAM RISE

Cookham Antiques
35 Station Parade. SL6 9BR. (Gary Lloyd Wallis). TVADA. Est. 1990. Open daily including Sun. SIZE: Large. *STOCK: Furniture including bookcases, desks, chests of drawers, 18th-20th C, £50-£1,000.* PARK: Easy and at rear. TEL: 01628 523224; mobile - 07778 020536. SER: Valuations; restorations.

DEDDINGTON

Deddington Antiques Centre
Laurel House, Bull Ring, Market Sq. OX15 0TT. (Mrs B. J. Haller). TVADA. Est. 1972. Open 10-5, including Sun. SIZE: 27 dealers. *STOCK: Furniture, Georgian to 1930's, £100-£4,000;* *porcelain, silver, pictures, jewellery, 1700-1930, £5-£5,000; collectables, £10-£200.* LOC: Off A4260 Oxford-Banbury road at Deddington traffic lights. PARK: Easy, free. TEL: 01869 338968; fax - 01869 338916. SER: Valuations. FAIRS: TVADA.

DORCHESTER-ON-THAMES

Dorchester Antiques
The Barn, 3 High St. OX10 7HH. (J. and S. Hearnden). LAPADA. TVADA. Est. 1992. Open Tues.-Sat. 10-5. SIZE: Medium. *STOCK: Furniture including chairs and decorative country pieces, 18th-19th C.* LOC: Opposite Abbey. PARK: Easy. TEL: 01865 341373. SER: Restorations; finder. FAIRS: TVADA.

Hallidays (Fine Antiques) Ltd
The Old College, High St. OX10 7HL. LAPADA. TVADA. CINOA. Est. 1950. Open 9-5, Sat. 10-1 and 2-4. SIZE: Large. *STOCK: Furniture, 17th-19th C, £100-£70,000; paintings, 18th-19th C, £100-£20,000; decorative and small items, pine and marble mantelpieces, firegrates, fenders, 18th-20th C; room panelling.* LOC: 8 miles south-east of Oxford. PARK: At rear. TEL: 01865 340028; fax - 01865 341149. FAIRS: Olympia. VAT: Stan/Spec.

HALFWAY, Nr. Newbury

Alan Walker   BADA
Halfway Manor. RG20 8NR. TVADA. Open by appointment. SIZE: Large. *STOCK: Fine barometers and weather instruments.* LOC: 4 miles west of Newbury on A4. PARK: Easy. TEL: 01488 657670; mobile - 07770 728397; website - www.alanwalker-barometers.com. SER: Restorations.

HUNTERCOMBE

The Country Seat
Huntercombe Manor Barn. RG9 5RY. (Harvey Ferry and William Clegg). LAPADA. TVADA. Est. 1965. Open 9-5.30, Sun. by appointment. SIZE: Large. *STOCK: Furniture - signed and designed, 1700-1970; garden and architectural/panelling; art pottery and metalwork, lighting and Whitefriars glass.* LOC: 200 yds down right-hand turn off A4130 Nettlebed-Wallingford. PARK: Easy. TEL: 01491 641349; fax - 01491 641533; e-mail - ferry &clegg@thecountryseat.com; websites - www. thecountryseat.com and www.whitefriars glass.com. SER: Restorations. VAT: Spec.

MARLOW

Marlow Antique Centre
35 Station Rd. SL7 1NW. TVADA. Est. 1995.
Open 10.30-5, Sun. 11-4. SIZE: 30+ dealers.
*STOCK: 18th-20th C furniture, collectors' china
from Worcester to Clarice Cliff, Staffordshire
figures and dogs, chandeliers, silver, decorative
glass, writing slopes, tea caddies, postcards,
pens, cuff-links, equestrian items, jewellery.*
LOC: Town centre. PARK: Nearby. TEL: 01628
473223; fax - 01628 478989. SER: International
shipping and packing.

NETTLEBED, Nr. Henley-on-Thames

Willow Antiques and the Nettlebed Antique Merchants
The Barns, 1 High St. RG9 5DA. (Willow Bicknell,
Michael Plummer and Laurie Brunton). TVADA.
Est. 1984. Open 10-5.30, Sun. 11-4, other times by
appointment. SIZE: Large. *STOCK: Decorative, fine
and unusual furniture, objects and decorations,
including architectural and garden items, 17th C to
1970s, including Gothic, Aesthetic, Arts and Crafts
and Art Deco.* LOC: Between Wallingford and
Henley on A4074. PARK: Easy. TEL: 01491
642062/628811; mobile - 07770 554559. SER:
Finder; copy and design; advice on period design for
house and garden. FAIRS: TVADA. VAT: Spec.

NORTH ASTON

Elizabeth Harvey-Lee
1 West Cottages, Middle Aston Lane. OX25 5QB.
Est. 1986. Open by appointment. *STOCK:
Original prints, 15th-20th C; artists' etchings,
engravings, lithographs, £100-£6,000.* LOC: 6
miles from junction 10, M40, 15 miles north of
Oxford. TEL: 01869 347164. SER: Illustrated
catalogue available twice yearly (£20 p.a.).
FAIRS: London Original Print, Royal Academy;
Olympia (June and Nov); Art on Paper, Royal
College of Art. VAT: Spec.

OXFORD

Antiques on High Ltd
85 High St. OX1 4BG. (Paul Lipson and Sally
Young). TVADA. Est. 1982. Open 10-5, Sun. and
Bank Holidays 11-5. SIZE: Large - 35 dealers.
*STOCK: Small antiques and collectables including
jewellery, silver and plate, ceramics, glass,
antiquities, watches, books and coins, 17th-20th C.*
LOC: Opposite Queen's Lane. PARK: St Clements,
Westgate, Seacourt/Thornhill Park and Ride. TEL:
01865 251075. SER: Valuations; restorations (jewellery, silver including replating). FAIRS: TVADA.

PANGBOURNE

Rita Butler
4a Station Rd. RG8 7AN. TVADA. Est. 1999.
Open 10-5. *STOCK: General antiques including
brass and bronze; early 19th C to early 20th C
ceramics especially Art Deco; glass, early 1800's.*
PARK: Opposite. TEL: 0118 984 5522; mobile -
07752 936327. FAIRS: TVADA; Thames.

READING

Rupert Landen Antiques
Church Farm, Reading Rd., Woodcote. RG8
0QX. TVADA. Open by appointment only.
STOCK: Late 18th to early 19th C furniture.
TEL: 01491 682396; mobile - 07974 732472.

SONNING-ON-THAMES

Cavendish Fine Arts   BADA
**The Dower House. RG4 6UL. (Janet Middlemiss
and Guy Hazel). LAPADA. TVADA. Est. 1972.
Open by appointment only. *STOCK: Fine
Queen Anne and English Georgian furniture,
glass and porcelain.* TEL: 01189 691904;
mobile - 07831 295575. SER: Valuations;
shipping; interior decoration. FAIRS:
Olympia; Chelsea; BADA; TVADA. VAT:
Stan/Spec.**

TETSWORTH, Nr. Thame

The Swan at Tetsworth
High St. OX9 7AB. TVADA. Est. 1995. Open 7
days 10-6. SIZE: 40+ rooms. LOC: A40, 5
minutes from junctions 6 and 8, M40. PARK:
Own large. TEL: 01844 281777; fax - 01844
281770; website - www.theswan.co.uk; e-mail -
antiques@theswan.co.uk. SER: Restorations
(clocks, cabinet work and gilding).

WALLINGFORD

The Lamb Arcade
83 High St. OX10 0BX. TVADA. Open 10-5, Sat.
10-5.30. *STOCK: As below plus books, crafts and
ephemera.* TEL: 01491 835166. SER: Restorations (furniture).

Summers Davis Antiques Ltd
Calleva House, 6 High St. OX10 0BP. (Graham
Wells). LAPADA. CINOA. TVADA. Est. 1917.
Open 9-5.30, Sat. 9-5, Sun. 11-5. SIZE: Large.
*STOCK: English and Continental furniture,
decorative items and objects.* Not Stocked: Silver,
shipping goods. LOC: From London, shop is on

left, 50yds. from Thames Bridge. PARK: Opposite, behind castellated gates. TEL: 01491 836284; fax - 01491 833443; e-mail - antiques@summers davis.co.uk; website - www.summers-davies antique-furniture.com. VAT: Spec.

WANTAGE

The Arbery Centre
Market Place. OX12 8AB. (Cedarstar Ltd.). TVADA. Est. 2000. Open 9.30-5, Sun. 11.30-5. SIZE: Large. *STOCK: Wide range of general antiques and collectables including 20th C paintings, costumes, pine and country furniture, silver, gramophones, maps, books on French furniture.* TEL: 01235 769325; fax - 01235 765242.

Stephen Orton Antiques
The Antiques Warehouse, Shirburn Rd. OX49 5BZ. TVADA. Open Mon.-Fri. 9-5, other times by appointment. SIZE: Warehouse. *STOCK: 18th-19th C furniture, some decorative items.* LOC: 2 mins. from exit 6, M40. TEL: 01491 613752; e-mail - Orton.Antiques@virgin.net. SER: Supply and pack containers; valuations; restorations; buying agent. VAT: Stan/Spec.

WARFIELD

Moss End Antique Centre
Moss End Garden Centre. RG12 6EJ. TVADA. Est. 1988. Open 10.30-5. CL: Mon. SIZE: Large - 25 dealers. *STOCK: General antiques and collectables.* LOC: A3095. PARK: Own. TEL: 01344 861942. FAIRS: TVADA (Spring and Autumn).

WENDOVER

Sally Turner Antiques
Hogarth House, High St. HP22 6DU. LAPADA. TVADA. Open 10-5. CL: Wed. and Sun. except Dec. SIZE: 7 showrooms + barn. *STOCK: Decorative and period furniture, general antiques and jewellery.* PARK: Rear of shop. TEL: 01296 624402; fax - same; mobile - 07860 201718.

WINDSOR AND ETON

Marcelline Herald Antiques
41 High St., Eton. SL4 6BD. LAPADA, TVADA. Est. 1993. Open Tues.,Thurs., Fri. and Sat. 10-5, other days by appointment. SIZE: Medium. *STOCK: Furniture, £500-£15,000; mirrors, pelmets and screens, £200-£2,500; ceramics, lamps and prints, £50-£1,000; all 18th to early* *19th C.* PARK: Loading only. TEL: 01753 833924; fax - 0118 971 4683; home - same; e-mail - marcelline.herald@virgin.net. FAIRS: TVADA; Decorative Antiques and Textiles. VAT: Spec.

Peter J. Martin
40 High St., Eton. SL4 6BD. TVADA. Est. 1963. Open 9-1 and 2-5. CL: Sun. SIZE: Large and warehouse. *STOCK: Period, Victorian and decorative furniture and furnishings, £50-£20,000; metalware, £10-£500, all from 1800.* PARK: 50yds. opposite. TEL: 01753 864901; home - 01753 863987. SER: Restorations; shipping arranged; buys at auction. VAT: Stan/Spec.

WOODSTOCK

Chris Baylis Country Chairs
16 Oxford St. OX20 1TS. TVADA. Open 10.30-5.30, Sun. 11-5, appointment advisable to view stock. *STOCK: English country chairs, from 1780; sets of rush seated chairs including ladder and spindle backs, Windsors and kitchen chairs.* TEL: 01993 813887; fax - 01993 812379; e-mail - info@realwoodfurniture.co.uk; website - www.realwoodfurniture.co.uk.

Bees Antiques
30 High St. OX20 1TG. (Jo and Jim Bateman). TVADA. Est. 1991. Open 10-1 and 1.30-5, Sun. 11-5. CL: Tues. SIZE: Small. *STOCK: Pottery, porcelain and glass, 18th-20th C, £30-£1,500; small furniture, 19th to early 20th C, £50-£2,000; metalware, 19th C, £30-£200; jewellery, 19th-20th C, £30-£1,000.* LOC: Just off A3440 Oxford/Stratford-on-Avon road, in town centre. PARK: Opposite. TEL: 01993 811062; home - 01993 771593; mobile - 07702 603419. SER: Valuations; buys at auction (as stock).

John Howard   BADA
19 High St. OX20 1TE. LAPADA. TVADA. CADA. Open 10-5.30. SIZE: Small. *STOCK: 18th-19th C British pottery especially rare Staffordshire animal figures, bocage figures, lustre, 18th C creamware and unusual items.* PARK: Easy. TEL: 0870 4440678; fax - same; mobile - 07831 850544; e-mail - john@john howard.co.uk; website - www.antiquepottery. co.uk and www.Staffordshires.com. SER: Packing; insurance service to USA. FAIRS: Olympia; BADA. VAT: Spec.

Span Antiques
6 Market Place. OX20 1TA. TVADA. Est. 1978. Open 10-1 and 2-5, Sun 1-5. SIZE: Medium. LOC: Near Town Hall. PARK: Easy. TEL: 01993 811332.

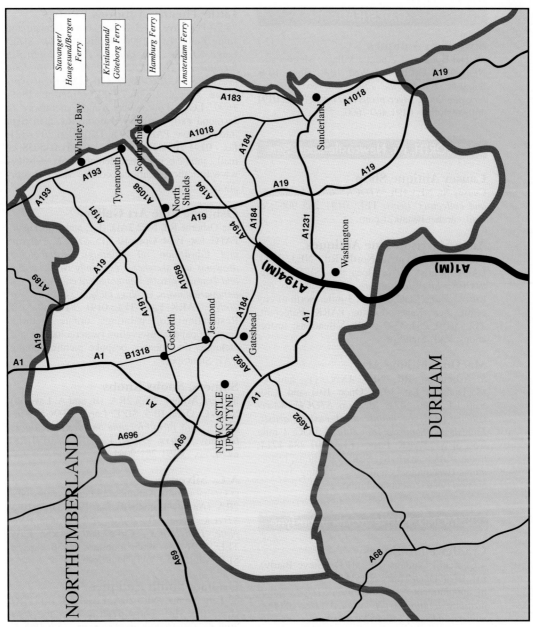

Stavanger/ Haugesund/Bergen Ferry

Kristiansand/ Göteborg Ferry

Hamburg Ferry

Amsterdam Ferry

Whitley Bay

A193

Tynemouth

South Shields

North Shields

A193

A191

A19

A189

A19

A1058

A194

A1058

A183

A1018

A184

A19

A184

A194

A19

Sunderland

A1018

A19

A1231

Washington

A194(M)

A1(M)

Gosforth

Jesmond

A184

Gateshead

A1

A1

B1318

A1

A692

A1

A592

NEWCASTLE UPON TYNE

A696

A69

A69

A68

NORTHUMBERLAND

DURHAM

Dealers and Shops in Tyne and Wear

				Sunderland	1
Gateshead	1	Newcastle-upon-Tyne	8	Tynemouth	1
Gosforth	3	North Shields	1	Washington	2
Jesmond	8	South Shields	1	Whitley Bay	3

GATESHEAD

Sovereign Antiques
35 The Boulevard, Antique Village, Metrocentre. NE11 9YN. Open Mon.-Wed. 10-8, Thurs. 10-9, Sat. 9-6. *STOCK: Fine antique and modern jewellery, diamonds, silver, prints and maps.* TEL: 0191 460 9604; fax - 0191 460 7600.

GOSFORTH, Nr. Newcastle-upon-Tyne

Causey Antique Shop
Causey St. NE3 4DL. *STOCK: Silver, Victoriana and collectors' items.* TEL: 0191 285 9062; e-mail - archer.l@talk21.com.

Anna Harrison Fine Antiques
Grange Park, Great North Rd. NE3 2DQ. LAPADA. Est. 1976. Open 9-5. SIZE: Large. *STOCK: English furniture, porcelain, oils and watercolours.* LOC: A6125, 3 miles north of city centre, near Regent Centre. PARK: Forecourt. TEL: 0191 284 3202. SER: Valuations; restorations. VAT: Stan/Spec.

MacDonald Fine Art
8 Ashburton Rd. NE3 4XN. (T. and C. MacDonald). Est. 1976. Open 10-1 and 2.30-5.30. CL: Wed. SIZE: Medium. *STOCK: Watercolours and oils, mainly north-eastern artists, English and Scottish, 18th-20th C.* LOC: 1 mile west of A1. PARK: Easy. TEL: 0191 284 4214; home - 0191 285 6188. SER: Valuations; restorations (watercolours and oils); framing; buys at auction (watercolours and oils).

JESMOND, Nr. Newcastle-upon-Tyne

Cradlewell Antiques
4 Churchill Gardens. NE2 1LD. (Steve Bardy). Est. 1979. Open Thurs.-Sat. 11-5, Tues. and Wed. by appointment. SIZE: Medium. *STOCK: Small furniture, lighting, Art Nouveau, Art Deco, 20th C modern design, £50-£500; ceramics, bakelite telephones and radios, £20-£200.* LOC: Left off A1058 coast road to shops at lights just before Cradlewell bypass. PARK: Easy. TEL: 0191 212 1500; mobile - 07966 246101.

Owen Humble
11-12 Clayton Rd. NE2 4RP. LAPADA. Est. 1958. Open 6 days. SIZE: Large and warehouse. *STOCK: Furniture, general antiques.* PARK: Easy. TEL: 0191 281 4602; fax - 0191 281 9076; e-mail - antiques@owenhumble.com. SER: Restorations. VAT: Stan/Spec.

Little Theatre Antiques Centre
75-79 Fern Ave. NE2 2RA. (Louise Bennett and John Bell). Est. 1994. Open 10-5.30. SIZE: Large. *STOCK: Victorian and Edwardian British furniture, £200-£3,000; north-east England pressed glass, 1860-1930, £20-£250; French furniture 1900's, £500-£2,000; ceramics, 1880-1990.* LOC: Follow city centre motorway to Jesmond exit, north up Osborne Rd. then right into Fern Ave. PARK: Own. TEL: 0191 209 4321; fax - 0191 209 4320; mobile - 07951 035038; e-mail - john@bennett-bell.demon.co.uk; website - www.littletheatreantiques.co.uk. SER: Restorations (furniture).

Osborne Fine Art Gallery
18c Osborne Rd. NE2 2AD. (F.T. and J. Jackman). FATG. Est. 1974. Open 10-5.15. *STOCK: Victorian and Edwardian oil paintings, watercolours, drawings and sketches - especially Northumbrian and Tyneside artists; topographical engravings and antiquarian maps, etchings including marine, 19th-20th C.* PARK: Easy. TEL: 0191 281 6380. SER: Restorations (oil paintings, ornate Victorian frames); paper conservation (watercolours, maps, etchings, documents); bespoke picture-framing. VAT: Stan/Spec.

Shiners, Snobs Knobs
81 Fern Avenue, NE2 2RA. (B. and A. Lawson). SALVO. Open 10-5. SIZE: Large. *STOCK: Fireplaces, door furniture, pine and vestibule doors, lighting, fenders.* PARK: Easy. TEL: 0191 281 6474; fax - 0191 281 9041.

A.C. Silver
at Graham Smith Antiques, 83 Fern Avenue. NE2 2RA. (Andrew Campbell). Est. 1980. Open 10-5. *STOCK: Silver, 17th-20th C, £50-£15,000; silver plate, 19th-20th C, £50-£1,000.* PARK: Easy. TEL: 0191 281 5065; mobile - 07836 286218. SER: Valuations. VAT: Stan/Spec.

Graham Smith Antiques
83 Fern Avenue. NE2 2RA. LAPADA. Est. 1999. Open 10-5. SIZE: Large. *STOCK: Furniture, 18th-20th C, £50-£8,000; works of art, 18th-19th C, £100-£2,000; smalls, 18th-20th C, £10-£2,000.* LOC: Follow signs to Fern Avenue Antiques Village off Osborne Rd. PARK: Easy. TEL: 0191 281 5065; mobile - 07836 251873. SER: Valuations. FAIRS: Newark. VAT: Stan/Spec.

Turnburrys
257 Jesmond Rd. NE2 1LB. Est. 1995. Open 9-6, Sun. 12-3. SIZE: Large. *STOCK: Period, antique and bespoke fireplaces; original and bespoke vestibule doors: radiators, Victorian to 1920's, £100-£500; over mantel mirrors.* LOC: Off

Cradlewell by-pass, next to Jesmond Dene. PARK: Easy. TEL: 0191 281 1770; fax - 0191 240 2569. SER: Valuations; restorations (doors, furniture and fireplaces). FAIRS: Traditional Homes & Period Living, London. VAT: Stan.

NEWCASTLE-UPON-TYNE

Davidson's The Jewellers Ltd
94 and 96 Grey St. NE1 6AG. (Anthony and Helen Davidson). NAG. Est. 1898. Open 9-5.30. *STOCK: Jewellery, silver.* TEL: 0191 232 2551/232 2895.

Dog Leap Antiques
61 Side. NE1 3JE. Est. 1950. Open 9.15-1 and 2-5, Sat. 9.30-1. SIZE: Small. *STOCK: Antique engravings and reproduction prints.* LOC: Bottom of Dean St. PARK: Easy. TEL: 0191 232 7269.

Intercoin
103 Clayton St. NE1 5PZ. Open 9-4.30. *STOCK: Coins and items of numismatic interest; jewellery, silver.* LOC: City centre. TEL: 0191 232 2064.

Steve Johnson Medals & Militaria
PO Box 1SP. NE99 1SP. *Medals and militaria.* Fax - 01207 547073; e-mail - steve@wwmeinc. com; website - www.wwmeinc.com. *Mail Order and Online.*

Owen's Jewellers
14 and 153 Shields Rd., Byker. NE6 1DR. (D.W. Robertson). Est. 1968. Open 9-5. *STOCK: Jewellery.* TEL: 0191 265 4332/8699.

R.D. Steedman
9 Grey St. NE1 6EE. ABA. Est. 1907. Open 9-5. CL: Sat. pm. *STOCK: Rare and secondhand books.* LOC: Central. TEL: 0191 232 6561. FAIRS: Olympia Book.

NORTH SHIELDS

Maggie May's
(Incorporating Tynemouth Fine Art) 49 Kirton Park Terrace. NE29 0LJ. (Miss M.L. Hayes). Est. 1960. Open Thurs.-Sat. 11-5.30. SIZE: Medium. *STOCK: General antiques and collectors' items, Art Deco, Victorian and Edwardian furniture, china, glass; paintings and watercolours, especially Northumbrian artists, 1800-1950; Continental furniture, glassware, porcelain, decorative items, gramophones.* LOC: Opposite The Gunner Inn. TEL: 0191 237 6933. SER: Valuations; restorations; framing; French polishing; buys at auction.

SOUTH SHIELDS

The Curiosity Shop
16 Frederick St. NE33 5EA. (G.D. Davies.). Est. 1969. CL: Wed. SIZE: Large. *STOCK: General antiques, paintings, jewellery, furniture, Royal Doulton.* PARK: Free. TEL: 0191 456 5560; fax - 0191 427 7597; e-mail - cdandgdno3@blueyonder. co.uk. FAIRS: Newark.

SUNDERLAND

Peter Smith Antiques
12-14 Borough Rd. SR1 1EP. LAPADA. Est. 1968. Open 9.30-4.30, Sat. 10-1, other times by appointment. SIZE: Warehouse. *STOCK: Georgian, Victorian, Edwardian longcase clocks, shipping goods, £5-£15,000.* LOC: 10 miles from A1(M); towards docks/Hendon from town centre. PARK: Easy. TEL: 0191 567 3537/567 7842; fax - 0191 514 2286; home - 0191 514 0008; e-mail - petersmithantiques@btinternet.com; website - www.petersmithantiques.co.uk. SER: Valuations; restorations; some shipping; containers packed; buys at auction. VAT: Stan/Spec.

TYNEMOUTH

Ian Sharp Antiques
23 Front St. NE30 4DX. LAPADA. Est. 1988. Open 10-1 and 1.30-5.30 or by appointment. SIZE: Small. *STOCK: Furniture, 19th to early 20th C; British pottery including northern especially Maling and Sunderland lustreware, 18th to early 20th C.* PARK: Easy. TEL: 0191 296 0656; fax - same; e-mail - iansharp@sharpantiques.demon. co.uk; website - www.sharpantiques.demon.co.uk. FAIRS: Newark. VAT: Global/ Spec.

WASHINGTON

Harold J. Carr Antiques
Field House, Rickleton. NE38 9HQ. Est. 1970. Open by appointment. *STOCK: General antiques and furniture.* TEL: 0191 388 6442. SER: Shippers.

Grate Expectations (Fireplaces)
Unit 6, Lee Close, Pattinson North Industrial Estate. NE38 8QF. (Geoffrey Moore). Est. 1983. Open 9-5. SIZE: Large. *STOCK: Fireplaces, £95-£650; fireplace accessories, £10-£125; both 19th C.* LOC: Close to A1 and A19. PARK: Easy. TEL: 0191 416 0609. SER: Restorations (cast-iron refurbishment, repair and welding). VAT: Stan.

Northumbria Pine
54 Whitley Rd. NE26 2NF. (C. and V. Dowland). Est. 1979. Open 9-5.30. SIZE: Small. *STOCK: Stripped pine and reproduction items.* LOC: Cullercoats end of Whitley Rd., behind sea front. PARK: Easy. TEL: 0191 252 4550. VAT: Stan.

Oliver's Bookshop
48A Whitley Rd. NE26 2NF. (J. Oliver). Est. 1986. Open 11-5. CL: Tues. and Wed. SIZE: Small. *STOCK: Antiquarian and secondhand books, 50p to £500.* PARK: Easy. TEL: 0191 251 3552. SER: Valuations. FAIRS: Tynemouth Book.

Treasure Chest
2 and 4 Norham Rd. NE26 2SB. Est. 1974. Open 10.30-1 and 2-4. CL: Wed. and Thurs. SIZE: Small. *STOCK: General antiques.* LOC: Just off main shopping area of Park View, leading to Monkseaton Railway Station. PARK: Easy. TEL: 0191 251 2052.

Jane Lindsay, 1838.

From an article entitled "Schoolgirl Samplers Featuring Animals And Houses" by Rebecca Scott which appeared in the September 2001 issue of **Antique Collecting**. For more details and to subscribe see page 21.

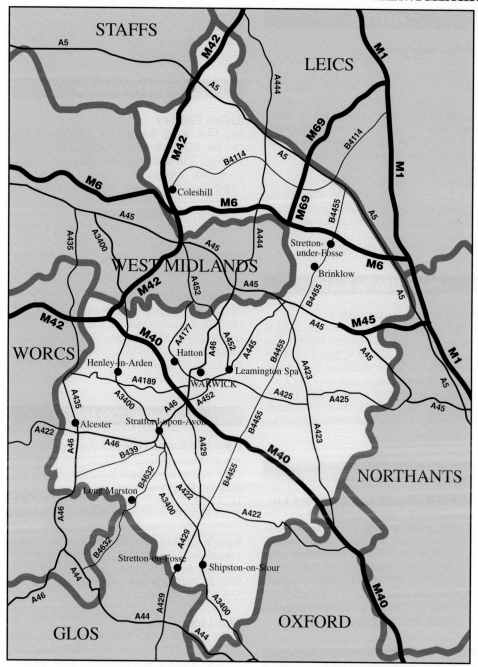

STAFFS

LEICS

WEST MIDLANDS

WORCS

NORTHANTS

GLOS

OXFORD

Coleshill

Stretton-under-Fosse

Brinklow

Hatton

Henley-in-Arden

Leamington Spa

WARWICK

Alcester

Stratford-upon-Avon

Long Marston

Stretton-on-Fosse

Shipston-on-Stour

Dealers and Shops in Warwickshire

Alcester	2	Henley-in-Arden	3	Stratford-upon-Avon	10
Brinklow	1	Leamington Spa	4	Stretton-on-Fosse	1
Coleshill	1	Long Marston	1	Stretton-under-Fosse	1
Hatton	1	Shipston-on-Stour	3	Warwick	16

High St. Antiques
11A High St. B49 5AE. (V.F.S. and J.F. Baldwin).
Est. 1979. Open Fri. 12-5 and Sat. 10-5 or by
appointment. SIZE: Small. *STOCK: Glass and
china, 18th-20th C, £5-£200; postcards and Art
Deco china.* LOC: On left-hand side near church
coming from Stratford-on-Avon road. PARK:
Rear of High St. TEL: 01789 764009; fax - 01789
766325. SER: Valuations.

Malthouse Antiques Centre
Market Place. B49 5AE. (J. and P. Allcock). Est.
1982. Open 10-5, Sun. 1-4. SIZE: Large. *STOCK:
Furniture, china, silver, collectables and objets
d'art, 18th-20th C, £1-£2,000.* LOC: Adjacent to
town car park. TEL: 01789 764032.

The Victorian Ironmonger
The Old Garage, 70 Broad St. CV23 0LN.
(Marlene and Dave Thompson). SALVO. Est.
1993. Open Fri. and Sat. 10-5, Sun. 11-3. SIZE:
Medium. *STOCK: Door furniture, 17th to early
20th C, £2-£500; fireplaces, 19th C, £150-£1,500;
architectural items, 17th to early 20th C, £25-
£2,000.* PARK: Easy. TEL: 01788 832292; home -
same; website - www.thevictorianironmonger.
co.uk. VAT: Spec.

Coleshill Antiques and Interiors Ltd
12 and 14 High St. B46 1AZ. (A.J. Webster). Est.
1958. Open Tues.-Sat. 9.30-5 or by appointment.
SIZE: Large. *STOCK: Continental porcelain, furniture, jewellery, silver and decorative items.* LOC:
1 mile from NEC. PARK: Easy. TEL: 01675
467416; fax - 01675 462931; e-mail - enq@
coleshillantiques-com; website - www.coleshill
antiques-com. SER: Valuations; restorations; repairs;
interior design. VAT: Stan/Spec.

The Stables Antique Centre
Hatton Country World, Dark Lane. CV35 8XA.
(John and Margaret Colledge). Est. 1990. Open
10-5 including Sun. SIZE: Large - 25 units.
*STOCK: Furniture, 18th-19th C, £50-£3,000;
china, 19th-20th C, £5-£200; clocks, 18th-19th C,
£200-£4,000; linen, glass, brass and copper;
paintings and prints, jukeboxes, radios, gramo-*

phones, kitchenalia and jewellery. LOC: Just off
A4177 Solihull-Warwick road, 5 minutes from
junction 15, M40. PARK: Own. TEL: 01926
842405. SER: Valuations.

Arden Gallery
B95 5AN. (G.B. Horton). Est. 1963. Open 1-6.
CL: Sat. SIZE: Medium. *STOCK: Oil paintings,
Victorian, £20-£1,000; watercolours, all periods,
to £1,500; portrait miniatures.* LOC: A3400.
PARK: Easy. TEL: 01564 792520. VAT: Spec.

Colmore Galleries Ltd
52 High St. B95 5AN. LAPADA. Open 11-5.30,
Sat. 11-4.30. *STOCK: Pictures, 19th-20th C.* TEL:
01564 792938; fax - same. SER: Valuations;
restorations; framing.

Henley Antiques Centre
92 High St. B95 5DM. (Mrs Rosie Montague and
Mrs Gill Rayson). Open 10.30-5, Sun and Bank
Holidays 11-4. SIZE: Large. *STOCK: Furniture,
porcelain and collectables, 19th to early 20th C,
£20-£2,000.* TEL: 01564 795979; mobile - 07950
324262. SER: Valuations.

David & Karol Hooper Antiques
The Elephant House, 38-40 Morton St. CV32
5SY. Open by appointment only. *STOCK: General
antiques, fairground, circus and unusual items.*
TEL: 01926 429679; mobile - 07831 241284;
07775 850219.

King's Cottage Antiques
4 Windsor St. CV32 5EB. (G. and A. Jackson).
LAPADA. Est. 1993. Open 9.30-5. SIZE: Medium.
*STOCK: Early oak and country furniture, 16th-
18th C.* TEL: 01926 422927.

The Light Gallery
36 Regent St. CV32 5EG. (Gary Jones). Est.
1988. Open 9.30-5.30, Sat. 9-6. SIZE: Medium.
*STOCK: Lighting and especially glass shades,
19th to early 20th C, £25-£2,500; reproduction
period-style lighting, shades and components, £2-
£1,000.* LOC: Town centre. PARK: Easy. TEL:
01926 422421. SER: Valuations. VAT: Stan.

Yesterdays
21 Portland St. CV32 5EY. (Shona Caldwell).
Est. 1986. Open Tues.-Sat. 10-5. SIZE: Medium.
STOCK: Furniture, George III to Edwardian,

£75-£3,500; china, prints, 1850-1910, £10-£200. Not Stocked: Pine. LOC: Parallel to The Parade. PARK: Easy. TEL: 01926 450238.

LONG MARSTON, Nr. Stratford-upon-Avon

Barn Antiques Centre
Station Rd. CV37 8RB. (Bev and Graham Simpson). Est. 1978. Open every day 10-5. SIZE: Large - 40+ dealers. *STOCK: Georgian, Victorian, Edwardian and later furniture, collectables, silver, porcelain, china, kitchenalia, fireplaces, linen, pictures, 18th C to 1950, £5-£2,000.* LOC: Take B4632 from Stratford-upon-Avon to Mickleton, brown tourist signs en route. PARK: Adjacent. TEL: 01789 721399; fax - 01789 721390; e-mail - info@barnantique.co.uk.

SHIPSTON-ON-STOUR

Fine-Lines (Fine Art)
The Old Rectory Lodge, West St. CV36 4HD. (L.W. and R.M. Guthrie). LAPADA. Est. 1975. Open seven days by appointment only. SIZE: Medium. *STOCK: British and European watercolours, pastels, drawings and selected oils, from 1850, £300-£20,000.* LOC: 2 mins. from town centre. PARK: Easy and nearby. TEL: 01608 662323 (answerphone); e-mail - lwg@guthrie.abelgratis. co.uk; websites - www.fine-linesfineart.co.uk and www.finelinesfineart.co.uk. SER: Valuations; restorations, cleaning and framing; buys at auction (paintings, watercolours and drawings). VAT: Spec.

Pine and Things
Portobello Farm, Campden Rd. CV36 4PY. (Richard Wood). Est. 1991. Open 9-5. SIZE: Large - 6 showrooms. *STOCK: Pine, 18th-19th C, £50-£2,000.* LOC: A429. PARK: Easy. TEL: 01608 663849; home - same; website - www. pinethings.co.uk. VAT: Stan/Spec.

'Time in Hand'
11 Church St. CV36 4AP. (F.R. Bennett). Open 9-1 and 2-5.30 or by appointment. SIZE: Large. *STOCK: Longcase, carriage and wall clocks, barometers.* PARK: Free - Banbury Road. TEL: 01608 662578. SER: Restorations (clocks, watches, barometers and mechanical instruments).

STRATFORD-UPON-AVON

Arbour Antiques Ltd
Poet's Arbour, Sheep St. CV37 6EF. (R.J. Wigington). Est. 1952. Open 9-5, Sat. by appoint-ment. *STOCK: Arms and armour.* LOC: From town centre towards Theatre and River, behind Lamb's Café through archway at right. TEL: 01789 293453. VAT: Spec.

Bow Cottage Antiques
At The Antique Shop, 30 Henley St. CV37 6QW. (R. Harvey-Morgan). Open 10-5.30. *STOCK: English porcelain, glass, silver, paintings, engravings, maps, books; general antiques, all 18th-20th C, £5-£150+.* TEL: 01789 205883; e-mail - bowcotantiques@aol.com.

Burman Antiques
34 College St. CV37 6BW. (J. and J. Burman Holtom). Est. 1973. Open by appointment only. *STOCK: Ruskin ware, pot-lids, fishing tackle.* TEL: 01789 295164. SER: Restorations (clocks).

Howards Jewellers
44a Wood St. CV37 6JG. (Howards of Stratford Ltd). NAG. Est. 1985. Open 9.30-5.30. *STOCK: Jewellery, silver, objets d'art, 19th C.* LOC: Town centre. PARK: Nearby. TEL: 01789 205404. SER: Valuations; restorations (as stock). VAT: Stan/Spec.

The Loquens Gallery
The Minories, Rother St. CV37 6NF. (S. and J. Loquens). Est. 1980. Open 9.30-5, Sun. by appointment. SIZE: Medium. *STOCK: English watercolours, some oil paintings, late 18th to early 20th C, to £5,000.* LOC: From island in town centre, follow Wood St. to Rother St. junction, entrance to Minories is on right. PARK: Easy. TEL: 01789 297706. SER: Valuations; restorations (cleaning watercolours, relining oils); framing. VAT: Stan/Spec.

Paul Sandby, Nursery Tea, watercolour over pencil heightened with a grey wash border, 3in. x 3¼in., £4,000 in 1997. (Sotheby's)

From an article entitled "Paul and Thomas Sandby" by Charles Hind which appeared in the October 2001 issue of **Antique Collecting**. For more details and to subscribe see page 21.

George Pragnell Ltd

5 & 6 Wood St. CV37 6JA. NAG. Open 9.15-5.30. SIZE: Large. *STOCK: Fine jewellery, silver, clocks and watches.* LOC: Town centre. PARK: Nearby. TEL: 01789 267072; fax - 01789 415131; e-mail - enquiries@pragnell.co.uk; website - www.pragnell.co.uk. SER: Valuations; repairs; remodelling. FAIRS: NEC. VAT: Stan/Spec.

Stratford Antique Centre

Ely St. CV37 6LN. (N.Sims). Open 10-5.30 every day. SIZE: 60 dealers. *STOCK: General antiques.* TEL: 01789 204180.

The Stratford Antiques and Interiors Centre Ltd

Dodwell Industrial Park, Evesham Rd. CV37 9ST. (Andrew and Suzanna Kerr). Est. 1980. Open 10-5 including Sun., evenings by appointment. SIZE: 25+ dealers. *STOCK: Georgian, Victorian, Edwardian and shipping furniture, £100-£8,000; china and smalls, 19th-20th C, £5-£300; reclaimed pine, £50-£2,000.* LOC: B439. PARK: Easy. TEL: 01789 297729; fax - 01789 297710; website - www.stratfordantiques.co.uk. SER: Valuations; restorations; buys at auction. FAIRS: Newark and Ardingly.

The Stratford Bookshop

45A Rother St. CV37 6LT. (J. and S. Hill). PBFA. Est. 1993. Open 10-6. SIZE: Medium. *STOCK: Secondhand and out-of-print books.* LOC: From island in town centre follow Wood St., left into Rother St., shop on corner of Ely St. PARK: Easy. TEL: 01789 298362; e-mail - stratfordbshop@aol.com. FAIRS: PBFA (Stratford, Monmouth).

Robert Vaughan

20 Chapel St. CV37 6EP. (C.M. Vaughan). ABA. Est. 1953. Open 9.30-5.30. SIZE: Medium. *STOCK: Antiquarian and out-of-print books, maps and prints.* LOC: Town centre. PARK: Easy. TEL: 01789 205312. SER: Valuations; buys at auction (books). VAT: Stan.

STRETTON-ON-FOSSE

Astley House - Fine Art

The Old School. GL56 9SA. (David, Nanette and Caradoc Glaisyer). LAPADA. CADA. Est. 1973. Open by appointment. SIZE: Large. *STOCK: Large decorative oil paintings, 19th-21st C.* LOC: Village centre. PARK: Easy. TEL: 01608 650601; fax - 01608 651777; e-mail - astart333@aol.com; website - www.art-uk.com. SER: Exhibitions; mailing list. VAT: Spec.

Patrick and Gillian Morley Antiques

Antique Furniture and Works of Art
Always something rare and
unusual in stock
62, WEST STREET, WARWICK, CV34 6AW

Tel: (01926) 494464 (Shop)

STRETTON-UNDER-FOSSE, Nr. Rugby

The Old Forge
29 Main St. CV23 0PF. (A. Blackburn). Est. 1991. Open Fri., Sat. and Sun. 11-4 pm. SIZE: Large. *STOCK: Hardwood furniture, £50-£5,000; pine, £50-£1,000; ceramics, £5-£300; glass, £5-£100.* LOC: Half mile from The Fosse Way, 2 miles north of Brinklow and 8 miles north east of Coventry. PARK: Easy. TEL: 01788 832191; e-mail - r.black2330@aol.com; website - www.oldforge.antiques.co.uk. SER: Buys at auction (furniture).

WARWICK

Duncan M. Allsop
68 Smith St. CV34 4HS. ABA. Est. 1965. Open 9.30-5.30. SIZE: Medium. *STOCK: Antiquarian and modern books.* PARK: Nearby. TEL: 01926 493266; fax - same; mobile - 07770 895924.

Apollo Antiques Ltd
The Saltisford, Birmingham Rd. CV34 4TD. (R.H. Mynott). LAPADA. Est. 1968. Open 9-6, Sat. 9.30-12.30. SIZE: Large. *STOCK: English furniture, 18th-19th C; Continental and gothic revival furniture, sculpture, paintings, Arts and Crafts and decorative items.* PARK: Easy. TEL: 01926 494746; fax - 01926 401477; e-mail -mynott@apollo antiques.com; website - www. apolloantiques.com. VAT: Stan/Spec

William J. Casey Antiques
9 High St. CV34. (William and Pat Casey). LAPADA. Est. 1970. Open 10-5, Sun. by appointment. SIZE: Large. *STOCK: Furniture, 18th-20th C, £750-£7,500.* LOC: Town Centre. PARK: Nearby. TEL: 01926 499199; home - 01562 777507. VAT: Spec.

Castle Antiques
24 Swan St. CV34 4BJ. (Julia Reynolds). Est. 1979. Open 10-5, Sun. by appointment. SIZE: Medium. *STOCK: China including Shelley, and linen, 19th-20th C, £5-£500; furniture, 19th to early 20th C, £100-£3,000.* LOC: Town centre. PARK: Easy - at rear. TEL: 01926 401511; fax - 01926 492469. SER: Restorations (ceramics). FAIRS: Heritage Museum, Gaydon. VAT: Spec.

John Goodwin and Sons
20-22 High St.,CV34 4AP. Open 9.30-5.30. SIZE: Shop (+ warehouse on request - 20 mins. away) . *STOCK: Furniture, clocks, ceramics, oil paintings, collectables.* TEL: 01926 853332. SER: Restorations (furniture).

Russell Lane Antiques
2-4 High St. CV34 4AP. (R.G.H. Lane). Open 10-5. *STOCK: Fine jewellery and silver.* TEL: 01926 494494.

Patrick and Gillian Morley Antiques
62 West St. CV34 6AW. LAPADA. Est. 1968. SIZE: Large. *STOCK: Furniture, 17th to late 19th C; unusual and decorative items, sculpture, carvings; all £250-£50,000.* PARK: Easy. TEL: 01926 494464; e-mail - morleyantiques@ tinyworld.co.uk. SER: Valuations; buys at auction. VAT: Spec.

Patrick and Gillian Morley Antiques Warehouse
Unit 7 Cape Industrial Estate, Cattell Rd. LAPADA. Est. 1968. Open 9-5.30, Sat. and Sun. by appointment. SIZE: Large. *STOCK: 17th to late 19th C fine furniture, unusual and decorative items, sculpture, carvings, £250-£50,000.* LOC: Close to J15, off M40. PARK: Opposite. TEL: 01926 498849; e-mail - morleyantiques@ tinyworld.co.uk. VAT: Spec.

Christopher Peters Antiques

28 West St. CV34 6AN. (Chris and Jill Peters). Est. 1987. Open 10-5, other times by appointment. SIZE: Shop + workshop and barns. *STOCK: Country antiques, original painted furniture, decorative items; 18th C French provincial furniture.* TEL: 01926 494106; fax - 02476 303300; website - www.christopher petersantiques.co.uk. SER: Design and installation of original unfitted kitchens; French polishing, restorations and repairs. VAT: Stan/Spec.

Buckle; silver and pearl. 1900-4. £1,300-£1,800. (Tadema Gallery)

From an article entitled "Collecting Archibald Knox" by Stephen A. Martin which appeared in the December 2001/January 2002 issue of **Antique Collecting**. For more details and to subscribe see page 21.

James Reeve

at Quinneys of Warwick, 9 Church St. CV34 4AB. Est. 1865. Open 9.30-5.30. CL: Sat. pm. *STOCK: Furniture, mahogany, oak, and rosewood, 17th-18th C, £80-£30,000; furniture, 19th C, £50-£10,000; glass, copper, brass, pewter, china.* TEL: 01926 498113. VAT: Stan/Spec.

Don Spencer Antiques

36a Market Place. CV34 4SH. Est. 1963. Open daily. SIZE: Large. *STOCK: Desks, 1850-1920, £500-£5,000; dining furniture and bookcases, 1800-1920, £500-£3,000.* PARK: Easy. TEL: 01926 499857/407989; home - 01564 775470; website - www.antique-desks.co.uk. VAT: Stan/ Spec.

Summersons

172 Emscote Rd. CV34 5QN. (Peter Lightfoot). BHI. Est. 1969. Open 10-5, Sat. 10-1. SIZE: Small. *STOCK: Clocks and barometers.* PARK: Free. TEL: 01926 400630; fax - same; mobile - 07770 300695; e-mail - clocks@summersons.com; website - www.summersons.com. SER: Restorations; repairs; materials and parts. VAT: Spec.

Tango Art Deco & Antiques

46 Brook St. CV34 4BL. (Jenny and Martin Wills). Open Thurs., Fri. and Sat. 10-5. SIZE: Medium. *STOCK: Art Deco and general including Clarice Cliff, Susie Cooper, Myott, Burleigh, Carlton, Crown Devon, small furniture, mirrors, light shades; £5-£1,000.* LOC: Town centre. PARK: Free nearby. TEL: 01926 496999; home/fax - 0121 704 4969; e-mail - info@tango-artdeco.co.uk; website - www. tango-artdeco.co.uk. VAT: Spec.

Vintage Antiques Centre

36 Market Place. CV34 4SH. (Peter Sellors). Est. 1977. Open 10-5.30, Sun. 11.30-4.30. SIZE: 15 dealers + cabinets. *STOCK: Ceramics, glass, collectables and small furniture, 19th-20th C.* PARK: Easy. TEL: 01926 491527. FAIRS: NEC; National Glass.

The Warwick Antique Centre

20-22 High St. CV34 4AP. Est. 1973. Open 10-5. SIZE: 25 dealers. *STOCK: Porcelain, silver and plate, jewellery, coins, militaria, books, furniture, stamps, metalware, toys, collectables, postcards, glass.* TEL: 01926 491382/495704.

West Rock Antiques

19 West Rock, Birmingham Rd., The Saltisford. CV34 4SG. (Christina Goodson). Est. 1974. Open 9.30-5.30, Sat. 10-4. SIZE: Medium. *STOCK: Furniture, £200-£5,000, decorative items, £5-£500; both 19th C; general antiques, to 1940, £50-£100.* PARK: At rear. TEL: 01926 411175; fax - 01926 411176. SER: Valuations.

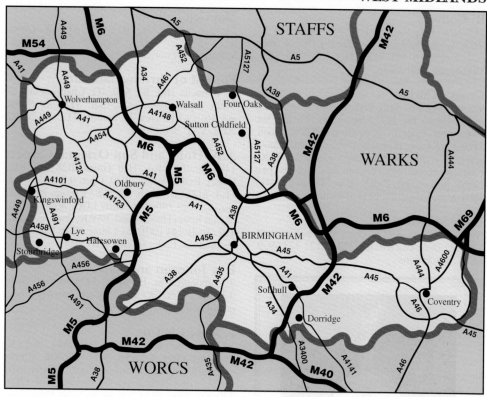

Dealers and Shops in the West Midlands

Birmingham	18	Halesowen	2	Solihull	2
Coventry	2	Kingswinford	1	Stourbridge	3
Dorridge	1	Lye	2	Sutton Coldfield	3
Four Oaks	1	Oldbury	1	Walsall	3
				Wolverhampton	9

BIRMINGHAM

Peter Asbury Antiques
Greenfield House Farm, 6 Hales Lane, Smethwick, Warley. B67 6RS. (Mrs Susan Asbury). Est. 1986. Open 9.30-5. *STOCK: General antiques.* PARK: Limited. TEL: 0121 558 0579. SER: Repairs (doll, teddy bear).

Paul Baxter
B47 6LS. Open by appointment only. *STOCK: Oriental ceramics and general antiques.* TEL: 01564 824920.

The Birmingham Antique Centre
1403-1407 Pershore Rd., Stirchley. B30 2JR. Est. 1960. Open 9-5.30, Sun. 10-5. *STOCK: General antiques, collectables, shipping furniture, trade display cabinets.* TEL: 0121 459 4587/689 6565.

Carleton Gallery
91 Vivian Rd., Harborne. B17 0DR. (D. Dunnett). Est. 1986. Open 9-5.30, Wed. 9-1. *STOCK: Maps and prints.* TEL: 0121 427 2487; e-mail - artworld@ukonline.co.uk.

Chesterfield Antiques
181 Gravelly Lane. B23 5SG. (Mara Cirjanic). Est. 1977. Open 9.30-5.30. *STOCK: General antiques and fine art.* TEL: 0121 373 3876.

Peter Clark Antiques
36 St. Mary's Row, Moseley. B13 8JG. LAPADA. Open 9-5.30. SIZE: Medium. *STOCK: Furniture, mid-17th C to early 20th C, £175-£2,500.* LOC: Centre of Moseley. PARK: At rear. TEL: 0121 449 8245. SER: Valuations; restorations (furniture). VAT: Stan/Spec.

R. Collyer
185 New Rd., Rubery. B45 9JP. Open 9-5.30. *STOCK: Secondhand jewellery.* LOC: 1 mile from junction 4, M5. TEL: 0121 453 2332. SER: Valuations; restorations.

Cross's Curios
928 Pershore Rd., Selly Park. B29 7PY. (John and Valerie Cross). Est. 1972. Open Thurs., Fri. and Sat. 10-6, other times by appointment. SIZE: Small. *STOCK: Old toys, juvenalia, dolls, tinplate, teddies, furniture, china, jewellery and collectables.* LOC: From city centre, take Pershore Rd., shop just past Pebble Mill on left. PARK: Easy. TEL: 0121 415 4866. SER: Valuations; buys at auction.

Dolly Mixtures
B68 0AU. Est. 1979. Open by appointment. *STOCK: Dolls and teddies.* TEL: 0121 422 6959. SER: Restorations.

The extraordinary ostrich egg cup and cover, one of only eight other examples known to exist, which topped the sale of antiques from Scawby Hall with a London trade bid of £60,000.

From an Auction Report by Christopher Wight of the Contents of Scawby Hall held at Sotheby's Olympia on 11th April 2002 which appeared in the June 2002 issue of **Antique Collecting.** For more details and to subscribe see page 21.

Maurice Fellows
21 Vyse St., Hockley. B18 6LE. *STOCK: Objets d'art, jewellery.* TEL: 0121 554 0211. SER: Valuations; restorations.

Format of Birmingham Ltd
18 Bennetts Hill. B2 5QJ. (G. Charman and D. Vice). Open 9.30-5. CL: Sat. *STOCK: Coins, medals.* PARK: New St. station. TEL: 0121 643 2058. VAT: Stan/Spec.

A.W. Hone and Son Oriental Carpets
1486 Stratford Rd., Hall Green. B28 9ET. (Ian Hone). BORDA. Est. 1949. Open 9.30-5.30, Sun. 11-4. SIZE: Medium. *STOCK: Persian rugs and carpets, late 19th C to date.* LOC: A34 south of city on Robin Hood Island. PARK: Own forecourt. TEL: 0121 744 1001; fax - same. SER: Valuations; restorations; finder service.VAT: Stan.

Rex Johnson and Sons
8 Corporation St. B2 4RN. (D. Johnson). Open 9.15-5.15. *STOCK: Gold, silver, jewellery, porcelain and glass.* TEL: 0121 643 9674.

F. Meeks & Co
197 Warstone Lane, Hockley. B18. (M.L. and S.R. Durham). Open 9-5, Sat. 9-12. *STOCK: Clocks especially longcase, mantel and wall; vintage wrist watches and antique pocket watches; all £100-£10,000.* TEL: 0121 236 9058. SER: Valuations; restorations (clocks); clock and watch parts supplied. VAT: Stan/Spec.

Piccadilly Jewellers
105 New St. B2 4HD. (R. and R. Johnson). Open 10-5. *STOCK: Jewellery, silver and objects.* TEL: 0121 643 5791.

David Temperley Fine and Antiquarian Books
19 Rotton Park Rd., Edgbaston. B16 9JH. (D. and R.A. Temperley). Resident. Est. 1967. Open 9.30-5.30 by prior appointment. SIZE: Small. *STOCK: Fine antiquarian and rare books,16th-20th C especially fine bindings, illustrated and private press; fine colour plate books - natural history, costume, travel, British topography and atlases; early and rare English and European playing cards.* LOC: 150 yards off Hagley Rd. (A456) and under 2 miles from city centre. 4 miles junction 3, M5. PARK: Easy. TEL: 0121 454 0135; fax - 0121 454 1124. SER: Valuations; restorations (book binding and paper); buys at auction (antiquarian books).

Warley Antique Centre
146 Pottery Rd., Warley Woods. B68 9HD. (Angela Hamilton). Open six days. SIZE: 70 cabinets and 4 furniture showrooms. *STOCK: Antiques, furnishings and collectables including Ruskin, Worcester, Doulton, clocks, silver, mainly*

19th-20th C. LOC: Off the A456 or A4123, junctions 2/3, M5. PARK: Easy. TEL: 0121 434 3813; mobile - 07702 976759.

The Windmill Gallery
c/o Snell & Prideaux Ltd., 6 Ernest St., Holloway Head. B1 1NS. (M. and C. Ashton). Est. 1985. Open 9-5.30, Sat. and Sun. by appointment. SIZE: Medium. *STOCK: Watercolours and drawings, 18th-20th C, £100-£3,000+.* LOC: City centre. PARK: Easy. TEL: 0121 622 3986; fax - 0121 666 6630. SER: Valuations; restorations; mounting, framing. VAT: Spec.

COVENTRY

Antiques Adventure
Rugby Rd., Binley Woods. CV3 2AW. (N. and J. Green). Est. 1969. Open 9.30-5.30, (winter 10-4.30), Sat. and Sun. 10-5. SIZE: Large. *STOCK: Georgian, Victorian, Edwardian, contemporary, 1950's and 1960's furniture and effects.* LOC: Just off A46 eastern bypass, entrance off A428 Rugby road. PARK: Easy. TEL: 02476 453878; fax - 02476 445847; e-mail - sales@antiques adventure.com; website - www.antiques adventure. com. SER: Deliveries (UK); shipping advice. VAT: Global/Spec/Stan.

Luckmans Antiques
40 Far Gosford St. CV1 5DW. (K. Harris). Est. 1977. Open 12.30-6. CL: Tues. SIZE: Small. *STOCK: Bric-a-brac, books, medals, post and cigarette cards.* PARK: Easy. TEL: 02476 223842.

DORRIDGE, Nr. Solihull

Dorridge Antiques & Collectables
7 Forest Court. (C. Swift). Est. 1995. Open 11-6. SIZE: 2 floors. *STOCK: Furniture, ceramics, silver, militaria, paintings and prints, general antiques and collectables.* LOC: Between Birmingham and Stratford, 10 minutes from NEC. PARK: Free. TEL: 01564 779336; home - 01564 779768.

FOUR OAKS, Nr. Sutton Coldfield

M. Allen Watch and Clockmaker
76A Walsall Rd. B74 4QY. (M.A. Allen). Est. 1969. Open 9-5.30, Sun. by appointment. SIZE: Small. *STOCK: Vintage wristwatches - Omega, Longines, Girard, Perregaux and Jaeger le Coultre; clocks - Vienna regulators, 1820-1880, mantel and wall clocks.* LOC: By Sutton Park, close to television mast. PARK: Easy. TEL: 0121 308 6117; home - 0121 308 8134. SER: Valuations; restorations (clocks and watches). VAT: Stan/Spec.

HALESOWEN

S.R. Furnishing and Antiques
Unit 1, Eagle Trading Estate, Stourbridge Rd. B63 3UA. (S.Willder). Est. 1975. *STOCK: General antiques and shipping furniture.* TEL: Mobile - 07860 820221.

Tudor House Antiques
68 Long Lane. B62 9LS. (D. Taylor). Open 9.30-5.30. *STOCK: Doors, fireplaces, pine including kitchens and furniture.* TEL: 0121 561 5563.

KINGSWINFORD

Unicorn Antiques & Reproductions
29-30 High St., Wall Heath. DY6 0JA. (J.C. Vaughan). Est. 1998. Open Tues.,Wed. and Fri. 10.15-4.15, Sat.10.15-5. SIZE: Medium. *STOCK: 19th C and reproduction furniture, china and collectables, £5-£1,000.* LOC: A449. PARK: Easy. TEL: 01384 288122. SER: Restorations (furniture).

LYE, Nr. Stourbridge

Lye Antique Furnishings
206 High St. DY9 8JY. (P. Smith). Est. 1979. Open 9-5. SIZE: Medium. *STOCK: Furniture, china, glass, metalware, jewellery and collectors' items.* PARK: Easy. TEL: 01384 897513; mobile - 07976 765142. SER: Valuations.

Retro Antiques
Antique Warehouse, The Yard, Star St. DY9 8TU. (M. McHugo). Est. 1980. Open 9.30-5. CL: Sat. SIZE: Large. *STOCK: Furniture - Victorian, Edwardian, garden and shipping, £5-£1,000; cast iron, metalwork, architectural items.* LOC: Off Stourbridge to Birmingham Rd. PARK: Easy. TEL: 01384 894042/442065; mobile - 07860 307446. FAIRS: Ardingly and Newark. VAT: Stan.

OLDBURY

The Glory Hole
431 Moat Rd. B68 8EJ. (Colin Dickens). Est. 1985. Open 9.30-5.30, Tues. 12-5.30, Sat.10-5.30. SIZE: Small. *STOCK: Furniture, 19th-20th C, £50-£100; china, 20th C, £5-£100.* PARK: Easy. TEL: 0121 544 1888; home - 0121 561 3573. SER: Valuations. FAIRS: Malvern Showground, Peterborough Festival, Norwich Sports Centre.

SOLIHULL

Renaissance
18 Marshall Lake Rd., Shirley. B90 4PL. (S.K. Macrow). MGMC. Est. 1981. Open 9-5. SIZE:

Small. *STOCK: General antiques.* LOC: Near Stratford Rd. TEL: 0121 745 5140. SER: Restorations (repairs, re-upholstery and polishing).

Tilleys Antiques
B91 2ES. (S.A. Alpren). GADAR. Open by appointment only. *STOCK: British glass, Oriental pottery, porcelain, shipping goods; silver, 19th C; Worcester.* TEL: 0121 704 1813. SER: Valuations; restorations (jewellery, silver); clock and watch repairs.

STOURBRIDGE

Oldswinford Gallery
106 Hagley Rd., Oldswinford. DY8 1QU. (A.R. Harris). Open 9.30-5. CL: Mon. and Sat. p.m. *STOCK: 18th-20th C oil paintings, watercolours, antiquarian prints and maps.* TEL: 01384 395577. SER: Restorations; framing.

Regency Antique Trading Centre
116 Stourbridge Rd. DY9 7BU. (D. Bevan). Open 9.30-5. SIZE: 2 floors. *STOCK: General antiques and collectables, fireplaces and pine.* PARK: Free. TEL: 01384 868778; fax - 01384 825466; e-mail - regencytrading@aol.com; website - www.regency-antiques.co.uk. SER: Stripping.

Retro
48 Worcester St. DY8 1AS. (M. McHugo). Open Thurs., Fri. and Sat. 9.30-5. *STOCK: Furniture.* TEL: 01384 442065.

SUTTON COLDFIELD

Thomas Coulborn and Sons   BADA
Vesey Manor, 64 Birmingham Rd. B72 1QP. (P. Coulborn). Est. 1939. Open 9.15-5.30 (1hr. lunch). SIZE: Large. *STOCK: General antiques, 1600-1830; fine English and Continental furniture, 17th-18th C; paintings and clocks.* LOC: 3 miles from Spaghetti Junction. From Birmingham A5127 through Erdington, premises on main road opposite cinema. PARK: Easy. TEL: 0121 354 3974; fax - 0121 354 4614; e-mail - art@coulborn.com; website - www.coulborn.com. SER: Valuations; restorations (furniture and paintings); buys on commission. VAT: Spec.

Driffold Gallery
78 Birmingham Rd. B72 1QR. (David Gilbert). Est. 1974. Open 10.30-6. *STOCK: Oil paintings and watercolours, 19th C to contemporary.* LOC: Town centre approach. PARK: Own. TEL: 0121 355 5433. SER: Valuations; restorations.

H. and R.L. Parry Ltd
23 Maney Corner. B72 1QL. Est. 1925. Open 9.30-5. CL: Wed. SIZE: Medium. *STOCK: Porcelain, silver and jewellery, all periods; metalware, paintings.* LOC: A38 from Birmingham road into Sutton. Cinema on right, on corner of service road in which premises are situated. TEL: 0121 354 1178. SER: Valuations. VAT: Stan/Spec.

WALSALL

The Doghouse (Antiques)
309 Bloxwich Rd. WS2 7BD. (John and Kate Rutter). Est. 1971. Open 9-5.30, Sun. (Oct.-March) 2-5.30. SIZE: Large. *STOCK: General antiques, fireplaces, architectural items.* LOC: B4210. PARK: At rear. TEL: 01922 630829; fax - 01922 631236; website - www.doghouseantiques.co.uk. VAT: Stan/Spec.

Hardwick Antiques
317B Chester Rd., Aldridge. WS9 0PH. (P. Chatfield). Est. 1992. Open 11-5. CL: Wed. am. *STOCK: Jewellery, silver, porcelain, furniture.* LOC: Opposite Ruby Rest. PARK: Easy. TEL: 0121 353 1489; mobile - 07740 870954. SER: Valuations.

L.P. Antiques (Mids) Ltd
The Old Brewery, Short Acre St. WS2 8HW. (Pierre Farouz). Est. 1982. Open daily, Sun. by appointment. SIZE: Warehouse. *STOCK: French, Spanish and other Continental decorative furniture - armoires, buffets, mirrors and tables; reproduction chairs, wrought iron.* LOC: Junction 10, M6, A454 towards town centre, left on A34 towards Cannock. PARK: Own. TEL: 01922 746764; fax - 01922 611316; e-mail - pierre.farouz@virgin.net; website - www.lpantiques.co.uk. FAIRS: Newark. VAT: Stan.

WOLVERHAMPTON

Afantiques
WV11 1PE. Open by appointment only. *STOCK: Clocks, wrist and pocket watches.* TEL: 01902 731167.

Antiquities
75-76 Dudley Rd. Est. 1968. Open 10-6. *STOCK: General antiques.* TEL: 01902 459800.

Doveridge House Antiques   BADA
P O Box 1856. WV3 9XH. (Cdr. Harry and Mrs. Jean Bain). LAPADA. CINOA. Est. 1967. Open by appointment. *STOCK: 17th-19th C English and Continental furniture, fine art, clocks, decorative artifacts.* TEL: 01902 312211.

SER: Valuations; restorations (furniture and oils); interior design; export. FAIRS: Advisers to NEC Antiques for Everyone.

Martin-Quick Antiques
Unit E2, Long Lane, Cosford. TF11 8PJ. (C.R. Quick). LAPADA. Est. 1965. Open by appointment or by chance. SIZE: Large. *STOCK: 18th-19th C English and French and upholstered furniture and shipping goods.* LOC: 1 mile from junction 3, M54. PARK: Easy. TEL: 01902 754703; home - 01902 752908; mobile - 07774 124859; e-mail - cqantiques @aol.com. SER: Packing and shipping. FAIRS: Newark. VAT: Stan/Spec.

Newhampton Road Antiques
184/184A Newhampton Rd. East, Whitmoreans. WV1 4PQ. (Robert and Linda Hill). Est. 1982. Open 10-3.30. SIZE: Small. *STOCK: General antiques and collectables, Victorian and Edwardian, £50-£1,500.* LOC: From A449 left at Wolverhampton football ground. PARK: Easy. TEL: 01902 712583. SER: Valuations. FAIRS: Newark, Swinderby.

No 9 Antiques
9 Upper Green, Tettenhall. WV6 8QQ. Open 10-5.30. CL: Mon. and Tues. SIZE: Medium. *STOCK: Furniture, 18th-19th C, £200-£1,000; ceramics, silver and prints, 19th C, £25-£500; works of art, £25-£100.* LOC: Corner of the Green. PARK: Easy. TEL: 01902 755333.

The Red Shop
7 Hollybush Lane, Penn. (B. Savage). Open 9.30-5.30. *STOCK: Furniture including pine.* TEL: 01902 342915.

Martin Taylor Antiques
140b and 323 Tettenhall Rd. WV6 0BQ. LAPADA. Est. 1976. Open 8.30-5.30, Sat. 9.30-4. SIZE: Large + showroom. *STOCK: Furniture, mainly 1800-1930, for the UK, USA, Japanese, and Italian market, £50-£10,000.* LOC: One mile from town centre on A41. PARK: Easy. TEL: 01902 751166; showroom - 01902 751122; fax - 01902 746502; mobile - 07836 636524; home - 01785 284539; e-mail - enquiries@mtaylor-antiques.co.uk; website - www.mtaylor-antiques.co.uk. SER: Restorations; French polishing. VAT: Stan/Spec.

Wolverhampton Antiques and Collectors Market
Basement of Retail Market, Salop St. WV3 0SF. (D. Lymer-Jones). Open Tues., Wed. and Fri. 9-4, Sat. 9-5. SIZE: 20 units. *STOCK: China, glass, jewellery, militaria, books and comics, linen, football memorabilia, 19th C, £5-£1,000.* LOC: Wolverhampton ring road, exit Chapel Ash island, market signposted. PARK: Easy - Peel St. and Pitt St. TEL: 01902 851103.

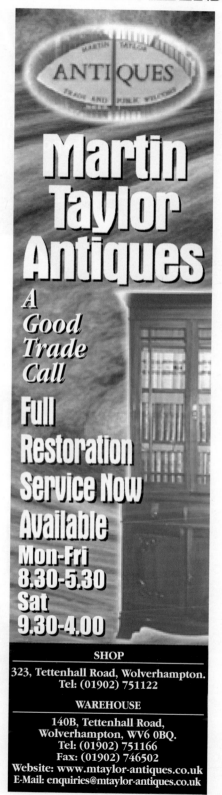

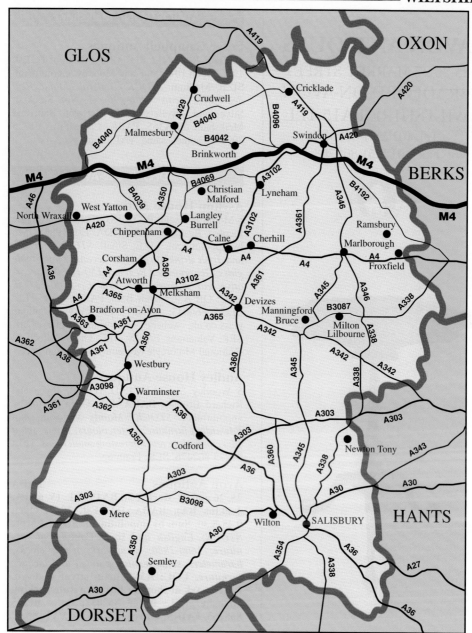

AVON ANTIQUES
25-26-27 MARKET STREET
BRADFORD-ON-AVON
WILTSHIRE BA15 1LL
Tel. (01225) 862052
Fax: (01225) 868763

*Eight showrooms of 17th, 18th
and early 19th century furniture,
clocks, barometers, metalwork,
some textiles, painted and
lacquered furniture*

**Member of the British Antique
Dealers Association**

ATWORTH, Nr. Melksham

Peter Campbell Antiques
59 Bath Rd. SN12 8JY. (P. R. Campbell). Est. 1976. Open 10-5, Sun. and Mon. by appointment. SIZE: Medium. *STOCK: General antiques and decorative items, 18th-19th C.* Not Stocked: Silver and jewellery. LOC: Between Bath and Melksham on A365. PARK: Easy. TEL: 01225 709742; home - same. VAT: Stan/Spec.

BRADFORD-ON-AVON

Asylum House Antiques
5 Mount Pleasant. BA15 1SJ. (Peter and Maggie Jacobs). Resident. BABAADA. Est. 1986. Open by appointment. SIZE: Small. *STOCK: English and Irish drinking glasses, decanters and table glass, Georgian and Regency, £50-£2,000; decorative gilt mirrors, 18th-19th C, £500-£3,000.* LOC: Off A363 from Bath. PARK: Easy. TEL: 01225 866043; e-mail - info@asylum-antique glass.co.uk; website - www.antiqueglasses.biz. SER: Valuations. FAIRS: NEC; Glass Collectors' (National Motorcyle Museum). VAT: Stan/Spec.

Audley House Antiques
5 Woolley St. BA15 1AD. (David, Joyce and Richard Brown). BABAADA. Open 9-6 or by appointment. *STOCK: Mainly Victorian and Edwardian furniture; watercolours, prints, small silver, porcelain and interesting small items.* TEL: 01225 862476. SER: Framing.

Avon Antiques   BADA
25, 26 and 27 Market St. BA15 1LL. (V. and A. Jenkins BA). BABAADA. Est. 1963. Open 9.45-5.30, Sun. by appointment. SIZE: Large. *STOCK: English and some Continental furniture, 1600-1880; metalwork, treen, clocks, barometers, some textiles, painted and lacquer furniture.* LOC: A363, main street of town. PARK: Ask at shop for key to private parking opposite. TEL: 01225 862052; fax - 01225 868763. FAIRS: Grosvenor House. VAT: Spec.

Mac Humble Antiques   BADA
7-9 Woolley St. BA15 1AD. (W. Mc. A. and B.J. Humble). BABAADA. Est. 1979. Open 9.30-5.30, Sat. 9.30-1. SIZE: Medium. *STOCK: 17th-19th C oak, mahogany, fruitwoods, metalware, treen, samplers, silkwork pictures, decorative objects.* PARK: Nearby. TEL: 01225 866329; fax - same; e-mail - mac.humble@virgin.net; website - www.machumbleantiques.co.uk. SER: Valuations; restorations. FAIRS: BADA (March); Olympia (Nov). VAT: Stan/Spec.

BRADFORD ON AVON

Probably the best town for period antique furniture outside London

AVON ANTIQUES

Established 1963

25-26-27 MARKET STREET, BRADFORD ON AVON, WILTSHIRE BA15 1LL
TELEPHONE: (01225) 862052   ANDREW & VIBEKE JENKINS

MAC HUMBLE ANTIQUES

EST. 1979

18th & 19th Century Furniture, Metalware, Treen and Needlework.
Decorative items. Valuations & Restorations.

7-9 Woolley Street, Bradford-on-Avon, Wiltshire BA15 1AD

Telephone: (01225) 866329 Facsimile: (01225) 866329
E-mail: mac.humble@virgin.net

MOXHAMS ANTIQUES

Roger, Jill and Nicholas Bichard   Est. 1967

*One of the largest stocks of good period furniture and
accessories outside London: collectors and dealers welcome*

17, 23 & 24 Silver Street, Bradford on Avon, Wiltshire BA15 1JZ
Tel: (01225) 862789 Fax: (01225) 867844 Home: (01380) 828677
E-mail: jill@moxhams-antiques.demon.co.uk

Trevor Waddington OBE
ANTIQUE CLOCKS

★ Offering quality antique clocks,
restored and fully guaranteed

★ Showroom open
by appointment

★ Stock details on
request/website

5 TROWBRIDGE RD., BRADFORD ON AVON
Tel: 01225 862351
www.antiques-uk.co.uk/waddington

MEMBER OF THE
BRITISH HOROLOGICAL
INSTITUTE

Asylum House Antiques

Established 1985

Georgian drinking glasses & decanters, decorative gilt mirrors

By appointment   01225 866043
www.antiqueglasses.biz

*An excellent place to stop for lunch with good pubs, cafes and
restaurants in the centre of this beautiful Wiltshire town.*

Moxhams Antiques

17, 23 and 24 Silver St. BA15 1JZ. (R., J. and N. Bichard). LAPADA. BABAADA. Est. 1967. Open 9-5.30 or by appointment. SIZE: Large. *STOCK: English and Continental furniture, clocks, 1650-1850; European and Oriental pottery and porcelain, 1700-1850; decorative items, 1600-1900, all £50-£50,000.* PARK: Own, at rear. TEL: 01225 862789; fax - 01225 867844; home - 01380 828677/01225 755026; e-mail - jill@moxhams-antiques.demon.co.uk. VAT: Spec.

Town and Country Antiques   BADA

34 Market St. BA15 1LL. (Rosemary Drewett and Michael Hughes). Open 10-5, Sat. 10-1, other times by appointment. SIZE: Large. *STOCK: Fine period furniture, metalware, caddies, boxes and period decorative items.* PARK: Nearby. TEL: 01225 867877; fax - same. VAT: Spec.

Trevor Waddington Antique Clocks

5 Trowbridge Rd. BA15 1EE. MBHI. BABAADA. Est. 1996. Strictly by appointment. SIZE: Small. *STOCK: 18th-19th C clocks - longcase, £3,000-£13,000; wall, £750-£2,000; carriage, bracket and mantel, £500-£5,000.* LOC: Quarter mile south of town bridge on A363. PARK: Easy. TEL: 01225 862351; home/fax - same; website - www.antiques-uk.co.uk/waddington. SER: Valuations; restorations (BADA/West Dean Dip. conservator).

BRINKWORTH, Nr. Malmesbury

North Wilts Exporters

Farm Hill House. SN15 5AJ. (M. Thornbury). Est. 1972. Open Mon.-Sat. or by appointment. *STOCK: Imported Continental pine, 18th-19th C; shipping goods.* LOC: Off M4, junction 16 Malmesbury road. TEL: 01666 510876; mobile - 07836 260730; e-mail - mike@northwilts.demon.co.uk; website - www.northwiltsantiqueexporters.com. SER: Valuations; shipping; import and export. VAT: Stan/Global.

CALNE

Calne Antiques

London Rd. SN11 0AB. (M. Blackford). GMC. Est. 1981. Open 10-5 seven days. *STOCK: Antique pine and country furniture, Victorian to 1930's; mahogany, oak and walnut.* LOC: A4, next to White Hart Hotel. PARK: Own. TEL: 01249 816311; fax - same. SER: Furniture made to order; free-standing kitchens.

Clive Farahar and Sophie Dupré - Rare Books, Autographs and Manuscripts

Horsebrook House, 15 The Green. SN11 8DQ. Open by appointment. SIZE: Medium. *STOCK: Rare books on voyages and travels, autograph letters and manuscripts, 15th-20th C, £5-£5,000.* LOC: Off A4 in town centre. PARK: Easy. TEL: 01249 821121; fax - 01249 821202; e-mail - post@farahardupre.co.uk or farahar_dupre@compuserve.com; website - www.farahardupre.co.uk. SER: Valuations; buys at auction (as stock). FAIRS: ABA; Universal Autograph Collectors' Club. VAT: Stan.

Hilmarton Manor Press

Hilmarton Manor. SN11 8SB. (H. Baile de Laperriere). Est. 1967. Open 9-6. SIZE: Medium. *STOCK: New and out-of-print, some antiquarian, art related books including fine, applied, dictionaries and reference.* LOC: 3 miles from Calne on A3102 towards Swindon. PARK: Easy. TEL: 01249 760208; fax - 01249 760379. SER: Buys at auction.

CHERHILL, Nr. Calne

P.A. Oxley Antique Clocks and Barometers

The Old Rectory, Main Rd. SN11 8UX. LAPADA. BABAADA. Est. 1971. Open 9.30-5, other times by appointment. CL: Wed. SIZE: Large. *STOCK: Longcase, bracket, carriage clocks and barometers, 17th-19th C, £500-£30,000.* LOC: A4, not in village. PARK: Easy. TEL: 01249 816227; fax - 01249 821285; e-mail - info@paoxley.com; website - www.british-antiqueclocks.com. VAT: Spec.

CHIPPENHAM

Cross Hayes Antiques

Unit 6 Westbrook Farm, Draycot Cerne. SN15 5LH. (D. Brooks). LAPADA. Est. 1975. Open 9-5 or by appointment. SIZE: Warehouse. *STOCK: Furniture, 1850-1930, Victorian, Edwardian and shipping oak.* TEL: 01249 720033; fax - same; home - 01666 822062; website - www.crosshayes.co.uk; e-mail - david@crosshayes.co.uk. SER: Packing and shipping. VAT: Stan/Spec.

CHRISTIAN MALFORD, Nr. Chippenham

Harley Antiques

The Comedy. SN15 4BS. (G.J. Harley). Est. 1959. Open 9-6 including Sun. or later by appointment. SIZE: Large. *STOCK: Furniture, 18th-19th C, £250-£6,000; decorative objects, £30-£8,000.*

P.A.Oxley

Antique Clocks & Barometers
Established 1971

**The Old Rectory · Cherhill · Near Calne
Wiltshire SN11 8UX**
Telephone (01249) 816227 Fax (01249) 821285
Visit our Web site - Full stock & prices
www.british-antiqueclocks.com
E-mail: info@paoxley.com

Established in 1971, P.A. Oxley is one of the
largest quality antique clock and barometer
dealers in the U.K. Current stock includes over
30 quality restored **longcase clocks** ranging in
price from £3,500 to £30,000. In addition we
have a fine selection of **bracket clocks,
carriage clocks** and **barometers**.

We do not exhibit at antique fairs, and
therefore our extensive stock can only be
viewed at our large showrooms on the main A4
London to Bath road at Cherhill or on our
website address shown above.

**Full shipping facilities are available to any
country in the world.** U.K. customers are
provided with a free delivery and setting up
service combined with a twelve month guarantee.

**If your desire is for a genuine antique clock
or barometer** then please visit us at Cherhill
where you can examine our large stock and
discuss your exact requirement. If time is short
and you cannot visit us we will send you a
selection of colour photographs from which
you can buy with confidence.

**Hours of opening are 9.30-5.00 every day
except Wednesday.** Sunday and evening
appointments can easily be arranged. We look
forward to welcoming you to our establishment.

The Association of Art and Antique Dealers

LOC: B4069, 4 miles off M4, junction 17. PARK: Own. TEL: 01249 720112; home - same; fax - 01249 720553. SER: Colour brochure available (export only). VAT: Stan. *Trade Only.*

CODFORD, Nr. Warminster

Tina's Antiques
75 High St. BA12 0ND. (T.A. Alder). Open 9-6, Sat. 9-1. *STOCK: General antiques.* TEL: 01985 850828.

CORSHAM

Matthew Eden
Pickwick End. SN13 0JB. Resident. Est. 1951. SIZE: Large. *STOCK: Country house furniture and garden items, 17th-19th C.* LOC: A4 between Chippenham and Bath. TEL: 01249 713335; fax - 01249 713644. SER: Shipping. FAIRS: Chelsea Flower Show. VAT: Spec.

CRICKLADE, Nr. Swindon

Edred A.F. Gwilliam
Candletree House, Bath Rd. SN6 6AX. Est. 1976. Open by appointment. SIZE: Medium. *STOCK: Arms and armour, swords, pistols, long guns, £50-£20,000+.* PARK: Easy. TEL: 01793 750241; fax - 01793 750359. SER: Valuations; buys at auction. FAIRS: Major arms. VAT: Stan/Spec.

CRUDWELL

Philip A. Ruttleigh Antiques incorporating Crudwell Furniture
Odd Penny Farm. SN16 9SJ. Est. 1990. Open 9-5 and by appointment. CL: Sat. SIZE: Small. *STOCK: Furniture including pine in the paint, and decorative items, £10-£2,000.* LOC: Next to RAF Kemble on A429, 5 minutes from Cirencester, 15 mins from junction 17, M4. TEL: 01285 770970; website - www.crudwellfurniture. co.uk. SER: Furniture restoration, including stripping; bead blasting for architectural antiques.

DEVIZES

Cross Keys Jewellers
The Ginnel, Market Pl. SN10 1HN. (D. and D. Pullen). Est. 1967. Open 9-5. *STOCK: Jewellery, silver.* LOC: Alley adjacent Nationwide Building Society. PARK: Easy. TEL: 01380 726293. SER: Valuations; repairs; restringing (pearls). VAT: Stan.

St Mary's Chapel Antiques
Northgate St. SN10 1JL. (Richard Sankey). BABAADA. Est. 1971. Open 10-6, Wed. by appointment. SIZE: Large. *STOCK: Original painted and Continental furniture, decorative accessories, garden items.* LOC: Just off Market Square. PARK: Easy. TEL: 01380 721399; e-mail - richard@rsankey.freeserve.co.uk; website - www.st-marys-chapel-Antiques.org.uk. SER: Restorations. FAIRS: BABAADA.

FROXFIELD

Blanchard
Bath Rd. LAPADA. Est. 1940. Open 9.30-6. SIZE: Large. *STOCK: 18th-20th C antiques and decorative pieces including garden furniture.* TEL: 01488 680666; fax - 01488 680668.

LANGLEY BURRELL, Nr. Chippenham

Harriet Fairfax Fireplaces and General Antiques
Langley Green. SN15 4LL. Open by appointment only. *STOCK: China, glass, dolls, furniture, fabrics and needlework; architectural items and fittings, brass and iron knobs, knockers; fireplaces, pine and iron, 1780-1950.* TEL: 01249 652030. SER: Design consultancy.

LYNEHAM, Nr. Chippenham

Pillars Antiques
10 The Banks. SN15 4NS. (K. Clifford). Resident. Est. 1986. Open 10-5, including Sun. CL: Wed. and Thurs. SIZE: Large. *STOCK: Victorian and Edwardian pine, shipping oak.* LOC: B4069 Chippenham road, 1 mile from village. PARK: Easy. TEL: 01249 890632; home - same.

MALMESBURY

Antiques - Rene Nicholls
56 High St. SN16 9AT. (Mrs. R. Nicholls). Est. 1980. Open 10-5.30, Sun. by appointment. SIZE: Small. *STOCK: English pottery and porcelain, 18th to early 19th C, £50-£900; small furniture.* PARK: Opposite. TEL: 01666 823089; home - same.

Andrew Britten Antiques
48 High St. SN16 9AT. (T.M. Tyler and T.A. Freeman). Est. 1975. Open 9.30-6. SIZE: Medium. *STOCK: Furniture, decorative brass, wood, glass*

and porcelain items, £15-£500. PARK: Opposite. TEL: 01666 823376; fax - 01666 825563. VAT: Spec.

Lyon Oliver Antiques

Laynes House, Oaksey. SN16 9SE. TADA. Prior telephone call advisable. *STOCK: English and Irish country house furniture, large mirrors, upholstery and decorative sculpture.* TEL: 01666 577603; e-mail - lyon@lyon-oliver.demon.co.uk.

MANNINGFORD BRUCE

Indigo

Dairy Barn. SN9 6JW. (Richard and Marion Lightbown). Est. 1982. Open 9-1 and 2-5. CL: Sat. SIZE: Large. *STOCK: 19th C Indian and Chinese furniture, Chinese lacquer cabinets, £400-£2,000; Far Eastern architectural items, 18th-19th C, £500-£3,000; small collectibles and accessories from India, China, Tibet, Japan and Indonesia.* LOC: A345 south of Marlborough. PARK: Easy. TEL: 01672 564722; fax - 01672 564733; e-mail - sales@indigo-uk.com; website - www.indigo-uk.com. VAT: Stan.

MARLBOROUGH

Bowmoore Gallery

4 London Rd. SN8 1PH. Est. 1968. Open Wed.-Sun. 10-6 or by appointment. *STOCK: 20th C oil paintings and watercolours, small collectables, interior design and garden items.* PARK: Easy. TEL: 01672 513593; mobile - 07818 054448; e-mail - bowmoore@supanet.com. SER: Framing and restorations.

Brocante Antiques Centre

6 London Rd. SN8 1PH. (Robert Stenhouse and Peter Randall). Est. 1986. Open 10-5. SIZE: Large. *STOCK: Furniture including French, £50-£1,500; ceramics including Staffordshire, £5-£1,000; all 18th-20th C; collectables.* LOC: A4 entering Marlborough. PARK: Easy. TEL: 01672 516512; fax - same; e-mail - brocante@brocante antiques.co.uk; website - www.brocanteantiques. co.uk. SER: Valuations; restorations (furniture). VAT: Global.

Cook of Marlborough Fine Art Ltd

High Trees House, Savernake Forest. SN8 4NE. (W.J. Cook). LAPADA. BAFRA. Est. 1963. Open by appointment only. SIZE: Medium. *STOCK: Furniture, 18th to early 19th C; objets d'art, 18th-19th C.* LOC: 1.5 miles from Marlborough

on A346 towards Burbage. PARK: Easy. TEL: 01672 513017; fax - 01672 514455. SER: Valuations; restorations (furniture including polishing and gilding); buys at auction (furniture). FAIRS: Olympia; Harrogate; Claridges; Chester; Tatton Park. VAT: Stan/Spec.

Katharine House Gallery

Katharine House, The Parade. SN8 1NE. (C.C. Gange). Est. 1983. Open 10-5.30. SIZE: Medium. *STOCK: Furniture, 18th-19th C, £200-£2,000; decorative items, £100-£1,000; Chinese, Roman and Greek antiquities, 2000BC-1000AD, £100-£1,000; 20th C British paintings and prints, £10-£1,000; books, £5-£500.* PARK: Easy. TEL: 01672 514040; home - same. VAT: Stan/Spec.

Two lustre ware dishes, c.1880. Sold for £2,000 each in 1999.

Over the past year, auctions and exhibitions have highlighted the growing interest in pottery by William De Morgan. This is reflected in steadily rising prices, making this master potter from the late 19th century hot property.

From an article entitled "William De Morgan" by Johanna Freidwall which appeared in the October 2001 issue of **Antique Collecting**. For more details and to subscribe see page 21.

Robert Kime Antiques

P O Box 454 SN8 3UR. Est. 1968. Open by appointment only. STOCK: Decorative, period furniture. TEL: 01264 73126; e-mail - rdkime@aol.com. VAT: Spec.

The Marlborough Parade Antique Centre

The Parade. SN8 1NE. (T. Page). Est. 1985. Open 10-5 including Sun. SIZE: 57 dealers. STOCK: Good quality furniture, paintings, silver, porcelain, glass, clocks, jewellery, copper, brass and pewter, £5-£5,000. LOC: Adjacent A4 in town centre. PARK: Easy. TEL: 01672 515331. SER: Valuations; restorations (furniture, porcelain, copper, brass). VAT: Spec.

The Military Parade Bookshop

The Parade. SN8 1NE. (G. and P. Kent). STOCK: Military history books especially regimental histories and the World Wars. LOC: Next to The Lamb. TEL: 01672 515470; fax - 01980 630150; e-mail - enquiry@militaryparadebooks.com; website - www.militaryparadebooks.com.

The Table Gallery Antiques

4 Kingsbury St. SN8 1HU. (Paul Martin). Open 10-5.30, Sun. by appointment. STOCK: Country vernacular, mainly English, table treen, metalware, clocks, Welsh dressers, court cupboards, settles - bacon, curved and box; tables, Thames Valley and Windsor chairs, all 17th to early 19th C; decorative items - rushlight candlesticks, trivets, inglenook toasters, bible boxes, spice and food cupboards. TEL: 01672 511188; fax - same. SER: Valuations; restorations; sourcing; reference book library.

Annmarie Turner Antiques

22 Salisbury Rd. SN8 4AD. Resident. Est. 1960. Open 10-6, Sun. by appointment. SIZE: Small. STOCK: British oak, fruitwood, pine and primitive country furniture, £50-£1,500; treen and kitchenalia, £5-£100; allied decorative items and the unusual, £20-£500, 17th C to 1920's. Not Stocked: Mahogany, jewellery, silver, reproduction. LOC: Left side of first roundabout approaching town from Hungerford on A4. PARK: Easy and at rear. TEL: 01672 515396; home - same. SER: Valuations. VAT: Spec.

MELKSHAM

Dann Antiques Ltd

Unit 1, Avonside Enterprise Park, New Broughton Rd. SN12 8BS. (G. Low). BABAADA. Est. 1983. Open 9-5.30, Sat. 9-1. SIZE: Large. STOCK: 18th-19th C English furniture; French and decorative *pieces, lighting, fenders, mirrors, pottery, porcelain.* PARK: Own. TEL: 01225 707329; fax - 01225 790120; e-mail - 113665.1341@compuserve. com; website - www.dannantiques.com. SER: Restorations. VAT: Stan/Spec.

Alan Jaffray
16 Market Place. SN12 6EX. BABAADA. Est. 1956. Open Mon.-Fri. 9-5. SIZE: Large. *STOCK: Furniture and smalls, 18th-19th C, £50-£2,000.* LOC: Main Bath to Devizes Rd. PARK: On premises. TEL: 01225 702269; fax - 01225 790413; e-mail - jaffray.antiques@talk21.com. VAT: Stan/Spec.

King Street Curios
8 King St. SN12 6HD. Est. 1991. SIZE: 20 units. *STOCK: China, discontinued Denby, USSR, glass, jewellery, Art Deco, kitchenalia, furniture.* LOC: A350. PARK: Own at rear. TEL: 01225 790623. FAIRS: Oasis, Swindon; Neeld Hall, Chippenham; Templemeads (Brunel), Bristol.

MERE, Nr. Warminster

Louis Stanton   **BADA**
P O Box 2839. BA12 6BY. (L.R. and S.A. Stanton). CINOA. Est. 1965. Open by appointment only. *STOCK: Early English oak furniture, medieval sculpture and works of art, metalware, unusual decorative items.* **TEL: 01747 860747; fax - same. SER: Valuations; buys at auction.**

MILTON LILBOURNE, Nr. Pewsey

Rupert Gentle Antiques   **BADA**
The Manor House. SN9 5LQ. Est. 1954. Open 9.15-6. SIZE: Medium. *STOCK: English and Continental domestic metalwork, 1650-1850; treen, decorative objects, needlework and domestic accessories.* **LOC: From Hungerford on A4 take A338 for Pewsey. PARK: Easy. TEL: 01672 563344; fax - 01672 563563. SER: Valuations; buys at auction. VAT: Stan/Spec.**

NEWTON TONY, Nr. Salisbury

Ray Best Antiques
Owl Cottage SP4 0HF. LAPADA. Est. 1964. Open by appointment. *STOCK: 17th-18th C oak and mahogany furniture, pottery, English Delft, textiles and metalware.* LOC: 5 mins. from A303, just off A338. PARK: Easy. TEL: 01980 629528; mobile - 07831 766340; e-mail - raybestantiques @hotmail.com; website - www.raybestantiques. co.uk. FAIRS: Bath; Harrogate; Snape; NEC.

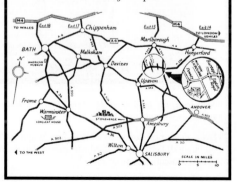

NORTH WRAXHALL, Nr. Chippenham

Delomosne and Son Ltd   BADA
Court Close. SN14 7AD. (T.N.M. Osborne and M.C.F. Mortimer). BABAADA. Articles on chandeliers, glass and porcelain. Est. 1905. Open Mon.-Fri. 9.30-5.30, other times by appointment. SIZE: Large. *STOCK: English and Irish glass, pre-1830, £20-£20,000; glass chandeliers, English and European porcelain, needlework, papier mâché and treen.* LOC: Off A420 between Bath and Chippenham. PARK: Easy. TEL: 01225 891505; fax - 01225 891907; website - www.delomosne.co.uk. SER: Valuations; buys at auction. FAIRS: International Ceramic; Winter Olympia. VAT: Spec.

RAMSBURY, Nr. Marlborough

Heraldry Today
Parliament Piece. SN8 2QH. Est. 1954. Open 9.30-4.30. CL: Sat. *STOCK: Heraldic and genealogical books and manuscripts, £3-£10,000.* PARK: Own. TEL: 01672 520617; fax - 01672 520183; e-mail - heraldry@heraldrytoday. co.uk; website - www. heraldrytoday.co.uk. SER: Book search.

Inglenook Antiques
59 High St. SN8 2QN. (Dennis White). Est. 1969.

Open 10-1 and 2-5, prior telephone call advisable. CL: Mon. and Wed. except by appointment. SIZE: Small. *STOCK: Oil lamps, £50-£850; clocks, barometers and spare parts, £150-£4,000; some furniture.* LOC: 3 miles from A4 between Hungerford and Marlborough. PARK: Easy. TEL: 01672 520261; home - same. SER: Restorations (longcase clock movements only).

SALISBURY

Antique and Collectors Market
37 Catherine St. SP1 2DH. Open 10-5. SIZE: Large. *STOCK: Silver, plate, china, glass, toys, books, taxidermy, prints, pens and furniture.* TEL: 01722 326033.

The Avonbridge Antiques and Collectors Market
United Reformed Church Hall, Fisherton St. SP2 7RG. Open Tues. 9-3.30. SIZE: 15 dealers. *STOCK: General antiques.* TEL: 01202 669061.

The Barn Book Supply
88 Crane St. SP1 2QD. (J. and J. Head). Est. 1958. Open 9.30-5. CL: Sat. *STOCK: Antiquarian books on angling, shooting, horses, deerstalking.* TEL: 01722 327767; fax - 01722 339888.

Non-train toy models at the Barry Potter sale included this Meccano crane, constructed from 1920s nickel metal, which sold at £1,500.

From an Auction Report by Christopher Wight on Trains and Toys held at Barry Potter Auctions, Rugby on 9th-10th February 2002 which appeared in the April 2002 issue of **Antique Collecting**. For more details and to subscribe see page 21.

Boston Antiques
223 Wilton Rd. and warehouse at Wilton. SP2 7JY. Est. 1964. Open by appointment. SIZE: Small. *STOCK: 17th-19th C fine furniture.* PARK: Opposite. TEL: 01722 322682; 08702 417452; e-mail - derek@strangecorp.com. VAT: Stan/Spec.

Robert Bradley Antiques
71 Brown St. SP1 2BA. Est. 1970. Open 9.30-5.30. CL: Sat. *STOCK: Furniture, 17th-18th C; decorative items.* TEL: 01722 333677; fax - 01722 339922. VAT: Spec.

Ronald Carr
6 St. Francis Rd. SP1 3QS. (R.G. Carr). Est. 1983. Open by appointment. SIZE: Small. *STOCK: Modern British etchings, wood engravings and colour wood cuts, £5-£1,000.* LOC: 1 mile north of city on A345. PARK: Easy. TEL: 01722 328892; home - same. SER: Buys at auction.

Castle Galleries
81 Castle St. SP1 3SP. (John C. Lodge). Est. 1971. Open 9-4.30, Sat. 9-1. CL: Mon. and Wed. *STOCK: General antiques, coins and medals.* PARK: Easy. TEL: 01722 333734; mobile - 07890 225059; e-mail - johnlodge@bun.com.

Edward Hurst Antiques
The Garden Room, Netherhampton. SP2 8PU. Est. 1983. Open 9.30-5.30, Sat. by appointment. SIZE: Medium. *STOCK: English furniture and associated works of art, 1650-1820.* LOC: Just west of Salisbury. PARK: Easy. TEL: 01722 743042. VAT: Spec.

Pennyfarthing Antiques
52-54 Winchester St. SP1 1HG. (Mike and Bernadett Scott). Open 9-5.30, Sun. 11-4. SIZE: Medium. *STOCK: Country furniture including Windsor arm chairs, 18th to early 20th C, £50-£1,000.* PARK: Easy. TEL: 01722 505955. SER: Restorations (furniture).

Salisbury Antiques Warehouse Ltd
94 Wilton Rd. SP2 7JJ. (R.W and Mrs. C. Wallrock). LAPADA. Est. 1964. Open 9-5.30, Sat. 10-4, Sun. by appointment. SIZE: Large. *STOCK: 18th-19th C English and Continental furniture, decorative works of art, clocks and pictures, £1,000-£15,000; small items, £100-£1,000.* LOC: A36 Warminster-Southampton road. PARK: Easy. TEL: 01722 410634; fax - 01722 410635; mobile - 07768 877069; home - 01590 672515. Restorations (gilding). VAT: Stan/Spec.

527

William Sheppee
Old Sarum Airfield. SP4 6BJ. (W. Hiley and J. Hedges). Est. 1989. Open Mon.-Fri. by appointment only. SIZE: Large. *STOCK: Indian and Chinese antiques and antique replica mirrory.* PARK: Easy. TEL: 01722 334454; fax - 01722 337754; e-mail - sales@williamsheppee.com. VAT: Stan. *Trade Only.*

Chris Wadge Clocks
83 Fisherton St. SP2 7ST. Open 9-4. CL: Mon. *STOCK: Clocks, movements and spare parts.* TEL: 01722 334467; e-mail - cwclocks@aol.com. SER: 400 day specialist.

SEMLEY

Dairy House Antiques
Station Rd. SP7 9AN. (Miss I. Moyes). Open 9.30-5.30. SIZE: Large. *STOCK: Furniture, paintings, decorative items, 1600-1900.* TEL: 01747 853317.

SWINDON

Penny Farthing Antiques Arcade
Victoria Centre, 138/9 Victoria Rd., Old Town. SN1 3BU. (Ann Farthing). Est. 1977. Open 10-5. SIZE: Large. *STOCK: Furniture, silver, porcelain, watches, clocks.* LOC: On left on hill between Old Town and college. PARK: Prospect Place. TEL: 01793 536668. VAT: Stan.

Sambourne House Antiques Ltd
50-51 The Arcade, Brunel Shopping Centre. SN1 1LL. (T. and Mrs K. Cove). Est. 1984. Open 10-5, Sun. 10-4. SIZE: Large. *STOCK: Restored 19th C pine, £120-£2,000; reclaimed 19th C pine, £50-£1,500; reproduction smalls, £2-£90.* LOC: 1.5 miles off junction 16, M4, towards Swindon. PARK: Easy. TEL: 01793 610855; fax - same. SER: Stripping; specialist pine importer. VAT: Stan/Global.

Allan Smith Antique Clocks
162 Beechcroft Rd., Upper Stratton. SN2 7QE. Est. 1988. Open anytime by appointment. SIZE: Large. *STOCK: 50-60 longcase clocks including automata, moonphase, painted dial, brass dial, 30 hour, 8 day, London and provincial, £1,950-£39,500; occasionally stick and banjo barometers, mantel, wall, bracket, Vienna and lantern clocks.* LOC: Near Bakers Arms Inn. PARK: Own. TEL: 01793 822977; mobile - 07778 834342; e-mail - allansmithclocks@lineone.net: website - www.allan-smith-antique-clocks.co.uk. VAT: Spec.

Traditional Beds
11 Newport St., Old Town. SN1 3DX. (J. and M. Brown). Open 10-5.30. CL: Wed. SIZE: Medium. *STOCK: Pine, traditional brass and iron beds, china, lace, linen and costume jewellery.* LOC: From M4, junction 15 or 16 follow signs to Old Town. PARK: 100yds. TEL: 01793 520259. VAT: Stan/Spec.

Victoria Bookshop
30 Wood St., Old Town. SN1 4AB. (S. Austin). Est. 1965. Open 9.30-5. SIZE: Large. *STOCK: Books, most subjects, old postcards.* LOC: Middle of Old Town shopping area. PARK: Nearby. TEL: 01793 527364.

WARMINSTER

Cassidy's Antiques
7 Silver St. BA12 8PS. (M. Cassidy). BABAADA. Est. 1989. Open 9-5, Sat. 10-5. SIZE: Medium. *STOCK: Furniture, 17th-19th C, £200-£1,500.* PARK: Easy. TEL: 01985 213313; e-mail - matcas@supanet.com. SER: Restorations (furniture and cabinet making).

Choice Antiques
4 Silver St. BA12 8PS. (Avril Bailey). Open 10-5.30. SIZE: Medium. *STOCK: General antiques and decorative items, 18th-19th C, £25-£2,000.* PARK: Easy. TEL: 01985 218924. VAT: Stan/Spec.

Isabella Antiques
11 Silver St. BA12 8PS. (B.W. Semke). BABAADA. Est. 1990. Open 10-5. SIZE: Medium. *STOCK: Furniture, late 18th C to late 19th C, £100-£5,000; boxes and mirrors, 19th C, £50-£1,000.* LOC: Main road. PARK: Easy. TEL: 01985 218933. SER: Buys at auction (furniture). VAT: Spec.

Maxfield House Antiques
Maxfield House, 16 Silver St. BA12 8PS. (Martyn and Rosemary Reynolds). BABAADA. Est. 1992. Open 10-5 or by appointment. SIZE: Small. *STOCK: Mainly English oak and mahogany, 18th-20th C; town and country furniture; pictures and decorative objects; all £50-£2,000.* LOC: Main Bath road leading into Silver St. PARK: Easy. TEL: 01985 212121; home - same; mobile - 07703 877196; e-mail - maxfield@ooh.co.uk; website - www.maxfield-antiques.com.

Obelisk Antiques
2 Silver St. BA12 8PS. (P. Tanswell). LAPADA. BABAADA. Open 10-1 and 2-5.30. SIZE: Large. *STOCK: English and Continental furniture, 18th-19th C; decorative items, objets d'art.* TEL: 01985 846646; fax - 01985 219901.

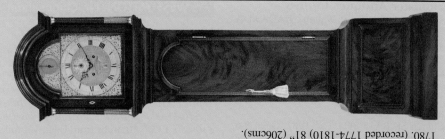

Warminster Antiques Centre
6 Silver St. BA12 8TT. (P. Walton). BABAADA. Est. 1970. Open 10-5. SIZE: 15 dealers. *STOCK: Furniture, home embellishments, textiles, silver, jewellery, collectors' items.* PARK: Easy. TEL: 01985 847269; mobile - 07860 584193. FAIRS: Newark.

K. and A. Welch
1A Church St. BA12 8PG. Est. 1967. Open 8-6, Sat. 9-1. SIZE: Large. *STOCK: Shipping furniture, 18th-19th C, £10-£2,000.* LOC: A36 west end of town. PARK: Own. TEL: 01985 214687; home - 01985 213433. VAT: Stan/Spec.

Starting from 1900, when car accessories were not only the epitome of quality and craftsmanship, but also in many cases minor works of art, this book covers lamps, mirrors, clocks, horns, dashboard instruments, tools, clothing, badges, mascots, containers, cigarette cards, publicity material, maps, trophies, motoring novelties, toy cars and pedal cars. There is also a section on post-1950 memorabilia and items connected with motor racing.

"…this is a book you will find hard to put down"   **Automobile**

ISBN 1 85149 293 3, 304pp., 143 col. 814 b.&w. illus. **£25.00**

Available from the
ANTIQUE COLLECTORS' CLUB
Sandy Lane, Old Martlesham,
Woodbridge, Suffolk IP12 4SD, UK.
For your free copy of the catalogue:
Tel: **01394 389950** or Fax: **01394 389999**
Email: sales@antique-acc.com
Website: www.antique-acc.com

WEST YATTON, Nr. Chippenham

Heirloom & Howard Limited
Manor Farm. SN14 7EU. (D.S. Howard). BABAADA. Est. 1972. Open 10-5.30, Sat. 11-5 or by appointment. SIZE: Medium. *STOCK: Porcelain mainly Chinese armorial and export, 18th C, £100-£5,000; heraldic items, 18th-19th C, £10-£1,000; portrait engravings, 17th-19th C, £10-£50.* LOC: 10 miles from Bath, 1/4 mile off A420 Chippenham/Bristol road. Transport from Chippenham station (4 miles) if required. PARK: Own. TEL: 01249 783038; fax - 01249 783039. SER: Valuations; buys at auction (Chinese porcelain). VAT: Spec.

WESTBURY

Ray Coggins Antiques
1 Fore St. BA13 3AU. Open 9-5.30. *STOCK: Antique and decorative furniture and architectural fittings.* TEL: 01373 826574.

WILTON, Nr. Salisbury

Bay Tree Antiques
26 North St. SP2 0HJ. Open 9-5.30 or by appointment. SIZE: Medium. *STOCK: General antiques, specialising in period English furniture.* TEL: 01722 743392.

Hingstons of Wilton
36 North St. SP2 0HJ. Est. 1976. Open 9-5, Sat. 10-4. SIZE: Large. *STOCK: 18th-20th C furniture, clocks, pictures and objects.* PARK: Easy. TEL: 01722 742263; home - 01722 714742; mobile - 07887 870569; website - www.hingstons-antiques. co.uk.

Carol Musselwhite Antiques
6 West St. SP2 0DF. Est. 1990. Open 10-5. CL: Mon. and Jan. SIZE: Medium. *STOCK: Porcelain and pottery especially discontinued Denby, pre 1980, linen and lace, £1-£300.* LOC: Village centre. PARK: 30 metres. TEL: 01722 742573.

A.J. Romain and Sons
The Old House, 11 and 13 North St. SP2 0HA. *STOCK: Furniture, mainly 17th-18th C; early oak, walnut and marquetry; clocks, copper, brass and miscellanea.* TEL: 01722 743350. VAT: Stan/Spec.

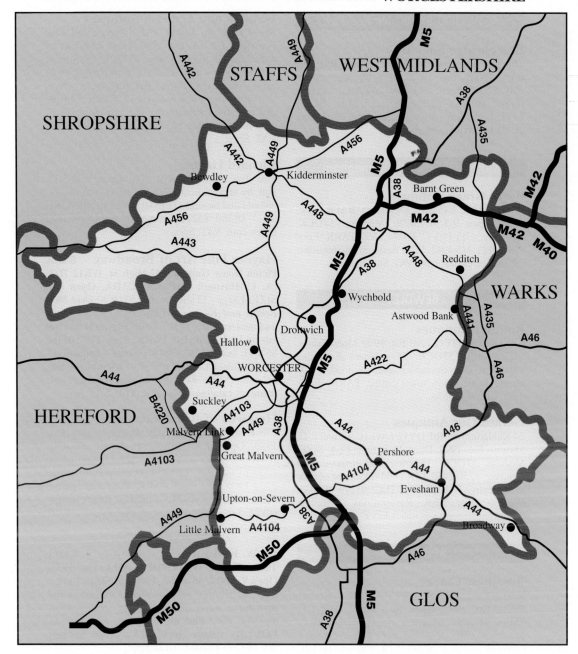

Dealers and Shops in Worcestershire

Astwood Bank	1	Great Malvern	8	Redditch	1
Barnt Green	1	Hallow	1	Suckley	1
Bewdley	2	Kidderminster	3	Upton-upon-Severn	1
Broadway	8	Little Malvern	1	Worcester	12
Droitwich	2	Malvern Link	2	Wychbold	1
Evesham	2	Pershore	3		

ASTWOOD BANK, Nr. Redditch

Bracebridge Fine Art
The Old Bakehouse, 1242 Evesham Rd. B96
6AA. FATG. Est. 1987. Open by appointment
only. *STOCK: 18th-20th C oil paintings, and rare
signed limited edition prints.* TEL: 01527
893557; website - www.BracebridgeFinarArt.co.
uk. SER: Archive information.

BARNT GREEN, Nr. Birmingham

Barnt Green Antiques
93 Hewell Rd. B45 8NL. (N. Slater). BAFRA. Est.
1965. Open 9-5.30. SIZE: Medium. *STOCK:
Furniture, 17th-19th C, £100-£5,000.* PARK: Easy.
TEL: 0121 445 4942. SER: Restorations (furniture,
gilt frames, clocks, oils). VAT: Stan/Spec.

BEWDLEY

Bewdley Antiques
62A Load St. DY12 2AP. Est. 1999. Open 7 days.
SIZE: Small. *STOCK: 25 cabinets displaying
19th-20th C collectables and decorative furniture.* LOC: A456 town centre. PARK: Easy.
TEL: 01299 405636.

Gerard Guy Antiques
24 Kidderminster Rd. DY12 1AG. (C. G. and P. G.
Mason). Est. 1990. Open 11-5, Sun. 12-4. SIZE:
Medium. *STOCK: Victorian and stripped pine
furniture, £250-£450.* LOC: Old A456, just outside
town centre. PARK: Easy. TEL: 01299 400032;
home - same. SER: Restorations (stripping,
refinishing, repairs and upholstery).

BROADWAY

Broadway Clocks
Kennel Lane, High St. WR12 7DP. (R. J. Kemp).
FBHI. Est. 1992. Open 10-1 and 2.15-5. CL:
Thurs. *STOCK: Longcase clocks, 17th-19th C,
£1,500-£6,000; also bracket, French mantel,
carriage and wall clocks.* LOC: 30 yds up lane
next to Lloyds Bank. TEL: 01386 852458. SER:
Clock restorations and repairs. VAT: Stan/Spec.

Broadway Dolls and Bears
76 High St. WR12 7AJ. (Janice Longhi). Open 7
days 10-5. *STOCK: Antique and modern artist's
dolls and teddy bears.* TEL: 01386 858323. SER:
Teddy bear museum; restorations (bears and
dolls).

Fenwick and Fenwick Antiques
88-90 High St. WR12 7AJ. (George and Jane
Fenwick). CADA. Est. 1980. Open 10-6 and by
appointment. SIZE: Large. *STOCK: Furniture,
oak, mahogany and walnut, 17th to early 19th C;
samplers, boxes, treen, Tunbridgeware, Delft,
decorative items and corkscrews.* PARK: Outside
and own by arrangement. TEL: 01386 853227;
after hours - 01386 841724; fax - 01386 858504.
VAT: Spec.

Richard Hagen
Yew Tree House. WR12 7DT. Open 9.30-5.30,
Sun. by appointment. *STOCK: 20th C oils, watercolours and bronzes.* TEL: 01386 853624/858561;
fax - 01386 852172; e-mail - fineart@richard
hagen.com. VAT: Spec.

Haynes Fine Art of Broadway   BADA
**Picton House Galleries, 42 High St. WR12 7DT.
(A. C. Haynes). LAPADA. CADA. Open 9-6.
SIZE: Large - 12 showrooms. *STOCK: Over 2000
British and European 16th-21st C oil paintings
and watercolours.* LOC: From Lygon Arms, 100
yds up High St. on left. PARK: Easy. TEL: 01386
852649; fax - 01386 858187; e-mail - enquiries@
haynes-fine-art.co.uk; website - www.haynesfine
art.com. SER: Free valuations; restorations;
framing; catalogue available (£10). VAT: Spec.**

Howards of Broadway
27a High St. WR12 7DP. (Robert Light). Est.
1989. Open 9.30-5.30. SIZE: Small. *STOCK:
Jewellery, 1750 to modern, £20-£5,000; silver,
1700 to modern, £20-£5,000; objects of vertu,
1700-1900, £50-£500.* PARK: Easy and nearby.
TEL: 01386 858924; e-mail - robert.light@
talk21.com. SER: Valuations; restorations. VAT:
Stan/Spec.

H. W. Keil Ltd   BADA
**Tudor House. WR12 7DP. CADA. Est. 1925.
Open 9. 15-12. 45 and 2. 15-5. 30. SIZE: Large.
*STOCK: Walnut, oak, mahogany and rosewood
furniture; early pewter, brass and copper,
tapestry, glass and works of art, 17th-18th C.*
LOC: By village clock. TEL: 01386 852408;
fax - 01386 852069. VAT: Spec.**

John Noott Galleries   BADA
**58 High St., 14 Cotswold Court, and at The
Lygon Arms, High St. WR12 7AA. LAPADA.
CADA. Est. 1972. Open 9. 30-1 and 2-5. SIZE:
Large. *STOCK: Paintings, watercolours and
bronzes, 19th C to Contemporary.* PARK: Easy.
TEL: 01386 854868/858969; fax - 01386 854919.
SER: Valuations; restorations; framing. VAT:
Stan/Spec.**

DROITWICH

Robert Belcher Antiques
128 Worcester Rd. WR9 8AN. (Robert & Wendy Belcher). Est. 1986. Open 9.30-5.30, Sun. by appointment. CL: Mon. SIZE: Large. *STOCK: Furniture, 18th-19th C, £500-£10,000; ceramics, silver, glass, paintings and prints, 19th-20th C, £50-£1,000.* PARK: Easy. TEL: 01905 772320. SER: Valuations; restorations; picture framing. FAIRS: NEC. VAT: Spec.

Grant Books
The Coach House, New Rd., Cutnall Green. WR9 0PQ. Est. 1976. Open 9-5 or by appointment. CL: Sat. SIZE: Small. *STOCK: Books, prints, pictures, clubs, golfiana, £5-£1,000.* LOC: A442 Droitwich to Kidderminster road. PARK: Easy. TEL: 01299 851588; fax - 01299 851446; e-mail - golf@grantbooks.co.uk; website - www.golf books-memorabilia.com.

EVESHAM

Bookworms of Evesham
81 Port St. WR11 6AF. (T. J. Sims). PBFA. Est. 1999. Open 10-5, Mon. by appointment. SIZE: Small. *STOCK: Books - Gloucestershire and Worcestershire, 19th-20th C, £5-£1,200; John Moore, 20th C, £5-£75; general books, 19th-20th C, from 50p.* PARK: Behind premises. TEL: 01386 45509. SER: Valuations; restorations; buys at auction. FAIRS: PBFA - Bath, Cheltenham, Cirencester and Churchdown. VAT: Stan.

Magpie Jewellers and Antiques and Magpie Arms & Armour
Manchester House 1 High St. WR11 4DA. (R. J. and E. R. Bunn). Est. 1975. Open 9-5.30. SIZE: Large. *STOCK: Silver, jewellery, furniture, general antiques, arms and armour, books, stamps and coins.* TEL: 01386 41631.

GREAT MALVERN

Carlton Antiques
43 Worcester Rd. WR14 4RB. (Dave Roberts). Open 10-5. *STOCK: Edwardian postcards and cigarette cards; Victorian and Edwardian furniture, stripped pine; oil paintings, watercolours and prints.* TEL: 01684 573092; e-mail - dave@ carlton-antiques.com; website - www.carlton-antiques.com. SER: Valuations.

Foley Furniture
Foley Bank. WR14. (Dave Roberts). *STOCK: Furniture - shipping, modern and old; postcards, cigarette cards, books, pictures, sheet music and general collectables.* TEL: 01684 891255; website - www.carlton-antiques.com.

Great Malvern Antiques
Salisbury House, 6 Abbey Rd. WR14 3HG. (Leonard Sutton and Robert J. Rice). Est. 1966. Open by appointment. SIZE: Large. *STOCK: Decorative furniture and objects, 1800-1940.* LOC: Near theatres. PARK: Easy. TEL: 01684 575490; home - same; e-mail - gmantiques@dial. pipex.com. SER: Valuations. FAIRS: Decorative Antiques & Textile, Bath Decorative Antiques. VAT: Stan/Spec. *Trade Only.*

Malvern Bookshop
7 Abbey Rd. WR14 3ES. (Howard and Julie Hudson). Open 10-5. SIZE: 5 rooms. *STOCK: Antiquarian, secondhand books and remainders.* LOC: Near GPO by Priory steps. PARK: Short stay on road above. TEL: 01684 575915; e-mail - browse@malvern-bookshop.co.uk.

Malvern Studios
56 Cowleigh Rd. WR14 1QD. (L. M. Hall). BAFRA. Open 9-5.15, Fri. and Sat. 9-4.45. CL: Wed. *STOCK: Period, Edwardian painted and inlaid furniture, general furnishings.* TEL: 01684 574913; fax - 01684 569475. SER: Restorations; woodcarving; polishing; interior design. VAT: Stan/Spec.

Miscellany Antiques
20 Cowleigh Rd. WR14 1QD. (Ray and Liz Hunaban). Resident. Est. 1974. SIZE: Medium showroom + trade warehouse. *STOCK: Victorian, Edwardian and Georgian furniture, including shipping goods, £300-£20,000; some porcelain, silver, bronzes and jewellery.* LOC: B4219 to Bromyard. PARK: Own. TEL: 01684 566671; fax - 01684 560562; mobile - 07836 507954; e-mail - liz.hunaban@virgin.net; website - www.free space.virgin.net/liz.hunaban/index.htm. SER: Valuations. VAT: Stan/Spec.

Promenade Antiques
41 Worcester Rd. WR14 4RB. (Mark Selvester). Open 10-5, Sun. 12-5. CL: Tues. *STOCK: General antiques, including Victorian and Edwardian furniture, bric-a-brac and books.* TEL: 01684 566876.

Whitmore
Teynham Lodge, Chase Rd., Upper Colwall. WR13 6DT. (John and Stella Whitmore). BNTA. Est. 1965. *STOCK: British and foreign coins,*

1700-1950; trade tokens, 1650-1900; commemorative medallions, 1600-1950; all £1-£500. TEL: 01684 540651; 01684 541417; e-mail - teynhaml@netscapeonline.co.uk. *Postal Only.*

HALLOW, Nr. Worcester

Antique Map and Print Gallery
April Cottage, Main Rd. WR2 6LS. (M. A. and G. P. Nichols). Open by appointment only. *STOCK: Antiquarian maps, prints and books, Baxter and Le Blond prints.* LOC: Approx. 4 miles from Worcester on the Tenbury Wells Rd. PARK: Easy. TEL: 01905 641300; e-mail - antiquemap@aol.com. SER: Greetings cards reproduced from original prints.

KIDDERMINSTER

The Antique Centre
5-8 Lion St. DY10 1PT. (Vivien Bentley). Est. 1980. Open 10-5. SIZE: Large. *STOCK: Furniture, early 18th C to 1930's, £10-£2,000; collectables, to 1930's, £1-£1,000; Victorian, Edwardian and reproduction fireplaces.* LOC: Off Bromsgrove St. PARK: Easy. TEL: 01562 740389; fax - same; mobile - 07980 300660. SER: Valuations; restorations (furniture including stripping, jewellery repairs and commissions).

B. B. M. Jewellery and Antiques
8 and 9 Lion St. DY10 1PT. (W. V. and A. Crook). BJA. Est. 1977. Open 10-5. CL: Tues. SIZE: Medium. *STOCK: Jewellery, 19th C, £50-£3,000; coins, £5-£1,000; general antiques, £5-£500.* LOC: Adjacent Youth Centre, off ring road. PARK: Easy. TEL: 01562 744118. SER: Valuations; restorations (jewellery, porcelain, silver). VAT: Stan/Spec/Global.

Gemini Antiques & Gallery
152 Offmore Rd. DY10 1SB. (D. A. Southern). Resident. Est. 1985. Open 10-5.30. CL: Wed. SIZE: Medium. *STOCK: Furniture, 19th-20th C, £100-£500; porcelain, 18th-19th C, £50-£500; mirrors, 19th-20th C, £100-£300.* LOC: Off Birmingham Rd. /off Chester road. PARK: Easy. TEL: 01562 824109. SER: Valuations; restorations (desk leathers, upholstery, polishing); buys at auction. FAIRS: Malvern and Birmingham. VAT: Stan.

LITTLE MALVERN

St. James Antiques
De Lys Wells Rd. WR14 4JL. (H. Van Wyngaarden).

Est. 1991. Open 10-5 or by appointment. *STOCK: Continental and English pine furniture, lighting and rugs.* PARK: Easy. TEL: 01684 563404. VAT: Stan.

MALVERN LINK

Kimber & Son
6 Lower Howsell Rd. WR14 1EF. (E. M. and M. E. Kimber). Est. 1956. Open 9-5.30, Sat. 9-1. *STOCK: 18th-20th C antiques for English, Continental and American markets.* TEL: 01684 574339; home - 01684 572000. FAIRS: Newark. VAT: Stan/Spec.

Malvern Link Antiques Centre
154 Worcester Rd. WR14 1AA. (Trevor Guiver, Roger Hales and Paul Shaw). Open 10-5.30, Sun. 11-5. SIZE: Large. *STOCK: General furnishings and beds, 19th to early 20th C, £100-£2,000; collectables, china, £5-£100; fireplaces, from 19th C, £75-£2,000.* LOC: A449 entering Malvern Link. PARK: Easy. TEL: 01684 575750; home - 01684 575904/572491. SER: Restorations; French polishing; buys at auction. VAT: Stan/Spec.

PERSHORE

The Drawing Room - Interiors & Antiques
9 Bridge St. WR10 1AJ. (Janet Davie). IDS. Est. 1980. Open 9.30-5, Sat. 9.30-1. CL: Thurs. SIZE: Medium. *STOCK: Decorative pieces including antique and reproduction furniture, lighting, mirrors, framed prints and engravings, £50-£20,000.* PARK: Easy (in main square or opposite). TEL: 01386 555747; fax - 01386 555071. SER: Valuations; interior design. VAT: Stan/Spec.

Hansen Chard Antiques
126 High St. WR10 1EA. (P. W. Ridler). BSc LBHI. Est. 1984. Open Tues. , Wed. , Fri. and Sat. 10-4 or by appointment. SIZE: Large. *STOCK: Clocks, barometers, models, tools, books, antique and secondhand, £5-£4,000.* LOC: On A44. PARK: Easy. TEL: 01386 553423; home - same. SER: Valuations; restorations (as stock); buys at auction (as stock). FAIRS: Brunel, Midlands, Haydock Park and Balderton Clock. VAT: Spec.

S. W. Antiques
Abbey Showrooms, Newlands. WR10 1BP. (A. M. Whiteside). Est. 1978. Open 9-5. SIZE: Large. *STOCK: 19th-20th C furniture including beds and bedroom furniture, to £4,000.* Not Stocked:

Jewellery, small items. LOC: 2 mins. from Abbey. PARK: Own. TEL: 01386 555580; fax - 01386 556205; website - www.sw-antiques.co.uk. VAT: Stan/Spec.

REDDITCH

Lower House Fine Antiques

Lower House, Far Moor Lane, Winyates Green. B98 0QX. (Mrs J. B. Hudson). Est. 1987. Usually open but prior appointment advisable. SIZE: Small. *STOCK: Furniture, 17th to early 20th C, £100-£4,000; silver and plate, 18th to early 20th C, £10-£1,000; oil lamps, 19th C, £50-£500.* Not Stocked: Pine furniture. LOC: 3 miles due east Redditch town centre and half a mile from Coventry Highway island, close to A435. PARK: Own. TEL: 01527 525117; home - same; e-mail - LWSE.antiques@Tesco.net. SER: Valuations; restorations (including porcelain).

SUCKLEY

Holloways

Lower Court. WR6 5DE. (Edward and Diana Holloway). Open 9-5, Sun. in summer. SIZE: Large. *STOCK: Garden ornaments and furniture, £20-£5,000.* LOC: A44 from Worcester towards Leominster, left at Knightwick, 3 miles, situated in front of village church. PARK: Easy. TEL: 01886 884665; website - www.holloways.co.uk. SER: Valuations; restorations; buys at auction. VAT: Stan/Spec.

UPTON-UPON-SEVERN

The Highway Gallery

40 Old St. WR8 0HW. (J. Daniell). Est. 1969. Open 10.30-5, but appointment advisable. CL: Thurs. and Mon. SIZE: Small. *STOCK: Oils, watercolours, 19th-20th C, £100-£10,000.* Not Stocked: Prints. LOC: 100yds. from crossroads towards Malvern. PARK: Easy. TEL: 01684 592645; home - 01684 592909; fax - 01684 592909; e-mail - mr.daniell@ukonline.co.uk. SER: Valuations; restorations (reline and clean); buys at auction (pictures).

A selection of treen from the McElhatton Collection.

From an article entitled "Treen Trends" by Nic McElhatton which appeared in the September 2001 issue of **Antique Collecting**. For more details and to subscribe see page 21.

Antique Warehouse

Rear of 74 Droitwich Rd, Barbourne. WR3 8BW. (D. Venn). Open 9-5, Sat. 10-4.30. *STOCK: General antiques, shipping, restored pine and satin walnut, Victorian doors and fireplaces.* PARK: Easy. TEL: 01905 27493. SER: Stripping (wood and metalwork).

Antiques and Curios

50 Upper Tything. WR1 1JZ. (Brian W. Inett). Est. 1981. Open 9.30-5.30. SIZE: Large - 6 dealers on three floors. *STOCK: 18th to early 20th C furniture, oak, mahogany, walnut, especially Victorian and Edwardian desks, dining and bedroom, decorative and upholstered, furnishings, mirrors, pictures, clocks, curios, treen, objets d'art.* LOC: From Birmingham A38 into Worcester on right-hand side. PARK: Easy. TEL: 01905 25412/764547. SER: Restorations; re-polishing; upholstery; valuations.

The Barber's Clock

37 Droitwich Rd. WR3 7LG. (Graham Gopsill). Est. 1990. Open 9-5, Mon. 10-5, Sun. 1-4. SIZE: Medium. *STOCK: Clocks, 19th C to Art Deco, £350-£1,000; gramophones and phonographs, 20th C, £250-£475+.* PARK: Own. TEL: 01905 29022; home - 01905 779011. SER: Valuations; restorations (clocks and gramophones).

Bygones by the Cathedral

Cathedral Sq. WR1. (Gabrielle Doherty Bullock). LAPADA. FGA. DGA. Est. 1946. Open 9.30-5.30, Sat. 9.30-1 and 2-5.30. SIZE: Medium. *STOCK: Furniture, 17th-19th C; silver, Sheffield plate, jewellery, paintings, glass; English and Continental pottery and porcelain especially Royal Worcester.* LOC: Adjacent main entrance to Cathedral. TEL: 01905 25388. VAT: Spec.

Bygones of Worcester

55 Sidbury. WR1 2HU. (Gabrielle Bullock). LAPADA. FGA. Est. 1946. Open 9.30-1 and 2-5.30. *STOCK: 17th-20th C walnut, oak, mahogany and exotic wood furniture, brass and copper, oil paintings, porcelain, pottery and glass and decorative objects.* LOC: Opposite car park near approach to the cathedral. PARK: Opposite. TEL: 01905 23132. VAT: Stan/Spec.

Gray's Antiques

29 The Tything. WR1 1JL. (David Gray). Open 8.30-5.30. *STOCK: General antiques and soft furnishings.* TEL: 01905 724456; fax - 01905 723433; e-mail - enqs@grays-interiors.com.

Gray's Interiors

35 The Tything. WR1 1JL. Open 8.30-5.30. *STOCK: Chandeliers, chairs, sofas, soft furnishings.* TEL: 01905 21209; e-mail - enqs@grays-interiors.com.

Heirlooms

46 Upper Tything. WR1 1JZ. (D. Tarran and L. Rumford). Open 9.30-4.30. *STOCK: General antiques, objets d'art, Royal Worcester porcelain and prints.* TEL: 01905 23332.

Sarah Hodge

Peachley Manor, Hallow Lane, Lower Broadheath. WR2 6QL. Resident. Est. 1985. Open daily including Sun. SIZE: Large. *STOCK: General antiques, country bygones, pine and kitchenalia.* LOC: Off B4204, 3 miles N. W. Worcester. PARK: Easy. TEL: 01905 640255.

M. Lees and Sons

Tower House, Severn St. WR1 2NB. LAPADA. Resident. Est. 1955. Open 9.15-5.15, Sat. by appointment. CL: Thurs. pm. SIZE: Medium. *STOCK: Furniture, 1780-1880; porcelain, 1750-1920; mirrors, Oriental and decorative.* LOC: At southern end of Worcester Cathedral adjacent to Edgar Tower; near Royal Worcester Porcelain Museum and factory. PARK: Easy. TEL: 01905 26620; mobile - 07860 826218. VAT: Stan/Spec.

Round the Bend

1 Deansway. WR1 2JD. Open 10-5.30. *STOCK: Eccentricities, brocante-type goods and jolly junk.* LOC: Corner of Cathedral Square. TEL: 01905 616516.

Worcester Antiques Centre

15 Reindeer Court, Mealcheapen St. WR1 4DF. (Stephen Zacaroli). Est. 1992. Open 10-5. *STOCK: Pottery and porcelain, 1750-1950, £10-£2,000; silver, 1750-1940, £10-£3,000; jewellery, 1800-1940, £5-£2,000; furniture, 1650-1930, £50-£5,000.* PARK: Loading only or 50 yards. TEL: 01905 610680/1. SER: Valuations; restorations. FAIRS: NEC (April and Aug); East Berkshire (May and Oct).

D & J Lines Antiques

Papermill Lane. WR9 0DE. (Derek and Jill Lines). By appointment only. SIZE: Medium. *STOCK: Oak and country furniture, 17th-18th C, £500-£8,000; metalware, 18th-19th C, £50-£500; Persian carpets, 19th-20th C, £50-£1,000.* TEL: 01527 861282. SER: Valuations; restorations; desk re-leathering.

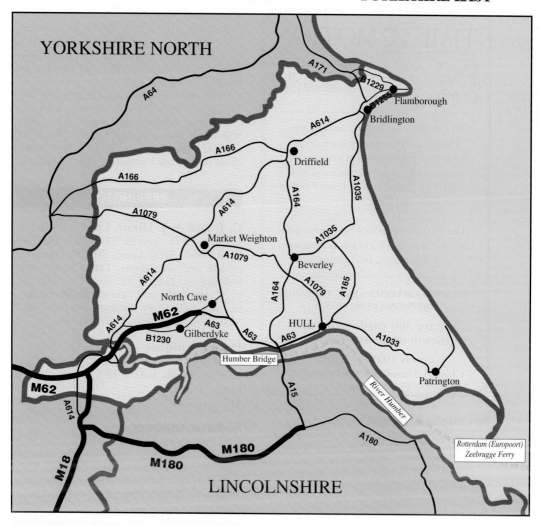

Dealers and Shops in Yorkshire East

Beverley	5	Flamborough	1	Market Weighton	3
Bridlington	3	Gilberdyke	1	North Cave	1
Driffield	3	Hull	7	Patrington	1

BEVERLEY

Karen Guest Antiques
24 Saturday Market Place. HU17. NAG registered Valuer and Jeweller. HRD Dip. of Diamond Grading. Open 9.15-5. SIZE: Medium. *STOCK: Jewellery and silver, 18th-20th C, £50-£15,000.* PARK: Easy. TEL: 01482 882334; fax - same. SER: Valuations; restorations. VAT: Stan/Spec.

Hawley Antiques
5 North Bar Within. HU17 8AP. LAPADA. Est. 1966. Open 10-4, Sat. 9.30-5. SIZE: Medium. *STOCK: General antiques, furniture, pottery, porcelain, glass, oil paintings, watercolours, silver.* LOC: Town centre. TEL: 01482 868193; mobile - 07850 225805; e-mail - john@hawleys. org.uk. SER: Restorations (fine furniture); valuations; buys at auction. FAIRS: Newark. VAT: Stan/Spec.

St Crispin Antique Centre
11 Butcher Row. HU17 0AA. (Chris Fowler and Jill Northgraves). Est. 1971. Open 10-5, Sun. 10.30-4. SIZE: 70+ dealers. *STOCK: Ceramics, glass and furniture.* TEL: 01482 869583. SER: Valuations.

James H. Starkey Galleries
49 Highgate. HU17 0DN. Est. 1968. Open 9.30-4.30, Sat. by appointment. SIZE: Medium. *STOCK: Oil paintings, 16th-19th C; drawings and watercolours, 17th-19th C.* LOC: Opposite minster. PARK: Easy. TEL: 01482 881179; fax - 01482 861644. SER: Valuations; restorations (paintings); buys at auction. VAT: Stan/Spec.

Time and Motion
1 Beckside. HU17 0PB. (Peter A. Lancaster). FBHI. Est. 1977. Open 10-5. CL: Thurs. SIZE: Medium. *STOCK: English longcase clocks, 18th-19th C, £1,500-£8,000; English, German and French mantel and wall clocks, 19th C, £300-£3,500; aneroid and mercurial barometers, 18th-19th C, £150-£3,000.* LOC: 1 mile from town centre and minster, 300 yards from Army Museum of Transport. PARK: Easy. TEL: 01482 881574; home - same. SER: Valuations; restorations (clocks and barometers). VAT: Stan/Spec.

BRIDLINGTON

C. J. and A. J. Dixon Ltd
1st Floor, 23 Prospect St. YO15 2AE. Est. 1969. Open 9.30-5. SIZE: Large. *STOCK: British war medals and decorations.* LOC: Town centre. PARK: Easy. TEL: 01262 676877/603348; fax - 01262 606600; e-mail - chris@dixonsmedals.co.uk; website - www.dixonsmedals.com. SER: Valuations; renovations. VAT: Stan/Spec.

Priory Antiques
47-49 High St. YO16 4PR. (P. R. Rogerson). Est. 1979. Open Tues. and Fri. 10-5, Sat. 10-12. SIZE: Large. *STOCK: Georgian and Victorian furniture.* TEL: 01262 601365.

Sedman Antiques
106 Cardigan Rd. YO15 3LR. (R. H. S. and M. A. Sedman). Est. 1971. Open 10-5.30, Sun. by appointment. *STOCK: General antiques, period and shipping furniture, Oriental porcelain, Victorian collectors' items.* TEL: 01262 675671.

DRIFFIELD

The Antique Pine & Country Furniture Shop
58A Middle St. North. YO25 6SU. (D. A. Smith). Est. 1977. Open 9.30-5.30, Sat. 9.30-5, Sun. by appointment. SIZE: Medium + warehouse. *STOCK: Furniture including pine and country, 18th to early 20th C, £50-£2,000; furniture designed and made to order, from £50+.* LOC: Main street. PARK: Easy. TEL: 01377 256321; home - same; fax - 01377 256070; e-mail - dave@pine-on-line.co.uk; website - www.pine-on-line.co.uk. SER: Restorations.

The Crested China Co
Station House. YO25 6PX. (D. Taylor). Est. 1978. By appointment or by chance. *STOCK: Goss and crested china.* PARK: Easy. TEL: 01377 257042

(24 hr.); e-mail - dt@thecrestedchinacompany. com; website - www.thecrestedchinacompany. com. SER: Sales catalogues.

Karen Guest Antiques
80A Middle St. South. YO25 7QE. NAG registered Valuer and Jeweller. HRD Diploma of Diamond Grading. Est. 1989. Open 9.30-5. SIZE: Small. *STOCK: Jewellery and silver, 18th-20th C, £50-£5,000.* TEL: 01377 241467; website - www. michaelphilips.com. SER: Valuations; restorations. VAT: Stan/Spec.

FLAMBOROUGH, Nr. Bridlington

Lesley Berry Antiques
The Manor House. YO15 1PD. (Mrs L. Berry). Resident. Est. 1972. Open 9.30-5.30, other times by appointment. SIZE: Small. *STOCK: Furniture, silver, jewellery, amber, Whitby jet, oils, watercolours, prints, copper, brass, textiles, fountain pens, secondhand and antiquarian books on-line.* Not Stocked: Shipping goods. LOC: On corner of Tower St. and Lighthouse Rd. PARK: Easy. TEL: 01262 850943; e-mail - lb@flamboroughmanor. co.uk; website - www. flamborough manor.co.uk. SER: Buys at auction.

GILBERDYKE

Lewis E. Hickson FBHI
Antiquarian Horologist, Sober Hill Farm. HU15 2TB. Est. 1965. Open by appointment only. SIZE: Small. *STOCK: Longcase, bracket clocks, barometers and instruments.* TEL: 01430 449113. SER: Restorations; repairs.

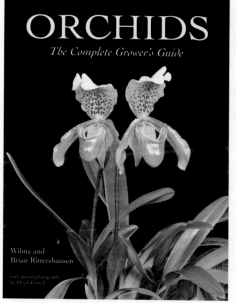

HULL

Grannie's Parlour
33 Anlaby Rd. HU1 2PG. (A. and Mrs. N. Pye). Est. 1974. Open 11-5. CL: Thurs. *STOCK: General antiques, ephemera, Victoriana, dolls, toys, kitchenalia.* LOC: Near railway and bus station. PARK: Nearby. TEL: 01482 228258; home - 01482 341020.

Grannie's Treasures
1st Floor, 33 Anlaby Rd. HU1 2PG. (Mrs N. Pye). Est. 1974. Open 11-5. CL: Thurs. *STOCK: Advertising items, dolls prams, toys, small furniture, china and pre-1940s clothing.* LOC: Near railway and bus station. PARK: Nearby. TEL: 01482 228258; home - 01482 341020.

David Hakeney Antiques
P O Box 65. HU10 7XT. Est. 1970. Open by appointment only. *STOCK: Porcelain, silver, clocks and watches, 19th C and Edwardian furniture, decorative items.* TEL: 01482 651177; fax - same; mobile - 07860 507774. FAIRS: NEC (April, Aug. and Dec.); Newark; Harrogate. VAT: Global.

Hull Antique Centre
Anderson Wharf, Wincolmlee. HU2 8AH. (Melvin Anderson). Est. 1975. Open 9-5, Sat. and Sun. 10-4. SIZE: Large. *STOCK: Furniture, period, Victorian and Edwardian, 17th to early 20th C, £50-£3,000.* LOC: From M64 take Clive Sullivan Way. PARK: Easy. TEL: 01482 609958. SER: Valuations. FAIRS: Newark, Swinderby, York, Ardingly, Harrogate, Birmingham. VAT: Stan/Spec.

Imperial Antiques
397 Hessle Rd. HU3 4EH. (M. Langton). Est. 1982. Open 9-5.30. *STOCK: British stripped pine furniture, antique, old and reproduction.* TEL: 01482 327439. FAIRS: Newark, Ardingly. VAT: Stan.

Kevin Marshall's Antiques Warehouse
17-20A Wilton St., Holderness Rd. HU8 7LG. Est. 1981. Open 10-5 including Sun. SIZE: Large. *STOCK: Bathroom ware, architectural items, fires, lighting, furniture and reproductions, 19th C, £5-£5,000.* LOC: 1st right off Dansom Lane South. PARK: Easy. TEL: 01482 326559; fax - same; e-mail - kevinmarshall@antiquewarehouse.karoo.co.uk. SER: Valuations; restorations; boardroom tables made to order. VAT: Stan/Spec.

Sandringham Antiques
64a Beverley Rd. HU5 1NE. (P. Allison). Est. 1968. *STOCK: General antiques.* TEL: 01482 847653/320874.

MARKET WEIGHTON, Nr. York

Garforth Gallery
57 Market Place. YO43 3AJ. Est. 1956. Open 10.30-4. CL: Thurs. SIZE: Small. *STOCK: Paintings, prints, maps, clocks, jewellery, silver, some porcelain, £20-£600.* LOC: On main road in town centre. TEL: 01430 803173. SER: Valuations; restorations.

Houghton Hall Antiques
Cliffe/North Cave Rd. YO43 3RE. (M. E. Watson). Est. 1965. Open daily 8-4, Sun. 11-4. SIZE: Large. *STOCK: Furniture, 17th-19th C, £5-£8,000; china, 19th C, £1-£600; paintings and prints, £20-£1,000; objets d'art.* Not Stocked: Coins, guns. LOC: Turn right on new by-pass from York (left coming from Beverley), ¾ mile, signposted North Cave - sign on entrance. PARK: Easy. TEL: 01430 873234. SER: Valuations; restorations (furniture); buys at auction. FAIRS: New York. VAT: Stan/Spec.

Pieter Plantenga
49 Holme Rd. YO43 3EW. Open 9-4.30. *STOCK: Stripped pine, general furniture.* TEL: 01430 872473.

NORTH CAVE

Penny Farthing Antiques
Albion House, 18 Westgate. (C. E. Dennett). Est. 1987. Open 9.30-6. SIZE: Medium. *STOCK: 19th-20th C furniture, Victorian brass and iron bedsteads, £25-£2,000; linen, textiles and samplers, 18th-20th C, £5-£500; general collectables, china and glass, 19th-20th C, £5-£500.* LOC: Main road (B1230). PARK: Easy. TEL: 01430 422958; mobile - 07980 624583. SER: Valuations; buys at auction. FAIRS: Newark.

PATRINGTON

Clyde Antiques
12 Market Place. HU12 0RB. (S. M. Nettleton). Est. 1978. Open 10-5. CL: Sun., Mon. and Wed. except by appointment. SIZE: Medium. *STOCK: General antiques.* PARK: Easy. TEL: 01964 630650; home - 01964 612471. SER: Valuations. VAT: Stan.

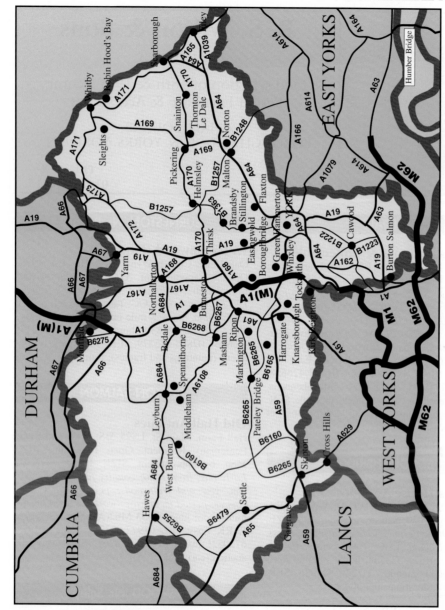

Dealers and Shops in North Yorkshire

						Sleights	1
Bedale	1	Green Hammerton	1	Masham	1	Snainton	1
Boroughbridge	3	Harrogate	25	Middleham	2	Spennithorne	1
Brandsby	1	Hawes	1	Northallerton	1	Stillington	2
Burneston	1	Helmsley	3	Norton	1	Thirsk	5
Burton Salmon	1	Kirk Deighton	1	Pateley Bridge	2	Thornton le Dale	1
Cawood	1	Knaresborough	4	Pickering	2	Tockwith	1
Cross Hills	1	Leyburn	1	Ripon	4	West Burton	1
Easingwold	5	Lythe	1	Robin Hood's Bay	1	Whitby	5
Filey	1	Malton	2	Scarborough	2	Whixley	1
Flaxton	1	Manfield	1	Settle	5	Yarm	1
Gargrave	4	Markington	1	Skipton	3	York	16

George III Mahogany Bureau in original condition.

R. S. Wilson & Sons
Antiques

Good selection of 18th & 19th Century
Period Furniture & Accessories

4 HALL SQUARE,
BOROUGHBRIDGE, N. YORKS. YO51 9AN.

EST.
1917

TEL/FAX
01423 322417

BEDALE

Bennett's Antiques & Collectables
7 Market Place. DL8 1ED. (Paul and Kim Bennett). Est. 1996. Open 9-5, Sun. by appointment. SIZE: Large. *STOCK: Furniture, 18th to early 20th C, £100-£10,000; fine art, 19th to early 20th C, £100-£6,000; clocks, 19th to early 20th C, £200-£4,000; collectables, 19th-20th C, £20-£2,000; local works of art, 20th C, £100-£1,000.* LOC: Off A1. PARK: Easy and free. TEL: 01677 427900; fax - 01677 426858; mobile - 07711 054219; e-mail - info@bennetts.uk.com; website - www.bennetts.uk.com. SER: Restorations; clock repairs; exhibitions of Yorkshire artists. VAT: Spec.

BOROUGHBRIDGE

St. James House Antiques
St. James Sq. YO51 9AR. (J. D. Wilson). Est. 1989. Open 9-5.30, Sun. by appointment. SIZE: Small. *STOCK: Period and later furniture, brass, copper and china.* LOC: Town centre. PARK: Own. TEL: 01423 322508; home - same; fax - 01423 326690; mobile - 07720 544926. SER: Valuations; restorations; upholstery.

R. S. Wilson and Sons
4 Hall Square. YO51 9AN. Est. 1917. Open 9-5.30, Thurs. and Sun. by appointment. *STOCK: 17th-19th C furniture and accessories.* PARK: Nearby. TEL: 01423 322417; fax - same. VAT: Stan/Spec.

BRANDSBY

L. L. Ward and Son
Bar House. YO61 4RQ. (R. Ward). Est. 1970. Open 8.30-5. *STOCK: Antique pine.* TEL: 01347 888651

BURNESTON, Nr. Bedale

W. Greenwood (Fine Art)
Oak Dene, Church Wynd. DL8 2JE. Est. 1978. Open by appointment. *STOCK: Paintings and watercolours, 19th-20th C, £100-£5,000; frames, £20-£500; mirrors.* LOC: Take B6285 left off A1 northbound, house ¼ mile on right. PARK: Easy. TEL: 01677 424830; home - 01677 423217; mobile - 07885 175279. SER: Valuations; restorations (paintings and frames); framing.

BURTON SALMON

Old Hall Antiques
Hall Farm, Main St. LS25 5JS. (J. T. and S. G. Fenteman). Resident. Open Tues.-Sun. 10-5, Mon. by appointment. SIZE: Large. *STOCK: Early oak, from 1600; country furniture in oak, elm, yew and fruitwoods; pewter, brass, and copper; period metalware; works of art.* LOC: 3 miles from junction 33 M62(A1) just off A162. PARK: Easy. TEL: 01977 607778; home - 01977 672052; fax - 01977 678261. SER: Buys at auction (early oak). VAT: Spec.

CAWOOD, Nr. Selby

Cawood Antiques
Sherburn St. YO8 3SS. (J. E. Gilham). Open 8-5. *STOCK: Furniture, copper, brass, weapons, medals, golfing memorabilia and collectors' items.* PARK: Easy. TEL: 01757 268533.

CROSS HILLS, Nr. Keighley

Heathcote Antiques
Skipton Rd. Junction. BD20 7DS. (M. Webster). Resident. Est. 1979. Open 10-5.30, Sun. 12.30-4.30. CL: Mon. and Tues. SIZE: Very large

showroom + trade warehouse. *STOCK: Furniture, clocks, barometers, unstripped English pine, pottery, porcelain, brass and metal wares.* PARK: Easy. TEL: 01535 635250; fax - 01535 637205; mobile - 07836 259640.

EASINGWOLD

Country House Furniture
108 Long St. YO61 3HY. (Mrs. J. O'Brien). Est. 1958. Open 10.15-5. *STOCK: Period pine and country furniture including upholstery and decorative items.* Not Stocked: Reproduction. PARK: Easy. TEL: 01347 822977.

Milestone Antiques
Farnley House, 101 Long St. YO61 3HY. (A. B. and S. J. Streetley). Est. 1982. Open daily, Sun. by appointment. SIZE: Medium. *STOCK: Mahogany and oak furniture especially dining tables, upholstered armchairs and sofas; longcase and wall clocks; all 18th to early 20th C.* LOC: Old A19, village centre. PARK: Easy. TEL: 01347 821608; home - same; e-mail - milestoneantiques-easingwold@fsmail.net. SER: Valuations. VAT: Stan/Spec.

Old Flames
30 Long St. YO61 3HT. (P. Lynas and J. J. Thompson). Est. 1988. Open 10-5. SIZE: Medium. *STOCK: Fireplaces, 18th-19th C, £100-£4,000; lighting, 19th C, £100-£5,000; architectural items, 18th-19th C, £50-£2,000.* PARK: Easy. TEL: 01347 821188; website - www.salvoweb.com/dealers/old-flames. SER: Valuations. FAIRS: Newark. VAT: Stan/Spec.

Mrs B. A. S. Reynolds
42 Long St. YO61 3HT. *STOCK: General antiques, Victorian.* TEL: 01347 821078.

The White House Antiques & Architectural Reclamation
Thirsk Rd. YO61 3NF. (G. Hood). Resident. Est. 1960. Usually open but prior 'phone call advisable. *STOCK: Rural and domestic bygones, stone troughs, architectural reclamation and garden ornaments.* LOC: 1 mile north of Easingwold, 200 yds from northern junction of bypass (A19). PARK: Easy. TEL: 01347 821479.

FILEY

Cairncross and Sons
31 Bellevue St. YO14 9HU. (G. Cairncross). Open 9.30-12.45 and 2-4.30. CL: Wed. pm. *STOCK: Medals, uniforms, insignia, cap badges.* Not Stocked: Weapons. TEL: 01723 513287.

FLAXTON, Nr. York

Elm Tree Antiques
YO60 7RJ. (R. and J. Jackson). Est. 1975. Open 9-5, (winter - 4.30) Sun. 10-5 (winter - Sat. and Sun. 10-4). SIZE: Large. *STOCK: Furniture, 17th C to Edwardian; small items, £5-£5,000, Staffordshire figures.* LOC: 1 mile off A64. PARK: Easy. TEL: 01904 468462; home - same; website - www.elmtreeantiques.co.uk. SER: Valuations; restorations (cabinet making, polishing and upholstery). FAIRS: Newark.

GARGRAVE, Nr. Skipton

Antiques at Forge Cottage
22A High St. BD23 3RB. Est. 1979. Open Wed. - Sat. 10-5. *STOCK: Pottery and porcelain.* LOC: A65. PARK: Easy. TEL: 01756 748272; mobile - 07860 525579; e-mail - philina@carrol. fsnet. co. uk. SER: Restorations; valuations. FAIRS: NEC; GMEX; Newark. VAT: Spec.

Bernard Dickinson
Estate Yard, West St. BD23 3PH. (H. H. and A. E. Mardall). Resident. Est. 1958. Open 9-5.30 or by appointment. *STOCK: Early English furniture.* LOC: Just off A65 Skipton-Settle road. PARK: Easy. TEL: 01756 748257. VAT: Spec.

Gargrave Gallery
48 High St. BD23 3RB. (B. Herrington). Appointment advisable. *STOCK: General antiques, oak, mahogany, metal, paintings, 18th to early 20th C.* LOC: A65. PARK: Easy. TEL: 01756 749641.

R. N. Myers and Son
BADA
Endsleigh House, High St. BD23 3LX. Est. 1890. Open 9-5.30 or by appointment. SIZE: Medium. *STOCK: Furniture, oak, mahogany, 17th to early 19th C; pottery, porcelain and metalware.* Not Stocked: Victoriana, weapons, coins, jewellery. LOC: A65. Skipton-Settle road. PARK: Behind shop and opposite. TEL: 01756 749587. SER: Valuations. VAT: Spec.

GREEN HAMMERTON, Nr. York

The Main Pine Co
Grangewood, The Green. YO26 8BQ. (C. and K. M. Main). Est. 1976. Open 9-5. SIZE: Large. *STOCK: Pine furniture, 18th-19th C, £100-£1,500; reproductions from reclaimed pine.* LOC: Just off A59. PARK: Easy. TEL: 01423 330451; home - 01423 331078; fax - 01423 331278; e-mail - sales@mainpinecompany.com; website - www.mainpinecompany.com. SER: Export; containers packed. VAT: Stan.

THE GINNEL ANTIQUES CENTRE HARROGATE		THE RED HOUSE ANTIQUES CENTRE YORK

50 specialist dealers with datelines stock in each centre
(see listings under Harrogate and York)

The Ginnel
Off Parliament St. (Opp. Debenhams)
HARROGATE 01423 508857

The Red House
Duncombe Place (100 yds. Minster)
YORK 01904 637000

HARROGATE

Nigel Adamson
Flat 1, 19 Park View. HG1 5LY. (N. J. G. Adamson). Est. 1863. Open by appointment only. *STOCK: Furniture, 17th to early 19th C; porcelain, Chinese, English and Continental.* TEL: 01423 528924; mobile - 07957 686493. SER: Valuations; restorations (furniture, porcelain). VAT: Spec.

Armstrong   BADA
10-11 Montpellier Parade. HG1 2TJ. (M. A. Armstrong). LAPADA. Est. 1983. Open 10-5.30. SIZE: Medium. *STOCK: Fine English furniture, 18th to early 19th C; glasses and works of art, 18th C.* **PARK: Easy. TEL: 01423 506843. FAIRS: Olympia (June, Nov). VAT: Spec.**

Bryan Bowden
Oakleigh, 1 Spacey View, Leeds Rd., Pannal. HG3 1LQ. Est. 1969. By appointment only. SIZE: Small. *STOCK: English pottery and porcelain, 1750-1850; small Georgian furniture.* LOC: 2. 5 miles south of Harrogate on Leeds road. PARK: Easy. TEL: 01423 870007; home - same. SER: Valuations; restorations (pottery and porcelain); buys at auction (English pottery and porcelain). FAIRS: Northern; Buxton; Wakefield Ceramic. VAT: Spec.

Derbyshire Antiques Ltd
27 Montpellier Parade. HG1 2TG. (R. C. Derbyshire). Est. 1960. Open 10-5.30. SIZE: Medium. *STOCK: Early oak and walnut, 16th-18th C; Georgian furniture to 1820; decorative items.* TEL: 01423 503115/564242; fax - 01423 709762. VAT: Spec.

Dragon Antiques
10 Dragon Rd. HG1 5DF. (P. F. Broadbelt). Resident. Est. 1954. Open 11-6. Always avail-able. SIZE: Small. *STOCK: Victorian art glass, £30-£300; art pottery, postcards, GB and foreign.* LOC: 5 mins. from town centre, opposite Dragon Road car park. PARK: Easy. TEL: 01423 562037.

Garth Antiques
16 Montpellier Parade. HG1 2TG. (J. and I. Chapman). LAPADA. Est. 1978. Open 10-5.30. SIZE: Large. *STOCK: Furniture, 18th-19th C, £500-£7,000; oils and watercolours, £200-£5,000.* PARK: Pay and Display, outside shop. TEL: 01423 530573. SER: Restorations; upholstery. VAT: Stan/Spec.

The Ginnel Antiques Centre
The Ginnel. HG1 2RB. (Pauline Stephenson). Est. 1986. Open 9.30-5.30. SIZE: Large. *STOCK: All date-lined and vetted - see individual entries.* LOC: Off Parliament St. opposite Debenhams. PARK: Nearby. TEL: 01423 508857; website - www.ginnel.co.uk and www.ginnel.com. SER: Courier. Below are listed the specialist dealers at this centre.

Anglo-Scandinavian
Cutlery, silver plate, inkwells, collectors' and decorative items.

Appleton Antiques
19th-20th pottery including Carlton, Moorcroft, Linthorpe, Poole and crested china; drinking glasses, paintings, small furniture.

Fiona Aston
Objets d'art including porcelain and miniatures.

M. Bedi
Fine 19th C furniture and paintings.

Brackmoor Antiques
Silver, porcelain and objets d'art.

Catkins Jewellery
Victorian and Edwardian jewellery, Royal Worcester porcelain.

J.E. Chew
19th to early 20th C silver and plate.

The Clock Inn
(R.K. Mayes). *Clocks.* SER: Repairs; restorations.

D. Cocking
19th to early 20th C oil paintings and watercolours.

Mary Cooper
Antique costumes and textiles, to 1929, including lace, fans, shawls, linen, quilts, samplers, wool and beadwork.

Cornmill Antiques
19th to early 20th C china, especially Royal Doulton.

G. Ford & Sons Ltd. (I.G.F. Thomson)
18th-19th C mahogany and country furniture.

Jeffrey and Pauline Glass
Porcelain and glass, objets d'art, 19th to early 20th C.

R. Himsworth
Silver and jewellery.

James & Morton Fine Art & Antiques
19th C furniture, oil paintings and watercolours.

S. Judge
20th C pottery and porcelain including Shelley, Doulton, Bretby, Charlotte Rhead, Moorcroft.

G. Kendall
Furniture and collectables.

Kismet
Art Deco Jewellery.

Ian. P. Legard
18th-19th C silver.

Brian Loomes
Longcase clocks, small period furniture.

E.R. Marris
19th C silver.

Sheila Morgan
Victorian collectables.

O'Flynn
19th-20th C prints and books.

Octavia Antiques
1920's, 1930's pottery and porcelain.

Parker Gallery
19th to early 20th C oils and watercolours, £100-£3,000.

Paul Raine
19th C silver.

Graham Reed Fine Art
19th C porcelain, mirrors and pictures.

G. Rhodes
19th C furniture and objets d'art.

G.M. Ritchie
Porcelain, copper and brass, linen.

Rose Fine Art
19th to early 20th C prints and engravings.

Alan Sharp
English pottery and porcelain, 1750-1850.

Stella-Mar
Fine 19th C furniture and furnishings, objets d'art.

Tango Curios
19th-20th C collectables.

John Tee
Oriental rugs.

C.E. Tweedale
Victorian and Edwardian pottery.

E.H. Ward
Pottery, porcelain and glass.

Ann Wilkinson
Silver, porcelain and jewellery.

Eileen Wilson
Victorian and Edwardian jewellery.

Michael Green Pine & Country Antiques

Library House, Regent Parade. HG1 5AN. Est. 1976. Open 8.30-5.30, Sat. 8.45-4, Sun. by appointment. SIZE: Medium. *STOCK: Oak, mahogany and pine furniture, from 17th C, £5-£3,000; treen, kitchenalia and collectors treasures.* LOC: Overlooking the Stray. PARK: Easy. TEL: 01423 560452. SER: Valuations; restorations; stripping. VAT: Stan/Spec.

Havelocks

13-17 Westmoreland St. HG1 5AY. (Philip Adam). Est. 1989. Open 10-5 including Sun. SIZE: Large. *STOCK: Original pine, oak, general antique furniture.* LOC: A59 towards Skipton, turn left into Westmoreland St. PARK: Free. TEL: 01423 506721. SER: Valuations; restorations; stripping and finishing.

London House Oriental Rugs and Carpets

9 Montpellier Parade. HG1 2TJ. Est. 1981. Open 10-5. SIZE: Medium. *STOCK: Persian, Turkish, Indian, Tibetan, Nepalese and Afghan rugs and carpets, 19th-20th C, £25-£5,000; kelims and camel bags, 19th-20th C, £25-£2,000.* LOC: Town centre on The Stray. PARK: Easy. TEL: 01423 567167; home - 01937 845123. SER: Valuations; restorations (handmade rugs). VAT: Stan.

David Love   BADA

10 Royal Parade. HG1 2SZ. Est. 1969. Open 9-1 and 2-5.30. SIZE: Large. *STOCK: Furniture, English, 17th-19th C; pottery and porcelain, English and Continental; decorative items, all periods.* LOC: Opposite Pump Room Museum. PARK: Easy. TEL: 01423 565797/525567. SER: Valuations; buys at auction. VAT: Stan/Spec.

Charles Lumb and Sons Ltd   BADA

2 Montpellier Gardens. HG1 2TF. (F. and A. R. Lumb). Est. 1920. Open 10-1 and 2-6. SIZE: Medium. *STOCK: Furniture, 17th to early 19th C; metalware, period accessories.* PARK: 20yds. immediately opposite. TEL: 01423 503776; home - 01423 863281; fax - 01423 530074. VAT: Spec.

McTague of Harrogate

17/19 Cheltenham Mount. HG1 1DW. (P. McTague). Open 11-5. CL: Mon. SIZE: Medium. *STOCK: Prints, watercolours, some oil paintings, mainly 18th to early 20th C.* LOC: From Conference Centre on Kings Rd., go up Cheltenham Parade and turn first left. PARK: Easy. TEL: 01423 567086; fax - 01423 564539. VAT: Stan/Spec.

Montpellier Mews Antique Market

Montpellier St. HG1 2TG. Open 10-5. SIZE: Various dealers. *STOCK: General antiques - porcelain, jewellery, furniture, paintings, interior decor, golf memorabilia, linen, glass and silver.* LOC: Behind Weatherells Antiques. TEL: 01423 530484.

Ogden of Harrogate Ltd   BADA

38 James St. HG1 1RQ. Est. 1893. Open 9. 15-5. SIZE: Large. *STOCK: Jewellery, English silver and plate.* PARK: Easy. TEL: 01423 504123; fax - 01423 522283; e-mail - sales@ ogden-of-harrogate.co.uk; website - www. ogden-of-harrogate.co.uk. SER: Repairs; restorations; valuations. VAT: Stan/Spec.

Paraphernalia

38A Cold Bath Rd. HG2 0NA. (Peter F. Hacker). Est. 1986. Open 10-5. *STOCK: Wallplates, crested and commemorative china, cutlery, glass including carnival, Mauchlineware, bric-a-brac, small furniture.* PARK: Outside shop. TEL: Evenings - 01423 567968. FAIRS: Newark.

Paul M. Peters Antiques

15a Bower Rd. HG1 1BE. LAPADA. Est. 1967. Open 10-5. CL: Sat. SIZE: Medium. *STOCK: Chinese and Japanese ceramics and works of art, 17th-19th C; European ceramics and glass, 18th-19th C; European metalware, scientific instruments and unusual objects.* LOC: Town centre, at bottom of Station Parade. PARK: Easy. TEL: 01423 560118. SER: Valuations. VAT: Stan/Spec.

Elaine Phillips Antiques Ltd   BADA

1 and 2 Royal Parade. HG1 2SZ. (Colin, Elaine and Louise Phillips). Est. 1968. Open 9.30-5.30, other times by appointment. SIZE: Large. *STOCK: Oak furniture, 1600-1800; country furniture, 1700-1840; some mahogany, 18th to early 19th C; period metalwork and decoration.* LOC: Opposite Crown Hotel, Montpellier Quarter. PARK: Nearby. TEL: 01423 569745; fax - 01977 620868; e-mail - ep@heliscott.co.uk. FAIRS: Harrogate (Spring, Autumn). VAT: Spec.

Smith's (The Rink) Ltd

Dragon Rd. HG1 5DR. Est. 1906. Open 9-5.30, Sun. 11-4.30. SIZE: Large. *STOCK: General antiques, 1750-1820, £150; Victoriana, 1830-1900, £50.* LOC: From Leeds, right at Prince of Wales roundabout, left at next roundabout, ½ mile on Skipton Rd., left into Dragon Rd. PARK: Easy. TEL: 01423 567890. VAT: Stan/Spec.

Sutcliffe Galleries   BADA

5 Royal Parade. HG1 2SZ. Est. 1947. Open 10-5. *STOCK: Paintings, 19th C.* LOC: Opposite Crown Hotel. TEL: 01423 562976; fax - 01423 528729; website - www.sutcliffegalleries.co.uk. SER: Valuations; restorations; framing. FAIRS: Harrogate. VAT: Spec.

Thorntons of Harrogate

1 Montpellier Gdns. HG1 2TF. LAPADA. Est. 1971. Open 9.30-5.30. SIZE: Medium. *STOCK: 17th-19th C furniture, metalware, clocks, paintings, porcelain, scientific instruments.* PARK: Easy. TEL: 01423 504118; fax - 01423 528400; e-mail - info@harrogateantiques.com; website - www. harrogateantiques.com. SER: Valuations. FAIRS: Harrogate (Spring). VAT: Spec.

Walker Galleries Ltd

BADA

6 Montpellier Gdns. HG1 2TF. LAPADA. Est. 1972. Open 9.30-1 and 2-5.30. SIZE: Medium. *STOCK: Oil paintings and watercolours, 18th C furniture.* TEL: 01423 567933; fax - 01423 536664; e-mail - wgltd@aol.com; websites - www.walkergalleries.com and www.walker fineart.co.uk. SER: Valuations; restorations; framing. FAIRS: BADA, London; Harrogate: Olympia. VAT: Spec.

Weatherell's of Harrogate Antiques and Fine Arts

29 Montpellier Parade. HG1 2TG. LAPADA. Open 9-5.30. SIZE: Large. *STOCK: Period and fine decorative furniture.* TEL: 01423 507810/ 525004; fax - 01423 520005.

Chris Wilde Antiques

134 King's Rd. HG1 5HY. (C. B. Wilde). LAPADA. Est. 1996. Open 10-5 or by appointment. SIZE: Large. *STOCK: Furniture, 1680-1920, £300-£8,000; longcase clocks, 1720-1920, £500-£5,000; ceramics, glass and pictures.* LOC: North side of town. PARK: Easy. TEL: 01423 525855; mobile - 07831 543268; e-mail - chris@ harrogate.com; website - www.antiques. harrogate. com. SER: Valuations. VAT: Stan/Spec.

Yorkshire Country Wines & Antiques

The Mill, Glasshouses. HG3 5QH. (Richard Brown). Est. 1980. Open Wed.-Sun. 11.30-4.30, (reduced hours Jan. and Feb) - most times by appointment. SIZE: Medium. *STOCK: Oak and country furniture, 17th-19th C, £50-£5,000.* LOC: 1/4 mile from crossroads of B6165. PARK: Easy. TEL: 01423 711947; fax - same; home - 01423 711223. VAT: Spec.

Sturman's Antiques

Main St. DL8 3QW. LAPADA. Open 10-5 including Sun. *STOCK: Georgian and Victorian furniture; porcelain, silver plate, paintings; longcase, wall and mantel clocks.* PARK: Opposite. TEL: 01969 667742; fax - same. VAT: Spec.

E. Stacy-Marks Limited

10 Castlegate. YO62 5BZ. Est. 1889. *STOCK: Paintings, English, Dutch and Continental schools, 18th-20th C.* TEL: 01439 771950; fax - 01439 771859.

Westway Pine

Carlton Lane. YO62 5HB. (J. and J. Dzierzek). Est. 1987. Open 9-5, Sat. 10-5, other times by appointment. SIZE: Medium. *STOCK: Pine furniture, 19th C, £20-£2,000.* LOC: From A170 from Scarborough, first right into town, first left, then left again 100m. PARK: Easy. TEL: 01439 771399. SER: Valuations; restorations (pine).

York Cottage Antiques

7 Church St. YO62 5AD. (G. and E. M. Thornley). LAPADA. Est. 1976. Open Fri. and Sat. 10-4 or by appointment. *STOCK: Early oak and country furniture; 18th-19th C metalware.* LOC: Opposite church. PARK: Adjacent. TEL: 01439 770833; home - same.

Elden Antiques

23 Ashdale View. LS22 4DS. (E. and D. Broadley). Est. 1970. Open 9-6, Sat. 12-5.30. SIZE: Medium. *STOCK: General antiques including furniture.* LOC: Main road between Wetherby and Knaresborough. PARK: Easy. TEL: 01937 584770; home - same; e-mail - elden. antiques@virgin.net.

Robert Aagaard & Co

Frogmire House, Stockwell Rd. HG5 0JP. Est. 1961. Open 9-5, Sat. 10-4. SIZE: Medium. *STOCK: Chimney pieces, marble fire surrounds and interiors.* LOC: Town centre. PARK: Own. TEL: 01423 864805. VAT: Stan.

Bowkett

9 Abbey Rd. HG5 8HY. (E. S. Starkie). Resident. Est. 1919. Open 9-6. SIZE: Medium. *STOCK: Chairs, small furniture, brass, copper, pot-lids, Goss, books.* LOC: By the river at the lower road bridge. PARK: Easy. TEL: 01423 866112. SER: Restorations (upholstery and small furniture).

Omar (Harrogate) Ltd

21 Boroughbridge Rd. Est. 1946. Open by appointment. *STOCK: Persian, Turkish, Caucasian rugs and carpets.* PARK: Easy. TEL: 01423 863199; fax - same. SER: Cleaning and restoration. VAT: Stan.

John Thompson Antiques

Swadforth House, Gracious St. HG5 8DT. LAPADA. Est. 1968. *STOCK: 18th-19th C furniture and related decorative objects.* PARK: Easy. TEL: 01423 864698. FAIRS: Olympia. VAT: Spec.

LEYBURN

Thirkill Antiques
Newlands, Worton. DL8 3ET. Est. 1963. *STOCK: Musicals, pottery, porcelain, small furniture, 18th-19th C.* PARK: Easy. TEL: 01969 650725. SER: Restorations.

LYTHE, Nr. Whitby

Lythe Cottage Antiques
High St. (Mrs. Lynne Robinson). *STOCK: Victorian, Edwardian, early oak and country cottage furniture.* LOC: Three miles from Whitby towards Staithes. PARK: Easy. TEL: Mobile - 07961 828679. SER: Valuations.

MALTON

Malton Antique Market
2 Old Maltongate. YO17 0EG. (Mrs M. A. Cleverly). Est. 1970. Open 9.30-12.30 and 2-5. CL: Thurs. SIZE: Medium. *STOCK: Furniture, Georgian to Victorian, to £1,500; glass, bric-a-brac, porcelain, pottery, copper, brass, silver and plate.* LOC: From York take A64, shop is at main traffic light junction in Malton. PARK: 20yds. further. TEL: 01653 692732.

Talents Fine Arts Ltd
7 Market Place. YO17 7LP. (L. Vaughan). Est. 1986. Open daily. SIZE: Medium. *STOCK: Oils, watercolours and prints, £500-£3,000; contemporary local artists.* LOC: A64 near church. PARK: Easy. TEL: 01653 600020. SER: Restorations; framing.

MANFIELD, Nr. Darlington

Joan and David White
Lucy Cross Cottage. DL2 2RJ. Est. 1975. Open after prior telephone call. *STOCK: Georgian, Victorian and export furniture.* LOC: B6275, Scotch Corner to Piercebridge road, on left 3 miles after leaving A1. PARK: Easy. TEL: 01325 374303; mobile - 07779 206036. VAT: Stan/Spec.

MARKINGTON, Nr. Harrogate

Daleside Antiques
Hinks Hall Lane. HG3 3NU. Est. 1978. Open 8-5, Sat. and Sun. by appointment. *STOCK: Pine furniture, decorative items, architectural features and fittings, 18th-19th C, £50-£3,500; Georgian mahogany furniture; Victorian shop fittings.* TEL: 01765 677888; fax - 01765 677886; e-mail - sales@daleside.net; website - www.daleside.net. SER: Containers; restorations. VAT: Stan.

MASHAM, Nr. Ripon

Aura Antiques
1-3 Silver St. HG4 4DX. (R. and R. Sutcliffe). Est. 1985. Open 9.30-4.30, Sun. by appointment. SIZE: Medium. *STOCK: Furniture especially period mahogany dining furniture, 18th to mid-19th C, £50-£5,000; metalware - brass and copper, fenders, £5-£250; china, glass, silver and decorative objects, £5-£1,000; all 18th-19th C.* LOC: Corner of Market Sq. PARK: Easy. TEL: 01765 689315; home - 01765 658192; e-mail - Robert@aura-antiques.co.uk; website - www. aura-antiques.co.uk. SER: Valuations; delivery throughout UK. VAT: Spec.

MIDDLEHAM, Nr. Leyburn

Castle Antiques Centre
34 Market Pl. DL8 4QW. (Derek and Joanne Jarvill). Est. 1994. Open 10-5.30 including Sun., Tues by appointment. SIZE: Medium (5 rooms). *STOCK: Georgian, Victorian and Edwardian furniture, pottery, porcelain, glass, clocks, metalware, treen, Art Nouveau, jewellery, general antiques and collectables.* LOC: Town centre. PARK: Easy. TEL: 01969 624655.

Middleham Antiques
The Corner Shop, Kirkgate. DL8 4PF. (Mike Pitman). Est. 1984. Open 10-5.30 most days, Wed. by appointment - prior 'phone call advisable. *STOCK: Pre 1830 oak and country furniture, longcase clocks, curios, ceramics, pewter, £20-£7,000.* PARK: Easy. TEL: 01969 622982; fax - same; websites - www.middlehamonlin.com/middleham-antiques.htm.

NORTHALLERTON

Collectors Corner
145/6 High St. DL7 8SL. (J. Wetherill). Est. 1972. Open 10-4 or by appointment. CL: Thurs. *STOCK: General antiques, collectors' items.* LOC: Opposite GPO. TEL: 01609 777623; home - 01609 775199.

NORTON, Nr. Malton

Northern Antiques Company
2 Parliament St., Scarborough Rd. YO17 9HE. (Sara Ashby-Arnold). Est. 1991. Open 9-1 and 2-5, Sat. 9.30-12.30, Sun. and evenings by appointment. SIZE: Medium. *STOCK: Country oak furniture, from 17th C, £200-£2,000; pine, Georgian to Victorian, to £1,000; upholstered sofas and chairs, cast-iron and wooden beds, decorative items and prints, from 19th C, to £800; some contemporary interior design items.* LOC: From Malton town centre on old Scarborough Rd., through Norton, shop on right above Aga shop. PARK: Easy. TEL: 01653 697520.

PATELEY BRIDGE

Brian Loomes
Calf Haugh Farm. HG3 5HW. (Brian and Joy Loomes). (Author of clock reference books). Est. 1966. Open strictly by appointment. SIZE: Medium. *STOCK: British clocks especially longcase, wall, bracket and lantern, pre-1840, £500-£15,000.* Not Stocked: Foreign clocks. LOC: From Pateley Bridge, first private lane on left on Grassington Rd. (B6265). PARK: Own. TEL: 01423 711163; home and fax - same; website - www.brianloomes.com. VAT: Spec.

Pateley Bridge Antiques
The Apothecary's House, 35 High St. HG3 5JZ. (A. D. Gora). Est. 1995. Open Mon. -Fri. 10-5.30 or by appointment. SIZE: Medium. *STOCK: Oak and country furniture, 17th-18th C, £100-£10,000; longcase clocks, £1,000-£3,000; metalware including copper and pewter, 17th-19th C, £30-£500.* LOC: Ripon-Grassington road. PARK: Almost opposite. TEL: 01423 711004; e-mail - info@earlyoak.co.uk; website - www.earlyoak.co.uk. SER: Valuations.

PICKERING

Country Collector
11-12 Birdgate. YO18 7AL. (G. and M. Berney). Est. 1991. Open 10-5. CL: Wed. SIZE: Small. *STOCK: Ceramics, including blue and white and Art Deco pottery, and collectables, 1800-1940, £10-£1,000.* LOC: Top of the Market Place, at crossroads of A169 and A170. PARK: Eastgate. TEL: 01751 477481. SER: Valuations; buys at auction (ceramics). VAT: Stan.

C. H. Reynolds Antiques
The Old Curiosity Shop, 122 Eastgate. YO18

7DW. Est. 1947. Open 9.30-5.30, Sun. by appointment. *STOCK: General antiques.* PARK: Free, outside shop. TEL: 01751 472785.

RIPON

Milton Holgate   BADA
P O Box 77. HG4 3XX. Est. 1972. By appointment only. *STOCK: Fine English furniture and accessories, 17th-19th C.* TEL: 01765 620225.

Sigma Antiques and Fine Art
The Old Opera House, Water Skellgate. HG4 1BH. (D. Thomson). Est. 1963. Open 10.30-5, other times by appointment. SIZE: Large. *STOCK: 17th-20th C furniture, furnishing items, pottery, porcelain, objets d'art, paintings, jewellery and collectors' items.* LOC: Near Town centre. PARK: Nearby. TEL: 01765 603163; fax - same; e-mail - sigmaantiques@aol.com. VAT: Spec.

Skellgate Curios
2 Low Skellgate. HG4 1BE. (J. I. Wain and P. S. Gyte). Est. 1974. Open 11-5. CL: Wed. *STOCK: Furniture, decorative antiques, period jewellery, silver, brass, copper and collectors items.* TEL: 01765 601290; home - 01765 635336/635332.

ROBIN HOOD'S BAY

John Gilbert Antiques
King St. YO22 4SH. Est. 1990. Open Sat. 10-1 and 2-5, Sun. 11-4, other days by appointment. SIZE: Small. *STOCK: Country furniture, 18th-19th C, £100-£1,000; oak furniture from 1650, £250-£1,500; Victorian furniture, £50-£1,000; treen, £5-£150.* LOC: At bottom of old village, between Bay and Dolphin Hotels. PARK: Top of hill. TEL: Home - 01947 880528. SER: Valuations; restorations (furniture).

SCARBOROUGH

Hanover Antiques & Collectables
33 St Nicolas Cliff. YO11 2ES. (R. E. and P. J. Baldwin). Est. 1976. Open 10-4. CL: Wed. pm. *STOCK: Small collectables, medals, badges, toys, 50p-£500.* PARK: Nearby. TEL: 01723 374175.

Shuttleworths
7 Victoria Rd. YO11 1SB. (L. R. Shuttleworth). Open 10-4. CL: Wed. *STOCK: General antiques.* TEL: 01723 366278.

SETTLE

Mary Milnthorpe and Daughters Antique Shop
Market Place. BD24 9DX. Est. 1958. Open 9.30-5. CL: Wed. SIZE: Small. *STOCK: Antique and 19th C jewellery and English silver.* LOC: Opposite Town Hall. PARK: Easy. TEL: 01729 822331. VAT: Stan/Spec.

Nanbooks
Roundabout, 41 Duke St. BD24 9DJ. (J. L. and N. M. Midgley). Resident. Est. 1955. Open Tues., Fri. and Sat. 11-12.30 and 2-5.30. CL: Nov. -Feb. SIZE: Small. *STOCK: English pottery, porcelain including Oriental, glass, general small antiques, 17th-19th C, to £500.* Not Stocked: Jewellery. LOC: A65. PARK: Easy. TEL: 01729 823324.

Anderson Slater Antiques
6 Duke St. BD24 7DW. (K. C. Slater). Est. 1962. Open 10-1 and 2-5. CL: Wed. SIZE: Medium. *STOCK: Furniture, 18th-19th C, £200-£4,000; porcelain, 18th-19th C, £25-£500; pictures, 19th-20th C, £200-£1,500.* LOC: Main street out of Market Place. PARK: Nearby. TEL: 01729 822051. SER: Valuations; restorations (furniture and porcelain); buys at auction. VAT: Stan/Spec.

E. Thistlethwaite
The Antique Shop, Market Sq. BD24 9EF. Est. 1972. Open 9-5. CL: Wed. SIZE: Medium. *STOCK: Country furniture and metalware, 18th-19th C.* LOC: Town centre, A65. PARK: Forecourt. TEL: 01729 822460. VAT: Stan/Spec.

SKIPTON

Adamson Armoury
Otley Rd. BD23 1ET. (J. K. Adamson). Est. 1975. Open by appointment only. SIZE: Medium. *STOCK: Weapons, 17th-19th C, £10-£1,000.* LOC: A65, 200yds. from town centre. PARK: At rear. TEL: 01756 791355. SER: Valuations. FAIRS: London.

Corn Mill Antiques
High Corn Mill, Chapel Hill. BD23 1NL. (Mrs M. Hawkridge). Est. 1984. Open 10-4. CL: Tues. and Wed. SIZE: Medium. *STOCK: Oak, mahogany and walnut furniture, £300-£2,000; porcelain, silver plate, prints, pictures, brass and copper, £20-£500; all Georgian to 1920's.* Not Stocked: Jewellery, gold and silver. LOC: From town centre take Grassington Road, Chapel Hill is first right. PARK: Easy. TEL: 01756 792440; home - 01729 830489. SER: Valuations. VAT: Spec.

Manor Barn
Providence Mill, The Old Foundry Yard, Cross St. BD23 2AE. (Manor Barn Furniture Ltd). Est. 1972. Open 9-5. *STOCK: Pine, 17th-19th C and reproduction; oak.* PARK: Easy. TEL: 01756 798584; fax - 01756 798536. VAT: Stan/Spec.

SLEIGHTS, Nr. Whitby

Eskdale Antiques
164 Coach Rd. YO22 4BH. (Philip Smith). Est. 1978. Open 9-5.30 including Sun. SIZE: Medium. *STOCK: Pine furniture and farm bygones, 19th-20th C, £50-£500.* LOC: Main Pickering road. PARK: Easy. TEL: 01947 810297; home - same. SER: Valuations; buys at auction.

SNAINTON, Nr. Scarborough

Antony, David & Ann Shackleton
19 & 72 High St. YO13 9AE. Resident. Est. 1984. Open every day. SIZE: Medium. *STOCK: Long-case clocks, Victorian rocking horses, Georgian and Victorian furniture, collectables, £1-£3,500.* LOC: A170, equidistant Scarborough and

Pickering. PARK: Easy. TEL: 01723 859577/ 850172. SER: Restorations (furniture, longcase clocks, rocking horses).

SPENNITHORNE, Nr. Leyburn

N. J. and C. S. Dodsworth
Thorney Hall. DL8 5PW. Est. 1973. Open by appointment. SIZE: Medium. *STOCK: Furniture, clocks and small items, 17th-19th C.* LOC: Off A684. TEL: 01969 622277. VAT: Margin

STILLINGTON

Pond Cottage Antiques
Brandsby Rd. YO61 1NY. (C. M. and D. Thurstans). Resident. Est. 1970. Open seven days 9-5. SIZE: Medium. *STOCK: Pine, kitchenalia, country furniture, treen, metalware, brass, copper.* LOC: B1363 York to Helmsley Rd. PARK: Own. TEL: 01347 810796.

Rose Fine Art and Antiques
Fox Inn Farm, Easingwold Rd. YO61 1LS. (Mr and Mrs S. Rose). Est. 1984. Open by appointment. *STOCK: Pictures, 18th to early 20th C, £5-£2,000.* PARK: Easy. TEL: 01347 810554. SER: Valuations; restorations (pictures). *Trade Only.*

THIRSK

Classic Rocking Horses
from Windmill Antiques. (B. and J. Tildesley). Est. 1980. Open by appointment only. *STOCK: Restored antique rocking horses and authentic replicas of Victorian rocking horses, £1,500-£5,000.* TEL: 01845 501330; fax - 01845 501700; e-mail - info@classicrockinghorses.co.uk; website - www.classicrockinghorses.co.uk.

Cottage Antiques and Curios
1 Market Place. YO7 1HQ. (Mrs E. H. and S. R. Ballard). Est. 1970. Open 9-4. CL: Wed. *STOCK: Victorian porcelain and glass, £5-£500; paintings, £20-£1,000, furniture, from 1750, £20-£1,000; brass, copper, silver and plated ware, £5-£500.* PARK: Easy. TEL: 01845 522536/523212.

Kirkgate Fine Art & Conservation
The Studio, 3 Gillings Yard. YO7 1SY. (Richard Bennett). ABPR. UKIC. SSCR. Est. 1979. Open by appointment. SIZE: Small. *STOCK: Oil paintings, £50-£2,000; watercolours, £50-£500; both 19th to mid-20th C.* LOC: Joins Market Place. PARK: Nearby. TEL: 01845 524085; home - same. SER: Restorations (oil paintings and framing); buys at auction.

Millgate Pine & Antiques
12 Millgate. YO7 1AA. (T. D. and M. Parvin). Est. 1990. Open 10-5, Sun. 10-5. SIZE: Large + warehouse. *STOCK: English and European pine especially doors.* PARK: Nearby. TEL: 01845 523878; e-mail - babs.jenkins@btinternet.com. SER: Repairs; stripping; restorations.

Potterton Books
The Old Rectory, Sessay. YO7 3LZ. (Clare Jameson). Open 9-5. SIZE: Large. *STOCK: Classic reference works on art, architecture, interior design, antiques and collecting.* TEL: 01845 501218; fax - 01845 501439; e-mail - pottertonbooks@sagehost.co.uk; website - www. pottertonbooks.co.uk. SER: Book search; catalogues. FAIRS: London; Frankfurt; Paris; New York; Milan; Dubai.

THORNTON DALE, Nr. Pickering

Stable Antiques
4 Pickering Rd. YO18 7LG. (Mrs S. Kitching Walker). Open 2-5, mornings by appointment. CL: Mon. SIZE: Medium. *STOCK: Porcelain, £5-£500; furniture, £20-£700; silver, glass, brass, plate, copper, collectors' items, £5-£150, all 19th C to 1930's.* LOC: A170. PARK: Easy. TEL: 01751 474332; home - 01751 474435; e-mail - yvonne@stable-antiques.co.uk; website - www. stable-antiques.co.uk. SER: Valuations.

(Left) A caneware jug with applied figures and an unusual hawthorn border, c.1825-35. (Centre) An earthenware soup dish transfer-printed in green with the 'Steamer Forfarshire' pattern, from a service made for use on board the ship, which was wrecked in 1838. (Right) A brown-glazed and gilded lidless Cadogan teapot, c.1825-35. Each piece bears a factory mark.

From an article entitled "Rockingham Pottery and Porcelain 1745-1842" by Alwyn and Angela Cox which appeared in the November 2001 issue of **Antique Collecting**. For more details and to subscribe see page 21.

TOCKWITH, Nr. York

Tomlinsons

Moorside. YO26 7QG. LAPADA. Est. 1971. Open, trade only, Mon-Fri. 8-4.30 or by appointment. Club members - Sat. 9-4.30 and Sun. 10-4. SIZE: Large. *STOCK: Furniture, £10-£20,000; clocks, porcelain, silver plate and decorative items, £10-£5,000.* LOC: A1 Wetherby take B1224 towards York. After 3 miles turn left on to Rudgate. At end of this road turn left, business 200m on left. PARK: Easy. TEL: 01423 358833; fax - 01423 358188; e-mail - sales@tomlinson.demon.co.uk; website - www.antique-furniture.co.uk. SER: Export; restorations; container packing, desk leathering. VAT: Stan/Spec.

WEST BURTON, Nr. Leyburn

The Old Smithy

DL8 4JL. (Bill Woodbridge, Lynn Watkinson and Pete and Elaine Dobbing). Est. 2000. Open 10-4, prior telephone call advisable for winter opening. SIZE: Small. *STOCK: General antiques, silver and jewellery, collectables, £5-£300; clocks and small furniture, £50-£1,000; all 18th-20th C.* LOC: Between Leyburn and Hawes, take Kettlewell road. PARK: Easy. TEL: 01969 663224; fax - same; mobile - 07881 985555. SER: Valuations; buys at auction. *Trade Only.*

WHITBY

Age of Jazz

85 Church St. YO22 4BH. (P. A. Smith). Est. 1983. Open 10.30-12.30 and 1-5 (Sat. and Sun. only Nov. to Mar.). SIZE: Medium. *STOCK: Clarice Cliff, £100-£750.* LOC: A174. PARK: Nearby. TEL: 01947 600512. SER: Valuations; buys at auction (Clarice Cliff).

The Bazaar

7 Skinner St. YO21 3AH. (F. A. Doyle). Est. 1970. Open 10.30-5.30. *STOCK: Jewellery, furniture, general antiques, 19th C.* TEL: 01947 602281.

'Bobbins' Wool, Crafts, Antiques

Wesley Hall, Church St. YO22 4DE. (D. and P. Hoyle). Open 10-5 every day. SIZE: Small. *STOCK: General antiques especially oil lamps, bric-a-brac, kitchenalia, 19th-20th C.* LOC: Between Market Place and steps to Abbey on cobbled East Side. PARK: Nearby (part of Church St. is pedestrianised). TEL: 01947 600585 (answerphone). SER: Repairs and spares (oil lamps). VAT: Stan.

Caedmon House

14 Station Sq. YO21 1DU. (E. M. Stanforth). Est. 1977. Open 12-4.30. SIZE: Medium. *STOCK: General, mainly small, antiques including jewellery, dolls, Disney and china, especially Dresden, to £1,200.* PARK: Easy. TEL: 01947 602120; home - 01947 603930. SER: Valuations; restorations (china); repairs (jewellery). VAT: Stan/Spec.

Coach House Antiques

75 Coach Rd., Sleights. YO22 5BT. (C. J. Rea). Resident. Est. 1973. Open Sat. from 10 and by appointment. SIZE: Small. *STOCK: Furniture, especially oak and country; metalware, paintings, pottery, textiles, unusual and decorative items.* LOC: On A169, 3 miles south west of Whitby. PARK: Easy, opposite. TEL: 01947 810313.

WHIXLEY

Garth Antiques

The Old School, Franks Lane. YO26 8AP. (I. Chapman). LAPADA. Est. 1978. Open Tues-Sat. 10-5. SIZE: Medium. *STOCK: Furniture, 18th-19th C, £50-£3,000; brass and copper, 19th C, £1-£500; oils and watercolours, £5-£3,000.* LOC: A59, turn towards Whixley at the Cattle/Whixley junction, then left opposite The Anchor into old village, next to Village Hall. PARK: Easy. TEL: 01423 331055; fax - 01423 331733. SER: Restorations. VAT: Stan/Spec.

YARM, Nr. Stockton-on-Tees

Ruby Snowden Antiques

10 High St. TS15 9QZ. (R. H. Snowden). Est. 1977. Open 9-5.30, Wed. 9-5, Sun. by appointment. SIZE: Medium. *STOCK: Furniture, 1700-1930's, £50-£2,000; porcelain and Staffordshire, £5-£200; jewellery, silver, glass, copper and brass.* PARK: Easy. TEL: 01642 801188; home - 01642 830246. SER: Valuations. VAT: Stan/Spec.

YORK

Barbican Bookshop

24 Fossgate. YO1 9TA. PBFA. Est. 1961. Open 9.15-5.30. *STOCK: Antiquarian books.* LOC: City centre. PARK: Multi-storey nearby. TEL: 01904 653643; fax - 01904 653643; e-mail - mail@barbicanbookshop.co.uk; website - www.barbican bookshop.co.uk. VAT: Stan.

Bishopsgate Antiques

23/24 Bishopsgate St. YO2 1JH. (R. Wetherill). Open 9. 15-6, Sun. 12-5. *STOCK: General antiques.* TEL: 01904 623893; fax - 01904 626511.

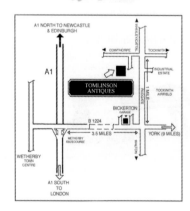

Barbara Cattle

BADA

45 Stonegate. YO1 8AW. Open 9-5.30. *STOCK: Jewellery and silver, Georgian to date.* TEL: 01904 623862. SER: Valuations; repairs; restorations.

Cavendish Antiques & Collectors Centre

44 Stonegate. YO1 8AS. (Anthony Gilberthorpe). Est. 1996. Open seven days 9-6. SIZE: Large. *STOCK: Wide range of general antiques, £1-£7,000.* LOC: In pedestrianised thoroughfare between minster and main shopping area. PARK: Nearby. TEL: 01904 621666/613888; fax - 01904 644400. VAT: Stan.

Coulter Galleries

YO24 1LX. Open by appointment only. *STOCK: Watercolours and oils, pre-1900; frames.* TEL: 01904 702101; fax - 01904 701908; e-mail - R. Coulter@tesco.net.

Ruth Ford Antiques

39 Fossgate. YO1 9TF. Est. 1976. Open 11.30-4.30. CL: Wed. SIZE: Small. *STOCK: 18th-19th C country furniture, pine, treen and collectables, £5-£1,000.* LOC: Near Merchant Adventurers Hall. PARK: Nearby. TEL: Home - 01904 632864.

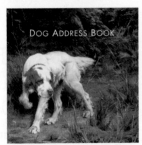
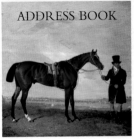

The French House (Antiques) Ltd.
74 Micklegate. YO1 6LF. (S. B. and M. J. Hazell). Est. 1995. Open 9.30 -5.30. SIZE: Large. *STOCK: Wooden beds, 18th-19th C, £900-£2,500; gilt mirrors, 19th C, £300-£2,000; lighting, 19th-20th C, £200-£1,000; all French.* LOC: Main entry to city from A64. PARK: Side streets. TEL: 01904 624465; fax - 01904 629965. SER: Restorations (cabinet making, upholstery, French polishing, painting). VAT: Margin.

Golden Memories of York
14 Newgate. YO1 7LA. (M. S. and D. J. Smith). NAG. Est. 1991. Open 9-5.30. SIZE: Small. *STOCK: Antique and secondhand jewellery and silver, £5-£3,000.* LOC: Adjacent York market, off Parliament St. PARK: Multi-storey. TEL: 01904 655883. VAT: Stan/Spec.

Minster Gate Bookshop
8 Minster Gates. YO1 2HL. (N. Wallace). Est. 1970. Open 9.30-5.30. SIZE: Large. *STOCK: Antiquarian and secondhand books; old maps and prints.* LOC: Opposite south door of minster. PARK: Nearby. TEL: 01904 621812. SER: Valuations; restorations; book finding.

Robert Morrison and Son   BADA
Trentholme House, 131 The Mount. YO24 1DU. (C. and P. Morrison). Est. 1870. Open 9-5, Sat. 9-3. SIZE: Large. STOCK: English furniture, 1700-1900; porcelain and clocks. LOC: Near racecourse, one mile from city centre on Leeds Rd. From A1, take A64 to outskirts of York, then take A1036 York west road. PARK: Easy. TEL: 01904 655394; email - info@york-antiques.com; website - www. york-antiques.com. VAT: Stan/Spec.

The Red House Antiques Centre
Duncombe Place. (Ginnel Antiques Centres - P. Stephenson). Open Mon.-Sat. 9.30-6, (June-Sept. 9.30-8), Sun. 10.30-5.30. LOC: 200 yards from Minster. TEL: 01904 637000; e-mail - enquiries@redhouseyork; website - www.red houseyork.co.uk. SER: Shipping; packing; arts and antiques lectures. Below are listed the specialist dealers at this centre.

Algar Antiques
General 19th and 20th C antiques.

Antiquai
19th C ceramics and glass.

Appleton Antiques
19th-20th C pottery including Moorcroft, Carlton, Linthorpe and crested china.

Fiona Aston
19th C porcelain, silver and objets d'art.

J. Barrington of Bond Street
Fine 18th-19th C furniture and paintings.

Margaret Bedi
18th-19th C furniture, oil paintings and water-colours.

Bootham Antiques
19th C silver, porcelain, glass and curios.

Brackmoor Antiques
Silver.

Bygones
Jewellery and dolls.

J.E. Chew
Silver.

C.W. Collectables
19th to early 20th C ceramics.

Cookes Cottage Antiques
19th C furniture and paintings.

I. Drake
18th-19th C figurines and ceramics.

D. Goodfellow
Reference books.

Graham and Dianne
Militaria.

Robert M. Himsworth
Fine York and provincial silver.

Hogarth Antiques
Silver, plate, porcelain and treen.

Laurel Bank Antiques
Georgian, Victorian and Edwardian furniture, longcase, wall and mantel clocks.

Catherine Lough
19th C French furniture and furnishings, decorative items and objets d'art.

Lycurgus Glass
19th-20th C decorative art glass and mirrors.

Stella Mar Antiques
19th C furniture and furnishings, porcelain, metalware, treen and objets d'art.

Maurice and Linda
Silver and military badges.

Rory Meyler
Dolls and teddies.

Olivia Meyler
Jewellery and Russian artefacts.

John Moor
Ancient art and antiques.

Needful Things
Silver, ceramics, north east glass, Davidsons.

Nichola
General antiques.

F. O'Flynn
Antique prints, maps and books.

S. Ogley
General antiques.

Past and Present
Buttons, badges, costume accessories, lace and costume jewellery.

Peacock Antiques
Thimbles and 19th C ceramics.

Anne Powell
18th-19th C ceramics, Tunbridgeware and silver.

P.W. Raine
Silver, pewter, metalware and ceramics.

G. Rhodes
19th C furniture and paintings.

Rose Fine Art
19th C prints and maps.

E. Schwetje
Silver and glassware.

Small Fish Antiques
19th C furniture, mirrors, glass, pottery, toys, advertising materials and ephemera.

L. Spooner
Luggage and leather goods.

Station Road Antiques
Silver and jewellery.

Gordon Steel
Silver, jewellery, glass, treen and pipes.

John Tee
Fine Irish silver.

Topaz Antiques
Victorian and Edwardian jewellery.

C.E. Tweedale
Victorian and Edwardian pottery and porcelain.

Upstairs-Downstairs
Kitchenalia, garden tools and bygones.

A. Wardale
Textiles and decorative items.

Paul Wheeler
Glass, pottery, porcelain and metalware.

Gwen Wood
Belleek.

Wycliffe Antiques
19th C ceramics, pot-lids, Baxter and Le Blond prints.

Jack Yarwood
18th-19th C wood, metalware and objets d'art.

J. Smith
47 The Shambles. YO1 7LX. BNTA. Est. 1963. Open 9.30-4.30. SIZE: Small. *STOCK: Numismatic items, £5-£1,000; British stamps, £1-£100.* TEL: 01904 654769; fax - 01904 677988. VAT: Stan/Spec.

Ken Spelman
70 Micklegate. YO1 6LF. (P. Miller and A. Fothergill). ABA. Est. 1948. SIZE: Large. *STOCK: Secondhand and antiquarian books especially fine arts and literature, 50p-£10,000.* PARK: Easy. TEL: 01904 624414; fax - 01904 626276; e-mail - rarebooks@kenspelman.com; website - www.kenspelman.com. SER: Valuations; buys at auction (books); catalogues issued. FAIRS: Bath, Oxford, York, Harrogate, Cambridge, Edinburgh and London PBFA and ABA. VAT: Spec.

St. John Antiques
26 Lord Mayor's Walk. YO3 7HA. (R. and N. Bell). Est. 1985. Open 10-5. CL: Mon. *STOCK: Victorian stripped pine, curios, blue and white pottery.* LOC: Near Minster. PARK: At rear. TEL: 01904 644263. SER: Stripping and finishing.

Stonegate Antiques Centre
41 Stonegate. YO1 8AW. (Anthony Gilberthorpe). Est. 1996. Open seven days 9-6. SIZE: Large. *STOCK: Wide range of general antiques, from £1-£7,000.* LOC: In pedestrianised thoroughfare between mister and main shopping area. PARK: Nearby. TEL: 01904 613888/ 621666; fax - 01904 644400. VAT: Stan.

York Antiques Centre
2 Lendal. YO1 8AA. Open 10-5. SIZE: 20 dealers. *STOCK: Antiques and collectable items, 18th-20th C.* LOC: Opposite the museum gardens. PARK: Easy. TEL: 01904 641445/641582.

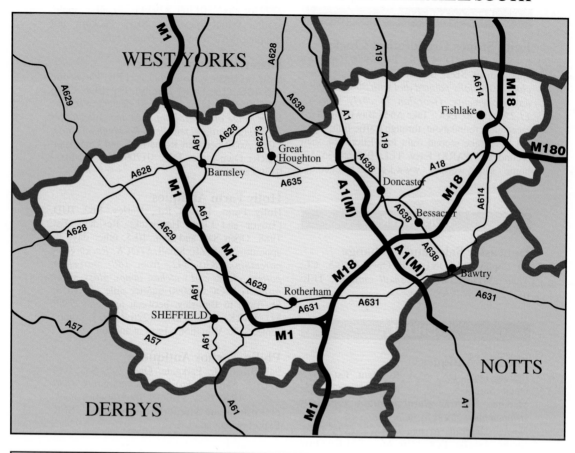

Dealers and Shops in South Yorkshire

Barnsley	2	Doncaster	1	Rotherham	4
Bawtry	1	Fishlake	1	Sheffield	18
Bessacarr	1	Great Houghton	1		

BARNSLEY

Charisma Antiques Trade Warehouse
The Old Chapel, 6b Market St., Hoyland. S74 9QR. (J. C. Simmons). Est. 1976. Open 10-5. SIZE: Large. *STOCK: Furniture, shipping goods, pictures.* LOC: 1. 5 miles off M1, exit 36. PARK: Easy. TEL: 01226 747599; home - 01226 790482.

Christine Simmons Antiques
St. Paul's Former Methodist Chapel, Market St., Hoyland. S74 9QR. Est. 1976. Open 10-4. SIZE: Medium. *STOCK: Smalls and pictures.* LOC: 1. 5 miles from exit 36, M1. PARK: Easy. TEL: 01226 747599/790482.

BAWTRY, Nr. Doncaster

Swan Antiques
2 Swan St. DN10 6JQ. (Mary Richardson and Sarah Philipson). Est. 1984. Open 10-5 including Sun. SIZE: Large. *STOCK: Furniture, silver, ceramics, collectables, costume jewellery.* LOC: 3 miles from A1, south of Doncaster. PARK: Easy. TEL: 01302 710301. FAIRS: Newark; Alexandra Palace.

BESSACARR, Nr. Doncaster

Keith Stones Grandfather Clocks
5 Ellers Drive. DN4 7DL. Est. 1988. Open by appointment. SIZE: Small. *STOCK: Grandfather clocks especially painted dial with 30 hour and 8 day movements, Georgian to early 19th C, £1,250-£3,750.* LOC: Take A638 Bawtry road off racecourse roundabout, through traffic lights after 3/4 mile, take second right into Ellers Rd. then second left. PARK: Easy. TEL: 01302 535258; home - same; website - www.kstones.fsnet.co.uk. SER: Valuations.

DONCASTER

Doncaster Sales and Exchange
20 Copley Rd. DN1 2PF. Open 9.30-5. CL: Thurs. *STOCK: General small antiques.* TEL: 01302 344857. VAT: Stan.

FISHLAKE

Fishlake Antiques
Pinfold Lane. DN7 5LA. Resident. Est. 1972. Open Sat. 1-5, and by appointment. SIZE: Medium. *STOCK: Rural furniture especially stripped pine; clocks including longcase and wall clocks, Victorian to mid-19th C, £30-£2,000; smalls, £3-£70.* LOC: Off A63. PARK: Own. TEL: 01302 841411.

GREAT HOUGHTON, Nr. Barnsley

Farmhouse Antiques
7 High St. S72 0AA. (Anita L. Calvert). Est. 1992. Open Mon., Tues. 1.30-4.30, Thurs. and Sat. 10.30-12 and 1.30-4.30, other times by appointment. SIZE: Medium. *STOCK: 19th-20th C furniture, ceramics, glass, textiles, linen, kitchenalia, Susie Cooper, Art Deco, soft furnishings.* LOC: Village centre. PARK: Easy. TEL: 01226 754057; home - 01226 753263; mobile - 07887 722202. FAIRS: Leeds Armouries Art Deco; Elsecar Heritage Centre.

ROTHERHAM

Roger Appleyard Ltd
Fitzwilliam Rd., Eastwood Trading Estate. S65 1SL. LAPADA. Open 8-5, Sat. 8-12. SIZE: Large. *STOCK: General antiques, £5-£10,000.* LOC: A630. PARK: Easy. TEL: 01709 367670/

377770; fax - 01709 829395; e-mail - apple. antiques@dial.pipex.com. SER: Packing and shipping. VAT: Stan/Spec. *Trade Only.*

Foster's Antique Centre
Foster's Garden Centre, Doncaster Rd., Thrybergh. S65 4BE. (The Foster Family). Est. 1996. Open 10-4.30, Sun. 11-5. SIZE: 20 dealers. *STOCK: Wide range of general antiques and collectables including furniture, jewellery, Rockingham china.* LOC: A630 between Rotherham and Doncaster. PARK: Own large. TEL: 01709 850337; fax - 01709 851905.

Holly Farm Antiques
Holly Farm, Harley Rd., Harley. S62 7UD. (Trevor and Linda Hardwick). Resident. Est. 1988. Open Sat. and Sun. 10-5, other days by appointment. SIZE: Small. *STOCK: Rockingham porcelain, 1830-1842, from £80; porcelain, pottery, clocks and watches, lamps, glass, silver, furniture.* LOC: B6090 quarter mile off A6135 Sheffield to Barnsley, between junctions 35/36 M1. PARK: Own. TEL: 01226 744077; home - same. SER: Valuations; buys at auction.

Philip Turnor Antiques
94a Broad St., Parkgate. Open 9-5, Sat. 10-4. *STOCK: Shipping furniture including oak, 1880-1940.* PARK: Easy. TEL: 01709 524640; e-mail - philipsfurniture@turnorfreeserve.co.uk. SER: Export (Japan and USA).

SHEFFIELD

Acorn Antiques
298-300 Abbeydale Rd. S7 1FL. (R. C. and B. C. Priest). Est. 1984. Open 10-5. SIZE: Medium. *STOCK: Furniture, 19th-20th C, £20-£500; bronzes, sculptural and unusual items.* LOC: A625 to Bakewell. PARK: Easy. TEL: 0114 255 5348; home - same.

Beech House
361 Abbeydale Rd. S7 1FS. (J. M. and A. J. Beech). Est. 1996. Open 10-5. CL: Thurs. SIZE: Small. *STOCK: Pine furniture, £250-£400; art and ceramics, £100-£5000.* LOC: 1 mile from city centre. PARK: Easy. TEL: 0114 250 1004; fax - same; mobile - 07970 196126. SER: Buys at auction (pine, rustic and country furniture).

Chapel Antiques Centre
99 Broadfield Rd. S8 0XH. Open 10-5, Sun. and Bank Holidays 11-5. SIZE: 20+ dealers. *STOCK: Furniture, textiles and accessories.* LOC: From city centre, 1 mile along A61 Chesterfield Rd., turn right. TEL: 0114 258 8288; fax - same.

Court House Antique Centre

2-6 Town End Rd., Ecclesfield. S35 9YY. (J. P. & K. E. Owram). Open 10.30-5, Sun. 11.30-5. SIZE: Large - 35+ dealers. *STOCK: Town and country furniture, French bedroom furniture, antiquarian maps, decorative items, ceramics, glass, clocks, barometers, kitchenalia, books, silver, jewellery, lighting, mirrors, collectables, £5-£5,000.* LOC: 2 miles from M1, junction 35. Down hill, bear left into Nether Lane, through lights to church, turn left 250 yards on right. PARK: Easy. TEL: 0114 257 0641.

Dronfield Antiques

375-377 Abbeydale Rd. S7 1FS. (H. J. Greaves). Est. 1968. Open 10.30-5.30. CL: Thurs. except by appointment. SIZE: Large + warehouses. *STOCK: Trade and shipping goods, Victoriana, glass, china.* LOC: A621, 1 mile south of city centre. PARK: Easy. TEL: 0114 2550172/2581821; home and fax - 0114 2556024. SER: Container packing facilities. VAT: Stan.

F S Antiques

Court House Antiques Centre, 2-6 Town End Rd., Ecclesfield. S35 9YY. Open 10.30-5, Sun. 11.30-4.30. SIZE: Small. *STOCK: Longcase, wall and mantel clocks, £150-£3,000.* LOC: 2 miles from M1, junction 35. PARK: Easy. TEL: 0114 25 70641; home - 01226 382805; mobile - 07949 399481; e-mail - antique@clocksforall.f9.co.uk; website - www.antiqueclocksforall.co.uk. SER: Restorations.

Alan Hill Books

Unit 4, Meersbrook Works, Valley Rd. S8 9FT. Est. 1980. Open 10-5. *STOCK: Antiquarian books, maps and prints.* TEL: 0114 255 6242; e-mail - alanhillbooks@supanet.com.

Peter James Antiques

336 Abbeydale Rd. S7 1FN. (P. J. Conboy). Est. 1980. Open 9.30-4.30. SIZE: Medium. *STOCK: Georgian, Victorian and Edwardian mahogany, walnut, oak and pine furniture.* PARK: Easy. TEL: 0114 2551554. SER: Restorations. VAT: Stan/Spec.

Kelly Lighting

679 Ecclesall Rd. S11 8TG. (Frank R. Kelly). Est. 1982. Open Fri. 9-5, Sat. 10.30-5, other days by appointment. SIZE: Small. *STOCK: Lighting - ceiling, wall, table and floor, Edwardian and Victorian, £160-£10,000.* LOC: Half mile from Sheffield Parkway End. PARK: Easy. TEL: 0114 267 8500; fax - 0114 268 3242; e-mail - sales @kellyantiquelighting.co.uk; website - www. kellylighting.co.uk. SER: Restorations (polishing, lacquering, re-wiring).

Langtons Antiques & Collectables

443 London Rd. /Courtyard, 100 Guernsey Rd., Heeley Bottom. S2 4HJ. (Langton Family). Est. 1999. Open 10-5. Sun. 10.30-4.30. SIZE: Large, 70+ dealers. *STOCK: Furniture, architectural items, military, china, porcelain, jewellery, clocks, Art Deco, from 1850, £5-£3,000.* LOC: M1, exit 33, A61 to city centre. PARK: Easy. TEL: 0114 258 1791. FAIRS: Newark. VAT: Stan.

Nichols Antique Centre

The Nichols Building, Shalesmoor. S3 8UJ. (T. and M. Vickers). Est. 1994. Open 10-5, Sat. and Sun. 10.30-4.30. SIZE: Large. *STOCK: Ceramics, fine furniture, clocks and collectables, mainly 19th-20th C, £50-£3,000.* LOC: A61, half mile from city centre. PARK: Easy. TEL: 0114 281 2811; fax - 0114 281 2812. SER: Valuations; restorations; re-upholstery. VAT: Stan.

The Oriental Rug Shop

763 Abbeydale Rd. S7 2BG. (Kian A. Hezaveh). Est. 1880. Open 10-5. *STOCK: Handmade rugs and carpets especially large carpets.* LOC: A621. TEL: 0114 2552240; fax - 0114 2509088; website - www.rugs.btinternet.co.uk.

Paraphernalia
66/68 Abbeydale Rd. S7 1FD. Est. 1972. *STOCK: General antiques, stripped pine, lighting, brass and iron beds.* TEL: 0114 2550203.

Renishaw Antiques
32 Main Rd., Renishaw. S21 3UT. (B. Findley). Open Mon.-Sat. 9-3. *STOCK: Furniture, architectural items, pine doors and leaded glass.* LOC: 1 mile off M1, junction 30. TEL: 01246 435521. SER: Door stripping.

N. P. and A. Salt Antiques and Barmouth Court Antiques Centre
Abbeydale House, Barmouth Rd. S7 2DH. LAPADA. Open 10-5, Sun. 11-4. SIZE: Large. *STOCK: Victorian furniture, shipping goods, smalls and toys.* TEL: 0114 2582672/2552711. SER: Valuations; packing; shipping; courier.

Sheffield Antiques Emporium
15 Clyde Rd., Heeley. S8 0YD. Est. 1994. Open 10-5, Sun. 11-5. SIZE: 70+ dealers. *STOCK: Furniture, collectables, linens, glass, militaria, china, books, Art Deco, £1-£5,000.* LOC: 1st right off Broadfield Rd., opposite Broadfield public house on Abbeydale Rd. PARK: Easy. TEL: 0114 258 4863/258 8288; fax - 0114 255 5609; website - www.sheffieldantiquesemporium.com.

Tilley's Vintage Magazine Shop
281 Shoreham St. (A. G. J. and A. A. J. C. Tilley). Est. 1978. Open Tues.-Sat. 9.30-4.30, other times by appointment. SIZE: Large. *STOCK: Magazines, comics, newspapers, books, postcards, programmes, posters, cigarette cards, prints, ephemera.* LOC: Opposite Sheffield United F. C. PARK: Easy. TEL: 0114 2752442; fax - same; e-mail - tilleys281@aol.com; website - www.tilleysmagazines.com. SER: Mail order; valuations.

Paul Ward Antiques
Owl House, 8 Burnell Rd., Owlerton. S6 2AX. Resident. Est. 1976. Open by appointment. SIZE: Large. *STOCK: Matched sets of Victorian dining and kitchen chairs, country chairs, general antiques.* LOC: 2 miles north of city on A61. TEL: 0114 2335980. VAT: Stan/Spec.

A group of 20th century copies of earlier pieces, recently exhibited under the title 'Pleasures & Pitfalls'. Without the benefit of experience and close inspection, all of these could be mistaken for genuine. (Delomosne)

From an article entitled "Fake 'Antique' Glassware" by Andy McConnell which appeared in the December 2001/January 2002 issue of **Antique Collecting**. For more details and to subscribe see page 21.

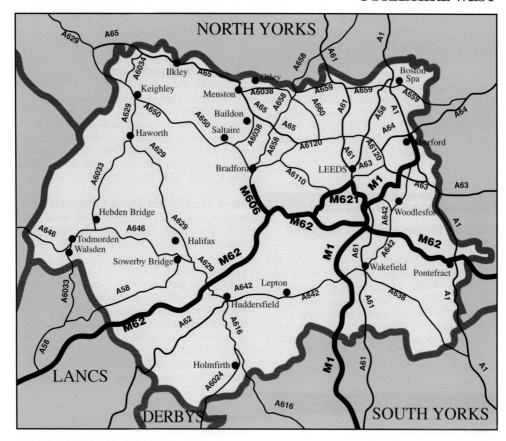

Dealers and Shops in West Yorkshire

		Otley	2
Aberford	1	Holmfirth	4	Pontefract	2
Baildon	1	Huddersfield	4	Saltaire	1
Boston Spa	1	Ilkley	3	Sowerby Bridge	2
Bradford	3	Keighley	1	Todmorden	3
Halifax	4	Leeds	9	Wakefield	1
Haworth	1	Lepton	1	Walsden	1
Hebden Bridge	1	Menston	2	Woodlesford	1

ABERFORD

Aberford Antiques Ltd t/a Aberford Country Furniture

Hicklam House. LS25 3DP. (J. W. H. Long and C. A. Robinson). Est. 1973. Open 9-5.30, Sundays 10-5.30. CL: Mon. SIZE: Large. *STOCK: French oak furniture; pine and mahogany, £10-£4,000; Victoriana and collectables, £5-£1,000.* LOC: Large detached property at south end of village. PARK: Easy. TEL: 0113 2813209; fax - 0113 2813121; e-mail - jwhlong@aol.com; website - www.aberfordpine.com.uk. VAT: Stan/Spec.

BAILDON, Nr. Bradford

The Baildon Furniture Co.

Spring Mills, Otley Rd. BD17 6AD. (Richard Parker). Est. 1972. Open 10.30-4.30, Sun. by appointment. SIZE: Large. *STOCK: Furniture, architectural fitments, pottery and metalware, 17th-20th C, £5-£5,000.* PARK: Easy. TEL: 01274 414345; fax - same; e-mail - baildon furniture@aol.com. SER: Valuations; restorations (cabinet work, repolishing, upholstery, pottery). VAT: Stan/Spec.

Tansu Japanese Antiques

Redbrick Mill, 218 Bradford Rd, Batley Carr. WF17 6JF. (Stephen P. Battye). Est. 1993. Open 9.30-5.30, Sun. 10.30-4.30. SIZE: Medium. *STOCK: Japanese granite lanterns, chests including shop display, wheeled trunks, caligraphy boxes, 1850-1900, £350-£20,000; kimono, 1930-1960, £20-£200.* LOC: Close to M1 and M62. PARK: Own large. TEL: 01924 460044/ 430002; fax - 01924 462844. SER: Valuations; restorations (Japanese antique furniture). VAT: Spec/Margin.

BOSTON SPA, By Wetherby

London House Oriental Rugs and Carpets

London House, High St. LS23 6AD. (M. A. and Mrs I. T. H. Ries). Open 10-5.30 including Sun. CL: Mon. SIZE: Large. *STOCK: Caucasian, Turkish, Afghan and Persian rugs, runners and carpets, £50-£10,000; kelims and textiles.* LOC: Off A1, south of Wetherby. PARK: Easy. TEL: 01937 845123; home - same. SER: Restorations (Oriental carpets and rugs); buys at auction (Oriental carpets and rugs). VAT: Stan.

BRADFORD

The Corner Shop

89 Oak Lane. BD9 4QU. (Miss Badland). Est. 1961. Open Tues. and Thurs. 2-5.30, Wed. 12.30-3.30 and Sat. 11-5.30. *STOCK: Pottery, small furniture, clocks and general items.*

Cottingley Antiques

286 Keighley Rd., Frizinghall. BD9. (Peter and Barbara Nobbs). Est. 1981. Open 9-5. SIZE: Medium. *STOCK: Victorian stripped and restored pine, £100-£500.* LOC: Right hand side of A650 from Keighley. PARK: Easy. TEL: 01274 545829; home - 01274 569091. SER: Restorations (furniture).

Heaton Antiques

1 Hammond Place, Emm Lane, Heaton. BD9 4AN. (T. Steward). Est. 1991. Open 10-5. CL: Mon. SIZE: Medium. *STOCK: Furniture, silver plate and bric-a-brac, pre 1930, £10-£1,000.* LOC: Near A650. PARK: Easy. TEL: 01274 480630. SER: Valuations. FAIRS: Harrogate.

HALIFAX

Collectors Old Toy Shop and Antiques

89 Northgate. HX1 1XF. (S. Haley). Est. 1983.

Open 10.30-4.30. CL: Thurs. SIZE: 2 floors. *STOCK: Collectors toys, clocks and antiques.* PARK: Nearby. TEL: 01422 360434/822148.

Halifax Antiques Centre

Queens Rd. HX1 4LR. (M. and A. Carroll). Est. 1981. Open Tues.-Sat. 10-5. SIZE: Large -30 dealers. *STOCK: Art Deco, jewellery, porcelain, linen, costume, pine, oak, mahogany, French and English furniture, kitchenalia, decorative collectables.* LOC: A58 to King Cross, turn at Trafalgar Inn into Queens Rd. corner, 3rd set of lights. PARK: Own. TEL: 01422 366657.

Muir Hewitt Art Deco Originals

Halifax Antiques Centre, Queens Rd. Mills. HX1 4LR. Est. 1982. Open Tues.-Sat. and Bank Holidays 10.30-5. CL: Mon. *STOCK: 20th C ceramics including Clarice Cliff, Susie Cooper, Charlotte Rhead, Shelley; furniture, metalware, lighting and mirrors.* LOC: 1 mile west of town centre off A58 (A646)Aachen Way/Burnley Rochdale road. Turn right at Trafalgar Inn traffic lights. Centre at 3rd set of traffic lights at junction of Queens Rd. and Gibbet St. PARK: Easy. TEL: 01422 347377; fax - same; website - www. muirhewitt.com. SER: Valuations. FAIRS: Ann Zierold Art Deco; Leeds Royal Armouries; Chester. VAT: Spec.

Andy Thornton Architectural Antiques Ltd

Victoria Mills, Stainland Rd., Greetland. HX4 8AD. Est. 1976. Open 8.30-5.30, Sat. 9-5. SIZE: Large. *STOCK: Architectural antiques - doors, stained glass, fireplaces, panelling, garden furniture, light fittings, pews and decor items.* LOC: Off junction 24, M62. PARK: Easy. TEL: 01422 377314; fax - 01422 310372. VAT: Stan.

HAWORTH, Nr. Keighley

Bingley Antiques

Springfield Farm Estate, Flappit. BD21 5PT. (J. B. and J. Poole). Est. 1965. Open Tues.-Sat. 8.30 -5. SIZE: Large. *STOCK: Furniture, 18th-19th C; shipping goods, porcelain, architectural antiques.* LOC: Near Haworth. PARK: Easy. TEL: 01535 646666; e-mail - john@bingleyantiques.com; website - www.bingleyantiques.com. VAT: Stan/Spec.

HEBDEN BRIDGE, Nr. Halifax

Cornucopia Antiques

9 West End. HX7 8JP. (C. Nassor). Open Thurs., Fri. and Sun. 1-5, Sat. 11-5. *STOCK: Furniture, Art*

Discover the world of Clarice Cliff
and all that Jazz

A wide selection of 1920's/30's ceramics by Clarice Cliff, Susie Cooper Charlotte Rhead, Shelley and others.

Furniture | Mirrors | Lamps | Chrome

Open Tuesday to Friday
10.30am-4.30pm

Saturday
10.30am-5.00pm

Closed
Sundays/Mondays

Clarice Cliff is a registered trademark of Josiah Wedgwood & Sons Limited, Barlaston.

Photography by Keith Paisley

ART DECO ORIGINALS
MUIR HEWITT

Tel/Fax: 01422 347377 www.muirhewitt.com

Halifax Antiques Centre,
Queens Road Mills, Queens Road/Gibbet Street,
Halifax, West Yorkshire, HX1 4LR England.

Deco, lighting, mirrors, stoves and bric-a-brac.
LOC: Town centre behind Pennine Information
Centre. PARK: Easy. TEL: 01422 844497.

HOLMFIRTH

Bruton Gallery
PO Box 145HD9 1YU. (Helen Robinson). Est.
1969. Open by appointment only. SIZE: Medium.
*STOCK: French sculpture, 19th-20th C, from
£1,000+; contemporary British art, to £10,000.*
PARK: Limited. TEL: Mobile - 0870 747 1800;
e-mail - art@BrutonGallery.co.uk; website -
www.BrutonGallery.co.uk. SER: Valuations;
buys at auction. FAIRS: Glasgow; Oxford;
London. VAT: Stan/Spec.

Chapel House Fireplaces
Netherfield House, St. Georges Rd., Scholes. HD9
1UH. (J. and M. Forster). Est. 1979. Open strictly
by appointment Tues. 9-7, Wed.-Sat. 9-5. SIZE:
Large. *STOCK: Georgian, Victorian and Edwardian
grates and mantels; French chimneypieces.*
PARK: Own. TEL: 01484 682275; e-mail - info
@chapelhousefireplaces.co.uk; website - www.
chapelhousefireplaces.co.uk. SER: Restorations.

The Toll House Bookshop
32/34 Huddersfield Rd. HD9 2JS. (E. V.
Beardsell). Est. 1978. Open 10-5. *STOCK: Books
including antiquarian.* TEL: 01484 686541.

Upperbridge Antiques
9 Huddersfield Rd. HD9 2JR. (I. and B. Ridings).
Open Wed., Thurs. and Sat. 1-5, Sun. 2-5. SIZE:
Small. *STOCK: Pottery, metalware, lighting,
linen, interesting items, Victorian to 1950's, £5-
£200.* Not Stocked: Clocks and jewellery. LOC:
A635. PARK: Nearby. TEL: 01484 687200.

HUDDERSFIELD

D. W. Dyson (Antique Weapons)
Wood Lea, Shepley. HD8 8ES. Est. 1974. Open
by appointment only. *STOCK: Antique weapons
including cased duelling pistols, armour, miniature arms, cigar and smoking related accessories, rare and unusual items.* LOC: Off A629.
PARK: Easy. TEL: 01484 607331; home - same.
SER: Valuations; buys at auction (antique
weapons); special presentation items made to
order in precious metals; restorations; interior
design; finder (film props). FAIRS: Dorchester
Hotel, London; Dortmund, Stuttgart and other
major foreign. VAT: Spec.

Huddersfield Picture Framing Co
Cloth Hall Chambers, Cloth Hall St. HD1 2EG.
(Miss Pamela Ward). Est. 1962. Open 9-5, Wed.
9-1, Sat. 9-4. SIZE: Large. *STOCK: Watercolours, picture mouldings, swept frames, ovals
and circles.* LOC: Between Market St. and New
St. PARK: Meters or nearby. TEL: 01484 546075;
home - 01484 687598. SER: Valuations; restorations (especially oil paintings). VAT: Stan.

Geoff Neary (incorporating Fillans Antiques Ltd)
2 Market Walk. HD1 2QA. NAG, FGA. Est.
1852. Open 9.30-5. 15. SIZE: Small. *STOCK:
English silver, 1700-1980; Sheffield plate, 1760-
1840, £50-£2,000; jewellery, 1800-1980, £50-
£20,000.* LOC: Town centre. PARK: Multi-
storey. TEL: 01484 531609. SER: Valuations;
restorations; buys at auction (English silver and
jewellery). VAT: Stan/Spec.

Objects of Vertu
26 Lidget St., Lindley. HD3 3JP. (Christopher J.
L. Dawes). Est. 1995. Open 10-5. CL: Mon. and
Wed. SIZE: Small. *STOCK: Silver, glass and
porcelain, 19th-20th C, £20-£400.* PARK:
Nearby. TEL: 01484 649515. SER: Valuations;
buys at auction. FAIRS: Newark; Elliott Antiques
& Collectors.

ILKLEY

Coopers of Ilkley
46-50 Leeds Rd. LS29 8EQ. LAPADA. Est.
1910. Open 9-1 and 2-5.30. SIZE: Large. *STOCK:
English and Continental furniture, pre-1900,
£100-£10,000; porcelain and metalware.* LOC:
A65. PARK: Own. TEL: 01943 608020. SER:
Valuations; restorations (furniture); buys at
auction. VAT: Stan/Spec.

The Grove Bookshop
10 The Grove. LS29 9EG. (Andrew and Janet
Sharpe). ABA, PBFA. Est. 1984. Open 9-5.30.
SIZE: Medium. *STOCK: Antiquarian books and
maps; topographical and sporting prints.* LOC:
200 yards from A65. PARK: Easy. TEL: 01943
609335; fax - 01943 817086; e-mail - antiquarian
@grovebookshop.co.uk; website - www.grove
bookshop.co.uk. SER: Valuations; restorations
(book-binding and framing); buys at auction (as
stock).

Jack Shaw and Co
The Old Grammar School, Skipton Rd. LS29 9EJ.
Est. 1945. Open Thurs., Fri. and Sat. 9.30 -12.45
and 2-5.30. *STOCK: Silver especially cutlery and
18th C domestic.* TEL: 01943 609467. VAT: Spec.

Clock House Antiques
2 Janet St. BD22 9ET. (P. A. Langham). Open Tues., Wed. and Thurs. 1-4, Sat. 11-4, Sun. 2-4. SIZE: Medium. *STOCK: Clocks, porcelain and small furniture.* PARK: Easy. TEL: 01535 648777. SER: Clock valuations and repairs.

Aladdin's Cave
19 Queens Arcade. LS1 6LF. (A. and R. Spencer). Est. 1954. SIZE: Small. *STOCK: Jewellery, £15-£5,000; collectors' items.* LOC: Town centre. PARK: 100 yards. TEL: 0113 245703. SER: Valuations; repairs. VAT: Stan.

Cottage Antiques
78 Otley Rd., Headingley. LS6 4BA. (David Atkinson). Est. 1989. Open 10-5. SIZE: Small. *STOCK: Furniture and clocks, 19th C, £50-£2,000; pottery, 20th C, £5-£500.* LOC: A660. PARK: Easy. TEL: 01132 955125; home - 01132 948136. SER: Valuations; restorations (furniture repolishing). FAIRS: Newark, Harrogate.

Geary Antiques
114 Richardshaw Lane, Stanningley, Pudsey. LS28 6BN. (J. A. Geary). Est. 1933. Open 10-5.30, Sun. 12-4. SIZE: Large + warehouse. *STOCK: Furniture, Georgian, Victorian and Edwardian; copper and brass.* LOC: 500 yds. from West Leeds Ring Rd. PARK: Easy. TEL: 0113 2564122. SER: Restorations (furniture); interior design. VAT: Stan/Spec.

Headrow Antiques Centre
Level 3 Headrow Shopping Centre, The Headrow. (Sally Hurrell). Est. 1991. Open 10-5, Sun. 11-4 (Nov.-Dec). SIZE: 25 dealers. *STOCK: Ceramics, jewellery and furniture, £5-£2,000.* LOC: City centre. PARK: NCP Albion St. TEL: 0113 2455344; home - 0113 2749494.

J. Howorth Antiques/Swiss Cottage Furniture
85 Westfield Crescent, Burley. LS3 1DJ. Est. 1986. Open 10-5.30, Sun. 1-5.30. CL: Tues. SIZE: Warehouse. *STOCK: Collectables, furniture, architectural items, £5-£3,000.* LOC: Town hall to Burley Rd., road opposite YTV. PARK: Easy. TEL: 0113 2306268/2429994. SER: Prop. hire for film and TV. FAIRS: Newark. VAT: Stan/Spec.

Oakwood Gallery
613 Roundhay Rd., Oakwood. Open 9-6. *STOCK: Fine paintings and prints.* PARK: Easy. TEL: 0113 2401348. SER: Framing; restorations; conservation.

The Piano Shop
39 Holbeck Lane. LS11 9UL. (B. Seals). Open 9-5. SIZE: 2 floors. *STOCK: Pianos, especially decorated cased grand.* LOC: 5 mins. from City centre. TEL: 0113 2443685; e-mail - thepianoshop@free net.co.uk; website - www.thepiano shop.co.uk. SER: Restorations; French polishing; hire.

Elizabeth Sexton, 1660. A rare 17th century band sampler.

From an article entitled "Schoolgirl Samplers featuring Animals and Houses" by Rebecca Scott which appeared in the September 2001 issue of **Antique Collecting**. For more details and to subscribe see page 21.

Swiss Cottage Furniture
85 Westfield Crescent. LS3 1DJ. (J. Howorth). Est. 1985. Open 10-5, Sun. 1-5. CL: Tues. SIZE: Large. *STOCK: Fireplaces, pine doors, 19th C, £75-£700; architectural salvage and collectables.* LOC: Behind Yorkshire TV Studios. PARK: Easy. TEL: 0113 242 9994. VAT: Stan/Spec.

Year Dot
16 Market St. Arcade. LS1 6DH. (A. Glithro). Est. 1977. Open 9.30-5. *STOCK: Jewellery, watches, silver, pottery, porcelain, glass, clocks, prints, paintings, bric-a-brac.* LOC: Briggate. TEL: 0113 2460860.

LEPTON, Nr. Huddersfield

K. L. M. & Co. Antiques
The Antique Shop, Wakefield Rd. HD8 0EL. (K. L. & J. Millington). Est. 1980. Open 10.30-5, other times by appointment. SIZE: 8 showrooms and warehouse. *STOCK: Furniture including stripped pine, satin walnut, to 1940's; pianos, all £25-£1,500.* LOC: A642 Wakefield road from Huddersfield, shop opposite village church. PARK: Easy and at rear. TEL: 01484 607763; home - 01484 607548. SER: Valuations. VAT: Stan.

MENSTON

Antiques
101 Bradford Rd. LS29. (W. and J. Hanlon). Est. 1974. Open 2.30-5. CL: Tues. and Wed. *STOCK: Handworked linen, textiles, pottery, porcelain, Art Nouveau, Art Deco, silver, plate, jewellery, small furniture, collectors items.* LOC: A65 near Harry Ramsden. PARK: Forecourt. TEL: 01943 877634; home - 01943 463693. FAIRS: Newark.

Park Antiques
2 North View, Main St. LS29 6JU. Resident. Est. 1975. Open Thurs.-Sat. 12-5.30. SIZE: Medium. *STOCK: Furniture, Georgian to Edwardian, £500-£5,000; decorative items, £100-£1,000, soft furnishings, £500-£2,000. Not Stocked: Pine, silver.* LOC: Opposite the park. PARK: Easy. TEL: 01943 872392. VAT: Stan/Spec.

OTLEY

Mayfair Antiques
26 Cross Green. LS21 1HD. (Ivor Hughes). Est. 1998. Open 10-6. CL: Wed. SIZE: Medium. *STOCK: French faience, garden antiques, metalware, 19th C; French decorative art, 1850-1930.*

LOC: A658, on left leaving Otley towards Harrogate. PARK: Easy. TEL: 01943 463380; mobile - 07802 740012; e-mail - ivor@frantique. fsnet.co.uk; website - www.frantique.co.uk. SER: Valuations; restorations (clocks and furniture); translation. FAIRS: Harrogate.

Otley Antique Centre
6 Bondgate. LS21 3AB. (A. Monkman). Est. 1991. Open 10-5, Wed. 10-4. SIZE: Small. *STOCK: 20th C collectables; jewellery, paintings, 19th-20th C: all £50-£100.* LOC: Top of High St., opposite parish church on Leeds road. PARK: Next to church. TEL: 01943 850342.

PONTEFRACT

Cottage Antiques
Heaton House, 24 Wakefield Rd., Ackworth. WF7 7AB. (Sheila Whittaker). Est. 1987. Open by appointment only. *STOCK: 18th-19th C pine and country furniture; bedroom and kitchen furniture, ceramics, linen and kitchenalia.* PARK: Easy. TEL: 01977 611146; mobile - 07944 853624. SER: Restorations (furniture). FAIRS: Newark (Stand F32).

D. Turner Antiques
The Old Coach House, Bondgate. (Dennise Turner). Est. 1988. Open 11-5. CL: Thurs. SIZE: Medium. *STOCK: Furniture, £30-£300; pottery, £20-£100, both late 19th to early 20th C; collectables, £5-£25.* LOC: Just off A1 towards town. PARK: Easy. TEL: 01977 798818; home - 01226 751802. SER: Valuations; buys at auction (furniture). FAIRS: Newark, Harrogate and Ardingly.

SALTAIRE, Nr. Shipley

The Victoria Centre
3-4 Victoria Rd. BD18 3LA. (M. and M. Gray and Andrew Draper). Est. 1995. Open 10.30-5.30. CL: Mon. and Tues. SIZE: Large - 40+ dealers. *STOCK: Wide range of general antiques including fine furniture, paintings, silver, clocks, porcelain, pine and collectables, £5-£10,000.* PARK: Nearby. TEL: 01274 530611. SER: Valuations; restorations (furniture and pictures). VAT: Stan/Spec.

SOWERBY BRIDGE, Nr. Halifax

Memory Lane
69 Wakefield Rd. HX6 2UX. (L. Robinson). Est. 1978. Open 10.30-5. SIZE: Warehouse + showroom. *STOCK: Pine, oak and teddy bears.* PARK: Easy. TEL: 01422 833223.

Talking Point Antiques

66 West St. HX6 3AP. (Paul Austwick). Est. 1986. Usually open Thurs., Fri., Sat. 10.30-5.30, prior telephone call advisable. *STOCK: Restored gramophones and phonographs, 78rpm records, gramophone accessories and related items.* PARK: Nearby. TEL: 01422 834126; e-mail - tpagrams@aol.com; website - www.talkingpoint gramophones.co.uk. SER: Restorations (gramophones). FAIRS: NEC.

TODMORDEN

Robert Davidson Antiques

56 Burnley Rd. OL14 5EY. (J. Ratcliff). Est. 1982. Open 10-5, Sun. by appointment. CL: Mon. SIZE: Medium + warehouse. *STOCK: Country, antique and quality furniture, £1-£3,500; small architectural items and curiosities.* LOC: A646 Burnley road. PARK: Easy. TEL: 01706 816053. SER: Valuations.

Echoes

650a Halifax Rd., Eastwood. OL14 6DW. (P. Oldman). Est. 1980. CL: Mon. and Tues. SIZE: Medium. *STOCK: Costume, textiles, linen and lace, £5-£500; jewellery, £5-£150; all 19th-20th C.* LOC: A646. PARK: Easy. TEL: 01706 817505; home - same. SER: Valuations; restorations (costume); buys at auction (as stock).

Todmorden Antiques Centre

Sutcliffe House, Halifax Rd. OL14 5DG. (Mr and Mrs Hoogeveen). Open 10-5, Sat. 10-4, Sun. 12-4. SIZE: 20 dealers. *STOCK: General antiques, furniture and jewellery.* TEL: 01706 818040.

WAKEFIELD

Robin Taylor Fine Arts

36 Carter St. WF1 1XJ. Open 9.30-5.30. *STOCK: Oils and watercolours.* TEL: 01924 381809.

WALSDEN, Nr. Todmorden

Cottage Antiques (1984) Ltd

788 Rochdale Rd. OL14 7UA. (G. Slater). Resident. Est. 1978. Open Tues.-Sun. SIZE: Medium. *STOCK: Country and decorative painted furniture, kitchenalia, collectables; elm and cherrywood reproductions.* LOC: A6033 Todmorden to Littleborough road. PARK: Easy. TEL: 01706 813612. SER: Restorations; pine stripping; import/export of European pine and collectables.

WOODLESFORD, Nr. Leeds

Trafalgar Antiques Centre

Trafalgar Works, Astley Lane, Bowers Row. LS26 8AN. Open 9-5.30, Sat. 10-5, Sun. 11-5.30. SIZE: Large. *STOCK: Mahogany, walnut and oak, 18th to early 20th C.* LOC: Off M62, junction 30 towards Garforth, into Swillington, 2 miles down Astley Lane. PARK: Own. TEL: 0113 287 5955; fax - 0113 287 5966. SER: Valuations; restorations. VAT: Stan/Spec

Paul Sandby, Couples strolling past musicians, pen and grey ink over pencil, 4½in. x 10½in., sold for £5,400 in 1997. (Sotheby's)

From an article entitled "Paul and Thomas Sandby" by Charles Hind which appeared in the October 2001 issue of **Antique Collecting**. For more details and to subscribe see page 21.

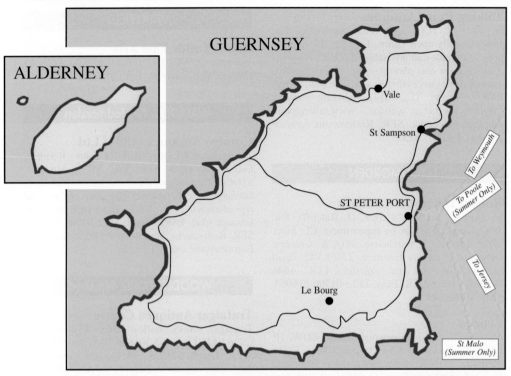

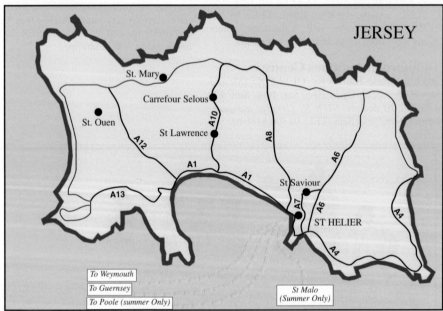

Dealers and Shops on the Channel Islands

			St Helier	11
ALDERNEY	2	St Sampson 2	St Lawrence	1
GUERNSEY		Vale 1	St. Mary	1
Le Bourg	1	JERSEY	St. Ouen	1
St Peter Port	6	Carrefour Selous 1	St Saviour	1

Alderney

Beverley J. Pyke - Fine British Watercolours
22 Victoria St. GY9 3TA. Est. 1988. Open by appointment only. *STOCK: 20th C watercolours, £150-£2,000.* TEL: 01481 824092.

Victoria Antiques
St. Catherine's, Victoria St. GY9 3TA. (P. A. Nightingale). Open 10-12.30 or by appointment. *STOCK: Period and Victorian furniture, glass, silver, china, jewellery, small objets d'art.* TEL: 01481 823260. SER: Valuations.

Guernsey

LE BOURG FOREST

Mark Blower Antiques
The Rectory. Est. 1978. Open by appointment only. SIZE: Small. *STOCK: Furniture, 18th C, £1,000-£20,000; garden ornament, pictures, 18th-19th C, £500-£5,000.* PARK: Easy. TEL:

01481 239098. SER: Valuations; restorations (furniture and pictures); fine art packing and shipping; buys at auction.

ST. PETER PORT

Stephen Andrews Gallery
5 College Terrace, Grange. GY1 2PX. (J. Geddes and S. Wilkowski). Est. 1984. Open 9.30-5. SIZE: Medium. *STOCK: Furniture, pottery and porcelain, paintings, 19th-20th C.* LOC: Main road. PARK: Adjacent. TEL: 01481 710380. SER: Buys at auction. FAIRS: Local.

Channel Islands Galleries Ltd
Trinity Square Centre, Trinity Sq. GY1 1LX. (G. P. and Mrs C. Gavey). Est. 1970. Open 10-5. SIZE: Medium. *STOCK: Antique maps, sea charts and prints of the Channel Islands; oil paintings, watercolours, Channel Islands' books, illustrated, historical, social, geographical and natural history; Channel Island banknotes and coins.* Not Stocked: General antiques. PARK: Easy. TEL: 01481 723247; home - 01481 247337; fax - 01481 714669; e-mail - geoff. gavey@cigalleries.f9.co.uk; website - www. cigalleries.f9.co.uk. SER: Framing.

The Collectors Centre
1 Sausmarez St. GY1 2PT. (Andrew Rundle). Est. 1984. Open 11-6. SIZE: Small. *STOCK: Prints, engravings, maps, coins, banknotes, stamps, postcards, books and ephemera.* PARK: Opposite. TEL: 01481 725209. SER: Valuations.

N. St. J. Paint & Sons Ltd
26-29 The Pollet. GY1 1WQ. (Michael St J. Paint). NAG. Est. 1947. Open 9-5. SIZE: Large. *STOCK: Jewellery and silver, 18th-20th C, £50-£25,000.* LOC: Town centre. TEL: 01481 721096; fax - 01481 710241; e-mail - paint@ guernsey.net. SER: Valuations; restorations (silver and jewellery).

The Pine Collection
La Route de la Garenne, Pitronnerie Road Industrial Estate, GY1 2RL. (P. Head). Est. 1986. Open 9.30-5.30. *STOCK: Pine.* TEL: 01481 726891.

St. James's Gallery Ltd
18-20 Smith St. GY1 2JQ. (Mrs C. O. Whittam). Est. 1955. Open 10-1 and 2-5, Sat. 10-1. SIZE: Large. *STOCK: Furniture, 19th C, £300-£30,000; paintings, 19th-20th C, £100-£20,000; silver, 19th-20th C, £10-£5,000.* LOC: Town centre, just off High St. PARK: Nearby. TEL: 01481 720070; fax - 01481 721132; home - 01481 723999.

The Old Curiosity Shop
Commercial Rd. GY2 4QP. Est. 1978. Open Sat. pm. *STOCK: Old and antiquarian books, prints, postcards, coins, ephemera, paintings, small furniture, china, glass, silver, brass, £1-£5,000.* TEL: 01481 45324. FAIRS: Organiser.

Ray & Scott Ltd
The Bridge. GY2 4QN. (M. J. Search). NAG. Open 9-5.15, Sat. 9-5. SIZE: Small. *STOCK: Jewellery, 19th C, £500-£1,000+.* PARK: Easy. TEL: 01481 244610; fax - same. SER: Valuations; restorations (jewellery and engraving).

Jersey

David Hick Interiors
Alexandra House. JE3 1GL. Est. 1977. Open Wed., Fri. and Sat. 9.30-5. CL: Aug. SIZE: Large and warehouse. *STOCK: Furniture and objets d'art.* PARK: Own. TEL: 01534 865965; fax - 01534 865448; e-mail - hickantiques@localdial.com. SER: Shipping (UK and overseas).

John Blench & Son
50 Don St. JE2 4TR. *STOCK: Fine books, bindings, local maps and prints.* TEL: 01534 725281; fax - 01534 758789; e-mail - segart@itl. net; website - www.selectiveeye.com.

John Cooper Antiques
16 The Market. JE2. *STOCK: General antiques.* TEL: 01534 723600.

Falle Fine Art Limited
94 Halkett Place. JE2 4WH. (John Falle). LAPADA. Est. 1993. Open Tues.-Fri. 11-5, Sat. 9.30-1, Mon. by appointment. SIZE: Large. *STOCK: 20th C paintings, watercolours and bronzes.* LOC: Opposite Public Library. PARK: Easy. TEL: 01534 887877; fax - 01534 723459; e-mail - gallery@fallefineart.com; website - www.fallefineart.com. SER: Valuations; restorations; exhibitions.

David Hick Antiques
45 Halkett Place. JE2 4WQ. Open 10-5, Thurs. 10-1. *STOCK: Furniture and smalls.* TEL: 01534 721162; fax - same; e-mail - hickantiques@ localdial.com.

Peter Le Vesconte's Collectables
62 Stopford Rd. JE2 4LZ. Est. 1979. Open 10-3. CL: Thurs. SIZE: Medium. *STOCK: Toys, 1920-1999, £5-£500; militaria, 1900-1945, £1-£500; small items, 1900-1970, £5-£300.* LOC: Road opposite Hotel de France. PARK: Easy. TEL: 01534 732481; fax - same. SER: Valuations; buys at auction (toys and militaria).

A. & R. Ritchie
7 Duhamel Place. JE2. Open 9.30-4.30. *STOCK: Militaria and jewellery.* TEL: 01534 873805.

Roberts Antiques
14 York St. JE2 3RQ. (Robert Michieli). Est. 1975. Open 9.30-4. 45. SIZE: Medium. *STOCK: English silver, ceramics, clocks, glass, jewellery, 19th C, £50-£10,000.* LOC: Opposite town hall. PARK: Easy. TEL: 01534 509071; home - 01534 865005; e-mail - count.roberto@jerseymail.co. uk. SER: Valuations; buys at auction (as stock).

The Selective Eye Gallery
50 Don St. JE2 4TR. (J. and P. Blench). Est. 1958. Open 9-5. CL: Thurs. and Sat. pm. SIZE: Medium. *STOCK: Oil paintings, 19th-20th C; maps, prints and antiquarian books, 16th-20th C.* Not Stocked: General antiques. LOC: Town centre. PARK: Multi-storey 100yds. TEL: 01534

725281; fax - 01534 758789; e-mail - segart@itl. net; website - www.selectiveeye.com. SER: Valuations; restorations (pictures). FAIRS: Jersey.

Thesaurus (Jersey) Ltd
3 James St. JE2 4TT. (I. Creaton). Est. 1973. Open 9-5.30. SIZE: Small. *STOCK: Antiquarian and out of print books, £1-£2,000; maps and prints.* Not Stocked: General antiques. LOC: Town centre. PARK: 100yds. TEL: 01534 37045. SER: Buys at auction. VAT: Spec.

Joan Thomson Antiques
12 Burrard St. JE2. Est. 1967. Open 10-3. CL: Thurs. SIZE: Medium. *STOCK: Smalls, £10-£500, jewellery, linen, collectors' items, Oriental.* PARK: Nearby. TEL: 01534 737206; home - 01534 856908.

Thomson's
60 Kensington Place and 44 Don St. JE2 3PA. Est. 1967. Open 10-6. SIZE: Large. *STOCK: General antiques and collectors's items, mainly furniture.* LOC: 60 Kensington Place at the side of Grand Hotel; 44 Don St. opposite Bonhams. PARK: Easy. TEL: 01534 723673/618673; mobile - 07797 766806. SER: Valuations.

ST. LAWRENCE

I. G. A. Old Masters Ltd
5 Kimberley Grove, Rue de Haut. (I. G. and Mrs C. B. V. Appleby). Est. 1953. Open by appointment. *STOCK: Old Master and 19th C paintings.* LOC: Near glass church. PARK: Easy. TEL: 01534 724226; home - same.

ST. MARY

Country House and Cottage Antiques
La Foret, Rue es Boeufs. JE3 3EQ. (Mrs Sarah Johnson). Resident. Est. 1985. Open Tues.-Sat. 10-5, Wed. 10-1 or by appointment. SIZE: Large. *STOCK: Furniture - Jacobean, Georgian, Victorian, Art Nouveau, Art Deco; china, glass, pictures and decorative items.* PARK: Easy. TEL: 01534 862547. SER: Valuations; restorations; interior design.

ST. OUEN

Stephen Cohu Antiques
La Ville de L'Eglise. JE3 2LR. Est. 1990. Open 10-5, Wed. 2-5, prior telephone call advisable. CL: Mon. SIZE: Medium + warehouse. *STOCK: Furniture and clocks, 18th-20th C, £50-£10,000;*

porcelain and pottery, 17th-20th C, £10-£2,000; glass, 18th-20th C, £5-£1,000. LOC: Opposite parish church. PARK: Own. TEL: 01534 485177; fax - same; mobile - 07797 723895. SER: Valuations; restorations (furniture and china); buys at auction. FAIRS: NEC and Newark.

ST. SAVIOUR

Grange Gallery - Fine Arts Ltd
10 Victoria Rd., JE2 7QG. (G. J. Morris). Est. 1973. Open 9-5.30. SIZE: Medium. *STOCK: 19th-20th C oil paintings and watercolours, local items, £10-£10,000.* LOC: 1 mile east of St Helier. PARK: Forecourt. TEL: 01534 720077; e-mail - morris@jerseymail.co.uk. SER: Valuations; restorations (paintings); framing.

A watercolour by Myles Birket Foster of an Italian coastal scene which appeared at Sotheby's. This tiny painting was immaculately preserved in the lining of a chest of drawers and attracted £5,400.

From an Auction Report by Christopher Wight of Sporting, Primitive and Selected Pictures held at Sotheby's South on 18th July 2001 which appeared in the September 2001 issue of **Antique Collecting**. For more details and to subscribe see page 21.

The Bell Gallery
13 Adelaide Park. BT9 6FX. (J. N. Bell). Est. 1964. Open Mon.-Thurs. 10-6 or by appointment. SIZE: Medium. *STOCK: British and Irish art, 19th-20th C.* LOC: Off Malone Rd. PARK: Easy. TEL: 028 9066 2998; bellgallery@btinternet. com; website - www.bellgallery.com. SER: Valuations; restorations (paintings); buys at auction. VAT: Stan/Spec.

Emerald Isle Books
539 Antrim Rd. BT15 3BU. ABA. Est. 1966. Open by appointment. *STOCK: Travel, Ireland, theology.* TEL: 028 9037 0798; fax - 028 9077 7288. SER: Catalogues available.

T. H. Kearney & Sons
Treasure House, 123 University St. BT7 1HP. Resident. *STOCK: Small antiques.* TEL: 028 9023 1055. SER: Restorations and upholstery. VAT: Stan.

Charlotte and John Lambe
41 Shore Rd. BT15 3PG. Open 10-5. CL: Sat. *STOCK: English and French furniture, 19th C; pictures and works of art.* TEL: 028 9037 0761.

Co. Antrim

The Country Antiques
219B Lisnevenagh Rd. BT41 2JT. (David Wolfenden). LAPADA. 1982. Open 10-6. SIZE: Large. *STOCK: Furniture, £200-£5,000; jewellery and porcelain, £100-£3,000; all 19th C.* LOC: Main Antrim-Ballymena line. PARK: Easy. TEL: 028 9442 9498; e-mail - antiquewolfirl@ aol.com; website - www.country-antiques wolfenden.co. uk. SER: Valuations; restorations. Dublin. VAT: Stan/Spec.

Dunluce Antiques
33 Ballytober Rd. BT57 8UU. (MrsC. Ross). Est. 1978. Open 2-6 or by appointment. CL: Fri. SIZE: Small. *STOCK: Furniture, £100-£5,000; porcelain and glass, £10-£2,000; silver, £10-£2,000; all Georgian to 1930's; paintings, mainly*

Irish, £100-£25,000. LOC: 1. 5 miles off Antrim coast rd. at Dunluce Castle. PARK: Easy. TEL: 028 2073 1140. SER: Restorations (porcelain).

Robert Christie Antiques
The Courtyard, 38 Scotch Quarter. BT38 7DP. IADA. Est. 1976. Open 11-5. SIZE: Medium. *STOCK: Furniture, 1750-1900, £200-£3,000; clocks, 1750-1900, £500-£2,000; decorative objects, 1800-1900, £50-£500.* PARK: Easy. TEL: 028 9336 1333/9334 1149; mobile - 07802 968846. SER: Valuations. FAIRS: Kings Hall, Belfast; all RDS fairs.

Parvis Sigaroudinia
Mountainview House, 40 Sandy Lane, Ballyskeagh. BT27 5TL. IADA. Est. 1974. Open by appointment at any time. *STOCK: Oriental and European carpets and tapestries (extra large sizes stocked); cushions, lamps, William Yeoward crystal, David Williams-Ellis bronze sculpture, decorative items.* LOC: Take Malone Road from Belfast, then Upper Malone Road towards Lisburn, cross Ballyskeagh bridge over M1, 1st left into Sandy Lane. PARK: Easy. TEL: 028 9062 1824; home - same; fax - 028 9062 3311; e-mail - parvissig@aol.com; website - www. parvis.co.uk. SER: Valuations; buys at auction; exhibitions held in Belfast. FAIRS: IADA in RDS Dublin and King's Hall, Belfast. VAT: Stan.

MacHenry Antiques
Caragh Lodge, Glen Rd., Jordanstown. BT37 0RY. (R. and A. MacHenry). IADA. Est. 1964. Open Fri. and Sat. 12-6 or by appointment. SIZE: Medium. *STOCK: Georgian and Victorian furniture and objects.* LOC: 6 miles from Belfast on M2/M5 to Whiteabbey village, left at traffic lights at Woody's, then left into Old Manse Rd. and continue into Glen Rd. PARK: Easy. TEL: 028 9086 2036; fax - 028 9085 3281; mobile - 07831 135226; e-mail - rupert.machenry@ ntlworld.com. SER: Valuations. FAIRS: Dublin, Belfast and Irish. VAT: Stan/Spec.

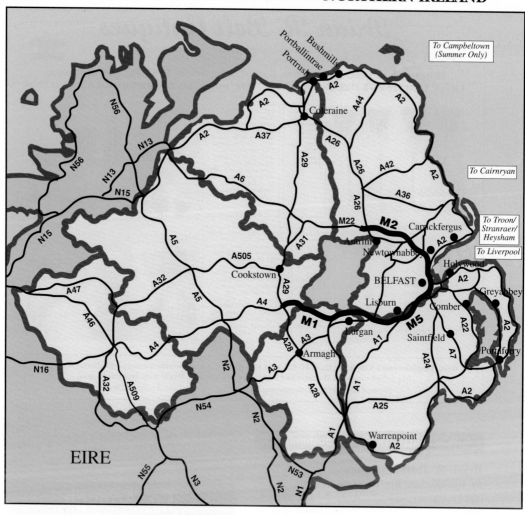

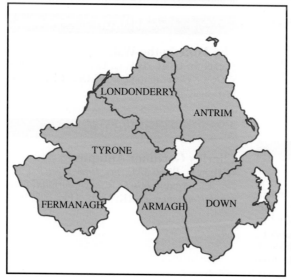

Brian R. Bolt Antiques

Early English & Continental Silver & Objects of Vertu; Arts & Crafts; Art Nouveau;
Art Deco & Post-War Design; Antique & 20th Century Glass; Treen etc.

88 Ballaghmore Road, Portballintrae, Bushmills, Co. Antrim, BT57 8RL, Northern Ireland.
Tel/Fax: (+44) 028 2073 1129; Mobile: 07712 579802; e-mail: brianbolt@antiques88.freeserve.co.uk

Set of four champagne flutes with silver-gilt textured stems, Stuart Devlin London 1978.

Irish silver milk jug, Charles Marsh, Dublin 1827; silver pepper mill with crest finial, London 1938; Victorian silver spill holder (military crest), John Eley, London 1847; Victorian silver Queen Anne style lighthouse caster, George Aldwinckle, London 1888; arts & crafts silver serving spoon, Kathleen Mary Hutchens (Kettering), hallmarked Birmingham 1931.

Art deco silver christening mug engraved with fish in the manner of Keith Murray, Mappin & Webb, London 1935 (jubilee hall-marks); Peter & Anne Bateman silver goblet (crested), London 1796.

Nathaniel Mills silver snuff box, Birmingham 1827; 18-cent. silver-mounted cowrie shell snuff box, unmarked probably Irish c.1740; Georg Jensen silver spoon London 1939; silver-mounted boar's tusk vesta case, London 1906; silver 'kidney bean' double sovereign case, Chester 1903; rare silver combination vesta, sovereign and stamp case with toothpick and pencil, Birmingham 1895; 17-cent. silver patch box engraved with tulips, maker's mark 'ME' only, English c.1690-95.

Write, telephone (until 9.00pm) or fax (+44) 028 2073 1129 daily or e-mail (brianbolt@antiques88.freeserve.co.uk) for free priced catalogue. Overseas and trade enquiries welcome. World-wide business by post.
Payment accepted by Mastercard and Visa together with guaranteed personal cheque.

PORTBALLINTRAE, Nr. Bushmills

Brian R. Bolt Antiques
88 Ballaghmore Rd. BT57 8RL. Open 11-5.30 and by appointment. CL: Wed. and Fri. *STOCK: Silver - small and unusual items, objects of vertu, snuff boxes, vesta cases, table, Scottish and Irish provincial; treen; English and Continental glass, antique and 20th C; art and studio glass and ceramics; Arts and Crafts, Art Nouveau and Art Deco jewellery and metalwork; vintage fountain pens.* TEL: 028 2073 1129; fax - same; e-mail - brianbolt@antiques88.freeserve.co.uk.   SER: Search; illustrated catalogues available; worldwide postal service; valuations.

PORTRUSH

Alexander Antiques
108 Dunluce Rd. BT56 8NB. (Mrs M. and D. Alexander). Est. 1974. Open 10-6. CL: Sun. except by appointment. SIZE: Large. *STOCK: Furniture, silver, porcelain, fine art, 18th-20th C; oils and watercolours, 19th-20th C.* Not Stocked: Militaria, jewellery, coins. LOC: 1 mile from Portrush on A2 to Bushmills. PARK: Easy. TEL: 028 7082 2783. SER: Valuations; buys at auction. VAT: Stan/Spec.

Co. Armagh

ARMAGH

The Hole-in-the-Wall
Market St. BT61 7BW. (I. Emerson). Est. 1953. *STOCK: General antiques.* LOC: City centre. VAT: Stan/Spec.

LURGAN

Charles Gardiner Antiques
48 High St. BT66 8AU. Est. 1968. Open 9-1 and 2-6. CL: Wed. *STOCK: Clocks, furniture and general antiques.* PARK: Own. TEL: 028 3832 3934.

Co. Down

COMBER

Bobby Douglas Antiques
9 Killinchy St. BT23 5SD. (B. and N. R. G. Douglas). Open by appointment only. SIZE: Medium and trade barn. *STOCK: Irish furniture, 18th-19th C, £1,000-£25,000; unusual collectors' items, 19th C, under £1,000.* PARK: Easy. TEL: 028 9752 8351. SER: Valuations. VAT: Stan/Spec. *Trade only.*

GREYABBEY, Nr. Newtownards

Phyllis Arnold Gallery Antiques
Hoops Courtyard. BT22 2NE. Est. 1968. Open Wed., Fri. and Sat. 11-5. *STOCK: General antiques, jewellery, small furniture, Irish paintings and watercolours, portrait miniatures, maps and engravings of Ireland.* TEL: 028 4278 8199; home - 028 9185 3322; fax - same. SER: Restorations (maps, prints, watercolours, portrait miniatures); conservation framing. FAIRS: Culloden.

Marjorie McAuley - The Antique Shop
9 Main St. BT22 2NE. Est. 1968. Open Wed. and Fri. 2-5.30 or by appointment. *STOCK: General antiques, Georgian, Victorian and modern silver, linens.* PARK: Easy. TEL: Home - 028 4273 8333.

HOLYWOOD

Herbert Gould and Co.
21-23 Church Rd. BT18 9BU. (Robert Brown). Est. 1897. Open 9. 15-5.30. SIZE: Medium. *STOCK: Pine, 19th C, £75-£200; collectables, architectural antiques, 19th-20th C, £10-£100.* LOC: 20 yards from maypole in town centre. PARK: Opposite. TEL: 028 9042 7916. SER: Valuations; pine stripping; buys at auction (as stock). VAT: Stan.

PORTAFERRY

Time & Tide Antiques
36 Shore Rd. BT22 1JZ. (D. Dunlop). Open Wed., Fri., Sat. and Sun. 12-5.30 or by appointment. SIZE: Medium. *STOCK: Clocks, barometers, marine instruments, pictures, nautical memorabilia and small furniture, £50-£10,000.* LOC: A20 from Newtownards through Greyabbey. PARK: On promenade. TEL: 028 4272 8935; home - same. SER: Valuations; restorations and repairs.

SAINTFIELD

Agar Antiques
92 Main St. BT24 7AD. (Rosie Agar). Est.1990. Open 11-5. SIZE: Medium. *STOCK: Furniture, mainly Victorian, some Georgian and Edwardian, £30-£1,000; light fittings, Victorian and Edwardian, £15-£650; general small items including oil lamps, £1-£500; jewellery, Victorian and Edwardian, £10-£350.* PARK: Nearby. TEL: 028 975 11214. SER: Valuations.

The Anvil Gallery
55 Main St. BT24. (Sheila Duff). Est. 1996. Open 11-5.30. CL: Mon. and Tues. SIZE: Small. *STOCK: Works of art including paintings and prints, ceramics, wallhangings, sculpture, furniture and jewellery, to £2,000.* PARK: Easy. TEL: 028 9751 1991; fax - same; home - 028 4488 1627; e-mail - sheilamduff@hotmail.com; website - www.anvilgallery.com.

Ashley Pine
88 Main St. BT24 7AB. (Mrs Truda K. Martin). Est. 1995. Open Mon. 1-5, Tues.-Fri. 10.30-5 and Sat. 10-5.30. SIZE: Small. *STOCK: General antiques and pine.* PARK: Easy. TEL: 028 9751 1855. SER: Restorations (furniture).

Attic Antiques
88 Main St. (Caesar and Reuben Doyle). Est. 1992. Open 10-5, Sat. 10-5.30. SIZE: Large. *STOCK: Victorian and Edwardian furniture, £50-£2,000; Victorian jewellery, £5-£1,000; bric-a-brac, to £100. (+ Irish, European and reclaimed pine, £30-£1,000 at Attic Pine).* PARK: Easy. TEL: 028 9751 1057. SER: Valuations.

Fine Art
45 Main St. BT24 7AB. Est. 2001. Open Tues. and Fri. 12-5, Sat. 10-5. SIZE: Small. *STOCK: Original paintings, £50-£3,000.* PARK: Easy. TEL: 028 9751 9200.

Peter Francis Antiques
92 Main St. BT24 7AD. Est. 1998. Open 11-5. SIZE: Medium. *STOCK: English, Irish and Oriental ceramics, 18th-20th C; English and Irish glass, mainly 18th-19th, some 20th C; smalls including ethnographic, Indian, European, bronzes, metalwork, treen and prints; all £5-£500.* PARK: Nearby. TEL: 028 9751 1214; e-mail irishantiq@aol.com. SER: Valuations.

Saintfield Antiques & Fine Books
68 Main St. BT24 7AB. (Joseph Leckey). Est. 1978. Open Thurs., Fri. and Sat. 11.30 -5. SIZE: Small. *STOCK: Silver, 18th-20th, £25-£750;*

porcelain, 18th-19th C, £50-£500; fine and antiquarian books, 19th-20th C, £10-£500. PARK: Easy. TEL: Home - 028 9752 8428; fax - same; e-mail - home@antiquesireland.com; website - www.antiquesireland.com. FAIRS: All L&M Ltd.

The Oriental Rug Shop
3 Fairview. (Mrs. Wendy Dallas). Est. 1993. Open Tues.-Sat. 11-5. SIZE: Small. *STOCK: Persian rugs and carpets, 1900-1970, £160-£5,000; 19th-20th C occasional furniture, £40-£400; bric-a-brac, to £100.* LOC: Top of main street. PARK: Easy. TEL: 07803 908791; mobile - 07762 912141. SER: Valuations (carpets and rugs); restorations; cleaning and repairs.

Town & Country Antiques
92 Main St. BT24 7AB. (Patrica Keller). Est. 1997. Open Wed. -Sat. 10.30-5. SIZE: Medium. *STOCK: Prints, botanical, ornithological and sporting, £100-£400; 18th-19th C French tapestries, £600-£1,500; French chandeliers £300-£600; Venetian, French and Victorian mirrors, £400-£700; Georgian, Victorian and Edwardian small mahogany furniture, £500-£1,000; table lamps, rugs and equestrian items, desks.* PARK: Easy. TEL: 028 4461 4721; home - same; fax - 028 4461 9716; mobile - 07710 840090; e-mail - l.w.k @btinternet.com. SER: Restorations (furniture, prints and tapestries). VAT: Stan.

Antiques and Fine Art Gallery
3 Charlotte St. BT34 3LF. (B. Woods). Est. 1991. Open 10.30-1 and 2.30-5.30. CL: Mon. and Wed. SIZE: Medium. *STOCK: Furniture, Georgian to Edwardian, £50-£5,000; paintings especially Irish, 20th C, £50-£10,000.* LOC: Turn off main road at Newry. PARK: Easy. TEL: 028 4175 2905. SER: Valuations. framing.

The Forge Antiques
24 Long Commons. BT52 1LH. (M. W. Walker). Est. 1977. Open 10-5.30. CL: Thurs. SIZE: Medium. *STOCK: General antiques, silver, clocks, jewellery, porcelain, paintings.* PARK: Easy. TEL: 028 7035 1339. VAT: Stan.

Homes, Pubs and Clubs
1-5 Portrush Rd. BT52 1RL. (McNulty Wholesalers). Resident. Est. 1983. Open 9-6, Sun. 2.30-6. SIZE: Large. *STOCK: Pine and mahogany, small interesting items.* LOC: Main Portrush road, near traffic lights. PARK: At rear. TEL: 028 7035 5733. SER: Valuations; restorations. FAIRS: Newark. VAT: Stan.

Co. Tyrone

Cookstown Antiques
16 Oldtown St. BT80 8EF. (G. Jebb). Est. 1976. Open Thurs. and Fri. 2-5.30, Sat. 10.30-5.30. SIZE: Small. *STOCK: Jewellery, silver, £10-£2,000; coins, £25-£200; pictures, ceramics and militaria, £5-£1,000; general antiques, all 19th-20th C. Not Stocked: Large furniture.* LOC: Going north, through both sets of traffic lights, on left at rear of estate agency. PARK: Easy. TEL: 028 8676 5279; fax - 028 8676 2946; home - 028 8676 2926. SER: Valuations; buys at auction.

The Saddle Room Antiques
4 Coagh St. BT80 8NG. (C. J. Leitch). Est. 1968. Open 10-5.30. CL: Mon. and Wed. SIZE: Medium. *STOCK: China, silver, furniture, glass, jewellery.* TEL: 028 8676 4045.

Fabric design in satin with a repeating tiger lily spray motif, edited by Cornille frères, c.1900–1903. (Musée de la Mode et du Textile, Paris; photograph L.-S. Jaulmes)

From an article entitled "Art Nouveau Designers at the Paris Salons 1895-1914" by Alastair Duncan which appeared in the February 2002 issue of **Antique Collecting**. For more details and to subscribe see page 21.

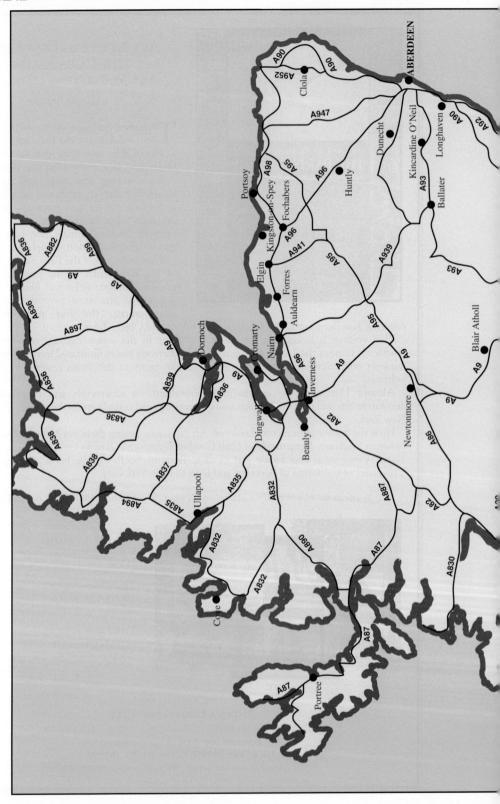

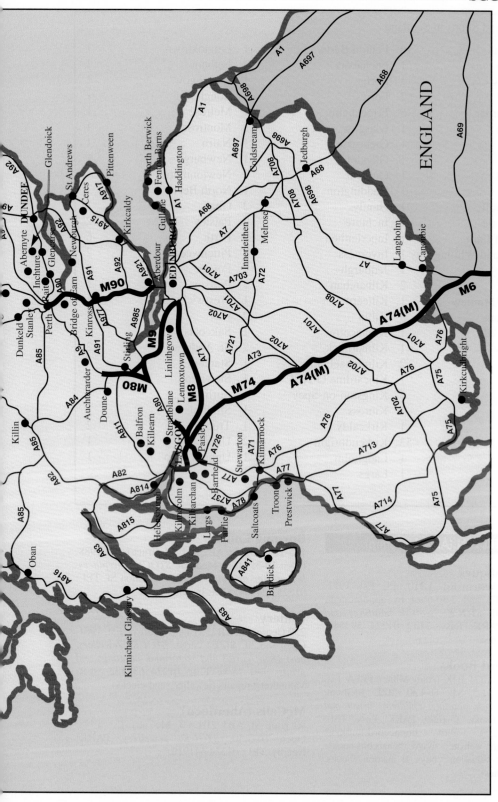

Dealers and Shops in Scotland

Aberdeen	10	Fenton Barns	1	Lennoxtown	1
Aberdour	1	Fochabers	4	Letham	1
Aberfeldy	1	Forfar	1	Linlithgow	1
Abernyte	2	Forres	1	Longhaven	1
Auchterarder	5	Friockheim	1	Melrose	1
Auldearn	1	Glasgow	16	Montrose	1
Balfron	1	Glencarse	1	Nairn	1
Ballater	1	Glendoick	1	Newburgh	1
Barrhead	1	Gullane	1	Newtonmore	1
Beauly	1	Haddington	1	North Berwick	3
Blair Atholl	1	Huntly	2	Oban	1
Blairgowrie	2	Inchture	2	Paisley	2
Bridge of Earn	1	Innerleithen	2	Perth	6
Brodick and Whiting Bay	1	Inverness	1	Pittenweem	2
Canonbie	1	Jedburgh	2	Portree	1
Ceres	2	Kilbarchan	2	Portsoy	1
Clola by Mintlaw	1	Killearn	1	Prestwick	1
Coldstream	3	Killin	2	Rait	1
Cove	1	Kilmacolm	1	Saltcoats	1
Cromarty	1	Kilmarnock	2	St. Andrews	2
Dornoch	2	Kilmichael Glassary	1	Stanley	1
Doune	1	Kincardine O'Neil	1	Stewarton	1
Dundee	3	Kingston-on-Spey	1	Stirling	1
Dunecht	1	Kinross	1	Strathblane	1
Dunkeld	1	Kirkcaldy	1	Troon	2
Edinburgh	53	Kirkcudbright	2	Ullapool	1
Elgin	1	Langholm	1	Upper Largo	1
Fairlie	1	Largs	1		

ABERDEEN (Aberdeenshire)

Atholl Antiques
322 Great Western Rd. AB10 6PL. Est. 1971. Open 10.30-1 and 2.30-6 or by appointment. SIZE: Small. *STOCK: Scottish paintings and furniture.* PARK: Easy. TEL: 01224 593547. VAT: Stan/Spec.

Bon-Accord Books
69-75 Spital. AB24 3HX. (Andy Milne). PBFA. Est. 1998. Open 11-5, Sat. 11-4.30. SIZE: Medium. *STOCK: Scottish, sporting, childrens, travel and antiquarian books, £5-£800.* PARK: Easy. TEL: 01224 643209; e-mail - bonaccord.books@ btinternet.com; website - www. bonaccord-books-co.uk. SER: Valuations; buys at auction (books, prints and maps).

Burning Embers
165-167 King St. AB2 3AE. (J. Bruce). Est. 1988. Open 10-5. SIZE: Medium. *STOCK: Fireplaces, bric-a-brac and pine.* LOC: Off Union St. TEL: 01224 624664. SER: Installations.

Gallery
239 George St. AB25 1ED. (M. Gray). Est. 1981. Open 9-5.30. SIZE: Large. *STOCK: Jewellery, post 1850; curios and Victoriana, paintings and prints, post 1800.* TEL: 01224 632522. SER: Valuations; repairs (jewellery and clocks).

McCalls (Aberdeen)
90 King St. AB1 2JH. (B. McCall). Est. 1948. Open 10-5.30. *STOCK: Jewellery.* PARK: Nearby. TEL: 01224 641916.

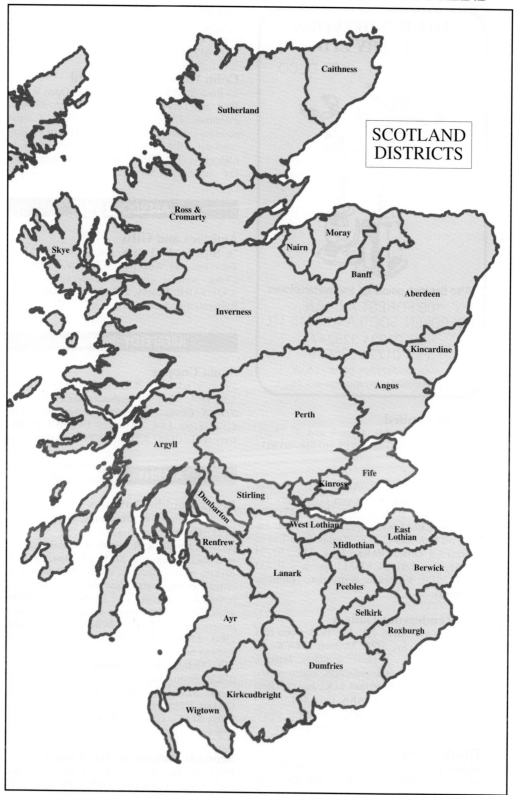

SCOTLAND
DISTRICTS

Caithness

Sutherland

Ross &
Cromarty

Skye

Nairn

Moray

Banff

Aberdeen

Inverness

Kincardine

Angus

Perth

Argyll

Fife

Kinross

Stirling

Dunbarton

West Lothian

East
Lothian

Renfrew

Midlothian

Berwick

Lanark

Peebles

Ayr

Selkirk

Roxburgh

Dumfries

Kirkcudbright

Wigtown

McCalls Limited
11 Bridge St. AB11 6JL. Open 9.30-5.30, Thurs. 9.30-8. *STOCK: Jewellery.* TEL: 01224 405303.

The Odd Lot
18 Adelphi, Union St. AB11 5BL. (George Knight-Mudie). Est. 1995. Open 11-4, Thurs. 10-5, Fri. and Sat. 10-5.30. SIZE: Small. *STOCK: Furniture, £30-£1,000; jewellery and china, £5-£750; all 19th-20th C.* LOC: 2 mins. from Tourist Information Office. PARK: Easy. TEL: 01224 592551; fax - 01224 575813; home - 07833 773772. SER: Valuations; restorations (furniture and china).

The Rendezvous Gallery
100 Forest Ave. AB15 4TL. Est. 1973. Open 10-1 and 2.30-6. CL: Fri. SIZE: Medium. *STOCK: Art Nouveau, Art Deco, glass, jewellery, bronzes, furniture, £100-£5,000; paintings, watercolours, Scottish School, £200-£6,000.* LOC: Just off Great Western Rd. to Braemar. PARK: Easy. TEL: 01224 323247; fax - 01224 326029; e-mail - info@ rendezvous-gallery.co.uk. VAT: Stan/Spec.

Thistle Antiques
28 Esslemont Ave. AB25 1SN. (P. and Mrs M. Bursill). LAPADA. Est. 1967. Open 10-5, Sat.

10-1. CL: Wed. SIZE: Medium. *STOCK: General antiques, Georgian and Victorian furniture, period lighting.* LOC: City centre. PARK: Easy. TEL: 01224 634692. VAT: Spec.

Colin Wood (Antiques) Ltd
25 Rose St. AB10 1TX. Est. 1968. Open 9.30-5, Wed. and Thurs. 10-5. SIZE: Medium. *STOCK: Furniture, 17th-19th C; works of art, Scottish paintings, prints and silver; specialist in maps of Scotland, 16th-19th C.* PARK: Multi-storey in Chapel St. TEL: 01224 644786 (answerphone); fax - same. VAT: Stan/Spec.

ABERDOUR (Fife)

Antiques and Gifts
26 High St. KY3 0SW. Est. 1976. CL: Mon., Tues. am. and Wed. pm. SIZE: Small. *STOCK: China, pottery, glass and collectables.* LOC: A921. PARK: Nearby. TEL: 01383 860523. SER: Restorations (china).

ABERFELDY (Perthshire)

Sonia Cooper
19 Bridgend. PH15 2DF. Est. 1983. Open Thurs.-Sat. 11-4, Mon. in summer. SIZE: Medium. *STOCK: China, glass, wood and metal, from 18th C, £1-£100.* LOC: 10 miles from A9. PARK: Easy. TEL: 01887 820266. SER: Buys at auction.

ABERNYTE (Perthshire)

Becca Gauldie Antiques
Scottish Antiques & Arts Centre. PH14 9SJ. Est. 1993. Centre open 10-5 including Sun. For personal appointment, telephone mobile number or e-mail in advance. SIZE: Medium. *STOCK: British, mainly Scottish, curios including snuff boxes, sewing items, Mauchline ware (painted, tartan, fern, transfer and photographic), 1800-1930, £50-£4,000; country furnishings, Scottish pottery, glass and quilts, decorators items, 1750-1900, £50-£5,000.* LOC: 1. 5 miles off A92 midway between Perth and Dundee. PARK: Easy. TEL: Mobile - 07770 741636; centre manager - 01828 686401; e-mail - becca@gauldie.freeserve. co.uk. SER: Buys at auction. FAIRS: Little Chelsea; Bailey, Harrogate; Denman, West London; NEC; SECC, Glasgow. VAT: Stan/Spec/Global/ Export.

Scottish Antique & Arts Centre
PH14 9SJ. (Templemans). Open 10-5 including Sun. SIZE: Large - 100 dealers. *STOCK: Furniture, £50-*

£5,000; accessories, £5-£2,000; collectibles, £5-£50; all 18th-19th C. LOC: 1.5 miles from A90 Perth-Dundee link road. PARK: Own. TEL: 01828 686401; fax - 01828 686199. SER: Valuations; restorations. VAT: Stan/Spec/Global.

AUCHTERARDER (Perthshire)

Ian Burton Antique Clocks
at The Antique Galleries, 125 High St. PH3 1AA. Open 9-5, Sat. 10-5. STOCK: Clocks. TEL: 01334 471426; mobile - 07785 114800; e-mail - ian@ianburton.com; website - www.ianburton.com.

Nigel Stacy-Marks Ltd
92 High St. PH3 1BJ. (Nigel and Ginny Marks). LAPADA. Open 10-5. SIZE: Medium. STOCK: Oils and watercolours, 19th-20th C, £250-£30,000; British etchings, late 19th C to mid 20th C, £100-£5,000. LOC: Opposite library, next to Tourist Information Centre. PARK: Easy. TEL: 01764 663525; fax - same; e-mail - paintings@stacy-marks.co.uk; website - www.stacy-marks.co.uk. SER: Valuations; restorations; framing; regular exhibitions (catalogues on request). FAIRS: Antiques For Everyone, SECC, Glasgow. VAT: Stan/Spec.

Times Past Antiques
Broadfold Farm. PH3 1DR. (J. M. Brown). Est. 1970. Open 8-4.30, weekends and holidays 10-3. SIZE: Large. STOCK: Stripped pine, 19th-20th C, from £50; shipping goods, £5-£500. LOC: From town centre take Abbey Rd. to flyover A9 at T junction. Turn left, 1st farm on left. PARK: Easy. TEL: 01764 663166; fax - same. SER: Restorations (pine); courier; container-packing.

John Whitelaw and Sons Antiques
125 High St. PH3 1AA. LAPADA. Open 9-5, Sat. 9-1 and 2-5. STOCK: General antiques; furniture, 17th-19th C. PARK: Easy. TEL: 01764 662482; fax - 01764 663577; e-mail - jwsantique@aol.com; website - www.whitelawantiques.com. VAT: Stan/Spec.

AULDEARN, Nr. Nairn (Nairnshire)

Auldearn Antiques
Dalmore Manse, Lethen Rd. IV12 5HZ. Est. 1980. Open 10-6 including Sun. SIZE: Medium. STOCK: Victorian linen and lace, kitchenalia, china, furniture, architectural items. LOC: 1 mile from village. TEL: 01667 453087; home - same.

BALFRON (Stirlingshire)

Amphora Galleries
16-18 Buchanan St. G63 0TT. (L. Ruglen). Resident. Est. 1961. Open 10-5.30 and by appointment. SIZE: Large. STOCK: General antiques, furniture, decorative items. LOC: A81. TEL: 01360 440329.

BALLATER (Aberdeenshire)

The McEwan Gallery
Bridge of Gairn. AB35 5UB. (D., P. and R. McEwan). LAPADA. Est. 1968. Open 2-5.30, Sun. 2-5, prior telephone call advisable during winter. SIZE: Medium. STOCK: 18th-20th C British and European paintings, specialising in Scottish; rare and elusive polar, Scottish, golf, sporting and natural history books. LOC: First house on the east side of A939 after its junction with A93 outside Ballater. PARK: Easy. TEL: 013397 55429; fax - 013397 55995. SER: Valuations; restorations (framing); buys at auction (paintings, watercolours, books); golf catalogues. VAT: Spec.

BARRHEAD, Nr. Glasgow (Renfrewshire)

C. P. R. Antiques and Services
96 Main St. G78 1SE. (C. Porterfield). Est. 1965. Open 10-1 and 1.30-5. CL: Tues. SIZE: Small. STOCK: Brass, furniture and curios, 19th-20th C, to £3,000. PARK: Easy. TEL: 0141 881 5379.

BEAULY (Inverness-shire)

Iain Marr Antiques
3 Mid St. IV4 7DP. (I. and A. Marr). HADA. Est. 1975. Open 10.30-1 and 2-5.30. CL: Thurs. STOCK: Silver, jewellery, clocks, porcelain, scientific instruments, arms, oils, watercolours, small furniture. LOC: Off Square, on left going north (next to Coffee Shop). PARK: Easy. TEL: 01463 782372; e-mail - info@iain-marr-antiques.com; website - www.iain-marr-antiques.com. VAT: Stan/Spec/Global.

BLAIR ATHOLL, Nr. Pitlochry (Perthshire)

Blair Antiques
By Bruar Falls. PH18 5TW. (Duncan Huie). Est. 1976. Open 9-5. CL: Thurs. STOCK: Period furniture, Scottish oil paintings, silver - some provincial, curios, clocks, pottery and porcelain. TEL: 01796 483264. SER: Valuations; buys at auction. VAT: Stan/Spec.

BLAIRGOWRIE (Perthshire)

Blairgowrie Books
3 Meadow Place, Wellmeadow. PH10 6NQ. (Marlene Hughes). Est. 1982. Open 10.30-1 and 2-5, Sat. 10.30-5, Sun. by appointment. CL: Tues. SIZE: Medium. *STOCK: Books - mainly on Scottish fishing, shooting, hunting and climbing, £2.50-£150; children's and general.* LOC: Next to river Ericht, town centre. PARK: Easy. TEL: 01250 875855. SER: Valuations.

Roy Sim Antiques
The Granary Warehouse, Lower Mill St. PH10 6AQ. (Roy and Ann Sim). Est. 1977. Open 9-5.30, Sun. 12-5. SIZE: Large. *STOCK: Furniture, clocks, silver, EPNS, collectable, decorative and furnishing items.* LOC: Town centre. PARK: Own. TEL: 01250 873860. SER: Shipping. VAT: Spec.

BRIDGE OF EARN (Perthshire)

Imrie Antiques
Back St. PH2 9AE. (Mr and Mrs I. Imrie). LAPADA. Est. 1969. Open 10-1 and 2-5.30. SIZE: Large. *STOCK: Victorian and 18th C shipping goods.* PARK: Easy. TEL: 01738 812784. VAT: Stan.

BRODRICK AND WHITING BAY (Isle of Arran)

Kames Antiques & Jewellery
Shore Rd. KA27 8AJ. (C. J. and J. M. Fieldhouse). Open 10-5. *STOCK: Furniture, porcelain, paintings, jewellery, collectables, objets d'art, silver and artists' materials.* TEL: 0177030 2213.

CANONBIE, Nr. Carlisle (Dumfriesshire)

The Clock Showrooms
DG14 0SY. (John R. Mann). MCWG. Est. 1987. Open by appointment. SIZE: Large. *STOCK: Clocks - over 80 restored longcase, 17th-19th C, £2,500-£90,000; bracket, 17th-19th C, £3,500-£35,000; wall, 19th C, £500-£6,000; small antiques and collectables.* LOC: Leave M6, junction 44, A7 north through Longtown, follow sign to village, premises next to Cross Keys Hotel. PARK: Easy. TEL: 013873 71337/71827; fax - 013873 71337; mobile - 07850 606147. SER: Valuations; restorations (clock movements, cases and dials); buys at auction (clocks). VAT: Stan.

CERES (Fife)

Ceres Antiques
1 High St. KY15. (Mrs E. Norrie). SIZE: Medium. *STOCK: General antiques, china and linen.* PARK: Easy. TEL: 01334 828384.

Steeple Antiques
38 Main St. KY15 5NH. (Mrs Elizabeth Hart). Est. 1980. Open 2-5 including Sun., mornings by appointment. CL: Wed. pm. SIZE: Medium. *STOCK: Porcelain including some Wemyss, 1800-1950, £5-£500; cutlery, silver and plate, £5-£200+; Victorian linen, some furniture, £50-£400.* LOC: 3 miles from Cupar. PARK: Easy. TEL: Home - 01334 828553. SER: Valuations; buys at auction (silver, china and furniture).

CLOLA BY MINTLAW, Nr. Peterhead (Aberdeenshire)

Clola Antiques Centre
Shannas School House. AB42 5AE. (Joan and David Blackburn). Est. 1985. Open 10-5, Sun. 11-4.30 or by appointment. SIZE: Large - 10 dealers. *STOCK: Victorian and Edwardian furniture, antique and modern jewellery, collectables, china and militaria.* LOC: 3 miles south of Mintlaw and 25 miles north of Aberdeen on A952. PARK: Own. TEL: 01771 624584; fax - 01771 624751; e-mail - clolaantique@aol.com; website - www. clolaantiquecentre.co.uk. FAIRS: Aberdeen.

COLDSTREAM (Berwickshire)

Coldstream Antiques
44 High St. TD12 4AS. (Mr and Mrs J. Trinder). Resident. Open daily. SIZE: Large. *STOCK: Furniture, 17th-20th C; general antiques, clocks, silver and shipping goods, 17th-19th C.* LOC: A697. TEL: 01890 882552. VAT: Stan/Spec.

Fraser Antiques
65 High St. TD12 4DL. Est. 1968. Open Tues.-Fri. 10-5, Sat. 9.30-5, other times by appointment. SIZE: Medium. *STOCK: Porcelain, glass, pictures, silver, small furniture, general antiques.* PARK: Easy. TEL: 01890 882450; fax - 01890 882451. SER: Valuations; restorations. VAT: Spec.

Hand in Hand
Hirsel Law Schoolhouse. (Mrs Ruth Hand). Est. 1969. Open by appointment. *STOCK: Paisley shawls, period costume, fine linens, quilts, curtains and interesting textiles.* PARK: Own. TEL: 01890 883496; e-mail - ruth.hand@virgin.

net; website - www.handinhand.uk.com. SER: Restorations; valuations. FAIRS: Textile (London, Manchester).

COVE (Argyll & Bute)

Cove Curios
Shore Rd. G84 0LR. (R. and K. J. Young). Open weekends and daily May-Sept., other times by appointment. *STOCK: General antiques.* PARK: Easy. TEL: 01436 842222. FAIRS: Glasgow.

CROMARTY (Ross-shire)

Cromarty Antiques
24 Church St. IV11 8XA. (Jean and Jenny Henderson). Est. 2000. Open summer - Wed., Thurs., Fri. and Sat. 10-5, other days by appointment. Winter - prior telephone call advisable. SIZE: Large. *STOCK: Georgian, Victorian and Edwardian fine furniture, especially dining room tables; porcelain, glass, metalware, silver including Scottish provincial.* LOC: On the Black Isle (just north of Inverness), follow signs for Cromarty from A9. PARK: Easy. TEL: 01381 600404; fax - 01381 610408; home - 01381 610269. FAIRS: Robert Soper - Hopetown House and Oxenfoord Castle; Galloway - Perth; Drumossie - Inverness. VAT: Spec.

DORNOCH (Sutherland)

Castle Close Antiques
Castle Close. IV25 3SN. (Mrs J. Maclean). Est. 1982. Open 10-1 and 2-5. CL: Thurs. pm. SIZE: Medium. *STOCK: General antiques including, furniture, stripped pine, porcelain, jewellery and silver, paintings.* PARK: Easy. TEL: 01862 810405; home - 01862 81057; e-mail - enquiries @castle-close-antiques.com. VAT: Spec.

Little Treasures
Shore Rd. IV25 3LS. (Allison Taylor). Est. 1993. Open 10-5, Sun. 12-4 (summer only). SIZE: Small. *STOCK: Jewellery, ceramics and glass, 19th-20th C, £5-£1,000.* LOC: Just off Cathedral Sq, road opposite Tourist Information. PARK: Easy. TEL: 01862 811175; e-mail - allison@ littletreasures.fsbusiness.co.uk; website - www. littletreasures.fsbusiness.co.uk. SER: Valuations.

DOUNE (Stirlingshire)

Scottish Antique & Arts Centre
FK16 6HD. (Robert Templeman). Est. 1999. Open 10-5 including Sun. SIZE: Large. *STOCK: General antiques, collectables, Georgian and Victorian furniture, jewellery, glass, paintings, books.* LOC: A84 Stirling to Callander road, 1 mile north of Doune. PARK: Own. TEL: 01786 841203; fax - 01786 842070; e-mail - victempleton @aol.com; website - www.scottish-antiques.com. VAT: Stan./Spec.

DUNDEE (Angus)

Angus Antiques
4 St. Andrews St. DD1 2EX. (Stanley Paget and John Czerek). Est. 1964. Open 10-4. CL: Sat. *STOCK: Militaria, badges, medals, swords, jewellery, silver, gold, collectors items, Art Nouveau, Art Deco, advertising and decorative items, tins, toys, teddy bears.* LOC: City centre. PARK: Nearby. TEL: 01382 322128.

Neil Livingstone
3 Old Hawkhill. DD2 1LS. LAPADA. Open any time by appointment. SIZE: Small. *STOCK: Jewellery, Continental furniture and decorative items, 18th-20th C.* TEL: 01382 907788/221751; fax - 01382 566332; mobile - 07775 877715; e-mail - neil@westportgallery.sagehost.co.uk. SER: Shipping worldwide.

Westport Gallery
48 Westport. DD1 5ER. Est. 1976. Open 9-5. SIZE: Medium. *STOCK: Antique jewellery.* LOC: City centre end of Perth Road, turn into Tay St. and bear left, shop on the left. PARK: Easy. TEL: 01382 221751; fax - 01382 229707. SER: Valuations; jewellery repairs. VAT: Stan/Spec.

DUNECHT (Aberdeenshire)

The Magic Lantern
Nether Corskie. AB32 7EL. (Mr and Mrs P Whyte). Est. 1978. SIZE: Medium. *STOCK: Georgian and Victorian furniture, £500-£2,000; silver and plate Victorian cutlery, £50-£100; china, porcelain, Scottish pottery, candlesticks, £25-£200.* LOC: A944, turn towards Kintore. PARK: Easy. TEL: 01330 860678; home - same. SER: Restorations (china).

DUNKELD (Perthshire)

Dunkeld Antiques
Tay Terrace. PH8 0AQ. (D. Dytch). LAPADA. Est. 1986. Open 10-5.30, Sun. 12-5.30. SIZE: Large. *STOCK: 18th-19th C items especially dining furniture, decorative boxes and clocks,*

Japanese ceramics, shooting and fishing memor-abilia, out of print books. LOC: Converted church, overlooking Tay river. PARK: Easy. TEL: 01350 728832; fax - 01350 727008. VAT: Spec.

EDINBURGH (Midlothian)

Antiques
48 Thistle St. EH2 1EN. (E. Humphrey). Est. 1946. Open mornings or by appointment. *STOCK: Paintings, etchings, china and glass.* TEL: 0131 226 3625.

Armchair Books
72 West Port. EH1 2LE. (David Govan). Est. 1993. Open 11-5.30 and most Sun. SIZE: Small. *STOCK: Books, secondhand and Victorian, £2-£50.* LOC: West from Grassmarket. PARK: Nearby. TEL: 0131 229 5927; e-mail - armchairbooks@hotmail.com. SER: Valuations; restorations (books).

Paddy Barrass
15 The Grassmarket. EH1 2HS. Est. 1974. Open 12-6, Sat. 10.30-5.30, Sun. in Aug. 2-7. SIZE: Small. *STOCK: Period clothing, textiles and household linen, 19th-20th C, £5-£500.* LOC: South side of High St., directly below castle. PARK: Easy. TEL: 0131 22630 87; website - www.vintagelinens.co.uk. SER: Valuations.

Bebes et Jouets
c/o Lochend Post Office. 165 Restalrig Rd. EH7 6HW. Est. 1988. Open by appointment only. SIZE: Small. *STOCK: Fine French and German dolls, vintage teddy bears, dolls' houses and miniature doll-related items, dolls' clothing and accessories.* LOC: ½ mile from Princes Street. PARK: Easy. TEL: 0131 332 5650; e-mail - bebesetjouets@u.genie.co.uk; website - www. you.genie.co.uk/bebesetjouets. SER: Photographs and videos of stock available.

Berland's of Edinburgh
143 Gilmore Place. EH3 9PW. (R. Melvin). Open 9-5. *STOCK: Restored antique light fittings.* TEL: 0131 228 6760.

Joseph Bonnar, Jewellers
72 Thistle St. EH2 1EN. Open 10.30-5 or by appointment. SIZE: Medium. *STOCK: Antique and period jewellery.* LOC: Parallel with Princes St. TEL: 0131 226 2811; fax - 0131 225 9438. VAT: Stan/Spec.

Bourne Fine Art Ltd
6 Dundas St. EH3 6HZ. (P. Bourne). Est. 1978. Open 10-6, Sat. 11-2. SIZE: Medium. *STOCK: British paintings, 1700-1950.* PARK: Easy. TEL: 0131 557 4050. SER: Valuations; restorations; buys at auction; framing. VAT: Stan/Spec.

Broughton Books
2A Broughton Place. EH1 3RX. (P. Galinsky). Est. 1964. Open Tues.-Fri. 12-6, Sat. 10.30-5.30. SIZE: Medium. *STOCK: Books, secondhand and antiquarian, £2. 50-£250.* LOC: Off Broughton St, close to Waverley station and top of Leith Walk. TEL: 0131 557 8010; home - 0131 478 0614.

Calton Gallery   BADA
10 Royal Terr. EH7 5AB. (A. G. Whitfield). Est. 1979. Open 10-6, Sat. by appointment. SIZE: Large. STOCK: Paintings, especially Scottish marine and watercolours, £100-£100,000; prints, £10-£1,000; sculpture, to £20,000; all 19th to early 20th C. PARK: Easy. TEL: 0131 556 1010; home - same; fax - 0131 558 1150. SER: Valuations; restorations (oils, watercolours, prints); buys at auction (paintings). VAT: Stan/Spec.

The Carson Clark Gallery -
Scotland's Map Heritage Centre
181-183 Canongate, The Royal Mile. EH8 8BN. (A. Carson Clark). FRGS. FBCartS. Est. 1969. Open 10.30-5.30. *STOCK: Maps, sea charts and prints.* TEL: 0131 556 4710; fax - same; e-mail - scotmap@aol.com. SER: Collections valued and purchased.

The Collectors Shop
49 Cockburn St. EH1 1BS. (D. Cavanagh). Est. 1960. Open 11-5. *STOCK: Coins, medals, militaria, cigarette and postcards, small collectors' items, jewellery, silver and plate.* Not Stocked: Postage stamps. TEL: 0131 226 3391. SER: Buys at auction.

Craiglea Clocks
88 Comiston Rd. EH10 5QJ. (R. J. Rafter). Est. 1977. Open 10-5. SIZE: Small. *STOCK: Antique clocks and barometers.* LOC: On Biggar road from Morningside. PARK: Adjacent streets. TEL: 0131 452 8568; website - www.craigleaclocks. com. SER: Restorations (clocks and barometers).

Da Capo Antiques
68 Henderson Row. EH3 5BJ. (Nick Carter). Est. 1975. Open Wed.-Sun. 10.30-5.30. SIZE: Small. *STOCK: General antiques including brass bedsteads and lighting, 18th to early 20th C, £500-£1,000.* LOC: Off Dundas St. PARK: Easy. TEL: 0131 557 1918; home - 0131 557 3621. SER: Valuations; restorations (furniture including upholstery). VAT: Spec.

Alan Day Antiques
25A Moray Place. EH3 6DA. LAPADA. Open by appointment only. *STOCK: Furniture, paintings, 18th-19th C; general antiques.* TEL: 0131 225 2590.

A. F. Drysdale Ltd
35 and 20 North West Circus Place. EH3 6TW. Est. 1974. Open 9.30-1 and 2-6. *STOCK: Quality Continental reproduction lamps, decorative furniture; antique prints.* TEL: 0131 225 4686. VAT: Stan.

George Duff Antiques
254 Leith Walk. EH6 5EL. Open by appointment. *STOCK: Shipping goods, pre-1940.* TEL: 0131 554 8164; home - 0131 337 1422. VAT: Stan. *Export Only.*

EASY - Edinburgh Architectural Salvage Yard
Unit 6, Couper St., Off Coburg St., Leith. EH6 6HH. Est. 1985. Open 9-5. SIZE: Large. *STOCK: Fireplaces, stained glass, roll-top baths, carriage gates, panelled doors, cast iron radiators.* TEL: 0131 554 7077; fax - 0131 55430 70; e-mail - enquiries@easy-arch-salv.co.uk; website - www.easy-arch-salv.co.uk.

Edinburgh Coin Shop
11 West Crosscauseway. EH8 9JW. (T. D. Brown). Open 10-5. *STOCK: Coins, medals, badges, militaria, postcards, cigarette cards, stamps, jewellery, clocks and watches, general antiques, bullion dealers.* TEL: 0131 668 2928/667 9095; fax - 0131 668 2926. VAT: Stan.

Donald Ellis incorporating Bruntsfield Clocks
7 Bruntsfield Place. EH10 4HN. (D. G. and C. M. Ellis). Est. 1970. Open 9.30-5.30. CL: Wed. pm. SIZE: Medium. *STOCK: Clocks and general antiques.* LOC: Opposite Links Garage at Bruntsfield Links. PARK: Nearby. TEL: 0131 229 4720. SER: Clock repairs. FAIRS: Buxton (May).

Georgian Antiques
10 Pattison St., Leith Links. EH6 7HF. LAPADA. Est. 1976. Open 8.30-5.30, Sat. 10-2. SIZE: 2 large warehouses. *STOCK: Furniture, Georgian, Victorian, inlaid, Edwardian; shipping goods, smalls, £10-£10,000.* LOC: Off Leith Links. PARK: Easy. TEL: 0131 553 7286; fax - 0131 5536299; e-mail - info@georgianantiques.net; website - www.georgianantiques.net. SER: Valuations; restorations; buys at auction; packing; shipping; courier. VAT: Stan/Spec.

Gladrags
17 Henderson Row. EH3 5DH. (Kate Cameron). Est. 1977. Open Tues.-Sat. 10.30-6. *STOCK: Period clothes, linen, lace, beadwork, silk and paisley shawls, costume jewellery, silks and satins, cashmeres and accessories.* TEL: 0131 557 1916.

Goodwin's Antiques Ltd
15-16 Queensferry St. and 106A-108 Rose St. EH2 4QW. Est. 1952. Open 9-5.30, Sat. 9-5. SIZE: Medium. *STOCK: Antique and modern silver and jewellery.* LOC: Off Princes St., west end. TEL: 0131 225 4717; fax - 0131 220 1412; Rose St. - 0131 220 1230. VAT: Stan/Spec.

Harlequin Antiques
30 Bruntsfield Place. EH10 4HJ. (C. S. Harkness). Est. 1995. Open 10-5 and Sun. (Dec. only) 12-4. SIZE: Small. *STOCK: Clocks and watches, silver, ceramics, small furniture, £25-£3,000.* LOC: 2 miles south of Princes St. (west end). PARK: Easy. TEL: 0131 228 9446. SER: Valuations; restorations (clocks); buys at auction (clocks).

Hawkins & Hawkins
9 Atholl Crescent. EH3 8HA. (Emma H. Hawkins). Resident. Est. 1989. Open by appointment only. SIZE: Medium. *STOCK: Taxidermy, 1890-1920, £100-£10,000; English furniture, 1800-1910, £500-£100,000.* LOC: Off Princes St. PARK: Easy. TEL: 0131 229 2828; fax - 0131 229 2128. FAIRS: Olympia (June). VAT: Spec/Stan.

Holyrood Architectural Salvage
Holyrood Business Park, 146 Duddingston Rd. West. EH16 4AP. (Ken Fowler). Est. 1993. Open 9-5. SIZE: Large. *STOCK: Georgian to reproduction fireplaces; rolltop and canopy baths; panelled doors.* LOC: 2 mins from Duddingston village - telephone for directions. PARK: Easy. TEL: 0131 661 9305; fax - 0131 656 9404. SER: Restorations (baths). VAT: Stan/Spec.

Gordon Inglis Antiques
8 Barclay Terrace. EH10 4HP. Est. 1990. Open 1-5, Tues., Thurs. and Sun. by appointment. SIZE: Small. *STOCK: British art and studio pottery including Doulton, Minton and especially Scottish hand-painted pottery - Wemyss, Bough and MacMerry, £200-£1,000.* LOC: 5 minutes from castle and Princes St. PARK: Easy. TEL: 0131 221 1192; fax - same; mobile - 07966 505219; website - www.inglisantiques.com. SER: Valuations; worldwide free delivery. FAIRS: Hopetoun House, Pollock House, Prestonfield and local.

Allan K. L. Jackson
67 Causewayside. EH9 1QF. Est. 1974. Open 10-6. SIZE: Medium. *STOCK: General small antiques, from Victorian, £5-100.* PARK: Easy. TEL: 0131 668 4532; mobile - 07989 236443. SER: Valuations.

Kaimes Smithy Antiques
79 Howdenhall Rd. EH14 2LQ. (J. Lynch). Est. 1972. Open 1.30-5. CL: Mon. and Thurs. SIZE: Medium. *STOCK: Furniture, clocks, porcelain, glass, paintings, curios, 18th-20th C, £10-£3,000.* LOC: From City bypass take A701 (at Straiton junction) into city centre, located at 1st set of traffic lights. PARK: Easy. TEL: 0131 441 2076/ 664 0124. SER: Valuations; restorations.

London Road Antiques
15 Earlston Place, London Rd. EH7 5SU. (R. Forrest and T. Hardie). Est. 1990. Open 10-5, Sun. 1-5, or by appointment. SIZE: Large + trade store. *STOCK: Georgian, Victorian and stripped pine furniture.* TEL: 0131 652 2790; e-mail - LRA@19thC.com; website - www.19thC.com. VAT: Spec.

J. Martinez Antiques
17 Brandon Terrace. EH3 5DZ. Est. 1975. Open 11-5. SIZE: Small. *STOCK: Clocks, jewellery and general antiques, mainly Victorian, £50-£1,000.* LOC: Off Dundas St. PARK: Easy. TEL: 0131 558 8720; fax - same. SER: Valuations; restorations (porcelain, clocks and watches); buys at auction. FAIRS: Midland Clock & Watch, NEC; Antique Clock & Watch, Haydock Park; Ingliston, Edinburgh; Freemasons Hall, Edinburgh.

John Mathieson and Co
48 Frederick St. EH2 1EX. Open 9-5.30, Sat. 9-4.30. *STOCK: Paintings, watercolours, prints.* TEL: 0131 225 6798. SER: Restorations (framing, gilding). VAT: Stan/Spec.

McNaughtan's Bookshop
3a and 4a Haddington Place. EH7 4AE. Est. 1957. Open 9.30-5.30. CL: Mon. *STOCK: Antiquarian books.* PARK: Limited. TEL: 0131 556 5897; fax - 0131 556 8220.

Montresor
35 St. Stephen St. EH3 5AH. (Pierre De Fresne and Gareth Jones). Est. 1989. Open 10.30-1 and 2-6. SIZE: Small. *STOCK: Costume and designer jewellery, 1850-1950, £50-£200; Art Deco and Art Nouveau lighting, china and glass, £50-£1,000.* LOC: North from Princes St. to Stockbridge. PARK: Easy. TEL: 0131 220 6877. SER: Valuations; restorations (paste jewellery).

T. and J. W. Neilson Ltd
76 Coburg St., Leith. EH6 6HJ. (J. and A. Neilson). Est. 1932. Open 9.30-5, Sat. 9.30-4. SIZE: Large. *STOCK: Fireplaces, 18th-20th C, £100-£20,000; interiors, stoves, fenders, fire irons; marble (including French), wood and stone chimney pieces.* LOC: Continuation of Ferry Rd. PARK: Own. TEL: 0131 554 4704; fax - 0131 555 2071; website - www. chimneypiece.co.uk. SER: Installations (fireplaces). VAT: Stan.

Now and Then (Toy Centre)
7 and 9 West Crosscauseway. EH8 9JW. Usually open from 2.30pm, prior telephone call advisable. *STOCK: Telephones, tin and diecast toys, clockwork and electric model trains, collectable mechanical ephemera, automobilia, juvenalia, clocks, gold and silver watches, small furniture, old advertisements, bric-a-brac.* LOC: City centre off A68. PARK: Nearby. TEL: 0131 668 2927; evenings - 0131 226 2867; mobile - 07976 360283; e-mail - nowandthenuk@aol.com. SER: Valuations; buys at auction.

Open Eye Gallery Ltd
75/79 Cumberland St. EH3 6RD. (T. and P. Wilson). Est. 1976. Open 10-6, Sat. 10-4. SIZE: Medium. *STOCK: Early 20th C etchings, contemporary paintings, ceramics and jewellery.* LOC: From Princes St. go east, left into Frederick St. right at bottom of hill. PARK: Easy. TEL: 0131 557 1020; e-mail - open.eye@virgin.net; website - www.openeyegallery.co.uk. SER: Valuations; restorations (paintings and ceramics); buys at auction. VAT: Mainly Spec.

H. Parry
Castle Antiques, 330 Lawnmarket. EH1 2PN. *STOCK: Silver, porcelain, English and Continental furniture, clocks.* TEL: 0131 225 7615.

R. L. Rose Oriental Carpets Ltd
8 Howe St. EH3 6TD. GMC. Est. 1919. Open 9.30-5.30. *STOCK: Antique, decorative, modern and fine old Oriental rugs and carpets.* PARK: Nearby. TEL: 0131 225 8785; fax - 0131 226 7827. SER: Valuations; repairs; cleaning.

Royal Mile Curios
363 High St. EH1 1PW. (L. Bosi and R. Eprile). Open 10.30-5. *STOCK: Jewellery and silver.* TEL: 0131 226 4050.

Royal Mile Gallery
272 Canongate, Royal Mile. EH8 8AA. (J. A. Smith). Est. 1970. Open 11.30-5. SIZE: Medium. *STOCK: Maps, engravings, etchings and lithographs.* LOC: Between castle and Holyrood Palace. PARK: New Street. TEL: 0131 558 1702; home - 0131 668 4007; e-mail james@royalmilegallery.co.uk. SER: Valuations; restorations; framing; buys at auction.

James Scott
43 Dundas St. EH3 6JN. Est. 1964. Open 11-1 and 2-5.30. CL: Thurs. pm. *STOCK: Curiosities, unusual items, silver, jewellery, small furniture.* TEL: 0131 556 8260; mobile - 07714 004370. VAT: Stan.

The Scottish Gallery
16 Dundas St. EH3 6HZ. (Aitken Dott Ltd). Est. 1842. Open 10-6, Sat. 10-4. *STOCK: 20th C and contemporary Scottish paintings and contemporary crafts.* LOC: New Town. TEL: 0131 558 1200; e-mail - mail@scottish-gallery.co.uk; website - www.scottish-gallery.co.uk. VAT: Stan/Spec.

Second Edition
9 Howard St. EH3 5JP. (Mr and Mrs W. A. Smith). Est. 1978. Open 12-5.30, Sat. 9.30-5.30. SIZE: Medium. *STOCK: Antiquarian and second-hand books, £10-£750; maps and prints, £7-£75; all late 19th to early 20th C.* LOC: 200 yards south of Royal Botanical Gardens. PARK: Nearby. TEL: 0131 556 9403; home - 0131 552 1850. SER: Valuations; book-binding.

The Talish Gallery
168 Canongate. EH8 8DF. (John R. Martin). Est. 1970. Open 11-3. SIZE: Medium. *STOCK: Silver, plate, collectors' items, rugs, pictures, small furniture, £10-£10,000.* LOC: Bottom of Royal Mile, opposite clock. PARK: Easy. TEL: 0131 557 8435. SER: Valuations. VAT: Spec.

The Thrie Estaits
49 Dundas St. EH3 6RS. (Peter D. R. Powell). Est. 1970. Open Tues.-Sat. 11-5. *STOCK: Pottery, porcelain, glass, contemporary and period paintings and prints, unusual and decorative items, some early oak and country furniture.* TEL: 0131 556 7084; e-mail - TheThrieEstaits@aol.com.

Trinity Curios
4-6 Stanley Rd., Trinity. (Alan Ferguson). Resident. Est. 1987. Open 10-5, Wed. and Sat. 12-6, Sun. 2-5. CL: Mon. SIZE: Medium. *STOCK: Furniture, ceramics and silver, 19th C, £50-£1,000.* LOC: From Ferry Rd. turn north on to Newhaven Rd., shop30 0 yards on left. PARK: Easy. TEL: 0131 552 8481. SER: Restorations (furniture including upholstery). VAT: Stan.

William Trist
111 St. Leonard's St. EH8 9RB. Open 6-7pm or by appointment. *STOCK: Period furniture, mainly Georgian.* TEL: 0131 667 0092. SER: Restorations.

Unicorn Antiques
65 Dundas St. EH3 6RS. (N. Duncan). Est. 1967. Usually open 10.30-7. SIZE: Medium. *STOCK: Architectural and domestic brassware, lights, mirrors, glass, china, cutlery and bric-a-brac.* Not Stocked: Weapons, coins, jewellery. LOC: From Princes St. turn into Hanover St. Dundas St. is a continuation of Hanover St. TEL: 0131 556 7176; home - 0131 332 9135.

John Whyte
116b Rose St. EH2 3JF. Est. 1928. Open 9.30-5. 15, Sat. 9.30-5. *STOCK: Jewellery, watches, clocks and silver.* TEL: 0131 225 2140. VAT: Stan.

Whytock and Reid
Sunbury House, Belford Mews. EH4 3DN. (D. C. Reid). Est. 1807. Open 9-5.30, Sat. 10-2. SIZE: Large. *STOCK: Furniture, English and Continental, 18th-19th C, £50-£20,000; Eastern rugs, carpets, £50-£10,000.* LOC: ½ mile from West End, off Belford Rd. PARK: Own. TEL: 0131 226 4911; fax - 0131 226 4595; website - www. whytockandreid.com. SER: Restorations (furniture, rugs); buys at auction; interiors. VAT: Stan/Spec.

Wild Rose Antiques
15 Henderson Row. EH3 5DH. (K. and E. Cameron). Est. 1975. Open Tues.-Sat. 10.30-6. *STOCK: General antiques - silver, jewellery, glass, pottery, porcelain, small furniture, objects, Paisley shawls, brassware.* TEL: 0131 557 1916.

Anthony Woodd Gallery
4 Dundas St. EH3 6HZ. Est. 1981. Open 10-6, Sat. 11-4. *STOCK: Scottish landscape, sporting and military pictures; furniture and decorative items.* TEL: 0131 558 9544/5; fax - 0131 558 9525; e-mail - sales@anthonywoodd.com; website - www. anthonywoodd.com. SER: Valuations; restorations; buys at auction; framing. VAT: Spec.

Young Antiques
185 Bruntsfield Place. EH10 4DG. (T. C. Young). Est. 1979. Open 10.30-1.30 and from 2.30. CL: Wed. pm. SIZE: Medium. *STOCK: Victorian and Edwardian furniture, £50-£1,000; ceramics, £20-£2,000; Persian rugs, oils and watercolours, £50-£1,500.* PARK: Easy. TEL: 0131 229 1361. SER: Valuations; buys at auction (art pottery).

ELGIN (Morayshire)

West End Antiques
35 High St. IV30 1EE. (F. Stewart). HADA. Est. 1969. Open 9.30-12.30 and 1.45-4.30, Wed. 9.30-12.30. *STOCK: Silver, clocks and watches, jewellery and bric-a-brac.* TEL: 01343 547531; home - 01343 543216/812556.

FAIRLIE (Ayrshire)

Fairlie Antique Shop
86 Main Rd. KA29 0AD. (E. A. Alvarino). Est. 1976. Open Thurs.-Sat. 12-5. SIZE: Small. *STOCK: Ornaments, £10-£1,000; small furniture, clocks and silver, £50-£2,000; jewellery; all Victorian or Edwardian.* LOC: A78. PARK: 25yds. TEL: 01475 568613; e-mail - sales@alvarinoantiques.com. SER: Valuations. FAIRS: NEC; SECC; Scone Palace; Hopetown House.

FENTON BARNS, Nr. North Berwick (East Lothian)

Deco by Design
Implement Shed West, EH39 5BW. (Bob Dobbie and Hazel Roberts). Est. 1990. Open Sat. 10.30-4.30, Sun. 11-4.30, other days by appointment. SIZE: Large. *STOCK: Art Deco furniture and lighting, £40-£3,500; general antiques, 19th-20th C, £5-£500.* LOC: 17 miles east of Edinburgh, off A1 - follow signs for Drem and Fenton Barns. PARK: Easy. TEL: 0402 059315; home - 0131 669 5771. SER: Valuations; buys at auction (Art Deco). FAIRS: Ingliston, Edinburgh. VAT: Stan.

FOCHABERS (Morayshire)

Antiques (Fochabers)
22 The Square. IV32. (J. and M. L. Holstead). Est. 1983. Open 10.15-5. SIZE: Medium. *STOCK: General collectables, Oriental, clocks including longcase, from 18th C oak to 1930's.* PARK: Easy. TEL: 01343 820838; home - 01343 820572.

Country Collectables
22 The Square. IV32. (A. Holstead). Open 10-1 and 2-5. *STOCK: Pine furniture and collectables.* PARK: Easy. TEL: 01303 820838; home - 01340 831663.

Pringle Antiques
High St. IV32 7EP. (G. A. Christie). Est. 1983. Open 10.30-4.30 April-Sept. SIZE: Medium.

STOCK: Furniture, Victorian, £20-£5,000; general antiques, pictures, brass, pottery, silver and jewellery. Not Stocked: Books and clothing. LOC: A96, premises are a converted church. PARK: Easy. TEL: 01343 821204; home - 01343 820599. VAT: Stan/Spec.

Marianne Simpson
61/63 High St. IV32 7DU. (M. R. Simpson). Est. 1990. Open Easter-Oct: Mon.-Sat. 10-1 and 2-4; Oct. -Easter: Tues., Thurs., Sat. 10-1 and 2-4, or by appointment. SIZE: Small. STOCK: Books and ephemera, 19th-20th C, £1-£100. LOC: A96. PARK: Easy. TEL: 01343 821192; home - same.

FORFAR (Angus)

Gow Antiques
Pitscandly Farm. DD8 3NZ. (Jeremy Gow). BAFRA. Est. 1986. Open by appointment. SIZE: Medium. STOCK: 17th-19th C furniture, £50-£20,000. LOC: 3 miles off A90, take B9134 out of Forfar, through Lunenhead, first right at sign Myreside, premises next left, in farmyard. PARK: Easy. TEL: 01307 465342; mobile - 07711 416786; e-mail - jeremy@gowantiques.co.uk; website - www.gowantiques.co.uk. SER: Restorations; valuations. FAIRS: Antiques For Everyone, Glasgow (Aug.).

FORRES (Morayshire)

Michael Low Antiques
45 High St. IV36 2PB. Est. 1967. Open 10-1 and 2-5. STOCK: Small antiques. TEL: 01309 673696.

FRIOCKHEIM, Nr. Arbroath (Angus)

M. J. and D. Barclay
29 Gardyne St. DD11 4SQ. Est. 1965. Open 2-5.30. CL: Thurs. STOCK: General antiques including furniture, jewellery, silver, porcelain and clocks. Not Stocked: Stamps, books, coins. PARK: Easy. TEL: 01241 828265. VAT: Stan.

GLASGOW (Lanarkshire)

All Our Yesterdays
6 Park Rd., Kelvinbridge. G4 9JG. (Susie Robinson). Est. 1989. Open 11.30-5.30. SIZE: Small. STOCK: Kitchenalia, mainly 1850-1949, £5-£500; smalls, especially decorative arts, advertising related items, books, etchings and postcards, mechanical items, crystals and minerals, smokers sundries and oddities, to £500. LOC: Near junction with Gt. Western Rd. and university. PARK: Easy. TEL: 0141 334 7788; answerphone/fax - 0141 339 8994; e-mail - antiques@allouryesterdays.fsnet.co.uk. SER: Valuations; buys at auction; search and hire.

E. A. Alvariño - Antiques
13 Radnor St., Kelvingrove. G3 7UA. Est. 1976. Open Mon.-Fri. 1-5. STOCK: Furniture, 18th-19th C, £50-£5,000; silver and ornaments, pictures, jewellery, clocks and instruments. LOC: Near Kelvingrove Art Gallery & Museum. PARK: Easy. TEL: 0141 334 1213; e-mail - sales@alvarinoantiques.com. SER: Valuations; restorations; buys at auction.

The Antiques Warehouse
Unit 3b, Yorkhill Quay Estate. G3 8QE. (P. Mangan). Open 9-5, Sat. 10-5, Sun. 12-5. SIZE: 19 dealers. STOCK: Antique pine, Oriental rugs and carpets, general antiques, furnishings, smalls and fine arts. TEL: 0141 334 4924. SER: Import and export worldwide.

The Roger Billcliffe Fine Art
134 Blythswood St. G2 4EL. Est. 1876. Open 9.30-5.30, Sat. 10-1. SIZE: Large. STOCK: British paintings, watercolours, drawings, sculpture, especially Scottish, from 1850; jewellery, metalwork, glass and woodwork. TEL: 0141 332 4027; fax - 0141 332 6573. VAT: Spec.

Brown's Clocks
13 Radnor St., Kelvingrove. G3 7UA. (J. Wilson and J. Cairns). Est. 1933. Open 9.30-5, Sat. 10.30-12.30. STOCK: Fine clocks and barometers. TEL: 0141 334 6308. SER: Restorations.

Butler's Furniture Galleries
39 Camelon Street, Carntyne Industrial Estate. G32 6JS. (Laurence Butler). Open 10-5 or by appointment. CL: Sat. SIZE: Large. STOCK: Georgian, Victorian and Edwardian furniture, £200-£5,000. LOC: From M8 from Edinburgh, off at Stepps Cutoff, right at traffic lights down to bottom of road. Left on to dual carriageway, right at first traffic lights and straight down to sign for industrial estate, turn right. PARK: Easy. TEL: 0141 778 5720; home - 0141 639 3396; mobile - 07950 312355. SER: Valuations; restorations; repolishing. VAT: Spec.

A. D. Hamilton and Co
7 St. Vincent Place. G1 2DW. (Jeffrey Lee Fineman). Est. 1890. Open 9-5. 15. SIZE: Small. STOCK: Jewellery and silver, 19th to early 20th C, £100-£3,000; British coins, medals and banknotes, £10-£1,000. LOC: City centre, next to George Square. PARK: Meters. TEL: 0141 221 5423; fax - 0141 248 6019. SER: Valuations. VAT: Stan/Spec.

Ewan Mundy Fine Art Ltd

Lower Ground Floor, 211 West George St. G2 2LW. Est. 1981. Open daily. SIZE: Medium. *STOCK: Fine Scottish, English and French oils and watercolours, 19th-20th C, from £250; Scottish and English etchings and lithographs, 19th-20th C, from £100; Scottish contemporary paintings, from £50.* LOC: City centre. PARK: Nearby. TEL: 0141 248 9755. SER: Valuations; restorations arranged; buys at auction (pictures). FAIRS: New York. VAT: Stan/Spec.

Pastimes Vintage Toys

126 Maryhill Rd. G20 7QS. (Gordon and Anne Brown). Est. 1980. Open 10-5. SIZE: Medium. *STOCK: Vintage toys, die-cast, railways and dolls' houses, from 1910, £1-£300.* LOC: From the west off junction 17, M8; from the east junction 16, M8. PARK: Easy. TEL: 0141 331 1008. SER: Valuations. VAT: Stan.

The Renaissance Furniture Store

103 Niddrie Rd., Queens Park. G42 8PR. (Bruce Finnie). Open 10.30-5, Sat. and Sun. 12.30-5. CL: Mon. *STOCK: General antiques; Arts and Crafts and Art Nouveau furniture; fire inserts and surrounds.* PARK: Easy. TEL: 0141 423 0022. SER: Buys at auction.

R. L. Rose Oriental Carpets Ltd

Unit 3b, Yorkhill Quay. G3 8QE. Open 9-5, Sat. 10-5, Sun. 12-5. *STOCK: Oriental and decorative carpets.* TEL: 0141 339 7290; fax - 0141 334 1499. SER: Repair; cleaning.

Jeremy Sniders Antiques

158 Bath St. G2 4TB. Est. 1983. Open 9-5, Sat. 10-5. SIZE: Medium. *STOCK: British decorative arts including furniture, 1850-1960, £30-£1,000; Scandinavian decorative arts including furniture, 1900 to date, £30-£5,000; silver, mainly 19th-20th C, £30-£3,000.* LOC: Next door to Christies. PARK: Nearby - Sauchiehall St. Centre. TEL: 0141 332 0043; fax - 0141 332 5505; e-mail - snidersantiques @aol.com; websites - www.jeremysnidersantiques. com and www.jeremysnidersantiques.co.uk. SER: Will source Scandinavian articles - eg. Georg Jensen, Royal Copenhagen, etc; repairs (Georg Jensen silverware). VAT: Spec.

Strachan Antiques

40 Darnley St., Pollokshields. G41 2SE. (Alex and Lorna Strachan). Est. 1990. Open 10-5, Sun. 12-5. SIZE: Warehouse. *STOCK: Furniture, especially Arts and Crafts, Art Nouveau and Glasgow Style, also Victorian and Edwardian, £50-£5,000; some decorative items.* LOC: 2 mins from M8, junction 20 westbound, junction 21 eastbound. PARK: Own. TEL: 0141 429 4411; e-mail - alex@strachan-antiques.freeserve.uk; website - www.strachanantiques.co.uk. FAIRS: SECC Glasgow. VAT: Stan/Spec.

Victoria Antiques Ltd

350 Pollokshaws Rd., G41 1QS. Est. 1963. Open 9.30-5, Sat. 10.30-4, Sun. 12.30-4. SIZE: Large. *STOCK: General antiques, Victoriana, shipping goods.* LOC: South side of city. TEL: 0141 423 7216; fax - 0141 423 6497. SER: Valuations; buys at auction. VAT: Stan/Spec.

The Victorian Village Antiques

93 West Regent St. G2 1PB. Open 10-5. SIZE: 3 floors. LOC: Near Hope St. PARK: At rear and meters. TEL: 0141 332 0808/9808. VAT: Stan/Spec. Below are listed the dealers at these premises.

Golden Oldies

Jewellery. SER: Repairs; commissions.

Cathy McLay - Saratoga Trunk

Textiles, lace, jewellery. TEL: 0141 331 2707.

Stuart Myler

Silverware.

Putting-on-the-Ritz

Art Deco, china, jewellery, 1920's curios. TEL: 0141 332 9808.

Rosamond Rutherford

Victorian jewellery, Scottish agate, silver, Sheffield plate. TEL: 0141 332 9808.

Tim Wright Antiques

147 Bath St. G2 4SQ. (T. and J. Wright). LAPADA. Est. 1971. Open 9. 45-5, Sat. 10.30-5. SIZE: 6 showrooms. *STOCK: Furniture, European and Oriental ceramics and glass, decorative items, silver and plate, brass and copper, mirrors and prints, textiles, samplers, all £50-£6,000.* LOC: On opposite corner to Christie's. PARK: Multi-storey opposite and meters. TEL: 0141 221 0364; fax - same; e-mail - tim@timwright-antiques.com; website - www.timwright-antiques.com. VAT: Mainly Spec.

GLENCARSE, Nr. Perth

Michael Young Antiques at Glencarse

PH2 7LX. Est. 1887. Open 10-6 and by appointment *STOCK: 17th-19th C furniture, paintings and silver.* LOC: A90 3 miles east of Perth. TEL: 01738 860001; fax - same; e-mail - volenti@ btopenworld.com.

GLENDOICK (Perthshire)

Glendoick Antiques

PH2 7NR. (Malcolm Wood). Est. 1995. Open 10.30-4.30 including Sun. SIZE: Large. *STOCK: Dining furniture, 17th-18th C, £1,000-£9,000; watercolours and oils, 18-19th C, £50-£2,000; general antiques, 18th-19th C, £50-£10,000.* LOC: A90. PARK: Easy. TEL: 01738 860870. VAT: Stan/Spec.

GUILLANE (East Lothian)

Gullane Antiques

5 Rosebery Place. EH31 2AN. (E. A. Lindsey). Est. 1981. Open 10.30-1 and 2.30-5. CL: Wed. and Thurs. SIZE: Medium. *STOCK: China and glass, 1850-1930, £5-£150; prints and watercolours, early 20th C, £25-£100; metalwork, 1900's, £5-£150.* LOC: 6 miles north of Haddington, off A1. PARK: Easy. TEL: 01620 842994.

HADDINGTON (East Lothian)

Leslie and Leslie

EH41 3JJ. Open 9-1 and 2-5. CL: Sat. *STOCK: General antiques.* PARK: Nearby. TEL: 01620 822241; fax - same. VAT: Stan.

HUNTLY (Aberdeenshire)

Bygones

1 Bogie St. AB54 8DX. (Sue and Bruce Watts). Est. 1966. Open Wed. and Sat. 10-2, other days by appointment. SIZE: Medium. *STOCK: Clocks and pocket watches, £50-£3,000; furniture, barometers, Victoriana, curios and collectables, 19th-20th C, £10-£3,000.* LOC: Off Duke Street, towards railway station. PARK: Nearby. TEL: 01466 794412. FAIRS: Swinderby; Newark.

Huntly Antiques

43 Duke St. AB54 8DT. (Mrs J. Barker). Open Mon. and Sat. 10-1 and 2-5, Thurs. 10-1, other times by appointment. SIZE: Small. *STOCK: Jewellery, china, glass and furniture, 19th-20th C, £5-£250.* LOC: Off Aberdeen/Inverness road. PARK: Easy. TEL: 01466 793307.

INCHTURE (Perthshire)

Inchmartine Fine Art

Inchmartine House. PH14 9QQ. (P. M. Stephens). Est. 1998. Open 9-5.30. SIZE: Medium. *STOCK: Mainly Scottish oils and watercolours, £150-£1,500.* LOC: Take A90 Perth/Dundee road, entrance on left at Lodge. PARK: Easy. TEL: 01828 686412; home - same; fax - 01828 686748; mobile - 07702 190128; e-mail - fineart@incmartine.freeserve.co.uk. FAIRS: Buxton; SECC (Glasgow); Chester. VAT: Spec.

C. S. Moreton (Antiques)

Inchmartine House. PH14 9QQ. (P. M. and Mrs M. Stephens). Est. 1922. Open 9-5.30. SIZE: Large. *STOCK: Furniture, £100-£10,000; carpets and rugs, £50-£3,000; ceramics, metalware; all 16th C to 1860; old cabinet makers' tools.* LOC: Take A90 Perth/Dundee road, entrance on left at Lodge. PARK: Easy. TEL: 01828 686412; home - same; fax - 01828 686748; mobile - 07702 190128; e-mail - moreton@inchmartine.freeserve.co.uk. SER: Valuations; cabinet making and repairs. FAIRS: Buxton; SECC (Glasgow); Chester. VAT: Mainly Spec.

INNERLEITHEN (Peeblesshire)

Keepsakes

96 High St. EH44 6HF. (Margaret Maxwell). CL: Tues., Wed. and lunchtimes. SIZE: Small. *STOCK: Ceramics and glass, £50-£200; dolls, teddies and toys, £100-£500; books, post and cigarette cards,*

£5-£25; jewellery, £5-£100; all 20th C. LOC: A72. PARK: Easy. TEL: 01896 831369; home - 01896 830701. FAIRS: Ingliston; some Border.

Last Century Antiques and Books
34 High St. EH44 6HF. (Gill and Keith Miller). Est. 1990. Open 11-5. SIZE: Small. *STOCK: General antiques, books, furniture, paintings and prints, £5-£100.* PARK: Easy. TEL: 01896 831759. SER: Valuations.

INVERNESS (Inverness-shire)

Gallery Persia
Upper Myrtlefield, Nairnside. IV2 5BX. (G. MacDonald). *STOCK: Persian, Turkoman, Afghanistan, Caucasus, Anatolian rugs and carpets, late 19th C to 1940, £500-£2,000+; quality contemporary pieces, £100+.* LOC: From A9 1st left after flyover, 1st left at roundabout, then 2. 25 miles on B9006, then 1st right, 1st left. PARK: Easy. TEL: 01463 798500; home - 01463 792198; fax - same; e-mail - mac@gallerypersia. co.uk; website - www. gallerypersia.co.uk. SER: Valuations; restorations (cleaning and repair). FAIRS: Game, Scone Palace, Perth (July).

JEDBURGH (Roxburghshire)

Mainhill Gallery
Ancrum. TD8 6XA. (Diana Bruce). Est. 1981. Open by appointment. SIZE: Medium. *STOCK: Oil paintings, watercolours, etchings, some sculpture and ceramics, 19th C to contemporary, £35-£7,000.* LOC: Just off A68, 3 miles north of Jedburgh, centre of Ancrum. PARK: Easy. TEL: 01835 830545; fax - 01835 830518. SER: Exhibitions; valuations. FAIRS: Glasgow; London; Edinburgh. VAT: Spec.

R. and M. Turner (Antiques Ltd)
34-36 High St. TD8 6AG. (R. J. Turner). LAPADA. Est. 1965. Open 9.30-5.30, Sat. 10-5. SIZE: Large. *STOCK: Furniture, clocks, porcelain, paintings, silver, jewellery, 17th-20th C and fine reproductions.* LOC: On A68 to Edinburgh. PARK: Own. TEL: 01835 863445; fax - 01835 863349. SER: Valuations; packing; shipping. VAT: Stan/Spec.

KILBARCHAN (Renfrewshire)

Gardner's The Antique Shop
Wardend House, Kibbleston Rd. PA10 2PN. (G. D., R. K. F. and D. D. Gardner). LAPADA. Est. 1950. Open to Trade 7 days, retail 9-6, Sat. 10-5.

SIZE: 11 showrooms. *STOCK: Smalls, furniture, general antiques.* LOC: 12 miles from Glasgow, at far end of Tandlehill Rd. 10 mins. from Glasgow Airport. PARK: Easy. TEL: 01505 702292; e-mail - gardantiques@cqm.co.uk; website - www.gardnersantiques.co.uk. SER: Valuations. VAT: Spec.

McQuade Antiques
7 Shuttle St. PA10 2JN. (W. G. & W. J. McQuade). Est. 1975. Open 10-5.30, Sun. 2-5.30. CL: Sat. SIZE: Large. *STOCK: Furniture, porcelain, clocks, brass and silver, 19th-20th C.* LOC: Next to Weavers Cottage. PARK: Easy. TEL: 01505 704249. SER: Valuations. FAIRS: Newark. VAT: Spec.

KILLEARN, Nr. Glasgow (Stirlingshire)

Country Antiques
G63 9AJ. (Lady J. Edmonstone). Est. 1975. Open Mon.-Sat. *STOCK: Small antiques and decorative items.* Not Stocked: Reproduction. LOC: A81. In main street. PARK: Easy. TEL: Home - 01360 770215. SER: Interior decoration.

KILLIN (Perthshire)

Maureen H. Gauld
Craiglea, Main St. FK21 8UN. Est. 1975. Open March-Oct. 10-5, Nov.-Feb. Thurs., Fri., Sat. SIZE: Medium. *STOCK: General antiques, furniture, silver, paintings and etchings, £5-£3,500.* PARK: Easy. TEL: 01567 820475; home - 01567 820605; e-mail - killingallery@fsbdial.co.uk; website - www.killingallery.co.uk.

Killin Gallery
Craiglea, Main St. FK21 8UN. (J. A. Gauld). Est. 1992. Open 10-5, Sun. by appointment. SIZE: Medium. *STOCK: Etchings and drypoints, £100-£1,000; paintings, £300-£3,000; furniture, £50-£500; all 1860-1960.* PARK: Easy. TEL: 01567 820605; fax - same. SER: Valuations.

KILMACOLM (Renfrewshire)

Kilmacolm Antiques Ltd
Stewart Place. PA13 4AF. (H. Maclean). Est. 1973. Open 10-1 and 2.30-5.30. CL: Sun. except by appointment. SIZE: Medium. *STOCK: Furniture, 18th-19th C, £100-£8,000; objets d'art, 19th C; jewellery, £5-£5,000; paintings, £100-£5,000.* LOC: First shop on right when travelling from Bridge of Weir. PARK: Easy. TEL: 01505 873149. SER: Restorations

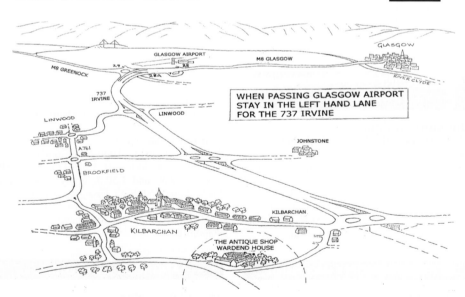

(furniture, silver, jewellery, porcelain). FAIRS: Hopetown, Pollock House, Edinburgh, Inverness. VAT: Stan/Spec.

KILMARNOCK (Ayrshire)

MacInnes Antiques
5c David Orr St., Bonnington. KA1 2KQ. (Mrs M. MacInnes). Est. 1973. Open by appointment. *STOCK: General antiques.* TEL: 01563 526739.

QS Antiques and Cabinetmakers
Moorfield Industrial Estate. KA2 0DP. (J. R. Cunningham and D. A. Johnson). Est. 1980. Open 9-5.30, Sat. 9-5. SIZE: Large. *STOCK: Furniture including stripped pine, 18th-19th C; shipping goods, architectural and collectors' items.* PARK: Easy. TEL: 01563 571071. SER: Restorations (upholstery, stripping); custom-built kitchens and furniture. VAT: Stan.

KILMICHAEL GLASSARY
By Lochgilphead (Argyllshire)

Rhudle Mill
PA31 8QE. (D. Murray). Est. 1979. Open daily, weekends by appointment. SIZE: Medium. *STOCK: Furniture, 18th C to Art Deco, £30-£3,000; small items and bric-a-brac, £5-£500.* LOC: Signposted 3 miles south of Kilmartin on A816 Oban to Lochgilphead road. PARK: Easy. TEL: 01546 605284; home - same. SER: Restorations (furniture); French polishing; buys at auction.

KINCARDINE O'NEIL, Nr. Aboyne (Aberdeenshire)

Dunmore Antiques
27 North Deeside Rd. AB34 5AA. (Pauline Baird). Est. 1988. Open Thurs., Fri. and Sat. 10-5, other times by appointment. SIZE: Small. *STOCK: China, 1800-1960, £10-£1,000; glass, silver, 20th C, £10-£500.* PARK: Easy. TEL: 013398 84449; home - 013398 82640; fax - same; e-mail - dunmore-antiques@talk21.com. SER: Valuations. FAIRS: Treetops, Newark. VAT: Global.

KINGSTON-ON-SPEY (Morayshire)

Collectables
Lein Rd. IV32 7NW. (J. Penman and B. Taylor). Est. 1987. Open daily including most weekends, prior telephone call required. SIZE: Small. *STOCK: Militaria and jewellery, lap desks, china,*

collectables, small silver, £5-£1,000. LOC: On B9105. PARK: Easy. TEL: 01343 870462. SER: Valuations. FAIRS: Inverness and Aberdeen.

KINROSS (Kinross)

Miles Antiques
Mill St. KY13 8DR. (K. and S. Miles). LAPADA. Est. 1979. Open Mon.-Fri. 12-5. SIZE: Large. *STOCK: Furniture including decorative, Georgian, Victorian and Edwardian, £100-£5,000; china and pottery, £50-£500.* LOC: Off M90, junction 6. Take right at High St. then second left. PARK: Easy. TEL: 01577 864858. SER: Restorations (upholstery, polishing, small repairs). VAT: Stan/Spec.

KIRKCALDY (Fife)

Second Notions Antiques
4B Normand Rd., Dysart. KY1 2XJ. (James Sinclair). Est. 1996. Open 12-5, Sat. 10-5. SIZE: Medium. *STOCK: General antiques especially furniture and longcase clocks, £2-£3000; shipping furniture.* LOC: A92. PARK: Easy. TEL: 01592 650505; home/fax - same. SER: Valuations; buys at auction. FAIRS: Swinderby.

KIRKCUDBRIGHT (Dumfries & Galloway)

The Antique Shop
67 St Mary St. DG6 4DU. (Paul and Marisa Mairs). Est. 1993. Open 10-5. *STOCK: General antiques, collectors' items, linen and lace, kichenalia, furniture and bric-a-brac, 18th-20th C, to £1,500.* LOC: Near entrance of town, at junction to Gatehouse of Fleet. PARK: Easy. TEL: 01557 332400; e-mail - mjmantiques@hotmail.com.

Osborne Antiques
41 Castle St. and 63 High St. DG6 4JD. (David and Robert A. Mitchell). LAPADA. Est. 1949. Open 9-12.30 and 1.30-5, or by appointment. SIZE: Large. *STOCK: Georgian and Victorian furniture, smalls.* PARK: Easy. TEL: 01557 330441; e-mail - mitch0106@hotmail.com. VAT: Stan/Spec.

LANGHOLM (Dumfriesshire)

The Antique Shop
High St. DG13 0DH. (R. and V. Baird). Est. 1970. Open 10.30-5. CL: Wed. pm. SIZE: Small. *STOCK: China, glass, pictures, 18th-20th C; jewellery, rugs, 19th-20th C; trade warehouse -*

furniture, shipping goods and antiquarian books. LOC: 20 miles north of Carlisle on A7. PARK: 100yds. TEL: 0138 73 80238. SER: Restorations (furniture).

LARGS (Ayrshire)

Narducci Antiques
11 Waterside St. KA30 9LN. (G. Narducci). Open Tues., Thurs. and Sat., 2.30-5.30 or by appointment - trade anytime. SIZE: Warehouse. *STOCK: General antiques and shipping goods.* TEL: 01475 672612; 01294 461687; fax - 01294 470002; mobile - 07771 577777; website - www. narducci-antiques.co.uk. SER: Packing and shipping; road haulage (Europe). *Mainly Trade and Export.*

LENNOXTOWN (Lanarkshire)

Campsie Antiques
2 Service St. G65. (R. Allen). Open 10-5.30, Sun. 12-4. SIZE: Small. *STOCK: Collectables.* LOC: A891. PARK: Easy. TEL: 01360 311100.

LETHAM, By Forfar (Angus)

Idvies Antiques
Idvies House. DD8 2QJ. (Tim Slingsby). Est. 1988. Open by appointment or chance (7 days). *STOCK: Furniture, 18th-19th C, £250-£1,500; pictures, 19th C, £100-£400; smalls, 18th-19th C, £5-£100.* LOC: Approximately 5 miles south-east from Forfar on B9128. PARK: Easy. TEL: 01307 818402; fax - 01307 818933; home - same; e-mail - tim.slingsby@icscotland.net. SER: Valuations; restorations; cabinet-making.

LINLITHGOW (West Lothian)

Mir Russki
Est. 1994. *STOCK: Russian silver, 18th C to 1917.* TEL: 01506 843973; website - www.russian silver.co.uk. SER: Mail order. FAIRS: NEC and other major.

LONGHAVEN, Nr. Peterhead (Aberdeenshire)

Grannie Used To Have One
Sanderling. AB42 0NX. (Mrs Jacqui Harvey). Est. 1991. Open Thurs. and Fri. 1-5, Sat. and Sun. 11-5, Mon and Tues and other times by appointment. SIZE: Large. *STOCK: Pottery including*

Scottish, 18th-19th C, £5-£2,000; porcelain and glass, wooden items, curios and furniture, 18th-20th C. LOC: A90 6 miles south of Peterhead. PARK: Own. TEL: 01779 813223; fax/home - same; e-mail - jacqui@grannieusedto.co.uk; website - www.grannieusedto.co.uk. SER: Valuations; buys at auction. FAIRS: Hilton Treetops, Aberdeen.

MELROSE (Borders)

Michael Vee Design - Birch House Antiques
High St. TD6 9PB. (Michael Vee and Enid Cranston). Est. 1990. Open 9.30-12.30 and 1.30-5, Sat. 9.30-4, Sun. by appointment. SIZE: Medium. *STOCK: Mirrors and lighting, French, English, decorative and some garden furniture, 1850-1920, £20-£5,000.* LOC: 1. 5 miles off A68. PARK: Easy. TEL: 01896 822116; home - 01896 822835. SER: Restorations; interior design.

MONTROSE (Angus)

Harper-James
25-27 Baltic St. DD10 8EX. (D. R. James). LAPADA. Resident. Est. 1990. Open 10-5, other times by appointment. SIZE: Large. *STOCK: Furniture, clocks, silver and jewellery, 1690-1910, £50-£6,000; ceramics and pottery, 1800-1945, £10-£650+; general antiques and curios, £2-£750.* LOC: From south turn right at Peel statue, then first left. PARK: Easy. TEL: 01674 671307; home - same; e-mail - antiques@telco40. net. SER: Valuations; restorations (furniture, upholstery); French polishing; export. FAIRS: Major U. K. VAT: Stan/Spec.

NAIRN (Nairnshire)

Moray Antiques
78 High St. IV12 4AU. (Mrs. Melanie Muir). Est. 1997. Open 10.30-1 and 2-5, Wed. 10.30-1, Sat. 10.30-5. SIZE: Medium. *STOCK: Victorian silver and plate, £50-£500; Victorian glass, 1920's-1930's pottery, £50-£200; 19th C furniture, £250-£2,000.* LOC: Sign on A96, 15 miles from Inverness. PARK: Easy. TEL: 01667 455570; fax - same. SER: Valuations; buys at auction.

NEWBURGH (Fife)

Newburgh Antiques
222 High St. KY14 6DZ. (Dorothy Fraser). Est. 1991. Open 10.30-12 and 1.30-5. CL: Mon. SIZE:

Small. *STOCK: Wemyss ware, 1882-1930, £100-£2,000; Scottish watercolours and oil paintings, 1800-1950's, £100-£1,500; furniture, 1750-1900, £200-£2,000.* LOC: A913. PARK: Easy. TEL: 01337 841026; home - 01337 827158; e-mail - antiques@wemyss-ware.com; website - www.wemyss-ware.com. SER: Valuations.

NEWTONMORE (Inverness-shire)

The Antique Shop
Main St. PH20 1DD. (J. Harrison). Est. 1990. Open 9.30-5.30. SIZE: Medium. *STOCK: Furniture, £20-£1,000; glass, china, silver, plate, copper, brass, secondhand books, vintage fishing tackle.* LOC: On A86 opposite Mains Hotel. PARK: Easy. TEL: 01540 673272. VAT: Global.

NORTH BERWICK (East Lothian)

Kirk Ports Gallery
49A Kirk Ports. EH39 4HL. (Alan Lindsey). Open 10-5. CL: Thurs. SIZE: Medium. *STOCK: Oil paintings, £100-£1,000; watercolours, £50-£600; etchings and prints, £30-£100; all 19th C to 1940.* LOC: Behind main street. PARK: Easy. TEL: 01620 894114. SER: Valuations.

Lindsey Antiques
49a Kirk Ports. EH39 4HL. (Stephen Lindsey). Est. 1993. Open 10-1 and 2-5. CL: Thurs. SIZE: Medium. *STOCK: Ceramics and glass, 1800-1935, £20-£500; furniture, 1750-1910, £150-£2,000.* LOC: Behind main street. PARK: Easy. TEL: 01620 894114. SER: Valuations.

Penny Farthing
23 Quality St. EH39 4HR. (S. Tait). Est. 1981. Open daily. SIZE: Medium. *STOCK: Secondhand books, collectables, 20th C, £5-£500.* LOC: On corner with High St. PARK: Easy. TEL: 01620 894400; fax - same. SER: Valuations; buys at auction. FAIRS: Scot, Meadowbank, Edinburgh.

OBAN (Argyllshire)

Oban Antiques
35 Stevenson St. PA34 5NA. (Peter and Pam Baker). Est. 1970. Open 10-5, some seasonal variation. SIZE: Medium. *STOCK: Furniture and general antiques, mainly 19th to early 20th C; books, prints, jewellery, silver, ceramics and collectables, £5-£1,500.* LOC: Off George (main) St. PARK: Easy. TEL: 01631 566203; e-mail - partners@obantiques.com; website - www.obantiques.com.

PAISLEY (Renfrewshire)

Corrigan Antiques
Woodlands, High Calside. PA2 6BY. Open by appointment only. SIZE: Small. *STOCK: Furniture and accessories.* LOC: 5 minutes from Glasgow Airport. TEL: 0141 889 6653; fax - 0141 848 9700; mobile - 07802 631110.

Paisley Fine Books
17 Corsebar Crescent. PA2 9QA. (Mr and Mrs B. Merrifield). Est. 1985. Open by appointment. SIZE: Small. *STOCK: Books on architecture, art, antiques and collecting.* TEL: 0141 581 0095; fax - 0141 884 2661; e-mail - bernieafc@aol.com. SER: Free book search; catalogues issued.

PERTH (Perthshire)

Ainslie's Antique Warehouse
Unit 3, Gray St. PH2 0JH. (T. S. and A. Ainslie). Open 9-5, by appointment at weekends. SIZE: Large. *STOCK: General antiques.* TEL: 01738 636825.

A. S. Deuchar and Son
10-12 South St. PH2 8PG. (A. S. and A. W. N. Deuchar). Est. 1911. Open 10-1 and 2-5. CL: Sat. SIZE: Large. *STOCK: Victorian shipping goods, furniture, 19th C paintings, china, brass, silver and plate.* LOC: Glasgow to Aberdeen Rd., near Queen's Bridge. PARK: Easy. TEL: 01738 626297; home - 01738 551452. VAT: Stan/Spec.

Hardie Antiques
25 St. John St. PH1 5SH. (T. G. Hardie). PADA. Est. 1980. Open 9.30-5, Sat. 10-4.30. SIZE: Medium. *STOCK: Jewellery and silver, 18th-20th C, £5-£5,000.* PARK: Nearby. TEL: 01738 633127; fax - same; home - 01738 551764; e-mail - info@timothyhardie.co.uk. SER: Valuations. VAT: Stan/Spec.

Henderson
5 North Methven St. PH1 5PN. (J. G. Henderson). Est. 1935. Open 9.30-5. CL: Wed. pm. SIZE: Small. *STOCK: Porcelain, glass, 1720-1950, £5-£500; silver, jewellery, medals, £1-£1,000.* Not Stocked: Furniture. LOC: A9. PARK: Easy. TEL: 01738 624836; home - 01738 621923. SER: Valuations. VAT: Stan.

Nigel Stacy-Marks Ltd
23 George St. PH1 5JY. (Nigel and Ginny Stacy-Marks). LAPADA. Open 9.30-5.30. SIZE: Medium. *STOCK: Oils and watercolours, 19th-20th C, £250-£30,000; British etchings, late 19th*

C to mid 20th C, £100-£5,000. LOC: Town centre, just south of museum. PARK: Nearby. TEL: 01738 626300; fax - 01738 620460; e-mail - paintings@stacy-marks.co.uk; website - www.stacy-marks.co.uk. SER: Valuations; restorations; framing; regular exhibitions (catalogues on request). FAIRS: Antiques For Everyone, SECC, Glasgow. VAT: Stan/Spec.

Yesterdays Today

267 High St. PH1 5QN. (Bill and Nora MacGregor). Est. 1996. Open 9-5. SIZE: Small. *STOCK: General collectables especially china, £25-£1,000.* LOC: Follow signs for Tourist Information Centre. PARK: Nearby. TEL: 01738 443534. SER: Valuations; buys at auction. VAT: Global.

PITTENWEEM (Fife)

The Antiques Shop

27 High St. KY10 2RQ. (R. J. Clark). Est. 1985. Open 10,30-5, Sun. 11-4. SIZE: Medium. *STOCK: Scottish pottery including Wemyss, furniture, 19th C, £100-£1,000; collectibles.* PARK: Easy. TEL: 01333 312870; home - 01333 720331; website - www.arbourantiques.co.uk. SER: Valuations.

The Little Gallery

20 High St. KY10 2LA. (Dr Ursula Ditchburn-Bosch). Est. 1988. Open 10-5, Sun. 2-5. CL: Mon. and Tues. SIZE: Small. *STOCK: China, 18th C to 1950's, £5-£100; small furniture, mainly Victorian, £30-£500; rustica, £5-£150; contemporary paintings, £40-£1,000.* LOC: From Market Sq. towards church, on right. PARK: Easy. TEL: 01333 311227; home - same. SER: Valuations.

PORTREE (Isle of Skye)

Croft Comforts Antiques

2 Wentworth St. IV51 9EJ. (Ms Fiona Middleton). Est. 1984. Open daily. CL: Tues. and Wed. Oct. to April. SIZE: Small. *STOCK: China, porcelain, curios and stoneware, 19th-20th C; furniture, 19th C and Edwardian.* PARK: Nearby. TEL: 01478 613762; fax - same. SER: Buys at auction.

PORTSOY (Banff)

Other Times Antiques

13-15 Seafield St. AB45 2QT. (D. McLean and T. Matheson). Est. 1986. Open 10-5 including Sun.

CL: Wed. *STOCK: General antiques, 1700-1950.* LOC: A98. PARK: At rear. TEL: 01261 842866. VAT: Stan/Spec.

PRESTWICK (Ayrshire)

Crossroads Antiques

7 The Cross. KA9 1AJ. (Timothy Okeeffe). Est. 1989. Open 9-5. SIZE: Medium. *STOCK: Furniture, 18th-20th C, £5-£1,000+; china and silver, 19th-20th C, £5-£500+.* PARK: Nearby. TEL: 01292 474004. SER: Valuations; buys at auction.

RAIT (Perthshire)

Rait Village Antiques Centre

PH2 7RT. Est. 1985. Open 10-5, Sun. 12.30-4.30. SIZE: 7 showrooms. *STOCK: General antiques, furniture.* LOC: Midway between Perth and Dundee, 1 mile north of A90. PARK: Easy. Below are listed the dealers at this centre. TEL: 01821 670379.

Fair Finds

(Lynda Templeman). *Large stock of antique and early 20th C country house furnishings, pictures, rugs, silver and clocks, £50-£10,000.* TEL: 01821 670379.

Gordon Loraine Antiques

(Liane and Gordon Loraine). *Georgian, Victorian and Edwardian furniture, decorative items and collectables.* TEL: 01821 670760.

J. and L. Newton

Upholstered furniture, antique pine, decorative accessories, textiles and cushions. TEL: 01821 670205

Rait Antiques

Period and decorative furniture, woodworking tools. TEL: 01821 670318.

Whimsical Wemyss

(Lynda Templeman and Chris Comben). *Wemyss-ware, £50-£3,000.* TEL: 01821 67039.

SALTCOATS (Ayrshire)

Narducci Antiques

Factory Place. KA21 5LA. (G. Narducci). Est. 1972. Open 10-1 and 2.30-5.30 or by appointment - trade anytime. *STOCK: Furniture, general antiques and shipping goods.* TEL: 01294 461687 and 01475 672612; mobiles - 07831 100152 and 07771 577777. SER: Packing, export, shipping and European haulage. *Mainly Trade and Export.*

SCOTLAND

ST. ANDREWS (Fife)

Old St. Andrews Gallery
9 Albany Place. KY16 9HH. (Mr and Mrs D. R. Brown). Est. 1973. CL: 1-2 daily. SIZE: Medium. *STOCK: Golf memorabilia, 19th C, £100-£20,000; silver, jewellery especially Scottish, 18th-20th C, £100-£10,000; general antiques, from 18th C, £50-£5,000.* LOC: Main street. PARK: Easy. TEL: 01334 477840. SER: Valuations; restorations (jewellery, silver); buys at auction (golf memorabilia). VAT: Stan.

St. Andrews Fine Art
84 Market St. KY16 9PA. (J. Carruthers). Open 10-5. *STOCK: Scottish oils, watercolours and drawings, 19th-20th C.* LOC: Main street. PARK: Easy. TEL: 01334 474080.

STANLEY (Perthshire)

Coach House Antiques Ltd
Charleston. PH1 4PN. (John Walker). Est. 1971. Open by appointment. SIZE: Medium. *STOCK: Period furniture, decorative items, 18th-19th C; garden furniture.* LOC: 9 miles north of Perth off A9. Take B9099 to Luncarty and Stanley, continue 2 miles through village, sign at end of road Charleston. PARK: Easy. TEL: 01738 828627; home - same; mobile - 07710 122244. SER: Valuations; restorations; buys at auction (furniture). VAT: Spec.

STEWARTON (Ayrshire)

Woolfsons of James Street Ltd t/a Past & Present
3 Lainshaw St. KA3 5BY. Est. 1983. Open 9.30-5.30, Sun. 12-5.30. SIZE: Medium. *STOCK: Furniture, £100-£500; porcelain, £25-£500; bric-a-brac, £5-£50; all from 1800.* LOC: Stewarton Cross. PARK: Easy. TEL: 01560 484113; fax - same. SER: Valuations; restorations (French polishing, upholstery, wood). VAT: Stan/Spec.

STIRLING (Stirlingshire)

Abbey Antiques
35 Friars St. FK8 1HA. (S. Campbell). Resident. Est. 1980. Open 9-5. SIZE: Small. *STOCK: Jewellery, £10-£5,000; silver and plate, £5-£1,000; furniture including pine, £20-£1,000; paintings, £50-£2,500; bric-a-brac, £1-£100; coins and medals, £1-£1,000; all 18th-20th C; china, porcelain, collectables.* LOC: Off Murray Place, part of main thoroughfare. PARK: Nearby. TEL: 01786 447840. SER: Valuations.

STRATHBLANE (Stirlingshire)

Whatnots
16 Milngavie Rd. G63 9EH. (F. Bruce). Est. 1965. *STOCK: Furniture, paintings, jewellery, silver and plate, clocks, small items, shipping goods, horse drawn and old vehicles.* LOC: A81, 10 miles NW of Glasgow. PARK: Easy. TEL: 01360 770310. VAT: Stan/Spec.

TROON (Ayrshire)

Old Troon Sporting Antiques
49 Ayr St. KA10 6EB. (R. S. Pringle). Est. 1984. CL: Wed. pm. and Sat. pm. SIZE: Medium. *STOCK: Golf items, 19th C, to £500+.* LOC: 5 minutes from A77. PARK: Easy. TEL: 01292 311822; home - 01292 313744; fax - 01292 313111. SER: Valuations; buys at auction (golf items). VAT: Stan.

Tantalus Antiques
79 Templehill. KA10 6BQ. (Iain D. Sutherland). BWCMG. Open 10-5, Sun. by appointment. SIZE: Medium. *STOCK: Furniture, clocks and watches, pictures and paintings, silverware, jewellery, ceramics.* LOC: Town centre, main road to the harbour. PARK: Easy. TEL: 01292 315999; fax - 01292 316611; e-mail - idsantique@aol.com; website - www.scottishantiques.com. SER: Valuations; restorations.

ULLAPOOL (Wester Ross)

Wishing Well Antiques
Shore St. IU26 2RL. (Simon and Eileen Calder). Est. 1988. Open 10-6, including Sun. in summer. SIZE: Medium. *STOCK: China, glass, silver, pottery, furniture, country artefacts, curiosities; books, prints and paintings.* LOC: Village centre, 50 miles from Inverness. PARK: Easy. TEL: 01854 613265; mobile - 07714 498569. SER: Valuations; restorations; wood stripping.

UPPER LARGO (Fife)

Waverley Antiques
13 Main St. KY8 6EL. (D. V. and C. A. St. Clair). Est. 1962. Open 10.30-5.30, Sun. by appointment. SIZE: Medium. *STOCK: Pictures, furniture, china, pottery, glass and works of art.* LOC: Coast road from Leven to St. Andrews. PARK: Easy. TEL: 01333 360437; home - same. SER: Valuations.

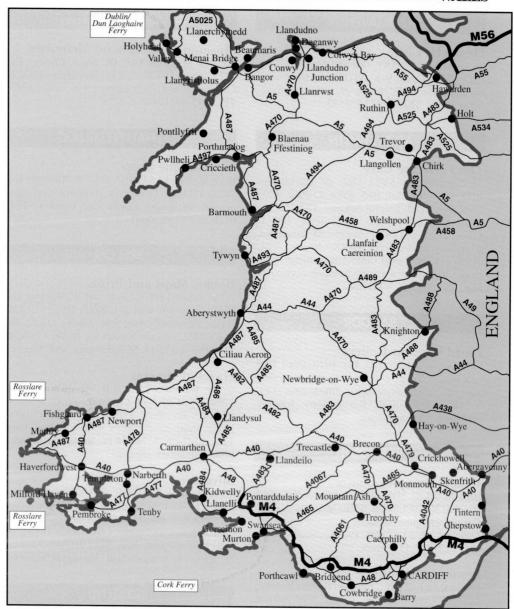

Dealers and Shops in Wales

Abergavenny	1	Chirk	1	Holt	1	Llanrwst	3	Porthcawl	1
								Porthmadog	1
Aberystwyth	1	Ciliau Aeron	1	Holyhead	1	Mathry	1	Pwllheli	1
Bangor	1	Colwyn Bay	2	Kidwelly	2	Menai Bridge	1	Ruthin	1
Barmouth	2	Conwy	2	Knighton	2	Milford Haven	1	Skenfrith	1
Barry	1	Cowbridge	3	Llandeilo	1	Monmouth	1	Swansea	5
Beaumaris	1	Criccieth	1	Llandudno	1	Mountain Ash	1	Templeton	1
Blaenau Ffestiniog	1	Crickhowell	1	Llandudno Junction	2	Murton	1	Tenby	2
Brecon	3	Deganwy	1	Llandysul	1	Narberth	1	Tintern	1
Bridgend	3	Fishguard	1	Llanelli	1	Newbridge-on-Wye	1	Trecastle	1
Caerphilly	1	Gorseinon	1	Llanerchymedd	1	Newport	1	Treorchy	1
Cardiff	7	Haverfordwest	2	Llanfair Caereinion	1	Pembroke	1	Trevor	1
Carmarthen	4	Hawarden	1	Llangollen	2	Pontarddulais	1	Tywyn	1
Chepstow	5	Hay-on-Wye	6	Llangristiolus	1	Pontllyfrii	1	Valley	1
								Welshpool	2

ABERGAVENNY

Henry H. Close
36 Cross St. NP3 3AY. (Mr and Mrs H. Close).
Est. 1968. Open 9-5. *STOCK: 18th-19th C
furniture, porcelain, pottery, glass, brass, copper,
silver, prints.* TEL: 01873 853583.

ABERYSTWYTH

The Furniture Cave
33 Cambrian St. SY23 1NZ. (P. David). Est.
1975. Open 9-5, Sat. 10-5. *STOCK: Pine, 1700-
1930, from £100; general antiques, Victorian and
Edwardian, £30-£3,000; small items, 19th C,
£10-£500; maps.* LOC: First right off Terrace Rd.,
at railway station end. PARK: Nearby. TEL:
01970 611234; e-mail - info@the-furniture-cave.
co.uk; website - www.the-furniture-cave.co.uk.
SER: Restorations. VAT: Spec.

BANGOR

David Windsor Gallery
173 High St. LL57 1NU. Est. 1970. Open 10-5.
CL: Wed. *STOCK: Oils and watercolours, 18th-
20th C; maps, engravings, lithographs.* TEL:
01248 364639. SER: Restorations; framing;
mounting. VAT: Stan/Spec.

BARMOUTH

Chapel Antiques Centre
High St. LL42 1DS. (Danny Jones). Est. 1985.
Open 10.30-5. CL: Wed. SIZE: Medium. *STOCK:
General antiques including furniture and glass,
18th-20th C, £5-£2,000.* PARK: Nearby. TEL:
01341 281377; fax - same.

Fronhouse Antiques
Jubilee Rd. LL42 1EE. (Tony and Barbara Howard).
Est. 1967. Open seven days 10-5. CL: Wed. and Sun.
Dec to Mar. SIZE: Small. *STOCK: Nautical items,
19th C £5-£250; oil lamps, bric-a-brac and small
furniture, £5-£200.* LOC: On corner of Church St.
PARK: Easy. TEL: 01341 280649; home/fax - same.
SER: Valuations; restorations (nautical items).
FAIRS: Swinderby, Newark.

BARRY

Flame 'n' Grate
99-100 High St. CF6 8DS. (A. Galsworthy).
Open 9-5.30. *STOCK: Antique and reproduction
fireplaces and surrounds.* TEL: 01446 744788.

BEAUMARIS (Anglesey)

Museum of Childhood Memories
1 Castle St. LL58 8AP. (R. and J. Brown). Est.
1973. Open 10.30-5. CL: Nov.-Feb. *STOCK:
Children's toys and memorabilia collectables.*
TEL: 01248 712498.

BLAENAU FFESTINIOG

The Antique Shop
Bryn Marian. LL41 3HD. (Mrs R. Roberts). Est.
1971. *STOCK: Victoriana, furniture, brass and
copper, oil lamps, clocks and watches.* TEL:
01766 830629/830041.

BRECON

Books, Maps and Prints
7 The Struet. LD3 7LL. (A. and W. Wakley). Est.
1961. Open 9-5, Wed. 9-1. SIZE: Large. *STOCK:
Books, maps and prints, from 17th C, £10-£1,000.*
LOC: A438, opposite Kwik Save. PARK: Opposite.
TEL: 01874 622714. SER: Framing. VAT: Stan.

Hazel of Brecon
6 The Bulwark. LD3 7LB. (H. Hillman). Est.
1969. Open 10-5.30. CL: Wed. SIZE: Medium.
STOCK: Jewellery, 19th-20th C, £20-£10,000.
LOC: Main square, town centre. PARK: Easy.
TEL: 01874 625274 (24 hr. answering service).
SER: Valuations; repairs.

Silvertime
6 The Bulwark. LD3 7LB. (L. Hillman). Open 10-
5.30. CL: Wed. SIZE: Small. *STOCK: Silver and
gold watches; antique and collectors' clocks; 19th-
20th C silver and plate.* LOC: Town centre, on
main square. PARK: Easy. TEL: 01874 625274 (24
hr. answering service). SER: Valuations; repairs.

BRIDGEND

Hart Antiques and Interiors
1A Dunraven Place. CF31 1JF. (Mrs Cheryl
Hart). Open 9-3. SIZE: Small. *STOCK: Textiles,
18th to early 20th C, £10-£1,000; lighting and
decorative accessories, mainly 19th C, French,
£5-£1,000.* LOC: Town centre, 100yds from Post
Office and Cenotaph. PARK: Easy. TEL: Mobile
- 07714 443429. SER: Interior design; FAIRS:
Shepton Mallet; specialist textile; soft furnishings
made to order.

J. & A. Antiques
1 Prince Rd., Kenfig Hill. CF33 6ED. (Jennifer
Lawson). Est. 1990. Open 10-12.30 and 2-4.30,

Wed. and Sat. 10-12.30. SIZE: Small. *STOCK: Furniture, china and clocks, 19th to early 20th C, £10-£600.* LOC: From A48 Pyle take B4281. PARK: Easy. TEL: 01656 746681; home - 01656 744709.

Nolton Antiques
66 Nolton St. CF31 3BP. (Gittings and Beynon). Est. 1997. Open 9.30-5. CL: Wed. SIZE: Large. *STOCK: General antiques including Clarice Cliff, majolica and Victorian furniture.* LOC: Turn off M4 at junction 35. PARK: Nearby. TEL: 01656 667774; website - www. welsh-antiques.com. SER: Valuations; buys at auction (named china).

CAERPHILLY

Yesterday's Future - G. J. Gittins and Son
10 Clive St. CF8 1GE. Open 9-4, Sat. 10-5. CL: Wed. *STOCK: General antiques, jewellery and shipping goods.* TEL: 02920 868835; e-mail - gittinsantiques@supornet.com.

CARDIFF

Cardiff Antiques Centre
10/12 Royal Arcade. CF1 2AE. Open 10-5.30. SIZE: 3 floors. *STOCK: Antiques, collectables and classic clothing.* LOC: Town centre. TEL: 02920 398891.

Jacobs Antique Centre
West Canal Wharf. CF10 5DB. Open Thurs.-Sat. 9.30-5. SIZE: Large - 50 dealers. *STOCK: General antiques and collectables.* LOC: 2 mins. from main railway and bus stations. PARK: 100yds. TEL: 02920 390939. SER: Valuations; restorations.

Kings Fireplaces, Antiques and Interiors
The Old Church, Adamsdown Sq., Adamsdown. CF2 1EZ. (B. Quinn). Est. 1984. Open 10-5. SIZE: Medium. *STOCK: Period fireplaces including French marble; Victorian and Edwardian furniture.* TEL: 02920 492439. SER: Restorations (furniture and fireplaces); fireplace installations. VAT: Stan.

Llanishen Antiques
26 Crwys Rd., Cathays. CF2 4NL. (Mrs J. Boalch). Open 10.30-4.30. CL: Wed. except by appointment. *STOCK: Furniture, silver, china, glass, bric-a-brac.* TEL: 02920 397244.

Pontcanna Old Books, Maps and Prints
1 Pontcanna St. CF11 9HQ. (W. A. Beynon). WBDA. Open 10-5. SIZE: Medium. *STOCK:*

Books, £1-£2,000; maps, 17th-19th C, £1-£1,000; prints, £1-£500. LOC: Off Cathedral Rd. PARK: Easy. TEL: 02920 641047; fax - same. SER: Valuations; buys at auction (books, maps and prints). FAIRS: Royal National; Bonnington Hotel. VAT: Stan.

Roberts Emporium
58-60 Salisbury Rd. CF24 4AD. Est. 1980. Open 11-5. SIZE: Large. *STOCK: General antiques, Victorian, £5-£1,000; collectables, 50's, 60's, 70's.* LOC: In road near Museum of Wales. PARK: Easy. TEL: 02920 235630; fax - 02920 395935; e-mail - robertsflea@yahoo.co.uk; website - www.robertsfleamarket.com. SER: Valuations; restorations (ceramics and furniture); buys at auction; prop. hire. FAIRS: Newark.

San Domenico Stringed Instruments
175 Kings Rd., Pontcanna. CF1 9DF. (H. W. Morgan). Est. 1978. Open 10-4, Sat. 10-1. SIZE: Small. *STOCK: Fine violins, violas, cellos and bows, mainly 18th-19th C, £300-£20,000.* LOC: Off Cathedral Rd. or Cowbridge Rd. PARK: Easy. TEL: 02920 235881; fax - 02920 344510; home - 02920 777156; e-mail - HWM@san-domenico.co.uk; website - www.san-domenico.co.uk. SER: Valuations; restorations; buys at auction. FAIRS: Musicora, Paris. VAT: Stan/Spec.

CARMARTHEN

Audrey Bull
2 Jacksons Lane. SA31 1QD. Open 10-5. *STOCK: Period and Welsh country furniture, general antiques especially jewellery and silver.* TEL: 01267 222655; home - 01834 813425. VAT: Spec.

Cwmgwili Mill
Bronwydd Arms. SA33 6HX. (M. J. Sandell). Est. 1950. Open 9-1 and 2-6, Sat. 9-1 and 2-6, Sun. by appointment. SIZE: Large. *STOCK: Furniture, oak, mahogany, pine, 18th-20th C.* PARK: Easy. TEL: 01267 231500; home - 01267 237215.

Merlins Antiques
Market Hall. SA31 1QY. (Mrs J. R. Perry). Est. 1984. Open 10-4.30. *STOCK: Small items - porcelain, pottery, glass, silver and plate, postcards.* TEL: 01267 233814.

The Mount Antiques Centre
1 and 2 The Mount, Castle Hill. SA31. (R. Lickley). Est. 1987. Open 10-5.30, Sun. 11-3. SIZE: Large. *STOCK: Fine furniture including country, 18th-19th C, £500-£1,000+; china and collectables, 19th-20th C, £50-£500; architectural salvage, musical instruments, 19th C, £50-*

£1,500. LOC: A40 near county hall. PARK: Easy. TEL: 01267 220005. SER: Valuations; restorations (furniture and china). FAIRS: Towy - Cowbridge, Bristol and Cardiff.

CHEPSTOW

Foxgloves
20 St. Mary St. NP16 5EW. (Lesley Brain). Est. 1994. Open 10ish-5. CL: Wed. SIZE: Medium. *STOCK: Period and antique furniture; pictures, china and objet d'art.* LOC: Central. PARK: Nearby. TEL: 01291 622386. SER: Restorations.

Glance Back Bookshop
17 Upper Church St. NP6 5EX. Open 10ish-5.30, including Bank Holidays, Easter-October. SIZE: 8 rooms. *STOCK: Books including antiquarian; stamps, coins, tokens, medals, postcards pre-1930, banknotes, military cap badges, antiquarian maps and prints.* LOC: Town centre. PARK: Easy. TEL: 01291 626562; e-mail - Greg@GlanceBack. Demon.co.uk. SER: Restorations (works of art on paper, canvas or board); framing and colouring.

Glance Gallery
17a Upper Church St. NP6 5EX. Open 10ish-5.30. SIZE: Large. *STOCK: Antiquarian prints and maps.* LOC: Town centre. PARK: Easy. TEL: 01291 626562; e-mail - Greg@GlanceBack. Demon.co.uk. SER: Valuations; restorations (canvas, board or paper); framing; hand-colouring.

Intaglio
(John Harrison). Est. 1995. By appointment only. SIZE: Small. *STOCK: Sculpture, marble, 19th to early 20th C, £500-£20,000.* PARK: Easy. TEL: 01291 621476 or 01873 810036; fax - 01291 621476; e-mail - intaglio@tiscali.co.uk; authorised seller on - Sothebys.com. SER: Valuations; restorations (cleaning and conservation); buys at auction (bronze and marble sculpture). FAIRS: NEC; Bailey.

Plough House Interiors
Upper Church St. NP6 5HU. (Mr and Mrs P. Jones). Est. 1972. Open 10-5, Sat. 10-4.30, Sun. by appointment. CL: Wed. SIZE: Large. *STOCK: Victorian and Edwardian furniture and shipping goods.* LOC: 2 miles from Severn Bridge and M4. PARK: Easy. TEL: 01291 625200; home - same. SER: Valuations; restorations; buys at auction. VAT: Stan/Spec.

CHIRK

Seventh Heaven
Chirk Mill. LL14 5BU. Est. 1971. Open every day. SIZE: Large. *STOCK: Brass, iron and wooden beds including half-tester, four-poster and canopied, mainly 19th C.* LOC: B5070, below village, off A5 bypass. PARK: Easy. TEL: 01691 777622/773563; fax - 01691 777313; website - www. seventh-heaven.co.uk; e-mail - requests@seventh-heaven.co.uk. VAT: Stan.

CILIAU AERON

K. W. Finlay Antiques
The Forge, Neuaddlwyd. SA48 8DQ. Est. 1969. Usually open but prior telephone call advisable. SIZE: Medium. *STOCK: Furniture, 18th-20th C, £50-£3,000.* Not Stocked: Militaria, jewellery, smalls. LOC: A482, 2.5 miles from Aberaeron. PARK: Easy. TEL: 01545 570536; home - same. VAT: Stan/Spec.

COLWYN BAY

North Wales Antiques - Colwyn Bay
58 Abergele Rd. LL29 7PP. (F. Robinson). Est. 1958. Open 9-5. SIZE: Large warehouse. *STOCK: Shipping items, Victorian, early oak, mahogany and pine.* LOC: On A55. PARK: Easy. TEL: 01492 530521; evenings - 01352 720253. VAT: Stan.

Russell Worby
P O Box 43. LL29 8WS. Est. 1996. Open by appointment only. SIZE: Small. *STOCK: Welsh country furniture, 18th-19th C, £250-£15,000.* LOC: 3 miles from A55 expressway. PARK: Easy. TEL: 01492 512794; home/fax - same.

CONWY

Paul Gibbs Antiques and Decorative Arts
25 Castle St. LL32 8AY. Open 10-5. *STOCK: Antiques and Decorative Arts, 1880-1940's; art pottery, especially major factories.* TEL: 01492 593429; fax - same.

Teapot World - Museum and Shop
25 Castle St. LL32 8AY. Open every day Easter to end Oct. *STOCK: Traditional and novelty teapots and tea-related items. Also permanent display of 1,000+ antique, rare and novelty teapots from 1730.* TEL: 01492 596533; 01492 593429; fax - same; website - www. teapotworld.co.uk.

COWBRIDGE

Cowbridge Antique Centre
75 Eastgate. CF7 7AA. (T. C. Monaghan). Est.

1974. Open 10-5. SIZE: Medium. *STOCK: Furniture, 18th-19th C, £50-£1,000+; ceramics, 18th-20th C, £10-£750; collectables, 19th-20th C, £10-£500.* LOC: Town centre. PARK: Easy. TEL: 01446 775841; home - same; e-mail - terryval@cowbridgeantiques.freeserve.co.uk. SER: Valuations; restorations; upholstery. FAIRS: NEC, Birmingham.

Eastgate Antiques

6 High St. CF7 7AG. (Liz Herbert). Est. 1984. Open 10-1 and 2-5.30. CL: Mon. SIZE: Medium. *STOCK: Furniture, silver, jewellery, 18th C to Edwardian.* LOC: Off A48. PARK: Nearby. TEL: 01446 775; home - 01446 773505. SER: Buys at auction (furniture). VAT: Stan/Spec.

Havard and Havard

59 Eastgate. CF71 7EL. (Philip and Christine Havard). LAPADA. Est. 1992. Open 10.30-1 and 2-5. CL: Mon. and Wed. SIZE: Small. *STOCK: Oak, mahogany and walnut furniture especially provincial, £100-£10,000; metalware and samplers, £25-£1,000; all 18th-19th C.* LOC: Main street, 500 yards after lights on right. PARK: Easy. TEL: 01446 775021; e-mail - cphavard@aol.com. SER: Valuations. VAT: Stan/Spec.

Renaissance Antiques

The Antiques Centre, Ebenezer Chapel, 48A Eastgate. CF7 7AB. (R. W. and J. A. Barnicott). Est. 1984. Open 10-5. SIZE: Small. *STOCK: Small furniture, Georgian, Victorian and Edwardian, £100-£3,000; brass, copper, plate, decorative ceramics, Staffordshire figures, objets d'art, 18th to 20th C, £5-£500.* Not Stocked: Coins, militaria, reproductions. LOC: Main street.

CRICCIETH

Capel Mawr Collectors Centre

21 High St. LL52 0BS. (Alan and Dee Turner). Resident. Est. 1998. Open in summer 10-5; winter - Tues., Fri. and Sat. only. SIZE: Large. *STOCK: Books, from 18th C, £1-£500; postcards, 1894-1960, £1-£50; Sylvac, £5-£100.* LOC: A497. PARK: Nearby. TEL: 01766 523600; home - 01766 523435; e-mail - books@capelmawr.idps.co uk. SER: Valuations. VAT: Stan.

CRICKHOWELL

Gallop and Rivers Architectural Antiques

Ty'r Ash, Brecon Rd. NP8 1SF. (G. P. Gallop and R. A. Rivers). Open 9.30-5. *STOCK: Architectural items, pine and country furniture.* TEL: 01873 811084. VAT: Stan.

DEGANWY

Acorn Antiques

Castle Buildings. LL31 9EJ. (K. S. Bowers-Jones). Open 10-5. *STOCK: Ceramics, glass, furniture, pictures, brass and copper, 19th C.* PARK: Opposite. TEL: 01492 584083.

FISHGUARD

Manor House Antiques

Main St. SA65 9HG. (R. E. Davies). Est. 1987. Open in summer 10-5, prior 'phone call advisable in winter. *STOCK: General antiques especially porcelain and pottery.* PARK: Easy. TEL: 01348 873260.

GORSEINON, Nr. Swansea

Gold and Silver Shop

1 Cross St. SA1 1BA. (D. Paine). Open 9-2. *STOCK: Gold and silver, general antiques.* TEL: 01792 891874.

HAVERFORDWEST

Kent House Antiques

Kent House, Market St. SA61 1NF. (G. Fanstone and P. Thorpe). Est. 1987. Open 10-5. CL: Mon. SIZE: Medium. *STOCK: Victoriana, decorative items, hand-made rugs, £5-£500+.* LOC: Town centre. PARK: Easy. TEL: 01437 768175; home - same. SER: Valuations; restorations (furniture, some china).

Gerald Oliver Antiques

14 Albany Terrace, St. Thomas Green. SA61 1RH. Est. 1957. Open 9.30-4.30. *STOCK: Furniture, pre-1910, £20-£6,000; ceramics, treen, metalwork, silver, from £20; unusual, decorative and local interest items.* LOC: Via Freemans Way by-pass and up Merlins Hill. PARK: Easy. TEL: 01437 762794. SER: Valuations. VAT: Spec.

HAWARDEN

On the Air Ltd

The Vintage Technology Centre, The Highway. CH5 3DN. (Steve Harris). Est. 1990. Open 10-5, Sun. 11-4.30. CL: Mon. Christmas to Easter. SIZE: Small. *STOCK: Vintage wireless, gramophones and telephones, £50-£500.* LOC: Near St. David's Park, Ewloe, opposite Crown & Liver public house. PARK: Rear of premises. TEL: 01244 530300; fax - same; website - www.vintageradio.co.uk. SER:

Valuations; restorations (vintage wireless and gramophones). FAIRS: National Vintage Communications, NEC and Wembley.

HAY-ON-WYE

Richard Booth's Bookshop Ltd
44 Lion St. and Hay Castle. HR3 5AA. (Richard and Hope Booth). WBA. Est. 1974. Open 7 days 9-5.30, later at weekends and during summer. SIZE: Very large. *STOCK: Books, magazines, photographs, records, postcards, leather bindings.* LOC: Town centre. TEL: 01497 820322; fax - 01497 821150; Hay Castle - 01497 820503; e-mail - enquiries @richardboothbookseller.com; website (Hay-on-Wye Bookbuyers Ltd) - www.booktown. org.

Hay Antique Market
6 Market St. HR3 5AF. Open 10-5, Sun. 11-5. SIZE: 17 units. *STOCK: Antiques and collectables.* LOC: By the Butter Market. PARK: Easy. TEL: 01497 820175.

Hebbards of Hay
7 Market St. HR3 5AF. (P. E. Hebbard). Est. 1958. Open 10-5. SIZE: Small. *STOCK: Pottery and porcelain.* LOC: A438, opposite the Post Office. PARK: Own. TEL: 01497 820413.

Lion Fine Arts
19 Lion St. HR3 5AD. (Charles Spencer). Est. 1986. Open Mon., Thurs. and Sat. 10-5, prior telephone call advisable other days. SIZE: Small. *STOCK: Pottery, porcelain and glass, 18th to mid 19th C, £25-£250; furniture, prints and objets d'art, £30-£900; some second-hand and antiquarian books.* LOC: Turn right from Oxford Rd. car park, then second turning left. PARK: Limited. TEL: 01497 821726; home - same.

Rose's Books
14 Broad St. HR3 5DB. (Maria Goddard). Resident. Est. 1982. Open 7 days. SIZE: Medium. *STOCK: Children's books, 1900-1960, £5-£25.* TEL: 01497 820013; fax - 01497 820031; e-mail - enquiry@rosesbooks.com; website - www.roses. books.com. VAT: Stan.

Mark Westwood Antiquarian Books
High Town. HR3 5AE. ABA. PBFA. Est. 1976. Open 10.30-5.30, including Sun. *STOCK: Antiquarian and secondhand books on most subjects, £2-£1,000.* TEL: 01497 820068. SER: Valuations; buys at auction (antiquarian books). VAT: Stan.

HOLT, Nr. Wrexham

Furn Davies Partnership
Rock Cottage, Bridge St. LL13 9JG. Open
Thurs., Fri. and Sat. 10-5, other times by appointment. *STOCK: Furniture, 18th-19th C: decorative items.* TEL: 01829 270210. SER: Valuations; restorations.

HOLYHEAD (Anglesey)

Gwynfair Antiques
74 Market St. LL65 1UW. (Mrs. A. D. McCann).
Est. 1984. Open 10.30-4.30. CL: Tues. and Thurs.
SIZE: Small. *STOCK: China, ornaments, £5-
£250, furniture, £20-£1,000, all 1860-1950's.*
PARK: Loading outside shop, parking 100 yds.
TEL: 01407 763740; home - same. SER:
Valuations.

KIDWELLY

Country Antiques (Wales) Ltd BADA
Castle Mill. SA17 4UU. (R. and L. Bebb). Est.
1971. Open Tues.-Sat. 10-5, prior arrangement
advisable. SIZE: Large. *STOCK: Welsh oak
furniture and folk art; Welsh dressers, cupboards,
clocks, pottery.* LOC: Leave bypass (A484), into
centre of village, turn opposite war memorial,
by Boot and Shoe public house. PARK: Easy.
TEL: 01554 890534; e-mail - info@country
antiqueswales.fsnet.co.uk; website - www.
richardbebb.com. SER: Valuations; lectures.
VAT: Stan/Spec.

Kidwelly Antiques
31 Bridge St. SA17 4UU. (R. and L. Bebb). Est.
1971. Open Tues.- Sat. 10-5, prior arrangement
advisable. SIZE: Large. *STOCK: Georgian and
Victorian furniture and accessories; collectables.*
LOC: Leave bypass (A484), into centre of
village. PARK: Opposite shop. TEL: 01554
890328. VAT: Stan/Spec.

KNIGHTON

Offa's Dyke Antique Centre
4 High St. LD7 1AT. (Mrs. H. Hood and I.
Watkins). Est. 1985. Open 10-1 and 2-5. SIZE:
Medium - 16 dealers. *STOCK: Pottery, bijouterie,
18th-19th C furniture, £5-£1,000.* LOC: Near
town clock. PARK: Easy. TEL: 01547 528635;
evenings - 01547 528940/560272.

Islwyn Watkins
4 High St. LD7 1AT. Est. 1978. Open 10-1 and 2-
5. SIZE: Small. *STOCK: Pottery including

ISLWYN WATKINS ANTIQUES

Detail of Sprigs on a Derbyshire/Yorkshire saltglazed jug
dated 1861. Jug 16" high.

EIGHTEENTH AND NINETEENTH CENTURY POTTERY,
COUNTRY ANTIQUES AND BYGONES.

*Opening times of shop: Mon-Sat. 10.00-1.00, 2.00-5.00
or by appointment.*

4 High Street, Knighton, Powys, LD7 1AT
Tel: (01547) 520145 Evenings: (01547) 528940

studio, 18th-20th C, £25-£1,000; country and
domestic bygones, treen, 18th-20th C, £5-£200;
small country furniture, 18th-19th C, £20-£600.
Not Stocked: Jewellery, silver, militaria.* LOC: By
town clock. PARK: Easy. TEL: 01547 520145;
home - 01547 528940. SER: Valuations.

LLANDEILO

Jim and Pat Ash
The Warehouse, 5 Station Rd. SA19 6NG. Est.
1977. Open 9.30-5. SIZE: Large. *STOCK:
Victorian and antique furniture, Welsh country,
oak, mahogany, walnut.* LOC: 50yds. off A40.
PARK: Easy. TEL: 01558 823726/822130; fax -
same. SER: Valuations. VAT: Stan/Margin/Export.

LLANDUDNO

The Antique Shop
24 Vaughan St. LL30 1AH. (C. G. Lee). Est.
1938. Open 9-5.30. SIZE: Medium. *STOCK:
Jewellery, silver, porcelain, glass, ivories, metalware, from 1700; period furniture, shipping
goods.* LOC: Near promenade. PARK: Easy.
TEL: 01492 875575.

LLANDUDNO JUNCTION

Collinge Antiques
Old Fyffes Warehouse, Conwy Rd. LL31 9LU. (Nicky Collinge). Est. 1978. Open seven days. SIZE: Large. *STOCK: General antiques including Welsh dressers, dining, drawing and bedroom furniture, clocks, porcelain and pottery, silver, copper and brass, paintings, prints, glass and collectables, mainly Victorian and Edwardian.* LOC: Just off A55, Deganwy exit (A546). PARK: Easy. TEL: 01492 580022; fax - same; e-mail - sales@collinge-antiques.co.uk; website - www.collinge-antiques.co.uk. SER: Valuations; restorations including French polishing; buys at auction. VAT: Stan/Spec.

The Country Seat
35 Conwy Rd. LL31 9LU. (Steve and Helen Roberts). Est. 1994. Open 10-5, Sun. 12.30-4.30. SIZE: Small. *STOCK: Old and interesting items including paintings, pottery and porcelain, jewellery, furniture, linen, ephemera and bric-a-brac; decorative arts, 19th-20th C.* LOC: Just off A55. PARK: Easy. TEL: 01492 573256; e-mail - hkjroberts@hotmail.com; website - www.thecountryseat.co.uk. FAIRS: Newark; Birmingham Rag; Chester Northgate; Wrexham.

LLANDYSUL, Nr. Newcastle Emlyn

Michael Lloyd Antiques
The Alma, Wind St. SA44 4BD. Est. 1987. Open by appointment. SIZE: Small. *STOCK: Country furniture, decorative items.* LOC: Village centre. TEL: 01559 363880. VAT: Stan/Spec. *Trade Only.*

LLANELLI

John Carpenter
SA14 7HA. Resident. Est. 1973. Open by appointment. SIZE: Large. *STOCK: Musical instruments, furniture, general antiques, shipping goods.* LOC: 5 minutes from Cross Hands. TEL: 01269 831094; e-mail - sales@cjcantiques.co.uk. SER: Repairs (musical instruments); container packing.

LLANERCHYMEDD (Anglesey)

Two Dragons Oriental Antiques
8 High St. LL71 8EA. Open by appointment. SIZE: Large warehouse. *STOCK: Chinese country furniture.* TEL: 01248 470204/470100. FAIRS: Newark.

LLANFAIR CAEREINION, Nr. Welshpool

Heritage Restorations
Maes y Glydfa. SY21 0HD. (Jo and Fran Gluck). Est. 1970. Open 9-5. SIZE: Large. *STOCK: Pine and country furniture, £50-£5,000; some oak and architectural items, all 18th-19th C.* LOC: A458 from Welshpool. Past village, after 2 miles take first left after river bridge and caravan park, then follow signs. PARK: Easy. TEL: 01938 810384; home - same; fax - 01938 810900; website - www.heritagerestorations.co.uk. SER: Restorations (furniture including pine stripping). VAT: Stan/Spec.

LLANGOLLEN

J. and R. Langford
12 Bridge St. LL20 8PF. (P. and M. Silverston). Est. 1960. CL: Thurs. pm. and 1-2 daily. SIZE: Medium. *STOCK: Furniture, £100-£7,000; pottery and porcelain, £50-£2,000; silver, general antiques, clocks, paintings, £20-£4,000; all 18th-20th C.* LOC: Turn right at Royal Hotel, shop on right. PARK: Easy. TEL: 01978 860182; home - 01978 860493. SER: Valuations.

Passers Buy (Marie Evans)
Oak St/Chapel St. LL20 8NR. (Mrs M. Evans). Est. 1970. Open 11-5 - always on Tues., Fri. and Sat, often on Mon., Wed. and Thurs. - prior 'phone call advisable, Sun. by appointment. SIZE: Medium. *STOCK: Furniture, Staffordshire figures, Gaudy Welsh, fairings and general antiques.* LOC: Just off A5. Junction of Chapel St. and Oak St. PARK: Easy. TEL: 01978 860861/757385. FAIRS: Anglesey (June and Oct.)

LLANGRISTIOLUS (Anglesey)

Michael Webb Fine Art
Cefn-Llwyn. LL62 5DN. LAPADA. Est. 1972. Open by appointment only. *STOCK: Victorian and 20th C oil paintings and watercolours.* TEL: 01407 840336. SER: Valuations; restorations; framing. FAIRS: NEC; Chester; Carmarthen; Newbury Racecourse; Anglesey. VAT: Spec.

LLANRWST

Carrington House
26 Ancaster Sq. LL26 0LD. (R. Newstead and John Roberts). Est. 1975. Open 10.30-1.30 and 2.30-5, Mon. pm. and Sun. by appointment. SIZE: Medium. *STOCK: 19th C pine, £200-£1,000; oak and mahogany, 19th-20th C, £150-£2,000.* LOC: From A55 take A470 towards Betws-y-Coed. PARK: Easy. TEL: 01492 642500; fax - same; home - 01492 641279; website - www.carringtonhouse.co.uk. SER: Valuations. VAT: Spec.

Prospect Books

18 Denbigh St. LL26 0LL. (M. R. and M. R. Dingle). WBA. Est. 1980. CL: Mon. SIZE: Small. *STOCK: Books.* LOC: A55. PARK: Easy. TEL: 01492 640111; fax - same; mobile - 07801 844430.

Snowdonia Antiques

LL26 0EP. (J. Collins). Est. 1961. Open 9-5.30, Sun. by appointment. SIZE: Medium. *STOCK: Period furniture especially longcase clocks.* LOC: Turn off A5 just before Betws-y-Coed on to A496 for 4 miles. PARK: Easy. TEL: 01492 640789. SER: Restorations (furniture); repairs (grandfather clocks).

MATHRY

Cartrefle Antiques

SA62 5AD. (M. Hughes and Y. Chesters). Open in summer 10-5.30 ; in winter Wed.-Sat. 10.30-4. *STOCK: General antiques especially jewellery.* PARK: Easy. TEL: 01348 831591/837868.

MENAI BRIDGE (Anglesey)

Better Days

The Basement, 31 High St. LL59 5EF. (Mr and Mrs S. Rutter). Est. 1988. Open 10.30-4.30, Wed. 11-1, Sat. 10.30-5. CL: Mon. SIZE: Small. *STOCK: Decorative smalls, early 19th to mid 20th C, £5-£200; furniture, late 19th to mid 20th C, £50-£1,000; metal and miscellaneous, mid 19th C to early 20th C, £10-£150.* PARK: Rear of premises. TEL: 01248 716657; e-mail - rosy@ breathemail.net SER: Buys at auction. FAIRS: Mona Showground, Anglesey.

MILFORD HAVEN

Milford Haven Antiques

Robert St. SA73 2JQ. Est. 1968. Open 10-5. *STOCK: General antiques.* TEL: 01646 692152.

MONMOUTH

Frost Antiques & Pine

8 Priory St. NP25 3BR. (Nicholas Frost). Resident. Est. 1960. Open 9-5, Sun. and other times by appointment. SIZE: Small. *STOCK: Pine furniture and Staffordshire pottery, 19th C, £100-£1,500.* PARK: Easy. TEL: 01600 716687; website - www.frostantiques.com. SER: Valuations; restorations (furniture); buys at auction (Victorian furniture and ceramics).

MOUNTAIN ASH

Trading Post

3-4 Oxford Buildings, Oxford St. CF45 3HE. (D. Francis and Julie Thomas). Open 10-5. CL: Thurs. SIZE: Large. *STOCK: Edwardian and Victorian pine, satinwood and mahogany furniture; Continental items, china, glass, pictures and textiles, especially Welsh wool blankets and quilts.* LOC: Take A4059 off A470. PARK: Opposite. TEL: 01443 478855; mobile - 07813 674253.

MURTON, Nr. Swansea

West Wales Antiques

18 Manselfield Rd. SA3 3AR. (W. H. Davies). LAPADA. Est. 1956. Open 10-1 and 2-5. CL: Mon. *STOCK: Porcelain, 18th C, £20-£800; Welsh porcelain, 1800-1820; 18th-19th C furniture, silver, pottery, glass, jewellery and collectors' items.* LOC: M4-A4067-B4436, entrance to Gower Peninsula. TEL: 01792 234318. VAT: Stan/Spec.

NARBERTH

Malt House Antiques

Back Lane. SA67 7AR. (P. Griffiths). Est. 1995. Open 10-5.30, Sun. 11-4. SIZE: Large. *STOCK: Country furniture, 18th-20th C, £5-£1,000.* LOC: Village centre. PARK: Easy. TEL: 01834 860303.

NEWBRIDGE-ON-WYE
Nr. Llandrindod Wells

Allam Antiques

Old Village Hall. LD1 6HL. (Paul Allam). Est. 1985. Open Sat. 10-5. SIZE: Medium. *STOCK: Furniture, 1700-1930, £50-£3,000.* LOC: A470. PARK: Easy. TEL: 01597 860654; home - 01597 860455. SER: Valuations; paint stripping.

NEWPORT (Pembs.)

The Carningli Centre

East St. SA42 05Y. (Ann Gent and Graham Coles). Est. 1994. Open 10-5.30, Sun. by appointment only. SIZE: Medium. *STOCK: Furniture, 17th-19th C, £50-£5,000; railwayana, nautical items, country collectables including oil lamps and tools, £1-£500; secondhand books, fine art gallery.* LOC: A487, town centre. PARK: Free in Long St. TEL: 01239 820724; website - www. carningli.co.uk. SER: Valuations; restorations (furniture); polishing; turning; buys at auction (railwayana). VAT: Spec.

PEMBROKE

Pembroke Antiques Centre
Wesley Chapel, Main St. SA71 4DE. (Michael Blake). Est. 1986. Open 10-5. SIZE: Large. *STOCK: Pine, oak, mahogany and shipping furniture; china, rugs, paintings, Art Deco enamel signs, kitchenalia, pottery, toys, curios and collectables.* PARK: Easy. TEL: 01646 687017.

PONTARDDULAIS, Nr. Swansea

The Emporium
112 St Teilo St. SA4 1SS. (Laura Jeremy). Est. 1992. Open 10.30-6. SIZE: Medium. *STOCK: Furniture, 1900-1950, £5-£500; Victorian metalware, collectables, bric-a-brac.* LOC: Off M4, junction 48. PARK: Easy. TEL: 01792 885185; e-mail - laura@the-emporium.freeserve.co.uk. SER: Restorations. FAIRS: Local.

PONTLLFRII, Nr. Caernarfon

Sea View Antiques
LL54 5EF. (David A. Ramsell). Resident. Est. 1995. Open daily. SIZE: Small. *STOCK: General antiques and collectables, 18th-20th C, £5-£1,500.* LOC: Main Caernarfon to Pwllheli road. PARK: Easy. TEL: 01286 660436.

PORTHCAWL

Harlequin Antiques
Dock St. CF36 3BL. (Ann and John Ball). Est. 1974. Open 10-4. *STOCK: General antiques; textiles; early 19th to 20th C books.* TEL: 01656 785910; mobile - 07980 837844.

PORTHMADOG

Huw Williams Antiques
Madoc St. LL49 9LR. Est. 1993. Open 10-5, Mon. 12-5. CL: Wed. SIZE: Small. *STOCK: Weapons, 18th-19th C, £50-£3,000; country furniture, 18th-19th C, £100-£1,000; general antiques, 19th-20th C, to £300.* LOC: Opposite entrance to main car park. PARK: Opposite. TEL: 01766 514741; mobile - 07785 747561; website - www.antiqueguns wales.co.uk. FAIRS: Stockport Arms; International Arms, Motorcycle Museum, Birmingham; Gwyn Davies, Mona, Anglesey; Big Brum (Rag Market).

PWLLHELI

Rodney Adams Antiques
Hall Place, Old Town Hall and 62 High St. LL53 5DH. Resident. Est. 1965. CL: Sun. except by appointment. *STOCK: Longcase clocks, country oak and pine furniture.* TEL: 01758 613173; evenings - 01758 614337. VAT: Stan/Spec.

RUTHIN

R. and S. M. Percival Antiques
Porth-y-Dwr, 65 Clwyd St. LL15 1HN. Est. 1979. Open daily, Sun. and Mon. by appointment. SIZE: Medium. *STOCK: Pine, mahogany and oak furniture and decorative smalls, 18th-19th C, £100-£1,000+.* PARK: Behind shop. TEL: 01824 704454; home - 01978 790370. SER: Valuations; buys at auction (furniture). FAIRS: Newark.

SKENFRITH, Nr. Abergavenny

Singleton Antiques
Birch Hill Farm. NP7 8UH. (J. W. & A. A. Chapman). Est. 1994. Open any time by appointment. SIZE: Medium. *STOCK: Oak, 17th-19th C, £200-£5,000; country furniture, 18th-19th C, £100-£2,000; decorative items and pictures, 18th-20th C, £10-£2,000.* LOC: Telephone for directions. PARK: Easy. TEL: 01600 750671; e-mail - singletonantiques @4mail-biz. SER: Valuations. VAT: Stan/Spec.

SWANSEA

James Allan
22 Park St. SA1 3DJ. (S. J. Allan). Est. 1929. Open 9.30-4.30. SIZE: Small. *STOCK: Jewellery, 1850 to date, £50-£5,000.* LOC: Off Kingsway, round corner from Mothercare. PARK: Nearby. TEL: 01792 652176. SER: Valuations. VAT: Stan.

Keith Chugg Antiques
Gwydr Lane, Uplands. Open 9-5.30, Sat. 9-1. *STOCK: Pianos and general antiques including furniture.* TEL: 01792 472477.

Clydach Antiques
83 High St., Clydach. SA6 5LJ. (R. T. Pulman). Open 10-5, Sat. 10-1. *STOCK: General antiques.* TEL: 01792 843209.

Dylan's Bookstore
Salubrious Passage. SA1 3RT. (J. M. Towns). ABA. PBFA. Est. 1971. Open 10-5, prior telephone call advisable. *STOCK: Antiquarian books on Welsh history and topography, Anglo/Welsh literature and general books.* PARK: Adjacent. TEL: 01792 655255; fax - same; mobile - 07850 759199; e-mail - jefftowns@dylans.com; website - www.dylans.com. FAIRS: London; Boston; Los Angeles; San Francisco.

Magpie Antiques
57 St. Helens Rd. SA1 4BH. (H. Hallesy). Est. 1984. Open 10-5. CL: Thurs. *STOCK: Ceramics*

including Swansea, Lllanelly and other Welsh potteries; oak and country furniture. PARK: Opposite. TEL: 01792 648722. SER: Valuations; restorations (furniture).

TEMPLETON, Nr. Narberth

Barn Court Antiques, Crafts & Tearoom
Barn Court. SA67 8SL. (D., A. and M. Evans). Est. 1989. Open 10-5. SIZE: Medium. *STOCK: Mahogany, walnut, rosewood and oak furniture, Georgian to late Victorian, £100-£3,000; china and glass, mainly Victorian, £10-£500.* LOC: Off A40 on A478 Narberth to Tenby road. PARK: Easy. TEL: 01834 861224; e-mail - info@barncourtantiques.com; website - www.barncourtantiques.com. VAT: Margin.

TENBY

Audrey Bull
15 Upper Frog St. SA70 7DJ. (Jonathan and Jane Bull). Est. 1945. Open 9.30-5. *STOCK: Period and Welsh country furniture, general antiques especially jewellery and silver.* TEL: 01834 843114; workshop - 01834 871873; home - 01834 813425. VAT: Spec.

Potboard Antiques
Astridge Farm. SA70 8RE. (Nigel and Gill Batten). Est. 1987. Open by appointment only. *STOCK: 18th-19th C pine and country furniture.* LOC: Three miles from Tenby. TEL: 01834 842699; fax - 01834 842788; website - www.potboard.co.uk. SER: Restorations (furniture, including stripping); buys at auction (pine). VAT: Spec.

TINTERN

Tintern Antiques
The Old Bakehouse. NP6 6SE. (Dawn Floyd). Open 9.30-5.30. *STOCK: Antique jewellery and general antiques.* TEL: 01291 689705.

TRECASTLE, Nr. Brecon

Trecastle Antiques Centre
The Old School. LD3 8YA. (A. Perry). Est. 1980. Open 10-5 including Sun. SIZE: Large. *STOCK: General antiques, £5-£1,500.* LOC: A40. PARK: Easy. TEL: 01874 638007. SER: Valuations; restorations. FAIRS: Newark, Shepton Mallet.

TREORCHY

Steven Evans Antiques
Melvin Wine Cellars, Regent St. CF42 6EP.

(Steven Evans). Est. 1981. Open 9-5, Sat 10-5. SIZE: Warehouse. *STOCK: Victorian mahogany, Edwardian to 1920's oak, shipping goods.* LOC: Junction 34, M4, then A4119. PARK: Own. TEL: 01443 776410/431756; fax - 01443 776982; mobile - 0778530 8567. SER: North American and Japanese market specialists; container packing and shipping. VAT: Stan/Spec.

TREVOR, Nr. Llangollen

Romantiques
Bryn Seion Chapel, Station Rd. LL20 7TP. (Miss S. E. Atkin). Est. 1994. Open 10-5 including Sun., or by appointment. SIZE: Large. *STOCK: Furniture, £50-£4,000; collectables, £1-£1,000; clocks and barometers, £50-£3,000.* LOC: Off A5 and A539 Llangollen roads. PARK: Easy. TEL: 01978 822879; mobile - 07778 279614; website - www.romantiques.co.uk. SER: Valuations; restorations (furniture, upholstery, clocks); courier. VAT: Stan/Spec.

TYWYN

Welsh Art
(Miles Wynn Cato). Open by appointment only (also in London). *STOCK: Welsh paintings, 1550-1950; Welsh portraits of all periods and historical Welsh material.* TEL: 020 7259 0306 and 01654 711715.

VALLEY, Nr. Holyhead (Anglesey)

Ann Evans
Carna Shop, Station Rd. LL65 3HB. Open Thurs.-Sat. 10-4.30, other days by appointment. *STOCK: Oak dressers, Welsh pottery, cranberry glass, Staffordshire figures.* PARK: Easy. TEL: 01407 741733.

WELSHPOOL

A. & H. Antiques
19 High St. SY21 7JP. Est. 1980. Open 10-5, Sat. 10-2. CL: Tues. SIZE: Small. *STOCK: Furniture, 18th-19th C; china.* LOC: Off A483. PARK: Easy. TEL: 01938 552421; home - same; e-mail - anh.antiques@amserve.net. SER: Valuations; buys at auction. FAIRS: Shepton Mallett. *Trade Only.*

F. E. Anderson and Son
5-6 High St. SY21 7JF. (D. and I. Anderson). LAPADA. Open daily. *STOCK: Furniture, 17th-19th C; mirrors, paintings and early metalware.* TEL: 01938 553340; home - 01938 590509; mobile - 07773 795931; e-mail - feandersonandson@yahoo.co.uk. FAIRS: Olympia; LAPADA.

Index of
Packers and Shippers:
Exporters of Antiques (Containers)

AR · GS International Transport Ltd.

SHIPPERS & PACKERS OF ANTIQUES, FINE ART & REMOVALS TO **ITALY**

Tel: 020 7833 3955 or 01444 414667
Fax: 020 7837 8672

North London Freight Centre,
York Way, Kings Cross, London N1 0BB

LONDON

Anglo Pacific International plc
Standard Rd., NW10 6DF. LAPADA. Tel: 020 8838 8008; fax - 020 8453 0225; e-mail - antiques@anglopacific.co.uk. *Specialist antique and fine art packers and shippers serving worldwide destinations by land, sea or air. Free estimates and advice. Courier sevices available.*

AR. GS International Transport Ltd
North London Freight Centre, York Way, Kings Cross, N1 0BB. Tel: 020 7833 3955; fax - 020 7837 8672. *Fine art and antiques removals by road transport, Europe, especially Italy, door-to-door service. Documentation.*

Art Logistics Ltd
2 Old Oak Common Lane. NW10 6DX. LAPADA. Tel: 020 8961 7627; fax - 020 8961 8764; e-mail - mail@antlogistics.co.uk. *Fine art packing, freight forwarding.*

B B F Fine Art Services Ltd
Copenhagen House, Copenhagen Place, E14 7DE. Tel: 020 7515 7005; fax - 020 7515 6001; e-mail - mailbox@bbfwwide.demon.co.uk; website - www.bbfwwide.demon.co.uk. *Fine art packers, worldwide shippers by sea, air and road.*

Robert Boys Shipping

Unit D Tunnel Avenue Trading Estate, Tunnel Avenue, Greenwich, SE10 0QH LAPADA. Tel: 020 8858 3355; fax - 020 8858 3344; e-mail - boysship@ftech.co.uk. *Worldwide shipping. Air and sea cargo. Specialists in fine art and furniture to Japan with part load containers to Japan on a weekly basis. Japanese speaking staff.*

Constantine Ltd

Constantine House, 134 Queens Rd., SE15 2HR. LAPADA. Tel: 020 7732 8123; fax - 020 7732 2631. *Specialists in the international movement of antiques and fine art for over a hundred and fifty years - services incorporate all requirements from case making to documentation and insurance. Freight groupage specialists.*

Davies Turner Worldwide Movers Ltd.

London Headquarters : 49 Wates Way, Mitcham, CR4 4HR. Tel: 020 7622 4393; fax - 020 7720 3897; e-mail - antiques@daviesturner.co.uk. *Fine art and antiques packers and shippers. Courier and finder service. Full container L.C.L. and groupage service worldwide.*

Focus Packing Services Ltd

37-39 Peckham Rd., SE5 8UH. Tel: 020 7703 4715; fax - same; e-mail - A.clough@tinyonline.co.uk.

Gander and White Shipping Ltd.

Head Office, 21 Lillie Rd., SW6 1UE. LAPADA. Tel: 020 7381 0571; fax - 020 7381 5428. *Specialist packers and shippers of antiques and works of art.*

Salmon's serene style was followed by William Clark of Greenock in this oil of shipping inside the West Harbour of the Clydeside port, which sold for £18,000.

From an Auction Report by Christopher Wight on the Maritime Sale held at Bonhams, New Bond Street, on 16th January 2002 which appeared in the March 2002 issue of **Antique Collecting**. For more details and to subscribe see page 21.

LONDON · NEW YORK · PARIS

UNITED KINGDOM

Gander & White Shipping Ltd.
21 Lillie Road, London SW6 1UE
Tel: 00 44 20 7381 0571
Fax: 00 44 20 7381 5428

Newpound, Wisborough Green, Billingshurst,
West Sussex RH14 0AY
Tel: 00 44 1403 70 00 44
Fax: 00 44 1403 70 08 14

FRANCE

Gander & White Shipping Ltd.
8, rue de Duras, 75008 Paris
Tél: 01 43 12 31 32
Fax: 01 43 12 31 33

USA

Gander & White Shipping Inc.
21-44, 44th Road, Long Island City
New York 11101
Tel: 00 1 718 784 8444
Fax: 00 1 718 784 9337

Hedleys Humpers Ltd

3 St Leonards Rd., North Acton NW10 6SX. LAPADA. Tel: 020 8965 8733 (10 lines); fax - 020 8965 0249; e-mail - info@hedleyshumpers. com; website - www.hedleyshumpers.com. *Weekly door to door services to Europe, plus part load shipments by air and sea worldwide. Offices in London, Paris, Nice, Avignon and New York.*

Interdean.Interconex

Central Way, Park Royal, NW10 7XW. Tel: 020 8961 4141; telex - 922119; fax - 020 8965 4484. *Antiques and fine art packed, shipped and airfreighted worldwide. Storage and international removals. Full container L.C.L. and groupage service worldwide.*

Kuwahara Ltd.

6 McNicol Drive, NW10 7AW. LAPADA. Tel: 020 8963 5995; fax - 020 8963 0100; e-mail - antiques@kuwahara.co.uk; website - www. kuwahara.co.uk. *Specialist packers and shippers of antiques and works of art. Regular groupage service to Japan.*

Locksons Services Ltd

See entry under Essex.

Momart Ltd

199-205 Richmond Rd., E8 3NJ. Tel: 020 8986 3624; fax - 020 8533 0122; e-mail - enquiries @momart.co.uk. *Fine art handling including transportation, case making and packing: import/export services, exhibition installation and storage.*

Stephen Morris Shipping plc

6 McNicol Drive. NW10 7AW. LAPADA. Tel: 020 8838 2929; fax - 020 8838 6969; e-mail - enquiries@stemo.co.uk; website - www.stemo. co.uk. *Specialist packers and shippers of antiques and fine art worldwide. Weekly European service.*

Nelson Shipping

Unit C3, Six Bridges Trading Estate, Marlborough Grove, SE1 5JT. Tel: 020 7394 7770; fax - 020 7394 7707. *Expert export and packing service.*

The Packing Shop

6-12 Ponton Rd., SW8 5BA. Tel: 020 7498 3255; fax - 020 7498 9017. *Fine art and antiques export packed. World-wide shipping, scheduled European vehicles, New York weekly consols. International exhibitions. High security bonded storage. New York office and warehouse.*

SOME ARE MORE EQUAL THAN OTHERS

ALAN FRANKLIN TRANSPORT
Specialist Carriers to the Continent

England
26 Black Moor Road, Verwood, Dorset BH31 6BB
Tel: +44 1202 826539 Fax: +44 1202 827337

France
2 Rue Etienne Dolet, 93400 St. Ouen, Paris
Tel: +33 1 40 11 50 00 Fax: +33 1 40 11 48 21

France
Quartier La Tour de Sabran, 84440 Robion (Vaucluse)
Tel: +33 4 90 76 49 00 fax: +33 4 90 76 49 02

Belgium
De Klerckstraat 41, B8300 Knokke
Tel: +32 50 623 579 Fax: +32 50 623 579

Our door to door weekly service throughout
Europe is well known and very reliable.
Visit our Paris warehouse and offices located
within the famous Paris flea market area.
Container and Air Freight Services Worldwide.

Pitt and Scott Ltd
60 Coronation Rd., NW10 7PX. Tel: 020 7278 5585; fax - 020 7278 5592; e-mail - enquiries@ pittandscott.co.uk. *Packers and shippers of antiques and fine art. Shipping, forwarding and airfreight agents. Comprehensive service provided for visiting antique dealers. Insurance arranged.*

Robinsons International
The Gateway, Staples Corner. NW2 7AJ. LAPADA. Tel: 020 8208 8484; fax - 020 8208 8488; website - www.robinsons-intl.com. *Specialist packers and shippers of antiques and fine art worldwide. Established over 100 years.*

T. Rogers and Co. Ltd
PO Box No. 8, 1A Broughton St., SW8 3QL. Tel: 020 7622 9151; fax - 020 7627 3318. *Specialists in storage, packing, removal, shipping and forwarding antiques and works of art. Insurance.*

BUCKINGHAMSHIRE

Clark's of Amersham
Higham Mead, Chesham. HP5 2AH. Tel: 01494 774186; fax - 01494 774196; website - www. bluelorry.com. *Removals and storage, domestic and commercial; export packing and shipping - worldwide door to door.*

CHESHIRE

The Rocking Chair Antiques
Unit 3, St. Peters Way, Warrington, WA27 7BL. Tel: 01925 652409; fax - same; mobile - 07774 492891. *Exporters and packers.*

DEVON

Barnstaple Removal
14/15 Meadow Way, Treebeech Rural Enterprise Park, Gunn, Barnstaple. EX32 7NZ. Tel: 01271 831164; fax - 01271 831165; e-mail - barnstaple. removals@sosi.net; website - www.barnstaple. removals.co.uk. *Container packing and shipping worldwide.*

Bishop's Blatchpack
Kestrel Way, Sowton Industrial Estate, Exeter, EX2 7PA. Tel: 01392 202040; fax - 01392 201251. *International fine art packers and shippers.*

DORSET

Alan Franklin Transport
26 Blackmoor Rd., Ebblake Industrial Estate, Verwood, BH31 6BB. LAPADA. Tel: 01202 826539; fax - 01202 827337; e-mail - afteurope @aol.com. *Container packing and shipping. Weekly door-to-door European service. Paris office - 2 Rue Etienne Dolet, 93400 St. Ouen, Paris. Tel: 00 33140 115000; fax - 00 33140 114821. South of France office - Quartier la tour de Sabran, 84440 Robion (Vaucluse). Tel: 00 33490 764900; fax - 00 33490 764902. Belgian office - De Klerckstraat 41, B8300, Knokke. Tel: 00 3250 623579; fax - same.*

ESSEX

Geo. Copsey and Co. Ltd
178 Crow Lane, Romford. RM7 0ES. Tel: 01708 740714 or 020 8592 1003. *Worldwide packers and shippers.*

Crown Relocations
Security House, Abbey Wharf Industrial Estate, Kingsbridge Rd., Barking, IG11 0BD. Tel: 020 8591 3388; fax - 020 8594 4571. *Packers and shippers - 12 offices throughout U.K.*

Lockson Services Ltd
Unit 1, Heath Park Industrial Estate, Freshwater Rd., Chadwell Heath, RM8 1RX. LAPADA. Tel: 020 8597 2889; fax - 020 8597 5265; mobile (weekends) - 07831 621428; New York office - 201 392 9800; fax - 201 392 8830; e-mail - enquiries@lockson.co.uk; website - www.lockson. co.uk. *Specialist packers and shippers of fine art and antiques by air, sea and road to the USA, Japan, Far East, Canada and other worldwide destinations. A complete personalised service. At all Olympia, Newark and Ardingly fairs.*

L.J. Roberton
Mallard House, 402 Roding Lane South, Woodford Green, IG8 8EY. LAPADA. Tel: 020 8551 9188; fax - 020 8551 9199; email: international@harrowgreen.com.

GLOUCESTERSHIRE

The Removal Company - Loveday & Loveday
2 Wilkinson Rd., Cirencester, GL7 1YT. Tel: 01285 651505. *Shipping and packing.*

The Shipping Company Ltd.

Bourton Industrial Park, Bourton-on-the-Water, GL54 2HQ. Tel: 01451 822451; fax - 01451 810985; website - www.theshippingcompanyltd. com. *Export packers and shippers specialising in the antique, fine art and interior design markets worldwide. Single, consolidated and full container shipments by air and sea. All risks insurance offered.*

A.J. Williams (Shipping)

607 Sixth Ave., Central Business Park, Hengrove, Bristol, BS14 9BZ. LAPADA. Tel: 01275 892166; fax - 01275 891333.

HAMPSHIRE

Robinsons International

16 Millbank St., Southampton, SO14 5QQ. LAPADA. Tel: 023 8022 0069; fax - 023 8033 1274; e-mail - southampton@robinsons-intl.com; website - www.robinsons-intl.com. *Specialist packers and shippers of antiques and fine art worldwide. Established over 100 years.*

Robinsons International

Telford Rd., Basingstoke, RG21 6YU. LAPADA. Tel: 01256 465533; fax - 01256 324959; website - www.robinsons-intl.com. *Specialist packers and shippers of antiques and fine art worldwide. Established over 100 years.*

KENT

Sutton Valence Antiques

Unit 4, Haslemere Estate, Sutton Rd. Maidstone, ME15 9NL. LAPADA. Tel: 01622 675332; fax - 01622 692593; e-mail - svantiques@aol.com; website - www.svantiques.co.uk. *Antique and shipping furniture. Container packing and shipping. Facilities for 20ft. and 40ft. containers, all documentation. Worldwide service.*

LANCASHIRE

Robinsons International

32 Stanley Rd., Manchester, M45 8QX. LAPADA. Tel: 0161 766 8414; fax - 0161 767 9057; website - www.robinsons-intl.com. *Specialist packers and shippers of antiques and fine art worldwide. Established over 100 years.*

MERSEYSIDE

John Mason International Ltd

35 Wilson Rd., Huyton Business Park, Liverpool, L36 6AE. LAPADA. Tel: 0151 449 3938. *Specialist packer, full and part container loads, groupage service worldwide, courier and finder service.*

MIDDLESEX

Air-Sea Packing Group Ltd

Air-Sea House, Third Cross Rd., Twickenham, TW2 5EB. Tel: 020 8893 3303; fax - 020 8893 3068; e-mail - sales@airseapacking.com; website - www.airseapacking.com. *Specialist packers and shippers.*

McN International

Unit 10 Shield Drive, West Cross Centre, Brentford, TW8 8EX. Tel: 020 8580 1001; fax - 020 8580 1002. *Fine interiors project management, antique and fine art shippers, incorporating Vitesse in conjunction with Federal Express.*

Nippon Express (UK) Ltd

Ocean Freight Division, Unit 7, Parkway Trading Estate, Cranford Lane, Heston, Hounslow, TW5 9NE. Tel: Commercial (Export) - 020 8737 4240; fax - 020 8737 4249; (Import) - 020 8737 4260; fax - 020 8737 4269; Removal (Cargo) - 020 8737 4200; fax - 020 8737 4209. *Mainly*

Japanese imports/exports, both commercial and removals. Also import/export all other Far East countries.

Sovereign International Freight Ltd

Sovereign House, 8-10 St. Dunstans Rd., Feltham, TW13 4JU. Tel: 020 8751 3131; fax - 020 8751 4517; e-mail - info@sovereignlondon.co.uk. *Heathrow Airport based shippers and packers registered to ISO 9002 quality. Holders of the Queen's Award for Export and National Training Award. Specialist in antiques and the fine art trades.*

Vulcan International Services Ltd

Unit 1A, Avia Park, Westgate 1, Staines Rd., Bedfont, TW14 8RS. LAPADA. Tel: 01784 244152; 01784 248183. *Fine art packers and shippers worldwide.*

OXFORDSHIRE

Cotswold Carriers

Unit 2 The Walk, Hook Norton Rd., Chipping Norton, OX7 5TG. Tel: 01608 730500; fax - 01608 730600. *Removals, storage, shipping, door-to-door Continental deliveries.*

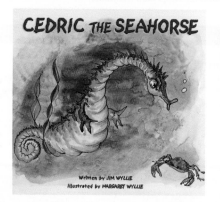

Robinsons International
Nuffield Way, Abingdon, OX14 1TN. LAPADA. Tel: 01235 552255; fax - 01235 553573; website - www.robinsons-intl.com. *Specialist packers and shippers of antiques and fine art worldwide. Established over 100 years.*

Hugh Thomas Shipping
Park House, Bladon, Woodstock. OX20 1RW. Tel: 01993 812817; fax - 01993 812912; e-mail - hughthomas@htshipping.com; website - www. htshipping.com. *Antique furniture exporter and shipper. Finder service. Single items or many shipped to all USA cities. Large free pick up area. Large dealer co-operative in USA. Full and half container rates also available.*

SOMERSET

Louis Degregorio
Old Bacon Factory, Huntspill Rd., Highbridge, TA9 3DE. Tel: 01278 788590/788603. *Packing, transport, shipping goods.*

Robinsons International
Aldermoor Way, Longwell Green, Bristol. BS30 7DA. LAPADA. Tel: 0117 980 5858; fax - 0117 980 5830; website - www.robinsons-intl.com. *Specialist packers and shippers of antiques and fine art worldwide. Established over 100 years.*

STAFFORDSHIRE

Crown Relocations
Crown House, Unit 1 Ninian Way, Tame Valley Industrial Estate, Wilnecote, Tamworth, B77 5ES Tel: 01827 264100; fax - 01827 264101.

Kenpack
69 Newcastle Rd., Leek, ST13 5RT. Tel: 01538 399670; fax - 01538 398175. *Open Mon.-Fri. 8.30-5. Container packing and export documentation.*

SURREY

W. Ede & Co
The Edes Business Park, Restmor Way, Wallington, SM2 5AA. Tel: 020 8773 9933; fax - 020 8773

Thickly painted in a broad style, 'A Sussex Cornfield', oil on canvas, 20in. x 30in., by Henry H. Parker (1858-1930) fetched £8,000 at Bonhams.

From an article entitled "19th Century Paintings" by Anthony J. Lester which appeared in the June 2002 issue of **Antique Collecting**. For more details and to subscribe see page 21.

Commercial Packing & Shipping Services

WORLD WIDE SHIPPING SERVICE

9011. *Worldwide packing and shipping, complete documentation and removals service, container packing.*

SUSSEX EAST

Global Services
West St., Lewes, BN7 2NJ. Tel: 01273 475903. *Packers and shippers of antiques, arms, armour and fine works of art.*

SUSSEX WEST

Gander and White Shipping Ltd
Newpound, Wisborough Green, Billingshurst, RH14 0AY. LAPADA. Tel: 01403 700044; fax - 01403 700814; e-mail - ukinfo@ganderand white.com. *Specialist packers and shippers of fine art and antiques.*

Martells International
Queen's Rd., East Grinstead RH19 1BA. Tel: 01342 321303; fax - 01342 317522. *National and international removers, export packers and shippers.*

TYNE AND WEAR

Owen Humble (Packing and Shipping) Ltd
Clayton House, Walbottle Rd., Lemington, Newcastle-upon-Tyne, NE15 9RU. Tel: 0191 267 7220. *Worldwide service.*

The Bubbles pattern (Z5257), part of the Fairyland Lustre range, decorated on a bone china Malfrey pot, 1920 to about 1929. (Special orders for this pattern were taken until 1941.) (Christie's Images)

From an article entitled "In Fairyland All Things Are Possible" by Andrew Casey which appeared in the December 2001/January 2002 issue of **Antique Collecting**. For more details and to subscribe see page 21.

Martin Bros. Ltd

The Old Sawmills, The Street,
Kilmington, Nr Warminster, Wilts. BA12 6RG
Tel: 01985 844 144, 112,   Fax: 01985 844 113
Specialist Carriers of Fine Art and Furniture
throughout mainland UK.

R.K. Neil Ltd -Scandinavia-

Tel: 01985 844 144, 112,   Fax: 01985 844 113
Specialist Carriers of Fine Art and Furniture to
Denmark, Sweden & Norway.
Weekly door to door service.

WEST MIDLANDS

The British Shop - Shipping U.S.A.
Old Sandwell House, Sandwell St., Walsall, WS1
3DR. Tel: 01922 721088; fax - 01922 723123;
(USA - 336 434 4645; fax - 336 434 7765) *Weekly
container from Birmingham to High Point, North
Carolina, USA. Pick-up and pack, no minimums.*

Robinsons International
22A Bartleet Rd., Washford, Redditch, B98 0DG.
LAPADA. Tel: 01527 830860; fax - 01527
500777; website - www.robinsons-intl.com.
*Specialist packers and shippers of antiques and
fine art worldwide. Established over 100 years.*

Clentons Removals Ltd.
94 Caldmore Road, Walsall. WS1 3PD. 01922
624431; fax - 01922 613053; e-mail - clentons
@yahoo.co.uk; website - www.clentonsremovals.
com. *Collections arranged in UK and Europe for
clients' goods. Storage available. Packing and
wrapping of all goods for container shipments.
All paperwork done for containers. Packing of
containers and shipment of containers.*

WILTSHIRE

Martin Bros Ltd
The Old Sawmills, The Street, Kilmington, Nr.
Warminster. BA12 6RG. Tel: 01985 844144; fax
- 01985 844113. *Specialist carriers of fine art and
furniture throughout mainland UK.*

WORCESTERSHIRE

Simon Hall Freight
Willersey Industrial Estate, Willersey, Nr.
Broadway, WR12 7RR. Tel: 01386 858555; fax -
01386 858501. *Specialist packers and shippers
for fine art and antiques world wide. UK
collections and deliveries. Humidity controlled
containerised and conventional storage.*

SCOTLAND

Crown Relocations
Containerbase, Gartsherrie Rd., Coatbridge,
Lanarkshire. ML5 2DT. Tel: 01236 449666; fax -
01236 449888. *Packers and shippers.*

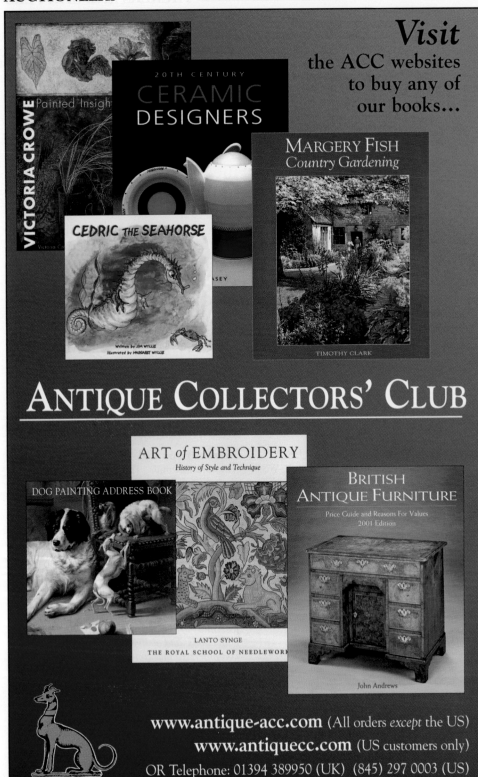

Index of Auctioneers

LONDON

Bloomsbury Book Auctions

3 and 4 Hardwick St., EC1R 4RY. Tel: 020 7833 2636/7; fax - 020 7833 3954; e-mail - info@ bloomsbury-book-auct.com; website - www. bloomsbury-book-auct.com. *Twenty-four sales a year of books on all subjects and of all values, manuscripts, autograph letters, prints, maps, drawings, photographs, posters and ephemera. Valuations. Collection service.*

Bonhams

101 New Bond St., W1S 1SR. Tel: 020 7629 6602; fax - 020 7629 8876; website - www. phillips-auctions.com. *Regular sales of fine furniture, paintings, ceramics, jewellery, silver, clocks, watches, Oriental works of art, textiles, books, musical instruments, works of art, stamps, medals and decorative arts.*

Bonhams Bayswater

10 Salem Rd., W2 4DL. Tel: 020 7313 2700. *Weekly, Mon., sales of furniture, works of art and carpets. Regular monthly sales of jewellery, ceramics and Oriental works of art and glass, silver, pictures. Specialist sales of pianos, fishing, chess and bicycles. Viewing Fri. 9-5, Sat. 10-5, Sun. 11-5 and other viewing dependent upon sale day.*

Bonhams & Brooks, Knightsbridge

Montpelier St., Knightsbridge, SW7 1HH. Tel: 020 7393 3900; fax - 020 7393 3905. *Regular auctions of vintage motor cars, automobilia, sporting items, watercolours, Old Masters, European and modern pictures, portrait miniatures, prints, carved frames, furniture, clocks and watches, Lalique, commercial scent bottles, Oriental and contemporary ceramics, objects of art, tribal art and antiquities, silver, jewellery, objects of vertu, books and manuscripts, antique and modern guns, musical instruments, Oriental carpets and rugs. Annual theme sales to coincide with Cowes Week, The Boat Show and The Westminster Dog Show, NY - pictures, sculptures and related works of art. Viewing Mon.-Fri. 9-4.30, Sun. 11-3.*

Bonhams Chelsea

65-69 Lots Rd., Chelsea, SW10 0RN. Tel: 020 7393 3900; fax - 020 7393 3906. *Regular sales of*

British, European and Russian pictures including watercolours, oils, prints and frames; clocks; ceramics including Art Nouveau & Art Deco; furniture, carpets & objects of art; light fittings and garden statuary; collectors items such as toys, dolls & teddies, textiles, cameras & scientific instruments, rock & pop, rare records & entertainment sales. Viewing Mon.-Fri. 9-4.30, Sun. 11-4.

Christie's

8 King St., St.James's, SW1Y 6QT. Tel: 020 7839 9060; fax - 020 7839 1611. *Porcelain, pottery, objets d'art and miniatures, pictures including Old Masters, English, Victorian, Continental, Impressionist, contemporary, prints, drawings, watercolours, Art Deco, Art Nouveau; Japanese and Chinese, Islamic and Persian works of art; glass, silver, jewellery, books, modern guns, furniture, carpets, tapestries, clocks and watches, garden statuary, photographs, Russian works of art, sculpture, wine, house sales (contents only).*

Christie's South Kensington Ltd

85 Old Brompton Rd., SW7 3LD. Tel: 020 7581 7611; fax - 020 7321 3311. *Sales of jewellery, silver, pictures, watercolours, drawings and prints; furniture and carpets, ceramics and works of art, printed books; costume, textiles and embroidery; toys and games, dolls, wines, Art Nouveau, Art Deco, cameras. Periodic sales of automata, mechanical music and vintage machines, motoring and aeronautical items including car mascots; Staffordshire portrait figures, miniatures.*

Criterion Auctioneers

53 Essex Rd., Islington. N1 2BN. Tel: 020 7359 5707; fax - 020 7354 9843; e-mail - info@ criterion-auctioneers.co.uk; website - www. criterion-auctioneers.co.uk. *Sales every Mon. at 5 pm of general antiques, reproduction and contemporary furniture, glass, china, rugs and smalls. Viewing Fri. 4-8, Sat. and Sun. 10-6, Mon. prior to sale.*

Stanley Gibbons Auctions

399 Strand, WC2R 0LX. Tel: 020 7836 8444; fax - 020 7836 7342; e-mail - auctions@stanley gibbons.co.uk; website - www.stanleygibbons. com. Est. 1901. *Regular auctions throughout the year.*

Glendining's and Co
101 New Bond St., W1S 1SR. Tel: 020 7493 2445. *Specialist auctioneers of coins and medals. Quarterly sales of coins; three sales annually of orders, decorations and medals.*

Harmers of London Stamp Auctioneers Ltd.
111 Power Rd., Chiswick, W4 5PY. Tel: 020 8747 6100; fax - 020 8996 0649. *Auctions of Great Britain, British Commonwealth, foreign countries, airmail stamps, also postal history and literature, stamp boxes, postal scales and related ephemera, monthly. Fully illustrated catalogues. Valuations for sale, probate or insurance.*

Hornsey Auctions Ltd
54-56 High St., Hornsey. N8 7NX. Tel: 020 8340 5334; fax - same. *Sales weekly on Wed. at 6.30. Viewing Tues. 5-7.30 and Wed. from 10. Open Thurs., Fri. 9.30-5.30 and Sat. 10-4 to take in for next auction.*

Lloyds International Auction Galleries Ltd
9 Lydden Rd., Wandsworth. SW18. Tel: 020 8788 7777; fax - 020 8874 5390; website - www. lloyds-auction.co.uk. *Fortnightly Saturday sales of antique and modern furniture, china, glassware, pictures and collectables. Website catalogue.*

Lots Road Galleries
71-73 Lots Rd., Chelsea, SW10 0RN. Tel: 020 7376 6800; fax - 020 7376 6899; website - www.lotsroad.com. *Auctions every Monday at 1 pm (modern and reproduction) and 6 pm (antique), approx. 600 lots of antique, traditional and decorative furniture, Oriental carpets, paintings, prints, ceramics, clocks, glass, silver, objets d'art and soft furnishings. On view Thurs. 5-7, Fri. 9-7, Sat. 10-4 and Sun. 11-5, all day Mon. Goods accepted Mon.-Fri. Payment by direct credit 9 days after the sale. Catalogue details and auction results by fax, phone or live auction line. Valuers, consultants and carriers. VAT registered.*

Onslows
The Depot, 2 Michael Rd. SW6 2AD. Tel: Mobile - 07831 473400; e-mail - bogue.onslows@ btinternet.com. *Sales 3-4 times a year including posters, railwayana, aero and motor, printed ephemera, Titanic and maritime, Louis Vuitton luggage. Viewing as published prior to sale.*

Rippon Boswell and Co.
The Arcade, South Kensington Station. SW7 2NA. Tel: 020 7589 4242. *International specialist auctioneers of old and antique Oriental carpets.*

Periodical auctions in London. Also in Germany, Switzerland, USA and Far East.

Rosebery Fine Art Ltd.
74-76 Knights Hill, West Norwood. SE27 0JD. Tel: 020 8761 2522; fax - 020 8761 2524. *Quarterly selected and monthly antique and collectors auctions on a Tues. and Wed. Fortnightly, Mon., general auctions. Specialist auctions of toys and collectors items, decorative arts, modern design, musical instruments, books and textiles held periodically.*

Sotheby's
34-35 New Bond St., W1A 2AA. Tel: 020 7293 5000. *Open for free valuations Mon.-Fri. 9-5. Daily sales of paintings, drawings, watercolours, prints, books and manuscripts, European sculpture and works of art, antiquities, silver, ceramics, glass, jewellery, Oriental works of art, furniture, musical instruments, clocks and watches, vintage cars, wine, postage stamps, coins, medals, toys and dolls and other collectors' items.*

Southgate Auction Rooms
55 High St., Southgate, N14 6LD. Tel: 020 8886 7888; website - www.southgateauctionrooms. com. *Weekly Mon. sales at 5 pm of jewellery, silver, china, porcelain, paintings, furniture. Viewing Sat. 9-12 noon and from 9 on day of sale.*

BEDFORDSHIRE

W. & H. Peacock
The Auction Centre, 26 Newnham St., Bedford, MK40 3JR. Tel: 01234 266366; website - www. peacockauctions.co.uk. Est. 1901. *Antiques sales first Fri. monthly. Viewing Fri. prior 9am-8pm. General sales every Sat. at 9.30.*

Douglas Ross (Auctioneers)
The Old Town Hall, Woburn. MK17 9PZ. Tel: 01525 290502. *Sales every four weeks on Thurs.*

BERKSHIRE

Dreweatt Neate
Donnington Priory, Donnington, Nr. Newbury, RG14 2JE. Tel: 01635 553553; fax - 01635 553599; e-mail - fineart@dreweatt-neate.co.uk; website - www.auctions.dreweatt-neate.co.uk. Est. 1759. *Sales on the premises mainly on a weekly basis. General furnishings - fortnightly on Tues. Antique furniture - six annually. Paintings, books, prints, silver and jewellery, ceramics - three of each annually. Buyers' premium 17.625% including VAT.*

Martin and Pole Nicholas
The Auction House, Milton Rd., Wokingham. RG40 1DB. Tel: 01189 790460; fax - 01189 776166. *Sale of antiques and collectables held usually on 3rd Wed. every month at above address.*

Thimbleby & Shorland
31 Great Knollys St., Reading. RG1 7HU. Tel: 01189 508611; fax - 01189 505896. Est. 1901. *Collective sales of antique and modern furniture held monthly at Reading Auction Market. Also sales and valuations of horse-drawn carriages and driving equipment with four sales annually in Reading.*

BUCKINGHAMSHIRE

Amersham Auction Rooms
125 Station Rd., Amersham. HP7 0AH. Tel: 01494 729292. *Weekly general and monthly selected antique sales held on Thurs. at 10.30.*

CAMBRIDGESHIRE

Bonhams
The Golden Rose, 17 Emmanuel Rd., Cambridge. CB1 1JW. Tel: 01223 366523. *Regular sales of good furniture, pictures, silver, ceramics and Victoriana. Enquiries to Clodagh Sapsford.*

Cheffins
The Cambridge Saleroom, 2 Clifton Rd., Cambridge. CB1 4BW. Tel: 01223 213343 (10 lines); website - www.cheffins.co.uk. *Regular fine art and general auction sales including pictures, furniture, works of art, silver and jewellery, ceramics and collectors' items.*

Grounds and Co.
2 Nene Quay, Wisbech. PE13 1AQ. Tel: 01945 585041/2. *Three specialist sales annually, each approximately 600 lots.*

Hyperion Auctions Ltd
Station Rd., St. Ives. PE27 5BH Tel: 01480 464140; fax - 01480 497552; e-mail - enquiries@ hyperionauctions.co.uk; website - www.hyperion auctions.co.uk. Est. 1995. *Regular sales of antiques and collectables.*

W. & H. Peacock
The Auction Centre, 75 New St., St Neots. PE19 1AJ. Tel: 01480 474550. *General sale every Thurs. at 11.*

Rowley Fine Art Auctioneers & Valuers
8 Downham Rd., Ely. CB6 1AH. Tel: 01353 699177; fax - 01353 699088; website - www.rowleyfineart.com. *Monthly general sales held on the 2nd Saturday. Regular sales of fine art and antiques at Tattersalls Sale Ring, Newmarket. Valuations.*

Willingham Auctions
25 High St., Willingham, CB4 5ES. Tel: 01954 261252/201396; website - www.willingham auctions.com. *Sales of antique and fine furniture, silver, ceramics, and clocks.*

CHESHIRE

Andrew, Hilditch and Son Ltd.
Hanover House, 1A The Square, Sandbach. CW11 0AP. Tel: 01270 767246/762048. *Quarterly sales of fine pictures and period furnishings. General and Edwardian furniture sales held weekly.*

Bonhams
New House, 150 Christleton Rd., Chester. CH3 5TD. Tel: 01244 313936; fax - 01244 340028. *22 salerooms countrywide including Chester.*

Cheyne's
38 Hale Rd., Altrincham. WA14 2EX. Tel: 0161 941 4879. *Bi-monthly sales held at St Peter's Assembly Rooms, Cecil Road, Hale. Viewing day prior 2-4.30 and 6-8 and sale morning 9-10.30.*

Halls Fine Art
Booth Mansion, 30 Watergate St., Chester. CH1 2LA. Tel: 01244 312300; fax - 01244 312112. *Quarterly antique sales (Fri.) and fortnightly Victoriana and collectors sales (Wed.).*

Frank R. Marshall and Co.
Marshall House, Church Hill, Knutsford. WA16 6DH. Tel: 01565 653284; fax - 01565 652341; e-mail - antiques@frankmarshall.co.uk. Est. 1948. *Regular sales of antique furniture, objets d'art, silver, pewter, glass, porcelain, pictures, brass and copper. Fortnightly household collective sales including bric-a-brac. Specialised sales at The Knutsford Auction Salerooms.*

Peter Wilson Fine Art Auctioneers
Victoria Gallery, Market St., Nantwich. CW5 5DG. Tel: 01270 623878; fax - 01270 610508; e-mail - auctions@peterwilson.co.uk; website - www.peterwilson co.uk. *Five catalogued (illustrated in colour) two-day sales each year. Uncatalogued auctions every Thursday - shipping goods and household effects (500+ lots).*

Wright Manley Auctioneers
Beeston Castle Salerooms, Tarporley. CW6 9NZ
Tel: 01829 262150; fax - 01829 262110.
Fortnightly Victoriana and household sales and quarterly catalogued fine art and furniture sales.

CORNWALL

Bonhams Cornwall
Cornubia Hall, Par. PL24 2AQ. Tel: 01726
814047. *Monthly sales of antiques, Victorian and later furnishings, silver, jewellery, pictures and collectors' items.*

Jefferys
The Auction Rooms, 5 Fore St., Lostwithiel.
PL22 0BP. Tel: 01208 872245; fax - 01208
873260; e-mail - jefferys.lostwithiel@btinternet.
com. *Fortnightly sales of antique furniture, ceramics, glass, jewellery, silver and plate, pictures, prints and collectors items, on Wed. at 10 am.*

Lambrays
Polmorla Walk Galleries, The Platt, Wadebridge.
PL27 7AE. Tel: 0120 881 3593. *Fortnightly sales of antiques and pine. Quarterly auctions of antiques and objets d'art. Illustrated catalogues.*

W. H. Lane & Son
Jubilee House, Queen St., Penzance. TR18 4DF.
Tel: 01736 361447; fax - 01736 350097; e-mail -
graham.bazley@btopenworld.com. *Six picture sales annually (specialists in the Newlyn and St. Ives Schools). Valuations for insurance, probate and family division.*

David Lay FRICS
The Penzance Auction House, Alverton,
Penzance. TR18 4RE. Tel: 01736 361414; fax -
01736 360035; e-mail - dlay@pzsw.fsnet.co.uk.
Regular sales of fine art, antiques, collectors' items, books and studio pottery. Three-weekly general household sales.

Martyn Rowe Auctioneers and Valuers
Triplets Business Park, Poldice Valley, Nr.
Chasewater, Truro. TR16 5PZ. Tel: 01209
822266; fax - 01209 821782. *Weekly on Thurs. at 10 am - Victorian, Edwardian and general sales. Viewing morning of sale and previous Wed 2-6 pm. Antique and picture sales - every 6-8 weeks. Collectors and sporting sales - every 6-8 weeks. Quarterly sales of vintage and classic motorcycles, cars and automobilia. House, commercial, industrial and receivership sales on site or at auction centre.*

CUMBRIA

Cumbria Auction Rooms
12 Lowther St., Carlisle. CA3 8DA. Tel: 01228
525259. *Twice weekly sales of Victorian and later furnishings and household effects. Quarterly catalogue sales of antiques and works of art.*

Mitchell's Auction Co.
The Furniture Hall, 47 Station Rd., Cockermouth.
CA13 9PZ. Tel: 01900 827800; fax - 01900
828073; e-mail - mfineart@aol.com. *Weekly (Thurs.) sales of antique, reproduction and modern furniture and effects, approximately 800 lots, starting at 9.30 am. Viewing Wed. 2-7 and throughout sale. Six fine art sales per annum, viewing prior Tues. 11-5 and Wed. 10-7 and prior to sale.*

Penrith Farmers' and Kidds plc
Skirsgill Saleroom, Skirsgill, Penrith. CA11
0DN. Tel: 01768 890781; fax - 01768 895058; e-mail - penrith.farmers@virgin.net. *Weekly sales of household furniture and effects on three Wed. each month, commencing 9.30am., view Tues. prior 3-6. Monthly sales of antiques and Victoriana on Wed., usually each month, except when quarterly sales of antiques and collectors' items are held at end of Mar., June, Sept. and Dec. - 10.30am. start. Viewing 2 days prior - Mon. 10-5, Tues. 10-7.*

James Thompson
64 Main St., Kirkby Lonsdale. LA6 2AJ. Tel:
015242 71555; fax - 015242 72939; e-mail-
sales@jthompson-auctioneers.co.uk; website -
www.jthompson-auctioneers.co.uk. Est. 1945.
Monthly two day sales of silver, ceramics, general antiques. Picture sales six times a year.

Thomson, Roddick and Medcalf
Coleridge House, Shaddongate, Carlisle. CA2
5TU. Tel: 01228 528939; fax - 01228 592128.
Est. 1880. *Monthly catalogue sales of antiques and collectors' items and regular specialist sales particularly antiquarian books, silver and pictures at Carlisle and Wigton. Monthly general furniture sales at Wigton.*

DERBYSHIRE

Armstrong Auctions
Midland Rd., Swadlincote, DE11 0AH. Tel:
01283 217772. *Weekly general sales and periodic antique sales held in Swadlincote Auction Rooms.*

Noel Wheatcroft & Son

Matlock Auction Gallery, The Old Picture Palace, Dale Rd., Matlock. DE4 3LU. Tel: 01629 57460; fax - 01629 57956; website - www.wheatcroft-noel.co.uk. Est. 1923. *Monthly sales of antiques and general items.*

DEVON

Bearne's

St Edmund's Court, Okehampton St., Exeter. EX4 1DU. Tel: 01392 207000. *Regular sales of antique furniture, works of art, silver, jewellery, collectors' items, books, clocks and watches, paintings, ceramics and glass, carpets and rugs.*

Bonhams

38/39 Southernhay East, Exeter, EX1 1PE. Tel: 01392 455955; fax - 01392 455962. *Seasonal sales of antiques and fine art held at Powderham Castle, near Exeter, to include silver, plated articles, European ceramics and glass, objects and works of art, clocks, antique furniture and West Country pictures.*

Bonhams & Brooks

Dowell St., Honiton. EX14 1LX. Tel: 01404 41872; fax - 01404 43137. *Regular monthly auctions of furniture, works of art, ceramics, silver and jewellery, collectors' items, wine, sporting and fishing memorabilia.*

S.J. Hales Antique & Fine Art Auctioneers & Valuers

87 Fore St., Bovey Tracey. TQ13 9AB. Tel: 01626 836684; fax - same; e-mail - info@sjhales.com; website - www.sjhales.com *Sales held at The Edgemoor Hotel, Haytor, Bovey Tracey monthly on Wed. at 10 am. Viewing Mon. 9-5, Tues. 9-7, Wed. 8-10 prior. Valuations.*

Kingsbridge Auction Sales

113 Fore St., Kingsbridge. TQ7 1BG. Tel: 01364 631439. *Regular sales of antique and general household furniture and effects.*

Lyme-Bay Auction Galleries

28 Harbour Rd., Seaton. EX12 2NA. Tel: 01297 22453. *General household and antique auctions held every four to six weeks.*

Potbury and Sons

The Auction Rooms, Temple St., Sidmouth, EX10 8LN. Tel: 01395 515555/517300; fax - 01395 512608. *Fortnightly sales; fine arts every two months.*

Rendells

Stone Park, Ashburton, TQ13 7RH. Tel: 01364 653017: fax - 01364 654251. *Sales every four weeks (Thurs. and Fri.) of antique and repro-duction furniture, ceramics, silver, jewellery, pictures, clocks and barometers, copper and brass, miscellanea, toys and collectables. No buyers premium.*

Taylor's

Honiton Galleries, 205 High St., Honiton, EX14 1LQ. Tel: 01404 42404. *Sales of paintings and prints, antiques, silver, books and porcelain.*

Ward and Chowen

Tavistock Auction Rooms, Market Rd., Tavistock, PL19 0BW. Tel: 01822 612603; fax - 01822 617311.

Whitton and Laing

32 Okehampton St., Exeter, EX4 1DY. Tel: 01392 252621; fax - 01392 496607. *Monthly auctions of antiques, silver and jewellery. Book and stamp auctions two or three times a year. Picture sales bi-monthly. General auctions weekly.*

DORSET

Bonhams Auctioneers

3 Cheap St., Sherborne. DT9 3PT. Tel: 01935 815271.

Cottees

The Market, East St., Wareham, BH20 4NR. Tel: 01929 552826; fax - 01929 554916; e-mail - auctions@cottees.fsnet.co.uk; website - www.auctionsatcottees.co.uk. Est. 1903. *Sales of furniture, silver and jewellery, pottery and porcelain etc. every two weeks, on Tues. Viewing previous day 2-5 and 6-8.*

Hy. Duke and Son

Fine Art Salerooms, Weymouth Avenue, Dorchester, DT1 1QS. Tel: 01305 265080; fax - 01305 260101; e-mail - enquiries@dukes-auctions.com. Est. 1823. *Regular six weekly sales including specialist sections of silver and jewellery, Oriental and English porcelain, English and Continental furniture, pictures, books and Oriental rugs. Complete valuation and advisory service, including insurance, probate and forward tax planning.*

Hy. Duke and Son

The Weymouth Salerooms, Nicholas St., Weymouth. Tel: 01305 761499; fax - 01305 260101. *Regular bi-weekly sales of Victoriana and later furniture and effects.*

House and Son

Lansdowne House, Christchurch Rd., Bournemouth, BH1 3JW. Tel: 01202 298044. *Fortnightly sales of selected furniture, pictures, books, silver, porcelain and glass. Catalogues £2.50 including postage.*

Wm. Morey and Sons

Salerooms, St. Michaels Lane, Bridport, DT6 3RB. Tel: 01308 422078; website - www. wmoreyandsons.co.uk. *Antique and general sales held every three to four weeks on Thurs.*

Riddetts of Bournemouth

177 Holdenhurst Rd., Bournemouth. BH8 8DQ. Tel: 01202 555686; fax - 01202 311004; e-mail - auctions@riddetts.co.uk; website - www.auction hammer.co.uk. Est. 1879. *Fortnightly sales of fine antiques, jewellery, silver, plate, pictures. Illustrated sale programme free. Catalogue subscription £45 p.a.*

DURHAM

Denis Edkins

Auckland Auction Rooms, 58 Kingsway, Bishop Auckland, DL14 7JF. Tel: 01388 603095. *General and antique sales from time to time.*

Barry Potter Auctions

Fleck Way, Thornaby, Stockton- on-Tees. TS17 9JZ. Tel: 01642 767116; fax - 01642 769478; e-mail - vicky@vectis.co.uk. *Sales of trains held six times a year at the Benn Hall, Rugby, viewing Fri. evening 5.30-7.30, and Sat. morning 8.30-10.30.*

Vectis Auctions Ltd

Fleck Way, Thornaby, Stockton-on-Tees. TS17 9JZ0. Tel:1642 750616; fax - 01642 769478; e-mail - vicky@vectis.co.uk. *Specialist sales held once a month on Wed. at the Community Centre, Buckingham, mainly diecast, dolls, teddies and lead. Two day sales held on Wed. and Thurs.*

Thomas Watson and Son

Northumberland St., Darlington, DL3 7HJ. Tel: 01325 462559. *Regular sales of antiques and good quality house contents.*

ESSEX

Ambrose

Ambrose House, Old Station Rd., Loughton. IG10 4LZ. Tel: 020 8502 3951; website - www. ambroseauction.co.uk. *Antique sales fortnightly/ monthly.*

Cooper Hirst Auctions

The Granary Salerooms, Victoria Rd., Chelmsford, CM2 6LH. Tel: 01245 260535. *Regular sales of antiques every 3 months and weekly Tues. sales of Victoriana, bric-a-brac etc.*

Reeman Dansie Howe & Son

Head Gate Auction Rooms, 12 Head Gate, Colchester, CO3 3BT. Tel: 01206 574271. *Sales held every Wed. Viewing Tues. 9-7 prior. Bi-monthly Fine Art sales.*

Simon H. Rowland

Chelmsford Auction Rooms, 42 Mildmay Rd., Chelmsford, CM2 0DZ. Tel: 01245 354251. *Regular sales by order of the Sheriff of Essex and private vendors.*

Saffron Walden Auctions

1 Market St., Saffron Walden, CB10 1JB. Tel: 01799 513281. *Sales of antique and fine furniture, antique effects and objets d'art held every six weeks.*

John Stacey & Sons (Leigh-on-Sea) Ltd

Leigh Auction Rooms, 86-90 Pall Mall, Leigh-on-Sea, SS9 1RG. Tel: 01702 477051. *Monthly sales of period and other furniture, works of art and collectors' items. Catalogue subscription £40.*

Stanfords

11 East Hill, Colchester, CO1 2QX. Tel: 01206 868070. *Weekly Tues. sales of antique and modern furniture, china, glass, silver and decorative items at 11.15 a.m. Occasional specialist sales of antique furniture and collectables, telephone for details.*

G.E. Sworder and Sons

14 Cambridge Rd., Stansted Mountfitchet. CM24 8BZ. Tel: 01279 817778; fax - 01279 817779; website - www.sworder.co.uk. Est. 1782. *Monthly auctions of antique furniture, ceramics, silver, pictures, clocks, decorative items. Twice yearly sporting sales. Viewing Fri. 10-5, Sat. and Sun. 10-1, Mon. 10-5, Tues. 9 am onwards prior to sale. Weekly Thurs. 11 am auction of Victorian, Edwardian and later furniture and collectables. Viewing morning of sale and Wed. 2-5. Fully illustrated catalogue available.*

Trembath Welch (incorporating J.M. Welch & Son)

Old Town Hall, Great Dunmow, CM6 1AU. Tel: 01371 873014; fax - 01371 878239. *At the Salerooms, Chequers Lane - selected antique furniture and effects sales quarterly. Sales of collectables, household furniture and antiques every two weeks. Catalogue subscription service available.*

BK The Property Assets Consultancy

Bisley House, Green Farm Business Park, Bristol Rd., Gloucester, GL2 4LY. Tel: 01452 880000; fax - 01452 880088; e-mail - artantiques@ bkonline.co.uk; website - www.bkonline.co.uk. *Free auction valuations; confidential valuation services. Auctions held regularly.*

Bristol Auction Rooms Ltd

St. John's Place, Apsley Rd., Clifton, Bristol, BS8 2ST. Tel: 0117 973 7201; fax - 0117 973 5671; website - www.bristolauctionrooms.co.uk. *Monthly auctions of antique furniture, clocks, rugs, textiles, paintings and prints, glass, pottery, porcelain, books and ephemera, silver, objects of vertu, toys and collectables. View Sat. prior 9.30-1; day prior from 9.30-7, and on day from 9 to sale at 10.30. Fortnightly auctions of Victorian and modern household furniture and effects. View day prior to sale from 12-6 and on day from 9 until sale at 10.30. Specialist auctions and house sales held throughout the year. Catalogue subscription service. Buyers' premium.*

Corinium Galleries

25 Gloucester St., Cirencester, GL7 2DJ. Tel: 01285 659057. Est. 1976. *Monday auctions of postcards and printed ephemera every six weeks.*

The Cotswold Auction Co.

Chapel Walk Saleroom, Chapel Walk, Cheltenham. GL50 3DS. Tel: 01242 256363; fax - 01242 571734; e-mail - info@cotswoldauction. co.uk. *Three sales monthly - specialist and general.*

Fraser Glennie and Partners

The Coach House, Upper Siddington, Cirencester, GL7 6HL. Tel: 01285 659677; fax - 01285 642256. *Monthly sales of antiques, other furniture, collectors' items and musical instruments at the Bingham Hall, Cirencester.*

Mallams Fine Art Auctioneers and Valuers

26 Grosvenor St., Cheltenham, GL52 2SG. Tel: 01242 235712; fax - 01242 241943. Est. 1788. *Regular sales of furniture, ceramics, paintings, textiles, rugs and works of art, sporting, toy and collectors items.*

Moore, Allen & Innocent

The Salerooms, Norcote, Cirencester, GL7 5RH. Tel: 01285 646050. Est. 1852. *Fortnightly sales of over 1,000 lots of antique and other furniture and effects. Quarterly sales of selected antiques. Bi-annual specialist picture and sporting sales. Fri. at 9.30. Viewing day prior 10.30-8. 10% buyers premium.*

The Cotswold Auction Company

City Chambers, 4/6 Clarence St., Gloucester. GL1 1DX. Tel: 01452 521177. *Sales of Georgian, Victorian, Edwardian and later furniture, ceramics, glass, metalwork, silver, plate, jewellery, miscellanea, collectors' items, books, pictures and outside effects every four to six weeks.*

Wotton Auction Rooms Ltd

(formerly Sandoe Luce Panes) Tabernacle Rd., Wotton-under-Edge, GL12 7EB. Tel: 01453 844733; fax - 01453 845448; website - www.wotton auctionrooms.co.uk. *Monthly 2-day sales of antiques and collectables, 1,500+ lots. Calendar cards on request. Valuations.*

Bonhams Auctioneers

54 Southampton Rd., Ringwood, BH24 1JD. Tel: 01425 473333.

Jacobs and Hunt Fine Art Auctioneers

Lavant St., Petersfield, GU32 3EF. Tel: 01730 233933; fax - 01730 262323; e-mail - auctions@ jacobsandhunt.co.uk; website - www. jacobsand hunt.co.uk. Est. 1895. *Monthly general antique sales held on Fri.*

George Kidner Auctioneers

The Old School, The Square, Pennington, Lymington. SO41 8GN. Tel: 01590 670070; fax - 01590 675167. Emsworth Rd. - 01590 679487. *Monthly specialist sales - furniture, works of art, silver and jewellery, collectors' items, oils, prints and watercolours, European ceramics, Oriental works of art, books and marine items, collectable toys, model railways and railwayana. Viewing - Mon. 9.30-4.30, Tues. 9.30-7. Also saleroom at Emsworth Rd., Lymington - Victorian, Edwardian and later furniture and effects. Viewing - day previous 9.30-7.*

May and Son

The Old Stables, 9A Winchester Rd., Andover, SP10 2EG. Tel: 01264 323417; fax - 01264 338841; e-mail - office@mayandson.com; website - www.mayandson.com. Est. 1940. *Monthly sales on 3rd Wed. of antique furniture and collectables at Penton Mewsey Village Hall (Lots from private sources only). Viewing previous day 8.30-6, and morning of sale from 8 am. Buyers premium 10% + tax.*

D.M. Nesbit and Co.

7 Clarendon Rd., Southsea, Portsmouth, PO5 2ED. Tel: 023 9286 4321; fax - 023 9229 5522. *Monthly sales of antique furniture, silver, porcelain and pictures.*

AUCTIONEERS

HEREFORDSHIRE

Brightwells
The Fine Art Saleroom, Ryelands Rd., Leominster, HR6 8NZ. Tel: 01568 611122; fax - 01568 610519. 1846. *Monthly 2-day sales of antiques and collectors' items (approx. 1,000 lots per sale). Two or three sales per month of antique and household effects.*

HERTFORDSHIRE

G E Sworder & Sons
Office - 42 St Andrews St., Hertford, SG14 1JA. Tel: 01992 583508; fax - same.

Tring Market Auctions
Brook St., Tring, HP23 5EF. Tel: 0144282 6446. *Fortnightly Sat. sales of antiques and collectables held at The Market Premises, Brook St., Tring. Fine art sales held on last Fri. of alternate months.*

ISLE OF WIGHT

Shanklin Auction Rooms
79 Regent St., Shanklin, PO37 7AP. Tel: 01983 863441. *Monthly auctions of antiques and fine arts.*

Ways
The Auction House, Garfield Rd., Ryde, PO33 2PT. Tel: 01983 562255; e-mail - ways@ways auctionrooms.fsbusiness.co.uk; website - www. waysauctionrooms.fsbusiness. co.uk. *Five-weekly sales of antique and modern furniture, silver, copper and brass, oils, watercolours and prints, jewellery, china, clocks. No buyers premium.*

KENT

Bonhams
49 London Rd., Sevenoaks, TN13 1AR. Tel: 01732 740310; fax - 01732 741842. *Monthly sales of antique furniture and objects of art.*

Bracketts
Fine Art Auctioneers, Auction Hall, Pantiles, Tunbridge Wells, TN2 5QL. Tel: 01892 544500; website - www.bfaa.co.uk. *Fortnightly Saturday sales of antique and later furniture and effects and specialist Tunbridge Ware sales.*

The Canterbury Auction Galleries
40 Station Rd. West, Canterbury, CT2 8AN. Tel: 01227 763337; fax - 01227 456770. *Bi-monthly auctions of fine art and antiques held on Tues. at 10.30, viewing Mon. prior 10-7. Auctions of Victorian and later furniture held on first Sat. monthly at 10, viewing Fri. prior 3-8. Valuations.*

Halifax Property Services
15 Cattle Market, Sandwich, CT13 9AW Tel: 01304 614369; fax - 01304 612023. *Antique and other furniture and effects on Wed., 16 sales per year. Held at The Drill Hall, The Quay, Sandwich.*

Hobbs Parker
Romney House, Ashford Market, Orbital Park, Ashford, TN24 0HB. Tel: 01233 502222; fax - 01233 502211. Est. 1850. *Monthly sales of antiques and household furniture.*

Hogben Fine Art Auctioneers & Valuers
Unit C Highfield Industrial Estate, Off Warren Rd., Folkestone. CT19 6DD. Tel: 01303 240808/ 246810; fax - 01303 246256. *Fine art saleroom - monthly sales.*

Ibbett, Mosely
125 High St., Sevenoaks, TN13 1UT. Tel: 01732 456731; fax - 01732 740910. Est. 1900. *Antiques and objets d'art.*

Lambert & Foster Auction Sale Room
102 High St., Tenterden, TN30 6HU. Tel: 01580 762083. *Four offices in Kent. Monthly general sales of antique and other furniture and effects.*

B.J. Norris
The Quest, West St., Harrietsham. ME17 1JD. Tel: 01622 859515; e-mail - norrisoz@globalnet. co.uk; website - www.antiquesbulletin.com/ bjnorris. *Regular sales at The Agricultural Hall, Maidstone at 10 am. Viewing from 8 am. on morning of sale.*

LANCASHIRE

Acorn Philatelic Auctions
PO Box 152, Salford, Manchester. M17 1BP. Tel: 0161 877 8818; e-mail - george@traffordbooks. fsnet.co.uk. Est. 1980. *Tues. sales, approximately every 5 weeks, held at Unit 6, Block C, Astra Business Centre, Guiness Rd., Trafford Park, Manchester. 10 per year all specialising in paper collectables - postage stamps and history, manuscripts, autographs, picture and cigarette cards, books, prints, drawings and watercolours. Sales commence at 2 pm., viewing Mon. previous 10.30-6.30, and sale morning 9-1.15.*

Capes Dunn & Co Fine Art Auctioneers & Valuers
The Auction Galleries, 38 Charles St., Manchester, M1 7DB. Tel: 0161 273 1911; fax - 0161 273 3474; e-mail - capesdunn@yahoo.

co.uk; website - www.ukauctioneers.com. Est. 1826. *Catalogues of weekly specialist sales available on request. Regional office in Lytham.*

Kingsway Auction Rooms Ltd
The Galleries, Kingsway, Ansdell, Lytham St. Annes, FY8 1AB. Tel: 01253 735442. *Sales of antique, reproduction and modern furnishings and appointments held fortnightly or every three weeks on Tues. Approximately 400-600 lots commencing 9.30. Viewing Fri. 2-4, Sat. 10-12, Mon. 9-4. Buyers' premium 15%.*

Warren & Wignall Ltd
The Mill, Earnshaw Bridge, Leyland. PR5 3PH. Tel: 01772 451430; fax - 01772 454516. *Sales of general antiques every three weeks. All sales Wed. at 10, viewing Tues. 9-7.*

LEICESTERSHIRE

Freckeltons
1 Leicester Rd., Loughborough, LE11 2AE. Tel: 01509 214564; fax - 01509 236114. Est. 1919. *Monthly sales of general antiques.*

Gilding's Auctioneers and Valuers
Roman Way, Market Harborough, LE16 7PQ. Tel: 01858 410414; fax - 01858 432956; e-mail - sales@gildings.co.uk; website - www.gildings. co.uk. *Regular antique and Victoriana sales and free, over-the-counter valuations.*

Heathcote Ball & Co
Castle Auction Rooms, 78 St. Nicholas Circle, Leicester, LE1 5NW. Tel: 0116 2536789; fax - 0116 2538517; e-mail - heathcote-ball@clara. co.uk. *Auctions every four to six weeks.*

LINCOLNSHIRE

DDM Auction Rooms Ltd
Old Courts Rd., Brigg. DN20 8JJ. Tel: 01652 650172; fax - 01652 650085. *Fine art and antique auctions every six weeks: Victorian and household auctions fortnightly on a Saturday. Valuations for insurance, probate and sale. Free valuation "clinic" every Thursday 9.30-12.*

Eleys Auctioneers
26 Wide Bargate, Boston, PE21 6RX. Tel: 01205 361687; fax - 01205 351091; e-mail - sales@j-eley.co.uk; website - www.eleysestateagents. co.uk. Est. 1882. *Regular antique and collectors sales.*

Thomas Mawer & Son Ltd
Dunston House, Portland St., Lincoln, LN5 7NN. Tel: 01522 524984; fax - 01522 535600; e-mail - auctions@thos-mawer.co.uk; website - www. thos-mawer.co.uk. *Sales on first Sat. every month at 10 am. Viewing Fri. prior 12-4 and sale morning from 8.30. Catalogue sales quarterly.*

Richardsons
Bourne Auction Rooms, Spalding Rd., Bourne, PE10 9LE. Tel: 01778 422686; fax - 01778 425726; e-mail - bourne-auctions@lineone.net. *Antiques sales every month. Antique and modern sales every other Sat. Various specific sales periodically, eg silver, clocks, bygones, transport.*

Marilyn Swain
The Old Barracks, Sandon Rd., Grantham, NG31 9AS. Tel: 01476 568861; fax - 01476 576100. *Bi-monthly antique, fine art and collectable sales. Fortnightly sales of Victorian and later furniture, general effects and collectables. Valuations.*

MERSEYSIDE

Cato Crane & Co
6 Stanhope St., Liverpool. L8 5RF. Tel: 0151 709 5559; fax - 0151 707 2454; e-mail - johncrane @cato-crane.co.uk. *Collectors, antiques, fine art and maritime sales fortnightly on Thurs. Viewing Wed. prior 10-3.*

Kingsley and Co. Auctioneers
3/4 The Quadrant, Hoylake. L47 2EE. Tel: 0151 632 5821; fax - 0151 632 5823. *Sales every Tues. at 10, of antiques, fine arts, general chattels. Viewing Sat. 9-12.30, Mon. 9-5 and Tues. 9-10.*

Outhwaite and Litherland
Kingsway Galleries, Fontenoy St., Liverpool, L3 2BE. Tel: 0151 236 6561; fax - 0151 236 1070; e-mail - auction@lots.uk.com; website - www.lots. uk.com. *Victorian, Edwardian and later furnishings - weekly Tues. Collectors cavalcade sale of general antiques and collectibles - monthly Tues. Fine art and antiques - quarterly Wed. Clocks, watches, scientific instruments - bi-annually Wed. Specialist sales of books, wines, stamps etc. periodically. Members of SOFAA. Branch offices at Southport and Hoylake, Wirral.*

MIDDLESEX

Bainbridge's
The Auction Room, Ickenham Rd., Ruislip. HA4 7DL. Tel: 01895 621991; fax - 01895 623622. *Monthly sales Thurs. at 11, viewing on sale day from 9.30 and day before 1-7.*

NORFOLK

James Beck Auctions
The Cornhall, Cattle Market St., Fakenham, NR21 9AW. Tel: 01328 851557. *Weekly sales of antique furniture and collectables every Thurs. at 11.*

Clowes Nash Auctions
Norwich Livestock & Commercial Centre, Hall Rd., Norwich, NR4 6EQ. Tel: 01603 504488. *Antiques and general furniture weekly sales.*

Ewings
Market Place, Reepham, Norwich, NR10 4JJ. Tel: 01603 870473. *Periodic sales of antiques and modern furniture and effects.*

Thos. Wm. Gaze and Son
Diss Auction Rooms, Roydon Rd., Diss, IP22 4LN. Tel: 01379 650306; fax - 01379 644313; website - www.twgaze.com. Est. 1857. *Weekly catalogue sales of antiques and cottage furniture on Fri. at 11am. Periodic specialist sales including fine antiques, rural bygones, architectural salvage and statuary, decorative arts, automobilia, toys and nostalgia, etc. Online catalogues.*

Horners Auctioneers
North Walsham Salerooms, Midland Rd., North Walsham. NR28 9JR. Tel: 01493 750225; fax - 01493 750506; e-mail - auction@horners.co.uk; website - www.horners.co.uk. *Special bi-monthly (Sat.) auctions of antiques and collectables held at Acle, viewing Fri. prior 10-8. Weekly general sales (Thurs. - Acle; Fri. - North Walsham). Details and catalogue on website.*

G.A. Key - Aylsham Salerooms
Auctioneers & Valuers, 8 Market Place, Aylsham, NR11 6EH. Tel: 01263 733195; fax - 01263 732140; e-mail - mail@aylshamsalerooms.co.uk; website - www.aylshamsalerooms.co.uk. Est. 1953. *Three weekly sales of period, antique and Victorian furniture, silver, porcelain etc. Bi-monthly picture sales - oils, watercolours and prints etc. Six book sales annually and regular collectors' sales. Weekly sales of modern and secondhand furniture.*

NORTHAMPTONSHIRE

Goldsmith Howard
15 Market Place, Oundle, PE8 4BA. Tel: 01832 272349. *Sales approximately bi-monthly.*

Southams
Corn Exchange, Thrapston, NN14 4JJ. Tel: 01832 734486. Est. 1900. *First Thurs. each month, viewing Wed. 9.30-8 sales of antiques and superior furniture, silver, plate, copper and brass, fine china, glass, Oriental rugs, oil paintings, watercolours and prints. 10% buyer's premium. Catalogues £2 including postage. Annual subscription £18.*

Wilfords Ltd.
76 Midland Rd., Wellingborough, NN8 1NB. Tel: 01933 222760/222762. *Weekly antique and general sales, Thurs. from 9.30 (1400 lots).*

NORTHUMBERLAND

Jack Dudgeon
76 Ravensdowne, Berwick-upon-Tweed. TD15 1DQ. Tel: 01289 332700; fax - 01289 332701; e-mail - jack@jackdudgeon.co.uk. *Antiques and fine arts, collectables every two months on Mon. Viewing Wed., Thurs., Fri. and Sat. prior.*

NOTTINGHAMSHIRE

Arthur Johnson and Sons (Auctioneers)
The Nottingham Auction Centre, Meadow Lane, Nottingham. NG2 3GY. Tel: 0115 986 9128; fax - 0115 986 2139. *Approximately 1,000 lots weekly on Sat. at 10 am of antique and shipping furniture, silver, gold, porcelain, metalware and collectables.*

Mellors & Kirk Fine Art Auctioneers
Gregory St., Nottingham. NG7 2NL. Tel: 0115 979 0000; e-mail - mellkirk@dircon.co.uk; website - www.mellors-kirk.com. *Sales every 6 weeks of antique furniture, clocks, pictures, ceramics, Oriental works of art, printed books and ephemera, collectors toys and dolls, coins and medals and other specialist sales. Weekly general sales of 500-800 lots Tues. 10.30, viewing Sat. 9-12 and Mon. 9-5.*

Neales
192-194 Mansfield Rd., Nottingham, NG1 3HU. Tel: 0115 962 4141; fax - 0115 985 6890; e-mail - fineart@neales.co.uk; website - www.neales. co.uk. *Bi-monthly specialist sales of paintings, drawings, prints and books; silver, jewellery, bijouterie and watches; European and Oriental ceramics and works of art, glass; furniture and decoration; clocks, barometers and mechanical music; metalwork, fabrics, needlework, carpets and rugs; collectors' toys and dolls; stamps, coins and medals, post and cigarette cards; autographs*

and collectors' items. Weekly collective sales (Mon.) of general antique and later furnishings, shipping goods and reproduction furnishings. Period and later ceramics, glass and decorative effects. Contents sales on the premises of town and country properties.

Richard Watkinson and Partners
17 Northgate, Newark, NG24 1EX. Tel: 01636 677154. *Monthly sales of antique and Victorian furniture, oil paintings, silver etc. Weekly sales of early 20th C and general household furniture.*

OXFORDSHIRE

Bonhams Auctioneers
39 Park End St., Oxford, OX1 1JD. Tel: 01865 723524; fax - 01865 791064; website - www. phillips-auctions.com. *Fortnightly sales of Victoriana and general effects. Specialist sales of fine furniture, rugs, works of art, silver, jewellery, ceramics, collectors' items and paintings throughout the year.*

Holloways
49 Parsons St., Banbury, OX16 5PF. Tel: 01295 817777; fax - 01295 817701; e-mail - enquiries@ hollowaysauctioneers.co.uk; website - www. hollowaysauctioneers.co.uk. *General or specialist sales on own premises every other week.*

Mallams
Fine Art Auctioneers, Bocardo House, 24A St. Michael's St., Oxford, OX1 2EB. Tel: 01865 241358; fax - 01865 725483; e-mail - oxford@ mallams.co.uk; website - www.mallams.co.uk/ fineart. Est. 1788. *Frequent sales of furniture, silver, paintings and works of art. House sales arranged on the premises.*

Mallams incorporating Messengers
Pevensey House, 27 Sheep St., Bicester, OX26 7JF. Tel: 01869 252901; fax - 01869 320283; e-mail - bicester@mallams.co.uk; website - www.mallams.co.uk/fineart. *Regular sales of antiques and later furniture, clocks, ceramics and glass, paintings, books and miscellany. Special annual garden sale.*

Simmons and Sons
32 Bell St., Henley-on-Thames. RG9 2BH. Tel: 01491 571111; fax - 01491 579833; website - www.simmonsandsons.com. *Eight antique and eight general sales per year held at The Saleroom Watcombe Manor, Ingham Lane, Watlington, Oxon. Sales start 10.30, viewing Sat. previous 9.30-12.30, Mon. prior 2-7, Tues. prior 10-6 and morning of sale.*

SHROPSHIRE

Hall and Lloyd, Auctioneers
Cosford Auction Rooms, Long Lane, Cosford. TF11 8PJ. Tel: 01902 375555; fax - 01902 375566. Est. 1882. *Monthly sales of Victoriana, shipping and modern furniture and effects. Fine art and antique sales every six weeks.*

Halls Fine Art
Welsh Bridge Salerooms, Shrewsbury, SY3 8LA. Tel: 01743 231212; fax - 01743 271014. *Weekly household and Victoriana sales (Fri.). Monthly catalogued antique sales.*

Perry and Phillips
Auction Rooms, Old Mill Antique Centre, Mill St., Bridgnorth, WV15 5AG. Tel: 01746 762248. *Monthly (Tues.) antiques and collectables.*

Walker Barnett and Hill
Cosford Auction Rooms, Long Lane, Cosford. TF11 8PJ. Tel: 01902 375555; fax - 01902 375556. *Monthly sales of Victoriana, reproduction, shipping, modern furniture and effects on Tues. 10.30. Fine art and antiques sales every 6-8 weeks.*

SOMERSET

Adam Auctions
28 Adam St., Bath. TA8 1PQ. Tel: 01278 783193/793709. *Monthly, usually Wed., sales of general antiques. Telephone for details.*

Aldridges of Bath
Newark House, 26-45 Cheltenham St., Bath, BA2 3EX. Tel: 01225 462830; fax - 01225 311319. *Fortnightly (Tues.) sales, broken down into specialist categories:- Antique furniture to include clocks and Oriental carpets; silver and porcelain, glass and metalware; paintings and prints; collector's sales; Victorian and general furniture. Viewing Sat. 9-12 and Mon. 9-6. Catalogues available upon annual subscription.*

Bonhams
1 Old King St., Bath, BA1 2JT. Tel: 01225 788988; fax - 01225 446675. *Regular sales of antique furniture and Victoriana as well as silver, pictures, books and fine wine, ceramics, glass and 20th C art and design.*

Clevedon Salerooms
Herbert Rd., Clevedon, BS21 7ND. Tel: 01275 876699; fax - 01275 343765; e-mail - clevedon. salerooms@cableinet.co.uk; website - www.

clevedon-salerooms.com. *Quarterly auctions of antique furniture, fine art and collectors' items. Fortnightly sales of Victorian, Edwardian and general furniture and effects. Occasional specialist sales and sales held on vendors' property. Valuations.*

Cooper & Tanner Chartered Surveyors
The Agricultural Centre, Standerwick, Frome, BA11 2QB. Tel: 01373 831010. Est. 1890. *Weekly sales of antiques and general household chattels Wed. 10.30 am. Viewing morning of sale. Haulage service.*

Gardiner Houlgate
9 Leafield Way, Corsham, Bath, SN13 9SW. Tel: 01225 812912; fax - 01225 811777; e-mail - auctions@gardiner-houlgate.co.uk. *Regular sales of antique furniture and works of art. Frequent sales of Victorian and later furnishings. Fortnightly jewellery sales, quarterly musical instrument sales, specialist clocks and watches sales. Valuations.*

Greenslade Taylor Hunt Fine Art
Magdalene House, Church Square, Taunton, TA1 1SB. Tel: 01823 332525; fax - 01823 353120. *Monthly, last Thurs., sales of antique furniture, ceramics, glass, metalwork, paintings and prints. Specialist sales of silver and jewellery; collectors items, printed books, clocks and watches, sporting. Fortnightly, Wed. sales of antique and shipping furniture, china, glass and effects.*

Lawrence Fine Art Auctioneers Ltd.
South St., Crewkerne, TA18 8AB. Tel: 01460 73041; fax - 01460 74627. *Specialist auctioneers and valuers. Regular sales of antiques and fine art. General sales every Wed.*

The London Cigarette Card Co. Ltd
Sutton Rd., Somerton, TA11 6QP. Tel: 01458 273452; fax - 01458 273515; e-mail - cards@londoncigcard.co.uk; website - www.london cigcard.co.uk. *Suppliers of thousands of different series of cigarette and trade cards and special albums. Publishers of catalogues, reference books and monthly magazine. Regular auctions in London and Somerset. S.A.E. for details. Showroom in West St. open Mon-Sat. or mail order.*

Tamlyn and Son
56 High St., Bridgwater, TA6 3BN. Tel: 01278 458241; fax - 01278 458242; saleroom - 01278 445251.

Wellington Salerooms
Mantle St., Wellington, TA21 8AR. Tel: 01823 664815. *Six-weekly sales of general antiques. Three-weekly sales of Victorian, Edwardian and shipping goods.*

STAFFORDSHIRE

Bagshaws Wintertons Fine Arts
The Estate Saleroom, 17 High St., Uttoxeter, ST14 7HP. Tel: 01889 562811; fax - 01889 563795. 1864. *Bi-monthly sales of Victorian and general household furniture and effects.*

John German
1 Lichfield St., Burton-on-Trent, DE14 3QZ. Tel: 01283 512244; fax - 01283 517896. *Occasional sales of major house contents; specialist fine art valuation department.*

Potteries Specialist Auctions
271 Waterloo Rd., Cobridge, Stoke-on-Trent. ST6 3HR. Tel: 01782 286622; fax - 01782 213777; e-mail - enquiries@potteriesauctions. com. *Specialist auctions every month, usually last Sat. at 11 am. Viewing Fri. prior 10-4.30.*

Louis Taylor Fine Art Auctioneers
Britannia House, 10 Town Rd., Hanley, Stoke-on-Trent. ST1 2QG. Tel: 01782 214111; fax - 01782 215283. Est. 1877. *Quarterly fine art sales including furniture, pictures, pottery, porcelain, silver and works of art. Specialist Royal Doulton and Beswick auctions. General Victoriana auctions held every two weeks.*

Wintertons
Lichfield Auction Centre, Fradley Park, Fradley, Lichfield, WS13 8NF. Tel: 01543 263256; fax - 01543 415348; e-mail - enquiries@wintertons. co.uk; website - www.wintertons.co.uk. Est. 1864. *Bi-monthly sales of antiques and fine art and sales of Victorian and general furniture every 2-3 weeks.*

SUFFOLK

Abbotts Auction Rooms
Campsea Ashe, Nr. Woodbridge, IP13 0PS. Tel: 01728 746323; fax - 01728 748173. *Extensive calendar of fine art and antique auctions held on Wed. Sales calendar and catalogues available. Weekly sales of Victoriana & household furniture held on Mon. Viewing Sat. 9-11 am.*

Boardman - Fine Art Auctioneers
Station Road Corner, Haverhill. CB9 0EY. Tel:

01440 730414. *Large sales held quarterly specialising in selected fine furniture (particularly oak), clocks and paintings.*

Bonhams Auctioneers
32 Boss Hall Rd., Ipswich, IP1 5DJ. Tel: 01473 740494. *Five two-day specialist sales annually at Bury St. Edmunds. Eight mixed sales in Ipswich.*

Diamond Mills and Co. Fine Art Auctioneers
117 Hamilton Rd., Felixstowe, IP11 7BL. Tel: 01394 282281 (3 lines). Ipswich office - 01473 218600. *Periodic fine art sales. Monthly general sales. Auctions at The Orwell Hall, Orwell Rd., Felixstowe.*

Durrant's
The Auction Rooms, Gresham Rd., Beccles. NR34 9QN. Tel: 01502 713490; e-mail - info@ durrantsauctionrooms.com. *Antique and general furniture auctions every Fri.*

Dyson & Son
The Auction Room, Church St., Clare. CO10 8PD. Tel: 01787 277993; e-mail - info@dyson-auctioneers.co.uk; website - www.dyson-auctioneers.co.uk. Est. 1978. *Sales of antiques and chattels every three weeks on Sat. at 11am., viewing Fri. 9am-9pm, Sat. from 9am.*

Lacy Scott and Knight Fine Art & Furniture
10 Risbygate St., Bury St. Edmunds, IP33 3AA. Tel: 01284 748600; fax - 01284 748620. *Quarterly sales of fine art including antique and decorative furniture, silver, pictures, ceramics etc. on behalf of executors and private vendors. Regular (every three weeks) sales of Victoriana and general household contents. Also quarterly sales of live steam models, scale models, diecast and tinplate toys.*

Neal Sons and Fletcher
26 Church St., Woodbridge, IP12 1DP. Tel: 01394 382263; fax - 01394 383030; e-mail - allatnsf @aol.com; website - www.nsf.co.uk. *Two special mixed antiques sales annually. Individual specialised sales and complete house contents sales as required. Household furniture sales on a Wed. of each month.*

Olivers
The Saleroom, Burkitts Lane, Sudbury, CO10 1HB. Tel: 01787 880305. *Fortnightly sales of Victorian and later furniture and household effects. Regular sales of antiques and works of art. Enquiries to James Fletcher FRICS.*

Clarke Gammon Fine Art Auctioneers
The Guildford Auction Rooms, Bedford Rd., Guildford, GU1 4SJ. Tel: 01483 880915; fax - 01483 880918.

Croydon Auction Rooms (Rosan and Co.) (incorporating E.Reeves Auctions)
145/151 London Rd., Croydon. CR0 2RG. Tel: 020 8688 1123. *Fortnightly, Sat., collective sales at 10, viewing Fri. prior.*

Ewbank Auctioneers
Burnt Common Auction Rooms, London Rd., Send, Woking. GU23 7LN. Tel: 01483 223101; fax - 01483 222171. *Monthly general and fine art sales on Thurs., viewing Wed. 10-8 and Tues. 2-5.*

Hamptons International
Baverstock House, 93 High St., Godalming, GU7 1AL. Tel: 01483 423567; fax - 01483 426392; e-mail - fineart@hamptons-int.com. *Regular (Wed. and Thurs.) fine art sales at 93 High Street, specialising in selected fine furniture, rugs, paintings and watercolours, porcelain, glass, jewellery, silver, objets d'art and books. Two sales each month of general and Victorian furniture, shipping goods and household effects, held on first and third Sat. House sales conducted on the premises when instructed. Valuations.*

Lawrences' - Auctioneers Limited
Norfolk House, 80 High St., Bletchingley, RH1 4PA. Tel: 01883 743323; fax - 01883 744578. *Six-weekly antique and reproduction furniture and effects.*

Parkins
18 Malden Rd., Cheam. SM3 8SD. Tel: 020 8644 6633/4. *Sales of general household furniture and effects 2nd and 4th Mon. at 10. Viewing Fri. 2-4 and Sat. 10-4. Special antique sale on 1st Mon. at 10. Small antiques and collectables one Fri. evening each month at 7 pm - please telephone for details.*

Richmond and Surrey Auctions
The Old Railway Parcels Depot, Kew Rd., Richmond. TW9 2NA. Tel: 020 8948 6677; fax - 020 8948 2021. Est. 1992. *Auctioneers, valuers and consultants. Sales every Thurs. 6pm.*

P.F. Windibank Fine Art Auctioneers & Valuers
The Dorking Halls, Reigate Rd., Dorking, RH4 1SG. Tel: 01306 884556/876280; fax - 01306

884669; e-mail - sjw@windibank.co.uk; website - www.windibank.co.uk. Est. 1945. *Antique auctions held every four to five weeks on Sat. at 10.30 am. Viewing Thurs. evening prior 5-9, Fri. prior 9-5 and morning of sale 8.15-10.15. Catalogues available 1 week before. 10% buyers premium.*

SUSSEX EAST

Burstow and Hewett

Abbey Auction Galleries and Granary Sale Rooms, Battle, TN33 0AT. Tel: 01424 772374. *Monthly sales of antique furniture, silver, jewellery, porcelain, brass, rugs etc. at the Abbey Auction Galleries. Also monthly evening sales of fine oil paintings, watercolours, prints, and engravings. At the Granary Sale Rooms - monthly sales of furniture, china, silver, brass, etc.*

Eastbourne Auction Rooms

Auction House, Finmere Rd., Eastbourne. BN22 8QL. Tel: 01323 431444; fax - 01323 417638; e-mail - enquiries@eastbourneauction.com. *Sales held weekly, usually Fri. and Sat. at 10 am.*

Gorringes inc. Julian Dawson

Terminus Rd., Bexhill-on-Sea. TN39 3LR. Tel: 01424 212994; fax - 01424 224035; website - www.gorringes.co.uk. *Fine art and antique sales held every six weeks.*

Gorringes inc. Julian Dawson

15 North St., Lewes. BN7 2PD. Tel: 01273 472503; fax - 01273 479559; website - www.gorringes.co.uk. *Fine art and antique sales held every six weeks.*

Gorringes inc. Julian Dawson

Garden St., Lewes. BN7 1XE. Tel: 01273 478221; fax - 01273 487369; website - www.gorringes.co.uk. *General sales held weekly on Mon. at 10.30.*

Edgar Horn's Fine Art Auctioneers

46/50 South St., Eastbourne, BN21 4XB. Tel: 01323 410419. *Fortnightly antique and later furniture and effects sales (Tues). Six specialist antique furniture, silver and jewellery, ceramics and glass, oil paintings and watercolours and works of art sales (Wed).*

Raymond P. Inman

The Auction Galleries, 35 and 40 Temple St., Brighton, BN1 3BH. Tel: 01273 774777; fax - 01273 735660. *Monthly sales of antiques, furniture, china, brass, pictures, silver, jewellery, collectables, etc.*

Scarborough Perry Fine Arts

Hove St., Hove. BN3 2GL. Tel: 01273 735266; fax - 01273 723813. Est. 1896. *Monthly sales of fine art including antique furniture, pictures, silver, Oriental carpets and rugs and ornamental items. Specialised sales of primitive art, coins, books and jewellery.*

Wallis and Wallis

West Street Auction Galleries, Lewes. BN7 2NJ. Tel: 01273 480208. Est. 1928. *Nine annual sales of arms and armour, militaria, coins and medals. Specimen catalogue £4.50. Current catalogues £7. Die-cast and tin plate toys and models - catalogue £5.50. Commission bids (without charge) accepted. Valuations.*

SUSSEX WEST

Henry Adams Fine Art Auctioneers

Baffins Hall, Baffins Lane, Chichester. PO19 1UA. Tel: 01243 532223; fax - 01243 532299; e-mail - enquiries@henryadamsfineart.co.uk; website - www.henryadamsfineart.co.uk. *Monthly catalogue specialist sales, usually on Wed. Viewing Sat. morning, Mon. and Tues. prior. Valuations for sales, insurance and probate.*

John Bellman Ltd

New Pound, Wisborough Green, Billingshurst. RH14 0AZ. Tel: 01403 700858; fax - 01403 700059. *Two day sale once a month - Thurs. am - ceramics and Oriental, Thurs. pm - silver, jewellery, clocks; Fri. am - collectors' items, works of art, paintings, Fri. pm - furniture. Viewing Sat. 9-12, Mon. 9-4, Tues. 9-7, Wed. 9-1. Book sales quarterly.*

Denham's

The Auction Galleries, Warnham, Nr. Horsham, RH12 3RZ. Tel: 01403 255699; fax - 01403 253837; e-mail - denhams@lineone.net. *Antique sales held monthly - good furniture of all periods, silver, jewellery, European and Oriental ceramics and collectors' items, paintings, drawings, prints and bronzes, metalware and Oriental carpets and rugs. Also monthly sales of general antiques, modern and shipping furniture. Periodic sales of books, stamps, coins and medals, arms and armour and specialist collections as advertised.*

R.H. Ellis and Sons

44/46 High St., Worthing. BN11 1LL. Tel: 01903 238999. *Monthly specialist auctions of antique, Victorian and Edwardian furniture and porcelain. Quarterly auctions of silver, watercolours, paintings, Oriental carpets and rugs.*

King & Chasemore

Midhurst Auction Rooms, West St., Midhurst, GU29 9NQ. Tel: 01730 812456; fax - 01730 814514. *General sales of antique and modern furniture and effects every six weeks.*

Sotheby's Sussex

Summers Place, Billingshurst, RH14 9AD. Tel: 01403 833500; fax - 01403 833699. *Regular sales of paintings, furniture, clocks, ceramics, glass, silver, jewellery, vertu, sporting guns, militaria, Oriental items and garden statuary.*

Stride and Son

Southdown House, St. John's St., Chichester, PO19 1XQ. Tel: 01243 780207; fax - 01243 786713. *Sales last Fri. monthly - antiques and general; periodic book and document sales.*

Worthing Auction Galleries

Fleet House, Teville Gate, Worthing, BN11 1UA. Tel: 01903 205565. *Monthly sales of antique, 20th C and reproduction furniture, ceramics, glass, silver, silver plate, jewellery, pictures and collectables. View Sat. prior 9-12, Fri. and Mon. prior 9-1 and 2-4. Sale Tues. and Wed. both days commencing at 10am.*

TYNE AND WEAR

Anderson and Garland

Fine Art Salerooms, Marlborough House, Marlborough Crescent, Newcastle-upon-Tyne, NE1 4EE. Tel: 0191 232 6278; fax - 0191 261 8665; e-mail - agarland@compuserve.com; website - www.auction-net.co.uk. *Regular sales of paintings, prints, antique furniture, silver and collectors' items.*

Anderson and Garland

Kepier Chare, Crawcrook, Ryton. NE40 4TS. Tel: 0191 413 8348. *Fortnightly sales of Victorian and later furnishings.*

Boldon Auction Galleries

24a Front St., East Boldon, NE36 0SJ. Tel: 0191 537 2630; website - www.boldonauctions.co.uk. *Quarterly antique auctions.*

Thomas N. Miller Auctioneers

Algernon Rd., Byker, Newcastle-upon-Tyne, NE6 2UN. Tel: 0191 265 8080; fax - 0191 265 5050; e-mail - millerlot1@aol.com. *Antique auctions every Wed. at 10 am.*

WARWICKSHIRE

Bigwood Auctioneers Ltd

The Old School, Tiddington, Stratford-upon-Avon, CV37 7AW. Tel: 01789 269415. *Monthly Victoriana sales. Monthly sales of fine furniture and works of art. Quarterly sales of wines, sporting goods and other specialist sales. Catalogues and calendars on request. Valuations for all purposes.*

Henley-in-Arden Auction Sales Ltd

The Estate Office, Warwick Rd., Henley-in-Arden, B95 5BH. Tel: 01564 792154. *Sales of antique and modern furniture and effects, second and fourth Sat. each month.*

Locke & England

18 Guy St., Leamington Spa, CV32 4RT. Tel: 01926 889100; e-mail - valuers@leauction.co.uk; websites - www.leauction.co.uk; www.invaluable.com. *Antique sales fortnightly/monthly.*

Warwick and Warwick Ltd

Chalon House, Scar Bank, Millers Rd., Warwick. CV34 5DB. Tel: 01926 499031; fax - 01926 491906. Est. 1958. *Philatelic auctioneers and private treaty specialists. Stamp auctions held monthly. Postcards, cigarette cards, autographs, ephemera, medals, militaria, coins, banknotes, sports memorabilia, and other collectables sold by auction periodically.*

WEST MIDLANDS

Biddle & Webb

Ladywood Middleway, Birmingham, B16 0PP. Tel: 0121 455 8042. *Fine art sales first Fri. monthly; antique sales on second Fri. monthly; silver, jewellery, medals, coins and watches on fourth Fri. monthly; toys, dolls, model railways and juvenalia sales on Fri. alternate months, all sales at 11. Weekly Tues. sales of Victoriana and collectables at 10.30. Three decorative art and 20th C ceramic sales a year.*

Bonhams

The Old House, Station Rd., Knowle, Solihull, B93 0HT. Tel: 01564 776151; fax - 01564 778069. *Specialised weekly sales of fine furniture, paintings, works of art, clocks, carpets; silver and jewellery; ceramics and 19th-20th C decorative arts; collectors items, toys, dolls, lace and linen, printed ephemera. Subscription available. Free sales programmes on request.*

Fellows and Sons
Augusta House, 19 Augusta St., Hockley, Birmingham, B18 6JA. Tel: 0121 212 2131; fax - 0121 212 1249; e-mail - info@fellows.co.uk; website - www.fellows.co.uk. Est. 1876. *Auctioneers and valuers of jewels, silver, fine art.*

Old Hill Antiques & Auction Rooms
220 Halesowen Rd., Old Hill, Cradley Heath. B64 6HN. Tel: 01384 411121. Est. 1990. *Auctioneers and valuers.*

Weller and Dufty Ltd
141 Bromsgrove St., Birmingham, B5 6RQ. Tel: 0121 692 1414; fax - 0121 622 5605. *Ten sales annually, approximately every five weeks, of antique and modern firearms, edged weapons, militaria etc. Periodic sales of specialist items - military vehicles and associated military equipment. Six fine art and antiques sales per year Postal bids accepted. Illustrated catalogue available.*

WILTSHIRE

Hamptons Auctioneers & Valuers
20 High St., Marlborough, SN8 1AA. Tel: 01672 516161; fax - 01672 515882. *Antique and selected quality furniture and effects sales first Wed. bi-monthly. General household sales first Wed. bi-monthly and every third Wed. monthly.*

Laynes House Auctions
Laynes House, Oaksey. SN16 9SE. Tel: 01666 577603; e-mail - lyon@lyon-oliver.demon.co.uk. *Twice yearly sales of decorative antiques.*

Swindon Auction Rooms
The Planks, Old Town, Swindon, SN3 1QP. Tel: 01793 615915. *Sales every two weeks.*

Woolley and Wallis
Salisbury Salerooms Ltd 51-61 Castle St., Salisbury, SP1 3SU. Tel: 01722 424500; fax - 01722 424508; e-mail - enquiries@woolley andwallis.co.uk; website - www.woolleyand wallis.co.uk. *Specialist sales of antique furniture, ceramics, pictures, silver and jewellery, rugs and textiles, books and wine. Fortnightly general sales. Written valuations for probate and insurance.*

WORCESTERSHIRE

Andrew Grant Fine Art
St Mark's House, St Mark's Court, Cherry Orchard, Worcester. WR5 3DL. Tel: 01905 357547; fax - 01905 763942; e-mail - fineart@ andrew-grant.co.uk. *Victoriana and collectables sales held monthly; fine art sales quarterly. Viewing day before sale.*

Griffiths & Charles
57 Foregate St., Worcester, WR1 1DZ. Tel: 01905 26464; e-mail - info@griffiths-charles.co.uk.

Philip Laney - FRICS - Fine Art
Malvern Auction Centre, Portland Rd., off Victoria Rd., Malvern. WR14 2TA. Tel: 01684 893933. *Monthly sales of antiques and collectors' items.*

Phipps and Pritchard
31 Worcester St., Kidderminster. DY10 1EQ. Tel: 01562 822244. *Regular eight-weekly sales of antique furniture, clocks and watches, watercolours and oil paintings, copper, brass, glass, china and porcelain, stamps and coins, silver. Private house sales also conducted.*

Philip Serrell - Auctioneers & Valuers
The Malvern Sale Room, Barnards Green Rd., Malvern. Tel: 01684 892314. *Bi-monthly catalogued antique and fine art auctions. Fortnightly general sales. Specialist on the premises sales. Free sales estimates.*

YORKSHIRE EAST

Gilbert Baitson
The Edwardian Auction Galleries, Wiltshire Rd, Hull. HU4 6PG. Tel: 01482 500500; after hours - 01482 645241; fax - 01482 500501; website - www.gilbert-baitson.co.uk. *Sales of antique and modern furnishings every Wed. at 10.30. Viewing day prior until 8 pm.*

Dee Atkinson & Harrison - Agricultural and Fine Arts
The Exchange Saleroom, Driffield, YO25 7LJ. Tel: 01377 253151; fax - 01377 241041; e-mail - exchange@dee-atkinson-harrison; website - www.dee-atkinson-harrison.co.uk. *Regular bi-monthly sales of antiques, Victorian, Edwardian and quality furnishings, paintings, silver, jewellery etc. Viewing two days prior. Fortnightly household sales. Biennial collectors' toys and sporting sales.*

H. Evans and Sons - Auctioneers & Valuers
1 Parliament St., Hull. HU1 2AR. Tel: 01482 323033; fax - 01482 211954. *Regular auctions of antiques and modern furniture and effects.*

Spencers Auctioneers and Estate Agents
The Imperial and Repository Salerooms, 18 Quay Rd., Bridlington, YO15 2AP. Tel: 01262 676724. Est. 1892. *General auctions every Thurs. Regular sales of antiques and fine arts.*

YORKSHIRE NORTH

Bairstow Eves Fine Art
West End Rooms, The Paddock, Whitby, YO21 3AX. Tel: 01947 820033/820011. *Monthly antiques sales. 10% buyers premium including VAT.*

Boulton and Cooper Ltd
St. Michaels House, Market Place, Malton, YO17 0LR. Tel: 01653 696151. *Members of SOFAA. Alternating monthly antique sales at Malton and York. Fortnightly general sales at Pickering.*

Hutchinson-Scott
The Grange, Marton-le-Moor, Ripon, HG4 5AT. Tel: 01423 324264. *Periodic general sales plus two or three catalogue sales annually. Specialist in fine antiques and works of art.*

Morphets of Harrogate
6 Albert St., Harrogate, HG1 1JL. Tel: 01423 530030; fax - 01423 500717; website - www. morphets.co.uk. Est. 1895. *Sales of antiques and works of art, interspersed with regular sales of general furniture and effects. Catalogue subscription scheme.*

Scarthingwell Auction Centre
Scarthingwell, Nr. Tadcaster. LS24 9PG. Tel: 01937 557955; fax - same; e-mail - scarthingwell @lineone.net; website - www.scarthingwell auctions.co.uk. *Evening antique and general sales held twice-monthly on Mon. and Tues. evenings, approx 1,000 lots. Viewing on prior Sun. 12-5 and sale days Mon. from 2pm and Tues. from 4pm.*

Stephensons
10 Colliergate, York. YO1 8BP. Tel: 01904 625533. *Six sales annually of antique and Victorian furniture, silver and paintings.*

Summersgill Auctioneers
8 Front St., Acomb, York, YO24 3BZ. Tel: 01904 791131. *Auctions of antiques and household effects and collectors' items.*

Tennants
The Auction Centre, Leyburn, DL8 5SG. Tel: 01969 623780; fax - 01969 624281. (Office - 34 Montpellier Parade, Harrogate. Tel: 01423 531661; fax - 01423 530990); e-mail - enquiry @tennants-ltd.co.uk; website - www.tennants. co.uk. *Minimum of three 1000 lot non-catalogue sales each month of antiques and later house contents, mainly on Sat. at 9.30, viewing Fri. 9-7. Three fine art sales each year. Catalogue subscription service. Specialist sales of collectors' items, books, etc.*

YORKSHIRE SOUTH

A.E. Dowse and Son
Cornwall Galleries, Scotland St., Sheffield, S3 7DE. Tel: 0114 2725858; fax - 0114 2490550; e-mail - aedowse@talk21.com. Est. 1915. *Monthly Sat. sales of antiques. Quarterly fine art and antique sales. Quarterly sales of diecast, tin plate and collectors' toys. Monthly sales of modern furniture and shipping goods.*

Wilkinson & Beighton Auctioneers
Woodhouse Green, Thurcroft, Rotherham. S66 9AQ. Tel: 01709 700005; fax - 01709 700244. *General sales every two weeks on Sun. from 11 am. Viewing Fri. 11-4 and sale day from 9 am. Quarterly sales of furniture and fine art.*

Wilkinson's Auctioneers
28 Netherhall Rd. Doncaster. DN1 2PW. Tel: 01302 814884; fax - 01302 814883. *Catalogue sales every two months, alternating between fine furniture, paintings, bronzes and effects and period oak, country furniture and carvings.*

YORKSHIRE WEST

Bonhams Auctioneers
Hepper House, 17a East Parade, Leeds, LS1 2BH. Tel: 0113 2448011; fax - 0113 2429875. *Quarterly fine sales of pictures, silver and jewellery, ceramics and furniture. Monthly general sales. Sales calendars sent on request.*

De Rome
12 New John St., Westgate, Bradford. BD1 2QY. Tel: 01274 734116/9. *Regular sales.*

Andrew Hartley Fine Arts
Victoria Hall Salerooms, Little Lane, Ilkley, LS29 8EA. Tel: 01943 816363; fax - 01943 817610; e-mail - info@andrewhartleyfinearts.co.uk; website - www.andrewhartleyfinearts.co.uk. Est. 1906. *Fifty sales annually including six good antique and fine art and other specialist sales.*

John H. Raby & Son
Salem Auction Rooms, 21 St. Mary's Rd., Bradford, BD8 7QL. Tel: 01274 491121. *Sales of antique furniture and pictures every four to six weeks, shipping goods and collectables every week.*

Bonhams & Brooks & Langlois Auctioneers

Westaway Chambers, Don St., St. Helier, Jersey, JE2 4TR. Tel: 01534 722441; fax - 01534 759354. *Regular antique and specialised auctions, general sales (Wed).*

Auction Rooms

Castle Laurie, Bankside, Falkirk. FK2 7XF. Tel: 01324 623000; fax - 01324 630343; e-mail - robert@auctionroomsfalkirk.co.uk; website - www.auctionroomsfalkirk.co.uk. *Weekly, Wed., sales at 6pm. Mixed sale of antique, general household and new furniture. Specialised sales are held, details available on website. Viewing Tues. 8-8, Wed. 8-6.*

Bonhams Scotland

65 George St., Edinburgh, Midlothian, EH2 2JL. Tel: 0131 225 2266. *Regular specialist sales of oils and watercolours, furniture, clocks, rugs and works of art, silver and jewellery, Oriental and European ceramics and books. Decorative arts, post war, garden and dolls and textiles sales are also held. Monthly general sales. Annual Scottish Sale, held during the Edinburgh Festival, includes important Scottish furniture, paintings, silver, books and sporting memorabilia.*

Frasers (Auctioneers)

8a Harbour Rd., Inverness, Inverness-shire, IV1 1SY. Tel: 01463 232395; fax - 01463 233634. *Weekly sales on Wed. at 6 pm.*

Leslie and Leslie

Haddington, East Lothian, EH41 3JJ. Tel: 01620 822241; fax - same. *Antique auctions every three months.*

Lindsay Burns & Co

6 King St., Perth. PH2 8JA0. Tel: 1738 633888; fax - 01738 441322; e-mail - lindsayburns@btconnect.com. *General sales bi-weekly on Thurs. at 10.30 am, viewing day prior 9-5. Quarterly fine art sales (illustrated colour catalogues available on website) held on Tues. Viewing previous Sat. 9-1 and Mon. 9-6.*

Loves Auction Rooms

52-54 Canal St., Perth, Perthshire, PH2 8LF. Tel: 01738 633337; fax - 01738 629830. *Regular sales of antique and decorative furniture, jewellery,* silver and plate, ceramics, works of art, metal-ware, glass, pictures, clocks, mirrors, pianos, Eastern carpets and rugs, garden furniture, architectural items. Weekly Fri. sales of Victoriana and household effects at 10.30. Specialist sales of books and collectors' items. Valuations.

Macdougalls Auctioneers & Valuers

Lower Breakish, Breakish, Isle of Skye. IV42 8QA. Tel: 01471 822777; fax - same. *Sales held every eight weeks of antiques and general furniture. Sales held Sat. at 2pm in Broadford Hall (10 mins. from the Skye bridge).*

McTear's

Clydeway Business Centre, 8 Elliot Place, Glasgow G3 8EP. Tel: 0141 221 4456; fax - 0141 204 5035;l e-mail - enquiries@mctears.co.uk; website - www.mctears.co.uk. *Weekly Fri. sales at 10.30 of antique, reproduction and shipping furniture, jewellery, silver, porcelain and paintings. Viewing prior Thurs. 10-4.*

John Milne

9 North Silver St., Aberdeen, Aberdeenshire, AB1 1RJ. Tel: 01224 639336. *Weekly general sales, regular catalogue sales of antiques, silver, paintings, books, jewellery and collectors' items.*

Paterson's

8 Orchard St., Paisley, Glasgow, PA1 1UZ. Tel: 0141 889 2435. Est. 1848. *Fortnightly Tues. sales.*

L.S. Smellie and Sons Ltd.

The Furniture Market, Lower Auchingramont Rd., Hamilton, Lanarkshire, ML10 6BE. Tel: 01698 282007. *Fine antiques auctions - third Thurs. in Feb., May, Aug. and Nov. Weekly sales every Mon. at 9.30 am. (600 lots) household furniture, porcelain and jewellery.*

Taylor's Auction Rooms

11 Panmure Row, Montrose, Angus, DD10 8HH. Tel: 01674 672775. *Antiques sales held every second Sat.*

Thomson, Roddick & Medcalf

20 Murray St., Annan, Dumfriesshire. DG12 6EG. Tel: 01387 279879. *Fortnightly sales of household furnishing and effects.*

Thomson, Roddick & Medcalf Ltd.

60 Whitesands, Dumfries, Dumfriesshire, DG1 2RS. Tel: 01387 279879. *Quarterly catalogued antique and collectors sales. Specialist sales of art pottery, silver, jewellery, sporting and fishing tackle. Fortnightly general sales.*

Thomson Roddick & Medcalf Ltd
44/3 Hardengreen Business Park, Eskbank, Edinburgh. EH22 3NX Tel: 0131 454 9090; fax - 0131 454 9191. *Weekly auctions of antiques and general furnishings, regular specialist sales, particularly Scottish provincial silver, quarterly catalogued fine art and antique sales; also quarterly sales in Dumfries and bi-monthly general sales in Annan.*

WALES

Dodds Property World
Victoria Auction Galleries, Mold, Flintshire, CH7 1EB. Tel: 01352 755705; fax - 01352 752542; e-mail - auctions@door-key.com; website - www. door-key.com. Est. 1952. *Weekly Wed. auctions of general furniture and shipping goods at 10.30am. Bi-monthly auctions of antique furniture, silver, porcelain and pictures etc. at 10.30am on Sat. Catalogues available.*

Peter Francis
Curiosity Salerooms, 19 King St., Carmarthen, South Wales SA31 1BH. Tel: 01267 233456/7; fax - 01267 233458; website - www.peter francis.co.uk. *Catalogued antiques and fine art sales every six weeks. Regular general sales.*

Newland Rennie Wilkins
87 Monnow St., Monmouth, Gwent, NP5 3EW. Tel: 01600 712916. *Periodic sales of antique furniture and effects, usually on Thurs.*

Harry Ray & Co
Lloyds Bank Chambers, Broad St., Welshpool. SY21 7RR. Tel: 01938 552555; e-mail - info@ harryray.com; website - www.harryray.com. Est. 1946. *Monthly country sales.*

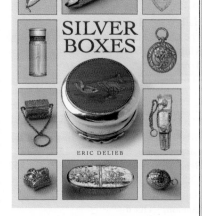

The silver box has fascinated and intrigued collectors for many centuries. It is perhaps safe to say that no other *objets de vertu* have attracted such vivid attention from maker and collector alike.

This book is a comprehensive study of the subject which concentrates on the development of the silver box in England from the 16th to the late 19th centuries.

The word 'box' covers snuffbox, pyx or lancet case, as long as it possesses a lid, hinged or otherwise, it is a box. The usual snuffboxes and vinaigrettes appear in plenty but have been carefully selected to show the ingenuity of silver craftsmen. Also included are 'special purpose' silver boxes: religious, dental and medical, skippet and seal, Masonic, jewel caskets, sweetmeat boxes, pomanders – even the unique sumptuous Henry VIII 'Barber-Surgeons' case' of circa 1512 with its glowing enamels. There is much hitherto unpublished material including pieces from private collections and articles from Livery Companies and other institutions.

Eric Delieb was a London antique silver dealer. He also devoted much of his time to research into Old English Silver. Author of a standard bibliography of books on hallmarks, many articles in antique journals and *Investing in Silver*, his name has become particularly associated with 'Collectors' Silver'.

ISBN 1 85149 313 1. 168pp., 160 col., 44 b.&w. **£29.50**

Available from the
ANTIQUE COLLECTORS' CLUB
Sandy Lane, Old Martlesham, Woodbridge, Suffolk IP12 4SD, UK.
For your free copy of the catalogue:
Tel: **01394 389950** or Fax: **01394 389999**
Email: sales@antique-acc.com Website: www.antique-acc.com

Fairs Calendar

In an attempt to make the Fairs listings for England more logical, we have rearranged the regional boundaries. At the beginning of each section there is a list of the counties included.
Because this list is compiled in advance, alterations or cancellations to the Fairs listed can occur. We strongly advise anyone wishing to attend a Fair, especially if they have to travel any distance, to telephone the organiser to confirm the details given.

LONDON (including Greater London)

Adams Antiques Fairs *020 7254 4054:*
Antiques & Collectors' Fair, The Royal Horticultural Hall, Lawrence Hall, Greycoat Street, Victoria, SW1 - **Jun 9; Jul 14; Sep 8, 22; Oct 13**
Antiques Fair, Chelsea Town Hall, King's Road, Chelsea, SW3 - **Jun 15; Jul 13; Sep 7; Dec 7**
Alison Vaissière 020 7399 8100:
The Grosvenor House Art & Antiques Fair, The Great Room, Le Méridien Grosvenor House, Park Lane, W1 - **Jun 12-18**
Antiquarian Booksellers' Association *020 7439 3118:*
The Olympia Book Fair, Olympia Exhibition Hall, W14 - **Jun 6-9**
The Chelsea Book Fair, Chelsea Old Town Hall, Kings Road, SW1 - **Nov 1-2**
Arms Fairs Ltd *01432 355416*
The London Arms Fair, The Royal National Hotel, Bedford Way, WC1 - **Sep 27-28**
BCAF *01428 661229:*
The Battersea Contemporary Art Fair, Battersea Arts Centre, Battersea Old Town Hall, 176 Lavender Hill, SW11 - **Nov 15-17**
Bead Society of Great Britain *01775 762996:*
13th Annual Beadwork & Bead Fair, Byron Hall, Harrow Leisure Centre, Harrow (NW London) - **Oct 6**
Centaur Exhibitions 020 7970 6543:
The HALI Antique Carpet & Textile Art Fair 2002, National Hall, Olympia Exhibition Centre, London W14 - **Jun 6-9**
Centre Exhibitions 0121 767 2596:
The LAPADA Antiques & Fine Art Fair, The Commonwealth Institute Galleries, Kensington High Street, W8 - **Oct 9-13**
Clarion Events Ltd 020 7370 8212:
The Summer Olympia Fine Art & Antiques Fair, The National Hall, Olympia Exhibition Centre, Hammersmith Road, W14 - **Jun 6-16**
The Winter Olympia Fine Art & Antiques Fair, The National Hall, Olympia Exhibition Centre, Hammersmith Road, W14 - **Nov 11-17**

DDI Fairs 0118 971 0353
The Westminster Ceramics & Glass Fair, Central Hall, Westminster, Storey's Gate, SW1 - **June 13-15**
DMG Fairs 01636 702326:
Antiques & Collectors' Fair, Hall 3, Wembley Exhibition Centre, Empire Way, Wembley - **Jun 4; Aug 26; Dec 27**
David Bannister 01242 514287:
Antique Map Fair, The Bonnington Hotel, Southampton Row, WC1 -**Jun 7-8; Jul 14; Aug 11; Sep 8; Oct 13; Nov 3; Dec 8**
Mr Dungate 01895 834694:
The Brunel Clock & Watch Fair, Brunel University, Kingston Lane, Uxbridge, Middx - **Jun 23; Sep 8; Dec 15**
Gay Hutson 020 8742 1611:
The 20/21 British Art Fair, Commonwealth Institute Galleries, Kensington High Street, W8 - **Sep 18-22**
Granny's Goodies 020 8693 5432:
The London International Antique & Artist Dolls, Toys, Miniatures & Teddy Bear Fair, Kensington Town Hall, Exhibition & Conference Centre, Hornton Street, W8 - **Jun 9; Sep 8; Nov 10**
Harvey (Management Services) Ltd 020 7624 5173:
The Winter Decorative Antiques & Textiles Fair, The Marquee, Battersea Park (through Chelsea Gate), SW11 - **Jan 22-27**
The Autumn Decorative Antiques & Textiles Fair, The Marquee, Battersea Park (through Chelsea Gate), SW11 - **Sep 24-29**
Haughton Fairs 020 7734 5491:
The 21st International Ceramics Fair & Seminar, The Park Lane Hotel, Piccadilly, W1 - **Jun 14-17**
Heritage Antiques Fairs 020 7624 5173:
Heritage Fairs at the Rembrandt Hotel, Thurloe Place (opposite the Victoria & Albert museum), London SW7 - **Jun 16; Jul 7; Sep 15; Oct 27; Nov 17; Dec 8**
Mainwarings Antique Fairs 01225 723094:
Chelsea Antiques Fair, Chelsea Town Hall,

PENMAN ANTIQUES FAIRS

Traditional & Decorative Antiques and Fine Art stylishly displayed, expertly authenticated & offered for sale by dealers of integrity.

2002

May 31- June 1   PETERSFIELD Antiques Fair, Hampshire

June 27 - 30   HOGHTON TOWER Art & Antiques Fair, Lancashire

July 25 - 28   KENSINGTON Art & Antiques Fair, The Town Hall

September 6-8 PETERSFIELD Antiques Fair, Hampshire

September 13-22 CHELSEA Antiques Fair

October 24-27 CHESTER Antiques & Fine Art Show, Cheshire

2003

January 16-19 WEST LONDON Antiques Fair, Kensington Town Hall

February 6 - 9 PETERSFIELD Antiques Fair

February 13-16 CHESTER Antiques & Fine Art Show

March 14-23   CHELSEA Antiques Fair, London SW3

April 24-27   CHELSEA ART Fair, London SW3

Details & Tickets via   www.penman-fairs.co.uk

Please check with Penmans or adverts before travelling any distance to fairs
Penman Antiques Fairs, Tel 01444 482514   info@penman-fairs.co.uk

King's Road, SW3 - **Jun 2, 30; Jul 21; Sep 8;
Nov 3, 17; Dec 8**
Marcel Fairs 020 8950 1844:
Antiques Fair, St Paul's Church Hall, The
Ridgeway, NW7 - **Jun 1**
P & A Antiques 020 8543 5075:
The London Textiles, Vintage Accessories Fair,
Hammersmith Town Hall, King Street, W6 -
Jun 30
The Brocante Fair, Royal Horticultural Hall's
Lindley Hall, Vincent Square, Westminster, SW1
- **Jun 2; Oct 20; Dec 1**
The London Antique Textiles Fair,
Hammersmith Town Hall, King Street, W6 -
Jun 8-9
Penman Fairs 01444 482514:
Chelsea Antiques Fair, Chelsea Old Town Hall,
Kings Road, SW3 - **Sep 13-22**
The Kensington Fine Art & Antiques Fair,
Kensington Town Hall, W8 - **Jul 26-28**
Pig & Whistle Promotions 020 8883 7061:
Alexandra Palace Antique & Collectors' Fair,
The Great Hall, Alexandra Palace, Wood Green,
N22 - **Sep 22; Nov 17**
Simmons Gallery 020 7831 2080:
The London Coin Fair, Holiday Inn (formerly
The Posthouse), London Bloomsbury, Coram
Street, WC1 - **Nov 9**
Talbot Promotions 020 8969 7011:
The International Antique Scientific & Medical
Instrument Fair, The Radisson SAS Portman
Hotel, Portman Square, W1 - **Oct 27**
*Towy Antiques Fairs 01267 236569 or 01792
402525:*
The Little Chelsea Antiques Fair, Chelsea Town
Hall, Kings Road, London SW3 - **Oct 7-8**
West Promotions 020 8641 3224:
The London Paper Money Fair, The Bonnington
Hotel, 92 Southampton Row, WC1 - **Jul 7;
Sep 1; Nov 17**

SOUTH EAST AND EAST ANGLIA

**Includes Bedfordshire, Cambridgeshire,
Essex, Hertfordshire, Kent, Norfolk, Suffolk,
Surrey, Sussex.**

Antiques & Collectors' World 01737 812 989:
Antiques & Collectors' Fair, Lingfield Park
Racecourse, Lingfield, Surrey (from M25
Junction 6, drive 5 miles south on A2) - **Jun 30**
Antique & Collectors' Fair, Goodwood
Racecourse, Goodwood, Near Chichester, West
Sussex - **June 3, 23; Aug 26**
Aztec Events 01702 549623:

Antique & Collectors' Fair, Harlow Sports
Centre, Hammarskjold Road, Harlow, Essex -
Oct 6; Nov 3; Dec 8
Antique & Collectors' Fair, Woodgreen Animal
Shelter, International Arena, London Road
(A1198), Godmanchester, Huntingdon, Cambs -
Jul 6-7; Sep 28-29
Antique & Collectors' Fair, Brentwood Centre,
International Hall, Doddinghurst Road,
Brentwood, Essex - **Jun 2-3; Aug 25-26; Oct
12-13**
Antique & Collectors' Fair, Norfolk
Showground, situated on the A47 Norwich
Southern Bypass at New Costessey - **Aug 10-11;
Nov 9-10**
Antique & Collectors' Fair, Suffolk
Showground, Bucklesham Road, Ipswich,
Suffolk - **Jun 18; Aug 20; Sep 7-8**
Best of Fairs 01787 280306:
Antiques & Collectors' Fair, The Old School,
Long Melford, Suffolk - **Jun 29-30; Jul 27-28;
Aug 24-26; Sep 28-29; Oct 26-27; Nov 23-24;
Dec 14-15, 28-29**
Antiques & Collectors' Fair, New Village Hall,
Copdock, Near Ipswich, Suffolk - **Jun 2; Jul 7;
Aug 4; Sep 1; Oct 13; Nov 3; Dec 1**
Big Surrey Fairs Ltd 020 8390 1230:
Antiques & Collectors' Fair, Tolworth
Recreation Centre, A3 Kingston Bypass, Hook
junction (A243), Fullers Way North, Surrey -
Jun 2; Jul 7; Aug 4; Sep 1; Oct 6
Antiques & Collectors' Fair, The Public Hall,
Stafford Road (A237/A23 M25, J7), Wallington,
Surrey - **Jul 14; Sep 29**
Antiques & Collectors' Fair, Civic Hall (near
High Street/London Road station), Guildford,
Surrey - **Jun 16; Sep 15; Oct 20**
Antique & Collectors' Fair, The Edge, Woolmer
Hill (A3/A287 south of Hindhead), Haslemere,
Surrey - **Jun 30; Sep 8; Oct 13**
Antiques & Collectors' Fair, Leisure Centre,
Hurst Road (A3050), Walton on Thames, Surrey
- **Jun 9; Oct 27**
*Camfair Antiques Fairs 01945 870160/07860
517048:*
Antiques Fair (1930 dateline), The Castle Hall,
Hertford, Herts - **Jun 29; Jul 20; Aug 24;
Sep 21; Oct 26; Nov 16; Dec 14**
Cooper Antiques Fair 01249 661111:
The 35th Annual Snape Antiques Fair, Snape,
Suffolk - **Jul 18-21**
Suffolk County Antiques Fair, Kentwall Hall,
Long Melford, Suffolk - **Nov 1-3**
Cross Country Fairs Ltd 0147483 4120:
Antiques & Collectors' Fair, The Copthorne

Effingham Park Hotel, West Park Road,
Copthorne (near East Grinstead), West Sussex -
**Jun 2; Jul 7; Aug 4; Sep 1; Oct 6; Nov 3;
Dec 1**
DMG Antiques Fairs 01636 702326:
International Antiques & Collectors' Fair, The
South of England Showground, Ardingly, West
Sussex - **Jul 16-17; Aug 4; Sep 10-11;
Oct 29-30**
International Antiques & Collectors' Fair, Kent
County Showground, Detling, Maidstone, Kent -
Jul 20-21; Sep 14-15; Nov 9-10
Antiques & Collectors' Fair, Rowley Mile
Racecourse, Newmarket, Suffolk - **Jun 16; Aug
11; Nov 24**
Antiques & Collectors' Fair, The South of
England Showground, Ardingly, West Sussex -
Aug 4
DPL Fairs 020 8205 1518:
Toy & Train Fair, Elm Court Youth &
Community Centre, Mutton Lane, Potters Bar,
Herts (M25 J24) - **Jun 2; Sep 8; Nov 3**
Camera Fair, Allum Hall, Allum Lane
(A5135/B5378) (opposite Elstree &
Borehamwood Station) - **Nov 10**
Toy & Train Fair, John Bunyan Upper School,
Mile Road (A5134, 8 miles west of Sandy
Roundabout), Bedford, Beds - **Jul 14; Sep 29;
Nov 24**
Camera Fair, St Peter's Catholic School,
Horseshoe Lane East, Merrow, Guildford,
Surrey (2 miles east of city centre, A25 towards
Dorking Close J10 M25 & A3) - **Jun 16; Oct 13**
Camera Fair, Francis Bacon School, Drakes
Drive, St Albans, Herts (1 mile London Colney
roundabout A1081/A414, M25 J22) - **Jul 21**
Galloway Antiques Fairs 01423 522122:
Antiques Fair, Seaford College, Near Petworth,
West Sussex - **Oct 18-20**
Antiques Fair, Stansted House, Rowlands Castle,
Hants/West Sussex - **Dec 6-8**
Antiques Fair, Cranleigh School, Cranleigh,
Surrey - **Jul 26-28**
Antiques Fair, Eridge Park, Near Crowborough,
East Sussex - **Sep 13-15**
Antiques Fair, Firle Place, Near Lewes, East
Sussex - **Nov 8-10**
Gemsco 01525 402596:
The 54th Luton Antiques Fair, Putteridge Bury
House (on the A505 Luton to Hitchin Road,
Beds - M1 exit 10) - **Oct 12-13**
The 4th Mid Beds Antiques Fair, Silsoe
Conference Centre, Silsoe, Beds (just off the A6,
midway between Luton & Bedford - M1
Junction 12) - **Nov 23-24**

Graham Deakin 01273 845141:
Ditchling Antique & Collectors' Fair, Ditchling
Village Hall, Lewes Road, West Sussex -
Jun 9; Sep 8; Dec 8
Graham Turner Antiques Fairs 01473 658224:
Antiques Fair, The Village (Memorial) Hall,
Long Melford, Suffolk - **Jun 5; Jul 3; Aug 7,
31-Sept 1; Sep 4; Oct 2; Nov 6, 16-17; Dec 4**
Antiques Fair, The Parish Hall, Marks Tey,
Essex - **Jun 12; Jul 10; Aug 14; Sep 11; Oct 9;
Nov 13; Dec 11**
Antiques Fair, Furze Hill, Banqueting Centre,
Margaretting, Near Chelmsford, Essex - **Sep 8;
Oct 13; Nov 10; Dec 8**
Little Easton Manor Fair, Little Easton Manor,
Near Great Dunmow, Essex - **Jul 13-14;
Oct 5-6**
Snape Special Four Day Annual Fair, The
Village Hall, Snape, Suffolk - **Jul 18-21**
Framlingham College Three Day Annual Fair,
Framlingham, Suffolk - **Aug 24-26**
Shuttleworth Mansion Two Day Fair,
Shuttleworth Mansion, Old Warden Park,
Biggleswade, Bedfordshire -**Nov 23-24**
Hallmark Antiques Fairs Ltd 01702 710383:
Antiques Fair, Southend Tennis & Leisure
Centre, Eastern Avenue, Southend on Sea, Essex
- **Sep 15**
Antiques Fair, The Palms Hotel, Southend
Arterial Road (A127), Romford, Essex - **Nov 10**
Antiques Fair, Courage Hall, Brentwood School,
Middleton Hall Lane, Brentwood, Essex -
Jun 23; Oct 6
Antiques Fair, Cressing Temple Barns (between
Witham & Braintree on the B1018), Essex -
Sep 7-8
Antiques Fair, Southend Cliffs Pavilion, Station
Road, Westcliff on Sea, Essex - **Nov 3**
Hands Militaria Fairs 01892 730233:
Militaria & Collectors' Fair, The Maltings,
Farnham, Surrey - **Jun 30; Aug 25; Oct 27;
Dec 8**
Militaria & Collectors' Fair, Wolsey Hall,
Cheshunt, Herts - **Jun 16; Oct 13; Dec 15**
Militaria & Collectors' Fair, Dorking Halls,
Dorking, Surrey - **Sep 1**
Militaria & Collectors' Fair, Barnhill
Community Centre, Hayes, Middlesex -
Nov 10
Militaria & Collectors' Fair, The Guildford
Civic, Guildford, Surrey - **Jul 28; Nov 24**
Militaria & Collectors' Fair: 2002 A Military
Odyssey - a large multi-period outdoor event at
the Kent County Showground, Detling, Near
Maidstone, Kent - **Sep 7-8**

Militaria & Collectors' Fair, The Grange, Midhurst, West Sussex - **Nov 17**

Harlequin Fairs 01462 671688:
Antiques Fair, Elstree Moat House Hotel (on A1 adjacent to Borehamwood exit, 2 miles south of M25), Herts - **Jun 30**
Saffron Walden Antiques & Fine Art Fair, Saffron Walden County High School, Audley End Road, Saffron Walden, Essex - **Jul 20-21; Sep 14-15; Nov 16-17**

Janba Fairs 01945 870160/07860 517048:
Antiques Fair, Burgess Hall, St Ivo Recreation Centre, St Ives, Cambridgeshire - **Aug 25-26; Oct 13; Nov 23-24**
Antiques Fair, Knights Hill Hotel, South Wootton, King's Lynn, Norfolk - **Sep 22; Oct 27; Dec 15**

Kyson Fairs 01473 735528:
Woodbridge Antiques Fair, Woodbridge Community Centre, Station Road, Woodbridge, Suffolk - **Jun 3; Aug 26; Sep 22; Oct 20; Nov 17; Dec 15**

Lomax Antiques Fairs 01603 737631:
The Tenth Langley Park Spring Antiques Fair, St Felix School, Southwold, Suffolk (AA signposted from the A12) (relocated due to a fire at Langley Park School, Loddon, Norfolk) - **Jun 1-3**
The Eleventh East Anglian Antique Dealers' Fair, Langley Park School, Loddon, Norfolk - **Oct 25-27**

Magnum Antiques Fairs 01491 681009:
Antiques Fair, The Grange Centre, Bepton Road, Midhurst, West Sussex - **Aug 4; Oct 6; Dec 1**

Ridgeway Fairs 01702 710383:
Antiques Fair, Marconi Sports & Social Club, Beehive Lane, Great Baddow, Chelmsford, Essex - **Oct 20**
Antiques Fair, Keys Hall, Eagle Way, Great Warley, Near Brentwood, Essex - **Nov 24**
Antiques Fair, Mill Hall, Bellingham Lane, Rayleigh, Essex - **Sep 22**
Antiques Fair, The Paddocks, Long Road, Canvey Island, Essex - **Nov 17**
Antiques Fair, Marconi Sports & Social Club, Gardiners Lane South, Basildon, Essex - **Aug 11**
Antiques Fair, Community Centre, Elm Road, Leigh on Sea, Essex - **Jul 28; Dec 8**
Antiques Fair, Sports & Leisure Centre, Main Road, Danbury, Essex - **Dec 1**
Antiques Fair, Marks Hall Estate, Coggeshall, Essex - **Aug 3-4**
Antiques Fair, Southend Bandstand, Clifftown Parade, Southend on Sea, Essex - **Jun 9; Aug 18**

Antiques Fair, The Belvedere, Billericay, Essex (just off A127) - **Jun 29-30; Aug 31; Sep 1**
Antiques Fair, Thurrock Civic Hall, Blackshott's Lane, Grays, Essex - **Oct 27**

Robert Bailey Fairs 01277 214699:
The 3rd West Sussex Antiques & Fine Art Fair (venue to be confirmed) - **Aug 16-18**
The 20th Hertfordshire Antiques & Fine Art Fair, Hatfield House, Hatfield, Hertfordshire - **Nov 1-3**

Robert Soper Exhibitions Ltd 01738 446534:
Antiques Fair, Goodwood House, Chichester, West Sussex - **Nov 15-17**

Shirley Mostyn Fairs - 01903 752961/755116:
Antiques Fair, Hove Town Hall, Norton Road, Hove, Sussex - **Jul 2; Sep 3; Dec 17**
Antiques Fair, The Brighton Centre, Kings Road, Brighton, Sussex - **Nov 7**

Take Five Fairs 020 8894 0218:
Antiques & Collectables Fair, Woking Leisure Centre, Kingfield Road, Woking, Surrey - **Jun 9; Jul 14; Aug 11; Sep 8; Oct 13; Dec 8**
Antiques & Collectables Fair, Canons Leisure Centre, Madeira Road, Mitcham, Surrey - **Jun 23; Jul 28; Aug 25; Sep 22; Oct 27; Nov 24**
Grand Glass Fair, Woking Leisure Centre, Kingfield Road, Woking, Surrey - **Sep 29**
Art Nouveau/Deco Fair, Woking Leisure Centre, Kingfield Road, Woking, Surrey - **Jun 3; Aug 26; Dec 27**

Trident Exhibitions Limited 01822 614671
www.buxtonantiquesfair.co.uk:
35th Surrey Antiques Fair, Guildford Civic, Guildford, Surrey - **Oct 3-6**

Wade Collectors' Club 01782 255255:
Wade Collectors' Meet, Mill Field, Arundel, West Sussex - **Jul 7**
Wade Extravaganza, Dunstable Leisure Centre, Bedfordshire - **Sep 29**
Wade Christmas Bonanza, Wade Collectors' Centre, Arundel, West Sussex - **Dec 7**

Wakefield Ceramics Fairs 01303 258635:
Ceramics Fair, Ramada Hotel (formerly Great Danes Hotel), Hollingbourne, Near Maidstone, Kent - **Jun 9; Jul 14; Aug 11; Sep 8; Oct 13; Nov 10; Dec 8**
Two Day Quality Dateline Antiques Fairs (Dateline 1940), Higham Park, Bridge, Near Canterbury, Kent - **Jun 1-2; Sep 28-29; Nov 30-Dec 1**
Two Day Quality Dateline Antiques Fairs (Dateline 1940), Sutton Valence School, Sutton Valence, Kent - **Oct 19-20**
Two Day Quality Dateline Antiques Fair (Dateline 1940), St Ronan's School, Gun Green,

Hawkhurst, Kent - **Jul 20-21**
Wonder Whistle Enterprises 020 7249 4050:
Antique Fair, The Exhibition Centre, Sandown
Park Racecourse, Esher, Surrey - **Jun 18; Oct 1;
Nov 5** (with firework party)

SOUTH WEST

**Includes Berkshire, Buckinghamshire,
Cornwall, Devon, Dorset, Gloucestershire,
Hampshire, Isle of Wight, Oxfordshire,
Somerset, Wiltshire.**

Adams Antiques Fairs 020 7254 4054:
Antiques Fair, Newbury Showground,
Chieveley, Berks (opposite Junction 13, M4) -
Aug 28; Oct 23; Dec 4
Athena Fayres 01489 584633:
Collectors' Fair, Lockswood Community Centre,
Locks Heath Shopping Centre, Centre Way,
Near Fareham, Hants - **Jun 8; Jul 13; Sep 14;
Oct 12; Nov 9; Dec 7**
Antiques & Collectables Fair, The Community
Centre, Mill Lane, Wickham, Hants (off the
A32) - **Jun 30; Jul 28; Aug 25; Sep 29;
Oct 27; Nov 24; Dec 29**
Cooper Antiques Fair 01249 661111:
The South Cotswolds Antiques Fair, Westonbirt
School, Near Tetbury, Glos - **Aug 16-18**
The North Cotswolds Antiques Fair, Stanway
House, Near Winchcombe, Glos - **Jul 5-7**
The South Cotswolds Xmas Antiques Fair,
Westonbirt School, Near Tetbury, Glos -
Dec 21-22
Crispin Fairs 0118 983 3020:
Antiques & Collectables Fair, St Crispin's Sports
Centre, London Road (A329), Wokingham,
Berks - **Jun 2; Jul 7; Aug 4; Sep 1; Oct 6;
Nov 3; Dec 1**
Antiques & Collectors' Fair, Victoria Hall,
Hartley Wintney, Hants (situated on the main
A30 between Camberley & Basingstoke) -
Jun 9; Sep 8; Oct 13; Nov 10; Dec 8
D & J Fairs - 01202 669061:
Antique & Collectors' Fair, Holy Angels Church
Hall, Lilliput Road, Lilliput, Poole, Dorset -
**Jun 29; Jul 27; Aug 31; Sep 28; Oct 26;
Nov 30; Dec 21**
DMG Antiques Fairs - 01636 702326:
Antiques & Collectors' Fair, The Royal Bath &
West Showground, Shepton Mallet, Somerset -
Jun 21-23; Sep 20-22; Nov 15-17
DPL Fairs 020 8205 1518:
Toy & Train Fair, Beaconsfield School,

Wattleton Road, Beaconsfield, Bucks - **Sep 21;
Nov 16**
Camera Fair, Beaconsfield School, Wattleton
Road, Beaconsfield, Bucks - **Sep 22; Dec 8**
Camera Fair, Trinity School, Love Lane,
Newbury, Berks - **Aug 11; Oct 20**
Devon County Antiques Fairs 01363 82571:
Westpoint Antiques & Collectables Fair,
Westpoint Exhibition Centre, Clyst St Mary,
Exeter, Devon - **Jul 6-7; Aug 31-Sep 1; Nov 2-3**
Matford Antiques & Collectables Fair, Exeter
Livestock Centre, Matford Park Road, Marsh
Barton, Exeter, Devon - **Jun 1; Aug 3; Sep 14;
Oct 12; Dec 7**
Yeovil Antique & Collectors' Fair, Westland
Sports & Social Club, Westbourne Close, Yeovil,
Somerset - **Jun 2; Aug 4; Oct 13; Dec 8**
Salisbury Antiques & Collectables Fair,
Salisbury Leisure Centre, The Butts, Hulse
Road, Salisbury, Wilts - **Jun 15; Sep 28; Nov 30**
E W Services Antiques Fairs 01933 225674:
Antiques & Collectors' Fair, Buckingham
Community Centre, Cornwalls Meadows
Shopping Precinct, Buckingham, Bucks - **Jun 1;
Jul 6; Aug 3; Sep 7; Nov 2**
Milton Keynes Antiques Fair, Middleton Hall,
Central Milton Keynes Regional Shopping
Centre, Milton Keynes, Bucks - **Oct 3-6**
Galloway Antiques Fairs 01423 522122:
Antiques Fair, Rookesbury Park, Wickham,
Hampshire - **Aug 23-26**
Gemsco 01525 402596:
1st South Bucks Antiques Fair, Missenden
Abbey, Great Missenden, Bucks (short distance
from M1, M25 & M40) - **Aug 31-Sep 1**
Grandma's Attic Antiques Fairs 01590 677687:
Antiques & Collectors' Fair, Winchester
Guildhall, The Broadway, Winchester (off the
M3), Hampshire - **Jun 2; Aug 4; Oct 6; Nov 3**
Antiques & Collectors' Fair, Brockenhurst
Village Hall, Highwood Road (off Sway Road),
New Forest, Brockenhurst, Hants - **Aug 25;
Nov 17**
Antiques & Collectors' Fair, Lyndhurst Park
Hotel, High Street, Lyndhurst, Hampshire -
Sep 8
Antiques & Collectors' Fair, Botleigh Grange
Hotel, Botley, Hedge End, Near Southampton,
Hampshire (Junction 7, M27) - **Oct 20**
Antiques & Collectors' Fair, The Masonic Hall
(bottom of High Street), Lymington, Hampshire
- **June 1; Aug 3, 24; Sep 7; Oct 5; Nov 2**
Antiques & Collectors' Fair, The Allendale
Centre, Hanham Road, Wimborne, Dorset -

Jun 3; Aug 26; Oct 13; Dec 29
Antiques & Collectors' Fair, Kingston Maurward
House, Dorchester, Dorset - **Jul 27-28;**
Sep 28-29; Nov 30-Dec 1
Antiques & Collectors' Fair, The Littledown
Centre, Castle Lane, north east of Bournemouth
(A3060), Dorset - **Oct 27**
Antiques & Collectors' Fair, Pavilion Ballroom
(Westover Road), Bournemouth - **Sep 14-15;**
Nov 9-10
Harlequin Fairs 01462 671688:
Antiques Fair, Centre for Epilepsy, Chalfont
Lane, Chalfont St Peter, Bucks - **Jun 2; Jul 7;**
Aug 4; Sep 1; Oct 6; Nov 3; Dec 1
Hyson Fairs Ltd 01647 231459:
Antiques & Collectors' Fair, The Pavilion, Sea
Front, Exmouth, Devon - **Jun 9; Jul 14;**
Aug 11; Sep 8; Oct 13; Nov 10; Dec 8
Antiques & Collectors' Fair, The Memorial Hall,
Holsworthy, Devon - **Jun 16; Jul 21; Aug 18;**
Sep 15; Oct 20; Dec 15
Glass & Pottery Fair, The Pavilion, Sea Front,
Exmouth, Devon - **Nov 23**
Quality Vetted Antiques & Collectors' Fair, The
Lower Exhibition Hall, Exeter University,
Devon - **Jul 28; Oct 6**
Textiles, Vintage Costume, Decorative Antiques
& Ephemera Fair, The Pavilion Sea Front,
Exmouth, Devon - **Sep 7; Nov 30**
Deco, 1950s, 60s & Modernist Fair, The
Pavilion Sea Front, Exmouth, Devon - **Nov 24**
Charity Antiques & Collectors' Fair in aid of
Leukaemia Research, Jubilee Hall, Chagford,
Devon - **Jun 29; Aug 24; Oct 26**
Jay Fairs 01235 815633:
Antiques & Collectors' Fair & Drive-In,
Crowmarsh Village Hall, Near Wallingford,
Oxon - **Aug 26**
Antiques & Collectors' Fair, Drayton Village
Hall, Near Abingdon, Oxon - **Sep 15; Nov 17**
Antiques & Collectors' Fair, The Village Hall,
Dorchester on Thames, Oxon - **Oct 13; Dec 8**
Quality Antiques Fair, Fawley Court, Henley on
Thames, Oxon - **Jul 28; Sep 22; Nov 24**
Legacy Fairs 01844 281311
Antiques & Collectors' Fair, Masonic Hall, Old
Beaconsfield, Bucks - **Jun 13; Jul 11; Sept 12;**
Oct 10; Nov 14; Dec 5
Magnum Antiques Fairs 01491 681009:
Antiques Fair, River Park Leisure Centre,
Gordon Road, Winchester, Hampshire - **Jun 3;**
Aug 26
Midas Fairs 01494 674170:
Antique Fair, The Bellhouse Hotel, Oxford Road

(A40), Beaconsfield, Bucks (from Junction 2,
M40, follow A40 sign to Gerrards Cross) -
Jun 9; Jul 14; Aug 11; Sep 8; Oct 13; Nov 10;
Dec 8
Two Day Fine Art & Antique Fair, The
Bellhouse Hotel, Oxford Road (A40),
Beaconsfield, Bucks (from Junction 2, M40,
follow A40 sign to Gerrards Cross) -
Aug 25-26
Penman Fairs 01444 482514:
Petersfield Antiques Fair, The Festival Hall,
Heath Road, Petersfield, Hants - **Sep 6-8**
Renaissance Fairs 01929 400343:
Antique & Collectors' Fair, Corfe Castle Village
Hall, Corfe Castle, Dorset - **Jun 2; Jul 7;**
Aug 4; Sep 1; Oct 6; Nov 3; Dec 1
Silhouette Fairs 01635 44338:
Antiques & Collectors' Fair, The Abbey Hall
(Guildhall), Abingdon, Oxon - **Jun 16; Jul 21;**
Aug 18; Sep 15; Oct 20; Nov 17; Dec 8
Talisman Fairs 01225 872522:
Bristol Antique & Collectors' Fair, Brunel Great
Train Shed, Temple Meads Station, Bristol -
Jun 9; Jul 14; Aug 11; Sep 8; Oct 13; Nov 10;
Dec 8
Antique & Collectors' Fair, St Margaret's Hall,
Bradford on Avon, Wilts - **Jun 15; Jul 13;**
Aug 10; Sep 7; Oct 19; Nov 16; Dec 7
Jazz Art Deco Fair, Ashton Court Mansion,
Bristol (west of Bristol city centre, from
Junction 18 or 19, M5, with direct access from
the A369 Portishead road) - **Oct 27**
Towy Antiques Fairs 01267 236569:
Antiques Fair, Newbury Racecourse, Berks (a
few miles from Junction 13, M4) - **Jun 15-16;**
Sep 28-29; Oct 9-10
Wakefield Ceramics Fairs 01303 258635:
Fine Quality Antique Porcelain & Pottery Fairs
(Dateline 1940), Burford School, Burford,
Oxfordshire - **Jul 13-14; Oct 5-6**
Fine Quality Antique Porcelain & Pottery Fairs
(Dateline 1940), The Michael Herbert Hall,
Wilton, Near Salisbury, Wiltshire - **Sep 14-15**
Wessex Fairs 01278 789568:
Antiques & Collectors' Fair, The Holiday Inn
(formerly Posthouse), Taunton (Junction 25, M5)
- **Sep 1; Oct 6; Nov 3; Dec 8**
Antiques & Collectors' Fair, Winter Gardens,
Weston Super Mare - **Jun 2-3, 23; Jul 28;**
Aug 25-26; Sep 22; Oct 27; Nov 24; Dec 29
Antiques & Collectors' Fair, Coombe Lodge,
Blagdon, Near Churchill (3 miles from
Churchill, A38 on Bath Road A368), North
Somerset - **Jun 30; Aug 4; Sep 29; Nov 17**

WEST MIDLANDS

Includes Birmingham, Coventry, Herefordshire, Shropshire, Staffordshire, Warwickshire, Worcestershire.

Bowman Antiques Fairs 07071 284 333:
Giant 3 Day Quality Antiques Fair, The Bingley Hall, County Showground, Weston Road, Stafford, Staffs (A518, 5 mins J14, M6) - **Jun 14-16; Aug 16-18; Oct 4-6; Dec 6-8**
Centre Exhibitions 0121 767 2760:
Antiques for Everyone, Hall 5, NEC, Birmingham, West Midlands - **Aug 8-11; Nov 28-Dec 1**
DMG Antiques Fairs 01636 702326:
Antiques & Collectors' Fair, The Three Counties Showground, Malvern, Worcs - **Jun 2; Jul 14; Aug 4; Sep 1; Oct 13; Nov 3; Dec 1**
Mr Dungate 01895 834694:
The Midland Clock & Watch Fair, National Motorcycle Museum (opposite NEC), Solihull, West Midlands - **Aug 18; Nov 3**
Patricia Hier 01260 271975:
The Original National Glass Collectors' Fair, The National Motorcycle Museum, Coventry Road, Bickenhill, Solihull, West Midlands (Junction 6 M42/A45) - **Nov 10**
Seven Promotions 01246 866143:
Antiques Fair, Kings Hall, Stoke, Staffordshire - **Jul 6-7; Oct 5-6; Dec 21-22**
Wakefield Ceramics Fairs 01303 258635:
Fine Quality Antique Porcelain & Pottery Fairs (Dateline 1940), The Bank House Hotel, Bransford, Worcs - **Jun 22-23; Nov 2-3**
Fine Quality Antique Porcelain & Pottery Fairs (Dateline 1940), The Allesley Hotel, Allesley, Coventry - **Nov 16-17**
Waverley Fairs 0121 550 4123:
Antique & Collectors' Fair, New Market Hall, Bromsgrove, Worcestershire - **every Wednesday**
Sunday Antique & Collectors' Fair, Kinver Community Centre, Kinver, Staffordshire (off A449, 5 miles north of Kidderminster) - **Jun 2; Jul 7; Aug 4; Sep 1; Oct 6; Nov 3; Dec 1**
Sunday Book Fair, Kinver Community Centre, Kinver, Staffordshire (off A449, 5 miles north of Kidderminster) - **Jun 16; Jul 21; Aug 18; Sep 15; Oct 20; Nov 17; Dec 15**
Sunday Antique & Collectors' Fair, New Market Hall, Bromsgrove, Worcestershire - **Jun 23; Jul 28; Aug 25; Sep 22; Oct 27 Nov 24; Dec 29**
Worcestershire Monthly Sunday Book Fair,
Powick village hall (from Worcester (Powick) take A449) - **Jun 9; Jul 14; Aug 11; Sep 8; Oct 13; Nov 10; Dec 8**

EAST MIDLANDS

Includes Derbyshire, Leicestershire, Lincolnshire, Northamptonshire, Nottinghamshire, Rutland, Sheffield.

Arthur Swallow Fairs 01298 27493/73188:
International Antiques & Collectors' Fair, RAF Swinderby (between Newark & Lincoln on the A46) - **Jun 7-9; Aug 16-18; Oct 18-20; Nov 29-Dec 1**
DMG Antiques Fairs 01636 702326:
International Antiques & Collectors' Fair, The Newark & Notts Showground, Newark, Notts - **Jun 10-11; Aug 19-20; Oct 21-22; Dec 2-3**
Jaguar Fairs Ltd 01332 831404:
Antiques Fair, Derby University, Kedleston Road, Derby - **Nov 2-3; Dec 14-15**
Antiques in the Park, Kedleston Hall, Derbyshire - **Jun 28-30; Sep 13-15**
Peak Fairs 01629 812449:
Antiques Fair, The Town Hall, Bakewell, Derbyshire - **every Saturday, Sunday & Monday**
Robert Bailey Fairs 01277 214699:
The 10th Buxton Autumn Fine Art & Antiques Fair, Pavilion Gardens, Buxton, Derbyshire - **Oct 18-20**
Seven Promotions 01246 866143:
Antiques Fair, Southwell Racecourse, Nottinghamshire - **Jun 15-16; Sep 21-22; Nov 16-17; Dec 14-15**
Top Hat Exhibitions 0115 941 9143/925 8769:
The National Art Deco Fair, Town Hall, Loughborough, Leics - **Jul 14; Sep 22; Nov 3**
Unicorn Fairs Ltd 0161 773 7001:
Antiques & Collectors' Fair, The Pavilion Gardens, Buxton, Derbyshire - **Jun 15-16; Jul 20-21; Aug 24-26; Oct 5-6; Nov 2-3, 30-Dec 1; Dec 28-29**

NORTH

Includes Cheshire, County Durham, Cumbria, Humberside, Lancashire, Manchester, Northumberland, Tyne and Wear, Yorkshire.

Abbey Antiques Fairs 01482 445785:
Antiques Fair, Willerby Manor, Hull, East Yorks - **Jun 30; Sep 22; Oct 27; Nov 24; Dec 15**
Antiques Fair, The Old Swan Hotel, Harrogate, North Yorks - **Jun 23; Sep 8; Nov 17; Dec 8, 29**

Albany Fairs 0191 584 2934:
Antiques Fair, The Village Hall, Pooley Bridge, Cumbria - **Jun 21-23; Jul 5-7, 19-21; Aug 2-4; Sep 13-15, 27-29; Oct 11-12; Nov 8-10**
Antiques Fair, The Community Centre, Lanchester, Co Durham - **Nov 17**
Antiques Fair, Bobbin Mill, Howtown (Pooley Bridge) - **Sep 6-8; Oct 4-6**

Cartmel Antiques Fairs 01253 396209:
Antiques Fair, The Village Hall, Cartmel, Cumbria - **Jun 28-30; Jul 18-21; Aug 15-18; Sep 5-8, 20-22; Oct 11-13, 25-27; Nov 15-17**

Colin Caygill Events 0191 261 9632:
Antiques & Collectors' Fair, The International Stadium, Gateshead, Tyne & Wear - **Jun 3; Jul 7; Sep 8; Nov 24**
Antiques & Collectors' Fair, The Newcastle Racecourse, Newcastle Upon Tyne, Tyne & Wear - **Jun 16; Sep 1; Nov 10**
Antiques & Collectors' Fair, The Graham Sports Centre, Durham University, Co Durham - **Jul 14; Sep 29; Nov 17**
Antiques & Collectors' Fair, The Wentworth Leisure Centre, Hexham, Northumberland - **Jun 18; Jul 16; Aug 20; Sep 10; Oct 8; Nov 5; Dec 10**
Antiques & Collectors' Fair, The Sands Centre, City of Carlisle, Cumbria - **Jun 9; Jul 21; Sep 22; Nov 3**
Antiques & Collectors' Fair, The Kendal Leisure Centre, Kendal, Cumbria - **Jun 30; Sep 15; Oct 27; Dec 1**
Antiques & Collectors' Fair, The County Hall, Durham City, Co Durham - **Aug 18; Oct 20; Dec 15**
Antiques & Collectors' Fair, Kirkley Hall, Ponteland, Northumberland - **Oct 5-6**
Antiques & Collectors' Fair, The Riverside Leisure Centre, Morpeth, Northumberland - **Jun 23; Aug 26; Dec 26**
Antiques & Collectors' Fair, Skirsgill Hall, PFK Mart, Penrith, Cumbria - **Jul 28; Oct 13**

Cooper Antiques Fairs 01249 661111:
The Cheshire County Antiques Fair, Arley Hall, Near Knutsford, Cheshire - **Jun 7-9; Oct 4-6**

Galloway Antiques Fairs 01423 522122:
Antiques Fair, The Old Swan Hotel, Harrogate, North Yorks - **Sep 20-22**
Antiques Fair, The Bowes Museum, Barnard Castle, Co Durham - **Oct 11-13**
Antiques Fair, Stonyhurst College, Near Clitheroe, Lancs - **Oct 25-27**
Antiques Fair, Naworth Castle, Brampton, Cumbria - **Aug 30-Sep 1**
The Duncombe Park Antiques Fair, Near Helmsley, North Yorks - **Jun 14-16; Nov 1-3**

Great Northern International Antiques & Collectors' Fairs 01325 380077:
Antiques & Collectors' Fair, Yorkshire Showground, Harrogate (on the A661 Harrogate/Wetherby Road) - **Jul 19-21; Sep 6-8; Nov 1-3**

Jaguar Fairs Ltd 01332 831404:
Antiques Fair, Wetherby Racecourse - **Jun 15-16; Jul 27-28; Aug 31-Sep 1; Oct 26-27**

Louise Walker 01823 323363:
The Harrogate Antique Fair, Fine Art Fair, The Harrogate International Centre (Hall A), Harrogate, North Yorks - **Sep 27-Oct 1**

N & B Fairs 01565 722144:
Antique & Collectors' Fair, Plumley Village Hall, Near Knutsford, Cheshire (M6, Junction 19 off A556) - **Jul 28; Aug 25; Sep 29; Oct 27; Nov 24**

Penman Antiques Fairs 01444 482514:
Chester Antiques & Fine Art Show, The County Grandstand, Chester Racecourse, Chester, Cheshire - **Oct 24-27**
The Hoghton Tower Fine Art & Antiques Fair, Near Preston, Lancashire (on A675, near M6 & M56) - **Jun 27-30**

Robert Bailey Fairs Ltd 01277 214699:
The 2nd Wirral Antiques & Fine Art Fair, Hulme Hall, Port Sunlight, Wirral, Cheshire - **Jun 14-16**
The 33rd Cheshire Summer Antiques & Fine Art Fair, Tatton Park, Knutsford, Cheshire - **Jul 12-14**
The 33rd Cheshire Autumn Antiques & Fine Art Fair, Tatton Park, Knutsford, Cheshire - **Sep 5-8**
The 52nd Northern Antiques Fair, Pavilions of Harrogate, Great Yorkshire Showground, Wetherby Road, Harrogate - **Sep 18-22**
The 3rd Wirral Antiques & Fine Art Fair, Hulme Hall, Port Sunlight, Wirral, Cheshire - **Oct 25-27**
The 24th Lancashire Christmas Antiques & Fine Art Fair, The Swallow Trafalgar Hotel (immediately off J31, M6, on A59 towards Clitheroe), Preston New Road, Samlesbury, Preston - **Nov 15-17**

Unicorn Fairs Ltd 0161 773 7001:
Antiques & Collectors' Fair, The Exhibition Halls, Park Hall, Charnock Richard, Lancs - **every Sunday**

SCOTLAND

Albany Fairs 0191 584 2934:
Antiques Fair, The Town Hall, Moffat, Dumfriesshire - **Jun 1-3, 28-30; Jul 25-27;**

Aug 23-26; Sep 19-21; Oct 24-26
Antiques Fair, Victory Memorial Hall, St Andrews, Fife - **Jun 14-16; Jul 12-14; Aug 30-Sep 1**
Antiques Fair, Town Hall, St Andrews, Fife - **Jun 18-19; Jul 16-17; Aug 7-10**
Centre Exhibitions 0121 767 2760:
Antiques for Everyone - Scotland, Scottish Exhibition & Conference Centre (SECC), Glasgow - **Aug 23-25**
Galloway Antiques Fairs 01423 522122:
Antiques Fair, Blair Castle, Blair Atholl, Pitlochry, Perthshire - **Jun 21-23**
Antiques Fair, Scone Palace, Perth - **Nov 15-17**
Robert Soper Exhibitions Ltd 01738 446534:
Antiques Fair, Hopetoun House, South Queensferry, Edinburgh - **Oct 11-13**
Antiques Fair, Pathhead, Near Edinburgh (off A68 Near Pathhead, 10 miles south of Edinburgh) - **Jun 14-16**

WALES

Allen Lewis Fairs 01202 604306:
The Antique Dealers' Fair of Wales, The Orangery, Margam Country Park, Port Talbot, West Glamorgan, South Wales (RAC signposted from Junction 38, M4) - **Sep 6-8**
The Portmeirion Antiques Fair, Portmeirion village, Gwynedd, North Wales (RAC signposted A487) - **Nov 1-3**
Towy Antiques Fairs 01267 236569:
Antique & Collectors' Fair, Brangwyn Hall, Guildhall, Swansea - **Oct 26-27**
Antiques & Collectors' Fair, The United Counties Showground, Carmarthen - **Jul 20-21; Sep 14-15; Dec 14-15**
Antique & Collectors' Fair, Sophia Gardens, Cardiff - **Sep 7-8**

IRELAND

L & M Fairs Ltd - 028 9752 8428:
Antique Fair, Methodist Church Hall, 262 Lisburn Road, Belfast - **Apr 6; May 4; Jun 1; Jul 6; Aug 3; Sep 7; Oct 5; Nov 2; Dec 7, 21; Jan 4, 2003; Feb 1, 2003; Mar 1, 2003**
Antique Fair, La Mon Country House Hotel, near Belfast - **Apr 17; Jun 19; Oct 30; Jan 29, 2003**
Antique Fair, Carrickfergus Town Hall (British Diabetic Association) - **May 25**
Antique Fair, Sydenham Methodist (church funds) - **Sep 14**
Antique Fair, Saintfield Second Presbyterian (church funds) - **Oct 26**
Antique Fair, Moira Presbyterian church hall (Animal Welfare) - **Nov 23**
Antique Fair, Crozier Hall, Armagh (Animal Welfare) - **Nov 30**
Antique Fair, Community Centre, Ballynahinch (Spa church funds) - **Dec 14**
Antique Fair, Greenisland Presbyterian church hall (church funds) - **Jan 11, 2003**
Antique Fair, Cregagh Presbyterian church, Belfast (church funds) - **Feb 22, 2003**

OVERSEAS

Antiquarius 2002 Antiques Show (203) 869 6899:
The Greenwich Civic Center, Harding Road, Old Greenwich, Connecticut, USA - **Dec 6-8**
Art Promotion Publi Gil - +32 (0)50 354 007:
Art Nocturne Knocke, 27th International Art & Antiques Fair, Scharpoord Cultural Centre, Knokke on Sea, Bruges, Belgium - **Aug 10-18**
Cawdell Douglas 020 7439 2822:
TEFAF Maastricht 2002 (The European Fine Art Fair), MEEC, Maastricht, The Netherlands - **Mar 8-17**
Three Fairs at Kölnmesse, Cologne (Kunst Messe Köln, International Fine Art & Antiques Fair; Kunst Köln 2002, International Art Fair; The 16th Antiquariatsmesse, International Antiquarian Book Fair) - **Apr 13-21**
Haughton Fairs - 020 7734 5491:
The International Asian Art Fair, Lincoln Center for the Performing Arts, Damrosch Park, W.62nd Street, New York City - **Mar 22-26**
The International Fine Art Fair, The Seventh Regiment Armory, Park Avenue at 67th Street, New York City - **May 10-15**
Wade Collectors' Club 01782 255255:
Wade Summer Fest, Raddison Hotel, CampHill, Pennsylvania, USA - **Jul 28-29**

Services

This section has been included to enable us to list those businesses which do not sell antiques but are in associated trades, mainly restorations. The following categories are included.

Art, Books, Carpets & Rugs, Ceramics, Clocks & Barometers, Consultancy, Courier, Enamel, Engraving, Fireplaces, Framing, Furniture, Glass, Insurance & Finance, Ivory, Jewellery & Silver, Locks & Keys, Metalwork, Musical Instruments, Photography, Reproduction Stonework, Suppliers, Textiles, Tortoiseshell, Toys.

We would point out that the majority of dealers also restore and can give advice in this field.

Below are listed the trade associations mentioned within this section.

BAFRA	-	British Antique Furniture Restorers' Assn
FATG	-	Fine Art Trade Guild
GADAR	-	Guild of Antique Dealers & Restorers
GMC	-	Guild of Master Craftsmen
MBHI	-	Member of British Horological Institute
UKIC	-	UK Institute for Conservation
CGCG	-	Ceramic & Glass Conservation Group
BTCM	-	British Traditional Cabinet Makers
BFMA	-	British Furniture Manufacturers' Assn
BCFA	-	British Contract Furniture Assn
ASFI	-	Assn of Suppliers to Furniture Industry
GAI	-	Guild of Architectural Ironmongers
MBWCG	-	Member British Watch & Clockmakers Guild

ART

The Antique Restoration Studio
See entry under Furniture.

Armor Paper Conservation Ltd
Glebe Cottage, 2 The Green, Garsington, Oxon. OX44 9DF. Tel: 01865 361741; fax - 01865 361815. TVADA. *Conservation and restoration of drawings, prints, watercolour paintings, documents and archive material.*

Paul Congdon-Clelford
The Conservation Studio, 59 Peverells Wood Ave., Chandler's Ford, Hants. SO53 2FX. Tel: 02380 268167; fax - same; e-mail - WinStudio @aol.com; website - www.conservationstudio. co.uk. IPC, ABPR, FATG, GADAR. Est. 1894. Open by appointment. *Conservators of oil paintings and works of art on paper; home consultations; collection and delivery in all areas. Conservators to museums and galleries.*

Kirkgate Fine Art & Conservation
The Studio, 3 Gillings Yard, Thirsk, Yorks North. YO7 1SY. (Richard Bennett). Tel: 01845 524085; home - same. UKIC, AABPR. SSCR. Est. 1979. Open by appointment. *Oil paintings cleaned and lined on the premises; gilt/gesso frames restored and repaired; framing.* LOC: 100 yards from Market Place, off Kirkgate.

Manor House Fine Arts
73 Pontcanna St. Cardiff, CF11 9HS. (S.K. Denley-Hill). Tel: 02920 227787; fax - 02920 641132; e-mail - valuers@manorhousefinearts. co.uk; website - www.manorhousefinearts.uk. National Association of Valuers & Auctioneers. Est. 1976. Open 10-5.30. *Auctioneers, valuers, restorers, fine arts, antiques and chattels.*

Stephen Messer Picture Restoration
Tarifa, Millstream Moorings, Mill Lane, Clewer, Windsor, Berks. SL4 5JH. Tel: 01753 622335. Associate member ABPR. *Restorations - paintings, mainly oils including re-lining, frames including gilding.*

Claudio Moscatelli Oil Painting Restoration

46 Cambridge St., London SW1V 4QH. (P. Moscatelli). Tel: 020 7828 1304; e-mail - claudio4 @btinternet.com. BPR. Open 10-6. *Oil paintings cleaned, relined, retouched and varnished.*

Plowden & Smith Ltd

190 St Ann's Hill, London SW18 2RT. Tel: 020 8874 4005; fax - 020 8874 7248; e-mail - Info@plowden-smith.co.uk; website - www. plowden-smith.co.uk. *Conservation and restoration of fine art and antiques. Specialist departments for furniture, ceramics, paintings, metal, stone, decorative arts, mounting/display.* VAT: Stan.

Colin A. Scott

1st Floor Studio, Anthony Hurst Antiques, 13 Church St., Woodbridge, Suffolk. IP12 1DS. Tel: 01394 388528. *Picture restoration and framing.*

Thicke Gallery

SA2 8BG. (T.G. Thicke). Tel: 01792 207515. Est. 1981. Open by appointment. *Advice on purchase/ sale of paintings; valuations; restorations (oils, watercolours, samplers).*

BOOKS

Brignell Bookbinders

2 Cobbles Yard, Napier St., Cambridge, Cambs. CB1 1HP. Tel: 01223 321280; fax - same. Society of Bookbinders, GMC. Est. 1982. *Book restoration, conservation including paper, leather photo cases, journal and thesis bindings, boxes and limited editions.* VAT: Stan.

The Manor Bindery Ltd.

Calshot Rd., Fawley, Southampton, Hampshire. SO4 1BB. Tel: 023 8089 4488; fax - 023 8089 9418. *Manufacturers of false books, either to use as a display or for cabinet makers to apply to doors and cupboards. Also decorative objects and accessories, various decorative replica book boxes. Leather library shelf edging.*

CARPETS AND RUGS

Barin Carpets Restoration

57a New Kings Rd., London SW6 4SE. Tel: 020 7731 0546. GMC. Conservation Register Museums and Galleries Commission. *Oriental carpets, rugs, European tapestries, Aubussons expertly cleaned, restored and lined. Expert advice, free estimates.*

The Restoration Studio

Unit 11 Kolbe House, 63 Jeddo Rd., London W12 9EE. (Ela Sosmowska). Tel: 020 8740 4977; website - www.restorationstudio.co.uk. Member Rug Restorers Assn. Est. 1987. Open 8-5. CL: Sat. *Restoration, cleaning, lining and mounting of tapestries, Aubusson carpets, kilims and all kinds of needlework.*

CERAMICS

The Antique Restoration Studio

See entry under Furniture.

G. Bagshaw Restorations

The Old Smithy, Capesthorne Hall Estate Yard, Siddington, Nr Macclesfield, Cheshire. SK11 9JX. Tel: 01625 860909; e-mail - gordon.bagshaw @lineone.net. Est. 1971. Open 10-5.30. *General restoration - mainly ceramics and clocks.*

China Repairers

The Old Coach House, King's Mews, off King Street, London N2 8DY. (V. Baron). Tel: 020 8444 3030; website - www.chinarepairers.co.uk. Est. 1952. Open 10-4. CL: Fri. and Sat. *Specialised restoration of all pottery and porcelain; restoration courses.*

The China Repairers

1 Street Farm Workshops, Doughton, Tetbury, Glos. GL8 8TH. Tel: 01666 503551. TADA. *Specialised restoration of porcelain and pottery, mirror frame gilding.*

Porcelain Repairs Ltd.

240 Stockport Rd., Cheadle Heath, Stockport, Cheshire. SK3 0LX. Tel: 0161 428 9599; fax - 0161 286 6702. CGCG, UKIC. Est. 1970. *Highest standard restorations of European and Oriental ceramics, especially underglaze blue and white, museum repairs, carat gilding and modelling. Cracks and crazing removed without any overpainting or glazing.*

CLOCKS AND WATCHES

Apollo Southerns

Penygraig Industrial Estate, Tonypandy, Mid. Glam., South Wales. CS40 1JA. Tel: 01443 420420. BJA; MBWCG; Jewellery Industry Distributors Assn. *Watch and clock replacement and restoration materials; specialised tools for the horological trade.* VAT: Stan. *Trade Only.*

G. Bagshaw Restorations

See entry under Ceramics.

Established in Portsea before 1880

E. HOLLANDER

1 BENNETT'S CASTLE
89 THE STREET
CAPEL
DORKING, SURREY RH5 5JX

Telephone: (01306) 713377

DAVID PAY

Maintains a family tradition
extending over five generations;
in the restoration of

CLOCKS
AND BAROMETERS

The Clock Gallery
Glebe Farm, Clarke's Rd., North Killingholme,
Lincs. DN40 3JQ. Tel: 01469 540901; fax -
01469 541512. Guild of Lincolnshire Craftsmen.
*Clock movements and dials, brass work. Agent
for several German clock movement makers.*
VAT: Stan.

Clive and Lesley Cobb
3 Pembroke Crescent, Hove, East Sussex. BN3
5DH. Tel: 01273 772649. Listed by the
Conservation Unit of the Museum and Galleries
Commission. Est. 1972. *Quality, sympathetic
restoration of lacquer clock cases and furniture,
and painted clock dials.*

Edmund Czajkowski and Son
See entry under Furniture.

Richard Higgins (Conservation)
See entry under Furniture.

E. Hollander (David Pay)
1 Bennetts Castle, 89 The Street, Capel, Dorking,
Surrey. RH5 5JX. Tel: 01306 713377; fax - 01306
712013. Open Mon.-Fri. 8-4.30 or by appointment. *Restoration of all forms of clocks,
mechanisms, cases, dials and barometers.*

A.C. Layne
48 Cecil St., Carlisle, Cumbria. CA1 1NT. Tel:
01228 545019. Open 8-11.30 and 1-4. *Repairs to
antique clocks.*

Robert B. Loomes
3 St Leonard's Street, Stamford, Lincs. PE9 1HD.
Tel: 01780 481319; website - www. dialrestorer.
co.uk. MBWCG. MBHI. Est. 1966. Open 9-5.
CL: Sat. *British antique clock restoration - longcase, lantern and bracket.* VAT: Stan/Spec.

William C. Mansell
24 Connaught St., Marble Arch, London W2 2AF.
(Bill and Karen Salisbury). Tel: 020 7723 4154;
fax - 020 7724 2273; e-mail - williammansell@
email.com; website - www.williammansell.co.uk.
MBHI. NAG. BWCG. Est. 1864. Open 9-6, Sat.
10-1. *Repair/restoration/sales of all types of
clocks, watches and barometers etc., also antique
jewellery and silverware. Online catalogue of
antique, vintage and modern watches, clocks,
jewellery and silverware.*

Meadows and Passmore Ltd
1 Ellen Street, Portslade, Brighton, East Sussex.
BN41 1EU. Tel: 01273 421321; fax - 01273
421322. *Clock and barometer parts, tools and
materials.*

Menim Restorations
Bow St., Langport, Somerset. Tel: 01458 252157.
GMC. Est. 1830. *Specialists in English clocks,
full cabinet making and horological service;
French polishing.*

Repton Clocks
Acton Cottage,48 High St., Repton, Derbys.
DE65 6GF. (P. Shrouder). Tel: 01283 703657; fax
- 01283 702367; e-mail - paul@pshrouder.
freeserve.co.uk. MBWCMG; MBHI. Open by
appointment 9-6. CL: Sat. *Antique and modern
watch and clock restoration; musical box repairs;
gear cutting; clocks made to order.*

The Restoration Shop
25 Broad St., Leominster, Herefs. HR6 8BT. (R.
Cookson). Tel: 01568 612281; fax - same. Open
10-4 or by appointment. *Restorations.* LOC:
Corner of A49 and New St.

Kevin Sheehan
15 Market Place, Tetbury, Glos. GL8 8DD. Tel:
01666 503099. Est. 1978. Open 9-4.30, Sat. 10-
12. *Specialist repairer of English and French
18th-19th C clocks. Written estimates given, all
work guaranteed. Awarded Royal Warrant.*

CONSULTANCY

Athena Antiques of Fleet.
59 Elvetham Rd., Fleet, Hants. GU13 8HH. (Richard Briant). Tel: 01252 615526; home - same; mobile - 07881 541748. Est. 1975. Available seven days by appointment. *Consultancy; valuations (jewellery, silver, clocks and furniture); restorations (clocks and furniture); buys at auction on commission; militaria.* LOC: Near Fleet railway station.

John Fell-Clark
Wall Farm, Harkstead Rd., Holbrook, Ipswich, Suffolk. IP9 2RQ. Tel: 01473 327707. LAPADA. Est. 1971. By appointment. *Valuations; restorations; consultancy and interior design; buys at auction (17th-20th C furniture and textiles).* VAT: Spec.

Geoffrey Godden
3 The Square, Findon, West Sussex. BN14 0TE. Tel: 01903 873456. *Consultant and lecturer in ceramics.*

Gerald Sattin   BADA
P O Box 20627, London NW6 7GA. (G. and M. Sattin). Tel: 020 8451 3295; fax - same; e-mail - gsattin@compuserve.com. Est. 1967. By appointment only. *Consultants and commission agents for the purchase of English and Continental porcelain, 1720-1900; English glass, 1700-1900; English silver, 1680-1920.* VAT: Stan/Spec.

COURIER

Antique Tours & Conrad Chauffeur Hire
11 Farleigh Rise, Monkton Farleigh, Nr. Bradford-on-Avon, Wilts. BA15 2QP. (John Veal). Tel: 01225 858527 (answerphone); fax - same; mobile - 07860 489831; e-mail - conradveal@hotmail.com. Est. 1988. *Chauffeur service for up to four persons; tours of antique shops, Fairs, dealers and warehouses in and around the West Country; packing and shipping arranged; air and sea port transfers; genealogical research undertaken.*

The English Room
London SW11 4PY. (Mrs Val Cridland). Tel: 020 7720 6655; mobile - 07770 275414; fax - 020 7978 2397. Est. 1985. By appointment only. *Search and courier (trade and private), London and country - shipment of goods purchased arranged.* VAT: Stan/Spec.

Janet Love Interiors
5A Furlong Road, London N7 8LS. Tel: 020 7619 9668; fax - 020 7619 9667; mobile - 07768 7815733. *Personal antique furniture shopping service and Olympia personal shopping service.*

Neil Robson Antiques Courier Service
10 Towrise, Sulgrave, Banbury, Oxon. OX17 2SB. Tel: 01295 760045; mobile - 07785 785447; e-mail - antiques.courier@virgin.net. TVADA. *Complete service for overseas buyers, throughout Britain and into Europe. Personalised itineraries covering all aspects of the trade - specialist dealers, fair, markets, auction, restorers and reproduction sources. Clients met at airport with spacious car or people carrier and accompanied throughout trip. Collection, packing, shipping and documentation of goods arranged.*

ENGRAVING

Eastbourne Engraving
12 North Street, Eastbourne, East Sussex. BN21 3HG. (D. Ricketts). Tel: 01323 723592. Est. 1882. Open Tues.-Fri. 9.15-4.45. *Engraving trophies, polishing, silver plating, repairs, hardwood plinths etc.*

The Woods Engraving Co
174 London Road, Southend-on-Sea, Essex. SS1 1PH. Tel: 01702 338754. GMC. Est. 1970. *Engraving for silversmiths, polishers and platers, jewellery manufacturers; chapter rings, barometer dials, etc.* VAT: Stan.

FIREPLACES

Antiques and Restoration
Old Town Hall, 965 Stockport Rd, Levenshulme, Manchester, Lancs. (A. Warburton). Tel: 0161 256 4644; mobile - 07976 985982. Open 10-5, Sun. 11-4. *Antiques, fireplaces and restoration, also carpentry and re-claimed pine furniture.*

FRAMING

Natural Wood Framing
Eight Bells Gallery, 14 Church St., Tetbury, Glos. GL8. Tel: 01666 505070. FATG. *Bespoke framing specialising in antiques, textiles and restorations. Contemporary and sporting art stocked.*

FURNITURE

Timothy Akers - Antique Furniture Restorations
The Forge, 39 Chancery Lane, Beckenham, Kent. BR3 2NR. Tel: 020 8650 9179; website - www. akersofantiques.com. BAFRA. *Restorations of 17th-19th C English furniture, longcase and bracket clocks.*

Alan's Antique Restorations
PO Box 355. Woking, Surrey. GU22 9QE. (A.V. Wellstead). Tel: 01483 724666; fax - 01483 750366.

Anthony Allen Antique Restorers
Old Wharf Workshop, Redmoor Lane, New Mills, High Peak, Derbys. SK22 3JL. Tel: 01663 745274. BAFRA. UKIC. Listed on Register of Conservation Unit Museums and Galleries Commission. *Early oak and walnut furniture; conservation; clocks, cases, and movements; artifacts and metalwork.*

The Antique Restoration Centre
14 Suffolk Rd., Cheltenham, Glos. GL50 2AQ.

(M.H.Smith-Wood). Tel: 01242 262549. Est. 1974. Open Mon-Fri 9.30-5. *All types of restoration - all restorers BADA qualified.*

The Antique Restoration Studio
The Stable Block, Milwich Rd. Stafford, Staffs. ST18 0EG. (P. Albright). Tel: 01889 505544; fax - 01889 505543; e-mail - ars@uk-hq.demon. co.uk; website - www.uk-hq.demon.co.uk. Open 9-5. *Repairs and restoration (furniture, rush and cane, French polishing, leatherwork and upholstery, ceramics, glassware, paintings, clocks and watches, rare books, documents and photographs). Five year guarantee on all work. Collection and delivery service. LOC: 4 miles NW of Stafford.*

Antiques and Restoration
See entry under Fireplaces.

Michael Barrington
The Old Rectory, Warmwell, Dorchester, Dorset. DT2 8HQ. Tel: 01305 852104; fax - 854822. BAFRA. UKIC. Est. 1983. *Conservator and restorer of 17th-20th C furniture, clocks, barometers, gilding, upholstery, metalwork, music boxes and barrel pianos, automatons and rocking horses, historic lighting eg. Colza Oil and Argand.*

Batheaston
20 Leafield Way, Corsham, Wilts. SN13 9SW. Tel: 01225 811295; fax - 01225 810501. BFMA. BCFA. *Oak reproduction furniture made from solid kiln dried timbers, antique hand finish. Extensive range of Windsor, ladderback and country Hepplewhite chairs; refectory, gateleg and other extendable tables, Welsh dressers, sideboards and other cabinet models. Trade Only.*

David Battle
Brightley Pound, Umberleigh, Devon. EX37 9AL. Tel: 01769 540483. BAFRA. Est. 1984. Open by appointment. *Cabinet making, restoration and conservation work; polishing, clock cases, veneer and marquetry work, woodturning. Specialists in 17th-19th C English and Continental furniture. Collections and deliveries.*

Keith Bawden - Restorer of Antiques
Mews Workshops, Montpellier Retreat, Cheltenham, Glos. GL50 2XG. Tel: 01242 230320. BAFRA. *All period furniture, plus restoration of items made from wood, metals, porcelain, pottery, fabrics, leather, ivory, papier-mâché, etc.*

Clive Beardall
104b High St., Maldon, Essex. CM9 5ET. Tel: 01621 857890; fax - 01621 850753; website - www.clivebeardall.co.uk. BAFRA. Est. 1982.

Belvedere Reproductions
11 Dove St., Ipswich, Suffolk. IP4 1NG. Tel: 01473 214573; fax - 01473 253229; mobile - 07860 782888. *Suppliers of traditionally constructed and hand polished oak and fruitwood country furniture.* VAT: Stan.

Berry & Crowther
The Workshops, Nine Whitestones, Stocksmoor, Huddersfield, West Yorks. HD4 6XQ. Tel: 01484 609800; fax - same; e-mail - peternberry@aol. com. Est. 1979. Open 9-6.30. *Fine antique restorers and conservators; restoration with traditional methods to highest standards on fine furniture and clocks. Insurance work approved.*

Rupert Bevan
40 Fulham High St., London SW6 3LQ. Tel: 020 7731 1919; fax - same. *Gilding, carving and painting.* Stan.

Peter Binnington
Barn Studio, Botany Farm, East Lulworth, Wareham, Dorset. BH20 5QH. Tel: 01929 400224; fax - 01929 400744. BAFRA. *Restoration of verre églomisé, giltwork, decorated surfaces, period furniture.*

Maxwell Black
Brookhouse Studios, Novington Lane, East Chiltington, Lewes, East Sussex. BN7 3AX. Tel: 01273 890175. Est. 1980. Open 8-4.30.

Martin Body - Giltwood Restoration
7 Addington Sq., London SE5 7JZ. Tel: 020 7703 4351. *Specialist conservation of fine gilded furniture and frames.*

Richard Bolton
Painswick House, The Old Dairy, Painswick, Glos. GL6 6TH. Tel: 01452 814881. BAFRA. Est. 1982. Open 9-5. CL: Sat. *All aspects of furniture restoration undertaken; tuition given.* LOC: At rear of Painswick House.

A.E. Booth & Son
Crows Nest, Edgeley Rd., Barton, Torquay, Devon. TQ2 8ND. Tel: 01803 312091. *Restorations, polishing, upholstery. Barometers, longcase, mahogany and walnut.*

Stuart Bradbury - M & S Bradbury
The Barn, Hanham Lane, Paulton, Somerset. BS39 7PF. Tel: 01761 418910. BAFRA. Est. 1989. Open 8-5. *All aspects of antique furniture restoration.*

Lawrence Brass
154 Sutherland Avenue, Maida Vale, London W9. Tel: 01225 852222. UKIC. Approved by the Museums and Galleries Commission. *Conservation and restoration of fine antiques, metal work, gilding and upholstery.*

A. J. Brett & Co Ltd
168c Marlborough Rd., London N19 4NP. Tel: 020 7272 8462; fax - 020 7272 5102; e-mail - ajbretts@aol.com; website - www.ajbrett.co.uk. GMC. Est. 1965. Open 7-3.30. *Restorers of antique furniture and upholstery; French polishing and gilding; free estimates.*

Bruton Classic Furniture Company Ltd.
Unit 1 Station Road Industrial Estate, Bruton, Somerset. BA10 0EH. Tel: 01749 813266; fax - same; mobile - 07973 342047. *Quality antique replica furniture - mahogany, teak and pine.*

Peter Campion Restorations
The Old Dairy, Rushley Lane, Winchcombe, Glos. GL54 5JE. Tel: 01242 604403; fax - same; website - www.petercampion.co.uk. BAFRA. Est. 1959. Open 9-5.30 or by appointment. *Furniture restoration, conservation, polishing, insurance work, furniture designed and made to order.* LOC: Opposite the exit of Sudeley Castle car park.

Cane & Able Antiques - Cane & Rush Furniture Restoration
The Limes, 22 The Street, Beck Row, Bury St. Edmunds, Suffolk. IP28 8AD. Tel: 01638 515529; fax - 01638 583905; e-mail - bob. caneandable2@hotmail.com. Est. 1991. *Specialists in antique and designer cane, upholstery and rush seating, furniture restoration and copying.*

John B. Carr - Charles Perry Restorations Ltd
Praewood Farm, Hemel Hempstead Rd., St. Albans, Herts. AL3 6AA. Tel: 01727 853487; fax - 01727 846668; e-mail - cperry@praewood. freeserve.co.uk. BAFRA.

Carvers & Gilders
9 Charterhouse Works, Eltringham St., London SW18 1TD. Tel: 020 8870 7047; fax - 020 8874 0470; e-mail - acc@carversandgilders.com; website - www.carversandgilders.com. UKIC; Master Carver's Assn; Furniture History Society; GMC. Est. 1979. *Restoration and conservation of fine decorative woodcarving and giltwood. Specialists in fine water gilding. Designers and makers of carved and giltwood furniture, mirror frames and other decorative pieces in both period and contemporary styles.* VAT: Stan.

Peter G. Casebow
Pilgrims, Mill Lane, Worthing, West Sussex. BN13 3DE. Tel: 01903 264045. BAFRA. *Period furniture, turning, marquetry, metalwork, fretwork, polishing.*

Graham Childs - Alpha (Antique) Restorations
High St., Compton, Newbury, Berks. RG20 6NL. Tel: 01635 578245; mobile - 07860 575203. BAFRA. *Fine oak, walnut and mahogany. Traditional hand finishes. Veneering and inlaying. Clock cases.*

Clare Hall Company
The Barns, Clare Hall, Cavendish Rd., Clare, Nr. Sudbury, Suffolk. CO10 8PJ. (Michael Moore). Tel: 01787 278445; fax - 01787 278803; 01787 277510 (ansaphone). Est. 1970. Open 8-4.30. *Replicas of 18th and 19th C floor standing and table globes. Full cabinet making especially four poster beds; restoration of all antiques and upholstery.* VAT: Stan/Spec.

Classic Reproductions
Swan Corner, Pewsey, Wilts. SN9 5HL. Tel: 01672 563333; fax - 01672 562391. *Suppliers of replica antiques from Java and manufacturers of custom designed pine furniture including tables, beds, chests, bookcases and desks.*

Benedict Clegg
Rear of 20 Camden Rd., Tunbridge Wells. Kent. TN1 2PT. Tel: 01892 548095. BAFRA.

Lucinda Compton of Compton & Schuster Ltd
The Old Laundry, Newby Hall, Ripon, North Yorks. HG4 5AE. Tel: 01423 324290; website - www.comptonandschuster.com. BAFRA. Conservation register. UKIC. Est. 1986. Open 9-5. CL: Sat. *Furniture - painted, gilded, lacquer, papier mâché, tôle.*

Compton & Schuster Ltd
Studio A133 Riverside Business Centre, Haldane Place, London SW18 4UQ. Tel: 020 8874 0762; fax - 020 8870 8060. BAFRA. *Conservation and restoration - lacquer, gilding, painted furniture, paper-mâché, tôle, architectural gilding.*

William Cook
167 Battersea High St., London SW11 3JS. Tel: 020 7736 5329 or 01672 513017. BAFRA. *18th C and English period furniture.*

William Cook
High Trees House, Savernake Forest, Marlborough, Wilts. SN8 4NE. Tel: 01672 513017. BAFRA.

Robert Crawley
75 St. Mary's Rd., Ealing, London W5 5RH. Tel: 020 8566 5074. BAFRA.

Crawley Studios
39 Woodvale, London SE23 3DS. Tel: 020 8516 0002; fax - same. BAFRA. Est. 1985. *Painted furniture, papier-mâché, tôle ware, lacquer and gilding.*

J.W. Crisp Antiques
1-9 Tennyson Rd., Wimbledon, London SW19 8SH. (Michael Murren). Tel: 020 8543 1118; fax - same. Est. 1926. Open by appointment. *Restoration of antique furniture and French polishing.*

Michael Czajkowski - Edmund Czajkowski and Son
96 Tor-o-Moor Rd., Woodhall Spa, Lincs. LN10 6SB. Tel: 01526 352895; fax - same; e-mail - sales@czajkowskiandson.co.uk BAFRA. *Furniture, clocks (including church) and barometers restored. Veneering, marquetry, English lacquer and boulle work, carving and gilding.*

D.H.R. Limited
8/10 Lea Lane, Thame Rd., Long Crendon, Aylesbury, Bucks. HP18 9RN. Tel: 01844 202213; fax - 01844 202214. BAFRA. *Boulle, cabinetwork, carving, gilding, lacquer, leather, marble, marquetry, ormolu, upholstery.*

D Restoration
4 Gleneldon Mews, London, SW16 2AZ. (Deborah Hurst). Tel: 020 8696 0315; e-mail - deborah.h@ukgateway.net. Est. 1996. Open 9-6. *French polishing, gilding, wood carving, restoration.*

Michael Dolling
Church Farm Barns, Glandford, Holt, Norfolk. NR25 7JR. Tel: 01263 741115. BAFRA.

Brian Duffy and Katie Keat - Hope & Piaget
12 and 13 Burmarsh Workshops, Marsden St., London NW5 3JA. Tel: 020 7267 6040; fax - same; e-mail - mail@hope-piaget.co.uk; website - www.hope-piaget.co.uk. BAFRA. UKIC.

Michael Durkee
Castle House, 1 Bennetts Field Estate, Wincanton, Somerset. BA9 9DT. Tel: 01963 33884; fax - 01963 31278. BAFRA. Conservation register. Open 8.30-5.30. CL: Sat. *Restoration, conservation and finishing of all styles of period furniture. Boulle and inlay work.*

EFMA

4 Northgate Close, Rottingdean, Brighton, East Sussex. BN2 7DZ. (Anthony and Patrick Hoole). Tel: 01273 589744; fax - 01273 589745; e-mail - info@efma.co.uk; website - www.efma.co.uk. Fed. of Sussex Industries, IDDA, Inst. of Export, Inst. of Linguists. Est. 1973. *Hand-finished reproductions in walnut, elm, myrtle, yew, mahogany, satinwood. Custom-work and bespoke polishing - 18th C, Biedermeier, Victorian, mahogany dining tables. Country furniture - distressed oak and cherry refectory, gateleg and coffee tables, Windsor chairs. Tables reproduced from old timber.* Stan.

D.S. Embling - The Cabinet Repair Shop

Woodlands Farm, Blacknest, Alton, Hants. GU34 4QB. Tel: 01252 794260. C&G London Inst; GMC; League of Professional Craftsmen. Est. 1977. *Antique and modern furniture restoration and repair including marquetry and veneering, French polishing, modern finishes. Parts made, wood turning, collection and delivery; insurance claim repairs.*

Everitt and Rogers

Dawsnest Workshop, Grove Rd., Tiptree, Essex. CO5 0JE. Tel: 01621 816508; fax - 01621 814685. GADAR. Est. 1969. *Expert antique furniture restoration.*

Duncan Everitt - D.M.E. Restorations Ltd

11 Church St., Ampthill, Beds. MK45 2PL. Tel: 01525 405819; fax - 01525 756177; e-mail - info@dmerestorations.com; website - www. dmerestorations.com. BAFRA. Est. 1986. *English and European furniture restoration.*

John Farbrother Furniture Restoration

Ivy House, Main St., Shipton-by-Beningbrough, York, North Yorks. YO30 1AB. Tel: 01904 470187; website - www.johnfarbrother.co.uk. GADAR. Est. 1987. *All repairs undertaken, refinishing process from complete strip to reviving existing finish. French polishing, oil, wax and lacquers. Pressurised fluid application woodworm treatment.*

Fauld Town and Country Furniture

Whitestone Park, Whitestone, Hereford, Herefs. HR1 3SE. Tel: 01432 851992; fax - 01432 851994; e-mail - enquiries@fauld.com; website - www.fauld.com. Est. 1972. Open 8-5, appointment advisable. *Windsor chairs, extensive range of farmhouse tables, dressers and racks and many other case pieces. Bespoke work a speciality to traditional styles and methods.* VAT: Stan.

Fenlan

17B Stilebrook Rd., Yardley Road Industrial Estate, Olney, Bucks. Tel: 01234 711799; fax - same. Est. 1982. *Furniture restoration. Restoration products and fittings supplied; cabinet making and non-caustic stripping.* VAT: Stan/Spec.

Andrew Foott

4 Claremont Rd., Cheadle Hulme, Cheshire. SK8 6EG. Tel: 0161 485 3559. *Sympathetic restoration and conservation of antique furniture and mercurial barometers; free advice and estimates; quality items occasionally for sale.*

Forge Studio Workshops

Stour St., Manningtree, Essex. CO11 1BE. Tel: 01206 396222. BAFRA. *Carving, general restoration, copying and bespoke cabinet making.*

Glen Fraser-Sinclair - G. and R. Fraser-Sinclair

Hays Bridge Farm, Brickhouse Lane, South Godstone, Surrey. RH9 8JW. Tel: 01342 844112. BAFRA. *18th C furniture.*

Alistair J. Frayling-Cork

2 Mill Lane, Wallingford, Oxon. OX10 0DH. Tel:

01491 826221. BAFRA. Est. 1979. *Antique and period furniture, clock cases, ebonising, wood turning, stringed instruments and brass fittings repaired.*

Georgian Cabinets Manufacturers Ltd
Unit 4 Fountayne House, 2-8 Fountayne Rd., London N15 4QL. Tel: 020 8885 1293; fax - 020 8365 1114. Est. 1964. *Manufacturers, restorers and polishers. Large stock of inlaid furniture.* LOC: Near Seven Sisters underground, Tottenham. VAT: Stan.

Sebastian Giles Furniture
11 Junction Mews, London W2 1PN. Tel: 020 7258 3721. BAFRA.

Melven Glander
Tel: 01284 828429. *Restoration and repair service to furniture, woodwork, clocks and period fixtures and fittings; free estimates and advice. Collection and delivery. Upholstery arranged.*

Gow Antiques & Restoration
Pitscandly Farm, Forfar, by Lunanhead, Angus, Scotland. DD8 3NZ. (Jeremy Gow). Tel: 01307 465342; mobile - 07711 416786; e-mail - Jeremy @gowantiques.co.uk; website - www.gow antiques.co.uk. BAFRA. Accredited by GMC, Historic Scotland and the Museums and Galleries Commission. Appointment advisable. *17th-19th C English and Continental furniture. Specialist in marquetry, tortoiseshell and fine furniture.*

Greycroft Antiques
Greycroft, Station Rd., Errol, Perthshire, Scotland. PH2 7SN. (D. and Mrs. J. Pickett). Tel: 01821 642221; home - same. Est. 1981. Open 10-5.30 or by appointment.

Jeffrey Hall - Malvern Studios
56 Cowleigh Rd., Malvern, Worcs. WR14 1QD. Tel: 01684 574913; fax - 01684 569475. BAFRA. Est. 1961. Open 9-5.15, Fri. and Sat. 9-4.45. CL: Wed. *Antique furniture restoration.*

Jeremy Hall - Peter Hall & Son
Danes Rd., Staveley, Kendal, Cumbria. LA8 9PL. Tel: 01539 821633; fax - 01539 821905.

John Hartley
Johnson's Barn, Waterworks Rd., Sheet, Petersfield, Hants. GU32 2BY. Tel: 01730 233792; fax - 01730 233922. BAFRA. *Comprehensive restoration and conservation service, including carving, gilding, painted furniture, lacquer, marquetry, boulle and architectural woodwork. Adviser to The National Trust.*

Philip Hawkins
Glebe Workshop, Semley, Shaftesbury, Dorset. SP7 9AP. Tel: 01747 830830; e-mail - hawkinssemley@hotmail.com. BAFRA. *16th to early 18th C oak furniture restoration.*

Roland Haycraft
The Lamb Arcade, Wallingford, Oxon. Tel: 01491 839622. *All aspects of antique restorations; one-off reproductions and copying service. Fine furniture designed and made to traditional standards.*

Michael Hedgecoe
21 Burrow Hill Green, Chobham, Surrey. GU24 8QS. Tel: 01276 858206; fax - 01276 857352. LAPADA. BAFRA. *General restorations, cabinet work, polishing, upholstery, chair making.*

Heritage Antiques
Unit 2 Trench Farm, Tilley Green, Wem, Shrops. SY4 5PJ. (R. Nelms). Tel: 01939 235463; fax - 01939 235416; e-mail - heritageantiques@ btconnect.com; website - www.heritageantiques. co.uk. GADAR. Est. 1989. Open 9-5, Sat. by appointment. *Furniture, including antique and fitted, full restoration service, antique boxes and clock cases a speciality.*

Alan Hessel
The Old Town Workshop, St. George's Close, Moreton-in-Marsh, Glos. GL56 0LP. Tel: 01608 650026; fax - same; e-mail - hessel@chal.pixex. com. BAFRA. Est. 1976. Open Mon.- Fri. 9-5 or by appointment. *Comprehensive restoration service. English and Continental fine period furniture.*

Richard Higgins (Conservation)
The Old School, Longnor, Nr. Shrewsbury, Shrops. SY5 7PP. Tel: 01743 718162; fax - 01743 718022; e-mail - richardhigginsco@aol.com. BAFRA. LBHI. Conservation Register Museums and Galleries Commission. Est. 1988. Open by appointment. *Comprehensive restoration of all fine furniture and clocks, including movements and dials; specialist work to boulle, marquetry, carving, turning, cabinet and veneer work, lacquer, ormolu, metalwork, casting, glazing, polishing, upholstery, cane and rush seating. Stocks of old timber, veneers, tortoiseshell etc. held to ensure sympathetic restoration.*

Stuart Hobbs Antique Furniture Restoration
Meath Paddock, Meath Green Lane, Horley, Surrey. RH6 8HZ. Tel: 01293 782349. GMC. BAFRA. *Full restoration service for period furniture.*

John Hubbard Antique Restorations
Castle Ash, Birmingham Rd., Blakedown, Worcs. DY10 3SE. Tel: 01562 701020; e-mail - jhantiques@aol.com; website - www.antiques bulletin.com/JohnHubbardAntiques. LAPADA. CINOA. GMC. Est. 1968. Open by appointment only. *Restorations of furniture including French polishing, desk leathers and upholstery.* VAT: Stan.

Christian Macduff Hunt - Hunt and Lomas
Village Farm Workshops, Preston Village, Cirencester, Glos. GL7 5PR. Tel: 01285 640111. BAFRA. *17th-19th C oak, mahogany, walnut, satinwood, carving.*

Donald Hunter
The Old School Room, Shipton Oliffe, Cheltenham, Glos. GL54 4JB. Tel: 01242 820755. *Restoration of fine antiques, cabinet making, water gilding, lacquer work, decorative finishes.*

Rodney F. Kemble
16 Crag Vale Terrace, Glusburn, Nr. Keighley, West Yorks. BD20 8QU. Tel: 01535 636954/ 633702. BAFRA. Est. 1987. Open 9-5.30. *Cabinet restorations, clock cases, traditional hand finishes and upholstery.*

Raymond Konyn Antique Restorations
The Old Wheelwright's, Brasted Forge, Brasted, Kent. TN16 1JL. Tel: 01959 563863; fax - 01959 561262; e-mail - antique@antique-restorations. org.uk; website - www.antique-restorations.org. uk. BAFRA. Est. 1979. Open by appointment. *Furniture, traditional upholstery, longcase and bracket clock cases, polishing, brass casting. Consultancy.* VAT: Spec.

Roderick Larwood
The Oaks, Station Rd., Larling, Norfolk. NR16 2QS. Tel: 01953 717937; fax - same. BAFRA. Est. 1983. Open 8-5.30. CL: Sat. *Brass inlay, 18th to early 19th C furniture; French polishing.*

E.C. Legg and Son
3 College Farm Buildings, Tetbury Rd., Cirencester, Glos. GL7 6PY. Tel: 01285 650695. Est. 1902. Open 9-5. CL: Sat. *Restoration of furniture and gilt frames; caning; re-leathering desk tops.*

David C. E. Lewry
Wychelms, 66 Gorran Avenue, Rowner, Gosport, Hants. PO13 0NF. Tel: 01329 286901; fax - 01329 289964; mobile - 07785 766844. BAFRA. Est. 1979. *17th to early 19th C furniture.*

John Lloyd
Bankside Farm, Ditchling Common, West Sussex. RH15 0SJTel: 01444 480388; fax - same; mobile - 07941 124772; e-mail - lloydjohn@ aol. com; website - www.johnlloydfurniture.co.uk. BAFRA. *Sympathetic restoration and conservation of English and Continental furniture; traditional hand finishing, veneering, marquetry and inlay work, carving and turning, gilding, upholstery, rush/cane work, leather lining and tooling, lock repairs and keys. Antique furniture copied or designed and made to order. Regular delivery/collection service to London.Short courses in furniture restoration and gilding.*

Lomas Pigeon & Co. Ltd
37 Beehive Lane, Great Baddow, Chelmsford, Essex. CM2 9TQ. Tel: 01245 353708; fax - 01245 355211; e-mail - wpigeon@compuserve.com; website - www.lomas/pigeon.co.uk. BAFRA. AMU. Est. 1938. Open 10-4, Sat. 9-12. CL:Wed. *Antique restoration, French polishing, traditional and modern upholstery. Retailers of fine furniture and rocking horses. Curtains and soft furnishings made to order. Leather table top linings.*

Timothy Long Restoration
St. John's Church, London Rd., Dunton Green, Sevenoaks, Kent. TN13 2 TE. Tel: 01732 743368; fax - 01732 742206. BAFRA. *Cabinet restoration, French polishing, upholstery.*

Bruce Luckhurst
The Little Surrenden Workshops, Ashford Rd., Bethersden, Kent. TN26 3BG. Tel: 01233 820589; fax - 01580 243068; e-mail - training@woodwise. newnet.co.uk; website - www. bruceluckhurst.co.uk. BAFRA. Est. 1976. *Conservation and restoration training plus comprehensive restoration service.*

Mortlake Antiques
Nelson House Workshop, Kaber, Kirkby Stephen, Cumbria. CA17 4EF. (C.J. and Miss J.A. Bate). Tel: 017683 71666. Est. 1945. *Antique furniture restoration.*

Timothy Naylor
24 Bridge Rd., Chertsey, Surrey. KT16 8JN. Tel: 01932 567129; fax - 01932 564948. BAFRA. *Antique furniture restoration.*

Nicholas J. Newman
22 Eastcroft Rd., West Ewell, Surrey. KT19 9TX. Tel: 020 8224 3347. Est. 1983. *Comprehensive restorations including exterior woodwork and locks.*

Ben Norris & Co
Knowl Hill Farm, Knowl Hill, Kingsclere, Newbury, Berks. RG20 4NY. Tel: 01635 297950;

fax - 01635 299851. BAFRA. *All aspects of furniture restoration including carving, gilding, copy chair making and architectural woodwork. Excellent storage facilities.* VAT: Stan.

Nigel Northeast Cabinet Makers
Furniture Workshops, Back Drove, West Winterslow, Salisbury, Wilts. SP5 1RY. Tel: 01980 862051; fax - 01980 863986; website - www.nigelnortheast.co.uk. GADAR. Est. 1982. *Antique restoration and French polishing. New furniture made to order, chairs made to complete sets. Cane and rush seating; fire and flood damage service.* VAT: Stan.

Simon Paterson Fine Furniture Restoration
Whitelands, West Dean, Chichester. West Sussex. PO18 0RL. Tel: 01243 811900; e-mail - hotglue@lineone.net. BAFRA.

Clive Payne
Unit 4 Mount Farm, Churchill, Chipping Norton, Oxon. OX7 6NP. Tel: 01608 658856; fax - same; mobile - 07801 088363. LAPADA. BAFRA.

Noel Pepperall
Dairy Lane Cottage, Walberton, Arundel, West Sussex. BN18 0PT. Tel: 01243 551282; e-mail - pepperall@amserve.net; website - www.pepperall. co.uk. BAFRA. *Antique furniture restoration.*

Eva-Louise Pepperall
Dairy Lane Cottage, Walberton, Arundel, West Sussex. BN18 0PT. Tel: 01243 551282; e-mail - pepperall@amserve.net; website - www.pepperall. co.uk. BAFRA. *Gilding and japanning.*

T. L. Phelps - Fine Furniture Restoration
8 Mornington Terrace, Harrogate, North Yorks. HG1 5DH. Tel: 01423 524604. BAFRA. UKIC. Conservation Register. Est. 1984. Open 8.30-1 and 2-6, Sat. and other times by appointment only. *Specialist restoration and conservation services; all cabinet work, including dining tables, large items; all veneer work; architectural woodwork; traditional hand polishing, colouring and waxed finishes. Condition and treatment reports,f reports for insurance loss adjustors.* LOC: Map available on request, easy parking outside property. VAT: Stan.

Pinewood Furniture Studio Ltd
1 Eagle Trading Estate, Stourbridge Rd., Halesowen, West Midlands. B63 3UA. Tel: 0121 550 8228; fax - 0121 585 5611. *Manufacturers of pine furniture. Special orders undertaken.* VAT: Stan.

Plain Farm Workshop
The Old Dairy, Plain Farm, East Tisted, Alton, Hants. GU34 3RT. (Simon Worte). Tel: 01420 588362. Est. 1990. Open 10-5.30. *18th to 19th C English furniture restoration.*

Plowden & Smith Ltd
See entry under Art.

Albert Plumb Furniture Co
Briarfield, Itchenor Green, Chichester, West Sussex. PO20 7DA. Tel: 01243 513700/1; fax - same. BAFRA. *Oak, walnut, mahogany and country furniture, upholstery and cabinet making.*

A.J. Ponsford Antiques at Decora
Northbrook Rd., off Eastern Ave., Barnwood, Glos. GL4 3DP. (A.J. and R.L. Ponsford). Tel: 01452 307700. Est. 1962. Open 8-5. CL: Sat. *Valuations; restorations (furniture); rushing; caning; upholstery; picture framing; manufacturers of period book simulations and decorative accessories.* LOC: Off junction 11A, M5. VAT: Stan.

Neil Postons Restorations
29 South St., Leominster, Herefordshire. HR6 8JQ. Tel: 01568 616677; fax - same; mobile - 07710 297602. UKIC. Registered with the Museums and Galleries Commission. Est. 1988. Open 8.45-5.30, Sat. and other times by appointment. *Antique and fine furniture restorations including re-construction, veneering, carving, turning, French and wax polishing, re-upholstery, rush and cane seating.*

Ludovic Potts Restorations
Unit 1/1A, Haddenham Business Park, Station Rd., Haddenham, Ely, Cambs. CB6 3XD. Tel: 01353 741537; fax - 01353 741822; e-mail - mail@restorers.co.uk. BAFRA.

The Real Wood Furniture Company
London House, 16 Oxford St, Woodstock, Oxon. OX20 1TS. (Chris Baylis). Tel: 01993 813887; fax - 01993 812379; e-mail - info@realwood furniture.co.uk; website - www.realwood furniture.co.uk. Open 10.30-5.30, Sun. 11-5. *Large stock of superb hand crafted country furniture in traditional antique styles - solid oak, ash and cherry. Tables, dressers etc made to order. Large range of rush seated, Windsor and kitchen style chairs.*

Rectory Bungalow Workshop
Station Rd., Elton, Nr. Bingham, Notts. NG13 9LF. (E.M. Mackie) Tel: 01949 850878. Est. 1981. Open by appointment only. *Restorations - cane and rush seating, painted furniture.*

Nicholas S. Reeve

Barton Grange, Worlingworth, Woodbridge, Suffolk. IP13 7PE. Tel: 01728 628121; fax - 01728 628676; mobile - 07850 817216; e-mail - enquiries@nreeve.flexnet.co.uk; on-line catalogue - www.nreeve.flexnet.co.uk. Est. 1860. *Makers of 16th-18th C oak and cherry English country period furniture.* VAT: Stan.

Riches

Wixamtree, 69 Wood Lane, Cottonend, Beds. MK45 3AP. (R.J. Jennings). Tel: 01234 742121. Est. 1980. *Re-upholstery, repairs and re-caning.*

Raymond Robertson - Tolpuddle Antique Restorers

The Stables, Southover House, Tolpuddle, Dorchester, Dorset. DT2 7HF. Tel: 01305 848739. West Dean/BADA Award Winner. *Furniture, clock and barometer cases, marquetry, veneering and boulle work, lacquer, lacquer, japaning and gilding, insurance work undertaken.*

R.S. Rust (Replicas)

83 Main Rd., Kesgrave, Ipswich, Suffolk. IP5 1AF. Tel: 01473 623092; e-mail - bobandedwina @onetel.net.uk. Est. 1977. Open Tues., Thurs., Fri. 9-5. *Replica hardwood furniture. Trade only.*

David A. Sayer - Courtlands Restorations

Courtlands, Park Rd., Banstead, Surrey. SM7 3EF. Tel: 01737 352429; fax - 01737 373255; e-mail - dsayer@courtlands98.freeserve.co.uk; website - www.antiquerestorationsurrey.com. BAFRA. Est. 1985. Open 8-5, Sat.and Sun. by appointment. *Comprehensive restoration service including repairs, polishing, carving, turning, veneering, gilding. Metal parts - replacement or repair.*

Michael Schryver Antiques Ltd

The Granary, 10 North Street, Dorking, Surrey, RH4 1DN. Tel: 01306 881110. Est. 1970. Open 8.30-5.30, Sat. 8-12. *Cabinet work, polishing, upholstery, metal work.* VAT: Stan/Spec.

Phillip Slater

93 Hewell Rd., Barnt Green, Worcs. B45 8NL. Tel: 0121 445 4942. BAFRA.

Alun Courtney Smith

45 Windmill Rd., Brentford, Middx. TW8 0QQ. Tel: 020 8568 5249; fax - same. BAFRA.

Eric Smith - Antique Furniture Restorations

The Church, Park Rd., Darwen, Lancs. BB3 2LD.

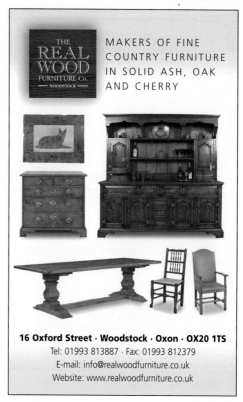
Tel: 01254 776222. BAFRA. UKIC. MA. Conservation Register Museums & Galleries Commission. *Restoration of longcase clocks and furniture. Comprehensive conservation and restoration of fine furniture.*

Alan & Kathy Stacey Tea Caddies & Fine Boxes

Yeovil, Somerset. Tel: 01963 441333; home - same; fax - 01963 441330; website - www. antiqueboxes. uk.com. LAPADA. BAFRA. Open every day by appointment. *Conservation, specialising in tea caddies, fine boxes, objects, tortoiseshell, ivory, MOP, Shagreen, horn, bone, exotic timber items. Worldwide collection and delivery, sales, maintenance of existing collections. Consultancy, valuations, search.* LOC: 2 miles from A303. PARK: Own. SER: Collection service from station. VAT: Stan.

Julian Stanley Woodcarving - Furniture

Unit 5 Bourton Link, Bourton Industrial Park, Bourton-on-the-Water, Glos. GL54 2HQ. Tel: 01451 822577; fax - same; e-mail - julian@ julianstanley-woodcarvingfurniture.co.uk; website - www.julianstanley-woodcarvingfurniture.co.uk. MCA. Est. 1983. *Carved furniture - the classical* work of the 18th C is re-created alongside contemporary designs, figure work and architectural pieces. Showroom on site includes contemporary paintings and sculpture. VAT: Stan/Spec.

Robert Tandy Restoration
Unit 5 Manor Workshops, Manor Park, West End, Nailsea, Bristol, Somerset. BS48 4DD. Tel: 01275 856378. BAFRA. *Furniture restoration especially 17th-19th C longcase clock cases; French polishing and traditional oil and wax finishing.* VAT: Stan.

Thakeham Furniture
Marehill Rd., Pulborough, West Sussex. RH20 2DY. (Timothy Chavasse). Tel: 01798 872006. Est. 1984. Open 9-5. CL: Sat. *Cabinet work, veneer repairs, wax and French polishing, turning, marquetry, carving, etc.* LOC: 1 mile east of Pulborough next to White Horse Inn.

Titian Studio
32 Warple Way, Acton, London W3 0DJ (Rodrigo and Rosaria Titian). Tel: 020 8222 6600; fax - 020 8749 2220; e-mail - enquiries@titianstudios. co.uk; website - www.titianstudios.co.uk. BAFRA. Est. 1963. Open 8.30-5.30. *Carving, gilding, lacquer, painted furniture, French polishing, Japanning.*

Clifford J. Tracy
Unit 3 Shaftesbury Industrial Centre, Icknield Way, Letchworth, Herts. SG6 1HE. (Clifford and Mark Tracy). Tel: 01462 684855; fax - 01462 684833. BAFRA. Est. 1961. Open 7-4, Fri. 7-3. CL:Sat. *General restorations including boulle, marquetry, leather lining, upholstery, period panelling.*

Treen Antiques
Treen House, 72 Park Rd., Prestwich, Manchester, Lancs. M25 0FA. (Simon J Feingold). Tel: 0161 720 7244; fax - same; mobile - 07973 471185; e-

mail - simonfeingold@hotmail.com; website - www.treenantiques.com. GADAR, RFS, FHS, UKIC. Est. 1988. Open by appointment. *Conservation and restoration of all antique furniture (including vernacular) and woodwork, with emphasis on preserving original finish. Research undertaken, housekeeping advice, environmental monitoring and all aspects of conservation. Furniture assessment and advice on purchase and sales. Courses in restoration work held on request. Listed in Bonham's Directory.*

Neil Trinder Furniture Restoration
Burrowlee House, Broughton Road, Hillsborough, Sheffield, South Yorks. S6 2AS. Tel: 0114 2852428. *Boulle, gilding, marquetry, carving, upholstery, fine furniture.*

William Trist
135 St Leonard's St., Edinburgh, Scotland. EH8 9RB. Tel: 0131 667 7775; fax - 0131 667 4333. BAFRA.

Tony Vernon
15 Follett Rd., Topsham, Devon. EX3 0JP. Tel: 01392 874635; e-mail - tonyvernon@antique wood.co.uk; website - www.antiquewood.co.uk. BAFRA. *Furniture, cabinet making, upholstery, gilding, veneering, inlay and French polishing.*

Fabio Villani
Clover, Alves, Forres, Scotland. IV36 2RA. Tel: 01343 850007; mobile - 07990 694972; e-mail - fabio@fabiovillani.co.uk; website - www. fabiovillani.co.uk. BAFRA. *Consultation and tuition for conservation of gilded frames and sculptures, objets d'art, furniture and wooden fittings. Traditional finishes and patina imitation. Lectures.*

W. Thomas Ltd.
12 Warwick Place. London. W9 2PX. Tel: 020 7286. Est. 1945. BAFRA.

E.F. Wall

32 Church St. Woodbridge, Suffolk. IP12 1DH. (Libby Wall). Tel: 01394 610511; fax - same; mobile - 07885 374917; e-mail - e.f.wall@ btinternet.co.uk; website - www.efwall.co.uk. Open 10-5.30. CL:Wed. *Makers of fine furniture.* VAT: Stan/Spec.

Barry J. Wateridge

Padouk, Portsmouth Rd., Bramshott Chase, Hindhead, Surrey. GU26 6DB. Tel: 01428 607235. *French polishing and antique furniture restorations.*

Weaver Neave and Daughter

17 Lifford St. Putney, London SW15 1NY. Tel: 020 8785 2464. *Re-caning and re-rushing of antique furniture in traditional manner with traditional materials.*

Gerald Weir Antiques

Unit 1, Riverside Industrial Park, Wherstead Rd., Ipswich, Suffolk. Tel: 01473 692300; fax - 01473 692333. Open by appointment. *Suppliers of reproduction oak furniture for European markets and decorative furniture for American markets. Trade Only.*

Laurence Whitfield

The Old School, Winstone, Cirencester, Glos. GL7 7JX. Tel: 01285 821342. BAFRA.

Wick Antiques

Fairlea House, 110-112 Marsh Lane, Lymington, Hants. SO41 8EE. Tel: 01590 677558; fax - same. *Furniture polishing, repairs, upholstery and re-gilding.* LAPADA.

Bryan Wigington - Antique Furniture Restoration

The Courtyard, 4 Hightown, Hay-on-Wye, Hereford, HR3 5AE. Tel: 01497 820545 (24 hr.) Est. 1961. Open any time by appointment. *Furniture conservation and restoration.* LOC: Behind Post Office.

Jonathan Wilbye

Blue Bell Farm, North Stainmore, Kirkby Stephen, Cumbria, CA17 4DY. Tel: 01768 341715. Est. 1983. *Full restoration service including all carving, inlay, turning and polishing. Longcase clock cases a speciality.*

Peter Williams Antique Furniture Restoration

Silkmill House, 4 Charlton Rd., Tetbury, Glos. GL8. Tel: 01666 502311. *Early oak, period mahogany, walnut and country furniture. Woodturning, French polishing and wax finish, gold tooled leather. Insurance claims. Antiques bought and sold. Established over 25 years.*

(Top row, and first and fifth of middle row) Buttons of bonded slices of red, white and blue. (Middle row, second and fourth) Woven by J. & J. Cash Ltd Coventry. (Centre) Painted wood. (Bottom row, first, second, fourth and fifth) White discs painted. (Centre) Contemporary.

From an article entitled "Commemorative Buttons" by Gillian Meredith which appeared in the October 2001 issue of **Antique Collecting**. For more details and to subscribe see page 21.

GLASS

The Antique Restoration Studio
See entry under Furniture.

Sargeant Restorations
21 The Green, Westerham, Kent. TN16 1AX. 01959 562130. *Restoration and cleaning of chandeliers, lustres and candelabra.*

INSURANCE AND FINANCE

The Art and Antiques Service
The Old Stores, High St., Elmdon, Saffron Walden, Essex. CB11 4NLTel: 01223 303051; fax - 01223 303071; mobile - 07850 932894; e-mail - artservice@clara.net. *Professional valuations and insurance for probate, family division. Buying specific items or total refurbishments including architectural - fireplaces, doors. Advice on building up or scaling down collections and placing items for sale.*

Lockson Insurance Consultants
29 Broomfield St, London E14 6BX. Tel: 020 7515 8600; fax - 020 7515 4866; e-mail - enquiries @lockson.co.uk; website - www.lockson.co.uk. *Specialists in all types of fine art, exhibition and memorabilia insurance.*

Anthony Wakefield & Company Ltd
4 Guildford Rd., Westcott, Dorking, Surrey. RH4 3NR. Tel: 01306 740555; fax - 01306 740770; e-mail - aw@anthonywakefield.com. Members IIB. Est. 1983. *Fine art and household insurance brokers; special terms for collectors; exclusive antique and fine art dealers policy with Axa Insurance UK plc; exclusive Connoisseur household policy with dealers/fairs extension.*

Windsor Insurance Brokers Ltd - Fine Art & Antiques Division
160-166 Borough High St., London SE1 1JR. Tel: 020 7407 7144; fax - 020 7827 9312. Lloyds Insurance Brokers. *Specialist Lloyd's brokers in antique and fine art dealers, fine art galleries, contemporary art galleries, restorers and conservators, antique centres, auctioneers and valuers "Heirloom" designed for dealers' own collections and household and all risks insurance brokers. Official brokers to LAPADA, BAFRA, The Fine Art Trade Guild, IDDA.*

IVORY

Coromandel
Wimbledon, London SW19. *See entry under London SW19 in dealer listing.*

E. and C. Royall Antiques
See entry under Metalwork.

Alan & Kathy Stacey Tea Caddies & Fine Boxes
See entry under Furniture.

JEWELLERY AND SILVER

Eastbourne Engraving
See entry under Engraving.

Goldcare
5 Bedford St., Middlesborough, Cleveland. TS1 2LL. Tel: 01642 231343; website - www.goldcare repairs.co.uk. *Jewellery repair, engraving, re-stringing, stone cutting. Restoration of silver and cutlery; brass, copper, pinchbeck restoration.* VAT: Stan.

LOCKS AND KEYS

Bramah Security Centres Ltd.
31 Oldbury Place, London W1U 5PT. Tel: 020 7935 7147; fax - 020 7935 2779. Open 8.30-5.30, Sat. 9-1. *Keys cut to old locks; old locks opened; repair of old locks; new locks made to an old design; original Bramah locks dated. Quotation provided. Overseas work undertaken.* LOC: Near Baker Street tube station. VAT: Stan.

METALWORK

Rupert Harris Conservation
Studio 5c, 1 Fawe St., London E14 6PD. Tel: 020 7515 2020; fax - 020 7987 7994; e-mail - enquiries@rupertharris.com; website - www. rupertharris.com. UKIC, IIC, NACE, SPAB, ICOM. Open by appointment. *Conservation of fine metalwork and sculpture including bronze, lead, zinc and electrotype; chandeliers, lanterns, gold and silver, fine ironwork, arms and armour, ecclesiastical metalwork, casting, replication and gilding; consultancy and maintenance. Appointed metalwork advisors to the National Trust for England and Wales.*

Optimum Brasses
7 Castle St., Bampton, Devon. EX16 9NS. (Robert and Rachel Byles). Tel: 01398 331515; fax - 01398 331164; e-mail - brass@obida.com; website - www.obida.com. Est. 1981. Open 9-1 and 2-4, Sat. and other times by appointment. *Over 5,000 replica brass handles etc. for antique furniture. Copying service.* LOC: On Wiveliscombe road. VAT: Stan.

Plowden & Smith Ltd
See entry under Art.

E. and C. Royall Antiques
10 Waterfall Way, Medbourne, Leics. LE16 8EE. Tel: 01858 565744. Open 9-5. *Restorations - bronzes, ivories, brass including inlay work, metalware, woodcarving, upholstery, French polishing.*

Shawlan Antiques Metal Restorers
Croydon/South London area. Tel: 020 8684 5082; fax - same. *High quality restoration of metalware, using traditional methods and materials. Over 25 years experience.*

MUSICAL INSTRUMENTS

J V Pianos & Cambridge Pianola
85 High St., Landbeach, Cambridge, Cambs. CB4 8DR. (Tom Poole) Tel: 01223 861348/861408; fax - 01223 441276; e-mail - ftpoole@talk21.com; website - www.cambridgepianolacompany.co.uk. Est. 1972. Open Mon.-Fri., prior 'phone call advisable, or by appointment. *Restoration and sales of period pianos, pianolas and player pianos; music rolls, repair materials, books and accessories.*

PHOTOGRAPHY

Gerry Clist Photography LMPA
London NW6. Tel: 020 7624 0716. *Specialising in sculptures, antiques and works of art photography - studio and location.*

REPRODUCTION STONEWORK

Hampshire Gardencraft
Rake Industries, Rake, Nr. Petersfield, Hants. GU31 5DR. Tel: 01730 895182; fax - 01730 893216; e-mail - sales@hampshire-gardencraft. com; website - www.hampshire-gardencraft.com Est. 1984. *Manufacturers of antiqued garden ornaments, troughs and pots in reconstituted stone in an old Cotswold stone finish. Many designs, catalogue available.*

UK's top aged stone statuary manufacturer. Family business, founded 1970. Friendly, helpful service. 400 different designs. 3 Unique finishes. Mythical Creatures. Classical Statuary. Contemporary Statuary. Heads, Hands, Feet & Torsos. Fruit, Finials, Obelisks & Stones. Pedestals, Urns, Vases & Troughs. Sundials, Seats, Birdbaths, Fountains

LUCAS GARDEN STATUARY
Firstland Park Estate, Albourne, West Sussex BN6 9JJ
Tel: +44 (0) 1273 494931
Fax: +44 (0) 1273 495125
www.lucasstone.co.uk
Email: trade@lucasstone.co.uk

Lucas Garden Statuary

Firstland Park Estate, Henfield Rd., Aldbourne, Hassocks, East Sussex BN6 9JJ. Tel: 01273 494931; fax - 01273 495125; e-mail - trade@lucasstone.co.uk; website - www.lucasstone.co.uk. Est. 1970. *Manufacturers of over 400 designs of aged stone statuary - mythical, classical, contemporary; head, hands, feet and torsos; fruit, finials, obelisks, pedestals, urns, vases and troughs, sundials, seats, birdbaths and fountains.*

SUPPLIERS

C. and A.J. Barmby

140 Lavender Hill, Tonbridge, Kent. TA9 2NJ. (Chris and Angela Barmby). Tel: 01732 771590; fax - same; e-mail - Bookpilot@aol.com. Est. 1980. Open by appointment. *Suppliers of display stands in wire, acrylic and wood; reference books and catalogues. Mail order service.* VAT: Stan.

Dauphin Museum Services Ltd

PO Box 602, Oxford, Oxon. OX44 9LU. (John Harrison-Banfield). Tel: 01865 343542; fax - 01865 343307. Est. 1985. Open 9-5, Sat. by appointment. Please telephone for directions.

Design and manufacture of stands, mounts, cabinets and environmental cases. Mounting service. Acrylic display stands - other materials utilised include glass, wood, metal, stone, marble, brass and bronze. Free mail order catalogue available.

Just Bros. and Co.

Roeder House, Vale Rd., London N4 1QA. Tel: 020 8880 2505; fax - 020 8802 0062; e-mail - just@freenet.co.uk. Member British Jewellery and Giftware Federation Ltd. Open 9-5, Fri. 9-12.30. *One of the largest suppliers of quality jewellery and presentation cases in Europe. Catalogue on request.*

Marshall Brass

Keeling Hall Rd., Foulsham, Norfolk. NR20 5PR. Tel: 01362 684105; fax - 01362 684280; e-mail - admin@marshall-brass.com; website - www.marshall-brass.com. GMC. *Suppliers of quality period furniture fittings in brass and iron.*

Martin and Co. Ltd

119 Camden St., Birmingham, West Midlands. B1 3DJ. Tel: 0121 233 2111; fax - 0121 236 0488; website - www.martin.co.uk-onlinecatalogue. ASFI, GAI. Open 9-5.30. CL: Sat. *Cabinet hardware supplied - handles, locks, hinges, castors etc.* LOC: Jewellery Quarter. *Trade Only.*

Alan Morris Wholesale

Stonecourt, Townsend, Nympsfield, Glos. GL10 3UF. Tel: 01453 861069. *Display stands - coated wire, plastic, acrylic and wood for plates, cups, saucers, bowls etc; wire and disc; jewellery boxes, polishing and cleaning cloths, peelable white labels and strung tickets. Mail order available.* VAT: Stan.

Relics of Witney Ltd.

35 Bridge St., Witney, Oxon. OX28 1DA. Tel: 01993 704611; website - www.tryrelics.co.uk. Est. 1987. Open 9-5. *Suppliers of furniture restoration material, brass castors, handles, locks, waxes and polish, upholstery and caning requisites, Farrow & Ball and reproduction paints, stencils, etc. Mail order also. Online catalogue.* LOC: Main road.

J. Shiner and Sons Ltd.

8 Windmill St., London W1T 2JE. Tel: 020 7636 0740; fax - 020 7580 0740. *Suppliers of brass handles, castors, locks, brass grills and leathers.*

Suffolk Brass

Thurston, Bury St. Edmunds, Suffolk. IP31 3SN. (Mark Peters). Tel: 01359 233383; fax - 01359

233384. Est. 1987. Open 8.30-5. CL: Sat. *Period replica cabinet fittings in brass and iron. One-off castings in lost wax or sand. Catalogue £5.* VAT: Stan. *Trade Only.*

The Victorian Ring Box Company
Unit 1, Fleetside, Gatehouse of Fleet, Kirkcudbrightshire, Scotland. DG7 2JY. (The Franca Bruno Company). Tel: 01557 814466/814054; fax - same; e-mail - victorianringbox.co.@scotland.com. Est.1990. By appointment only. *Manufacturers and distributors of high quality antique style presentation boxes; also available with sterling silver tops and in tartan.*

TEXTILES

The Textile Conservancy Company Ltd
Unit 3A Pickhill Business Centre, Smallhythe Road, Tenterden, Kent. TN30 7LZ. Tel: 01580 761600; fax - same; e-mail - alex@textile-conservation.co.uk; website - www.textile-conservation.co.uk. UKIC. Est. 1997. *Cleaning and repair of historic textiles, tapestries and rugs. Professional advice on correct storage and display.*

The Textile Restoration Studio
2 Talbot Rd., Bowdon, Altrincham, Cheshire. WA14 3JD. (Jacqueline and Michael Hyman). Tel: 0161 928 0020; fax - same; websites - www.textilerestoration.co.uk and www.conservationconsortium.com. Conservation Register, UK Institute for Conservation. Est. 1982. *Cleaning and repair of all antique textiles including tapestries, samplers, canvas work, beadwork, lace, costume, ecclesiastical vestments and furnishings, dolls and fans. Mail order catalogue of specialist textile conservation materials (free with large stamped addressed envelope).*

TORTOISESHELL

Alan & Kathy Stacey Tea Caddies & Fine Boxes
See entry under Furniture.

TOYS

Robert Mullis Rocking Restoration Services Ltd
55 Berkeley Rd., Wroughton, Swindon, Wilts. SN4 9BN. Tel: 01793 813583; fax - 01793 813577. British Toymakers Guild. *Full or partial restor-*ations *of antique horses, some wooden toy restoration. Traditional methods and materials used. Collection and delivery. New rocking horses made in five sizes, commissions undertaken.*

Tobilane Designs
The Toyworks, Holly House, Askham, Penrith, Cumbria. CA10 2PG. (Paul and Elaine Commander). Tel: 01931 712077; e-mail - tobilane@commander.clara.net; website - www.commander.clara.net/tobilane.htm. Est. 1985. Wed - Sat. 10-5, Sun. 11-4. CL: Mon. and Tues. *Traditional toymakers and restorers of old toys including rocking horses and teddies. Identification and valuation service.* LOC: Village centre, 5 miles south of Penrith. VAT: Stan.

Figured walnut and marquetry bonheur du jour *with gilt metal mounts, glazed panel doors flanking arched central mirror, inlaid fall front and cabriole legs. Illustrated by C. & R. Light in 1881. An 1860 version sold for £2,530 and an 1890, shown here, for £2,000 at Sotheby's South in January.*

From an article entitled "19th Century English Furniture - Gillows and the Ghost of Sam Jim" by John Andrews which appeared in the July/August 2001 issue of **Antique Collecting**. For more details and to subscribe see page 21.

ALPHABETICAL LIST OF TOWNS AND VILLAGES AND COUNTIES UNDER WHICH THEY ARE LISTED.

A

Abbots Langley, Herts.
Abbots Leigh, Somerset.
Aberdeen, Scotland.
Aberdour, Scotland.
Aberfeldy, Scotland.
Aberford, Yorks. West.
Abergavenny, Wales.
Abernyte, Scotland.
Aberystwyth, Wales.
Abinger Hammer, Surrey.
Abridge, Essex.
Accrington, Lancs.
Acle, Norfolk.
Acrise, Kent.
Adversane, Sussex West.
Alcester, Warks.
Aldeburgh, Suffolk.
Alderley Edge, Cheshire.
Aldermaston, Berks.
Alderney, C.I.
Alford, Lincs.
Alfreton, Derbys.
Alfriston, Sussex East.
Allington, Lincs.
Allonby, Cumbria.
Alnwick, Northumbs.
Alresford, Hants.
Alrewas, Staffs.
Alsager, Cheshire.
Alston, Cumbria.
Altrincham, Cheshire.
Amersham, Bucks.
Ampthill, Beds.
Andover, Hants.
Andoversford, Glos.
Angarrack, Cornwall.
Angmering, Sussex West.
Antrim, Co. Antrim, N. Ireland.
Appledore, Kent.
Armagh, Co. Armagh, N. Ireland.
Arthingworth, Northants.
Arundel, Sussex West.
Ascot, Berks.
Ascott-under-Wychwood, Oxon.

Ash, Kent.
Ash Vale, Surrey.
Ashbourne, Derbys.
Ashburton, Devon.
Ashby-de-la-Zouch, Leics.
Ashford, Kent.
Ashtead, Surrey.
Ashurst, Kent.
Astley Bridge, Lancs.
Aston Tirrold, Oxon.
Astwood Bank, Worcs.
Atcham, Shrops.
Attleborough, Norfolk.
Atworth, Wilts.
Auchterarder, Scotland.
Auldearn, Scotland.
Axbridge, Somerset.
Axminster, Devon.
Aylesby, Lincs.
Aylsham, Norfolk.

B

Bagshot, Surrey.
Baildon, Yorks. West.
Bakewell, Derbys.
Balcombe, Sussex West.
Baldock, Herts.
Balfron, Scotland.
Ballater, Scotland.
Balsham, Cambs.
Bampton, Devon.
Bangor, Wales.
Barham, Kent.
Barkham, Berks.
Barley Mow, Northants.
Barlow, Derbys.
Barmouth, Wales.
Barnard Castle, Durham.
Barnet, Herts.
Barnsley, Glos.
Barnsley, Yorks. South.
Barnstaple, Devon.
Barnt Green, Worcs.
Barrhead, Scotland.
Barrington, Somerset.
Barry, Wales.
Barton, Cambs.
Barton, Cheshire.
Basingstoke, Hants.
Bath, Somerset.

Batheaston, Somerset.
Batley, Yorks. West.
Battlesbridge, Essex.
Bawdeswell, Norfolk.
Bawtry, Yorks. South.
Baythorne End, Essex.
Beaconsfield, Bucks.
Beauly, Scotland.
Beaumaris (Anglesey), Wales.
Beccles, Suffolk.
Beckenham, Kent.
Bedale, Yorks. North.
Bedford, Beds.
Bedhampton, Hants.
Bedingfield, Suffolk.
Beech, Hants.
Beer, Devon.
Beeston, Notts.
Beetham, Cumbria.
Belfast, N. Ireland.
Belper, Derbys.
Bembridge, Isle of Wight.
Bentley, Suffolk.
Bere Regis, Dorset.
Berkeley, Glos.
Berkhamsted, Herts.
Berwick-on-Tweed, Northumbs.
Bessacarr, Yorks. South.
Betchworth, Surrey.
Beverley, Yorks. East.
Bewdley, Worcs.
Bibury, Glos.
Bicester, Oxon.
Bideford, Devon.
Biggleswade, Beds.
Billingham, Durham.
Billingshurst, Sussex West.
Bilsington, Kent.
Binfield, Berks.
Birchington, Kent.
Birdbrook, Essex.
Birkenhead, Merseyside.
Birmingham, West Mids.
Bishop's Castle, Shrops.
Bishop's Stortford, Herts.

Bishops Cleeve, Glos.
Blackburn, Lancs.
Blackmore, Essex.
Blackpool, Lancs.
Bladon, Oxon.
Blaenau Ffestiniog, Wales.
Blair Atholl, Scotland.
Blairgowrie, Scotland.
Blakeney, Glos.
Blandford Forum, Dorset.
Bletchingley, Surrey.
Blewbury, Oxon.
Bloxham, Oxon.
Blythburgh, Suffolk.
Bodmin, Cornwall.
Bollington, Cheshire.
Bolton, Lancs.
Bolton-by-Bowland, Lancs.
Borehamwood, Herts.
Boroughbridge, Yorks. North.
Boscastle, Cornwall.
Boston, Lincs.
Boston Spa, Yorks. West.
Botley, Hants.
Bottisham, Cambs.
Boughton, Kent.
Bourne, Lincs.
Bourne End, Bucks.
Bournemouth, Dorset.
Bowdon, Cheshire.
Bowness on Windermere, Cumbria.
Brackley, Northants.
Bradford, Yorks. West.
Bradford-on-Avon, Wilts.
Bradwell, Derbys.
Brambridge, Hants.
Bramley, Surrey.
Brampton, Cambs.
Brampton, Cumbria.
Brancaster Staithe, Norfolk.
Brandsby, Yorks. North.
Branksome, Dorset.
Brasted, Kent.
Braunton, Devon.

Brecon, Wales.
Brentwood, Essex.
Brereton, Staffs.
Bridge of Earn, Scotland.
Bridgend, Wales.
Bridgnorth, Shrops.
Bridlington, Yorks. East.
Bridport, Dorset.
Brierfield, Lancs.
Brightlingsea, Essex.
Brighton, Sussex East.
Brinklow, Warks.
Brinkworth, Wilts.
Bristol, Glos.
Brixham, Devon.
Broadstairs, Kent.
Broadway, Worcs.
Brockenhurst, Hants.
Brodick and Whiting Bay, Scotland.
Bromley, Kent.
Brook, Hants.
Broseley, Shrops.
Broughton Astley, Leics.
Broxted, Essex.
Bruton, Somerset.
Buckingham, Bucks.
Budleigh Salterton, Devon.
Bungay, Suffolk.
Burford, Oxon.
Burgess Hill, Sussex West.
Burghfield Common, Berks.
Burlton, Shrops.
Burneston, Yorks. North.
Burnham Market, Norfolk.
Burnham-on-Sea, Somerset.
Burnley, Lancs.
Burscough, Lancs.
Burton Salmon, Yorks. North.
Burton-on-Trent, Staffs.
Burwash, Sussex East.
Burwell, Cambs.
Bury, Lancs.
Bury St. Edmunds, Suffolk.
Bushey, Herts.
Bushmills, Co. Antrim, N. Ireland.
Buxton, Derbys.

C

Cadnam, Hants.
Caerphilly, Wales.
Caistor, Lincs.
Callington, Cornwall.
Calne, Wilts.
Camborne, Cornwall.
Cambridge, Cambs.
Cambridge, Glos.
Camelford, Cornwall.
Canonbie, Scotland.
Canterbury, Kent.
Cardiff, Wales.
Carhampton, Somerset.
Carlisle, Cumbria.
Carmarthen, Wales.
Carrefour Selous, St. Lawrence, Jersey, C.I.
Carrickfergus, Co. Antrim, N. Ireland.
Carshalton, Surrey.
Cartmel, Cumbria.
Castle Ashby, Northants.
Castle Donington, Leics.
Castletown, Isle of Man.
Cavendish, Suffolk.
Caversham, Berks.
Cawood, Yorks. North.
Ceres, Scotland.
Cerne Abbas, Dorset.
Chacewater, Cornwall.
Chagford, Devon.
Chale, Isle of Wight.
Chalfont St. Giles, Bucks.
Chalford, Glos.
Chalgrove, Oxon.
Chard, Somerset.
Cheadle Hulme, Cheshire.
Cheam, Surrey.
Chelmsford, Essex.
Cheltenham, Glos.
Chepstow, Wales.
Cherhill, Wilts.
Chertsey, Surrey.
Chesham, Bucks.
Chester, Cheshire.
Chesterfield, Derbys.
Chichester, Sussex West.
Chilcompton, Somerset.
Chilton, Oxon.
Chippenham, Wilts.
Chipping Campden, Glos.

Chipping Norton, Oxon.
Chipping Sodbury, Glos.
Chirk, Wales.
Chislehurst, Kent.
Chittering, Cambs.
Chobham, Surrey.
Chorley, Lancs.
Chorleywood, Herts.
Christchurch, Dorset.
Christian Malford, Wilts.
Church Stretton, Shrops.
Churt, Surrey.
Ciliau Aeron, Wales.
Cirencester, Glos.
Clare, Suffolk.
Cleethorpes, Lincs.
Cleobury Mortimer, Shrops.
Clevedon, Somerset.
Clitheroe, Lancs.
Clola by Mintlaw, Scotland.
Clutton, Somerset.
Coalville, Leics.
Cobham, Surrey.
Cockermouth, Cumbria.
Cocking, Sussex West.
Codford, Wilts.
Codsall, Staffs.
Coggeshall, Essex.
Coldstream, Scotland.
Coleraine, Co. Londonderry, N. Ireland.
Coleshill, Warks.
Colne, Lancs.
Coltishall, Norfolk.
Colwyn Bay, Wales.
Comber, Co. Down, N. Ireland.
Comberton, Cambs.
Congleton, Cheshire.
Conisholme, Lincs.
Connor Downs, Cornwall.
Consett, Durham.
Conwy, Wales.
Cooden, Sussex East.
Cookham Rise, Berks.
Cookstown, Co. Tyrone, N. Ireland.
Corbridge, Northumbs.
Corringham, Essex.
Corsham, Wilts.
Cottered, Herts.

Coulsdon, Surrey.
Cove, Scotland.
Coventry, West Mids.
Cowbridge, Wales.
Cowes, Isle of Wight.
Cowfold, Sussex West.
Coxley, Somerset.
Cranborne, Dorset.
Cranbrook, Kent.
Craven Arms, Shrops.
Crawley, Hants.
Crayford, Kent.
Crediton, Devon.
Cremyll, Cornwall.
Crewe, Cheshire.
Crewkerne, Somerset.
Criccieth, Wales.
Crickhowell, Wales.
Cricklade, Wilts.
Cromarty, Scotland.
Cromer, Norfolk.
Crosby Ravensworth, Cumbria.
Cross Hills, Yorks. North.
Cross in Hand, Sussex East.
Croydon, Surrey.
Crudwell, Wilts.
Cuckfield, Sussex West.
Cullompton, Devon.

D

Danbury, Essex.
Darlington, Durham.
Darlton, Notts.
Dartmouth, Devon.
Darwen, Lancs.
Datchet, Berks.
Davenham, Cheshire.
Deal, Kent.
Debden, Essex.
Debenham, Suffolk.
Deddington, Oxon.
Deganwy, Wales.
Depden, Suffolk.
Derby, Derbys.
Devizes, Wilts.
Disley, Cheshire.
Diss, Norfolk.
Ditchling, Sussex East.
Ditton Priors, Shrops.
Dobwalls, Cornwall.
Doncaster, Yorks. South.
Dorchester, Dorset.
Dorchester-on-Thames, Oxon.
Dorking, Surrey.

Dornoch, Scotland.
Dorridge, West Mids.
Douglas, Isle of Man.
Doune, Scotland.
Doveridge, Derbys.
Downham Market,
  Norfolk.
Driffield, Yorks. East.
Drinkstone, Suffolk.
Droitwich, Worcs.
Dronfield, Derbys.
Duffield, Derbys.
Dulverton, Somerset.
Dundee, Scotland.
Dunecht, Scotland.
Dunham-on-Trent, Notts.
Dunkeld, Scotland.
Dunsfold, Surrey.
Dunster, Somerset.
Durham, Durham.
Duxford, Cambs.

E

Earl Shilton, Leics.
Earsham, Norfolk.
Easingwold, Yorks.
  North.
East Budleigh, Devon.
East Dereham, Norfolk.
East Grinstead, Sussex
  West.
East Hagbourne, Oxon.
East Molesey, Surrey.
East Peckham, Kent.
East Pennard,
  Somerset.
East Rudham, Norfolk.
Eastbourne, Sussex
  East.
Ebrington, Glos.
Edenbridge, Kent.
Edgware, Middx.
Edinburgh, Scotland.
Elgin, Scotland.
Ely, Cambs.
Empingham, Rutland.
Emsworth, Hants.
Enderby, Leics.
Enfield, Middx.
Epsom, Surrey.
Ermington, Devon.
Eversley, Hants.
Evesham, Worcs.
Ewell, Surrey.
Exeter, Devon.
Exmouth, Devon.
Eye, Suffolk.

F

Fairford, Glos.

Fairlie, Scotland.
Fakenham, Norfolk.
Faldingworth, Lincs.
Falmouth, Cornwall.
Fareham, Hants.
Faringdon, Oxon.
Farnborough, Hants.
Farnham, Surrey.
Farningham, Kent.
Faversham, Kent.
Felixstowe, Suffolk.
Feniscowles, Lancs.
Fenton Barns,
  Scotland.
Filey, Yorks. North.
Finchingfield, Essex.
Finedon, Northants.
Finningham, Suffolk.
Fishguard, Wales.
Fishlake, Yorks. South.
Flamborough, Yorks.
  East.
Flaxton, Yorks. North.
Flimwell, Sussex East.
Flore, Northants.
Fochabers, Scotland.
Folkestone, Kent.
Fontmell Magna,
  Dorset.
Fordham, Cambs.
Fordingbridge, Hants.
Forest Row, Sussex
  East.
Forfar, Scotland.
Forres, Scotland.
Four Elms, Kent.
Four Oaks, West Mids.
Framlingham, Suffolk.
Frampton, Dorset.
Freshford, Somerset.
Freshwater, Isle of
  Wight.
Frinton-on-Sea, Essex.
Friockheim, Scotland.
Frome, Somerset.
Froxfield, Wilts.

G

Gainsborough, Lincs.
Gants Hill, Essex.
Gargrave, Yorks. North.
Gateshead, Tyne and
  Wear.
Gilberdyke, Yorks.
  East.
Gillingham, Dorset.
Glasgow, Scotland.
Glencarse, Scotland.
Glendoick, Scotland.
Glossop, Derbys.

Gloucester, Glos.
Godalming, Surrey.
Gomshall, Surrey.
Gorseinon, Wales.
Gosforth, Cumbria.
Gosforth, Tyne and
  Wear.
Gosport, Hants.
Goudhurst, Kent.
Grampound, Cornwall.
Grantham, Lincs.
Grasmere, Cumbria.
Gravesend, Kent.
Grays, Essex.
Great Baddow, Essex.
Great Bookham,
  Surrey.
Great Dunmow, Essex.
Great Glen, Leics.
Great Harwood, Lancs.
Great Houghton, Yorks.
  South.
Great Malvern, Worcs.
Great Missenden,
  Bucks.
Great Salkeld,
  Cumbria.
Great Shefford, Berks.
Great Shelford, Cambs.
Great Torrington,
  Devon.
Great Waltham, Essex.
Green Hammerton,
  Yorks. North.
Greyabbey, Co. Down,
  N. Ireland.
Greystoke, Cumbria.
Grimsby, Lincs.
Grimston, Leics.
Gt. Yarmouth, Norfolk.
Guildford, Surrey.
Gullane, Scotland.

H

Hacheston, Suffolk.
Haddenham, Bucks.
Haddington, Scotland.
Hadleigh, Suffolk.
Hadlow Down, Sussex
  East.
Hainault, Essex.
Hale, Cheshire.
Halesowen, West Mids.
Halesworth, Suffolk.
Halfway, Berks.
Halifax, Yorks. West.
Hallow, Worcs.
Halstead, Essex.
Hampton, Middx.
Harpenden, Herts.

Harpole, Northants.
Harrogate, Yorks. North.
Harston, Cambs.
Hartlepool, Durham.
Hartley Wintney,
  Hants.
Harwich, Essex.
Haslemere, Surrey.
Haslingden, Lancs.
Haslington, Cheshire.
Hastings, Sussex East.
Hatherleigh, Devon.
Hatton, Warks.
Haverfordwest, Wales.
Hawarden, Wales.
Hawes, Yorks. North.
Haworth, Yorks. West.
Hay-on-Wye, Wales.
Hayfield, Derbys.
Hayle, Cornwall.
Hayling Island, Hants.
Haywards Heath,
  Sussex West.
Heacham, Norfolk.
Headington, Oxon.
Headley, Hants.
Heanor, Derbys.
Heathfield, Sussex
  East.
Hebden Bridge, Yorks.
  West.
Helmsley, Yorks.
  North.
Helsby, Cheshire.
Hemel Hempstead,
  Herts.
Hemswell Cliff, Lincs.
Henfield, Sussex West.
Henley-in-Arden,
  Warks.
Henley-on-Thames,
  Oxon.
Hereford, Herefs.
Hertford, Herts.
Heswall, Merseyside.
Hexham, Northumbs.
High Wycombe, Bucks.
Highbridge, Somerset.
Hinckley, Leics.
Hindhead, Surrey.
Hingham, Norfolk.
Hitchin, Herts.
Hoby, Leics.
Hodnet, Shrops.
Holbeach, Lincs.
Holkham, Norfolk.
Holland-on-Sea, Essex.
Holmfirth, Yorks. West.
Holt, Norfolk.
Holt, Wales.

Holyhead (Anglesey), Wales.
Holywood, Co. Down, N. Ireland.
Honiton, Devon.
Hook, Hants.
Horley, Surrey.
Horncastle, Lincs.
Horsell, Surrey.
Horton, Berks.
Houghton, Sussex West.
Hoylake, Merseyside.
Huddersfield, Yorks. West.
Hull, Yorks. East.
Hungerford, Berks.
Hunstanton, Norfolk.
Huntercombe, Oxon.
Huntingdon, Cambs.
Huntly, Scotland.
Hursley, Hants.
Hurst, Berks.
Hurst Green, Sussex East.
Hurstpierpoint, Sussex West.
Hythe, Kent.

I
Ibstock, Leics.
Ilchester, Somerset.
Ilfracombe, Devon.
Ilkley, Yorks. West.
Ilminster, Somerset.
Inchture, Scotland.
Ingatestone, Essex.
Innerleithen, Scotland.
Inverness, Scotland.
Ipswich, Suffolk.
Ironbridge, Shrops.
Islip, Northants.
Iver, Bucks.
Ixworth, Suffolk.

J
Jedburgh, Scotland.
Jesmond, Tyne and Wear.

K
Keighley, Yorks. West.
Kelling, Norfolk.
Kelvedon, Essex.
Kendal, Cumbria.
Keswick, Cumbria.
Kettering, Northants.
Kew, Surrey.
Kew Green, Surrey.
Kidderminster, Worcs.

Kidwelly, Wales.
Kilbarchan, Scotland.
Killamarsh, Derbys.
Killearn, Scotland.
Killin, Scotland.
Kilmacolm, Scotland.
Kilmarnock, Scotland.
Kilmichael Glassary, Scotland.
Kincardine O'Neil, Scotland.
King's Lynn, Norfolk.
Kingsbridge, Devon.
Kingsclere, Hants.
Kingsley, Staffs.
Kingsthorpe, Northants.
Kingston-on-Spey, Scotland.
Kingston-upon-Thames, Surrey.
Kingswear, Devon.
Kingswinford, West Mids.
Kington, Herefs.
Kinross, Scotland.
Kirk Deighton, Yorks. North.
Kirkby Lonsdale, Cumbria.
Kirkby Stephen, Cumbria.
Kirkcaldy, Scotland.
Kirkcudbright, Scotland.
Kirton, Lincs.
Kirton in Lindsey, Lincs.
Knaresborough, Yorks. North.
Knebworth, Herts.
Knighton, Wales.
Knipton, Leics.
Knutsford, Cheshire.

L
Lake, Isle of Wight.
Laleham, Surrey.
Lamberhurst, Kent.
Lancaster, Lancs.
Landbeach, Cambs.
Langford, Notts.
Langford, Somerset.
Langholm, Scotland.
Langley Burrell, Wilts.
Largs, Scotland.
Launceston, Cornwall.
Lavenham,, Suffolk.
Le Bourg Forest, Guernsey, C.I.

Leamington Spa, Warks.
Leatherhead, Surrey.
Leavenheath, Suffolk.
Lechlade, Glos.
Leckhampstead, Berks.
Ledbury, Herefs.
Leeds, Yorks. West.
Leek, Staffs.
Leicester, Leics.
Leigh, Lancs.
Leigh-on-Sea, Essex.
Leighton Buzzard, Beds.
Leiston, Suffolk.
Lennoxtown, Scotland.
Leominster, Herefs.
Lepton, Yorks. West.
Letham, Scotland.
Lewes, Sussex East.
Leyburn, Yorks. North.
Lichfield, Staffs.
Limpsfield, Surrey.
Lincoln, Lincs.
Lindfield, Sussex West.
Linlithgow, Scotland.
Lisburn, Co. Antrim, N. Ireland.
Liss, Hants.
Little Chalfont, Bucks.
Little Dalby, Leics.
Little Haywood, Staffs.
Little Horsted, Sussex East.
Little Malvern, Worcs.
Littlebourne, Kent.
Littlehampton, Sussex West.
Littleton, Cheshire.
Littleton, Somerset.
Litton Cheney, Dorset.
Liverpool, Merseyside.
Llandeilo, Wales.
Llandudno, Wales.
Llandudno Junction, Wales.
Llandysul, Wales.
Llanelli, Wales.
Llanerchymedd (Anglesey), Wales.
Llanfair Caereinion, Wales.
Llangollen, Wales.
Llangristiolus (Anglesey), Wales.
Llanrwst, Wales.
Long Clawson, Leics.
Long Eaton, Derbys.
Long Hanborough, Oxon.

Long Marston, Warks.
Long Marton, Cumbria.
Long Melford, Suffolk.
Long Sutton, Lincs.
Longhaven, Scotland.
Looe, Cornwall.
Lostwithiel, Cornwall.
Loughborough, Leics.
Louth, Lincs.
Low Newton, Cumbria.
Lower Stondon, Beds.
Lubenham, Leics.
Ludlow, Shrops.
Lurgan, Co. Armagh, N. Ireland.
Luton, Beds.
Lydford, Devon.
Lye, West Mids.
Lymington, Hants.
Lymm, Cheshire.
Lyndhurst, Hants.
Lyneham, Wilts.
Lynton, Devon.
Lytchett Minster, Dorset.
Lythe, Yorks. North.

M
Macclesfield, Cheshire.
Maidencombe, Devon.
Maidenhead, Berks.
Maidstone, Kent.
Maldon, Essex.
Malmesbury, Wilts.
Malton, Yorks. North.
Malvern Link, Worcs.
Manchester, Lancs.
Manfield, Yorks. North.
Manningford Bruce, Wilts.
Manningtree, Essex.
Mansfield, Notts.
Manton, Rutland.
Marazion, Cornwall.
Margate, Kent.
Market Bosworth, Leics.
Market Deeping, Lincs.
Market Drayton, Shrops.
Market Harborough, Leics.
Market Weighton, Yorks. East.
Markington, Yorks. North.
Marlborough, Wilts.
Marlesford, Suffolk.
Marlow, Bucks.
Marple Bridge, Cheshire.

Martlesham, Suffolk.
Martock, Somerset.
Masham, Yorks. North.
Matching Green,
  Essex.
Mathry, Wales.
Matlock, Derbys.
Melbury Osmond,
  Dorset.
Melksham, Wilts.
Melrose, Scotland.
Melton Mowbray,
  Leics.
Menai Bridge, Wales.
Mendlesham Green,
  Suffolk.
Menston, Yorks. West.
Mere, Wilts.
Merstham, Surrey.
Merton, Devon.
Middle Aston, Oxon.
Middleham, Yorks.
  North.
Middleton Village,
  Lancs.
Middleton-in-Teesdale,
  Durham.
Midgham, Berks.
Midhurst, Sussex West.
Midsomer Norton,
  Somerset.
Mildenhall, Suffolk.
Milford, Surrey.
Milford Haven, Wales.
Milton Keynes, Bucks.
Milton Lilbourne,
  Wilts.
Minchinhampton, Glos.
Mobberley, Cheshire.
Modbury, Devon.
Monkton, Devon.
Monmouth, Wales.
Montrose, Scotland.
Morchard Bishop,
  Devon.
Morden, Surrey.
Morecambe, Lancs.
Morestead, Hants.
Moreton-in-Marsh,
  Glos.
Mountain Ash, Wales.
Much Wenlock,
  Shrops.
Murton, Wales.

N

Nairn, Scotland.
Nantwich, Cheshire.

Narberth, Wales.
Nayland, Suffolk.
Needham, Norfolk.
Needham Market,
  Suffolk.
Nelson, Lancs.
Nether Stowey,
  Somerset.
Nettlebed, Oxon.
New Bolingbroke,
  Lincs.
Newark, Notts.
Newbridge-on-Wye,
  Wales.
Newburgh, Scotland.
Newby Bridge,
  Cumbria.
Newby East, Cumbria.
Newcastle-under-Lyme,
  Staffs.
Newcastle-upon-Tyne,
  Tyne and Wear.
Newent, Glos.
Newhaven, Sussex
  East.
Newington, Kent.
Newmarket, Suffolk.
Newmills, Derbys.
Newport, Essex.
Newport, Isle of Wight.
Newport, Shrops.
Newport, Wales.
Newton Abbot, Devon.
Newton St. Cyres,
  Devon.
Newton Tony, Wilts.
Newtonmore, Scotland.
Newtownabbey, Co.
  Antrim, N. Ireland.
North Aston, Oxon.
North Berwick,
  Scotland.
North Cave, Yorks.
  East.
North Newton,
  Somerset.
North Petherton,
  Somerset.
North Shields, Tyne
  and Wear.
North Walsham,
  Norfolk.
North Wraxall, Wilts.
Northallerton, Yorks.
  North.
Northampton, Northants.
Northchapel, Sussex
  West.

Northfleet, Kent.
Northwich, Cheshire.
Norton, Durham.
Norton, Yorks. North.
Norwich, Norfolk.
Nottingham, Notts.
Nutley, Sussex East.

O

Oakham, Rutland.
Oban, Scotland.
Ockbrook, Derbys.
Odiham, Hants.
Okehampton, Devon.
Oldbury, West Mids.
Oldham, Lancs.
Ollerton, Notts.
Olney, Bucks.
Orford, Suffolk.
Ormskirk, Lancs.
Osgathorpe, Leics.
Oswestry, Shrops.
Otford, Kent.
Otley, Yorks. West.
Outwell, Cambs.
Oxford, Oxon.
Oxted, Surrey.

P

Paignton, Devon.
Painswick, Glos.
Paisley, Scotland.
Pangbourne, Berks.
Parkstone, Dorset.
Pateley Bridge, Yorks.
  North.
Patrington, Yorks. East.
Peasenhall, Suffolk.
Pembroke, Wales.
Penkridge, Staffs.
Penn, Bucks.
Penrith, Cumbria.
Penryn, Cornwall.
Penzance, Cornwall.
Pershore, Worcs.
Perth, Scotland.
Peterborough, Cambs.
Petersfield, Hants.
Petts Wood, Kent.
Petworth, Sussex West.
Pevensey, Sussex East.
Pevensey Bay, Sussex
  East.
Pickering, Yorks.
  North.
Pittenweem, Scotland.
Plumley, Cheshire.
Plymouth, Devon.

Polegate, Sussex East.
Polperro, Cornwall.
Pontarddulais, Wales.
Pontefract, Yorks.
  West.
Pontllyfrii, Wales.
Poole, Dorset.
Portaferry, Co. Down,
  N. Ireland.
Portballintrae, Co.
  Antrim, N. Ireland.
Porthcawl, Wales.
Porthmadog, Wales.
Portree, Scotland.
Portrush, Co. Antrim,
  N. Ireland.
Portsmouth, Hants.
Portsoy, Scotland.
Potter Heigham,
  Norfolk.
Potterspury, Northants.
Poulton-le-Fylde,
  Lancs.
Poynton, Cheshire.
Preston, Lancs.
Prestwick, Scotland.
Princes Risborough,
  Bucks.
Puckeridge, Herts.
Puddletown, Dorset.
Pulborough, Sussex
  West.
Pwllheli, Wales.

Q

Queen Camel,
  Somerset.
Queniborough,, Leics.
Quorn, Leics.

R

Rainford, Merseyside.
Rait, Scotland.
Ramsbury, Wilts.
Ramsey, Cambs.
Ramsgate, Kent.
Raughton Head,
  Cumbria.
Raveningham, Norfolk.
Ravenstonedale,
  Cumbria.
Rayleigh, Essex.
Reading, Berks.
Redbourn, Herts.
Redditch, Worcs.
Redhill, Surrey.
Redruth, Cornwall.
Reepham, Norfolk.

Reigate, Surrey.
Retford, Notts.
Richmond, Surrey.
Rickmansworth, Herts.
Ringmer, Sussex East.
Ringstead, Norfolk.
Ringway, Cheshire.
Ringwood, Hants.
Ripley, Derbys.
Ripon, Yorks. North.
Risby, Suffolk.
Robin Hood's Bay,
  Yorks. North.
Rochdale, Lancs.
Rochester, Kent.
Rodley, Glos.
Rolvenden, Kent.
Romiley, Cheshire.
Romsey, Hants.
Ross-on-Wye, Herefs.
Rothbury, Northumbs.
Rotherham, Yorks.
  South.
Rottingdean, Sussex
  East.
Rowlands Castle,
  Hants.
Roxwell, Essex.
Royston, Herts.
Rugeley, Staffs.
Rumford, Cornwall.
Runfold, Surrey.
Rushden, Northants.
Ruthin, Wales.
Ryde, Isle of Wight.
Rye, Sussex East.

S

Sabden, Lancs.
Saffron Walden, Essex.
Saintfield, Co. Down,
  N. Ireland.
Salisbury, Wilts.
Saltaire, Yorks. West.
Saltcoats, Scotland.
Samlesbury, Lancs.
Sandbach, Cheshire.
Sanderstead, Surrey.
Sandgate, Kent.
Sandhurst, Berks.
Sandhurst, Kent.
Sandwich, Kent.
Sawbridgeworth, Herts.
Scarborough, Yorks.
  North.
Scratby, Norfolk.
Screveton, Notts.
Scunthorpe, Lincs.

Seaford, Sussex East.
Seaton, Devon.
Seaview, Isle of Wight.
Sedbergh, Cumbria.
Seething, Norfolk.
Semley, Wilts.
Settle, Yorks. North.
Sevenoaks, Kent.
Shaftesbury, Dorset.
Shaldon, Devon.
Shanklin, Isle of Wight.
Shardlow, Derbys.
Sharrington, Norfolk.
Sheffield, Yorks. South.
Shefford, Beds.
Shenfield, Essex.
Shenton, Leics.
Shepton Mallet,
  Somerset.
Sherborne, Dorset.
Shere, Surrey.
Sheringham, Norfolk.
Shifnal, Shrops.
Shipston-on-Stour,
  Warks.
Shirley, Surrey.
Shoreham-by-Sea,
  Sussex West.
Shrewsbury, Shrops.
Sible Hedingham,
  Essex.
Sidcup, Kent.
Sidmouth, Devon.
Sileby, Leics.
Skenfrith, Wales.
Skipton, Yorks. North.
Slad, Glos.
Sleaford, Lincs.
Sleights, Yorks. North.
Snainton, Yorks. North.
Snape, Suffolk.
Snargate, Kent.
Solihull, West Mids.
Somersham, Cambs.
Somerton, Somerset.
Sonning-on-Thames,
  Berks.
South Brent, Devon.
South Harting, Sussex
  West.
South Molton, Devon.
South Petherton,
  Somerset.
South Shields, Tyne
  and Wear.
South Walsham,
  Norfolk.
Southampton, Hants.

Southborough, Kent.
Southend- on-Sea,
  Essex.
Southport, Merseyside.
Southwell, Notts.
Southwold, Suffolk.
Sowerby Bridge, Yorks.
  West.
Spalding, Lincs.
Spennithorne, Yorks.
  North.
St. Albans, Herts.
St. Andrews, Scotland.
St. Annes-on-Sea,
  Lancs.
St. Austell, Cornwall.
St. Helen Auckland,
  Durham.
St. Helier, Jersey, C.I.
St. Ives, Cambs.
St. Ives, Cornwall.
St. Lawrence, Jersey,
  C.I.
St. Leonards-on-Sea,
  Sussex East.
St. Mary, Jersey, C.I.
St. Neots, Cambs.
St. Ouen, Jersey, C.I.
St. Peter Port,
  Guernsey, C.I.
St. Sampson, Guernsey,
  C.I.
St. Saviour, Jersey,
  C.I.
Stafford, Staffs.
Staines, Surrey.
Stalham, Norfolk.
Stamford, Lincs.
Standlake, Oxon.
Stanley, Scotland.
Stansted, Essex.
Stanton upon Hine
  Heath, Shrops.
Staplehurst, Kent.
Staunton Harold, Leics.
Staveley, Cumbria.
Stewarton, Scotland.
Steyning, Sussex West.
Stickney, Lincs.
Stiffkey, Norfolk.
Stillington, Yorks.
  North.
Stirling, Scotland.
Stock, Essex.
Stockbridge, Hants.
Stockbury, Kent.
Stockland, Devon.
Stockport, Cheshire.

Stockton-on-Tees,
  Durham.
Stoke Ferry, Norfolk.
Stoke-on-Trent, Staffs.
Storrington, Sussex
  West.
Stotfold, Beds.
Stourbridge, West
  Mids.
Stow-on-the-Wold,
  Glos.
Stowmarket, Suffolk.
Stradbroke, Suffolk.
Stratford-upon-Avon,
  Warks.
Strathblane, Scotland.
Stretton, Cheshire.
Stretton-on-Fosse,
  Warks.
Stretton-under-Fosse,
  Warks.
Sturminster Newton,
  Dorset.
Suckley, Worcs.
Sudbury, Suffolk.
Sunderland, Tyne and
  Wear.
Sundridge, Kent.
Sunningdale, Berks.
Surbiton, Surrey.
Sutton, Surrey.
Sutton Bonington,
  Notts.
Sutton Bridge, Lincs.
Sutton Coldfield, West
  Mids.
Sutton Valence, Kent.
Sutton-in-Ashfield,
  Notts.
Sutton-on-Sea, Lincs.
Swaffham, Norfolk.
Swafield, Norfolk.
Swanage, Dorset.
Swansea, Wales.
Swindon, Wilts.
Swinford, Leics.
Swinstead, Lincs.

T

Tacolneston, Norfolk.
Taddington, Glos.
Tadley, Hants.
Tarleton, Lancs.
Tarporley, Cheshire.
Tarvin, Cheshire.
Tarvin Sands, Cheshire.
Tattenhall, Cheshire.
Tattershall, Lincs.

Taunton, Somerset.
Tavistock, Devon.
Taynton, Oxon.
Tedburn St Mary, Devon.
Teddington, Middx.
Teignmouth, Devon.
Telford, Shrops.
Templeton, Wales.
Tenby, Wales.
Tenterden, Kent.
Tetbury, Glos.
Tetsworth, Oxon.
Tewkesbury, Glos.
Teynham, Kent.
Thame, Oxon.
Thames Ditton, Surrey.
Thirsk, Yorks. North.
Thornbury, Glos.
Thornton le Dale, Yorks. North.
Tilston, Cheshire.
Tintern, Wales.
Titchfield, Hants.
Tockwith, Yorks. North.
Toddington, Beds.
Todenham, Glos.
Todmorden, Yorks. West.
Tonbridge, Kent.
Topsham, Devon.
Torquay, Devon.
Totnes, Devon.
Tottenhill, Norfolk.
Towcester, Northants.
Trawden, Lancs.
Trecastle, Wales.
Tregony, Cornwall.
Treorchy, Wales.
Tresillian, Cornwall.
Trevor, Wales.
Tring, Herts.
Troon, Scotland.
Truro, Cornwall.
Tunbridge Wells, Kent.
Tutbury, Staffs.
Tuxford, Notts.
Twickenham, Middx.
Twyford, Berks.
Twyford, Norfolk.
Tynemouth, Tyne and Wear.
Tywyn, Wales.

U

Uckfield, Sussex East.
Uffculme, Devon.

Ullapool, Scotland.
Ulverston, Cumbria.
Upper Largo, Scotland.
Uppingham, Rutland.
Upton-upon-Severn, Worcs.
Uttoxeter, Staffs.
Uxbridge, Middx.

V

Valley, Wales.
Ventnor, Isle of Wight.

W

Wadebridge, Cornwall.
Wadhurst, Sussex East.
Wainfleet, Lincs.
Wakefield, Yorks. West.
Wallasey, Merseyside.
Wallingford, Oxon.
Walsall, West Mids.
Walsden, Yorks. West.
Walton-on-Thames, Surrey.
Walton-on-the-Hill and Tadworth, Surrey.
Wansford, Cambs.
Wantage, Oxon.
Wareham, Dorset.
Warfield, Berks.
Wargrave, Berks.
Warlingham, Surrey.
Warminster, Wilts.
Warrenpoint, Co. Down, N. Ireland.
Warrington, Cheshire.
Warwick, Warks.
Washington, Tyne and Wear.
Watchet, Somerset.
Waterlooville, Hants.
Watford, Herts.
Watlington, Oxon.
Waverton, Cheshire.
Weedon, Northants.
Weeford, Staffs.
Welling, Kent.
Wellingborough, Northants.
Wellington, Somerset.
Wells, Somerset.
Wells-next-the-Sea, Norfolk.
Welshpool, Wales.
Wendover, Bucks.
West Auckland, Durham.

West Bridgford, Notts.
West Buckland, Somerset.
West Burton, Yorks. North.
West Byfleet, Surrey.
West Haddon, Northants.
West Kirby, Merseyside.
West Malling, Kent.
West Yatton, Wilts.
Westbury, Wilts.
Westcliff-on-Sea, Essex.
Westerham, Kent.
Weston, Herts.
Weston-Super-Mare, Somerset.
Weybridge, Surrey.
Weymouth, Dorset.
Whaley Bridge, Derbys.
Whalley, Lancs.
Wheathampstead, Herts.
Whimple, Devon.
Whitby, Yorks. North.
Whitchurch, Bucks.
Whitchurch, Shrops.
White Colne, Essex.
White Roding, Essex.
Whitefield, Lancs.
Whitehaven, Cumbria.
Whitley Bay, Tyne and Wear.
Whitstable, Kent.
Whitwick, Leics.
Whixley, Yorks. North.
Wickham Bishops, Essex.
Wickham Market, Suffolk.
Wickwar, Glos.
Widnes, Cheshire.
Wigan, Lancs.
Willingham, Cambs.
Williton, Somerset.
Wilmslow, Cheshire.
Wilstead (Wilshamstead), Beds.
Wilstone, Herts.
Wilton, Wilts.
Wimborne Minster, Dorset.
Wincanton, Somerset.
Winchcombe, Glos.

Winchester, Hants.
Windermere, Cumbria.
Windsor and Eton, Berks.
Wing, Rutland.
Wingham, Kent.
Winslow, Bucks.
Wisbech, Cambs.
Witney, Oxon.
Wittersham, Kent.
Woburn, Beds.
Woking, Surrey.
Wokingham, Berks.
Wolverhampton, West Mids.
Woodbridge, Suffolk.
Woodbury, Devon.
Woodford Green, Essex.
Woodhall Spa, Lincs.
Woodhouse Eaves, Leics.
Woodlesford, Yorks. West.
Woodseaves, Staffs.
Woodstock, Oxon.
Woodville, Derbys.
Wooler, Northumbs.
Woolhampton,, Berks.
Woolpit, Suffolk.
Woore, Shrops.
Worcester, Worcs.
Workington, Cumbria.
Worsley, Lancs.
Wortham, Suffolk.
Worthing, Sussex West.
Wraysbury, Berks.
Wrentham, Suffolk.
Writtle, Essex.
Wrotham, Kent.
Wroxham, Norfolk.
Wychbold, Worcs.
Wymeswold, Leics.
Wymondham, Leics.

Y

Yarm, Yorks. North.
Yarnton, Oxon.
Yazor, Herefs.
Yealmpton, Devon.
Yeovil, Somerset.
York, Yorks. North.
Yoxall, Staffs.
Yoxford, Suffolk.

Specialist Dealers' Index

Most antique dealers in Britain sell a wide range of goods from furniture, through porcelain and pottery, to pictures, prints and clocks. Much of the interest in visting antiques shops comes from this diversity. However, there are a number of dealers who specialise and the following is a list of these dealers. Most of them will stock a representative selection of the items found under their classification.

The name of the business, together with the area of London or the town and county under which the detailed entry can be found are given in the listing. Again we would like to repeat the advice given in the introduction that, if readers are looking for a particular item, they are advised to telephone first, before making a long journey.

CLASSIFICATIONS

Antiques Centres and Markets
Antiquarian Books
Antiquities
Architectural Items
Arms & Armour
Art Deco & Art Nouveau
Barometers - see also Clock Dealers
Beds
Brass (see Metalwork)
Bronzes
Carpets & Rugs
Cars & Carriages
Chinese Art - see Oriental
Church Furniture & Furnishings
Clocks & Watches
Coins & Medals
Dolls & Toys
Etchings & Engravings
Fire Related Items
Frames
Furniture-
   Continental (mainly French)
   Country
   Georgian
   Oak
   Pine
   Victorian
Garden Furniture, Ornaments & Statuary
Glass - see also Glass Domes &
  Paperweights
Glass Domes
Icons - see Russian Art
Islamic Art
Japanese Art - see Oriental
Jewellery - see Silver & Jewellery

Lighting
Maps & Prints
Metalware/work
Miniatures
Mirrors
Musical Boxes, Instruments & Literature
Nautical Instruments - see Scientific
Needlework - see Tapestries
Netsuke - see Oriental
Oil Paintings
Oriental Items
Paperweights
Photographs & Equipment
Porcelain & Pottery
Prints - see Maps
Rugs - see Carpets
Russian/Soviet Art
Scientific Instruments
Sculpture
Shipping Goods & Period Furniture for the
  Trade
Silver and Jewellery
Sporting Items & Associated Memorabilia
Sporting Paintings & Prints
Stamps
Tapestries, Textiles & Needlework
Taxidermy
Tools - including Needlework & Sewing
Toys - see Dolls
Trade Dealers - see Shipping Goods
Treen
Vintage Cars - see Carriages & Cars
Watercolours
Wholesale Dealers - see Shipping Goods
Wine Related Items

SPECIALIST DEALERS

Antique Centres & Markets

Georgian Village Antiques Market, London E17.
Angel Arcade, London N1.
Camden Passage Antiques Market and Pierrepont Arcade Antiques Centre, London N1.
The Fleamarket, London N1.
London Militaria Market, London N1.
The Mall Antiques Arcade, London N1.
Palmers Green Antiques Centre, London N13.
Southgate Antiques & Collectables, London N14.
Hampstead Antique and Craft Emporium, London NW3.
Alfies Antique Market, London NW8.
Bermondsey Antiques Market, London SE1.
Greenwich Antiques Market, London SE10.
Sydenham Antiques Centre, London SE26.
Cobwebs, London SE9.
Northcote Road Antiques Market, London SW11.
Antiquarius, London SW3.
Bourbon-Hanby Antiques Centre, London SW3.
Bond Street Antiques Centre, London W1.
Grays Antique Markets, London W1.
Admiral Vernon Antiques Market, London W11.
Arbras Gallery, London W11.
The Corner Portobello Antiques Supermarket, London W11.
Crown Arcade, London W11.
Kleanthous Antiques, London W11.
The Red Lion Antiques Arcade, London W11.
Roger's Antiques Gallery, London W11.
The Silver Fox Gallery (Portobello), London W11.
World Famous Portobello Market, London W11.
The Old Cinema Antique Department Store, London W4.
Kensington Church Street Antiques Centre, London W8.
Apple Market Stalls, London WC2.
Covent Garden Flea Market, London WC2.
The London Silver Vaults, London WC2.
Ampthill Antiques Emporium, Ampthill, Beds.
The Woburn Abbey Antiques Centre, Woburn, Beds.
Barkham Antique Centre, Barkham, Berks.
Great Grooms of Hungerford, Hungerford, Berks.
Hungerford Arcade, Hungerford, Berks.
Berkshire Antiques Centre, Midgham, Berks.
Moss End Antique Centre, Warfield, Berks.
Buck House Antique Centre, Beaconsfield, Bucks.
Buckingham Antiques Centre, Buckingham, Bucks.
Marlow Antique Centre, Marlow, Bucks.
Well Cottage Antiques Centre, Princes Risborough, Bucks.
Antiques at..Wendover Antiques Centre, Wendover, Bucks.
Winslow Antiques Centre, Winslow, Bucks.
Gwydir Street Antiques Centre, Cambridge, Cambs.

The Hive, Cambridge, Cambs.
Waterside Antiques Centre, Ely, Cambs.
Huntingdon Trading Post, Huntingdon, Cambs.
Fitzwilliam Antiques Centre, Peterborough, Cambs.
Guildhall Fair - Chester, Chester, Cheshire.
Davenham Antiques Centre, Davenham, Cheshire.
Antiques, Collectables and Crafts, Knutsford, Cheshire.
Knutsford Antiques Centre, Knutsford, Cheshire.
Northwich Antiques Centre, Northwich, Cheshire.
E. R. Antiques Centre, Stockport, Cheshire.
Tarporley Antique Centre, Tarporley, Cheshire.
Wilmslow Antiques, Wilmslow, Cheshire.
Bodmin Antiques Centre, Bodmin, Cornwall.
Waterfront Antiques Market, Falmouth, Cornwall.
Chapel Street Antiques Arcade, Penzance, Cornwall.
The Coinage Hall Antiques Centre, Truro, Cornwall.
The Cumbrian Antiques Centre, Brampton, Cumbria.
Carlisle Antiques Centre, Carlisle, Cumbria.
Cockermouth Antiques Market, Cockermouth, Cumbria.
Alfreton Antiques Centre, Alfreton, Derbys.
Chappells Antiques Centre, Bakewell, Derbys.
Bradwell Antiques Centre, Bradwell, Derbys.
Matlock Antiques and Collectables Centre, Matlock, Derbys.
Memory Lane Antiques Centre, Ripley, Derbys.
The Shambles, Ashburton, Devon.
North Devon Antiques Centre, Barnstaple, Devon.
The Antique Centre on the Quay, Exeter, Devon.
McBains Antiques, Exeter, Devon.
Phantique, Exeter, Devon.
The Quay Gallery Antiques Emporium, Exeter, Devon.
Honiton Antique Centre, Honiton, Devon.
St Leonards Antiques & Craft Centre, Newton Abbot, Devon.
Barbican Antiques Centre, Plymouth, Devon.
New Street Antique Centre, Plymouth, Devon.
Parade Antiques Market, Plymouth, Devon.
Sidmouth Antiques and Collectors Centre, Sidmouth, Devon.
The Antique & Interior Centre, South Molton, Devon.
Topsham Quay Antiques Centre, Topsham, Devon.
Hardy's Collectables, Bournemouth, Dorset.
Bridport Antiques Centre, Bridport, Dorset.
Colliton Antique Centre, Dorchester, Dorset.
Mr. Punch's Antique Market, Shaftesbury, Dorset.
Sherborne World of Antiques, Sherborne, Dorset.
Battlesbridge Antique Centre, Battlesbridge, Essex.
Church Hall Farm Antique & Craft Centre, Broxted, Essex.

Trinity Antiques Centre, Colchester, Essex.
Finchingfield Antiques Centre, Finchingfield, Essex.
Baddow Antique Centre, Great Baddow, Essex.
Gallerie Antiques, Hainault, Essex.
Townsford Mill Antiques Centre, Halstead, Essex.
Harwich Antiques Centre, Harwich, Essex.
ChrisPapworth Antique Clocks and Watches, Kelvedon, Essex.
Maldon Antiques and Collectors Market, Maldon, Essex.
Saffron Walden Antiques Centre, Saffron Walden, Essex.
Berkeley Antiques Market, Berkeley, Glos.
St. Nicholas Markets, Bristol, Glos.
Cheltenham Antique Market, Cheltenham, Glos.
Sixways Antique Centre, Cheltenham, Glos.
Cirencester Arcade, Cirencester, Glos.
Gloucester Antique Centre, Gloucester, Glos.
Jubilee Hall Antiques Centre, Lechlade, Glos.
Lechlade Arcade, Lechlade, Glos.
The Old Ironmongers Antiques Centre, Lechlade, Glos.
Antique Centre, Moreton-in-Marsh, Glos.
Windsor House Antiques Centre, Moreton-in-Marsh, Glos.
Durham House Antiques Centre, Stow-on-the-Wold, Glos.
Fox Cottage Antiques, Stow-on-the-Wold, Glos.
The Antiques Emporium, Tetbury, Glos.
Tewkesbury Antiques & Collectables Centre, Tewkesbury, Glos.
Dolphin Quay Antique Centre, Emsworth, Hants.
The Antiques Centre, Hartley Wintney, Hants.
Cedar Antiques Centre Ltd, Hartley Wintney, Hants.
Lymington Antiques Centre, Lymington, Hants.
Lyndhurst Antiques Centre, Lyndhurst, Hants.
The Folly Antiques Centre, Petersfield, Hants.
Samuels Spencers Antiques and Decorative Arts Emporium, Winchester, Hants.
Hereford Antique Centre, Hereford, Herefs.
Leominster Antiques Market, Leominster, Herefs.
Ross-on-Wye Antiques Centre, Ross-on-Wye, Herefs.
Bushey Antiques Centre, Bushey, Herts.
Hertford Antiques, Hertford, Herts.
The Herts and Essex Antiques Centre, Sawbridgeworth, Herts.
By George! Antiques Centre, St. Albans, Herts.
Royal Victoria Arcade, Ryde, Isle of Wight.
Beckenham Antiques & Collectors' Market, Beckenham, Kent.
Southdown House Antiques, Brasted, Kent.
Burgate Antique Centre, Canterbury, Kent.
Antiques at Cranbrook, Cranbrook, Kent.
Malthouse Arcade, Hythe, Kent.
Beehive, Petts Wood, Kent.

Barden House Antiques, Tonbridge, Kent.
Corn Exchange Antiques Centre, Tunbridge Wells, Kent.
Tunbridge Wells Antiques, Tunbridge Wells, Kent.
Castle Antiques Centre, Westerham, Kent.
Bolton Antique Centre, Bolton, Lancs.
Ironchurch Antiques Centre, Bolton, Lancs.
King's Mill Antique Centre, Burnley, Lancs.
Antiques and Crafts Centre, Chorley, Lancs.
Heskin Hall Antiques, Chorley, Lancs.
Belgrave Antique Centre, Darwen, Lancs.
Holden Wood Antiques Centre, Haslingden, Lancs.
The Assembly Rooms Market, Lancaster, Lancs.
G.B. Antiques Ltd, Lancaster, Lancs.
Lancaster Leisure Park Antiques Centre, Lancaster, Lancs.
Antiques Village, Manchester, Lancs.
The Ginnell Gallery Antique Centre, Manchester, Lancs.
The Antique Centre, Preston, Lancs.
Preston Antique Centre, Preston, Lancs.
Walter Aspinall Antiques, Sabden, Lancs.
Pendle Antiques Centre Ltd, Sabden, Lancs.
Oxford Street Antique Centre, Leicester, Leics.
Whitemoors Antiques and Fine Art, Shenton, Leics.
Portobello Row Antique & Collectors' Centre, Boston, Lincs.
Bourne Antiques & Arts, Bourne, Lincs.
Brownlow Antiques Centre, Faldingworth, Lincs.
Notions Antiques Centre, Grantham, Lincs.
Abbeygate Gallery & Antiques Centre, Grimsby, Lincs.
Astra House Antiques Centre, Hemswell Cliff, Lincs.
Hemswell Antiques Centres, Hemswell Cliff, Lincs.
Great Expectations, Horncastle, Lincs.
The Chapel Emporium Antique Centre, Long Sutton, Lincs.
Old Maltings Antique Centre, Louth, Lincs.
St. Martins Antiques Centre, Stamford, Lincs.
Phelps Antiques, Twickenham, Middx.
Coltishall Antiques Centre, Coltishall, Norfolk.
The Antiques & Collectors Centre (Diss), Diss, Norfolk.
Colbrook Antiques, Fakenham, Norfolk.
Fakenham Antique Centre, Fakenham, Norfolk.
Le Strange Old Barns Antiques, Arts & Craft Centre, Hunstanton, Norfolk.
The Old Granary Antiques and Collectors Centre, King's Lynn, Norfolk.
Cloisters Antique & Collectors Fair, Norwich, Norfolk.
St. Michael at Plea Antiques and Book Centre, Norwich, Norfolk.
Tombland Antiques Centre, Norwich, Norfolk.

SPECIALIST DEALERS

Ringstead Village Antique Centre, Ringstead, Norfolk.
Wells Antique Centre, Wells-next-the-Sea, Norfolk.
Antique and Collectors Fair, Wymondham, Norfolk.
Brackley Antique Cellar, Brackley, Northants.
E.K. Antiques, Finedon, Northants.
Finedon Antiques (Centre), Finedon, Northants.
The Village Antique Market, Weedon, Northants.
Antiques and Bric-a-Brac Market, Wellingborough, Northants.
Castle Gate Antiques Centre, Newark, Notts.
Newark Antiques Centre, Newark, Notts.
Newark Antiques Warehouse, Newark, Notts.
Tudor Rose Antiques Centre, Newark, Notts.
Top Hat Antiques Centre, Nottingham, Notts.
Antiques @ The George, Burford, Oxon.
Country Markets Antiques and Collectables, Chilton, Oxon.
Chipping Norton Antique Centre, Chipping Norton, Oxon.
The Quiet Woman Antiques Centre, Chipping Norton, Oxon.
Station Mill Antiques Centre, Chipping Norton, Oxon.
Deddington Antiques Centre, Deddington, Oxon.
Friday Street Antique Centre (The Ferret), Henley-on-Thames, Oxon.
Antiques on High Ltd, Oxford, Oxon.
TheSwan at Tetsworth, Tetsworth, Oxon.
The Lamb Arcade, Wallingford, Oxon.
The Arbery Centre, Wantage, Oxon.
Span Antiques, Woodstock, Oxon.
Yarnton Antiques Centre, Yarnton, Oxon.
Old Mill Antique Centre, Bridgnorth, Shrops.
Stretton Antiques Market, Church Stretton, Shrops.
Antique Centre, Cleobury Mortimer, Shrops.
Amanda's Secondhand Hypermarket, Newport, Shrops.
Princess Antique Centre, Shrewsbury, Shrops.
Shrewsbury Antique Centre, Shrewsbury, Shrops.
Shrewsbury Antique Market, Shrewsbury, Shrops.
Assembly Antiques Centre, Bath, Somerset.
Bartlett Street Antiques Centre, Bath, Somerset.
Bath Saturday Antiques Market, Bath, Somerset.
Paragon Antiques and Collectors Market, Bath, Somerset.
Crewkerne Antique Centre, Crewkerne, Somerset.
County Antiques, Ilminster, Somerset.
Somerton Antiques Centre, Somerton, Somerset.
Taunton Antiques Market - Silver Street, Taunton, Somerset.
Green Dragon Antiques Centre, Wincanton, Somerset.
Rugeley Antique Centre, Brereton, Staffs.
The Leek Antiques Centre (Barclay House), Leek, Staffs.

Antique Forum, Newcastle-under-Lyme, Staffs.
Windmill Antiques, Stafford, Staffs.
Old Chapel Antique & Collectables Centre, Tutbury, Staffs.
Tutbury Mill Antiques Centre, Tutbury, Staffs.
Blackbrook Antiques Village, Weeford, Staffs.
Clare Antique Warehouse, Clare, Suffolk.
Long Melford Antiques Centre, Long Melford, Suffolk.
The Old Town Hall Antique Centre, Needham Market, Suffolk.
The Risby Barn, Risby, Suffolk.
Snape Antiques and Collectors Centre, Snape, Suffolk.
Memories, Bramley, Surrey.
Mimbridge Antiques Centre, Chobham, Surrey.
Dorking House Antiques, Dorking, Surrey.
Pilgrims Antique Centre, Dorking, Surrey.
Victoria and Edward Antiques Centre, Dorking, Surrey.
Journeyman Antiques Centre, East Molesey, Surrey.
The Nostradamus Centre, East Molesey, Surrey.
Nostradamus II, East Molesey, Surrey.
Bourne Mill Antiques, Farnham, Surrey.
Maltings Monthly Market, Farnham, Surrey.
Haslemere Antique Market, Haslemere, Surrey.
Wood's Wharf Antiques Bazaar, Haslemere, Surrey.
Kingston Antique Market, Kingston-upon-Thames, Surrey.
Town & Country Decorative, Richmond, Surrey.
Shere Antiques Centre, Shere, Surrey.
Brighton Flea Market, Brighton, Sussex East.
Chateaubriand Antiques Centre, Burwash, Sussex East.
Eastbourne Antiques Market, Eastbourne, Sussex East.
Enterprise Collectors Market, Eastbourne, Sussex East.
The Old Town Antiques Centre, Eastbourne, Sussex East.
Pharoahs Antiques, Eastbourne, Sussex East.
George Street Antiques Centre, Hastings, Sussex East.
Church-Hill Antiques Centre, Lewes, Sussex East.
Cliffe Antiques Centre, Lewes, Sussex East.
The Emporium Antique Centre, Lewes, Sussex East.
Lewes Antique Centre, Lewes, Sussex East.
The Courtyard Antiques Market, Seaford, Sussex East.
Seaford's "Barn Collectors' Market" and Studio Bookshop, Seaford, Sussex East.
The Hastings Antique Centre, St. Leonards-on-Sea, Sussex East.
Old House Antique Centre, Adversane, Sussex West.

Nineveh House, Arundel, Sussex West.
Great Grooms Antique Centre, Billingshurst, Sussex West.
Almshouses Arcade, Chichester, Sussex West.
Chichester Antiques Centre, Chichester, Sussex West.
Spongs Antiques Centre, Lindfield, Sussex West.
Petworth Antique Market, Petworth, Sussex West.
Malthouse Antiques Centre, Alcester, Warks.
The Stables Antique Centre, Hatton, Warks.
Barn Antiques Centre, Long Marston, Warks.
Stratford Antique Centre, Stratford-upon-Avon, Warks.
The Stratford Antiques and Interiors Centre Ltd, Stratford-upon-Avon, Warks.
Vintage Antiques Centre, Warwick, Warks.
The Warwick Antique Centre, Warwick, Warks.
The Birmingham Antique Centre, Birmingham, West Mids.
Warley Antique Centre, Birmingham, West Mids.
Antiques Adventure, Coventry, West Mids.
Regency Antique Trading Centre, Stourbridge, West Mids.
Wolverhampton Antiques and Collectors Market, Wolverhampton, West Mids.
The Marlborough Parade Antique Centre, Marlborough, Wilts.
King Street Curios, Melksham, Wilts.
Antique and Collectors Market, Salisbury, Wilts.
The Avonbridge Antiques and Collectors Market, Salisbury, Wilts.
Dairy House Antiques, Semley, Wilts.
Warminster Antiques Centre, Warminster, Wilts.
Bewdley Antiques, Bewdley, Worcs.
Antiques and Curios, Worcester, Worcs.
Worcester Antiques Centre, Worcester, Worcs.
St Crispin Antique Centre, Beverley, Yorks. East.
Grannie's Treasures, Hull, Yorks. East.
Hull Antique Centre, Hull, Yorks. East.
The Ginnel Antiques Centre, Harrogate, Yorks. North.
Montpellier Mews Antique Market, Harrogate, Yorks. North.
Malton Antique Market, Malton, Yorks. North.
Castle Antiques Centre, Middleham, Yorks. North.
Cavendish Antiques & Collectors Centre, York, Yorks. North.
TheRed House Antiques Centre, York, Yorks. North.
Stonegate Antiques Centre, York, Yorks. North.
York Antiques Centre, York, Yorks. North.
Foster's Antique Centre, Rotherham, Yorks. South.
Court House Antique Centre, Sheffield, Yorks. South.
Nichols Antique Centre, Sheffield, Yorks. South.
Sheffield Antiques Emporium, Sheffield, Yorks. South.
Halifax Antiques Centre, Halifax, Yorks. West.

Headrow Antiques Centre, Leeds, Yorks. West.
Otley Antique Centre, Otley, Yorks. West.
The Victoria Centre, Saltaire, Yorks. West.
Todmorden Antiques Centre, Todmorden, Yorks. West.
Trafalgar Antiques Centre, Woodlesford, Yorks. West.
Scottish Antique & Arts Centre, Abernyte, Scotland.
Clola Antiques Centre, Clola by Mintlaw, Scotland.
The Antiques Warehouse, Glasgow, Scotland.
The Victorian Village Antiques, Glasgow, Scotland.
Rait Village Antiques Centre, Rait, Scotland.
Jacobs Antique Centre, Cardiff, Wales.
Hay Antique Market, Hay-on-Wye, Wales.
Offa's Dyke Antique Centre, Knighton, Wales.
Pembroke Antiques Centre, Pembroke, Wales.
Trecastle Antiques Centre, Trecastle, Wales.

Antiquarian Books

Ash Rare Books, London EC3.
Judith Lassalle, London N1.
Zeno Booksellers, London N12.
Barrie Marks Ltd, London N2.
Nicholas Goodyer, London N5.
Fisher and Sperr, London N6.
P.G. de Lotz, London NW3.
Keith Fawkes, London NW3.
H. Baron, London NW6.
Hosains Books and Antiques, London NW6.
Marcet Books, London SE10.
Rogers Turner Books, London SE10.
Classic Bindings, London SW1.
Thomas Heneage Art Books, London SW1.
Sims, Reed Ltd, London SW1.
Hünersdorff Rare Books, London SW10.
John Thornton, London SW10.
Paul Foster's Bookshop, London SW14.
Hanshan Tang Books, London SW15.
Earlsfield Bookshop, London SW18.
Russell Rare Books, London SW3.
Robin Greer, London SW6.
The Gloucester Road Bookshop, London SW7.
Paul Orssich, London SW8.
Altea Maps & Books, London W1.
G. Heywood Hill Ltd, London W1.
Holland & Holland, London W1.
Maggs Bros Ltd, London W1.
Marlborough Rare Books Ltd, London W1.
The O'Shea Gallery, London W1.
Paralos Ltd, London W1.
Pickering and Chatto, London W1.
Jonathan Potter Ltd, London W1.
Bernard Quaritch Ltd (Booksellers), London W1.
Robert G. Sawers, London W1.
Bernard J. Shapero Rare Books, London W1.

Henry Sotheran Ltd, London W1.
Crawley and Asquith Ltd, London W10.
Demetzy Books, London W11.
D. Parikian, London W14.
Adrian Harrington, London W8.
Atlantis Bookshop, London WC1.
Book Art & Architecture & Volume Gallery, London WC1.
Cinema Bookshop, London WC1.
Fine Books Oriental, London WC1.
Michael Finney Antique Prints and Books, London WC1.
Robert Frew Ltd, London WC1.
The Museum Bookshop, London WC1.
Skoob Russell Square, London WC1.
Bell, Book and Radmall, London WC2.
Blackwell's, London WC2.
David Drummond at Pleasures of Past Times, London WC2.
P. J. Hilton (Books), London WC2.
MarchpaneLondon WC2.
Henry Pordes Books Ltd, London WC2.
Reg and Philip Remington, London WC2.
Bertram Rota Ltd, London WC2.
Stage Door Prints, London WC2.
Storey's Ltd, London WC2.
Watkins Books Ltd, London WC2.
Nigel Williams Rare Books, London WC2.
Zwemmer, London WC2.
Books for Collectors Ltd, Toddington, Beds.
Eton Antique Bookshop, Windsor and Eton, Berks.
Penn Barn, Penn, Bucks.
The Bookshop, Cambridge, Cambs.
G. David, Cambridge, Cambs.
Galloway and Porter Ltd, Cambridge, Cambs.
Sarah Key, Cambridge, Cambs.
Stothert Old Books, Chester, Cheshire.
Lion Gallery and Bookshop, Knutsford, Cheshire.
Mereside Books, Macclesfield, Cheshire.
Iain Campbell, Widnes, Cheshire.
New Street Bookshop, Penzance, Cornwall.
Penzance Rare Books, Penzance, Cornwall.
Bonython Bookshop, Truro, Cornwall.
Norman Kerr - Gatehouse Bookshop, Cartmel, Cumbria.
Peter Bain Smith (Bookseller), Cartmel, Cumbria.
Archie Miles Bookshop, Gosforth, Cumbria.
Lakes Crafts & Antiques Gallery, Grasmere, Cumbria.
G.K. Hadfield, Great Salkeld, Cumbria.
The Book House, Ravenstonedale, Cumbria.
R. F. G. Hollett and Son, Sedbergh, Cumbria.
Michael Moon - Antiquarian Booksellers, Whitehaven, Cumbria.
Derventio Books, Derby, Derbys.
Dartmoor Bookshop, Ashburton, Devon.
Chantry Bookshop and Gallery, Dartmouth, Devon.
Exeter Rare Books, Exeter, Devon.

High Street Books, Honiton, Devon.
Honiton Old Bookshop, Honiton, Devon.
Geoffrey M. Woodhead, Honiton, Devon.
Graham York Rare Books, Honiton, Devon.
P.M. Pollak, South Brent, Devon.
R M Young Bookseller, South Molton, Devon.
Tavistock Books, Tavistock, Devon.
The Schuster Gallery, Torquay, Devon.
Collards Books, Totnes, Devon.
The Exchange, Totnes, Devon.
Pedlars Pack Books, Totnes, Devon.
Ancient and Modern Bookshop (including Garret's Antiques), Blandford Forum, Dorset.
Bridport Old Books, Bridport, Dorset.
Words Etcetera, Dorchester, Dorset.
Christopher Williams Antiquarian Bookseller, Parkstone, Dorset.
Antique Map and Bookshop, Puddletown, Dorset.
Chapter House Books, Sherborne, Dorset.
Keeble Antiques, Sherborne, Dorset.
Reference Works Ltd, Swanage, Dorset.
Books Afloat, Weymouth, Dorset.
Books & Bygones, Weymouth, Dorset.
Minster Books, Wimborne Minster, Dorset.
J. Shotton Antiquarian Books, Prints and Coins, Durham, Durham.
Castle Bookshop, Colchester, Essex.
Bookworm, Holland-on-Sea, Essex.
Cotham Hill Bookshop, Bristol, Glos.
Pastimes, Bristol, Glos.
David Bannister FRGS, Cheltenham, Glos.
Michael Rayner, Cheltenham, Glos.
Ian Hodgkins and Co. Ltd, Slad, Glos.
Tetbury Old Books & Coach House Antiques, Tetbury, Glos.
Laurence Oxley, Alresford, Hants.
Bookends, Emsworth, Hants.
Kingsclere Old Bookshop (Wyseby House Books), Kingsclere, Hants.
The Petersfield Bookshop, Petersfield, Hants.
Academy Books, Portsmouth, Hants.
Peter M. Daly, Winchester, Hants.
SPCK Bookshops, Winchester, Hants.
Bournville Books, Hereford, Herefs.
Castle Hill Books, Kington, Herefs.
Ross Old Book and Print Shop, Ross-on-Wye, Herefs.
Gillmark Gallery, Hertford, Herts.
Eric T. Moore, Hitchin, Herts.
Clive A. Burden Ltd, Rickmansworth, Herts.
Charles Dickens Bookshop, Cowes, Isle of Wight.
Ventnor Rare Books, Ventnor, Isle of Wight.
The Canterbury Bookshop, Canterbury, Kent.
Chaucer Bookshop, Canterbury, Kent.
J. Clarke-Hall Ltd, Deal, Kent.
Baggins Book Bazaar - The Largest Secondhand Bookshop in England, Rochester, Kent.

Sandwich Fine Books, Sandwich, Kent.
Baskerville Books, Tunbridge Wells, Kent.
Hall's Bookshop, Tunbridge Wells, Kent.
Taylor-Smith Books, Westerham, Kent.
Forest Books of Cheshire, Manchester, Lancs.
Gibb's Bookshop Ltd, Manchester, Lancs.
Eric J. Morten, Manchester, Lancs.
Halewood and Sons, Preston, Lancs.
Preston Book Co, Preston, Lancs.
The Book Shop, Castle Donington, Leics.
Anthony W. Laywood, Knipton, Leics.
Clarendon Books, Leicester, Leics.
ElaineLonsdale Bookseller and Bookbinder,
  Hemswell Cliff, Lincs.
P.J. Cassidy (Books), Holbeach, Lincs.
Golden Goose Books, Lincoln, Lincs.
Harlequin Gallery and Golden Goose Globe
  Restorers, Lincoln, Lincs.
Staniland (Booksellers), Stamford, Lincs.
C.K. Broadhurst and Co Ltd, Southport,
  Merseyside.
Ian Sheridan's Bookshop, Hampton, Middx.
Anthony C. Hall, Twickenham, Middx.
John Ives Bookseller, Twickenham, Middx.
Rita Shenton, Twickenham, Middx.
David Ferrow, Gt. Yarmouth, Norfolk.
Simon Gough Books, Holt, Norfolk.
The Old Reading Room Gallery and Tea Room,
  Kelling, Norfolk.
J & D Clarke Book and Print Dealers, Norwich,
  Norfolk.
The Tombland Bookshop, Norwich, Norfolk.
R.L. Cook, Sheringham, Norfolk.
Turret House, Wymondham, Norfolk.
The Old Hall Bookshop, Brackley, Northants.
Occultique, Northampton, Northants.
Park Gallery & Bookshop, Wellingborough,
  Northants.
Barter Books, Alnwick, Northumbs.
Priest Popple Books, Hexham, Northumbs.
Castle Antiques, Nottingham, Notts.
E.M. Lawson and Co, East Hagbourne, Oxon.
Richard J. Kingston, Henley-on-Thames, Oxon.
Richard Way Bookseller, Henley-on-Thames,
  Oxon.
Blackwell's Rare Books, Oxford, Oxon.
Jericho Books, Oxford, Oxon.
Thorntons of Oxford Ltd, Oxford, Oxon.
Waterfield's, Oxford, Oxon.
Toby English, Wallingford, Oxon.
Tooley Adams & Co, Wallingford, Oxon.
Goldmark Books, Uppingham, Rutland.
M. and M. Baldwin, Cleobury Mortimer, Shrops.
Candle Lane Books, Shrewsbury, Shrops.
George Bayntun, Bath, Somerset.
Camden Books, Bath, Somerset.
George Gregory, Bath, Somerset.
Patterson Liddle, Bath, Somerset.

Gresham Books, Crewkerne, Somerset.
Rothwell and Dunworth, Dulverton, Somerset.
Janet Clarke, Freshford, Somerset.
Steven Ferdinando, Queen Camel, Somerset.
Sterling Books, Weston-Super-Mare, Somerset.
Mike Abrahams Books, Lichfield, Staffs.
Besleys Books, Beccles, Suffolk.
Trinders' Fine Tools, Clare, Suffolk.
Abington Books, Finningham, Suffolk.
Claude Cox at College Gateway Bookshop,
  Ipswich, Suffolk.
R.G. Archer (Books), Lavenham,, Suffolk.
R.E. and G.B. Way, Newmarket, Suffolk.
Vandeleur Antiquarian Books, Epsom, Surrey.
J.W. McKenzie, Ewell, Surrey.
Thomas Thorp Bookseller, Guildford, Surrey.
Charles W. Traylen, Guildford, Surrey.
Lloyds of Kew, Kew, Surrey.
A. Burton-Garbett, Morden, Surrey.
Secondhand Bookshop, Oxted, Surrey.
Wagstaffs, Oxted, Surrey.
Reigate Galleries, Reigate, Surrey.
Raymond Slack FRSA & Shirley Warren,
  Sanderstead, Surrey.
Colin Page Antiquarian Books, Brighton, Sussex
  East.
Camilla's Bookshop, Eastbourne, Sussex East.
Roderick Dew, Eastbourne, Sussex East.
A. & T. Gibbard, Eastbourne, Sussex East.
Howes Bookshop, Hastings, Sussex East.
Bow Windows Book Shop, Lewes, Sussex East.
A. & Y. Cumming, Lewes, Sussex East.
The Fifteenth Century Bookshop, Lewes, Sussex
  East.
Chapter & Verse Booksellers, Rye, Sussex East.
The Book Jungle, St. Leonards-on-Sea, Sussex
  East.
R.D. Steedman, Newcastle-upon-Tyne, Tyne and
  Wear.
Oliver's Bookshop, Whitley Bay, Tyne and Wear.
The Stratford Bookshop, Stratford-upon-Avon,
  Warks.
Robert Vaughan, Stratford-upon-Avon, Warks.
Duncan M. Allsop, Warwick, Warks.
David Temperley Fine and Antiquarian Books,
  Birmingham, West Mids.
Clive Farahar and Sophie Dupré - Rare Books,
  Autographs and Manuscripts, Calne, Wilts.
Hilmarton Manor Press, Calne, Wilts.
The Military Parade Bookshop, Marlborough,
  Wilts.
Heraldry Today, Ramsbury, Wilts.
The Barn Book Supply, Salisbury, Wilts.
Victoria Bookshop, Swindon, Wilts.
Bookworms of Evesham, Evesham, Worcs.
Malvern Bookshop, Great Malvern, Worcs.
Antique Map and Print Gallery, Hallow, Worcs.
Potterton Books, Thirsk, Yorks. North.

Barbican Bookshop, York, Yorks. North.
Minster Gate Bookshop, York, Yorks. North.
Ken Spelman, York, Yorks. North.
Alan Hill Books, Sheffield, Yorks. South.
The Toll House Bookshop, Holmfirth, Yorks. West.
The Grove Bookshop, Ilkley, Yorks. West.
C.I Galleries Ltd, St. Peter Port, Guernsey, C.I.
John Blench & Son, St. Helier, Jersey, C.I.
The Selective Eye Gallery, St. Helier, Jersey, C.I.
Thesaurus (Jersey) Ltd, St. Helier, Jersey, C.I.
Emerald Isle Books, Belfast, N. Ireland.
Saintfield Antiques & Fine Books, Saintfield, Co. Down, N. Ireland.
Bon-Accord Books, Aberdeen, Scotland.
The McEwan Gallery, Ballater, Scotland.
Blairgowrie Books, Blairgowrie, Scotland.
Armchair Books, Edinburgh, Scotland.
Broughton Books, Edinburgh, Scotland.
McNaughtan's Bookshop, Edinburgh, Scotland.
Second Edition, Edinburgh, Scotland.
Marianne Simpson, Fochabers, Scotland.
Paisley Fine Books, Paisley, Scotland.
Books, Maps and Prints, Brecon, Wales.
Pontcanna Old Books, Maps and Prints, Cardiff, Wales.
Glance Back Bookshop, Chepstow, Wales.
Richard Booth's Bookshop Ltd, Hay-on-Wye, Wales.
Rose's Books, Hay-on-Wye, Wales.
Mark Westwood Antiquarian Books, Hay-on-Wye, Wales.
Dylan's Bookstore, Swansea, Wales.

Antiquities

C.J. Martin (Coins) Ltd, London N14.
Robin Symes Ltd, London SW1.
Aaron Gallery, London W1.
Charles Ede Ltd, London W1.
Hadji Baba Ancient Art, London W1.
Mansour Gallery, London W1.
Seaby Antiquities, London W1.
Rupert Wace Ancient Art Ltd, London W1.
Town Hall Antiques, Woburn, Beds.
Valued History, Ely, Cambs.
Potter's Antiques and Coins, Bristol, Glos.
Ancient & Oriental Ltd, Grimston, Leics.

Architectural Items

LASSCo, London EC2.
Westland London, London EC2.
Relic Antiques at Camden Passage, London N1.
Willesden Green Architectural SalvageLondon NW10.
Townsends, London NW8.
The Junk Shop, London SE10.
Lamont Antiques Ltd, London SE10.
The Old Station, London SE13.

Camberwell Architectural Salvage & Antiques, London SE5.
Crowther of Syon Lodge Ltd, London SW1.
Thornhill Galleries Ltd. in association with A. & R. Dockerill Ltd, London SW15.
Charles Edwards, London SW6.
Fairfax Antiques and Fireplaces, London SW6.
Architectural Antiques, London W6.
Architectural Antiques, Bedford, Beds.
T. Smith, Chalfont St. Giles, Bucks.
Solopark Plc, Cambridge, Cambs.
Nostalgia Architectural Antiques, Stockport, Cheshire.
Cheshire Brick and Slate Co, Tarvin Sands, Cheshire.
The Great Northern Architectural Antique Company Ltd, Tattenhall, Cheshire.
Architectural Antiques, Kendal, Cumbria.
W.R.S. Architectural Antiques, Low Newton, Cumbria.
Cumbria Architectural Salvage, Raughton Head, Cumbria.
Havenplan's Architectural Emporium, Killamarsh, Derbys.
Ashburton Marbles, Ashburton, Devon.
Rex Antiques, Chagford, Devon.
Fagins Antiques, Exeter, Devon.
Dorset Reclamation, Bere Regis, Dorset.
Talisman, Gillingham, Dorset.
Antique Fireplace Centre, Hartlepool, Durham.
Robert Mills Architectural Antiques Ltd, Bristol, Glos.
Original Architectural, Cirencester, Glos.
Cox's Architectural Reclamation Yard, Moreton-in-Marsh, Glos.
Architectural Heritage, Taddington, Glos.
Burgess Farm Antiques, Morestead, Hants.
The Pine Cellars, Winchester, Hants.
Baileys Home & Garden, Ross-on-Wye, Herefs.
Pattison's Architectural Antiques incorporating The Architectural Salvage Store, Chorleywood, Herts.
Curios of Chale, Chale, Isle of Wight.
Bygones Reclamation, Canterbury, Kent.
The Architectural Emporium, Tunbridge Wells, Kent.
Old Smithy, Feniscowles, Lancs.
Antique Fireplace Warehouse, Manchester, Lancs.
In-Situ Manchester, Manchester, Lancs.
In-Situ Manchester South Architectural Antiques, Manchester, Lancs.
Old Hall Farm, Long Clawson, Leics.
Lindsey Court Architectural Antiques, Horncastle, Lincs.
Antique Fireplaces, Liverpool, Merseyside.
Peco, Hampton, Middx.
Mongers, Hingham, Norfolk.
Stiffkey Antiques, Stiffkey, Norfolk.

Rococo Antiques, Architectural Goods and Furnishings, Weedon, Northants.

Woodside Reclamation (Architectural Antiques), Berwick-upon-Tweed, Northumbs.

Hallidays (Fine Antiques) Ltd, Dorchester-on-Thames, Oxon.

Aston Pine Antiques, Faringdon, Oxon.

Oxford Architectural Antiques, Faringdon, Oxon.

The Country Seat, Huntercombe, Oxon.

Willow Antiques and the Nettlebed Antique Merchants, Nettlebed, Oxon.

North Shropshire Reclamation, Burlton, Shrops.

David Bridgwater, Bath, Somerset.

Source, Bath, Somerset.

Walcot Reclamation, Bath, Somerset.

Chris's Crackers, Carhampton, Somerset.

Wells Reclamation Company, Coxley, Somerset.

Frome Reclamation, Frome, Somerset.

Castle Reclamation, Martock, Somerset.

Asianart.co.uk.Ltd, North Newton, Somerset.

Anvil Antiques Ltd, Leek, Staffs.

E.T. Webster, Blythburgh, Suffolk.

Antique Buildings Ltd, Dunsfold, Surrey.

Drummonds Architectural Antiques, Hindhead, Surrey.

The Packhouse, Runfold, Surrey.

Antique Church Furnishings, Walton-on-Thames, Surrey.

Brighton Architectural Salvage, Brighton, Sussex East.

Shiners, Snobs Knobs, Jesmond, Tyne and Wear.

Turnburrys, Jesmond, Tyne and Wear.

The Victorian Ironmonger, Brinklow, Warks.

Retro Antiques, Lye, West Mids.

Harriet Fairfax Fireplaces and General Antiques, Langley Burrell, Wilts.

Ray Coggins Antiques, Westbury, Wilts.

Holloways, Suckley, Worcs.

Kevin Marshall's Antiques Warehouse, Hull, Yorks. East.

Old Flames, Easingwold, Yorks. North.

The White House Antiques &

Architectural Reclamation, Easingwold, Yorks. North.

Robert Aagaard & Co, Knaresborough, Yorks. North.

Daleside Antiques, Markington, Yorks. North.

Renishaw Antiques, Sheffield, Yorks. South.

The Baildon Furniture Co., Baildon, Yorks. West.

Andy Thornton Architectural Antiques Ltd, Halifax, Yorks. West.

Swiss Cottage Furniture, Leeds, Yorks. West.

EASY - Edinburgh Architectural Salvage Yard, Edinburgh, Scotland.

Holyrood Architectural Salvage, Edinburgh, Scotland.

Gallop and Rivers Architectural Antiques, Crickhowell, Wales.

Arms & Armour

London Militaria Market, London N1.

Finchley Fine Art Galleries, London N12.

Laurence Corner, London NW1.

The Armoury of St. James's Military Antiquarians, London SW1.

Peter Dale Ltd, London SW1.

Blunderbuss Antiques, London W1.

Holland & Holland, London W1.

Michael German Antiques Ltd, London W8.

Robert Hales Antiques, London W8.

Trafalgar Square Collectors Centre, London WC2.

Anthony D. Goodlad, Chesterfield, Derbys.

Rex Antiques, Chagford, Devon.

Boscombe Militaria, Bournemouth, Dorset.

Sterling Coins and Medals, Bournemouth, Dorset.

Chris Grimes Militaria, Bristol, Glos.

Pastimes, Bristol, Glos.

Q & C Militaria, Cheltenham, Glos.

Military Curios, HQ84, Gloucester, Glos.

Hampton Gallery, Tetbury, Glos.

J F F Fire Brigade & Military Collectables, Bedhampton, Hants.

A. & R. Ritchie, St. Helier, Jersey, C.I.

H.S. Greenfield and Son, Gunmakers (Est. 1805), Canterbury, Kent.

Jean's Military Memories, Great Harwood, Lancs.

Anything Old & Military Collectables, Lancaster, Lancs.

Bus Stop Curios, Manchester, Lancs.

Garth Vincent Antique Arms and Armour, Allington, Lincs.

The Old Brigade, Kingsthorpe, Northants.

R. G. Antiques, Dunham-on-Trent, Notts.

Michael D. Long, Nottingham, Notts.

English Heritage, Bridgnorth, Shrops.

One Bell, Lavenham, Suffolk.

West Street Antiques, Dorking, Surrey.

Casque and Gauntlet Militaria, Farnham, Surrey.

Mark and David Hawkins The Lanes Armoury, Brighton, Sussex East.

St. Pancras Antiques, Chichester, Sussex West.

Arbour Antiques Ltd, Stratford-upon-Avon, Warks.

Edred A.F. Gwilliam, Cricklade, Wilts.

Magpie Jewellers and Antiques and Magpie Arms & Armour, Evesham, Worcs.

Cairncross and Sons, Filey, Yorks. North.

Hanover Antiques & Collectables, Scarborough, Yorks. North.

Adamson Armoury, Skipton, Yorks. North.

D.W. Dyson (Antique Weapons), Huddersfield, Yorks. West.

Angus Antiques, Dundee, Scotland.

Huw Williams Antiques, Porthmadog, Wales.

Art Deco & Art Nouveau

After Noah, London N1.

The Antique Trader, London N1.

SPECIALIST DEALERS

Style Gallery, London N1.
Tadema Gallery, London N1.
Mike Weedon, London N1.
Art Furniture, London NW1.
Beverley, London NW8.
Bizarre, London NW8.
The Studio, London NW8.
Behind the Boxes - Art Deco, London SE26.
Ciancimino Ltd, London SW1.
Gallery '25, London SW1.
Keshishian, London SW1.
Artchaos, London SW11.
Twentieth Century, London SW12.
The Arts & Crafts Furniture Co Ltd, London SW14.
After Noah, London SW3.
Butler and Wilson, London SW3.
David Gill, London SW3.
Gordon Watson Ltd, London SW3.
Victor Arwas Gallery - Editions Graphiques Gallery Ltd, London W1.
Liberty, London W1.
Mayfair Gallery, London W1.
B. and T. Antiques, London W11.
The Facade, London W11.
Hickmet Fine ArtsLondon W11.
Themes and Variations, London W11.
Peter Farlow, London W8.
Haslam and Whiteway, London W8.
John Jesse, London W8.
New Century, London W8.
Pruskin Gallery, London W8.
20th Century, Cambridge, Cambs.
Bizarre Decorative Arts North West, Altrincham, Cheshire.
Aldersey Hall Ltd, Chester, Cheshire.
Maggie Mays, Buxton, Derbys.
Lionel Geneen Ltd, Bournemouth, Dorset.
Omega, Newport, Essex.
Ruskin Decorative Arts, Stow-on-the-Wold, Glos.
Alexanders, Titchfield, Hants.
Peter Hoare Antiques, Southborough, Kent.
A.S. Antique Galleries, Manchester, Lancs.
Circa 1900, Liverpool, Merseyside.
Osiris Antiques, Southport, Merseyside.
Arbiter, Wallasey, Merseyside.
Aspidistra Antiques, Finedon, Northants.
Willow Antiques and the Nettlebed Antique Merchants, Nettlebed, Oxon.
Decorative Antiques, Bishop's Castle, Shrops.
Expressions, Shrewsbury, Shrops.
A J Antiques, Bath, Somerset.
Puritan Values at the Dome, Southwold, Suffolk.
Decodream, Coulsdon, Surrey.
The Olde Bakehouse Antiques, Dorking, Surrey.
The Gooday Gallery, Richmond, Surrey.
Cockrell Antiques, Surbiton, Surrey.
Art Deco Etc., Brighton, Sussex East.

Jezebel, Brighton, Sussex East.
Oasis Antiques, Brighton, Sussex East.
Wardrobe, Brighton, Sussex East.
Peter Hancock Antiques, Chichester, Sussex West.
Cradlewell Antiques, Jesmond, Tyne and Wear.
Tango Art Deco & Antiques, Warwick, Warks.
Muir Hewitt Art Deco Originals, Halifax, Yorks. West.
The Rendezvous Gallery, Aberdeen, Scotland.
Montresor, Edinburgh, Scotland.
Deco by Design, Fenton Barns, Scotland.
The Renaissance Furniture Store, Glasgow, Scotland.
Jeremy Sniders Antiques, Glasgow, Scotland.
Strachan Antiques, Glasgow, Scotland.
Rhudle Mill, Kilmichael Glassary, Scotland.
Paul Gibbs Antiques and Decorative Arts, Conwy, Wales.

Barometers - see also Clock Dealers

C.R. Frost and Son Ltd, London EC1.
The Antique Barometer Co., The Mall Antiques Arcade, London N1.
Patric Capon, London N1.
Strike One, London N5.
R.E. Rose FBHI, London SE9.
John Carlton-Smith, London SW1.
Trevor Philip and Sons Ltd, London SW1.
The Clock Clinic Ltd, London SW15.
Ronald Phillips Ltd, London W1.
Stair and Company Ltd, London W1.
Old Father Time Clock Centre, London W11.
Raffety & Walwyn, London W8.
The Clock Workshop, Caversham, Berks.
Alan Walker, Halfway, Berks.
The Old Malthouse, Hungerford, Berks.
M.V. Tooley, CMBHI, Chesham, Bucks.
John Beazor and Sons Ltd, Cambridge, Cambs.
Antique Barometers, Ramsey, Cambs.
T. W. Pawson - Clocks, Somersham, Cambs.
Derek and Tina Rayment Antiques, Barton, Cheshire.
Andrew Foott Antiques, Cheadle Hulme, Cheshire.
Mike Read Antique Sciences, St. Ives, Cornwall.
Musgrave Bickford Antiques, Crediton, Devon.
Honiton Clock Clinic, Honiton, Devon.
Barometer World Ltd, Merton, Devon.
Alan Jones Antiques, Okehampton, Devon.
Leigh C. Extence, Shaldon, Devon.
M.C. Taylor, Bournemouth, Dorset.
Timecraft Clocks, Sherborne, Dorset.
Tom Tribe and Son, Sturminster Newton, Dorset.
Mark Marchant (Antiques), Coggeshall, Essex.
Littlebury Antiques - Littlebury Restorations Ltd, Saffron Walden, Essex.
It's About Time, Westcliff-on-Sea, Essex.
Montpellier Clocks, Cheltenham, Glos.

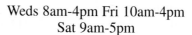
Bryden House Clocks & Antiques, Stow-on-the-Wold, Glos.

Antony Preston Antiques Ltd, Stow-on-the-Wold, Glos.

Styles of Stow, Stow-on-the-Wold, Glos.

Vanbrugh House Antiques, Stow-on-the-Wold, Glos.

Evans and Evans, Alresford, Hants.

Bryan Clisby Antique Clocks, Hartley Wintney, Hants.

The Clock Workshop (Winchester), Winchester, Hants.

G.E. Marsh Antique Clocks Ltd, Winchester, Hants.

Barometer Shop, Leominster, Herefs.

Robert Horton Antiques, Hertford, Herts.

John Chawner, Birchington, Kent.

Michael Sim, Chislehurst, Kent.

City Antiques Ltd, Rochester, Kent.

Neill RobinsonBlaxill, Sevenoaks, Kent.

Marks Antiques, Westerham, Kent.

Tankerton Antiques, Whitstable, Kent.

Drop Dial Antiques, Bolton, Lancs.

Harrop Fold Clocks (F. Robinson), Bolton-by-Bowland, Lancs.

Ingleside Antiques, Colne, Lancs.

N. Bryan-Peach Antiques, Wymeswold, Leics.

Robin Fowler (Period Clocks), Aylesby, Lincs.

David J. Hansord & Son, Lincoln, Lincs.

Timepiece Repairs, Lincoln, Lincs.

Rita Shenton, Twickenham, Middx.

Keith Lawson Antique Clocks, Scratby, Norfolk.

Peter Wiggins, Chipping Norton, Oxon.

Rosemary and Time, Thame, Oxon.

R.G. Cave and Sons Ltd, Ludlow, Shrops.

Adrian Donnelly Antique Clocks, Shrewsbury, Shrops.

Dodington Antiques, Whitchurch, Shrops.

Kembery Antique Clocks (inc. K. & D. Antique Clocks), Bath, Somerset.

Bernard G. House, Wells, Somerset.

Edward A. Nowell, Wells, Somerset.

James A. Jordan, Lichfield, Staffs.

Patrick Marney, Long Melford, Suffolk.

Suthburgh Antiques, Long Melford, Suffolk.

Trident Antiques, Long Melford, Suffolk.

Horological Workshops, Guildford, Surrey.

Surrey Clock Centre, Haslemere, Surrey.

B. M. and E. Newlove, Surbiton, Surrey.

Baskerville Antiques, Petworth, Sussex West.

'Time in Hand', Shipston-on-Stour, Warks.

Summersons, Warwick, Warks.

R. Collyer, Birmingham, West Mids.

P.A. Oxley Antique Clocks and Barometers, Cherhill, Wilts.

Inglenook Antiques, Ramsbury, Wilts.

Hansen Chard Antiques, Pershore, Worcs.
Time and Motion, Beverley, Yorks. East.
Lewis E. Hickson FBHI, Gilberdyke, Yorks. East.
Craiglea Clocks, Edinburgh, Scotland.

Beds
La Maison, London E1.
Tobias and The Angel, London SW13.
And So To Bed Limited, London SW6.
Simon Horn Furniture Ltd, London SW6.
Sleeping Beauty Antique Beds London SW6.
The French House (Antiques) Ltd, London SW8.
Hirst Antiques, London W11.
The Pine Merchants, Great Missenden, Bucks.
The Country Bedroom, Keswick, Cumbria.
Staveley Antiques, Staveley, Cumbria.
The Antiques Warehouse, Buxton, Derbys.
The Grove Antiques Centre, Honiton, Devon.
Pugh's Farm Antiques, Monkton, Devon.
Annterior Antiques, Plymouth, Devon.
Antique Bed Shop, Halstead, Essex.
Deja Vu Antiques, Leigh-on-Sea, Essex.
Antique Four-Poster Beds, Bristol, Glos.
Antique Bed Company, Emsworth, Hants.
Serendipity, Ledbury, Herefs.
Harriet Ann Sleigh Beds, Rolvenden, Kent.
House Things Antiques, Hinckley, Leics.
A Barn Full of Brass Beds, Conisholme, Lincs.
Graham Pickett Antiques, Stamford, Lincs.
Antiques & Gifts, Downham Market, Norfolk.
Rococo Antiques, Architectural Goods and
   Furnishings, Weedon, Northants.
Manor Farm Antiques, Standlake, Oxon.
Swans, Oakham, Rutland.
Bedsteads, Bath, Somerset.
Bed Bazaar, Framlingham, Suffolk.
Goodbreys, Framlingham, Suffolk.
Sleeping Beauty Antique Beds, Brighton, Sussex
   East.
The Victorian Brass Bedstead Company, Cocking,
   Sussex West.
Traditional Beds, Swindon, Wilts.
S.W. Antiques, Pershore, Worcs.
Penny Farthing Antiques, North Cave, Yorks. East.
The French House (Antiques) Ltd, York, Yorks.
   North.
Seventh Heaven, Chirk, Wales.

Brass - see Metalware

Bronzes
Furniture Vault, London N1.
Kevin Page Oriental Art, London N1.
Style Gallery, London N1.
Finchley Fine Art Galleries, London N12.
No. 28 Antiques, London NW8.
Tara Antiques, London NW8.
Robert Bowman, London SW1.

Victor Franses Gallery, London SW1.
M. and D. Lewis, London SW1.
Peter Nahum at The Leicester Galleries, London
   SW1.
Christine Bridge, London SW13.
Anthony James and Son Ltd, London SW3.
Victor Arwas Gallery - Editions Graphiques
   Gallery Ltd, London W1.
Barry Davies Oriental Art, London W1.
Eskenazi Ltd, London W1.
The Sladmore Gallery of Sculpture, London W1.
Elizabeth Bradwin, London W11.
Gavin Douglas Fine Antiques Ltd, London W11.
M. and D. Lewis, London W11.
David Brower Antiques, London W8.
H. and W. Deutsch Antiques, London W8.
John Jesse, London W8.
Pruskin Gallery, London W8.
Mary Wise & Grosvenor Antiques, London W8.
West End Galleries, Buxton, Derbys.
The John Davies Gallery, Stow-on-the-Wold, Glos.
Michael Sim, Chislehurst, Kent.
Apollo Antique Galleries, Westerham, Kent.
London House Antiques, Westerham, Kent.
Edward Cross - Fine Paintings, Weybridge, Surrey.

Carpets & Rugs
Alexander Juran and Co, London N4.
Kennedy Carpets, London N4.
Joseph Lavian, London N4.
David J. Wilkins, London NW1.
Sabera Trading Co, London NW2.
Soviet Carpet & Art Galleries, London NW2.
Orientalist, London NW5.
Robert Franses and Sons, London NW8.
Coats Oriental Carpets, London SE5.
Belgrave Carpet Gallery Ltd, London SW1.
Victor Franses Gallery, London SW1.
S. Franses Ltd, London SW1.
Keshishian, London SW1.
Iftikhar Bokhari, London SW10.
Gideon Hatch Rugs, London SW11.
Shaikh and Son (Oriental Rugs) Ltd, London
   SW19.
Gallery Yacou, London SW3.
Orientalist, London SW3.
Perez, London SW3.
Robert Stephenson, London SW3.
Perez Antique Carpets Gallery, London SW6.
Anglo Persian Carpet Co, London SW7.
Atlantic Bay Carpets Gallery, London SW7.
Heskia, London SW8.
David Aaron Ancient Arts & Rare Carpets,
   London W1.
Sibyl Colefax & John Fowler, London W1.
John Eskenazi Ltd, London W1.
Essie Carpets, London W1.
C. John (Rare Rugs) Ltd, London W1.

Mayfair Carpet Gallery Ltd, London W1.
Rabi Gallery Ltd, London W1.
Gordon Reece Gallery, London W1.
Vigo Carpet Gallery, London W1.
A. Zadah, London W1.
Fairman Carpets Ltd, London W11.
Graham and Green, London W11.
Rezai Persian Carpets, London W11.
David Black Oriental Carpets, London W2.
Oriental Rug Gallery Ltd, Windsor and Eton,
  Berks.
Peter Norman Antiques and Restorations, Burwell,
  Cambs.
J.L. Arditti, Christchurch, Dorset.
Christchurch Carpets, Christchurch, Dorset.
Hamptons, Christchurch, Dorset.
Eric Pride Oriental Rugs, Cheltenham, Glos.
Anthony Hazledine, Fairford, Glos.
Samarkand Galleries, Stow-on-the-Wold, Glos.
The Odiham Gallery, Odiham, Hants.
The Bakhtiyar Carpet Gallery, Stockbridge, Hants.
Oriental Rug Gallery Ltd, St. Albans, Herts.
Desmond and Amanda North, East Peckham,
  Kent.
Samovar Antiques, Hythe, Kent.
Woven Magic, Sevenoaks, Kent.
The Rug Gallery, Leicester, Leics.
Country and Eastern Ltd, Norwich, Norfolk.
M.D. Cannell Antiques, Raveningham, Norfolk.
Richard Purdon Antique Carpets, Burford, Oxon.
Thames Oriental Rug Co, Henley-on-Thames,
  Oxon.
Christopher Legge Oriental Carpets, Oxford,
  Oxon.
Oriental Rug Gallery Ltd, Oxford, Oxon.
Tattersall's, Uppingham, Rutland.
Haliden Oriental Rug Shop, Bath, Somerset.
Michael and Amanda Lewis Oriental Carpets and
  Rugs, Wellington, Somerset.
The Persian Carpet Studio, Long Melford, Suffolk.
Karel Weijand Fine Oriental Carpets, Farnham,
  Surrey.
Oriental Rug Gallery, Guildford, Surrey.
Clive Rogers Oriental Rugs, Staines, Surrey.
Lindfield Galleries - David Adam, Lindfield,
  Sussex West.
Persian Carpet Gallery of Petworth, Petworth,
  Sussex West.
A.W. Hone and Son Oriental Carpets,
  Birmingham, West Mids.
D & J Lines Antiques, Wychbold, Worcs.
London House Oriental Rugs and Carpets,
  Harrogate, Yorks. North.
Omar (Harrogate) Ltd, Knaresborough, Yorks.
  North.
The Oriental Rug Shop, Sheffield, Yorks. South.
London House Oriental Rugs and Carpets, Boston
  Spa, Yorks. West.

Parvis Sigaroudinia, Lisburn, Co. Antrim,
  N. Ireland.
R.L. Rose Oriental Carpets Ltd, Edinburgh,
  Scotland.
Whytock and Reid, Edinburgh, Scotland.
Young Antiques, Edinburgh, Scotland.
R.L. Rose Oriental Carpets Ltd, Glasgow,
  Scotland.
C.S. Moreton (Antiques), Inchture, Scotland.
Gallery Persia, Inverness, Scotland.
Nigel Stacy-Marks Ltd, Perth, Scotland.

Cars & Carriages
Finesse Fine Art, Dorchester, Dorset.
Fieldings Antiques, Haslingden, Lancs.
The Complete Automobilist, Bourne, Lincs.
C.A.R.S. (Classic Automobilia & Regalia
  Specialists), Brighton, Sussex East.
Whatnots, Strathblane, Scotland.

Chinese Art - see Oriental

Church Furniture & Furnishings
Whiteway and Waldron Ltd, London SW6.
Havenplan's Architectural Emporium, Killamarsh,
  Derbys.
Robert Mills Architectural Antiques Ltd, Bristol,
  Glos.
Antique Church Furnishings, Walton-on-Thames,
  Surrey.

Clocks & Watches
City Clocks, London EC1.
C.R. Frost and Son Ltd, London EC1.
Patric Capon, London N1.
Sugar Antiques, London N1.
Strike One, London N5.
North London Clock Shop Ltd, London SE25.
R.E. Rose FBHI, London SE9.
Camerer Cuss and Co, London SW1.
John Carlton-Smith, London SW1.
Charles Frodsham & Co Ltd, London SW1.
Harrods Ltd, London SW1.
Somlo Antiques, London SW1.
The Clock Clinic Ltd, London SW15.
W. F. Turk Antique Clocks, London SW20.
Norman Adams Ltd, London SW3.
Big Ben Antique Clocks, London SW6.
Gutlin Clocks and Antiques, London SW6.
A. & H. Page (Est. 1840), London SW7.
Carrington and Co. Ltd, London W1.
Mallett and Son (Antiques) Ltd, London W1.
Mallett at Bourdon House Ltd, London W1.
Pendulum of Mayfair Ltd, London W1.
Ronald Phillips Ltd, London W1.
Michael Rose - Source of the Unusual, London
  W1.
The Royal Arcade Watch Shop, London W1.

CATCH IT ON MY WEB !!!!
(www.oldfathertime.net)

MYSTERY ELECTRIC
TORSION
NOVELTY WALL
AUTOMATON
CONGREVE
CHRONOMETER
CARRIAGE LONGCASE
SKELETON ATMOS INDUSTRIAL

Old Father Time Clock Centre
101, Portobello Road, London, W11 2QB
020 8546 6299 (24 hrs/fax)
020 7727 3394 (shop)
07836 712088 (mobile)
clocks@oldfathertime.net (e-mail)
Friday – 10am-1pm
Saturday – 8am-2pm
or by appointment

Central Gallery (Portobello), London W11.
Gavin Douglas Fine Antiques Ltd, London W11.
Kleanthous Antiques, London W11.
Mayflower Antiques, London W11.
Old Father Time Clock Centre, London W11.
The Silver Fox Gallery (Portobello), London W11.
David Brower Antiques, London W8.
Raffety & Walwyn, London W8.
Roderick Antique Clocks, London W8.
Thomas Kettle Ltd, London WC2.
The London Silver Vaults, London WC2.
House of Clocks, Ampthill, Beds.
Melnick House of Ascot, Ascot, Berks.
The Clock Workshop, Caversham, Berks.
The Old Malthouse, Hungerford, Berks.
Times Past Antiques, Windsor and Eton, Berks.
Wyrardisbury Antiques, Wraysbury, Berks.
M.V. Tooley, CMBHI, Chesham, Bucks.
Robin Unsworth Antiques, Olney, Bucks.
Peter Norman Antiques and Restorations, Burwell,
    Cambs.
John Beazor and Sons Ltd, Cambridge, Cambs.
Antique Clocks, Harston, Cambs.
T. W. Pawson - Clocks, Somersham, Cambs.
Antiques & Curios (Steve Carpenter), Wisbech,
    Cambs.
Adams Antiques, Chester, Cheshire.
J. Luffman, Haslington, Cheshire.
Chapel Antiques, Nantwich, Cheshire.

Coppelia Antiques, Plumley, Cheshire.
Paul Jennings Antiques, Angarrack, Cornwall.
Little Jem's, Penzance, Cornwall.
Saint Nicholas Galleries Ltd. (Antiques and
    Jewellery), Carlisle, Cumbria.
G.K. Hadfield, Great Salkeld, Cumbria.
David Hill, Kirkby Stephen, Cumbria.
Thornbridge Antiques, Bakewell, Derbys.
Derbyshire Clocks, Glossop, Derbys.
Nimbus Antiques, Whaley Bridge, Derbys.
Around the Clock, Brixham, Devon.
Musgrave Bickford Antiques, Crediton, Devon.
Gold and Silver Exchange, Exeter, Devon.
John Nathan Antiques, Exeter, Devon.
Honiton Clock Clinic, Honiton, Devon.
Leigh C. Extence, Shaldon, Devon.
M.C. Taylor, Bournemouth, Dorset.
Derek J. Burgess - Horologist, Parkstone, Dorset.
Keeble Antiques, Sherborne, Dorset.
Timecraft Clocks, Sherborne, Dorset.
Tom Tribe and Son, Sturminster Newton, Dorset.
Eden House Antiques, West Auckland, Durham.
Mark Marchant (Antiques), Coggeshall, Essex.
Antique Clock Repair Shoppe, Gants Hill, Essex.
Memories, Great Dunmow, Essex.
It's About Time, Westcliff-on-Sea, Essex.
Antique Corner with A & C Antique Clocks,
    Bristol, Glos.
Montpellier Clocks, Cheltenham, Glos.
School House Antiques, Chipping Campden, Glos.
Arthur S. Lewis, Gloucester, Glos.
Jeffrey Formby Antiques, Moreton-in-Marsh,
    Glos.
Jillings Antiques - Distinctive Antique Clocks,
    Newent, Glos.
Keith Harding's World of Mechanical Music,
    Northleach, Glos.
Bryden House Clocks & Antiques, Stow-on-the-
    Wold, Glos.
Styles of Stow, Stow-on-the-Wold, Glos.
Vanbrugh House Antiques, Stow-on-the-Wold,
    Glos.
Evans and Evans, Alresford, Hants.
Clockwise, Emsworth, Hants.
Bryan Clisby Antique Clocks, Hartley Wintney,
    Hants.
A.W. Porter and Son, Hartley Wintney, Hants.
Barry Papworth, Lymington, Hants.
Gaylords, Titchfield, Hants.
The Clock Workshop (Winchester), Winchester,
    Hants.
G.E. Marsh Antique Clocks Ltd, Winchester,
    Hants.
Robin Lloyd Antiques, Ross-on-Wye, Herefs.
Howards, Baldock, Herts.
David Penney, Bishop's Stortford, Herts.
Robert Horton Antiques, Hertford, Herts.
The Clock Shop - Philip Setterfield of St. Albans,
    St. Albans, Herts.

Country Clocks, Tring, Herts.
Weston Antiques, Weston, Herts.
John Corrin Antiques, Douglas, Isle of Man.
Ye Olde Village Clock Shop, Freshwater, Isle of Wight.
John Chawner, Birchington, Kent.
Old Manor House Antiques, Brasted, Kent.
Michael Sim, Chislehurst, Kent.
Gem Antiques, Maidstone, Kent.
City Antiques Ltd, Rochester, Kent.
Michael Fitch Antiques, Sandgate, Kent.
Nancy Wilson, Sandwich, Kent.
Neill RobinsonBlaxill, Sevenoaks, Kent.
Gem Antiques, Sevenoaks, Kent.
Derek Roberts Fine Antique Clocks & Barometers, Tonbridge, Kent.
B.V.M. Somerset, Tonbridge, Kent.
Aaron Antiques, Tunbridge Wells, Kent.
Pantiles Spa Antiques, Tunbridge Wells, Kent.
The Vintage Watch Co., Tunbridge Wells, Kent.
The Old Clock Shop, West Malling, Kent.
Marks Antiques, Westerham, Kent.
Regal Antiques, Westerham, Kent.
Tankerton Antiques, Whitstable, Kent.
Drop Dial Antiques, Bolton, Lancs.
Harrop Fold Clocks (F. Robinson), Bolton-by-Bowland, Lancs.
Brittons - Watches and Antiques, Clitheroe, Lancs.
Ingleside Antiques, Colne, Lancs.
Fieldings Antiques, Haslingden, Lancs.
P.W. Norgrove - Antique Clocks, Haslingden, Lancs.
Charles Howell Jeweller, Oldham, Lancs.
H.C. Simpson and Sons Jewellers (Oldham)Ltd, Oldham, Lancs.
Hackler's Jewellers, Preston, Lancs.
Edmund Davies & Son Antiques, Whalley, Lancs.
Northern Clocks, Worsley, Lancs.
Lowe of Loughborough, Loughborough, Leics.
Old Timers, Swinford, Leics.
Charles Antiques, Whitwick, Leics.
N. Bryan-Peach Antiques, Wymeswold, Leics.
Trade Antiques, Alford, Lincs.
Robin Fowler (Period Clocks), Aylesby, Lincs.
Grantham Clocks, Grantham, Lincs.
MarcusWilkinson, Grantham, Lincs.
Second Time Around, Hemswell Cliff, Lincs.
David J. Hansord & Son, Lincoln, Lincs.
Timepiece Repairs, Lincoln, Lincs.
MarcusWilkinson, Sleaford, Lincs.
Penman Clockcare, Spalding, Lincs.
Kevin Whay's Clocks & Antiques, Hoylake, Merseyside.
Weldons Jewellery and Antiques, Southport, Merseyside.
Rita Shenton, Twickenham, Middx.
Village Clocks, Coltishall, Norfolk.
R.C. Woodhouse (Antiquarian Horologist), Hunstanton, Norfolk.

Tim Clayton Jewellery & Antiques, King's Lynn, Norfolk.
Jennifer and Raymond Norman Antiques, Needham, Norfolk.
Keith Lawson Antique Clocks, Scratby, Norfolk.
Parriss, Sheringham, Norfolk.
Norton Antiques, Twyford, Norfolk.
M.C. Chapman, Finedon, Northants.
Michael Jones Jeweller, Northampton, Northants.
Gordon Caris, Hexham, Northumbs.
David and Carole Potter Antiques, Nottingham, Notts.
Goodacre Engraving, Sutton Bonington, Notts.
Horseshoe Antiques and Gallery, Burford, Oxon.
Hubert's Antiques, Burford, Oxon.
Jonathan Howard, Chipping Norton, Oxon.
Craig Barfoot, East Hagbourne, Oxon.
Rosemary and Time, Thame, Oxon.
Witney Antiques, Witney, Oxon.
C. Reynolds Antiques, Oakham, Rutland.
Mytton Antiques, Atcham, Shrops.
R.G. Cave and Sons Ltd, Ludlow, Shrops.
Mitre House Antiques, Ludlow, Shrops.
Corner Farm Antiques, Shifnal, Shrops.
Adrian Donnelly Antique Clocks, Shrewsbury, Shrops.
Dodington Antiques, Whitchurch, Shrops.
Kembery Antique Clocks (inc. K. & D. Antique Clocks), Bath, Somerset.
Quiet Street Antiques, Bath, Somerset.
Bernard G. House, Wells, Somerset.
Edward A. Nowell, Wells, Somerset.
James A. Jordan, Lichfield, Staffs.
Winder's Fine Art and Antiques, Newcastle-under-Lyme, Staffs.
R.A. James - The Clock Shop, Tutbury, Staffs.
Clock House, Leavenheath, Suffolk.
Suthburgh Antiques, Long Melford, Suffolk.
Village Clocks, Long Melford, Suffolk.
Antique Clocks by Simon Charles, Sudbury, Suffolk.
Edward Manson (Clocks), Woodbridge, Suffolk.
Antique Clocks by Patrick Thomas, Dorking, Surrey.
The Coach House Antiques, Gomshall, Surrey.
Roger A. Davis Antiquarian Horologist, Great Bookham, Surrey.
Horological Workshops, Guildford, Surrey.
Surrey Clock Centre, Haslemere, Surrey.
Hill Rise Antiques, Richmond, Surrey.
B. M. and E. Newlove, Surbiton, Surrey.
S. Warrender and Co, Sutton, Surrey.
The Clock Shop Weybridge, Weybridge, Surrey.
Yellow Lantern Antiques Ltd, Brighton, Sussex East.
W. Bruford, Eastbourne, Sussex East.
John Cowderoy Antiques, Eastbourne, Sussex East.
Coach House Antiques, Hastings, Sussex East.

The Old Mint House, Pevensey, Sussex East.
Arundel Clocks, Arundel, Sussex West.
The Clock Shop, Hurstpierpoint, Sussex West.
Julian Antiques, Hurstpierpoint, Sussex West.
Churchill Clocks, Midhurst, Sussex West.
Baskerville Antiques, Petworth, Sussex West.
Thakeham Furniture, Pulborough, Sussex West.
Peter Smith Antiques, Sunderland, Tyne and Wear.
'Time in Hand, Shipston-on-Stour, Warks.
Summersons, Warwick, Warks.
R. Collyer, Birmingham, West Mids.
F. Meeks & Co, Birmingham, West Mids.
M. Allen Watch and Clockmaker, Four Oaks, West
   Mids.
Afantiques, Wolverhampton, West Mids.
Avon Antiques, Bradford-on-Avon, Wilts.
Moxhams Antiques, Bradford-on-Avon, Wilts.
Trevor Waddington Antique Clocks, Bradford-on-
   Avon, Wilts.
P.A. Oxley Antique Clocks and Barometers,
   Cherhill, Wilts.
Inglenook Antiques, Ramsbury, Wilts.
Salisbury Antiques Warehouse Ltd, Salisbury,
   Wilts.
Chris Wadge Clocks, Salisbury, Wilts.
Allan Smith Antique Clocks, Swindon, Wilts.
Broadway Clocks, Broadway, Worcs.
Hansen Chard Antiques, Pershore, Worcs.
The Barber's Clock, Worcester, Worcs.
Time and Motion, Beverley, Yorks. East.
Lewis E. Hickson FBHI, Gilberdyke, Yorks. East.
Milestone Antiques, Easingwold, Yorks. North.
Chris Wilde Antiques, Harrogate, Yorks. North.
Middleham Antiques, Middleham, Yorks. North.
Brian Loomes, Pateley Bridge, Yorks. North.
Tomlinsons, Tockwith, Yorks. North.
Keith Stones Grandfather Clocks, Bessacarr,
   Yorks. South.
Fishlake Antiques, Fishlake, Yorks. South.
F S Antiques, Sheffield, Yorks. South.
Stephen Cohu Antiques, St Ouen, Jersey, C.I.
Robert Christie Antiques, Carrickfergus, Co.
   Antrim, N. Ireland.
Time & Tide Antiques, Portaferry, Co. Down, N.
   Ireland.
Ian Burton Antique Clocks, Auchterarder,
   Scotland.
The Clock Showrooms, Canonbie, Scotland.
Craiglea Clocks, Edinburgh, Scotland.
Donald Ellis incorporating Bruntsfield Clocks,
   Edinburgh, Scotland.
Harlequin Antiques, Edinburgh, Scotland.
John Whyte, Edinburgh, Scotland.
West End Antiques, Elgin, Scotland.
Brown's Clocks, Glasgow, Scotland.
Bygones, Huntly, Scotland.
Silvertime, Brecon, Wales.
Snowdonia Antiques, Llanrwst, Wales.
Rodney Adams Antiques, Pwllheli, Wales.

Coins & Medals

George Rankin Coin Co. Ltd, London E2.
C.J. Martin (Coins) Ltd, London N14.
Christopher Eimer, London NW11.
Vale Stamps and Antiques, London SE3.
The Armoury of St. James's Military Antiquarians,
   London SW1.
Knightsbridge Coins, London SW1.
Beaver Coin Room, London SW5.
Michael Coins, London W8.
Simmons Gallery, London WC1.
Spink and Son Ltd, London WC1.
A.H. Baldwin and Sons Ltd, London WC2.
M. Bord (Gold Coin Exchange), London WC2.
PhilipCohen Numismatics, London WC2.
Trafalgar Square Collectors Centre, London WC2.
Valued History, Ely, Cambs.
B.R.M. Coins, Knutsford, Cheshire.
Souvenir Antiques, Carlisle, Cumbria.
Penrith Coin and Stamp Centre, Penrith, Cumbria.
Sterling Coins and Medals, Bournemouth, Dorset.
Dorset Coin Company, Parkstone, Dorset.
The Treasure Chest, Weymouth, Dorset.
Robin Finnegan (Jeweller), Darlington, Durham.
J. Shotton Antiquarian Books, Prints and Coins,
   Durham, Durham.
Potter's Antiques and Coins, Bristol, Glos.
Military Curios, HQ84, Gloucester, Glos.
Peter Morris, Bromley, Kent.
World Coins, Canterbury, Kent.
The Coin and Jewellery Shop, Accrington, Lancs.
Chard Coins, Blackpool, Lancs.
Gold and Silver Exchange, Gt. Yarmouth, Norfolk.
Clive Dennett Coins, Norwich, Norfolk.
Barbara Radman, Witney, Oxon.
Bath Stamp and Coin Shop, Bath, Somerset.
Neate Militaria & Antiques, Sudbury, Suffolk.
St. Pancras Antiques, Chichester, Sussex West.
Intercoin, Newcastle-upon-Tyne, Tyne and Wear.
Format of Birmingham Ltd, Birmingham, West
   Mids.
Castle Galleries, Salisbury, Wilts.
Whitmore, Great Malvern, Worcs.
B.B.M. Jewellery and Antiques, Kidderminster,
   Worcs.
C.J. and A.J. Dixon Ltd, Bridlington, Yorks. East.
Cookstown Antiques, Cookstown, Co. Tyrone,
   N. Ireland.
The Collectors Shop, Edinburgh, Scotland.
Edinburgh Coin Shop, Edinburgh, Scotland.
A.D. Hamilton and Co, Glasgow, Scotland.
Abbey Antiques, Stirling, Scotland.
Glance Back Bookshop, Chepstow, Wales.

Dolls & Toys

Donay Games & Pastimes, London N1.
Judith Lassalle, London N1.
Yesterday Child, London N1.
Dolly Land, London N21.

Bearly Trading of London, London SE20.
Engine 'n' Tender, London SE25.
Mimi Fifi, London W11.
Victoriana Dolls, London W11.
London Antique Gallery, London W8.
Tim Armitage, Nantwich, Cheshire.
Rosina's, Falmouth, Cornwall.
Ursus, Penzance, Cornwall.
Abbey House, Derby, Derbys.
Honiton Antique Toys, Honiton, Devon.
The Vintage Toy and Train Shop, Sidmouth, Devon.
Boscombe Models and Collectors Shop, Bournemouth, Dorset.
Tilly's Antiques, Leigh-on-Sea, Essex.
The Doll's House, Northleach, Glos.
Park House Antiques, Stow-on-the-Wold, Glos.
Peter Pan's of Gosport, Gosport, Hants.
The Attic, Baldock, Herts.
London House Antiques, Westerham, Kent.
Irving Antique Toys, Manchester, Lancs.
C. and K.E. Dring, Lincoln, Lincs.
Norwich Collectors Toyshop, Norwich, Norfolk.
Granny's Attic, Nottingham, Notts.
Angus Antiques, Dundee, Scotland.
Bebes et Jouets, Edinburgh, Scotland.
Now and Then (Toy Centre), Edinburgh, Scotland.
Pastimes Vintage Toys, Glasgow, Scotland.
Trench Puzzles, Stowmarket, Suffolk.
C.A.R.S. (Classic Automobilia & Regalia Specialists), Brighton, Sussex East.
Paul Goble Jewellers, Brighton, Sussex East.
Sue Pearson, Brighton, Sussex East.
Coach House Antiques, Hastings, Sussex East.
Recollect Dolls Hospital, Burgess Hill, Sussex West.
Antiquated, Petworth, Sussex West.
Museum of Childhood Memories, Beaumaris (Anglesey), Wales.
Cross's Curios, Birmingham, West Mids.
Dolly Mixtures, Birmingham, West Mids.
Broadway Dolls and Bears, Broadway, Worcs.
Grannie's Parlour, Hull, Yorks. East.
Classic Rocking Horses, Thirsk, Yorks. North.
Collectors Old Toy Shop and Antiques, Halifax, Yorks. West.
Memory Lane, Sowerby Bridge, Yorks. West.

Etchings & Engravings

Gladwell and Company London EC4.
Moreton Street Gallery, London SW1.
Old Maps and Prints, London SW1.
The Map House, London SW3.
Old Church Galleries, London SW3.
King's Court Galleries, London SW6.
Julie Collino, London SW7.
The Wyllie Gallery, London SW7.
Agnew's, London W1.

Victor Arwas Gallery - Editions Graphiques Gallery Ltd, London W1.
Royal Exchange Art Gallery at Cork St., London W1.
William Weston Gallery, London W1.
Justin F. Skrebowski Prints, London W11.
Foye Gallery, Luton, Beds.
The Lantern Shop Gallery, Sidmouth, Devon.
Antique Map and Bookshop, Puddletown, Dorset.
Oldfield Gallery, Portsmouth, Hants.
The Shanklin Gallery, Shanklin, Isle of Wight.
Peter Goodall, Ventnor, Isle of Wight.
G. and D.I. Marrin and Sons, Folkestone, Kent.
London House Antiques, Westerham, Kent.
Leicestershire Sporting Gallery and Brown Jack Bookshop, Lubenham, Leics.
Graftons of Market Harborough, Market Harborough, Leics.
P.J. Cassidy (Books), Holbeach, Lincs.
TRADA, Chipping Norton, Oxon.
The Barry Keene Gallery, Henley-on-Thames, Oxon.
Elizabeth Harvey-Lee, North Aston, Oxon.
Open Eye Gallery Ltd, Edinburgh, Scotland.
Royal Mile Gallery, Edinburgh, Scotland.
Ewan Mundy Fine Art Ltd, Glasgow, Scotland.
Mainhill Gallery, Jedburgh, Scotland.
Killin Gallery, Killin, Scotland.
Nigel Stacy-Marks Ltd, Perth, Scotland.
George Gregory, Bath, Somerset.
England's Gallery, Leek, Staffs.
King's Court Galleries, Dorking, Surrey.
Hampton Court Palace Antiques, East Molesey, Surrey.
Limpsfield Watercolours, Limpsfield, Surrey.
Reigate Galleries, Reigate, Surrey.
Palmer Galleries, Richmond, Surrey.
The Witch Ball, Brighton, Sussex East.
Faringdon Gallery, Arundel, Sussex West.
Osborne Fine Art Gallery, Jesmond, Tyne and Wear.
David Windsor Gallery, Bangor, Wales.
Ronald Carr, Salisbury, Wilts.
Heirloom & Howard Limited, West Yatton, Wilts.
The Drawing Room - Interiors & Antiques, Pershore, Worcs.

Fire Related Items

Westland London, London EC2.
House of Steel Antiques, London N1.
Chesney's Antique Fireplace Warehouse, London N19.
Amazing Grates - Fireplaces Ltd, London N2.
Acquisitions (Fireplaces) Ltd, London NW5.
Townsends, London NW8.
Under Milkwood, London SE24.
Ward Antiques, London SE7.
The Fireplace, London SE9.
Nigel A. Bartlett, London SW1.

Crowther of Syon Lodge Ltd, London SW1.
Nicholas Gifford-Mead, London SW1.
H.W. Poulter and Son, London SW10.
Thornhill Galleries Ltd. in association with A. & R. Dockerill Ltd, London SW15.
Mr Wandle's Workshop Ltd, London SW18.
O.F. Wilson Ltd, London SW3.
Fairfax Antiques and Fireplaces, London SW6.
Hollingshead and Co, London SW6.
Old World Trading Co, London SW6.
The Chiswick Fireplace Co., London W4.
Architectural Antiques, London W6.
Architectural Antiques, Bedford, Beds.
Below Stairs of Hungerford, Hungerford, Berks.
The Fire Place (Hungerford) Ltd, Hungerford, Berks.
Grosvenor House Interiors, Beaconsfield, Bucks.
Pillory House, Nantwich, Cheshire.
Nostalgia Architectural Antiques, Stockport, Cheshire.
Antique Fireplaces, Tarvin, Cheshire.
Hearth & Home, Penrith, Cumbria.
Staveley Antiques, Staveley, Cumbria.
Finishing Touches, Derby, Derbys.
Wooden Box Antiques, Woodville, Derbys.
Ashburton Marbles, Ashburton, Devon.
Antique Fireplace Centre, Plymouth, Devon.
Robson's Antiques, Barnard Castle, Durham.
Antique Fireplace Centre, Hartlepool, Durham.
Flame and Grate, Bristol, Glos.
Period Fireplaces, Bristol, Glos.
Original Architectural, Cirencester, Glos.
Cox's Architectural Reclamation Yard, Moreton-in-Marsh, Glos.
Baileys Home & Garden, Ross-on-Wye, Herefs.
Bygones Reclamation, Canterbury, Kent.
Victorian Fireplace, Canterbury, Kent.
Ward Antiques, Sidcup, Kent.
Past & Present, Clitheroe, Lancs.
Old Smithy, Feniscowles, Lancs.
Antique Fireplace Warehouse, Manchester, Lancs.
Colin Blakey Fireplaces, Nelson, Lancs.
House Things Antiques, Hinckley, Leics.
Britain's Heritage, Leicester, Leics.
Antique Fireplaces, Liverpool, Merseyside.
Peco, Hampton, Middx.
Marble Hill Gallery, Twickenham, Middx.
Rococo Antiques, Architectural Goods and Furnishings, Weedon, Northants.
Hallidays (Fine Antiques) Ltd, Dorchester-on-Thames, Oxon.
Aston Pine Antiques, Faringdon, Oxon.
Oxford Architectural Antiques, Faringdon, Oxon.
Burning Embers, Aberdeen, Scotland.
EASY - Edinburgh Architectural Salvage Yard, Edinburgh, Scotland.
Holyrood Architectural Salvage, Edinburgh, Scotland.
T. and J. W. Neilson Ltd, Edinburgh, Scotland.

The Renaissance Furniture Store, Glasgow, Scotland.
Walcot Reclamation, Bath, Somerset.
Brighton Architectural Salvage, Brighton, Sussex East.
Shiners, Snobs Knobs, Jesmond, Tyne and Wear.
Turnburrys, Jesmond, Tyne and Wear.
Grate Expectations (Fireplaces), Washington, Tyne and Wear.
Flame 'n' Grate, Barry, Wales.
Kings Fireplaces, Antiques and Interiors, Cardiff, Wales.
The Victorian Ironmonger, Brinklow, Warks.
Tudor House Antiques, Halesowen, West Mids.
Old Flames, Easingwold, Yorks. North.
Robert Aagaard & Co, Knaresborough, Yorks. North.
Chapel House Fireplaces, Holmfirth, Yorks. West.
Swiss Cottage Furniture, Leeds, Yorks. West.

Frames
Paul Mason Gallery, London SW1.
Nigel Milne Ltd, London SW1.
Arnold Wiggins and Sons Ltd, London SW1.
Paul Mitchell Ltd, London W1.
Rollo Whately Ltd, London W1.
Daggett Gallery, London W11.
Lacy Gallery, London W11.
Justin F. Skrebowski Prints, London W11.
The Fairhurst Gallery, Norwich, Norfolk.
Looking Glass of Bath, Bath, Somerset.
W. Greenwood (Fine Art), Burneston, Yorks. North.
Coulter Galleries, York, Yorks. North.

Furniture - Continental (mainly French)
Charlton House Antiques, London N1.
Gordon Gridley, London N1.
Michel André Morin, London N1.
Relic Antiques at Camden Passage, London N1.
C. Tapsell, London N1.
Frames Direct, London N12.
Relic Antiques Trade Warehouse, London NW1.
Deuxieme, London NW8.
The Galleries, London SE1.
Melbourne Antiques & Interiors, London SE22.
Robert E. Hirschhorn, London SE5.
Didier Aaron (London)Ltd, London SW1.
ADEC, London SW1.
Appley Hoare Antiques, London SW1.
Blanchard Ltd, London SW1.
Ross Hamilton Ltd, London SW1.
Harris Lindsay, London SW1.
Hermitage Antiques plc, London SW1.
Carlton Hobbs, London SW1.
Christopher Howe, London SW1.
Jeremy Ltd, London SW1.
M. and D. Lewis, London SW1.
McClenaghan, London SW1.

Mark Ransom Ltd, London SW1.
Rogier et Rogier, London SW1.
Un Francais á Londres, London SW1.
Thomas Kerr Antiques Ltd, London SW10.
McVeigh & Charpentier, London SW10.
Orientation, London SW10.
The Woodpigeon, London SW11.
Simon Coleman Antiques, London SW13.
Jorgen Antiques, London SW15.
Adams Room Antiques, London SW19.
No. 12, London SW3.
Prides of London, London SW3.
O.F. Wilson Ltd, London SW3.
275 Antiques, London SW6.
I. and J.L. Brown Ltd, London SW6.
Rupert Cavendish Antiques, London SW6.
Nicole Fabre, London SW6.
Birdie Fortescue Antiques, London SW6.
Judy Greenwood, London SW6.
Christopher Jones Antiques, London SW6.
Lewin, London SW6.
Sylvia Napier Ltd, London SW6.
M. Pauw Antiques, London SW6.
The French House (Antiques) Ltd, London
   SW8.
Adrian Alan Ltd, London W1.
H. Blairman and Sons Ltd., London W1.
Howard Antiques, London W1.
Mallett at Bourdon House Ltd, London W1.
Partridge Fine Arts plc, London W1.
Pelham Galleries Ltd, London W1.
Jacob Stodel, London W1.
Toynbee-Clarke Interiors Ltd, London W1.
Barham Antiques, London W11.
Canonbury, London W11.
Curá Antiques, London W11.
M. and D. Lewis, London W11.
Robin Martin Antiques, London W11.
David Alexander Antiques & Kate Thurlow,
   London W14.
Marshall Gallery, London W14.
David Brower Antiques, London W8.
Reindeer Antiques Ltd, London W8.
Sinai Antiques Ltd, London W8.
Pamela Teignmouth and Son, London W8.
David Litt Antiques, Ampthill, Beds.
Ulla Stafford Antiques, Binfield, Berks.
John A. Pearson Antiques, Horton, Berks.
Youll's Antiques, Hungerford, Berks.
La Maison, Bourne End, Bucks.
Jack Harness Antiques, Marlow, Bucks.
Archer's Antique and Country Furniture, Olney,
   Bucks.
Phoenix Antiques, Fordham, Cambs.
Ivor and Patricia Lewis Antique and Fine Art
   Dealers, Peterborough, Cambs.
Adams Antiques, Chester, Cheshire.
Harris & Holt, Chester, Cheshire.
French Countrystyle, Hale, Cheshire.

Antique Furniture Warehouse, Stockport,
   Cheshire.
Manchester Antique Company, Stockport,
   Cheshire.
Old Town Hall Antiques, Falmouth, Cornwall.
West End Galleries, Buxton, Derbys.
Merchant House Antiques, Honiton, Devon.
Pilgrim Antiques, Honiton, Devon.
Pugh's Farm Antiques, Monkton, Devon.
Colystock Antiques, Stockland, Devon.
Lionel Geneen Ltd, Bournemouth, Dorset.
Georgina Ryder, Frampton, Dorset.
Talisman, Gillingham, Dorset.
Deja Vu Antiques, Leigh-on-Sea, Essex.
August Antiques and Interiors, Moreton-in-Marsh,
   Glos.
Gary Wright Antiques, Moreton-in-Marsh, Glos.
Ashton Gower Antiques, Stow-on-the-Wold, Glos.
Oonagh Black, Stow-on-the-Wold, Glos.
Annarella Clark Antiques, Stow-on-the-Wold,
   Glos.
Antony Preston Antiques Ltd, Stow-on-the-Wold,
   Glos.
The Decorator Source, Tetbury, Glos.
Sieff, Tetbury, Glos.
Geoffrey Stead, Todenham, Glos.
Cotswold Antiques. com, Winchcombe, Glos.
Artemesia, Alresford, Hants.
Cedar Antiques Limited, Hartley Wintney, Hants.
David Lazarus Antiques, Hartley Wintney, Hants.
Phoenix Green Antiques, Hartley Wintney, Hants.
Csaky's Antiques, Hook, Hants.
Wick Antiques, Lymington, Hants.
Millers of Chelsea Antiques Ltd, Ringwood,
   Hants.
Antique Eyes, Stockbridge, Hants.
The Bakhtiyar Gallery, Stockbridge, Hants.
I. and J.L. Brown Ltd, Hereford, Herefs.
Great Brampton House Antiques Ltd, Hereford,
   Herefs.
Royal Standard Antiques, Cowes, Isle of Wight.
The Barn at Bislington, Bilsington, Kent.
Lennox Cato, Edenbridge, Kent.
Samovar Antiques, Hythe, Kent.
Henry Baines, Southborough, Kent.
Flower House Antiques, Tenterden, Kent.
Claremont Antiques, Tunbridge Wells, Kent.
Up Country, Tunbridge Wells, Kent.
J. Green and Son, Queniborough,, Leics.
Graham Pickett Antiques, Stamford, Lincs.
Birkdale Antiques, Southport, Merseyside.
Ron Green, Towcester, Northants.
Helios & Co (Antiques), Weedon, Northants.
Jonathan Fyson Antiques, Burford, Oxon.
Gateway Antiques, Burford, Oxon.
Antique English Windsor Chairs, Chipping
   Norton, Oxon.
Summers Davis Antiques Ltd, Wallingford, Oxon.
Witney Antiques, Witney, Oxon.

Swans, Oakham, Rutland.
Malthouse Antiques, Bridgnorth, Shrops.
Garrard Antiques, Ludlow, Shrops.
Jadis Ltd, Bath, Somerset.
Hennessy, Crewkerne, Somerset.
Pennard House Antiques, East Pennard, Somerset.
Gilbert & Dale, Ilchester, Somerset.
Edward Marnier Antiques, Shepton Mallet, Somerset.
Rostrum Antiques, South Petherton, Somerset.
Dix-Sept, Framlingham, Suffolk.
Heath-Bullocks, Godalming, Surrey.
Marryat, Richmond, Surrey.
Ripley Antiques, Ripley, Surrey.
Dermot and Jill Palmer Antiques, Brighton, Sussex East.
Graham Lower, Flimwell, Sussex East.
Graham Price Antiques Ltd, Polegate, Sussex East.
Julian Antiques, Hurstpierpoint, Sussex West.
Oliver Charles Antiques, Petworth, Sussex West.
Ruddy Antiques, Petworth, Sussex West.
Little Theatre Antiques Centre, Jesmond, Tyne and Wear.
Apollo Antiques Ltd, Warwick, Warks.
L.P. Antiques (Mids) Ltd, Walsall, West Mids.
Avon Antiques, Bradford-on-Avon, Wilts.
Moxhams Antiques, Bradford-on-Avon, Wilts.
St Mary's Chapel Antiques, Devizes, Wilts.
Brocante Antiques Centre, Marlborough, Wilts.
Obelisk Antiques, Warminster, Wilts.
Coopers of Ilkley, Ilkley, Yorks. West.
Charlotte and John Lambe, Belfast, N. Ireland.
Whytock and Reid, Edinburgh, Scotland.
Jeremy Sniders Antiques, Glasgow, Scotland.
Michael Vee Design - Birch House Antiques, Melrose, Scotland.

Furniture - Country

Michael Lewis Antiques, London N1.
At the Sign of the Chest of Drawers, London N6.
Relic Antiques Trade Warehouse, London NW1.
This and That (Furniture), London NW1.
M. and D. Seligmann, London NW3.
Robert E. Hirschhorn, London SE5.
Rogier et Rogier, London SW1.
The Furniture Cave, London SW10.
Robert Young Antiques, London SW11.
Simon Coleman Antiques, London SW13.
I. and J.L. Brown Ltd, London SW6.
Alistair Sampson Antiques Ltd, London W1.
Alan Hodgson Great Shefford Berks.
The Hampden Trading Company, Great Missenden, Bucks.
Jack Harness Antiques, Marlow, Bucks.
Simon and Penny Rumble Antiques, Chittering, Cambs.
A.P. and M.A. Haylett, Outwell, Cambs.
Boustead-Bland Antiques Chester, Cheshire.
Farmhouse Antiques, Chester, Cheshire.

Adams Antiques, Nantwich, Cheshire.
Julie Strachey, Connor Downs, Cornwall.
Blackwater Pine Antiques, Truro, Cornwall.
Simon Starkie Antiques, Cartmel, Cumbria.
David Hill, Kirkby Stephen, Cumbria.
Utopia Antiques Ltd, Low Newton Cumbria.
Sandgate Antiques, Penrith, Cumbria.
Winton Hall Antiques Ravenstonedale, Cumbria.
Peter Bunting Antiques, Bakewell Derbys.
Byethorpe Furniture Barlow Derbys.
Godolphin Antiques, Chagford, Devon.
Rex Antiques Chagford, Devon.
Cobweb Antiques, Cullompton, Devon.
Miller Antiques Cullompton Devon.
The Grove Antiques Centre, Honiton, Devon.
Pugh's Farm Antiques, Monkton, Devon.
Timepiece, Teignmouth, Devon.
Fine Pine Antiques, Totnes, Devon.
English Rose Antiques, Coggeshall, Essex.
Dean Antiques, Colchester, Essex.
The Stores Great Waltham, Essex.
Lennard Antiques Sible Hedingham Essex.
Denzil Verey, Barnsley, Glos.
J. and R. Bateman Antiques, Chalford, Glos.
John P. Townsend, Cheltenham, Glos.
Jon Fox Antiques, Moreton-in-Marsh, Glos.
Oonagh Black, Stow-on-the-Wold, Glos.
Annarella Clark Antiques, Stow-on-the-Wold, Glos.
Keith Hockin Antiques Stow-on-the-Wold, Glos.
Huntington Antiques Ltd, Stow-on-the-Wold, Glos.
The Chest of Drawers, Tetbury, Glos.
Peter Norden Antiques Tetbury Glos.
Westwood House Antiques and Beehive Antiques, Tetbury, Glos.
Cedar Antiques Limited Hartley Wintney, Hants.
Phoenix Green Antiques, Hartley Wintney, Hants.
Roy Precious Antiques & Fine Art, Hartley Wintney, Hants.
Burgess Farm Antiques, Morestead, Hants.
Millers of Chelsea Antiques Ltd, Ringwood, Hants.
The Pine Cellars, Winchester, Hants.
I. and J.L. Brown Ltd, Hereford, Herefs.
Robin Lloyd Antiques, Ross-on-Wye, Herefs.
M. and J. Russell, Yazor, Herefs.
Tim Wharton Antiques, Redbourn, Herts.
Dinah Stoodley & Celia Jennings Brasted, Kent.
Michael Pearson Antiques, Canterbury, Kent.
Douglas Bryan Cranbrook, Kent.
Swan Antiques, Cranbrook Kent.
Mill House Antiques, Goudhurst, Kent.
Henry Baines, Southborough, Kent.
Claremont Antiques, Tunbridge Wells, Kent.
Phoenix Antiques, Tunbridge Wells, Kent.
Up Country, Tunbridge Wells, Kent.
Edmund Davies & Son Antiques, Whalley, Lancs.
Quorn Pine and Decoratives, Quorn, Leics.
Rebecca Calvert Antiques Lincoln, Lincs.

Hunters Antiques & Interior Design Stamford Lincs.
Graham Pickett Antiques, Stamford, Lincs.
Sinclair's Stamford, Lincs.
Holt Antique Centre, Holt, Norfolk.
Paul Hopwell Antiques, West Haddon, Northants.
Mark Seabrook Antiques West Haddon, Northants.
Horseshoe Antiques and Gallery, Burford, Oxon.
Swan Gallery, Burford, Oxon.
Antique English Windsor Chairs, Chipping Norton, Oxon.
Key Antiques, Chipping Norton, Oxon.
Dorchester Antiques, Dorchester-on-Thames, Oxon.
Wychwood Antiques, Taynton Oxon.
Witney Antiques, Witney, Oxon.
Antiques of Woodstock Woodstock Oxon.
Chris Baylis Country Chairs Woodstock Oxon.
Ark Antiques, Bishop's Castle, Shrops.
John Clegg, Ludlow, Shrops.
Garrard Antiques, Ludlow, Shrops.
G. & D. Ginger Antiques Ludlow, Shrops.
Mackenzie & Smith Furniture Restoration, Ludlow, Shrops.
Marcus Moore Antiques, Stanton upon Hine Heath Shrops.
Dodington Antiques, Whitchurch, Shrops.
Lansdown Antiques, Bath, Somerset.
Piccadilly Antiques, Batheaston, Somerset.
Chez Chalon, Chard Somerset.
Hennessy, Crewkerne, Somerset.
Acorn Antiques, Dulverton, Somerset.
Anthony Sampson Antiques, Dulverton, Somerset.
Gilbert & Dale Ilchester Somerset.
Johnson's, Leek, Staffs.
The Suffolk Table Company, Debenham, Suffolk.
Dix-Sept Framlingham Suffolk.
TheTheatre Antiques Centre, Framlingham, Suffolk.
Noel Mercer Antiques, Long Melford, Suffolk.
Antiques Warehouse (incorporating The Woodbridge Trading Co.), Marlesford, Suffolk.
Suffolk House Antiques, Yoxford, Suffolk.
Stoneycroft Farm, Betchworth Surrey.
Cobham Galleries, Cobham, Surrey.
Harman's Antiques Dorking, Surrey.
Christopher's Antiques, Farnham, Surrey.
Elm House Antiques, Merstham, Surrey.
Anthony Welling Antiques, Ripley, Surrey.
E. and B. White, Brighton, Sussex East.
Hadlow Down Antiques, Hadlow Down, Sussex East.
Pastorale Antiques, Lewes, Sussex East.
Graham Price Antiques Ltd, Polegate, Sussex East.
Ringles Cross Antiques, Uckfield, Sussex East.
Park View Antiques, Wadhurst, Sussex East.
Antiquities, Arundel, Sussex West.
Michael Wakelin and Helen Linfield, Billingshurst, Sussex West.

Alexander Antiques, Henfield, Sussex West.
Angel Antiques, Petworth, Sussex West.
John Bird, Petworth, Sussex west.
J.C. Tutt Antiques, Petworth, Sussex West.
King's Cottage Antiques, Leamington Spa, Warks.
L.P. Antiques (Mids) Ltd, Walsall, West Mids.
Matthew Eden, Corsham, Wilts.
Annmarie Turner Antiques, Marlborough, Wilts.
Maxfield House Antiques, Warminster, Wilts.
D & J Lines Antiques Wychbold Worcs.
The Antique Pine & Country Furniture Shop Driffield, Yorks. East.
Elaine Phillips Antiques Ltd, Harrogate, Yorks. North.
Yorkshire Country Wines & Antiques Harrogate Yorks. North.
York Cottage Antiques, Helmsley, Yorks. North.
Middleham Antiques, Middleham, Yorks. North.
Northern Antiques Company, Norton, Yorks. North.
Pateley Bridge Antiques, Pateley Bridge, Yorks. North.
John Gilbert Antiques Robin Hood's Bay, Yorks. North.
E. Thistlethwaite, Settle, Yorks. North.
Coach House Antiques, Whitby, Yorks. North.
Ruth Ford Antiques, York, Yorks. North.
Fishlake Antiques, Fishlake, Yorks. South.
Robert Davidson Antiques Todmorden, Yorks. West.
Audrey Bull Carmarthen Wales.
The Mount Antiques Centre, Carmarthen, Wales.
Havard and Havard, Cowbridge, Wales.
Gallop and Rivers Architectural Antiques, Crickhowell, Wales.
Country Antiques (Wales) Ltd, Kidwelly, Wales.
Islwyn Watkins, Knighton, Wales.
Jim and Pat Ash, Llandeilo, Wales.
Collinge Antiques, Llandudno Junction, Wales.
Michael Lloyd Antiques Llandysul, Wales.
Heritage Restorations, Llanfair Caereinion, Wales.
Singleton Antiques, Skenfrith, Wales.
Audrey Bull, Tenby, Wales.

Furniture - Georgian

Peter Chapman Antiques and Restoration, London N1.
Furniture Vault, London N1.
Gordon Gridley, London N1.
Jonathan James, London N1.
Regent Antiques, London N1.
Restall Brown and Clennell Ltd, London N1.
C. Tapsell, London N1.
Vane House Antiques, London N1.
Finchley Fine Art Galleries, London N12.
Martin Henham (Antiques), London N2.
Betty Gould and Julian Gonnermann Antiques, London N6.
G. and F. Gillingham Ltd, London NW2.

Patricia Beckman Antiques, London NW3.
David Wainwright, London NW3.
Camden Art Gallery, London NW8.
Patricia Harvey Antiques and Decoration, London NW8.
Wellington Gallery, London NW8.
Young & Son, London NW8.
The Galleries, London SE1.
Tower Bridge Antiques, London SE1.
The Junk Shop, London SE10.
Robert E. Hirschhorn, London SE5.
Antique Warehouse, London SE8.
Anno Domini Antiques, London SW1.
Hilary Batstone Antiques inc. Rose Uniacke Interiors, London SW1.
John Bly, London SW1.
Ross Hamilton Ltd, London SW1.
Harrods Ltd, London SW1.
Hotspur Ltd, London SW1.
Christopher Howe, London SW1.
Humphrey-Carrasco, London SW1.
Jeremy Ltd, London SW1.
Anthony Outred, London SW1.
Westenholz Antiques Ltd, London SW1.
The Furniture Cave, London SW10.
Granville Antiques, London SW10.
Stephen Long, London SW10.
Pairs Antiques Ltd, London SW11.
The Dining Room Shop, London SW13.
Jorgen Antiques, London SW15.
H.C. Baxter and Sons, London SW16.
Adams Room Antiques, London SW19.
Norman Adams Ltd, London SW3.
Apter Fredericks Ltd, London SW3.
Richard Courtney Ltd, London SW3.
Robert Dickson and Lesley Rendall Antiques, London SW3.
Michael Foster, London SW3.
General Trading Co Ltd, London SW3.
Godson and Coles, London SW3.
Anthony James and Son Ltd, London SW3.
Peter Jones at PJ2, London SW3.
John Keil Ltd, London SW3.
Peter Lipitch Ltd, London SW3.
Prides of London, London SW3.
Charles Saunders Antiques, London SW3.
Clifford Wright Antiques Ltd, London SW3.
313 Antiques, London SW6.
Alasdair Brown, London SW6.
John Clay, London SW6.
Fergus Cochrane and Leigh Warren Antiques, London SW6.
George Floyd Ltd, London SW6.
HRW Antiques (London) Ltd, London SW6.
P.L. & M. James, London SW6.
Christopher Jones Antiques, London SW6.
L. and E. Kreckovic, London SW6.
Michael Luther Antiques, London SW6.
Michael Marriott Ltd, London SW6.

David Martin-Taylor Antiques, London SW6.
Ossowski, London SW6.
M. Pauw Antiques, London SW6.
Rogers & Co, London SW6.
Stephen Sprake, London SW6.
H. Blairman and Sons Ltd., London W1.
Antoine Cheneviere Fine Arts, London W1.
Sibyl Colefax & John Fowler, London W1.
Halcyon Days, London W1.
Patrick Jefferson, London W1.
Leuchars and Jefferson, London W1.
Mallett and Son (Antiques) Ltd, London W1.
Partridge Fine Arts plc, London W1.
Pendulum of Mayfair Ltd, London W1.
Ronald Phillips Ltd, London W1.
Scarisbrick and Bate Ltd, London W1.
Jeremy Seale Antiques/Interiors, London W1.
Stair and Company Ltd, London W1.
Toynbee-Clarke Interiors Ltd, London W1.
M. Turpin Ltd, London W1.
Windsor House Antiques LtdLondon W1.
B. and T. Antiques, London W11.
Butchoff Antiques, London W11.
The Coach House, London W11.
Michael Davidson, London W11.
Judy Fox, London W11.
Robin Martin Antiques, London W11.
Terence Morse and Son Ltd, London W11.
David Wainwright, London W11.
Trude Weaver, London W11.
Marshall Gallery, London W14.
J. Roger (Antiques) Ltd, London W14.
Aberdeen House Antiques, London W5.
Terrace Antiques, London W5.
Eddy Bardawil, London W8.
C. Fredericks and Son, London W8.
Lewis and Lloyd, London W8.
C.H. Major (Antiques) Ltd, London W8.
Reindeer Antiques Ltd, London W8.
Brian Rolleston Antiques Ltd, London W8.
Patrick Sandberg Antiques, London W8.
Pamela Teignmouth and Son, London W8.
Fluss and Charlesworth Ltd, London W9.
Paris Antiques, Ampthill, Beds.
Pilgrim Antiques, Ampthill, Beds.
S. and S. Timms Antiques Ltd, Shefford, Beds.
Town Hall Antiques, Woburn, Beds.
Ulla Stafford Antiques, Binfield, Berks.
John A. Pearson Antiques, Horton, Berks.
Roger King Antiques, Hungerford, Berks.
The Old Malthouse, Hungerford, Berks.
Turpins Antiques, Hungerford, Berks.
Widmerpool House Antiques, Maidenhead, Berks.
Rupert Landen Antiques, Reading, Berks.
Cavendish Fine Arts, Sonning-on-Thames, Berks.
John Connell - Wargrave Antiques, Wargrave, Berks.
Eton Antiques Partnership, Windsor and Eton, Berks.

Eton Gallery, Windsor and Eton, Berks.
Peter J. Martin, Windsor and Eton, Berks.
Times Past Antiques, Windsor and Eton, Berks.
The Cupboard Antiques, Amersham, Bucks.
June Elsworth - Beaconsfield Ltd, Beaconsfield, Bucks.
Grosvenor House Interiors, Beaconsfield, Bucks.
Period Furniture Showrooms, Beaconsfield, Bucks.
The Spinning Wheel, Beaconsfield, Bucks.
The Hampden Trading Company, Great Missenden, Bucks.
Country Furniture Shop, Penn, Bucks.
Bowood Antiques, Wendover, Bucks.
David's, Brampton, Cambs.
Peter Norman Antiques and Restorations, Burwell, Cambs.
Jess Applin Antiques, Cambridge, Cambs.
John Beazor and Sons Ltd, Cambridge, Cambs.
Tavistock Antiques, St. Neots, Cambs.
Sara Frances Antiques, Alderley Edge, Cheshire.
Church Street Antiques, Altrincham, Cheshire.
Andrew Foott Antiques, Cheadle Hulme, Cheshire.
Adams Antiques, Chester, Cheshire.
Boustead-Bland Antiques, Chester, Cheshire.
Harris & Holt, Chester, Cheshire.
Melody's Antiques, Chester, Cheshire.
Moor Hall Antiques, Chester, Cheshire.
Glynn Interiors, Knutsford, Cheshire.
John Titchner and Sons, Littleton, Cheshire.
David Bedale, Mobberley, Cheshire.
Chapel Antiques, Nantwich, Cheshire.
Coppelia Antiques, Plumley, Cheshire.
Saxon Cross Antiques Emporium, Sandbach, Cheshire.
Manchester Antique Company, Stockport, Cheshire.
Antique Chairs and Museum, Launceston, Cornwall.
Todd's, Launceston, Cornwall.
John Bragg Antiques, Lostwithiel, Cornwall.
Antiques & Fine Art, Penzance, Cornwall.
Victoria Antiques, Wadebridge, Cornwall.
Anthemion - The Antique Shop, Cartmel, Cumbria.
Jennywell Hall Antiques, Crosby Ravensworth, Cumbria.
Haughey Antiques, Kirkby Stephen, Cumbria.
Townhead Antiques, Newby Bridge, Cumbria.
Country Seat Antiques, Newby East, Cumbria.
Winton Hall Antiques, Ravenstonedale, Cumbria.
Ashbourne Antiques Ltd, Ashbourne, Derbys.
Pamela Elsom - Antiques, Ashbourne, Derbys.
Martin and Dorothy Harper Antiques, Bakewell, Derbys.
Thornbridge Antiques, Bakewell, Derbys.
Water Lane Antiques, Bakewell, Derbys.
Hackney House Antiques, Barlow, Derbys.
The Antiques Warehouse, Buxton, Derbys.

Ian Morris, Chesterfield, Derbys.
Brian Matsell, Derby, Derbys.
Wayside Antiques, Duffield, Derbys.
Shardlow Antiques Warehouse, Shardlow, Derbys.
Nimbus Antiques, Whaley Bridge, Derbys.
Wooden Box Antiques, Woodville, Derbys.
J. Collins and Son, Bideford, Devon.
John Prestige Antiques, Brixham, Devon.
Alison Gosling Antiques, Budleigh Salterton, Devon.
David J. Thorn, Budleigh Salterton, Devon.
Rex Antiques, Chagford, Devon.
Cullompton Old Tannery Antiques, Cullompton, Devon.
Mills Antiques, Cullompton, Devon.
McBains Antiques, Exeter, Devon.
Roderick Butler, Honiton, Devon.
The Grove Antiques Centre, Honiton, Devon.
Lombard Antiques, Honiton, Devon.
Maya Antiques, Honiton, Devon.
Merchant House Antiques, Honiton, Devon.
Pilgrim Antiques, Honiton, Devon.
Upstairs, Downstairs, Honiton, Devon.
W. J. Woodhams, Shaldon, Devon.
A. E. Wakeman & Sons Ltd, Tedburn St Mary, Devon.
Extence Antiques, Teignmouth, Devon.
Past and Present, Totnes, Devon.
Anthony James Antiques, Whimple, Devon.
Antiques for All, Blandford Forum, Dorset.
Lionel Geneen Ltd, Bournemouth, Dorset.
Sainsburys of Bournemouth Ltd, Bournemouth, Dorset.
David Mack Antiques, Branksome, Dorset.
Benchmark Antiques, Bridport, Dorset.
Hamptons, Christchurch, Dorset.
Tower Antiques, Cranborne, Dorset.
Michael Legg Antiques, Dorchester, Dorset.
Legg of Dorchester, Dorchester, Dorset.
Laburnum Antiques, Poole, Dorset.
Stocks and Chairs, Poole, Dorset.
Shaston Antiques, Shaftesbury, Dorset.
Heygate Browne Antiques, Sherborne, Dorset.
Piers Pisani Antiques, Sherborne, Dorset.
James Hardy Antiques Ltd, Barnard Castle, Durham.
Joan and David White Antiques, Barnard Castle, Durham.
Margaret Bedi Antiques & Fine Art, Billingham, Durham.
Alan Ramsey Antiques, Darlington, Durham.
Eden House Antiques, West Auckland, Durham.
Revival, Abridge, Essex.
Swan Antiques, Baythorne End, Essex.
Hutchison Antiques, Chelmsford, Essex.
Colton Antiques, Kelvedon, Essex.
Clive Beardall Antiques, Maldon, Essex.
West Essex Antiques (Stone Hall), Matching Green, Essex.

F.G. Bruschweiler (Antiques) Ltd, Rayleigh, Essex.

The Interior Design Shop, Saffron Walden, Essex.

W.A. Pinn and Sons, Sible Hedingham, Essex.

Harris Antiques (Stansted), Stansted, Essex.

Linden House Antiques, Stansted, Essex.

White Roding Antiques, White Roding, Essex.

Peter and Penny Proudfoot, Berkeley, Glos..

The Antiques Warehouse Ltd, Bristol, Glos.

Latchford Antiques, Cheltenham, Glos.

Triton Gallery, Cheltenham, Glos.

Forum Antiques, Cirencester, Glos.

Hares, Cirencester, Glos.

Rankine Taylor Antiques, Cirencester, Glos.

Patrick Waldron Antiques, Cirencester, Glos.

Bernard Weaver Antiques, Cirencester, Glos.

Blenheim Antiques, Fairford, Glos.

Mark Carter Antiques, Fairford, Glos.

August Antiques and Interiors, Moreton-in-Marsh, Glos.

Benton Fine Art, Moreton-in-Marsh, Glos.

Berry Antiques, Moreton-in-Marsh, Glos.

Dale House Antiques, Moreton-in-Marsh, Glos.

Seaford House Antiques, Moreton-in-Marsh, Glos.

Simply Antiques, Moreton-in-Marsh, Glos.

Gary Wright Antiques, Moreton-in-Marsh, Glos.

Robson Antiques, Northleach, Glos.

Ashton Gower Antiques, Stow-on-the-Wold, Glos.

Duncan J. Baggott, Stow-on-the-Wold, Glos.

Baggott Church Street Ltd, Stow-on-the-Wold, Glos.

Bryden House Clocks & Antiques, Stow-on-the-Wold, Glos.

Christopher Clarke Antiques Ltd, Stow-on-the-Wold, Glos.

Huntington Antiques Ltd, Stow-on-the-Wold, Glos.

T.M. King-Smith & Simon W. Nutter, Stow-on-the-Wold, Glos.

La Chaise Antique, Stow-on-the-Wold, Glos.

Roger Lamb Antiques & Works of Art, Stow-on-the-Wold, Glos.

Antony Preston Antiques Ltd, Stow-on-the-Wold, Glos.

Priests Antiques, Stow-on-the-Wold, Glos.

Queens Parade Antiques Ltd, Stow-on-the-Wold, Glos.

Michael Rowland Antiques, Stow-on-the-Wold, Glos.

Stow Antiques, Stow-on-the-Wold, Glos.

Styles of Stow, Stow-on-the-Wold, Glos.

Tudor House, Stow-on-the-Wold, Glos.

Vanbrugh House Antiques, Stow-on-the-Wold, Glos.

Wyndhams, Stow-on-the-Wold, Glos.

Arkangel Antiques, Tetbury, Glos.

Ball and Claw Antiques, Tetbury, Glos.

Breakspeare Antiques, Tetbury, Glos.

The Chest of Drawers, Tetbury, Glos.

Bobbie Middleton, Tetbury, Glos.

Paul Nash Antiques, Tetbury, Glos.

Peter Norden Antiques, Tetbury, Glos.

Porch House Antiques, Tetbury, Glos.

Berkeley Antiques, Tewkesbury, Glos.

Gainsborough House Antiques, Tewkesbury, Glos.

Cotswold Antiques. com, Winchcombe, Glos.

Prichard Antiques, Winchcombe, Glos.

Tudor Antiques & Fine Art Ltd, Alresford, Hants.

The Furniture Trading Co, Botley, Hants.

Nicholas Abbott, Hartley Wintney, Hants.

Andwells Antiques Limited, Hartley Wintney, Hants.

Antique House, Hartley Wintney, Hants.

Deva Antiques, Hartley Wintney, Hants.

David Lazarus Antiques, Hartley Wintney, Hants.

Phoenix Green Antiques, Hartley Wintney, Hants.

Csaky's Antiques, Hook, Hants.

Lita Kaye of Lyndhurst, Lyndhurst, Hants.

Millers of Chelsea Antiques Ltd, Ringwood, Hants.

Antique Eyes, Stockbridge, Hants.

The Bakhtiyar Gallery, Stockbridge, Hants.

Gasson Antiques and Interiors, Tadley, Hants.

Gaylords, Titchfield, Hants.

Burns and Graham, Winchester, Hants.

Winchester Antiques, Winchester, Hants.

Great Brampton House Antiques Ltd, Hereford, Herefs.

John Nash Antiques and Interiors, Ledbury, Herefs.

Serendipity, Ledbury, Herefs.

Jeffery Hammond Antiques, Leominster, Herefs.

Linden House Antiques, Leominster, Herefs..

Anthony Butt Antiques, Baldock, Herts.

Ralph and Bruce Moss, Baldock, Herts.

The Windhill Antiquary, Bishop's Stortford, Herts.

Tapestry Antiques, Hertford, Herts.

Michael Gander, Hitchin, Herts.

Hanbury Antiques, Hitchin, Herts.

Phillips of Hitchin (Antiques) Ltd, Hitchin, Herts.

Tom Salusbury Antiques, Hitchin, Herts.

J.N. Antiques, Redbourn, Herts.

Tim Wharton Antiques, Redbourn, Herts.

Charnwood Antiques and Arcane Antiques Centre, Sawbridgeworth, Herts.

John Bly, Tring, Herts.

New England House Antiques, Tring, Herts.

Weston Antiques, Weston, Herts.

Collins Antiques (F.G. and C. Collins Ltd.), Wheathampstead, Herts.

Michael Armson (Antiques) Ltd, Wilstone, Herts.

John Corrin Antiques, Douglas, Isle of Man.

Country House and Cottage Antiques, St Mary, Jersey, C.I.

Stephen Cohu Antiques, St Ouen, Jersey, C.I.

Stablegate Antiques, Barham, Kent.

David Barrington, Brasted, Kent.

Keymer Son & Co. Ltd, Brasted, Kent.

Roy Massingham Antiques, Brasted, Kent.
Tilings Antiques, Brasted, Kent.
Conquest House Antiques, Canterbury, Kent.
Chislehurst Antiques, Chislehurst, Kent.
Michael Sim, Chislehurst, Kent.
Vestry Antiques, Cranbrook, Kent.
Lennox Cato, Edenbridge, Kent.
Alan Lord Antiques, Folkestone, Kent.
Mill House Antiques, Goudhurst, Kent.
Newington Antiques, Newington, Kent.
J.D. and R.M. Walters, Rolvenden, Kent.
Christopher Buck Antiques, Sandgate, Kent.
Finch Antiques, Sandgate, Kent.
Michael Fitch Antiques, Sandgate, Kent.
Freeman and Lloyd Antiques, Sandgate, Kent.
David M. Lancefield Antiques, Sandgate, Kent.
James Porter Antiques, Sandwich, Kent.
Nancy Wilson, Sandwich, Kent.
Gem Antiques, Sevenoaks, Kent.
Steppes Hill Farm Antiques, Stockbury, Kent.
Sutton Valence Antiques, Sutton Valence, Kent.
Flower House Antiques, Tenterden, Kent.
The Pantiles Antiques, Tunbridge Wells, Kent.
Pantiles Spa Antiques, Tunbridge Wells, Kent.
Phoenix Antiques, Tunbridge Wells, Kent.
John Thompson, Tunbridge Wells, Kent.
Up Country, Tunbridge Wells, Kent.
Apollo Antique Galleries, Westerham, Kent.
Peter Dyke, Westerham, Kent.
London House Antiques, Westerham, Kent.
Marks Antiques, Westerham, Kent.
Taylor-Smith Antiques, Westerham, Kent.
Westerham Antiques Warehouse, Westerham,
    Kent.
Westerham House Antiques, Westerham, Kent.
Laurens Antiques, Whitstable, Kent.
Tankerton Antiques, Whitstable, Kent.
Silvesters, Wingham, Kent.
Brun Lea Antiques (J. Waite Ltd), Burnley, Lancs.
K.C. Antiques, Darwen, Lancs.
P.J. Brown Antiques, Haslingden, Lancs.
Luigino Vescovi, Morecambe, Lancs.
Brooks Antiques, Nelson, Lancs.
Alan Grice Antiques, Ormskirk, Lancs.
S.C. Falk, Rochdale, Lancs.
Old Bakehouse Antiques and Gallery, Broughton
    Astley, Leics.
Ken Smith Antiques Ltd, Enderby, Leics.
Sitting Pretty, Great Glen, Leics.
Withers of Leicester, Hoby, Leics.
Corry's, Leicester, Leics.
Treedale Antiques, Little Dalby, Leics.
Lowe of Loughborough, Loughborough, Leics.
Walter Moores and Son, Market Harborough,
    Leics.
J. Stamp and Sons, Market Harborough, Leics.
David E. Burrows, Osgathorpe, Leics.
J. Green and Son, Queniborough,, Leics.
Paddock Antiques, Woodhouse Eaves, Leics.

G. Baker Antiques, Horncastle, Lincs.
Alan Read - Period Furniture, Horncastle, Lincs.
Laurence Shaw Antiques, Horncastle, Lincs.
Laurence Shaw Antiques, Horncastle, Lincs.
David J. Hansord & Son, Lincoln, Lincs.
Dawson of Stamford Ltd, Stamford, Lincs.
Hunters Antiques & Interior Design, Stamford,
    Lincs.
Graham Pickett Antiques, Stamford, Lincs.
St. George's Antiques, Stamford, Lincs.
Robin Shield Antiques, Swinstead, Lincs.
Underwoodhall Antiques, Woodhall Spa, Lincs.
V.O.C. Antiques, Woodhall Spa, Lincs.
Stefani Antiques, Liverpool, Merseyside.
Colin Stock, Rainford, Merseyside.
Tony and Anne Sutcliffe Antiques, Southport,
    Merseyside.
Helen Horswill Antiques and Decorative Arts,
    West Kirby, Merseyside.
Tobias Jellinek Antiques, Twickenham, Middx.
Ivy House Antiques, Acle, Norfolk.
A.E. Bush and Partners, Attleborough, Norfolk.
M. and A. Cringle, Burnham Market, Norfolk.
Anne Hamilton Antiques, Burnham Market,
    Norfolk.
Market House, Burnham Market, Norfolk.
Roger Bradbury Antiques, Coltishall, Norfolk.
Peter Robinson, Heacham, Norfolk.
James Brett, Norwich, Norfolk.
Nicholas Fowle Antiques, Norwich, Norfolk.
John Howkins Antiques Ltd, Norwich, Norfolk.
Echo Antiques, Reepham, Norfolk.
Country House Antiques, Seething, Norfolk.
Leo Pratt and Son, South Walsham, Norfolk.
Stalham Antique Gallery, Stalham, Norfolk.
Norton Antiques, Twyford, Norfolk.
T.C.S. Brooke, Wroxham, Norfolk.
Courtyard Antiques, Brackley, Northants.
Simon Banks Antiques, Finedon, Northants.
M.C. Chapman, Finedon, Northants.
Robert Cheney Antiques, Finedon, Northants.
Huntershield Antiques and Granary Antiques,
    Flore, Northants.
Christopher Jones Antiques, Flore, Northants.
F. and C.H. Cave, Northampton, Northants.
Reindeer Antiques Ltd, Potterspury, Northants.
Barber Antiques, West Haddon, Northants.
Boadens Antiques, Hexham, Northumbs.
Hedley's of Hexham, Hexham, Northumbs.
ONeil's Antiques, Hexham, Northumbs.
James Miller Antiques, Wooler, Northumbs.
A.J. O'Sullivan Antiques, Darlton, Notts.
Antiques across the World, Nottingham, Notts.
David and Carole Potter Antiques, Nottingham,
    Notts.
Ranby Hall, Retford, Notts.
Strouds (of Southwell Antiques), Southwell, Notts.
Burford Antique Centre, Burford, Oxon.
Gateway Antiques, Burford, Oxon.

Hubert's Antiques, Burford, Oxon.
Anthony Nielsen Antiques, Burford, Oxon.
David Pickup, Burford, Oxon.
Swan Gallery, Burford, Oxon.
Rupert Hitchcox Antiques, Chalgrove, Oxon.
Georgian House Antiques, Chipping Norton, Oxon.
Hallidays (Fine Antiques) Ltd, Dorchester-on-Thames, Oxon.
Richard J. Kingston, Henley-on-Thames, Oxon.
The Country Seat, Huntercombe, Oxon.
de Albuquerque Antiques, Wallingford, Oxon.
Chris and Lin O'Donnell Antiques, Wallingford, Oxon.
Mike Ottrey Antiques, Wallingford, Oxon.
Summers Davis Antiques Ltd, Wallingford, Oxon.
Cross Antiques, Watlington, Oxon.
Stephen Orton Antiques, Watlington, Oxon.
Colin Greenway Antiques, Witney, Oxon.
W.R. Harvey & Co (Antiques) Ltd, Witney, Oxon.
Joan Wilkins Antiques, Witney, Oxon.
Witney Antiques, Witney, Oxon.
Antiques of Woodstock, Woodstock, Oxon.
The Chair Set - Antiques, Woodstock, Oxon.
Robin Sanders and Sons, Woodstock, Oxon.
Churchgate Antiques, Empingham, Rutland.
Swans, Oakham, Rutland.
T.J. Roberts, Uppingham, Rutland.
Woodman's House Antiques, Uppingham, Rutland.
Robert Bingley Antiques, Wing, Rutland.
Mytton Antiques, Atcham, Shrops.
Bayliss Antiques, Ludlow, Shrops.
R.G. Cave and Sons Ltd, Ludlow, Shrops.
Claymore Antiques, Ludlow, Shrops.
M. & R. Taylor Antiques and Sarah Taylor Interiors, Ludlow, Shrops.
Teme Valley Antiques, Ludlow, Shrops.
Valentyne Dawes Gallery, Ludlow, Shrops.
Raynalds Mansion, Much Wenlock, Shrops.
Corner Farm Antiques, Shifnal, Shrops.
Mansers Antiques, Shrewsbury, Shrops.
Marcus Moore Antiques, Stanton upon Hine Heath, Shrops.
Brian James Antiques, Telford, Shrops.
Dodington Antiques, Whitchurch, Shrops.
A J Antiques, Bath, Somerset.
Alderson, Bath, Somerset.
Lawrence Brass, Bath, Somerset.
Geoffrey Breeze, Bath, Somerset.
Mary Cruz, Bath, Somerset.
Jadis Ltd, Bath, Somerset.
Montague Antiques, Bath, Somerset.
Quiet Street Antiques, Bath, Somerset.
Piccadilly Antiques, Batheaston, Somerset.
M.G.R. Exports, Bruton, Somerset.
Chris's Crackers, Carhampton, Somerset.
Guy Dennler Antiques, Dulverton, Somerset.
Anthony Sampson Antiques, Dulverton, Somerset.
The Crooked Window, Dunster, Somerset.

Freshfords, Freshford, Somerset.
C.W.E. Dyte, Highbridge, Somerset.
Edward Marnier Antiques, Shepton Mallet, Somerset.
Rostrum Antiques, South Petherton, Somerset.
Edward A. Nowell, Wells, Somerset.
J.C. Giddings, Wiveliscombe, Somerset.
John Hamblin, Yeovil, Somerset.
Page Antiques, Leek, Staffs.
Winder's Fine Art and Antiques, Newcastle-under-Lyme, Staffs.
H.W. Heron and Son Ltd, Yoxall, Staffs.
Thompson's Gallery, Aldeburgh, Suffolk.
Saltgate Antiques, Beccles, Suffolk.
P. Dawson Furniture Restorers, Bentley, Suffolk.
Peppers Period Pieces, Bury St. Edmunds, Suffolk.
Cavendish Rose Antiques, Cavendish, Suffolk.
Robin Butler, Clare, Suffolk.
F.D. Salter Antiques, Clare, Suffolk.
Debenham Antiques, Debenham, Suffolk.
Denzil Grant Antiques, Drinkstone, Suffolk.
English and Continental Antiques, Eye, Suffolk.
TheTheatre Antiques Centre, Framlingham, Suffolk.
Hubbard Antiques, Ipswich, Suffolk.
J. and J. Baker, Lavenham,, Suffolk.
Warrens Antiques Warehouse, Leiston, Suffolk.
Sandy Cooke Antiques, Long Melford, Suffolk.
Alexander Lyall Antiques, Long Melford, Suffolk.
Seabrook Antiques, Long Melford, Suffolk.
Suthburgh Antiques, Long Melford, Suffolk.
Martlesham Antiques, Martlesham, Suffolk.
Frank Collins Antiques, Mendlesham Green, Suffolk.
Mary Palmer Antiques, Stradbroke, Suffolk.
Napier House Antiques, Sudbury, Suffolk.
David Gibbins Antiques, Woodbridge, Suffolk.
Hamilton Antiques, Woodbridge, Suffolk.
Anthony Hurst Antiques, Woodbridge, Suffolk.
Sarah Meysey-Thompson Antiques, Woodbridge, Suffolk.
J.C. Heather, Woolpit, Suffolk.
Suffolk House Antiques, Yoxford, Suffolk.
John Anthony Antiques, Bletchingley, Surrey.
G. D. Blay Antiques, Dorking, Surrey.
Dolphin Square Antiques, Dorking, Surrey.
Dorking Desk Shop, Dorking, Surrey.
Gallery Eleven, Dorking, Surrey.
Hampshires of Dorking, Dorking, Surrey.
Harman's Antiques, Dorking, Surrey.
Holmwood Antiques, Dorking, Surrey.
Malthouse Antiques, Dorking, Surrey.
Mayfair Antiques, Dorking, Surrey.
Norfolk House Galleries, Dorking, Surrey.
Elaine Saunderson Antiques, Dorking, Surrey.
The Vinery, Dorking, Surrey.
West Street Antiques, Dorking, Surrey.
A. E. Booth & Son, Ewell, Surrey.
Christopher's Antiques, Farnham, Surrey.

Heath-Bullocks, Godalming, Surrey.
The Coach House Antiques, Gomshall, Surrey.
M. J. Bowdery, Hindhead, Surrey.
Glencorse Antiques, Kingston-upon-Thames, Surrey.
Elm House Antiques, Merstham, Surrey.
Michael Andrews Antiques, Milford, Surrey.
F.G. Lawrence and Sons, Redhill, Surrey.
The Gallery, Reigate, Surrey.
M. & M. White Antique & Reproduction Centre, Reigate, Surrey.
Antique Mart, Richmond, Surrey.
Hill Rise Antiques, Richmond, Surrey.
Marryat, Richmond, Surrey.
J. Hartley Antiques Ltd, Ripley, Surrey.
Ripley Antiques, Ripley, Surrey.
Sage Antiques and Interiors, Ripley, Surrey.
Cockrell Antiques, Surbiton, Surrey.
B. M. and E. Newlove, Surbiton, Surrey.
Clifford and Roger Dade, Thames Ditton, Surrey.
Ian Caldwell, Walton-on-the-Hill and Tadworth, Surrey.
Church House Antiques, Weybridge, Surrey.
Weybridge Antiques, Weybridge, Surrey.
Alexandria Antiques, Brighton, Sussex East.
Dudley Hume, Brighton, Sussex East.
Patrick Moorhead Antiques, Brighton, Sussex East.
Michael Norman Antiques Ltd, Brighton, Sussex East.
TheNorth Laine Antiques Market, incorporating Alan Fitchett Antiques, Brighton, Sussex East.
Ben Ponting Antiques, Brighton, Sussex East.
Yellow Lantern Antiques Ltd, Brighton, Sussex East.
Dycheling Antiques, Ditchling, Sussex East.
Hadlow Down Antiques, Hadlow Down, Sussex East.
The Old Mint House, Pevensey, Sussex East.
Bragge and Sons, Rye, Sussex East.
East Street Antiques, Rye, Sussex East.
Herbert Gordon Gasson, Rye, Sussex East.
The Old House, Seaford, Sussex East.
Aarquebus Antiques, St. Leonards-on-Sea, Sussex East.
Bygones, Angmering, Sussex West.
Michael Wakelin and Helen Linfield, Billingshurst, Sussex West.
Frensham House Antiques, Chichester, Sussex West.
Gems Antiques, Chichester, Sussex West.
David Foord-Brown Antiques, Cuckfield, Sussex West.
Richard Usher Antiques, Cuckfield, Sussex West.
Ashcombe Coach House, Henfield, Sussex West.
Stable Antiques, Lindfield, Sussex West.
Callingham Antiques, Northchapel, Sussex West.
Antiquated, Petworth, Sussex West.
Baskerville Antiques, Petworth, Sussex West.

Ronald G. Chambers Fine Antiques, Petworth, Sussex West.
J. Du Cros Antiques, Petworth, Sussex West.
Elliott's, Petworth, Sussex West.
Richard Gardner Antiques, Petworth, Sussex West.
William Hockley Antiques, Petworth, Sussex West.
Oliver Charles Antiques, Petworth, Sussex West.
Red Lion Antiques, Petworth, Sussex West.
Georgia Antiques, Pulborough, Sussex West.
Thakeham Furniture, Pulborough, Sussex West.
Wilsons Antiques, Worthing, Sussex West.
Ian Sharp Antiques, Tynemouth, Tyne and Wear.
Yesterdays, Leamington Spa, Warks.
Apollo Antiques Ltd, Warwick, Warks.
William J. Casey Antiques, Warwick, Warks.
Patrick and Gillian Morley Antiques, Warwick, Warks.
James Reeve, Warwick, Warks.
Don Spencer Antiques, Warwick, Warks.
Peter Clark Antiques, Birmingham, West Mids..
Thomas Coulborn and Sons, Sutton Coldfield, West Mids..
Avon Antiques, Bradford-on-Avon, Wilts.
Mac Humble Antiques, Bradford-on-Avon, Wilts.
Moxhams Antiques, Bradford-on-Avon, Wilts.
Town and Country Antiques, Bradford-on-Avon, Wilts.
Harley Antiques, Christian Malford, Wilts.
Blanchard, Froxfield, Wilts.
Andrew Britten Antiques, Malmesbury, Wilts.
Brocante Antiques Centre, Marlborough, Wilts.
Cook of Marlborough Fine Art Ltd, Marlborough, Wilts.
Katharine House Gallery, Marlborough, Wilts.
Robert Kime Antiques, Marlborough, Wilts.
Alan Jaffray, Melksham, Wilts.
Ray Best Antiques, Newton Tony, Wilts.
Boston Antiques, Salisbury, Wilts.
Robert Bradley Antiques, Salisbury, Wilts.
Edward Hurst Antiques, Salisbury, Wilts.
Pennyfarthing Antiques, Salisbury, Wilts.
Salisbury Antiques Warehouse Ltd, Salisbury, Wilts.
Cassidy's Antiques, Warminster, Wilts.
Maxfield House Antiques, Warminster, Wilts.
Obelisk Antiques, Warminster, Wilts.
Bay Tree Antiques, Wilton, Wilts.
A.J. Romain and Sons, Wilton, Wilts.
Barnt Green Antiques, Barnt Green, Worcs.
Fenwick and Fenwick Antiques, Broadway, Worcs.
H.W. Keil Ltd, Broadway, Worcs.
Robert Belcher Antiques, Droitwich, Worcs.
Miscellany Antiques, Great Malvern, Worcs.
The Drawing Room -
Interiors & Antiques, Pershore, Worcs.
Lower House Fine Antiques, Redditch, Worcs.
Bygones by the Cathedral, Worcester, Worcs.
Bygones of Worcester, Worcester, Worcs.

M. Lees and Sons, Worcester, Worcs.
Priory Antiques, Bridlington, Yorks. East.
Houghton Hall Antiques, Market Weighton, Yorks. East.
Bennett's Antiques & Collectables, Bedale, Yorks. North.
St. James House Antiques, Boroughbridge, Yorks. North.
R.S. Wilson and Sons, Boroughbridge, Yorks. North.
Milestone Antiques, Easingwold, Yorks. North.
Elm Tree Antiques, Flaxton, Yorks. North.
Bernard Dickinson, Gargrave, Yorks. North.
R.N. Myers and Son, Gargrave, Yorks. North.
Nigel Adamson, Harrogate, Yorks. North.
Armstrong, Harrogate, Yorks. North.
Bryan Bowden, Harrogate, Yorks. North.
Derbyshire Antiques Ltd, Harrogate, Yorks. North.
Garth Antiques, Harrogate, Yorks. North.
David Love, Harrogate, Yorks. North.
Charles Lumb and Sons Ltd, Harrogate, Yorks. North.
Walker Galleries Ltd, Harrogate, Yorks. North.
Weatherell's of Harrogate Antiques and Fine Arts, Harrogate, Yorks. North.
Chris Wilde Antiques, Harrogate, Yorks. North.
Sturman's Antiques, Hawes, Yorks. North.
John Thompson Antiques, Knaresborough, Yorks. North.
Joan and David White, Manfield, Yorks. North.
Daleside Antiques, Markington, Yorks. North.
Aura Antiques, Masham, Yorks. North.
Milton Holgate, Ripon, Yorks. North.
Sigma Antiques and Fine Art, Ripon, Yorks. North.
Anderson Slater Antiques, Settle, Yorks. North.
Corn Mill Antiques, Skipton, Yorks. North.
Antony, David & Ann Shackleton, Snainton, Yorks. North.
N.J. and C.S. Dodsworth, Spennithorne, Yorks. North.
Tomlinsons, Tockwith, Yorks. North.
Garth Antiques, Whixley, Yorks. North.
Ruby Snowden Antiques, Yarm, Yorks. North.
Robert Morrison and Son, York, Yorks. North.
Peter James Antiques, Sheffield, Yorks. South.
The Baildon Furniture Co., Baildon, Yorks. West.
Bingley Antiques, Haworth, Yorks. West.
Coopers of Ilkley, Ilkley, Yorks. West.
Geary Antiques, Leeds, Yorks. West.
Park Antiques, Menston, Yorks. West.
Victoria Antiques, Alderney, Alderney, C.I.
Mark Blower Antiques, Le Bourg Forest, Guernsey, C.I.
St. James's Gallery Ltd, St. Peter Port, Guernsey, C.I.
Dunluce Antiques, Bushmills, Co. Antrim, N. Ireland.
Robert Christie Antiques, Carrickfergus, Co. Antrim, N. Ireland.

MacHenry Antiques, Newtownabbey, Co. Antrim, N. Ireland.
Time & Tide Antiques, Portaferry, Co. Down, N. Ireland.
Antiques and Fine Art Gallery, Warrenpoint, Co. Down, N. Ireland.
Colin Wood (Antiques) Ltd, Aberdeen, Scotland.
Coldstream Antiques, Coldstream, Scotland.
The Magic Lantern, Dunecht, Scotland.
Georgian Antiques, Edinburgh, Scotland.
London Road Antiques, Edinburgh, Scotland.
Whytock and Reid, Edinburgh, Scotland.
Gow Antiques, Forfar, Scotland.
E.A. Alvariño - Antiques, Glasgow, Scotland.
Butler's Furniture Galleries, Glasgow, Scotland.
Michael Young Antiques at Glencarse, Glencarse, Scotland.
Glendoick Antiques, Glendoick, Scotland.
C.S. Moreton (Antiques), Inchture, Scotland.
Kilmacolm Antiques Ltd, Kilmacolm, Scotland.
QS Antiques and Cabinetmakers, Kilmarnock, Scotland.
Rhudle Mill, Kilmichael Glassary, Scotland.
Miles Antiques, Kinross, Scotland.
Michael Vee Design - Birch House Antiques, Melrose, Scotland.
Harper-James, Montrose, Scotland.
Newburgh Antiques, Newburgh, Scotland.
Crossroads Antiques, Prestwick, Scotland.
Coach House Antiques Ltd, Stanley, Scotland.
Cwmgwili Mill, Carmarthen, Wales.
K.W. Finlay Antiques, Ciliau Aeron, Wales.
Cowbridge Antique Centre, Cowbridge, Wales.
Havard and Havard, Cowbridge, Wales.
Renaissance Antiques, Cowbridge, Wales.
Gerald Oliver Antiques, Haverfordwest, Wales.
Furn Davies Partnership, Holt, Wales.
Kidwelly Antiques, Kidwelly, Wales.
J. and R. Langford, Llangollen, Wales.
Snowdonia Antiques, Llanrwst, Wales.
Rodney Adams Antiques, Pwllheli, Wales.
Barn Court Antiques, Crafts & Tearoom, Templeton, Wales.
F.E. Anderson and Son, Welshpool, Wales.

Furniture - Oak

Robert E. Hirschhorn, London SE5.
Christopher Howe, London SW1.
The Furniture Cave, London SW10.
Robert Young Antiques, London SW11.
Apter Fredericks Ltd, London SW3.
Alistair Sampson Antiques Ltd, London W1.
Beedham Antiques Ltd, Hungerford, Berks.
Simon and Penny Rumble Antiques, Chittering, Cambs.
Melody's Antiques, Chester, Cheshire.
Adams Antiques, Nantwich, Cheshire.
Pillory House, Nantwich, Cheshire.
Simon Starkie Antiques, Cartmel, Cumbria.

Jennywell Hall Antiques, Crosby Ravensworth,
Cumbria.
Kendal Studios Antiques, Kendal, Cumbria.
Sandgate Antiques, Penrith, Cumbria.
Winton Hall Antiques, Ravenstonedale, Cumbria.
J H S Antiques, Ashbourne, Derbys.
Peter Bunting Antiques, Bakewell, Derbys.
Richard Glass, Whaley Bridge, Derbys.
Robert Byles and Optimum Brasses, Bampton,
Devon.
Rex Antiques, Chagford, Devon.
Cullompton Old Tannery Antiques, Cullompton,
Devon.
Alan Jones Antiques, Okehampton, Devon.
Colystock Antiques, Stockland, Devon.
A. E. Wakeman & Sons Ltd, Tedburn St Mary,
Devon.
Grant's Antiques, Barnard Castle, Durham.
Freemans Antiques, Roxwell, Essex.
Lennard Antiques, Sible Hedingham, Essex.
Peter and Penny Proudfoot, Berkeley, Glos.
J. and R. Bateman Antiques, Chalford, Glos.
William H. Stokes, Cirencester, Glos.
Mark Carter Antiques, Fairford, Glos.
Duncan J. Baggott, Stow-on-the-Wold, Glos.
Keith Hockin Antiques, Stow-on-the-Wold, Glos.
T.M. King-Smith & Simon W. Nutter, Stow-on-
the-Wold, Glos.
Priests Antiques, Stow-on-the-Wold, Glos.
Michael Rowland Antiques, Stow-on-the-Wold,
Glos.
Arthur Seager Antiques, Stow-on-the-Wold, Glos.
Day Antiques, Tetbury, Glos.
Peter Norden Antiques, Tetbury, Glos.
Westwood House Antiques and Beehive Antiques,
Tetbury, Glos.
Tudor Antiques & Fine Art Ltd, Alresford, Hants.
Underwood Oak, Alresford, Hants.
Quatrefoil, Fordingbridge, Hants.
Cedar Antiques Limited, Hartley Wintney, Hants.
Roy Precious Antiques & Fine Art, Hartley
Wintney, Hants.
Winchester Antiques, Winchester, Hants.
Robin Lloyd Antiques, Ross-on-Wye, Herefs.
M. and J. Russell, Yazor, Herefs.
Dobson's Antiques, Abbots Langley, Herts.
Tim Wharton Antiques, Redbourn, Herts.
Collins Antiques (F.G. and C. Collins Ltd.),
Wheathampstead, Herts.
R. Kirby Antiques, Acrise, Kent.
Dinah Stoodley & Celia Jennings, Brasted, Kent.
Michael Pearson Antiques, Canterbury, Kent.
Douglas Bryan, Cranbrook, Kent.
Vestry Antiques, Cranbrook, Kent.
Old English Oak, Sandgate, Kent.
Henry Baines, Southborough, Kent.
Edmund Davies & Son Antiques, Whalley, Lancs.
Boulevard Antique and Shipping Centre, Leicester,
Leics.

Treedale Antiques, Little Dalby, Leics.
Lowe of Loughborough, Loughborough, Leics.
RebeccaCalvert Antiques, Lincoln, Lincs.
Sinclair's, Stamford, Lincs.
Tobias Jellinek Antiques, Twickenham, Middx.
Pearse Lukies, Aylsham, Norfolk.
James Brett, Norwich, Norfolk.
Courtyard Antiques, Brackley, Northants.
Paul Hopwell Antiques, West Haddon, Northants.
Horseshoe Antiques and Gallery, Burford, Oxon.
Anthony Nielsen Antiques, Burford, Oxon.
Swan Gallery, Burford, Oxon.
Antique English Windsor Chairs, Chipping
Norton, Oxon.
Key Antiques, Chipping Norton, Oxon.
Witney Antiques, Witney, Oxon.
Antiques of Woodstock, Woodstock, Oxon.
G. & D. Ginger Antiques, Ludlow, Shrops.
Mackenzie & Smith Furniture Restoration,
Ludlow, Shrops.
Marcus Moore Antiques, Stanton upon Hine
Heath, Shrops.
Dodington Antiques, Whitchurch, Shrops.
Stuart Interiors Ltd, Barrington, Somerset.
Lawrence Brass, Bath, Somerset.
Anthony Sampson Antiques, Dulverton, Somerset.
The Crooked Window, Dunster, Somerset.
John Nicholls, Leigh, Staffs.
Winder's Fine Art and Antiques, Newcastle-under-
Lyme, Staffs.
P. Dawson Furniture Restorers, Bentley, Suffolk.
Peppers Period Pieces, Bury St. Edmunds, Suffolk.
Quercus, Debenham, Suffolk.
Denzil Grant Antiques, Drinkstone, Suffolk.
J. and J. Baker, Lavenham, Suffolk.
Noel Mercer Antiques, Long Melford, Suffolk.
Seabrook Antiques, Long Melford, Suffolk.
Suthburgh Antiques, Long Melford, Suffolk.
Trident Antiques, Long Melford, Suffolk.
Frank Collins Antiques, Mendlesham Green,
Suffolk.
Hamilton Antiques, Woodbridge, Suffolk.
Anthony Hurst Antiques, Woodbridge, Suffolk.
Suffolk House Antiques, Yoxford, Suffolk.
Stoneycroft Farm, Betchworth, Surrey.
Malthouse Antiques, Dorking, Surrey.
Sage Antiques and Interiors, Ripley, Surrey.
Anthony Welling Antiques, Ripley, Surrey.
B. M. and E. Newlove, Surbiton, Surrey.
Graham Lower, Flimwell, Sussex East.
Herbert Gordon Gasson, Rye, Sussex East.
Monarch Antiques, St. Leonards-on-Sea, Sussex
East.
Ringles Cross Antiques, Uckfield, Sussex East.
Park View Antiques, Wadhurst, Sussex East.
King's Cottage Antiques, Leamington Spa, Warks.
James Reeve, Warwick, Warks.
Mac Humble Antiques, Bradford-on-Avon, Wilts.
A.J. Romain and Sons, Wilton, Wilts.

H.W. Keil Ltd, Broadway, Worcs.
Old Hall Antiques, Burton Salmon, Yorks. North.
R.N. Myers and Son, Gargrave, Yorks. North.
Derbyshire Antiques Ltd, Harrogate, Yorks. North.
Elaine Phillips Antiques Ltd, Harrogate, Yorks.
  North.
Yorkshire Country Wines & Antiques, Harrogate,
  Yorks. North.
York Cottage Antiques, Helmsley, Yorks. North.
Middleham Antiques, Middleham, Yorks. North.
Pateley Bridge Antiques, Pateley Bridge, Yorks.
  North.
John Gilbert Antiques, Robin Hood's Bay, Yorks.
  North.
Coach House Antiques, Whitby, Yorks. North.
Cwmgwili Mill, Carmarthen, Wales.
Country Antiques (Wales) Ltd, Kidwelly, Wales.
Singleton Antiques, Skenfrith, Wales.

Furniture - Pine
Chest of Drawers, London N1.
Michael Lewis Antiques, London N1.
Old School (Gardens & Interiors), London N19.
At the Sign of the Chest of Drawers, London N6.
This and That (Furniture), London NW1.
Abbott Antiques and Country Pine, London SE26.
The Furniture Cave, London SW10.
The Pine Mine (Crewe-Read Antiques), London
  SW6.
Remember When, London W3.
The Pine Parlour, Ampthill, Beds.
Alan Hodgson, Great Shefford, Berks.
Dee's Antique Pine, Windsor and Eton, Berks.
Bourne End Antiques Centre, Bourne End, Bucks.
T. Smith, Chalfont St. Giles, Bucks.
The Pine Merchants, Great Missenden, Bucks.
Jack Harness Antiques, Marlow, Bucks.
Archer's Antique and Country Furniture, Olney,
  Bucks.
Pine Antiques, Olney, Bucks.
Ward Thomas Antiques, Balsham, Cambs.
Cambridge Pine, Bottisham, Cambs.
Rookery Farm Antiques, Ely, Cambs.
Marie West Antiques, Ely, Cambs.
Abbey Antiques, Ramsey, Cambs.
Melody's Antiques, Chester, Cheshire.
Steven Blackhurst, Crewe, Cheshire.
Town House Antiques, Marple Bridge, Cheshire.
Chapel Antiques, Nantwich, Cheshire.
Sue Ledger Antiques, Stockport, Cheshire.
The White House, Waverton, Cheshire.
Pine and Period Furniture, Grampound, Cornwall.
Blackwater Pine Antiques, Truro, Cornwall.
Ben Eggleston Antiques, Long Marton, Cumbria.
Utopia Antiques Ltd, Low Newton, Cumbria.
Friargate Pine Company Ltd, Derby, Derbys.
Pine Antiques Workshop, Doveridge, Derbys.
Michael Allcroft Antiques, Hayfield, Derbys.
Wooden Box Antiques, Woodville, Derbys.

W.G. Potter and Son, Axminster, Devon.
Robert Byles and Optimum Brasses, Bampton,
  Devon.
Cobweb Antiques, Cullompton, Devon.
Cullompton Old Tannery Antiques, Cullompton,
  Devon.
C Short Antiques, Great Torrington, Devon.
Annterior Antiques, Plymouth, Devon.
Colystock Antiques, Stockland, Devon.
King Street Curios, Tavistock, Devon.
Timepiece, Teignmouth, Devon.
Fine Pine Antiques, Totnes, Devon.
Chorley-Burdett Antiques, Bournemouth, Dorset.
English Rose Antiques, Coggeshall, Essex.
Partners in Pine, Coggeshall, Essex.
Dean Antiques, Colchester, Essex.
Revival, Colchester, Essex.
Phoenix Trading, Frinton-on-Sea, Essex.
The Stores, Great Waltham, Essex.
Fox and Pheasant Antique Pine, White Colne,
  Essex.
Denzil Verey, Barnsley, Glos.
Oldwoods, Bristol, Glos.
Relics - Pine Furniture, Bristol, Glos.
John P. Townsend, Cheltenham, Glos.
Parlour Farm Antiques, Cirencester, Glos.
Kelly Antiques, Rodley, Glos.
Berkeley Antiques, Tewkesbury, Glos.
Thornbury Antiques, Thornbury, Glos.
Campden Country Pine Antiques, Winchcombe,
  Glos.
The Furniture Trading Co., Botley, Hants.
Squirrels, Brockenhurst, Hants.
C.W. Buckingham, Cadnam, Hants.
The Pine Barn, Crawley, Hants.
The Pine Emporium, Hursley, Hants.
Burgess Farm Antiques, Morestead, Hants.
Smith & Sons, Ringwood, Hants.
The Pine Cellars, Winchester, Hants.
Waterfall Antiques, Ross-on-Wye, Herefs.
Dobson's Antiques, Abbots Langley, Herts.
Country Life Interiors, Bushey, Herts.
The Pine Emporium, Hemel Hempstead, Herts.
Seaview Antiques, Seaview, Isle of Wight.
Richard Back 2 Wood, Appledore, Kent.
Antique and Design, Canterbury, Kent.
Pinetum, Canterbury, Kent.
Vestry Antiques, Cranbrook, Kent.
Farningham Pine, Farningham, Kent.
Harriet Ann Sleigh Beds, Rolvenden, Kent.
Old English Pine, Sandgate, Kent.
Claremont Antiques, Tunbridge Wells, Kent.
Ann and Peter Christian, Blackpool, Lancs.
R.H. Latham Antiques, Tarleton, Lancs.
House Things Antiques, Hinckley, Leics.
Old Hall Farm, Long Clawson, Leics.
Country Pine Antiques, Market Bosworth, Leics.
David E. Burrows, Osgathorpe, Leics.
Quorn Pine and Decoratives, Quorn, Leics.

R. A. James Antiques, Sileby, Leics.
Bell Antiques, Grimsby, Lincs.
Kate, Hemswell Cliff, Lincs.
Andrew Thomas, Stamford, Lincs.
Antiques & Gifts, Downham Market, Norfolk.
Earsham Hall Pine, Earsham, Norfolk.
Heathfield Antiques & Country Pine, Holt,
   Norfolk.
Holt Antique Centre, Holt, Norfolk.
Echo Antiques, Reepham, Norfolk.
Laila Gray Antiques, Kingsthorpe, Northants.
The Country Pine Shop, West Haddon, Northants.
Bailiffgate Antique Pine, Alnwick, Northumbs.
Jack Spratt Antiques, Newark, Notts.
Harlequin Antiques, Nottingham, Notts.
Aston Pine Antiques, Faringdon, Oxon.
Cotswold Pine & Associates, Middle Aston, Oxon.
Ark Antiques, Bishop's Castle, Shrops.
Garrard Antiques, Ludlow, Shrops.
Arty Faherty, Market Drayton, Shrops.
Lansdown Antiques, Bath, Somerset.
Antiques and Country Pine, Crewkerne, Somerset.
Hennessy, Crewkerne, Somerset.
Burton Antiques, Burton-on-Trent, Staffs.
Justin Pinewood Ltd, Burton-on-Trent, Staffs.
Country Cottage Interiors, Kingsley, Staffs.
Antiques Within Ltd, Leek, Staffs.
Anvil Antiques Ltd, Leek, Staffs.
Gemini Trading, Leek, Staffs.
Roger Haynes - Antiques Finder, Leek, Staffs.
Coblands Farm Antiques, Depden, Suffolk.
TheTheatre Antiques Centre, Framlingham,
   Suffolk.
Joyce Hardy Pine and Country Furniture,
   Hacheston, Suffolk.
Orwell Furniture For Life, Ipswich, Suffolk.
Mildenhall Antiques, Mildenhall, Suffolk.
House of Christian, Ash Vale, Surrey.
Cherub Antiques, Carshalton, Surrey.
M. & M. White Antique & Reproduction Centre,
   Reigate, Surrey.
The Packhouse, Runfold, Surrey.
Antique Church Furnishings, Walton-on-Thames,
   Surrey.
Hadlow Down Antiques, Hadlow Down, Sussex
   East.
Pastorale Antiques, Lewes, Sussex East.
Graham Price Antiques Ltd, Polegate, Sussex East.
Bob Hoare - Pine Antiques, Ringmer, Sussex East.
Ann Lingard - Rope Walk Antiques, Rye, Sussex
   East.
Park View Antiques, Wadhurst, Sussex East.
Antiquities, Arundel, Sussex West.
Squire's Pantry Pine and Antiques, Cowfold,
   Sussex West.
Stable Antiques, Lindfield, Sussex West.
John Bird, Petworth, Sussex west.
Red Lion Antiques, Petworth, Sussex West.
Stewart Antiques, Petworth, Sussex West.

Northumbria Pine, Whitley Bay, Tyne and Wear.
Pine and Things, Shipston-on-Stour, Warks.
Christopher Peters Antiques, Warwick, Warks.
Tudor House Antiques, Halesowen, West Mids.
North Wilts Exporters, Brinkworth, Wilts.
Philip A. Ruttleigh Antiques incorporating
   Crudwell Furniture, Crudwell, Wilts.
Pillars Antiques, Lyneham, Wilts.
Sambourne House Antiques Ltd, Swindon, Wilts.
Gerard Guy Antiques, Bewdley, Worcs.
St. James Antiques, Little Malvern, Worcs.
The Antique Pine & Country Furniture Shop,
   Driffield, Yorks. East.
Imperial Antiques, Hull, Yorks. East.
Pieter Plantenga, Market Weighton, Yorks. East.
L.L. Ward and Son, Brandsby, Yorks. North.
Old Hall Antiques, Burton Salmon, Yorks. North.
Heathcote Antiques, Cross Hills, Yorks. North.
Country House Furniture, Easingwold, Yorks.
   North.
Milestone Antiques, Easingwold, Yorks. North.
The Main Pine Co, Green Hammerton, Yorks.
   North.
Michael Green Pine & Country Antiques,
   Harrogate, Yorks. North.
Havelocks, Harrogate, Yorks. North.
Westway Pine, Helmsley, Yorks. North.
Daleside Antiques, Markington, Yorks. North.
Northern Antiques Company, Norton, Yorks.
   North.
Manor Barn, Skipton, Yorks. North.
Eskdale Antiques, Sleights, Yorks. North.
Millgate Pine & Antiques, Thirsk, Yorks. North.
Ruth Ford Antiques, York, Yorks. North.
St. John Antiques, York, Yorks. North.
Fishlake Antiques, Fishlake, Yorks. South.
Beech House, Sheffield, Yorks. South.
Peter James Antiques, Sheffield, Yorks. South.
Aberford Antiques Ltd t/a Aberford Country
   Furniture, Aberford, Yorks. West.
Cottingley Antiques, Bradford, Yorks. West.
K.L.M. & Co. Antiques, Lepton, Yorks. West.
Cottage Antiques, Pontefract, Yorks. West.
Memory Lane, Sowerby Bridge, Yorks. West.
Cottage Antiques (1984) Ltd, Walsden, Yorks.
   West.
The Pine Collection, St. Peter Port, Guernsey, C.I.
Herbert Gould and Co., Holywood, Co. Down, N.
   Ireland.
Ashley Pine, Saintfield, Co. Down, N. Ireland.
Attic Antiques, Saintfield, Co. Down, N. Ireland.
Homes, Pubs and Clubs, Coleraine, Co.
   Londonderry, N. Ireland.
Times Past Antiques, Auchterarder, Scotland.
London Road Antiques, Edinburgh, Scotland.
Country Collectables, Fochabers, Scotland.
QS Antiques and Cabinetmakers, Kilmarnock,
   Scotland.
Abbey Antiques, Stirling, Scotland.

The Furniture Cave, Aberystwyth, Wales.
Cwmgwili Mill, Carmarthen, Wales.
Jim and Pat Ash, Llandeilo, Wales.
Heritage Restorations, Llanfair Caereinion, Wales.
Carrington House, Llanrwst, Wales.
Frost Antiques & Pine, Monmouth, Wales.
Trading Post, Mountain Ash, Wales.
R. and S. M. Percival Antiques, Ruthin, Wales.
Potboard Antiques, Tenby, Wales.

Furniture - Victorian
Old Cottage Antiques, London E11.
Peter Chapman Antiques and Restoration, London
    N1.
Furniture Vault, London N1.
Jonathan James, London N1.
Chris Newland Antiques, London N1.
Regent Antiques, London N1.
Restall Brown and Clennell Ltd, London N1.
Marcus Ross Antiques, London N1.
C. Tapsell, London N1.
Finchley Fine Art Galleries, London N12.
Frames Direct, London N12.
Betty Gould and Julian Gonnermann Antiques,
    London N6.
Dome Antiques (Exports) Ltd, London N7.
Solomon, London N8.
G. and F. Gillingham Ltd, London NW2.
Patricia Beckman Antiques, London NW3.
David Wainwright, London NW3.
Camden Art Gallery, London NW8.
Church Street Antiques, London NW8.
Just Desks, London NW8.
Wellington Gallery, London NW8.
Young & Son, London NW8.
The Galleries, London SE1.
Tower Bridge Antiques, London SE1.
The Junk Shop, London SE10.
The Waterloo Trading Co., London SE10.
Robert Whitfield Antiques, London SE10.
Abbott Antiques and Country Pine, London SE26.
Oola Boola Antiques London, London SE26.
Ward Antiques, London SE7.
Antique Warehouse, London SE8.
Hilary Batstone Antiques inc. Rose Uniacke
    Interiors, London SW1.
John Bly, London SW1.
Ross Hamilton Ltd, London SW1.
Harrods Ltd, London SW1.
Christopher Howe, London SW1.
Humphrey-Carrasco, London SW1.
M. and D. Lewis, London SW1.
Westenholz Antiques Ltd, London SW1.
Granville AntiquesLondon SW10.
Christopher Edwards, London SW11.
Garland Antiques, London SW11.
Overmantels, London SW11.
Pairs Antiques Ltd, London SW11.
A. and J. Fowle, London SW16.

Just a Second, London SW18.
General Trading Co Ltd, London SW3.
Prides of London, London SW3.
275 Antiques, London SW6.
Alasdair Brown, London SW6.
John Clay, London SW6.
Fergus Cochrane and Leigh Warren Antiques,
    London SW6.
HRW Antiques (London) Ltd, London SW6.
L. and E. Kreckovic, London SW6.
Michael Luther Antiques, London SW6.
David Martin-Taylor Antiques, London SW6.
Rogers & Co, London SW6.
Stephen Sprake, London SW6.
Adrian Alan Ltd, London W1.
Jeremy Seale Antiques/Interiors, London W1.
Windsor House Antiques LtdLondon W1.
Barham Antiques, London W11.
Butchoff Antiques, London W11.
Judy Fox, London W11.
Graham and Green, London W11.
M. and D. Lewis, London W11.
Terence Morse and Son Ltd, London W11.
Myriad Antiques, London W11.
David Wainwright, London W11.
Trude Weaver, London W11.
Marshall Gallery, London W14.
Craven Gallery, London W2.
Aberdeen House Antiques, London W5.
Terrace Antiques, London W5.
Haslam and Whiteway, London W8.
Lewis and Lloyd, London W8.
Pamela Teignmouth and Son, London W8.
Paris Antiques, Ampthill, Beds.
Pilgrim Antiques, Ampthill, Beds.
S. and S. Timms Antiques Ltd, Shefford, Beds.
Manor Antiques, Wilstead (Wilshamstead), Beds.
Town Hall Antiques, Woburn, Beds.
Melnick House of Ascot, Ascot, Berks.
Roger King Antiques, Hungerford, Berks.
Hill Farm Antiques, Leckhampstead, Berks.
Widmerpool House Antiques, Maidenhead, Berks.
Rupert Landen Antiques, Reading, Berks.
John Connell - Wargrave Antiques, Wargrave,
    Berks.
Eton Antiques Partnership, Windsor and Eton,
    Berks.
Peter J. Martin, Windsor and Eton, Berks.
Studio 101, Windsor and Eton, Berks.
Times Past Antiques, Windsor and Eton, Berks.
The Cupboard Antiques, Amersham, Bucks.
June Elsworth - Beaconsfield Ltd, Beaconsfield,
    Bucks.
Period Furniture Showrooms, Beaconsfield,
    Bucks.
The Spinning Wheel, Beaconsfield, Bucks.
Robin Unsworth Antiques, Olney, Bucks.
Country Furniture Shop, Penn, Bucks.
Bowood Antiques, Wendover, Bucks.

David's, Brampton, Cambs.
Jess Applin Antiques, Cambridge, Cambs.
Comberton Antiques, Comberton, Cambs.
Ivor and Patricia Lewis Antique and Fine Art Dealers, Peterborough, Cambs.
Antiques & Curios (Steve Carpenter), Wisbech, Cambs.
Sara Frances Antiques, Alderley Edge, Cheshire.
Church Street Antiques, Altrincham, Cheshire.
Andrew Foott Antiques, Cheadle Hulme, Cheshire.
Boustead-Bland Antiques, Chester, Cheshire.
Moor Hall Antiques, Chester, Cheshire.
The Old Warehouse Antiques, Chester, Cheshire.
W. Buckley Antiques Exports, Congleton, Cheshire.
Affordable Antiques, Hale, Cheshire.
Glynn Interiors, Knutsford, Cheshire.
John Titchner and Sons, Littleton, Cheshire.
Chapel Antiques, Nantwich, Cheshire.
Saxon Cross Antiques Emporium, Sandbach, Cheshire.
Limited Editions, Stockport, Cheshire.
Victoria Imports, Stockport, Cheshire.
Country Living Antiques, Callington, Cornwall.
Old Town Hall Antiques, Falmouth, Cornwall.
Antique Chairs and Museum, Launceston, Cornwall.
John Bragg Antiques, Lostwithiel, Cornwall.
Antiques & Fine Art, Penzance, Cornwall.
Victoria Antiques, Wadebridge, Cornwall.
Anthemion - The Antique Shop, Cartmel, Cumbria.
Haughey Antiques, Kirkby Stephen, Cumbria.
Country Seat Antiques, Newby East, Cumbria.
Taylor Robinson Antiques, Alfreton, Derbys.
Thornbridge Antiques, Bakewell, Derbys.
Water Lane Antiques, Bakewell, Derbys.
Hackney House Antiques, Barlow, Derbys.
The Antiques Warehouse, Buxton, Derbys.
Maggie Mays, Buxton, Derbys.
Ian Morris, Chesterfield, Derbys.
Wayside Antiques, Duffield, Derbys.
Nimbus Antiques, Whaley Bridge, Derbys.
Wooden Box Antiques, Woodville, Derbys.
John Prestige Antiques, Brixham, Devon.
Alison Gosling Antiques, Budleigh Salterton, Devon.
Mills Antiques, Cullompton, Devon.
Electique, Exeter, Devon.
McBains Antiques, Exeter, Devon.
Lombard Antiques, Honiton, Devon.
Merchant House Antiques, Honiton, Devon.
Upstairs, Downstairs, Honiton, Devon.
Farthings, Lynton, Devon.
Pugh's Farm Antiques, Monkton, Devon.
W. J. Woodhams, Shaldon, Devon.
Past and Present, Totnes, Devon.
Anthony James Antiques, Whimple, Devon.
Woodbury Antiques, Woodbury, Devon.

Antiques for All, Blandford Forum, Dorset.
Chorley-Burdett Antiques, Bournemouth, Dorset.
Victorian Chairman, Bournemouth, Dorset.
David Mack Antiques, Branksome, Dorset.
Benchmark Antiques, Bridport, Dorset.
Hamptons, Christchurch, Dorset.
Tower Antiques, Cranborne, Dorset.
Michael Legg Antiques, Dorchester, Dorset.
Hardy Country, Melbury Osmond, Dorset.
Laburnum Antiques, Poole, Dorset.
Stocks and Chairs, Poole, Dorset.
Shaston Antiques, Shaftesbury, Dorset.
Heygate Browne Antiques, Sherborne, Dorset.
Piers Pisani Antiques, Sherborne, Dorset.
James Hardy Antiques Ltd, Barnard Castle, Durham.
Joan and David White Antiques, Barnard Castle, Durham.
Margaret Bedi Antiques & Fine Art, Billingham, Durham.
Alan Ramsey Antiques, Darlington, Durham.
Paraphernalia, Norton, Durham.
Eden House Antiques, West Auckland, Durham.
Revival, Abridge, Essex.
Swan Antiques, Baythorne End, Essex.
Hutchison Antiques, Chelmsford, Essex.
Argentum Antiques, Coggeshall, Essex.
Memories, Great Dunmow, Essex.
Colton Antiques, Kelvedon, Essex.
Deja Vu Antiques, Leigh-on-Sea, Essex.
Tilly's Antiques, Leigh-on-Sea, Essex.
Clive Beardall Antiques, Maldon, Essex.
West Essex Antiques (Stone Hall), Matching Green, Essex.
F.G. Bruschweiler (Antiques) Ltd, Rayleigh, Essex.
Bush Antiques, Saffron Walden, Essex.
The Interior Design Shop, Saffron Walden, Essex.
Harris Antiques (Stansted), Stansted, Essex.
Linden House Antiques, Stansted, Essex.
It's About Time, Westcliff-on-Sea, Essex.
White Roding Antiques, White Roding, Essex.
Peter and Penny Proudfoot, Berkeley, Glos.
The Antiques Warehouse Ltd, Bristol, Glos.
Bristol Guild of Applied Art Ltd, Bristol, Glos.
Cotham Antiques, Bristol, Glos.
Oldwoods, Bristol, Glos.
Latchford Antiques, Cheltenham, Glos.
Cottage Farm Antiques, Chipping Campden, Glos.
Patrick Waldron Antiques, Cirencester, Glos.
Bernard Weaver Antiques, Cirencester, Glos.
Blenheim Antiques, Fairford, Glos.
Mark Carter Antiques, Fairford, Glos.
August Antiques and Interiors, Moreton-in-Marsh, Glos.
Benton Fine Art, Moreton-in-Marsh, Glos.
Berry Antiques, Moreton-in-Marsh, Glos.
Dale House Antiques, Moreton-in-Marsh, Glos.
Seaford House Antiques, Moreton-in-Marsh, Glos.

Simply Antiques, Moreton-in-Marsh, Glos.
Gary Wright Antiques, Moreton-in-Marsh, Glos.
Robson Antiques, Northleach, Glos.
Ashton Gower Antiques, Stow-on-the-Wold, Glos.
Christopher Clarke Antiques Ltd, Stow-on-the-Wold, Glos.
T.M. King-Smith & Simon W. Nutter, Stow-on-the-Wold, Glos.
La Chaise Antique, Stow-on-the-Wold, Glos.
Queens Parade Antiques Ltd, Stow-on-the-Wold, Glos.
Styles of Stow, Stow-on-the-Wold, Glos.
Tudor House, Stow-on-the-Wold, Glos.
Wyndhams, Stow-on-the-Wold, Glos.
Ball and Claw Antiques, Tetbury, Glos.
Balmuir House Antiques, Tetbury, Glos.
The Chest of Drawers, Tetbury, Glos.
Bobbie Middleton, Tetbury, Glos.
Porch House Antiques, Tetbury, Glos.
Berkeley Antiques, Tewkesbury, Glos.
Cotswold Antiques. com, Winchcombe, Glos.
Tudor Antiques & Fine Art Ltd, Alresford, Hants.
The Furniture Trading Co, Botley, Hants.
Eversley Antiques, Eversley, Hants.
Former Glory, Gosport, Hants.
Antique House, Hartley Wintney, Hants.
Deva Antiques, Hartley Wintney, Hants.
Plestor Barn Antiques, Liss, Hants.
Wick Antiques, Lymington, Hants.
The Gallery, Portsmouth, Hants.
Antique Eyes, Stockbridge, Hants.
Elizabeth Viney Antiques, Stockbridge, Hants.
Gasson Antiques and Interiors, Tadley, Hants.
Gaylords, Titchfield, Hants.
Winchester Antiques, Winchester, Hants.
Warings of Hereford, Hereford, Herefs.
John Nash Antiques and Interiors, Ledbury, Herefs.
Serendipity, Ledbury, Herefs.
Jeffery Hammond Antiques, Leominster, Herefs.
Linden House Antiques, Leominster, Herefs.
Anthony Butt Antiques, Baldock, Herts.
Wareside Antiques, Cottered, Herts.
Tapestry Antiques, Hertford, Herts.
Hanbury Antiques, Hitchin, Herts.
Phillips of Hitchin (Antiques) Ltd, Hitchin, Herts.
Tom Salusbury Antiques, Hitchin, Herts.
J.N. Antiques, Redbourn, Herts.
Charnwood Antiques and Arcane Antiques Centre, Sawbridgeworth, Herts.
New England House Antiques, Tring, Herts.
Collins Antiques (F.G. and C. Collins Ltd.), Wheathampstead, Herts.
The Old Bakery Antiques, Wheathampstead, Herts.
Michael Armson (Antiques) Ltd, Wilstone, Herts.
John Corrin Antiques, Douglas, Isle of Man.
Royal Standard Antiques, Cowes, Isle of Wight.
Stablegate Antiques, Barham, Kent.

Courtyard Antiques, Brasted, Kent.
Keymer Son & Co. Ltd, Brasted, Kent.
Roy Massingham Antiques, Brasted, Kent.
Conquest House Antiques, Canterbury, Kent.
Chislehurst Antiques, Chislehurst, Kent.
Alan Lord Antiques, Folkestone, Kent.
Mill House Antiques, Goudhurst, Kent.
Samovar Antiques, Hythe, Kent.
Newington Antiques, Newington, Kent.
Northfleet Hill Antiques, Northfleet, Kent.
J.D. and R.M. Walters, Rolvenden, Kent.
Finch Antiques, Sandgate, Kent.
Michael Fitch Antiques, Sandgate, Kent.
David M. Lancefield Antiques, Sandgate, Kent.
Forge Antiques and Restorations, Sandhurst, Kent.
Gem Antiques, Sevenoaks, Kent.
Staplehurst Antiques, Staplehurst, Kent.
Steppes Hill Farm Antiques, Stockbury, Kent.
Kentdale Antiques, Tunbridge Wells, Kent.
The Pantiles Antiques, Tunbridge Wells, Kent.
Pantiles Spa Antiques, Tunbridge Wells, Kent.
Phoenix Antiques, Tunbridge Wells, Kent.
Up Country, Tunbridge Wells, Kent.
Apollo Antique Galleries, Westerham, Kent.
Peter Dyke, Westerham, Kent.
Marks Antiques, Westerham, Kent.
Taylor-Smith Antiques, Westerham, Kent.
Westerham Antiques Warehouse, Westerham, Kent.
Westerham House Antiques, Westerham, Kent.
Laurens Antiques, Whitstable, Kent.
Tankerton Antiques, Whitstable, Kent.
Silvesters, Wingham, Kent.
Charles International Antiques, Wrotham, Kent.
Brun Lea Antiques (J. Waite Ltd), Burnley, Lancs.
Folly Antiques, Clitheroe, Lancs.
K.C. Antiques, Darwen, Lancs.
P.J. Brown Antiques, Haslingden, Lancs.
R.J. O'Brien and Son Antiques Ltd, Manchester, Lancs.
Luigino Vescovi, Morecambe, Lancs.
Brooks Antiques, Nelson, Lancs.
European Fine Arts and Antiques, Preston, Lancs.
The Glory Hole, Earl Shilton, Leics.
Ken Smith Antiques Ltd, Enderby, Leics.
Sitting Pretty, Great Glen, Leics.
House Things Antiques, Hinckley, Leics.
Withers of Leicester, Hoby, Leics.
Corry's, Leicester, Leics.
J. Stamp and Sons, Market Harborough, Leics.
J. Green and Son, Queniborough,, Leics.
Charles Antiques, Whitwick, Leics.
Grantham Furniture Emporium, Grantham, Lincs.
G. Baker Antiques, Horncastle, Lincs.
Seaview Antiques, Horncastle, Lincs.
Laurence Shaw Antiques, Horncastle, Lincs.
Laurence Shaw Antiques, Horncastle, Lincs.
C. and K.E. Dring, Lincoln, Lincs.
Graham Pickett Antiques, Stamford, Lincs.

Sinclair's, Stamford, Lincs.
St. George's Antiques, Stamford, Lincs.
The Antique Shop, Sutton Bridge, Lincs.
Robin Shield Antiques, Swinstead, Lincs.
Underwoodhall Antiques, Woodhall Spa, Lincs.
V.O.C. Antiques, Woodhall Spa, Lincs.
Stefani Antiques, Liverpool, Merseyside.
Colin Stock, Rainford, Merseyside.
Tony and Anne Sutcliffe Antiques, Southport,
    Merseyside.
Gallerie Veronique, Enfield, Middx.
Hunter's of Hampton, Hampton, Middx.
Ivy House Antiques, Acle, Norfolk.
A.E. Bush and Partners, Attleborough, Norfolk.
M. and A. Cringle, Burnham Market, Norfolk.
Antiques & Gifts, Downham Market, Norfolk.
Peter Robinson, Heacham, Norfolk.
Norfolk Galleries, King's Lynn, Norfolk.
Eric Bates and Sons Ltd., North Walsham, Norfolk.
Nicholas Fowle Antiques, Norwich, Norfolk.
John Howkins Antiques Ltd, Norwich, Norfolk.
Echo Antiques, Reepham, Norfolk.
Country House Antiques, Seething, Norfolk.
Leo Pratt and Son, South Walsham, Norfolk.
Stalham Antique Gallery, Stalham, Norfolk.
Jubilee Antiques, Tottenhill, Norfolk.
Brackley Antiques, Brackley, Northants.
Courtyard Antiques, Brackley, Northants.
Simon Banks Antiques, Finedon, Northants.
Robert Cheney Antiques, Finedon, Northants.
Huntershield Antiques and Granary Antiques,
    Flore, Northants.
Christopher Jones Antiques, Flore, Northants.
F. and C.H. Cave, Northampton, Northants.
Bryan Perkins Antiques, Wellingborough,
    Northants.
Barber Antiques, West Haddon, Northants.
Boadens Antiques, Hexham, Northumbs.
Hedley's of Hexham, Hexham, Northumbs.
ONeil's Antiques, Hexham, Northumbs.
James Miller Antiques, Wooler, Northumbs.
A.J. O'Sullivan Antiques, Darlton, Notts.
Fair Deal Antiques, Mansfield, Notts.
Antiques across the World, Nottingham, Notts.
Harlequin Antiques, Nottingham, Notts.
David and Carole Potter Antiques, Nottingham,
    Notts.
Ranby Hall, Retford, Notts.
Strouds (of Southwell Antiques), Southwell, Notts.
Burford Antique Centre, Burford, Oxon.
Gateway Antiques, Burford, Oxon.
Hubert's Antiques, Burford, Oxon.
Anthony Nielsen Antiques, Burford, Oxon.
David Pickup, Burford, Oxon.
Rupert Hitchcox Antiques, Chalgrove, Oxon.
Georgian House Antiques, Chipping Norton,
    Oxon.
Hallidays (Fine Antiques) Ltd, Dorchester-on-
    Thames, Oxon.

Richard J. Kingston, Henley-on-Thames, Oxon.
The Country Seat, Huntercombe, Oxon.
de Albuquerque Antiques, Wallingford, Oxon.
Chris and Lin O'Donnell Antiques, Wallingford,
    Oxon.
Cross Antiques, Watlington, Oxon.
Stephen Orton Antiques, Watlington, Oxon.
Colin Greenway Antiques, Witney, Oxon.
W.R. Harvey & Co (Antiques) Ltd, Witney, Oxon.
Joan Wilkins Antiques, Witney, Oxon.
Bees Antiques, Woodstock, Oxon.
Robin Sanders and Sons, Woodstock, Oxon.
Swans, Oakham, Rutland.
T.J. Roberts, Uppingham, Rutland.
Woodman's House Antiques, Uppingham, Rutland.
Robert Bingley Antiques, Wing, Rutland.
Mytton Antiques, Atcham, Shrops.
Malthouse Antiques, Bridgnorth, Shrops.
Portcullis Furniture, Craven Arms, Shrops.
Hodnet Antiques, Hodnet, Shrops.
Bayliss Antiques, Ludlow, Shrops.
Claymore Antiques, Ludlow, Shrops.
M. & R. Taylor Antiques and Sarah Taylor
    Interiors, Ludlow, Shrops.
Valentyne Dawes Gallery, Ludlow, Shrops.
Corner Farm Antiques, Shifnal, Shrops.
 Mansers Antiques, Shrewsbury, Shrops.
Brian James Antiques, Telford, Shrops.
A J Antiques, Bath, Somerset.
Antiques of Bath, Bath, Somerset.
The Antiques Warehouse, Bath, Somerset.
Lawrence Brass, Bath, Somerset.
Geoffrey Breeze, Bath, Somerset.
Mary Cruz, Bath, Somerset.
Montague Antiques, Bath, Somerset.
Tim Snell Antiques, Bath, Somerset.
Piccadilly Antiques, Batheaston, Somerset.
M.G.R. Exports, Bruton, Somerset.
Chris's Crackers, Carhampton, Somerset.
Guy Dennler Antiques, Dulverton, Somerset.
C.W.E. Dyte, Highbridge, Somerset.
Edward Marnier Antiques, Shepton Mallet,
    Somerset.
Rostrum Antiques, South Petherton, Somerset.
Selwoods, Taunton, Somerset.
John Hamblin, Yeovil, Somerset.
Gilligans Antiques, Leek, Staffs.
Page Antiques, Leek, Staffs.
Brett Wilkins Ltd, Lichfield, Staffs.
Winder's Fine Art and Antiques, Newcastle-under-
    Lyme, Staffs.
White House Antiques, Uttoxeter, Staffs.
H.W. Heron and Son Ltd, Yoxall, Staffs.
Thompson's Gallery, Aldeburgh, Suffolk.
Saltgate Antiques, Beccles, Suffolk.
P. Dawson Furniture Restorers, Bentley, Suffolk.
Peppers Period Pieces, Bury St. Edmunds, Suffolk.
Cavendish Rose Antiques, Cavendish, Suffolk.
Robin Butler, Clare, Suffolk.

SPECIALIST DEALERS

Debenham Antiques, Debenham, Suffolk.
English and Continental Antiques, Eye, Suffolk.
A. Abbott Antiques, Ipswich, Suffolk.
The Edwardian Shop, Ipswich, Suffolk.
Hubbard Antiques, Ipswich, Suffolk.
Warrens Antiques Warehouse, Leiston, Suffolk.
Alexander Lyall Antiques, Long Melford, Suffolk.
Mary Palmer Antiques, Stradbroke, Suffolk.
Gainsborough Antiques, Sudbury, Suffolk.
Napier House Antiques, Sudbury, Suffolk.
Ashe Antiques Warehouse, Wickham Market, Suffolk.
Hamilton Antiques, Woodbridge, Suffolk.
Anthony Hurst Antiques, Woodbridge, Suffolk.
R.A and S.M. Lambert and Son, Woodbridge, Suffolk.
J.C. Heather, Woolpit, Suffolk.
Wrentham Antiques, Wrentham, Suffolk.
House of Christian, Ash Vale, Surrey.
Country Antiques, Bagshot, Surrey.
Dolphin Square Antiques, Dorking, Surrey.
Dorking Desk Shop, Dorking, Surrey.
Gallery Eleven, Dorking, Surrey.
Harman's Antiques, Dorking, Surrey.
Holmwood Antiques, Dorking, Surrey.
Malthouse Antiques, Dorking, Surrey.
Mayfair Antiques, Dorking, Surrey.
Norfolk House Galleries, Dorking, Surrey.
The Vinery, Dorking, Surrey.
West Street Antiques, Dorking, Surrey.
A. E. Booth & Son, Ewell, Surrey.
The Antiques Warehouse, Farnham, Surrey.
Christopher's Antiques, Farnham, Surrey.
The Coach House Antiques, Gomshall, Surrey.
M. J. Bowdery, Hindhead, Surrey.
Glencorse Antiques, Kingston-upon-Thames, Surrey.
Elm House Antiques, Merstham, Surrey.
Michael Andrews Antiques, Milford, Surrey.
F.G. Lawrence and Sons, Redhill, Surrey.
The Gallery, Reigate, Surrey.
Antique Mart, Richmond, Surrey.
Hill Rise Antiques, Richmond, Surrey.
Marryat, Richmond, Surrey.
Sage Antiques and Interiors, Ripley, Surrey.
Cockrell Antiques, Surbiton, Surrey.
B. M. and E. Newlove, Surbiton, Surrey.
Brocante, Weybridge, Surrey.
Church House Antiques, Weybridge, Surrey.
Weybridge Antiques, Weybridge, Surrey.
Alexandria Antiques, Brighton, Sussex East.
Ashton's Antiques, Brighton, Sussex East.
Dudley Hume, Brighton, Sussex East.
Patrick Moorhead Antiques, Brighton, Sussex East.
The North Laine Antiques Market, incorporating Alan Fitchett Antiques, Brighton, Sussex East.
Ben Ponting Antiques, Brighton, Sussex East.
Colonial Times, Cross in Hand, Sussex East.

Dycheling Antiques, Ditchling, Sussex East.
Timothy Partridge Antiques, Eastbourne, Sussex East.
Hadlow Down Antiques, Hadlow Down, Sussex East.
Coach House Antiques, Hastings, Sussex East.
The Old Mint House, Pevensey, Sussex East.
Graham Price Antiques Ltd, Polegate, Sussex East.
East Street Antiques, Rye, Sussex East.
The Old House, Seaford, Sussex East.
Aarquebus Antiques, St. Leonards-on-Sea, Sussex East.
Bygones, Angmering, Sussex West.
W.D. Priddy Antiques, Chichester, Sussex West.
Richard Usher Antiques, Cuckfield, Sussex West.
Stable Antiques, Lindfield, Sussex West.
Callingham Antiques, Northchapel, Sussex West.
Antiquated, Petworth, Sussex West.
Baskerville Antiques, Petworth, Sussex West.
J. Du Cros Antiques, Petworth, Sussex West.
Elliott's, Petworth, Sussex West.
Richard Gardner Antiques, Petworth, Sussex West.
Red Lion Antiques, Petworth, Sussex West.
Ruddy Antiques, Petworth, Sussex West.
Georgia Antiques, Pulborough, Sussex West.
Wilsons Antiques, Worthing, Sussex West.
Little Theatre Antiques Centre, Jesmond, Tyne and Wear.
Ian Sharp Antiques, Tynemouth, Tyne and Wear.
Yesterdays, Leamington Spa, Warks.
Apollo Antiques Ltd, Warwick, Warks.
William J. Casey Antiques, Warwick, Warks.
John Goodwin and Sons, Warwick, Warks.
Patrick and Gillian Morley Antiques, Warwick, Warks.
James Reeve, Warwick, Warks.
Don Spencer Antiques, Warwick, Warks.
Peter Clark Antiques, Birmingham, West Mids.
Retro Antiques, Lye, West Mids.
Martin Taylor Antiques, Wolverhampton, West Mids.
Audley House Antiques, Bradford-on-Avon, Wilts.
Mac Humble Antiques, Bradford-on-Avon, Wilts.
Cross Hayes Antiques, Chippenham, Wilts.
Blanchard, Froxfield, Wilts.
Andrew Britten Antiques, Malmesbury, Wilts.
Brocante Antiques Centre, Marlborough, Wilts.
Cook of Marlborough Fine Art Ltd, Marlborough, Wilts.
Katharine House Gallery, Marlborough, Wilts.
Alan Jaffray, Melksham, Wilts.
Boston Antiques, Salisbury, Wilts.
Pennyfarthing Antiques, Salisbury, Wilts.
Salisbury Antiques Warehouse Ltd, Salisbury, Wilts.
Cassidy's Antiques, Warminster, Wilts.
Isabella Antiques, Warminster, Wilts.
Maxfield House Antiques, Warminster, Wilts.
Obelisk Antiques, Warminster, Wilts.

K. and A. Welch, Warminster, Wilts.
Hingstons of Wilton, Wilton, Wilts.
Barnt Green Antiques, Barnt Green, Worcs.
Robert Belcher Antiques, Droitwich, Worcs.
Carlton Antiques, Great Malvern, Worcs.
Miscellany Antiques, Great Malvern, Worcs.
Gemini Antiques & Gallery, Kidderminster, Worcs.
S.W. Antiques, Pershore, Worcs.
Lower House Fine Antiques, Redditch, Worcs.
M. Lees and Sons, Worcester, Worcs.
Priory Antiques, Bridlington, Yorks. East.
Houghton Hall Antiques, Market Weighton, Yorks. East.
Penny Farthing Antiques, North Cave, Yorks. East.
Bennett's Antiques & Collectables, Bedale, Yorks. North.
St. James House Antiques, Boroughbridge, Yorks. North.
R.S. Wilson and Sons, Boroughbridge, Yorks. North.
Milestone Antiques, Easingwold, Yorks. North.
Elm Tree Antiques, Flaxton, Yorks. North.
Garth Antiques, Harrogate, Yorks. North.
David Love, Harrogate, Yorks. North.
Chris Wilde Antiques, Harrogate, Yorks. North.
Sturman's Antiques, Hawes, Yorks. North.
John Thompson Antiques, Knaresborough, Yorks. North.
Lythe Cottage Antiques, Lythe, Yorks. North.
Joan and David White, Manfield, Yorks. North.
Milton Holgate, Ripon, Yorks. North.
Sigma Antiques and Fine Art, Ripon, Yorks. North.
John Gilbert Antiques, Robin Hood's Bay, Yorks. North.
Anderson Slater Antiques, Settle, Yorks. North.
Corn Mill Antiques, Skipton, Yorks. North.
Antony, David & Ann Shackleton, Snainton, Yorks. North.
Robert Morrison and Son, York, Yorks. North.
Acorn Antiques, Sheffield, Yorks. South.
Peter James Antiques, Sheffield, Yorks. South.
N.P. and A. Salt Antiques and Barmouth Court Antiques Centre, Sheffield, Yorks. South.
Paul Ward Antiques, Sheffield, Yorks. South.
Aberford Antiques Ltd t/a Aberford Country Furniture, Aberford, Yorks. West.
The Baildon Furniture Co., Baildon, Yorks. West.
Bingley Antiques, Haworth, Yorks. West.
Geary Antiques, Leeds, Yorks. West.
Park Antiques, Menston, Yorks. West.
Victoria Antiques, Alderney, Alderney, C.I.
St. James's Gallery Ltd, St. Peter Port, Guernsey, C.I.
Country House and Cottage Antiques, St Mary, Jersey, C.I.
Stephen Cohu Antiques, St Ouen, Jersey, C.I.
Charlotte and John Lambe, Belfast, N. Ireland.

The Country Antiques, Antrim, Co. Antrim, N. Ireland.
Dunluce Antiques, Bushmills, Co. Antrim, N. Ireland.
Robert Christie Antiques, Carrickfergus, Co. Antrim, N. Ireland.
MacHenry Antiques, Newtownabbey, Co. Antrim, N. Ireland.
Time & Tide Antiques, Portaferry, Co. Down, N. Ireland.
Attic Antiques, Saintfield, Co. Down, N. Ireland.
Antiques and Fine Art Gallery, Warrenpoint, Co. Down, N. Ireland.
Colin Wood (Antiques) Ltd, Aberdeen, Scotland.
Coldstream Antiques, Coldstream, Scotland.
The Magic Lantern, Dunecht, Scotland.
Dunkeld Antiques, Dunkeld, Scotland.
Alan Day Antiques, Edinburgh, Scotland.
Georgian Antiques, Edinburgh, Scotland.
London Road Antiques, Edinburgh, Scotland.
Whytock and Reid, Edinburgh, Scotland.
Young Antiques, Edinburgh, Scotland.
Pringle Antiques, Fochabers, Scotland.
Gow Antiques, Forfar, Scotland.
E.A. Alvariño - Antiques, Glasgow, Scotland.
Butler's Furniture Galleries, Glasgow, Scotland.
Strachan Antiques, Glasgow, Scotland.
Michael Young Antiques at Glencarse, Glencarse, Scotland.
Kilmacolm Antiques Ltd, Kilmacolm, Scotland.
QS Antiques and Cabinetmakers, Kilmarnock, Scotland.
Rhudle Mill, Kilmichael Glassary, Scotland.
Miles Antiques, Kinross, Scotland.
Michael Vee Design - Birch House Antiques, Melrose, Scotland.
Newburgh Antiques, Newburgh, Scotland.
A.S. Deuchar and Son, Perth, Scotland.
The Antiques Shop, Pittenweem, Scotland.
Crossroads Antiques, Prestwick, Scotland.
Cwmgwili Mill, Carmarthen, Wales.
The Mount Antiques Centre, Carmarthen, Wales.
Plough House Interiors, Chepstow, Wales.
K.W. Finlay Antiques, Ciliau Aeron, Wales.
North Wales Antiques - Colwyn Bay, Colwyn Bay, Wales.
Cowbridge Antique Centre, Cowbridge, Wales.
Havard and Havard, Cowbridge, Wales.
Renaissance Antiques, Cowbridge, Wales.
Furn Davies Partnership, Holt, Wales.
Kidwelly Antiques, Kidwelly, Wales.
Collinge Antiques, Llandudno Junction, Wales.
J. and R. Langford, Llangollen, Wales.
Carrington House, Llanrwst, Wales.
Trading Post, Mountain Ash, Wales.
R. and S. M. Percival Antiques, Ruthin, Wales.
Barn Court Antiques, Crafts & Tearoom, Templeton, Wales.
Steven Evans Antiques, Treorchy, Wales.

Garden Furniture, Ornaments & Statuary
LASSCo, London EC2.
Westland London, London EC2.
Gordon Gridley, London N1.
House of Steel Antiques, London N1.
Old School (Gardens & Interiors), London N19.
Relic Antiques Trade Warehouse, London NW1.
David Wainwright, London NW3.
Crowther of Syon Lodge Ltd, London SW1.
Chelminski, London SW6.
Charles Edwards, London SW6.
Sylvia Napier Ltd, London SW6.
M. Pauw Antiques, London SW6.
Mallett at Bourdon House Ltd, London W1.
Myriad Antiques, London W11.
J. D. Marshall, London W4.
Below Stairs of Hungerford, Hungerford, Berks.
Garden Art, Hungerford, Berks.
The Antique Garden, Chester, Cheshire.
Cheshire Brick and Slate Co, Tarvin Sands,
    Cheshire.
The Great Northern Architectural Antique
    Company Ltd, Tattenhall, Cheshire.
Haughey Antiques, Kirkby Stephen, Cumbria.
Dorset Reclamation, Bere Regis, Dorset.
Talisman, Gillingham, Dorset.
I. Westrope, Birdbrook, Essex.
Jon Fox Antiques, Moreton-in-Marsh, Glos.
Robson Antiques, Northleach, Glos.
Duncan J. Baggott, Stow-on-the-Wold, Glos.
Architectural Heritage, Taddington, Glos.
Jardinique, Beech, Hants.
Bygones Reclamation, Canterbury, Kent.
Adams Arts & Antiques Ltd, Farningham, Kent.
Jimmy Warren Antiques, Littlebourne, Kent.
The Architectural Emporium, Tunbridge Wells,
    Kent.
Folly Antiques, Clitheroe, Lancs.
Lindsey Court Architectural Antiques, Horncastle,
    Lincs.
Mongers, Hingham, Norfolk.
The Potting Shed, Holkham, Norfolk.
Reindeer Antiques Ltd, Potterspury, Northants.
The Country Seat, Huntercombe, Oxon.
John Garner, Uppingham, Rutland.
David Bridgwater, Bath, Somerset.
Source, Bath, Somerset.
Walcot Reclamation, Bath, Somerset.
Dix-Sept, Framlingham, Suffolk.
Drummonds Architectural Antiques, Hindhead,
    Surrey.
Sweerts de Landas, Ripley, Surrey.
The Packhouse, Runfold, Surrey.
Brighton Architectural Salvage, Brighton, Sussex
    East.
Dermot and Jill Palmer Antiques, Brighton,
    Sussex East.
Antiquated, Petworth, Sussex West.
John Bird, Petworth, Sussex West.

Riverbank, Petworth, Sussex West.
Matthew Eden, Corsham, Wilts.
Holloways, Suckley, Worcs.
The White House Antiques & Architectural
    Reclamation, Easingwold, Yorks. North.
Coach House Antiques Ltd, Stanley, Scotland.

Glass - see also Glass Domes & Paperweights
Carol Ketley Antiques, London N1.
Mike Weedon, London N1.
Wilkinson plc, London SE6.
Pullman Gallery, London SW1.
Christine Bridge, London SW13.
The Dining Room Shop, London SW13.
Mark J. West - Cobb Antiques Ltd, London SW19.
W.G.T.Burne (Antique Glass) Ltd, London SW20.
Thomas Goode and Co (London) Ltd, London W1.
Ronald Phillips Ltd, London W1.
Wilkinson plc, London W1.
Mercury Antiques, London W11.
Neil Phillips Ltd., London W11.
Tomkinson Stained Glass, London W11.
Craven Gallery, London W2.
Denton Antiques, London W8.
Jeanette Hayhurst Fine Glass, London W8.
Peter Shepherd Antiques, Hurst, Berks.
Cavendish Fine Arts, Sonning-on-Thames, Berks.
Berkshire Antiques Co Ltd, Windsor and Eton,
    Berks.
Gabor Cossa Antiques, Cambridge, Cambs.
Saxon Cross Antiques Emporium, Sandbach,
    Cheshire.
Antiques, Marazion, Cornwall.
Just Glass, Alston, Cumbria.
Elizabeth and Son, Ulverston, Cumbria.
Martin and Dorothy Harper Antiques, Bakewell,
    Derbys.
Robson's Antiques, Barnard Castle, Durham.
Potter's Antiques and Coins, Bristol, Glos.
Latchford Antiques, Cheltenham, Glos.
Rankine Taylor Antiques, Cirencester, Glos.
Grimes House Antiques & Fine Art, Moreton-in-
    Marsh, Glos.
Denys Sargeant, Westerham, Kent.
Jack Moore Antiques and Stained Glass, Trawden,
    Lancs.
Keystone Antiques, Coalville, Leics.
Liz Allport-Lomax, Norwich, Norfolk.
Dorothy's Antiques, Sheringham, Norfolk.
Laurie Leigh Antiques, Oxford, Oxon.
Joan Wilkins Antiques, Witney, Oxon.
Bees Antiques, Woodstock, Oxon.
Frank Dux Antiques, Bath, Somerset.
Somervale Antiques, Midsomer Norton, Somerset.
Mary Palmer Antiques, Stradbroke, Suffolk.
Marryat, Richmond, Surrey.
David R. Fileman, Steyning, Sussex West.
Asylum House Antiques, Bradford-on-Avon, Wilts.
Delomosne and Son Ltd, North Wraxall, Wilts.

Dragon Antiques, Harrogate, Yorks. North.
York Cottage Antiques, Helmsley, Yorks. North.
Dunluce Antiques, Bushmills, Co. Antrim, N. Ireland.
Brian R. Bolt Antiques, Portballintrae, Co. Antrim, N. Ireland.

Glass Domes
Get Stuffed, London N1.
John Burton Natural Craft Taxidermy, Ebrington, Glos.
Heads 'n' Tails, Wiveliscombe, Somerset.

Icons - see Russian Art

Islamic Art
Hosains Books and Antiques, London NW6.
Atlantic Bay Carpets Gallery, London SW7.
DavidAaron Ancient Arts & Rare Carpets, London W1.
Aaron Gallery, London W1.
Emanouel Corporation (UK) Ltd, London W1.
Hadji Baba Ancient Art, London W1.
Mansour Gallery, London W1.
Bashir Mohamed Ltd, London W1.
Axia Art Consultants Ltd, London W11.
Sinai Antiques Ltd, London W8.
Clive Rogers Oriental Rugs, Staines, Surrey.

Japanese Art - see Oriental

Jewellery -see Silver

Lighting
Carlton Davidson Antiques, London N1.
Turn On Lighting, London N1.
David Malik and Son Ltd, London NW10.
No. 28 Antiques, London NW8.
B.C. Metalcrafts, London NW9.
Wilkinson plc, London SE6.
Blanchard Ltd, London SW1.
Hermitage Antiques plc, London SW1.
Carlton Hobbs, London SW1.
Christopher Howe, London SW1.
Jeremy Ltd, London SW1.
Lion, Witch and Lampshade, London SW1.
McClenaghan, London SW1.
Rogier et Rogier, London SW1.
Carlton Davidson Antiques, London SW10.
H.W. Poulter and Son, London SW10.
Joy McDonald Antiques, London SW13.
W.G.T.Burne (Antique Glass) Ltd, London SW20.
275 Antiques, London SW6.
The Antique Lamp Shop, London SW6.
Christopher Bangs, London SW6.
Fergus Cochrane and Leigh Warren Antiques, London SW6.
Charles Edwards, London SW6.
Hector Finch Lighting, London SW6.

Judy Greenwood, London SW6.
Hollingshead and Co, London SW6.
Michael Luther Antiques, London SW6.
Sylvia Napier Ltd, London SW6.
Old World Trading Co, London SW6.
M. Pauw Antiques, London SW6.
Stephen Sprake, London SW6.
The French House (Antiques) Ltd, London SW8.
W. Sitch and Co. Ltd., London W1.
Stair and Company Ltd, London W1.
M. Turpin Ltd, London W1.
Wilkinson plc, London W1.
Jones Antique Lighting, London W11.
Marshall Gallery, London W14.
J. D. Marshall, London W4.
Mrs. M.E. Crick Chandeliers, London W8.
Denton Antiques, London W8.
George and Peter Cohn, London WC1.
Manor Antiques, Wilstead (Wilshamstead), Beds.
Below Stairs of Hungerford, Hungerford, Berks.
Temple Lighting (Jeanne Temple Antiques), Milton Keynes, Bucks.
Starlight Period Lighting, Wansford, Cambs.
Victoria Imports, Stockport, Cheshire.
Peter Johnson, Penzance, Cornwall.
Staveley Antiques, Staveley, Cumbria.
The Lantern Shop Gallery, Sidmouth, Devon.
Triton Gallery, Cheltenham, Glos.
Antony Preston Antiques Ltd, Stow-on-the-Wold, Glos.
Queens Parade Antiques Ltd, Stow-on-the-Wold, Glos.
Government House, Winchcombe, Glos.
Fritz Fryer Antique Lighting, Ross-on-Wye, Herefs.
Magic Lanterns, St. Albans, Herts.
Chislehurst Antiques, Chislehurst, Kent.
The Architectural Emporium, Tunbridge Wells, Kent.
Denys Sargeant, Westerham, Kent.
Period Style Lighting, Enfield, Middx.
The Stiffkey Lamp Shop, Stiffkey, Norfolk.
Barclay Antiques, Headington, Oxon.
Haygate Gallery, Telford, Shrops.
Ian McCarthy, Clutton, Somerset.
Post House Antiques, Bletchingley, Surrey.
Libra Antiques, Hurst Green, Sussex East.
Woodall and Emery Ltd, Balcombe, Sussex West.
David R. Fileman, Steyning, Sussex West.
The Light Gallery, Leamington Spa, Warks.
Delomosne and Son Ltd, North Wraxall, Wilts.
Inglenook Antiques, Ramsbury, Wilts.
Lower House Fine Antiques, Redditch, Worcs.
Old Flames, Easingwold, Yorks. North.
Bobbins Wool, Crafts, Antiques, Whitby, Yorks. North.
Kelly Lighting, Sheffield, Yorks. South.
Berland's of Edinburgh, Edinburgh, Scotland.
Michael Vee Design - Birch House Antiques, Melrose, Scotland.

Maps & Prints

Ash Rare Books, London EC3.
Judith Lassalle, London N1.
York Gallery Ltd, London N1.
The Totteridge Gallery, London N20.
John Denham Gallery, London NW6.
Gallery Kaleidoscope incorporating Scope, London NW6.
The Warwick Leadlay Gallery, London SE10.
Julian Hartnoll, London SW1.
Paul Mason Gallery, London SW1.
Old Maps and Prints, London SW1.
The Parker Gallery, London SW1.
Michael Parkin Fine Art Ltd, London SW1.
Henry Sotheran Ltd, London SW1.
Gallery Lingard, London SW3.
Stephanie Hoppen Ltd, London SW3.
The Map House, London SW3.
Old Church Galleries, London SW3.
20th Century Gallery, London SW6.
King's Court Galleries, London SW6.
Michael Marriott Ltd, London SW6.
Trowbridge Gallery, London SW6.
York Gallery Ltd, London SW6.
Paul Orssich, London SW8.
Altea Maps & Books, London W1.
Andrew Edmunds, London W1.
H. Fritz-Denneville Fine Arts Ltd, London W1.
Map World, London W1.
The O'Shea Gallery, London W1.
Jonathan Potter Ltd, London W1.
Bernard J. Shapero Rare Books, London W1.
Stephen Somerville (W.A.) Ltd, London W1.
Henry Sotheran Ltd, London W1.
Crawley and Asquith Ltd, London W10.
Justin F. Skrebowski Prints, London W11.
Connaught Galleries, London W2.
The Lucy B. Campbell Gallery, London W8.
Adrian Harrington, London W8.
Austin/Desmond Fine Art, London WC1.
Michael Finney Antique Prints and Books, London WC1.
Robert Frew Ltd, London WC1.
Grosvenor Prints, London WC2.
Lee Jackson, London WC2.
Stage Door Prints, London WC2.
Storey's Ltd, London WC2.
The Witch Ball, London WC2.
Melnick House of Ascot, Ascot, Berks.
Graham Gallery, Burghfield Common, Berks.
The Studio Gallery, Datchet, Berks.
Omniphil Prints, Chesham, Bucks.
Penn Barn, Penn, Bucks.
The Lawson Gallery, Cambridge, Cambs.
Sebastian Pearson Paintings Prints and Works of Art, Cambridge, Cambs.
J. Alan Hulme, Chester, Cheshire.
Moor Hall Antiques, Chester, Cheshire.
Lion Gallery and Bookshop, Knutsford, Cheshire.

Iain Campbell, Widnes, Cheshire.
John Maggs, Falmouth, Cornwall.
Souvenir Antiques, Carlisle, Cumbria.
Archie Miles Bookshop, Gosforth, Cumbria.
Kendal Studios Antiques, Kendal, Cumbria.
R. F. G. Hollett and Son, Sedbergh, Cumbria.
Medina Gallery, Barnstaple, Devon.
Medina Gallery, Bideford, Devon.
Chantry Bookshop and Gallery, Dartmouth, Devon.
Graham York Rare Books, Honiton, Devon.
The Lantern Shop Gallery, Sidmouth, Devon.
Birbeck Gallery, Torquay, Devon.
The Schuster Gallery, Torquay, Devon.
Bridport Old Books, Bridport, Dorset.
Words Etcetera, Dorchester, Dorset.
F. Whillock, Litton Cheney, Dorset.
Antique Map and Bookshop, Puddletown, Dorset.
Keeble Antiques, Sherborne, Dorset.
The Swan Gallery, Sherborne, Dorset.
The Treasure Chest, Weymouth, Dorset.
J. Shotton Antiquarian Books, Prints and Coins, Durham, Durham.
Castle Bookshop, Colchester, Essex.
Newport Gallery, Newport, Essex.
Cleeve Picture Framing, Bishops Cleeve, Glos.
Alexander Gallery, Bristol, Glos.
Cotham Hill Bookshop, Bristol, Glos.
David Bannister FRGS, Cheltenham, Glos.
Kenulf Fine Arts, Stow-on-the-Wold, Glos.
Talbot Court Galleries, Stow-on-the-Wold, Glos.
Vanbrugh House Antiques, Stow-on-the-Wold, Glos.
Tetbury Gallery, Tetbury, Glos.
Laurence Oxley, Alresford, Hants.
Kingsclere Old Bookshop (Wyseby House Books), Kingsclere, Hants.
The Petersfield Bookshop, Petersfield, Hants.
Oldfield Gallery, Portsmouth, Hants.
TheOlympic Gallery, Southampton, Hants.
Bell Fine Art, Winchester, Hants.
Ross Old Book and Print Shop, Ross-on-Wye, Herefs.
Gillmark Gallery, Hertford, Herts.
Eric T. Moore, Hitchin, Herts.
Clive A. Burden Ltd, Rickmansworth, Herts.
James of St Albans, St. Albans, Herts.
The Shanklin Gallery, Shanklin, Isle of Wight.
Ventnor Rare Books, Ventnor, Isle of Wight.
The Canterbury Bookshop, Canterbury, Kent.
Chaucer Bookshop, Canterbury, Kent.
Cranbrook Gallery, Cranbrook, Kent.
G. and D.I. Marrin and Sons, Folkestone, Kent.
The China Locker, Lamberhurst, Kent.
Langley Galleries, Rochester, Kent.
London House Antiques, Westerham, Kent.
Halewood and Sons, Preston, Lancs.
Leicestershire Sporting Gallery and Brown Jack Bookshop, Lubenham, Leics.

P.J. Cassidy (Books), Holbeach, Lincs.
Golden Goose Books, Lincoln, Lincs.
Harlequin Gallery and Golden Goose Globe Restorers, Lincoln, Lincs.
Norman Blackburn, Stamford, Lincs.
The Boydell Galleries, Liverpool, Merseyside.
David Ferrow, Gt. Yarmouth, Norfolk.
Baron Art, Holt, Norfolk.
The Old Reading Room Gallery and Tea Room, Kelling, Norfolk.
J & D Clarke Book and Print Dealers, Norwich, Norfolk.
Crome Gallery and Frame Shop, Norwich, Norfolk.
Right Angle, Brackley, Northants.
Park Gallery & Bookshop, Wellingborough, Northants.
TRADA, Chipping Norton, Oxon.
The Barry Keene Gallery, Henley-on-Thames, Oxon.
Elizabeth Harvey-Lee, North Aston, Oxon.
Magna Gallery, Oxford, Oxon.
Sanders of Oxford Ltd, Oxford, Oxon.
Toby English, Wallingford, Oxon.
Tooley Adams & Co, Wallingford, Oxon.
Churchgate Antiques, Empingham, Rutland.
The Old House Gallery, Oakham, Rutland.
Marc Oxley Fine Art, Uppingham, Rutland.
The Mount, Woore, Shrops.
Andrew Dando, Bath, Somerset.
Patterson Liddle, Bath, Somerset.
Sarah Russell Antiquarian Prints, Bath, Somerset.
Trimbridge Galleries, Bath, Somerset.
Michael Lewis Gallery - Antiquarian Maps & Prints, Bruton, Somerset.
Julian Armytage, Crewkerne, Somerset.
House of Antiquity, Nether Stowey, Somerset.
Besleys Books, Beccles, Suffolk.
King's Court Galleries, Dorking, Surrey.
Vandeleur Antiquarian Books, Epsom, Surrey.
Reigate Galleries, Reigate, Surrey.
Palmer Galleries, Richmond, Surrey.
Leoframes, Brighton, Sussex East.
The Witch Ball, Brighton, Sussex East.
A. & T. Gibbard, Eastbourne, Sussex East.
Murray Brown, Pevensey Bay, Sussex East.
Baynton-Williams, Arundel, Sussex West.
The Antique Print Shop, East Grinstead, Sussex West.
Julia Holmes Antique Maps and Prints, South Harting, Sussex West.
Osborne Fine Art Gallery, Jesmond, Tyne and Wear.
Robert Vaughan, Stratford-upon-Avon, Warks.
Carleton Gallery, Birmingham, West Mids.
Bracebridge Fine Art, Astwood Bank, Worcs.
Antique Map and Print Gallery, Hallow, Worcs.
McTague of Harrogate, Harrogate, Yorks. North.
Minster Gate Bookshop, York, Yorks. North.

Alan Hill Books, Sheffield, Yorks. South.
The Grove Bookshop, Ilkley, Yorks. West.
Oakwood Gallery, Leeds, Yorks. West.
C.I Galleries Ltd, St. Peter Port, Guernsey, C.I.
John Blench & Son, St. Helier, Jersey, C.I.
The Selective Eye Gallery, St. Helier, Jersey, C.I.
Thesaurus (Jersey) Ltd, St. Helier, Jersey, C.I.
Phyllis Arnold Gallery Antiques, Greyabbey, Co. Down, N. Ireland.
Colin Wood (Antiques) Ltd, Aberdeen, Scotland.
The McEwan Gallery, Ballater, Scotland.
Calton Gallery, Edinburgh, Scotland.
The Carson Clark Gallery, Edinburgh, Scotland.
Royal Mile Gallery, Edinburgh, Scotland.
David Windsor Gallery, Bangor, Wales.
Books, Maps and Prints, Brecon, Wales.
Pontcanna Old Books, Maps and Prints, Cardiff, Wales.
Glance Back Bookshop, Chepstow, Wales.
Glance Gallery, Chepstow, Wales.

Metalware/work
House of Steel Antiques, London N1.
Robert Young Antiques, London SW11.
Christopher Bangs, London SW6.
Jack Casimir Ltd, London W11.
Johnny Von Pflugh Antiques, London W11.
Manor Antiques, Wilstead (Wilshamstead), Beds.
Christopher Sykes Antiques, Woburn, Beds.
Below Stairs of Hungerford, Hungerford, Berks.
The Fire Place (Hungerford) Ltd, Hungerford, Berks.
Turpins Antiques, Hungerford, Berks.
Berkshire Metal Finishers Ltd, Sandhurst, Berks.
Peter J. Martin, Windsor and Eton, Berks.
Sundial Antiques, Amersham, Bucks.
Phoenix Antiques, Fordham, Cambs.
A.P. and M.A. Haylett, Outwell, Cambs.
The Antique Shop, Chester, Cheshire.
Simon Starkie Antiques, Cartmel, Cumbria.
Pamela Elsom - Antiques, Ashbourne, Derbys.
J H S Antiques, Ashbourne, Derbys.
Martin and Dorothy Harper Antiques, Bakewell, Derbys.
Water Lane Antiques, Bakewell, Derbys.
Roderick Butler, Honiton, Devon.
Morchard Bishop Antiques, Morchard Bishop, Devon.
Alan Jones Antiques, Okehampton, Devon.
J.B. Antiques, Wimborne Minster, Dorset.
William H. Stokes, Cirencester, Glos.
Christopher Clarke Antiques Ltd, Stow-on-the-Wold, Glos.
Country Life Antiques, Stow-on-the-Wold, Glos.
Keith Hockin Antiques, Stow-on-the-Wold, Glos.
Huntington Antiques Ltd, Stow-on-the-Wold, Glos.
Tudor House, Stow-on-the-Wold, Glos.
Prichard Antiques, Winchcombe, Glos.

Cedar Antiques Limited, Hartley Wintney, Hants.
Michael Gander, Hitchin, Herts.
James Porter Antiques, Sandwich, Kent.
V.O.C. Antiques, Woodhall Spa, Lincs.
Peter Robinson, Heacham, Norfolk.
James Brett, Norwich, Norfolk.
M.D. Cannell Antiques, Raveningham, Norfolk.
Huntershield Antiques and Granary Antiques,
    Flore, Northants.
Rococo Antiques, Architectural Goods and
    Furnishings, Weedon, Northants.
Mark Seabrook Antiques, West Haddon,
    Northants.
Jonathan Fyson Antiques, Burford, Oxon.
Horseshoe Antiques and Gallery, Burford, Oxon.
Anthony Nielsen Antiques, Burford, Oxon.
Mike Ottrey Antiques, Wallingford, Oxon.
Joan Wilkins Antiques, Witney, Oxon.
Brian and Caroline Craik Ltd, Bath, Somerset.
Source, Bath, Somerset.
Ian McCarthy, Clutton, Somerset.
Bernard G. House, Wells, Somerset.
Peppers Period Pieces, Bury St. Edmunds, Suffolk.
Anthony Welling Antiques, Ripley, Surrey.
Heritage Antiques, Brighton, Sussex East.
Park View Antiques, Wadhurst, Sussex East.
Michael Wakelin and Helen Linfield,
    Billingshurst, Sussex West.
J. Du Cros Antiques, Petworth, Sussex West.
Retro Antiques, Lye, West Mids.
Avon Antiques, Bradford-on-Avon, Wilts.
Town and Country Antiques, Bradford-on-Avon,
    Wilts.
Harriet Fairfax Fireplaces and General Antiques,
    Langley Burrell, Wilts.
Rupert Gentle Antiques, Milton Lilbourne,
    Wilts.
H.W. Keil Ltd, Broadway, Worcs.
D & J Lines Antiques, Wychbold, Worcs.
Garth Antiques, Harrogate, Yorks. North.
Charles Lumb and Sons Ltd, Harrogate, Yorks.
    North.
Elaine Phillips Antiques Ltd, Harrogate, Yorks.
    North.
York Cottage Antiques, Helmsley, Yorks. North.
Aura Antiques, Masham, Yorks. North.
E. Thistlethwaite, Settle, Yorks. North.
Garth Antiques, Whixley, Yorks. North.
Geary Antiques, Leeds, Yorks. West.
Unicorn Antiques, Edinburgh, Scotland.
Tim Wright Antiques, Glasgow, Scotland.

Miniatures

D.S. Lavender (Antiques) Ltd, London W1.
S.J. Phillips Ltd, London W1.
H. and W. Deutsch Antiques, London W8.
Michael Sim, Chislehurst, Kent.
Regal Antiques, Westerham, Kent.
Arden Gallery, Henley-in-Arden, Warks.

Mirrors

Anno Domini Antiques, London SW1.
Chelsea Antique Mirrors, London SW1.
Ossowski, London SW1.
Overmantels, London SW11.
Joy McDonald Antiques, London SW13.
Norman Adams Ltd, London SW3.
Anthony James and Son Ltd, London SW3.
Peter Lipitch Ltd, London SW3.
Clifford Wright Antiques Ltd, London SW3.
275 Antiques, London SW6.
Judy Greenwood, London SW6.
House of Mirrors, London SW6.
Christopher Jones Antiques, London SW6.
Stair and Company Ltd, London W1.
M. Turpin Ltd, London W1.
Valerie Howard, London W8.
Through the Looking Glass Ltd, London W8.
R. Wilding, Wisbech, Cambs.
Richmond Antiques, Bowdon, Cheshire.
Keeble Antiques, Sherborne, Dorset.
Simpsons - Mirrors & Carvings, Brentwood,
    Essex.
Triton Gallery, Cheltenham, Glos.
Ashton Gower Antiques, Stow-on-the-Wold, Glos.
Stow Antiques, Stow-on-the-Wold, Glos.
Arkangel Antiques, Tetbury, Glos.
Balmuir House Antiques, Tetbury, Glos.
Burns and Graham, Winchester, Hants.
The Windhill Antiquary, Bishop's Stortford, Herts.
Claymore Antiques, Ludlow, Shrops.
Looking Glass of Bath, Bath, Somerset.
Molland Antique Mirrors, Leek, Staffs.
Maria Cass Interiors, Nayland, Suffolk.
The Gallery, Reigate, Surrey.
Dermot and Jill Palmer Antiques, Brighton,
    Sussex East.
Shirley Ann's Antiques - International Interiors,
    Brighton, Sussex East.
Julian Antiques, Hurstpierpoint, Sussex West.
Asylum House Antiques, Bradford-on-Avon,
    Wilts.
Gemini Antiques & Gallery, Kidderminster,
    Worcs.
The Drawing Room - Interiors & Antiques,
    Pershore, Worcs.
W. Greenwood (Fine Art), Burneston, Yorks.
    North.
The French House (Antiques) Ltd, York, Yorks.
    North.
Michael Vee Design - Birch House Antiques,
    Melrose, Scotland.

Musical Boxes, Instruments & Literature

Boxes and Musical Instruments, London E8.
Vincent Freeman, London N1.
Tony Bingham, London NW3.
Otto Haas (A. and M. Rosenthal), London NW3.
Talking Machine, London NW4.

H. Baron, London NW6.
Robert Morley and Co Ltd, London SE13.
J & A Beare Ltd, London W1.
Peter Biddulph, London W1.
Pelham Galleries Ltd, London W1.
Mayflower Antiques, London W11.
Travis and Emery, London WC2.
Times Past Antiques, Windsor and Eton, Berks.
J.V. Pianos and Cambridge Pianola Company, Landbeach, Cambs.
Mill Farm Antiques, Disley, Cheshire.
Miss Elany, Long Eaton, Derbys.
M.C. Taylor, Bournemouth, Dorset.
Mark Marchant (Antiques), Coggeshall, Essex.
Arthur S. Lewis, Gloucester, Glos.
Keith Harding's World of Mechanical Music, Northleach, Glos.
Vanbrugh House Antiques, Stow-on-the-Wold, Glos.
Evans and Evans, Alresford, Hants.
Thwaites Fine Stringed Instruments, Watford, Herts.
Old Smithy, Feniscowles, Lancs.
Norfolk Polyphon Centre, Bawdeswell, Norfolk.
The Violin Shop, Hexham, Northumbs.
R.R. Limb Antiques, Newark, Notts.
Laurie Leigh Antiques, Oxford, Oxon.
Graham Webb, Brighton, Sussex East.
John Cowderoy Antiques, Eastbourne, Sussex East.
Pianos Galore, Little Horsted, Sussex East.
The Barber's Clock, Worcester, Worcs.
Thirkill Antiques, Leyburn, Yorks. North.
The Piano Shop, Leeds, Yorks. West.
K.L.M. & Co. Antiques, Lepton, Yorks. West.
Talking Point Antiques, Sowerby Bridge, Yorks. West.
San Domenico Stringed Instruments, Cardiff, Wales.
John Carpenter, Llanelli, Wales.
Keith Chugg Antiques, Swansea, Wales.

Nautical Instruments - see Scientific

Needlework - see Tapestries

Netsuke - see Oriental

Oil Paintings
Gladwell and CompanyLondon EC4.
Peter Chapman Antiques and Restoration, London N1.
Swan Fine Art, London N1.
Finchley Fine Art Galleries, London N12.
Martin Henham (Antiques), London N2.
Lauri Stewart - Fine Art, London N2.
The Totteridge Gallery, London N20.
Barkes and Barkes, London NW1.
Leask Ward, London NW3.

Duncan R. Miller Fine Arts, London NW3.
Newhart (Pictures) Ltd, London NW3.
John Denham Gallery, London NW6.
Gallery Kaleidoscope incorporating Scope, London NW6.
Camden Art Gallery, London NW8.
Nicholas Drummond/Wrawby Moor Art Gallery Ltd, London NW8.
Patricia Harvey Antiques and Decoration, London NW8.
The Greenwich Gallery, London SE10.
Didier Aaron (London)Ltd, London SW1.
Ackermann & Johnson, London SW1.
Verner Åmell Ltd, London SW1.
Antiquus, London SW1.
Artemis Fine Arts Limited, London SW1.
Chris Beetles Ltd, London SW1.
John Bly, London SW1.
Brisigotti Antiques Ltd, London SW1.
Miles Wynn Cato, London SW1.
Chaucer Fine Arts Ltd, London SW1.
Cox and Company, London SW1.
Simon C. Dickinson Ltd, London SW1.
Douwes Fine Art Ltd, London SW1.
Eaton Gallery, London SW1.
Frost and Reed Ltd (Est. 1808), London SW1.
Martyn Gregory Gallery, London SW1.
Ross Hamilton Ltd, London SW1.
Harrods Ltd, London SW1.
Julian Hartnoll, London SW1.
Hazlitt, Gooden and Fox Ltd, London SW1.
Hermitage Antiques plc, London SW1.
Carlton Hobbs, London SW1.
Derek Johns Ltd, London SW1.
MacConnal-Mason Gallery, London SW1.
The Mall Galleries, London SW1.
Paul Mason Gallery, London SW1.
Mathaf Gallery Ltd, London SW1.
Matthiesen Fine Art Ltd., London SW1.
Messums, London SW1.
Moreton Street Gallery, London SW1.
Guy Morrison, London SW1.
Peter Nahum at The Leicester Galleries, London SW1.
Paisnel Gallery, London SW1.
The Parker Gallery, London SW1.
Michael Parkin Fine Art Ltd, London SW1.
Portland Gallery, London SW1.
Steven Rich & Michael Rich, London SW1.
Julian Simon Fine Art Ltd, London SW1.
Bill Thomson - Albany Gallery, London SW1.
Trafalgar Galleries, London SW1.
Tryon Gallery (incorporating Malcolm Innes), London SW1.
Rafael Valls Ltd, London SW1.
Rafael Valls Ltd, London SW1.
Johnny Van Haeften Ltd, London SW1.
Waterman Fine Art Ltd, London SW1.
Whitford Fine Art, London SW1.

SPECIALIST DEALERS

Wildenstein and Co Ltd, London SW1.
Jonathan Clark & Co, London SW10.
Collins and Hastie Ltd, London SW10.
Lane Fine Art Ltd, London SW10.
Langton Street Gallery, London SW10.
Offer Waterman and Co. Fine Art, London SW10.
Park Walk Gallery, London SW10.
Pairs Antiques Ltd, London SW11.
Regent House Gallery, London SW11.
New Grafton Gallery, London SW13.
John Spink, London SW13.
Ted Few, London SW17.
The David Curzon Gallery, London SW19.
The Andipa Gallery, London SW3.
Campbell's of Walton Street, London SW3.
Gallery Lingard, London SW3.
Stephanie Hoppen Ltd, London SW3.
20th Century Gallery, London SW6.
Rupert Cavendish Antiques, London SW6.
Charles Edwards, London SW6.
Julie Collino, London SW7.
The Taylor Gallery Ltd, London SW7.
The Wyllie Gallery, London SW7.
Agnew's, London W1.
Victor Arwas Gallery - Editions Graphiques Gallery Ltd, London W1.
TheBritish Art Gallery, London W1.
Browse and Darby Ltd, London W1.
Burlington Paintings Ltd, London W1.
Andrew Clayton-Payne Ltd, London W1.
P. and D. Colnaghi & Co Ltd, London W1.
Connaught Brown plc, London W1.
Dover Street Gallery, London W1.
Elwes and Hanham Ltd, London W1.
The Fine Art Society plc, London W1.
H. Fritz-Denneville Fine Arts Ltd, London W1.
Deborah Gage (Works of Art) Ltd, London W1.
The Graham Gallery, London W1.
Richard Green, London W1.
Patrick Jefferson, London W1.
Maas Gallery, London W1.
Mallett and Son (Antiques) Ltd, London W1.
Mallett Gallery, London W1.
Marlborough Fine Art (London) Ltd, London W1.
Messums (Contemporary), London W1.
John Mitchell and Son, London W1.
Partridge Fine Arts plc, London W1.
W.H. Patterson Fine Arts Ltd, London W1.
Pyms Gallery, London W1.
Royal Exchange Art Gallery at Cork St., London W1.
Stephen Somerville (W.A.) Ltd, London W1.
Spink Leger Pictures, London W1.
Stoppenbach & Delestre Ltd, London W1.
William Thuillier, London W1.
Walpole Gallery, London W1.
Waterhouse and Dodd, London W1.
The Weiss Gallery, London W1.

Wilkins and Wilkins, London W1.
Williams and Son, London W1.
Crawley and Asquith Ltd, London W10.
Butchoff Antiques, London W11.
Caelt Gallery, London W11.
The Coach House, London W11.
Curá Antiques, London W11.
Charles Daggett Gallery, London W11.
Fleur de Lys Gallery, London W11.
Gavin Graham Gallery, London W11.
Lacy Gallery, London W11.
Milne and Moller, London W11.
Richard Philp, London W11.
Piano Nobile Fine Paintings, London W11.
Justin F. Skrebowski Prints, London W11.
Stern Art Dealers, London W11.
Johnny Von Pflugh Antiques, London W11.
Marshall Gallery, London W14.
Manya Igel Fine Arts Ltd, London W2.
Aberdeen House Antiques, London W5.
Ealing Gallery, London W5.
Baumkotter Gallery, London W8.
Pawsey and Payne, London W8.
Abbott and Holder, London WC1.
Austin/Desmond Fine Art, London WC1.
Baroq & David Ball Antiques, Leighton Buzzard, Beds.
Foye Gallery, Luton, Beds.
Woburn Fine Arts, Woburn, Beds.
Omell Galleries, Ascot, Berks.
Graham Gallery, Burghfield Common, Berks.
The Studio Gallery, Datchet, Berks.
John A. Pearson Antiques, Horton, Berks.
The Coworth Gallery, Sunningdale, Berks.
H.S. Wellby Ltd, Haddenham, Bucks.
Penn Barn, Penn, Bucks.
Cambridge Fine Art Ltd, Cambridge, Cambs.
Sebastian Pearson Paintings Prints and Works of Art, Cambridge, Cambs.
Storm Fine Arts Ltd, Great Shelford, Cambs.
Baron Fine Art, Chester, Cheshire.
Harris & Holt, Chester, Cheshire.
Harper Fine Paintings, Poynton, Cheshire.
Copperhouse Gallery - W. Dyer & Sons, Hayle, Cornwall.
Tony Sanders Penzance Gallery and Antiques, Penzance, Cornwall.
St. Breock Gallery, Wadebridge, Cornwall.
Peter Haworth, Beetham, Cumbria.
The Gallery, Penrith, Cumbria.
R. F. G. Hollett and Son, Sedbergh, Cumbria.
Kenneth Upchurch, Ashbourne, Derbys.
J. Collins and Son, Bideford, Devon.
Medina Gallery, Bideford, Devon.
Godolphin Antiques, Chagford, Devon.
Mill Gallery, Ermington, Devon.
Honiton Fine Art, Honiton, Devon.
Skeaping Gallery, Lydford, Devon.
Farthings, Lynton, Devon.

Gordon Hepworth Fine Art, Newton St. Cyres, Devon.
Michael Wood Fine Art, Plymouth, Devon.
Birbeck Gallery, Torquay, Devon.
Hampshire Gallery, Bournemouth, Dorset.
The Swan Gallery, Sherborne, Dorset.
Margaret Bedi Antiques & Fine Art, Billingham, Durham.
T.B. and R. Jordan (Fine Paintings), Stockton-on-Tees, Durham.
Brandler Galleries, Brentwood, Essex.
Neil Graham Gallery, Brentwood, Essex.
S. Bond and Son, Colchester, Essex.
Newport Gallery, Newport, Essex.
Galerie Lev, Woodford Green, Essex.
Peter and Penny Proudfoot, Berkeley, Glos.
Cleeve Picture Framing, Bishops Cleeve, Glos.
The Priory Gallery, Bishops Cleeve, Glos.
Alexander Gallery, Bristol, Glos.
Manor House Gallery, Cheltenham, Glos.
Triton Gallery, Cheltenham, Glos.
Peter Ward Fine Paintings, Cheltenham, Glos.
School House Antiques, Chipping Campden, Glos.
The Titian Gallery, Chipping Campden, Glos.
Astley House - Fine Art, Moreton-in-Marsh, Glos.
Astley House - Fine Art, Moreton-in-Marsh, Glos.
Benton Fine Art, Moreton-in-Marsh, Glos.
Berry Antiques, Moreton-in-Marsh, Glos.
Grimes House Antiques & Fine Art, Moreton-in-Marsh, Glos.
Nina Zborowska, Painswick, Glos.
Baggott Church Street Ltd, Stow-on-the-Wold, Glos.
Cotswold Galleries, Stow-on-the-Wold, Glos.
The John Davies Gallery, Stow-on-the-Wold, Glos.
The Fosse Gallery, Stow-on-the-Wold, Glos.
Kenulf Fine Arts, Stow-on-the-Wold, Glos.
Roger Lamb Antiques & Works of Art, Stow-on-the-Wold, Glos.
Styles of Stow, Stow-on-the-Wold, Glos.
Balmuir House Antiques, Tetbury, Glos.
Tetbury Gallery, Tetbury, Glos.
Antique House, Hartley Wintney, Hants.
Roy Precious Antiques & Fine Art, Hartley Wintney, Hants.
Century Fine Arts, Lymington, Hants.
Robert Perera Fine Art, Lymington, Hants.
The Petersfield Bookshop, Petersfield, Hants.
The Wykeham Gallery, Stockbridge, Hants.
Bell Fine Art, Winchester, Hants.
Lacewing Fine Art Gallery, Winchester, Hants.
Webb Fine Arts, Winchester, Hants.
Linden House Antiques, Leominster, Herefs.
The Shanklin Gallery, Shanklin, Isle of Wight.
Cooper Fine Arts Ltd, Brasted, Kent.
Michael Sim, Chislehurst, Kent.
Francis Iles, Rochester, Kent.
Langley Galleries, Rochester, Kent.
Sundridge Gallery, Sundridge, Kent.

Nicholas Bowlby, Tunbridge Wells, Kent.
Pantiles Spa Antiques, Tunbridge Wells, Kent.
Redleaf Gallery, Tunbridge Wells, Kent.
Apollo Antique Galleries, Westerham, Kent.
Peter Dyke, Westerham, Kent.
London House Antiques, Westerham, Kent.
Fulda Gallery Ltd, Manchester, Lancs.
St. James Antiques, Manchester, Lancs.
European Fine Arts and Antiques, Preston, Lancs.
Henry Donn Gallery, Whitefield, Lancs.
Corry's, Leicester, Leics.
Leicestershire Sporting Gallery and Brown Jack Bookshop, Lubenham, Leics.
P. Stanworth (Fine Arts), Market Bosworth, Leics.
Graftons of Market Harborough, Market Harborough, Leics.
Robin Shield Antiques, Swinstead, Lincs.
Ailsa Gallery, Twickenham, Middx.
Baron Art, Holt, Norfolk.
The Old Reading Room Gallery and Tea Room, Kelling, Norfolk.
The Bank House Gallery, Norwich, Norfolk.
Crome Gallery and Frame Shop, Norwich, Norfolk.
The Fairhurst Gallery, Norwich, Norfolk.
Mandell's Gallery, Norwich, Norfolk.
The Westcliffe Gallery, Sheringham, Norfolk.
Staithe Lodge Gallery, Swafield, Norfolk.
Norton Antiques, Twyford, Norfolk.
Coughton Galleries Ltd, Arthingworth, Northants.
Right Angle, Brackley, Northants.
Castle Ashby Gallery, Castle Ashby, Northants.
Dragon Antiques, Kettering, Northants.
Clark Galleries, Towcester, Northants.
Ron Green, Towcester, Northants.
Bryan Perkins Antiques, Wellingborough, Northants.
The Bell Gallery, Belfast, N. Ireland.
Boadens Antiques, Hexham, Northumbs.
Anthony Mitchell Fine Paintings, Nottingham, Notts.
H.C. Dickins, Bloxham, Oxon.
Horseshoe Antiques and Gallery, Burford, Oxon.
Hubert's Antiques, Burford, Oxon.
The Stone Gallery, Burford, Oxon.
Swan Gallery, Burford, Oxon.
Georgian House Antiques, Chipping Norton, Oxon.
Hallidays (Fine Antiques) Ltd, Dorchester-on-Thames, Oxon.
The Barry Keene Gallery, Henley-on-Thames, Oxon.
Churchgate Antiques, Empingham, Rutland.
Fine Art of Oakham, Oakham, Rutland.
The Old House Gallery, Oakham, Rutland.
John Garner, Uppingham, Rutland.
Marc Oxley Fine Art, Uppingham, Rutland.
John Boulton Fine Art, Broseley, Shrops.
Teme Valley Antiques, Ludlow, Shrops.

SPECIALIST DEALERS

Valentyne Dawes Gallery, Ludlow, Shrops.
Wenlock Fine Art, Much Wenlock, Shrops.
The Mount, Woore, Shrops.
Adam Gallery, Bath, Somerset.
Mary Cruz, Bath, Somerset.
Anthony Hepworth Fine Art Dealers, Bath,
   Somerset.
Trimbridge Galleries, Bath, Somerset.
Freshfords, Freshford, Somerset.
The Court Gallery, Nether Stowey, Somerset.
Nick Cotton Fine Art, Watchet, Somerset.
Sadler Street Gallery, Wells, Somerset.
Everett Fine Art Ltd, West Buckland, Somerset.
England's Gallery, Leek, Staffs.
Thompson's Gallery, Aldeburgh, Suffolk.
J. and J. Baker, Lavenham, Suffolk.
Trident Antiques, Long Melford, Suffolk.
Peasenhall Art and Antiques Gallery, Peasenhall,
   Suffolk.
The Falcon Gallery, Wortham, Suffolk.
Suffolk House Antiques, Yoxford, Suffolk.
Cider House Galleries Ltd, Bletchingley, Surrey.
Cobham Galleries, Cobham, Surrey.
The Whitgift Galleries, Croydon, Surrey.
Antique Clocks by Patrick Thomas, Dorking,
   Surrey.
Hampton Court Palace Antiques, East Molesey,
   Surrey.
Glencorse Antiques, Kingston-upon-Thames,
   Surrey.
Bourne Gallery Ltd, Reigate, Surrey.
The Gallery, Reigate, Surrey.
Roland Goslett Gallery, Richmond, Surrey.
Marryat, Richmond, Surrey.
Piano Nobile Fine Paintings, Richmond, Surrey.
Cedar House Gallery, Ripley, Surrey.
Sage Antiques and Interiors, Ripley, Surrey.
B. M. and E. Newlove, Surbiton, Surrey.
Edward Cross - Fine Paintings, Weybridge, Surrey.
Willow Gallery, Weybridge, Surrey.
John Day of Eastbourne Fine Art, Eastbourne,
   Sussex East.
Stewart Gallery, Eastbourne, Sussex East.
Murray Brown, Pevensey Bay, Sussex East.
E. Stacy-Marks Limited, Polegate, Sussex East.
Lannards Gallery, Billingshurst, Sussex West.
Chichester Gallery, Chichester, Sussex West.
The Canon Gallery, Petworth, Sussex West.
Oliver Charles Antiques, Petworth, Sussex West.
Georgia Antiques, Pulborough, Sussex West.
Wilsons Antiques, Worthing, Sussex West.
Anna Harrison Fine Antiques, Gosforth, Tyne and
   Wear.
MacDonald Fine Art, Gosforth, Tyne and Wear.
Osborne Fine Art Gallery, Jesmond, Tyne and
   Wear.
Arden Gallery, Henley-in-Arden, Warks.
Colmore Galleries Ltd, Henley-in-Arden, Warks.
Fine-Lines (Fine Art), Shipston-on-Stour, Warks.

Astley House - Fine Art, Stretton-on-Fosse, Warks.
Oldswinford Gallery, Stourbridge, West Mids.
Driffold Gallery, Sutton Coldfield, West Mids.
Salisbury Antiques Warehouse Ltd, Salisbury,
   Wilts.
Bracebridge Fine Art, Astwood Bank, Worcs.
Richard Hagen, Broadway, Worcs.
Haynes Fine Art of Broadway, Broadway, Worcs.
John Noott Galleries, Broadway, Worcs.
The Highway Gallery, Upton-upon-Severn, Worcs.
James H. Starkey Galleries, Beverley, Yorks. East.
W. Greenwood (Fine Art), Burneston, Yorks.
   North.
Garth Antiques, Harrogate, Yorks. North.
Sutcliffe Galleries, Harrogate, Yorks. North.
Walker Galleries Ltd, Harrogate, Yorks. North.
E. Stacy-Marks Limited, Helmsley, Yorks. North.
Thirkill Antiques, Leyburn, Yorks. North.
Talents Fine Arts Ltd, Malton, Yorks. North.
Rose Fine Art and Antiques, Stillington, Yorks.
   North.
Kirkgate Fine Art & Conservation, Thirsk, Yorks.
   North.
Garth Antiques, Whixley, Yorks. North.
Coulter Galleries, York, Yorks. North.
Oakwood Gallery, Leeds, Yorks. West.
Robin Taylor Fine Arts, Wakefield, Yorks. West.
Mark Blower Antiques, Le Bourg Forest,
   Guernsey, C.I.
C.I Galleries Ltd, St. Peter Port, Guernsey, C.I.
St. James's Gallery Ltd, St. Peter Port, Guernsey,
   C.I.
Falle Fine Art Limited, St Helier, Jersey, C.I.
The Selective Eye Gallery, St. Helier, Jersey, C.I.
I.G.A. Old Masters Ltd, St. Lawrence, Jersey, C.I.
Grange Gallery - Fine Arts Ltd, St. Saviour,
   Jersey, C.I.
Dunluce Antiques, Bushmills, Co. Antrim, N.
   Ireland.
Antiques and Fine Art Gallery, Warrenpoint, Co.
   Down, N. Ireland.
Atholl Antiques, Aberdeen, Scotland.
The Rendezvous Gallery, Aberdeen, Scotland.
Colin Wood (Antiques) Ltd, Aberdeen, Scotland.
Nigel Stacy-Marks Ltd, Auchterarder, Scotland.
The McEwan Gallery, Ballater, Scotland.
Bourne Fine Art Ltd, Edinburgh, Scotland.
Calton Gallery, Edinburgh, Scotland.
John Mathieson and Co, Edinburgh, Scotland.
Open Eye Gallery Ltd, Edinburgh, Scotland.
The Scottish Gallery, Edinburgh, Scotland.
Anthony Woodd Gallery, Edinburgh, Scotland.
Young Antiques, Edinburgh, Scotland.
The Roger Billcliffe Fine Art, Glasgow, Scotland.
Ewan Mundy Fine Art Ltd, Glasgow, Scotland.
Michael Young Antiques at Glencarse, Glencarse,
   Scotland.
Glendoick Antiques, Glendoick, Scotland.
Inchmartine Fine Art, Inchture, Scotland.

Mainhill Gallery, Jedburgh, Scotland.
Killin Gallery, Killin, Scotland.
Kilmacolm Antiques Ltd, Kilmacolm, Scotland.
Newburgh Antiques, Newburgh, Scotland.
Kirk Ports Gallery, North Berwick, Scotland.
Nigel Stacy-Marks Ltd, Perth, Scotland.
St. Andrews Fine Art, St. Andrews, Scotland.
Abbey Antiques, Stirling, Scotland.
David Windsor Gallery, Bangor, Wales.
Michael Webb Fine Art, Llangristiolus (Anglesey), Wales.
Welsh Art, Tywyn, Wales.

Oriental Items
Nanwani and Co, London EC3.
Japanese Gallery, London N1.
Laurence Mitchell Antiques Ltd, London N1.
Kevin Page Oriental Art, London N1.
Marcus Ross Antiques, London N1.
Yingguoren Ltd, London N1.
Leask Ward, London NW3.
Malcolm Rushton - Early Oriental Art, London NW3.
B.C. Metalcrafts, London NW9.
Coats Oriental Carpets, London SE5.
Ciancimino Ltd, London SW1.
Brian Harkins Oriental Art, London SW1.
Jeremy Mason (Sainsbury & Mason), London SW1.
Orientation, London SW10.
Hungry Ghost, London SW3.
Sebastiano Barbagallo, London SW6.
Sylvia Napier Ltd, London SW6.
Daphne Rankin and Ian Conn, London SW6.
Redroom, London SW6.
Brandt Oriental Art, London W1.
Paul Champkins, London W1.
Barry Davies Oriental Art, London W1.
Eskenazi Ltd, London W1.
John Eskenazi Ltd, London W1.
Robert Hall, London W1.
Gerard Hawthorn Ltd, London W1.
Roger Keverne, London W1.
Sydney L. Moss Ltd, London W1.
Nicholas S. Pitcher Oriental Art, London W1.
Robert G. Sawers, London W1.
A & J Speelman Ltd, London W1.
Toynbee-Clarke Interiors Ltd, London W1.
Jan van Beers Oriental Art, London W1.
Linda Wrigglesworth Ltd, London W1.
M.C.N. Antiques, London W11.
The Nanking Porcelain Co. Ltd, London W11.
Oriental Furniture and Arts, London W4.
AntikWest AB, London W8.
Gregg Baker Asian Art, London W8.
Berwald Oriental Art, London W8.
David Brower Antiques, London W8.
Cohen & Cohen, London W8.

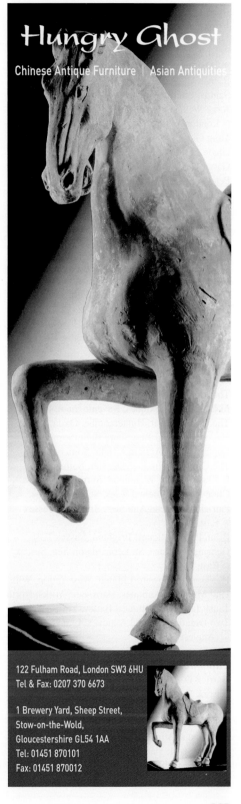

H. and W. Deutsch Antiques, London W8.
J.A.N. Fine Art, London W8.
Japanese Gallery, London W8.
Peter Kemp, London W8.
S. Marchant & Son, London W8.
R. and G. McPherson Antiques, London W8.
Santos, London W8.
Jorge Welsh Oriental Porcelain & Works of Art, London W8.
Yang Guifei, London W8.
Glade Antiques, Marlow, Bucks.
Gabor Cossa Antiques, Cambridge, Cambs.
Peter Johnson, Penzance, Cornwall.
Brian Matsell, Derby, Derbys.
David L.H. Southwick Rare Art, Kingswear, Devon.
The Dragon and the Phoenix, South Molton, Devon.
Mere Antiques, Topsham, Devon.
Lionel Geneen Ltd, Bournemouth, Dorset.
Hungry Ghost, Stow-on-the-Wold, Glos.
Oriental Gallery, Stow-on-the-Wold, Glos.
Artique, Tetbury, Glos.
Tudor Antiques & Fine Art Ltd, Alresford, Hants.
Oriental Rug Gallery Ltd, St. Albans, Herts.
Michael Sim, Chislehurst, Kent.
Mandarin Gallery - Oriental Art, Otford, Kent.
Flower House Antiques, Tenterden, Kent.
The Rug Gallery, Leicester, Leics.
M.D. Cannell Antiques, Raveningham, Norfolk.
The Country Seat, Huntercombe, Oxon.
Haliden Oriental Rug Shop, Bath, Somerset.
Lopburi Art & Antiques, Bath, Somerset.
The Crooked Window, Dunster, Somerset.
Robin Kennedy, Richmond, Surrey.
Clive Rogers Oriental Rugs, Staines, Surrey.
Patrick Moorhead Antiques, Brighton, Sussex East.
Brian Page Antiques, Brighton, Sussex East.
Gensing Antiques, St. Leonards-on-Sea, Sussex East.
Heirloom & Howard Limited, West Yatton, Wilts.
Paul M. Peters Antiques, Harrogate, Yorks. North.
Tansu Japanese Antiques, Batley, Yorks. West.
Two Dragons Oriental Antiques, Llanerchymedd (Anglesey), Wales.

Paperweights

Garrick D. Coleman, London W11.
Garrick D. Coleman, London W8.
Sweetbriar Gallery, Helsby, Cheshire.
Portique, Bournemouth, Dorset.
Todd and Austin Antiques of Winchester, Winchester, Hants.
The Stone Gallery, Burford, Oxon.
David R. Fileman, Steyning, Sussex West.

Photographs & Equipment

Vintage Cameras Ltd, London SE26.
Jessop Classic Photographica, London WC1.
Medina Gallery, Barnstaple, Devon.
Medina Gallery, Bideford, Devon.
Peter Pan's Bazaar, Gosport, Hants.

Pottery & Porcelain

Diana Huntley, London N1.
Carol Ketley Antiques, London N1.
Laurence Mitchell Antiques Ltd, London N1.
The Collector Limited, London N11.
Finchley Fine Art Galleries, London N12.
Martin Henham (Antiques), London N2.
Sabera Trading Co, London NW2.
Klaber and Klaber, London NW3.
Albert Amor Ltd, London SW1.
Ross Hamilton Ltd, London SW1.
M. and D. Lewis, London SW1.
Stephen Long, London SW10.
Robert Young Antiques, London SW11.
The Dining Room Shop, London SW13.
Rogers de Rin, London SW3.
Thomas Goode and Co (London) Ltd, London W1.
Harcourt Antiques, London W1.
Brian Haughton Antiques, London W1.
Alistair Sampson Antiques Ltd, London W1.
Judy Fox, London W11.
M. and D. Lewis, London W11.
Mercury Antiques, London W11.
Schredds of Portobello, London W11.
Staffordshire Pride, London W11.
Garry Atkins, London W8.
David Brower Antiques, London W8.
Davies Antiques, London W8.
H. and W. Deutsch Antiques, London W8.
Hope and Glory, London W8.
Jonathan Horne, London W8.
Valerie Howard, London W8.
Roderick Jellicoe, London W8.
Peter Kemp, London W8.
Libra Antiques, London W8.
London Antique Gallery, London W8.
E. and H. Manners, London W8.
Simon Spero, London W8.
Stockspring Antiques, London W8.
Mary Wise & Grosvenor Antiques, London W8.
Anchor Antiques Ltd, London WC2.
Baroq & David Ball Antiques, Leighton Buzzard, Beds.
Nick & Janet's Antiques, Leighton Buzzard, Beds.
Ulla Stafford Antiques, Binfield, Berks.
Cavendish Fine Arts, Sonning-on-Thames, Berks.

Berkshire Antiques Co Ltd, Windsor and Eton, Berks.
Gabor Cossa Antiques, Cambridge, Cambs.
Abbey Antiques, Ramsey, Cambs.
Aldersey Hall Ltd, Chester, Cheshire.
The Antique Shop, Chester, Cheshire.
Cameo Antiques, Chester, Cheshire.
K D Antiques, Chester, Cheshire.
Made of Honour, Chester, Cheshire.
Watergate Antiques, Chester, Cheshire.
Littles Collectables, Congleton, Cheshire.
Imperial Antiques, Stockport, Cheshire.
Antiques, Marazion, Cornwall.
Tregony Antiques, Tregony, Cornwall.
Alan Bennett, Truro, Cornwall.
Saint Nicholas Galleries Ltd. (Antiques and Jewellery), Carlisle, Cumbria.
Souvenir Antiques, Carlisle, Cumbria.
Dower House Antiques, Kendal, Cumbria.
Kendal Studios Antiques, Kendal, Cumbria.
Kenneth Upchurch, Ashbourne, Derbys.
The Good Olde Days, Ockbrook, Derbys.
Bampton Gallery, Bampton, Devon.
Selected Antiques & Collectables, Barnstaple, Devon.
David J. Thorn, Budleigh Salterton, Devon.
Mere Antiques, Topsham, Devon.
Birbeck Gallery, Torquay, Devon.
Box of Porcelain, Dorchester, Dorset.
Heygate Browne Antiques, Sherborne, Dorset.
Reference Works Ltd., Swanage, Dorset.
Grant's Antiques, Barnard Castle, Durham.
James Hardy Antiques Ltd, Barnard Castle, Durham.
Robson's Antiques, Barnard Castle, Durham.
E J Markham & Son Ltd, Colchester, Essex.
Bush House, Corringham, Essex.
Bush Antiques, Saffron Walden, Essex.
Harris Antiques (Stansted), Stansted, Essex.
Barling Fine Porcelain Ltd, Wickham Bishops, Essex.
Julian Tatham-Losh, Andoversford, Glos.
Cotham Antiques, Bristol, Glos.
Stuart House Antiques, Chipping Campden, Glos.
Sodbury Antiques, Chipping Sodbury,, Glos.
Berry Antiques, Moreton-in-Marsh, Glos.
Seaford House Antiques, Moreton-in-Marsh, Glos.
Church Street Antiques Centre, Stow-on-the-Wold, Glos.
Wyndhams, Stow-on-the-Wold, Glos.
Artemesia, Alresford, Hants.
Graylings Antiques, Andover, Hants.
Platt's of Lymington, Lymington, Hants.
Lita Kaye of Lyndhurst, Lyndhurst, Hants.
Lane Antiques, Stockbridge, Hants.

Goss and Crested China Centre and Goss Museum, Waterlooville, Hants.
Dinah Stoodley & Celia Jennings, Brasted, Kent.
W.W. Warner (Antiques), Brasted, Kent.
Serendipity, Deal, Kent.
Steppes Hill Farm Antiques, Stockbury, Kent.
Pantiles Spa Antiques, Tunbridge Wells, Kent.
The Emporium Antiques, Collectibles & Craft Centre, Welling, Kent.
Old Corner House Antiques, Wittersham, Kent.
Village Antiques, Manchester, Lancs.
Priory Collectables, Preston, Lancs.
Underwoodhall Antiques, Woodhall Spa, Lincs.
Ivy House Antiques, Acle, Norfolk.
Roger Bradbury Antiques, Coltishall, Norfolk.
Peter Robinson, Heacham, Norfolk.
Richard Scott Antiques, Holt, Norfolk.
Liz Allport-Lomax, Norwich, Norfolk.
Malcolm Turner, Norwich, Norfolk.
Dorothy's Antiques, Sheringham, Norfolk.
Leo Pratt and Son, South Walsham, Norfolk.
T.C.S. Brooke, Wroxham, Norfolk.
Peter Jackson Antiques, Brackley, Northants.
R. and M. Nicholas, Towcester, Northants.
Hedley's of Hexham, Hexham, Northumbs.
David and Carole Potter Antiques, Nottingham, Notts.
Swan Gallery, Burford, Oxon.
Bees Antiques, Woodstock, Oxon.
John Howard, Woodstock, Oxon.
Robin Sanders and Sons, Woodstock, Oxon.
The Old House Gallery, Oakham, Rutland.
T.J. Roberts, Uppingham, Rutland.
Micawber Antiques, Bridgnorth, Shrops.
Tudor House Antiques, Ironbridge, Shrops.
Teme Valley Antiques, Ludlow, Shrops.
David and Sally March Antiques, Abbots Leigh, Somerset.
Andrew Dando, Bath, Somerset.
Quiet Street Antiques, Bath, Somerset.
T J Atkins, Taunton, Somerset.
Eveline Winter, Rugeley, Staffs.
The Potteries Antique Centre Ltd, Stoke-on-Trent, Staffs.
The Pottery Buying Centre, Stoke-on-Trent, Staffs.
Top of the Hill (Ceramic Search), Stoke-on-Trent, Staffs.
White House Antiques, Uttoxeter, Staffs.
AD Antiques, Woodseaves, Staffs.
John Read, Martlesham, Suffolk.
David Gibbins Antiques, Woodbridge, Suffolk.
Red House Antiques, Yoxford, Suffolk.
Churt Curiosity Shop, Churt, Surrey.
Decodream, Coulsdon, Surrey.
Dolphin Square Antiques, Dorking, Surrey.

SPECIALIST DEALERS

The Olde Bakehouse Antiques, Dorking, Surrey.
Marryat, Richmond, Surrey.
Helena's Collectables, Shere, Surrey.
Susan Becker, Walton-on-Thames, Surrey.
Brocante, Weybridge, Surrey.
Patrick Moorhead Antiques, Brighton, Sussex East.
Yellow Lantern Antiques Ltd, Brighton, Sussex East.
Stewart Gallery, Eastbourne, Sussex East.
Southdown Antiques, Lewes, Sussex East.
Herbert Gordon Gasson, Rye, Sussex East.
Gems Antiques, Chichester, Sussex West.
Magic of Quimper, Littlehampton, Sussex West.
Richard Gardner Antiques, Petworth, Sussex West.
William Hockley Antiques, Petworth, Sussex West.
Ian Sharp Antiques, Tynemouth, Tyne and Wear.
Coleshill Antiques and Interiors Ltd, Coleshill, Warks.
Burman Antiques, Stratford-upon-Avon, Warks.
Castle Antiques, Warwick, Warks.
H. and R.L. Parry Ltd, Sutton Coldfield, West Mids.
Moxhams Antiques, Bradford-on-Avon, Wilts.
Antiques - Rene Nicholls, Malmesbury, Wilts.
Heirloom & Howard Limited, West Yatton, Wilts.
Bygones by the Cathedral, Worcester, Worcs.
Bygones of Worcester, Worcester, Worcs.
M. Lees and Sons, Worcester, Worcs.
Worcester Antiques Centre, Worcester, Worcs.
The Crested China Co, Driffield, Yorks. East.
Nigel Adamson, Harrogate, Yorks. North.
Bryan Bowden, Harrogate, Yorks. North.
David Love, Harrogate, Yorks. North.
York Cottage Antiques, Helmsley, Yorks. North.
Country Collector, Pickering, Yorks. North.
Nanbooks, Settle, Yorks. North.
Anderson Slater Antiques, Settle, Yorks. North.
Age of Jazz, Whitby, Yorks. North.
Ruby Snowden Antiques, Yarm, Yorks. North.
Holly Farm Antiques, Rotherham, Yorks. South.
Muir Hewitt Art Deco Originals, Halifax, Yorks. West.
St. James's Gallery Ltd, St. Peter Port, Guernsey, C.I.
Stephen Cohu Antiques, St Ouen, Jersey, C.I.
The Country Antiques, Antrim, Co. Antrim, N. Ireland.
Dunluce Antiques, Bushmills, Co. Antrim, N. Ireland.
Steeple Antiques, Ceres, Scotland.
Gordon Inglis Antiques, Edinburgh, Scotland.
Young Antiques, Edinburgh, Scotland.
Tim Wright Antiques, Glasgow, Scotland.

Miles Antiques, Kinross, Scotland.
Grannie Used To Have One, Longhaven, Scotland.
Harper-James, Montrose, Scotland.
Newburgh Antiques, Newburgh, Scotland.
The Antiques Shop, Pittenweem, Scotland.
Nolton Antiques, Bridgend, Wales.
Paul Gibbs Antiques and Decorative Arts, Conwy, Wales.
Manor House Antiques, Fishguard, Wales.
Hebbards of Hay, Hay-on-Wye, Wales.
Islwyn Watkins, Knighton, Wales.
J. and R. Langford, Llangollen, Wales.
Passers Buy (Marie Evans), Llangollen, Wales.
Frost Antiques & Pine, Monmouth, Wales.
West Wales Antiques, Murton, Wales.
Magpie Antiques, Swansea, Wales.

Prints - see Maps

Rugs - see Carpets

Russian/Soviet Art
Barkes and Barkes, London NW1.
Soviet Carpet & Art Galleries, London NW2.
Hermitage Antiques plc, London SW1.
Jeremy Ltd, London SW1.
Mark Ransom Ltd, London SW1.
The Andipa Gallery, London SW3.
Richardson and Kailas Icons, London SW6.
Antoine Cheneviere Fine Arts, London W1.
Wartski Ltd, London W1.
Temple Gallery, London W11.
The Mark Gallery, London W2.
Mir Russki, Linlithgow, Scotland.

Scientific Instruments
Finchley Fine Art Galleries, London N12.
Victor Burness Antiques and Scientific Instruments, London SE1.
Peter Laurie Antiques, London SE10.
Thomas Mercer (Chronometers) Ltd, London SW1.
Trevor Philip and Sons Ltd, London SW1.
Langford's Marine Antiques, London SW10.
Captain O.M. Watts, London W1.
Peter Delehar, London W11.
Mayflower Antiques, London W11.
Johnny Von Pflugh Antiques, London W11.
Gillian Gould at Ocean Leisure, London WC2.
Arthur Middleton, London WC2.
Christopher Sykes Antiques, Woburn, Beds.
Principia Fine Art, Hungerford, Berks.
Mike Read Antique Sciences, St. Ives, Cornwall.
Branksome Antiques, Branksome, Dorset.
Nautical Antique Centre, Weymouth, Dorset.

The Chart House, Shenfield, Essex.
Chris Grimes Militaria, Bristol, Glos.
Country Life Antiques, Stow-on-the-Wold, Glos.
Barometer Shop, Leominster, Herefs.
Michael Sim, Chislehurst, Kent.
Bernard G. House, Wells, Somerset.
Patrick Marney, Long Melford, Suffolk.
Roy Arnold, Needham Market, Suffolk.
Odin Antiques, Brighton, Sussex East.
Time & Tide Antiques, Portaferry, Co. Down, N. Ireland.

Sculpture

Mike Weedon, London N1.
Duncan R. Miller Fine Arts, London NW3.
No. 28 Antiques, London NW8.
Tara Antiques, London NW8.
Robert E. Hirschhorn, London SE5.
Robert Bowman, London SW1.
Chaucer Fine Arts Ltd, London SW1.
Christopher Gibbs Ltd, London SW1.
Nicholas Gifford-Mead, London SW1.
Hazlitt, Gooden and Fox Ltd, London SW1.
Daniel Katz Ltd, London SW1.
Whitford Fine Art, London SW1.
Jonathan Clark & Co, London SW10.
Ted Few, London SW17.
Joanna Booth, London SW3.
ChelminskiLondon SW6.
Agnew's, London W1.
Adrian Alan Ltd, London W1.
Victor Arwas Gallery - Editions Graphiques Gallery Ltd, London W1.
Browse and Darby Ltd, London W1.
Eskenazi Ltd, London W1.
The Fine Art Society plc, London W1.
The Graham Gallery, London W1.
Patrick Jefferson, London W1.
Messums (Contemporary), London W1.
The Sladmore Gallery of Sculpture, London W1.
Stoppenbach & Delestre Ltd, London W1.
Curá Antiques, London W11.
Hickmet Fine ArtsLondon W11.
Hirst Antiques, London W11.
Milne and Moller, London W11.
Richard Philp, London W11.
Piano Nobile Fine Paintings, London W11.
Wolseley Fine Arts Ltd, London W11.
Quatrefoil, Fordingbridge, Hants.
Lacewing Fine Art Gallery, Winchester, Hants.
Cooper Fine Arts Ltd, Brasted, Kent.
Francis Iles, Rochester, Kent.
Nicholas Bowlby, Tunbridge Wells, Kent.
London House Antiques, Westerham, Kent.
Pearse Lukies, Aylsham, Norfolk.

James Brett, Norwich, Norfolk.
The Barry Keene Gallery, Henley-on-Thames, Oxon.
AnthonyHepworth Fine Art Dealers, Bath, Somerset.
Everett Fine Art Ltd, West Buckland, Somerset.
Piano Nobile Fine Paintings, Richmond, Surrey.
Apollo Antiques Ltd, Warwick, Warks.
Patrick and Gillian Morley Antiques, Warwick, Warks.
Bruton Gallery, Holmfirth, Yorks. West.
Calton Gallery, Edinburgh, Scotland.
The Roger Billcliffe Fine Art, Glasgow, Scotland.
Mainhill Gallery, Jedburgh, Scotland.
Intaglio, Chepstow, Wales.

Shipping Goods & Period
Furniture to the Trade

Regent Antiques, London N1.
Keith Skeel Antiques, London N1.
Madeline Crispin Antiques, London NW1.
Antique Trade Warehouse, London SE1.
Tower Bridge Antiques, London SE1.
The Waterloo Trading Co., London SE10.
Oola Boola Antiques London, London SE26.
Tavistock Antiques, St. Neots, Cambs.
R. Wilding, Wisbech, Cambs.
W. Buckley Antiques Exports, Congleton, Cheshire.
Paul Jennings Antiques, Angarrack, Cornwall.
Ben Eggleston Antiques, Long Marton, Cumbria.
Michael Allcroft Antiques, Newmills, Derbys.
Shardlow Antiques Warehouse, Shardlow, Derbys.
John Prestige Antiques, Brixham, Devon.
Fagins Antiques, Exeter, Devon.
McBains Antiques, Exeter, Devon.
Sandy's Antiques, Bournemouth, Dorset.
Alan Ramsey Antiques, Darlington, Durham.
G.T. Ratcliff Ltd, Kelvedon, Essex.
Bristol Trade Antiques, Bristol, Glos.
Alan Lord Antiques, Folkestone, Kent.
Sutton Valence Antiques, Sutton Valence, Kent.
Charles International Antiques, Wrotham, Kent.
West Lancs. Antique Exports, Burscough, Lancs.
P.J. Brown Antiques, Haslingden, Lancs.
R.J. O'Brien and Son Antiques Ltd, Manchester, Lancs.
G G Exports, Middleton Village, Lancs.
Tyson's Antiques, Morecambe, Lancs.
John Robinson Antiques, Wigan, Lancs.
Boulevard Antique and Shipping Centre, Leicester, Leics.
Trade Antiques, Alford, Lincs.
Antique & Secondhand Traders, Bourne, Lincs.

SPECIALIST DEALERS

Grantham Furniture Emporium, Grantham, Lincs.
C. and K.E. Dring, Lincoln, Lincs.
Bridge Antiques, Sutton Bridge, Lincs.
Old Barn Antiques Warehouse, Sutton Bridge, Lincs.
Swainbanks Ltd, Liverpool, Merseyside.
Molloy's Furnishers Ltd, Southport, Merseyside.
Tony and Anne Sutcliffe Antiques, Southport, Merseyside.
Sheila Hart and John Giles, Aylsham, Norfolk.
Pearse Lukies, Aylsham, Norfolk.
John Roe Antiques, Islip, Northants.
Bryan Perkins Antiques, Wellingborough, Northants.
T. Baker, Langford, Notts.
Fair Deal Antiques, Mansfield, Notts.
Mitre House Antiques, Ludlow, Shrops.
M.G.R. Exports, Bruton, Somerset.
T.M. Dyte Antiques, Highbridge, Somerset.
Asianart.co.uk.Ltd., North Newton, Somerset.
J.C. Giddings, Wiveliscombe, Somerset.
Burton Antiques, Burton-on-Trent, Staffs.
Cordelia and Perdy's Antique Junk Shop, Lichfield, Staffs.
Brett Wilkins Ltd, Lichfield, Staffs.
Goodbreys, Framlingham, Suffolk.
A. Abbott Antiques, Ipswich, Suffolk.
The Edwardian Shop, Ipswich, Suffolk.
Laurence Tauber Antiques, Surbiton, Surrey.
The Old Mint House, Pevensey, Sussex East.
John H. Yorke Antiques, St. Leonards-on-Sea, Sussex East.
Peter Smith Antiques, Sunderland, Tyne and Wear.
Martin Taylor Antiques, Wolverhampton, West Mids.
North Wilts Exporters, Brinkworth, Wilts.
Cross Hayes Antiques, Chippenham, Wilts.
Harley Antiques, Christian Malford, Wilts.
Pillars Antiques, Lyneham, Wilts.
K. and A. Welch, Warminster, Wilts.
Joan and David White, Manfield, Yorks. North.
Tomlinsons, Tockwith, Yorks. North.
Roger Appleyard Ltd, Rotherham, Yorks. South.
Philip Turnor Antiques, Rotherham, Yorks. South.
Dronfield Antiques, Sheffield, Yorks. South.
N.P. and A. Salt Antiques and Barmouth Court Antiques Centre, Sheffield, Yorks. South.
Times Past Antiques, Auchterarder, Scotland.
Imrie Antiques, Bridge of Earn, Scotland.
Neil Livingstone, Dundee, Scotland.
George Duff Antiques, Edinburgh, Scotland.
Georgian Antiques, Edinburgh, Scotland.
Narducci Antiques, Largs, Scotland.
A.S. Deuchar and Son, Perth, Scotland.
Narducci Antiques, Saltcoats, Scotland.

Michael Lloyd Antiques, Llandysul, Wales.
Steven Evans Antiques, Treorchy, Wales.

Silver & Jewellery

George Rankin Coin Co. Ltd, London E2.
Finecraft Workshop Ltd, London EC1.
Jonathan Harris (Jewellery) Ltd, London EC1.
Hirsh Ltd, London EC1.
Joseph and Pearce Ltd, London EC1.
A.R. Ullmann Ltd, London EC1.
D. Horton, London EC2.
Nanwani and Co, London EC3.
Searle and Co Ltd, London EC3.
Eclectica, London N1.
Rosemary Hart, London N1.
John Laurie (Antiques) Ltd, London N1.
Sugar Antiques, London N1.
M. Tisdall Antiques, London N1.
Creek Antiques, London SE10.
Vale Stamps and Antiques, London SE3.
A.D.C. Heritage Ltd, London SW1.
N. Bloom & Son (1912) Ltd, London SW1.
J.H. Bourdon-Smith Ltd, London SW1.
Cornucopia, London SW1.
Kenneth Davis (Works of Art) Ltd, London SW1.
Alastair Dickenson Fine Silver Ltd, London SW1.
N. and I. Franklin, London SW1.
Harvey and Gore, London SW1.
Kojis Antique Jewellery Ltd, London SW1.
Longmire Ltd (Three Royal Warrants), London SW1.
Nigel Milne Ltd, London SW1.
thesilverfund.com, London SW1.
Mary Cooke Antiques Ltd, London SW14.
James Hardy and Co, London SW3.
McKenna and Co, London SW3.
Christine Schell, London SW3.
Gordon Watson Ltd, London SW3.
M.P. Levene Ltd, London SW7.
A. & H. Page (Est. 1840), London SW7.
Fay Lucas Artmetal, London SW8.
Armour-Winston Ltd, London W1.
Victor Arwas Gallery - Editions Graphiques Gallery Ltd, London W1.
Asprey & Garrard Ltd, London W1.
Paul Bennett, London W1.
Bentley & Skinner Ltd, London W1.
Daniel Bexfield Antiques, London W1.
Bond Street Silver Galleries, London W1.
John Bull (Antiques) Ltd JB Silverware, London W1.
Carrington and Co. Ltd, London W1.
Sandra Cronan Ltd, London W1.
A. B. Davis Ltd, London W1.
Simon Griffin Antiques Ltd, London W1.

Hancocks and Co, London W1.

Holmes Ltd, London W1.

Johnson Walker & Tolhurst Ltd, London W1.

D.S. Lavender (Antiques) Ltd, London W1.

Marks Antiques, London W1.

Moira, London W1.

Richard Ogden Ltd, London W1.

S.J. Phillips Ltd, London W1.

David Richards and Sons, London W1.

Michael Rose - Source of the Unusual, London W1.

Tessiers Ltd, London W1.

Wartski Ltd, London W1.

Central Gallery (Portobello), London W11.

The Coach House, London W11.

Kleanthous Antiques, London W11.

Portobello Antique Store, London W11.

Schredds of Portobello, London W11.

The Silver Fox Gallery (Portobello), London W11.

Colin Smith and Gerald Robinson Antiques, London W11.

Craven Gallery, London W2.

M. McAleer, London W2.

H. and W. Deutsch Antiques, London W8.

Green's Antique Galleries, London W8.

John Jesse, London W8.

Howard Jones - The Silver Shop, London W8.

Lev (Antiques) Ltd, London W8.

Nortonbury Antiques, London WC1.

Thomas Kettle Ltd, London WC2.

Koopman Ltd & Rare Art (London) LtdLondon WC2.

The London Silver Vaults, London WC2.

The Silver Mouse Trap, London WC2.

Styles Silver, Hungerford, Berks.

Berkshire Antiques Co Ltd, Windsor and Eton, Berks.

Turks Head Antiques, Windsor and Eton, Berks.

Buckies, Cambridge, Cambs.

D.J. Massey and Son, Alderley Edge, Cheshire.

Cameo Antiques, Chester, Cheshire.

Kayes of Chester, Chester, Cheshire.

Lowe and Sons, Chester, Cheshire.

Watergate Antiques, Chester, Cheshire.

D.J. Massey and Son, Macclesfield, Cheshire.

Imperial Antiques, Stockport, Cheshire.

Little Jem's, Penzance, Cornwall.

Alan Bennett, Truro, Cornwall.

Saint Nicholas Galleries Ltd. (Antiques and Jewellery), Carlisle, Cumbria.

Elizabeth and Son, Ulverston, Cumbria.

Mark Parkhouse Antiques and Jewellery, Barnstaple, Devon.

Timothy Coward Fine Silver, Braunton, Devon.

David J. Thorn, Budleigh Salterton, Devon.

Gold and Silver Exchange, Exeter, Devon.

Mortimers, Exeter, Devon.

John Nathan Antiques, Exeter, Devon.

Boase Antiques, Exmouth, Devon.

Otter Antiques, Honiton, Devon.

Extence Antiques, Teignmouth, Devon.

G.B. Mussenden and Son Antiques, Jewellery and Silver, Bournemouth, Dorset.

Geo. A. Payne and Son Ltd, Bournemouth, Dorset.

R.E. Porter, Bournemouth, Dorset.

Portique, Bournemouth, Dorset.

Tregoning Antiques, Bournemouth, Dorset.

Batten's Jewellers, Bridport, Dorset.

Greystoke Antiques, Sherborne, Dorset.

Henry Willis (Antique Silver), Sherborne, Dorset.

Georgian Gems Antique Jewellers, Swanage, Dorset.

Heirlooms Antique Jewellers and Silversmiths, Wareham, Dorset.

James Hardy Antiques Ltd, Barnard Castle, Durham.

Robson's Antiques, Barnard Castle, Durham.

Robin Finnegan (Jeweller), Darlington, Durham.

Argentum Antiques, Coggeshall, Essex.

Elizabeth Cannon Antiques, Colchester, Essex.

Grahams of Colchester, Colchester, Essex.

E J Markham & Son Ltd, Colchester, Essex.

J. Streamer Antiques, Leigh-on-Sea, Essex.

Harris Antiques (Stansted), Stansted, Essex.

Whichcraft Jewellery, Writtle, Essex.

Peter and Penny Proudfoot, Berkeley, Glos.

Cotham Antiques, Bristol, Glos.

Grey-Harris and Co, Bristol, Glos.

Kemps, Bristol, Glos.

Jan Morrison, Bristol, Glos.

Greens of Cheltenham Ltd, Cheltenham, Glos.

Martin and Co. Ltd, Cheltenham, Glos.

Scott-Cooper Ltd, Cheltenham, Glos.

Ross Hardie, Chipping Campden, Glos.

Sodbury Antiques, Chipping Sodbury,, Glos.

Walter Bull and Son (Cirencester) Ltd, Cirencester, Glos.

Rankine Taylor Antiques, Cirencester, Glos.

Squirrel Collectors Centre, Basingstoke, Hants.

A.W. Porter and Son, Hartley Wintney, Hants.

Barry Papworth, Lymington, Hants.

Meg Campbell, Southampton, Hants.

Warings of Hereford, Hereford, Herefs.

Abbey Antiques - Fine Jewellery & Silver, Hemel Hempstead, Herts.

Forget-me-Knot Antiques, St. Albans, Herts.

Christopher Wharton Goldsmiths, St. Albans, Herts.

J. and H. Bell Antiques, Castletown, Isle of Man.

R. J. Baker, Canterbury, Kent.

SPECIALIST DEALERS

Owlets, Hythe, Kent.

Gem Antiques, Maidstone, Kent.

Kaizen International Ltd, Rochester, Kent.

Gem Antiques, Sevenoaks, Kent.

Steppes Hill Farm Antiques, Stockbury, Kent.

Chapel Place Antiques, Tunbridge Wells, Kent.

Glassdrumman Antiques, Tunbridge Wells, Kent.

Kent & Sussex Gold Refiners, Tunbridge Wells, Kent.

Pantiles Spa Antiques, Tunbridge Wells, Kent.

The Coin and Jewellery Shop, Accrington, Lancs.

Ancient and Modern, Blackburn, Lancs.

Mitchell's Antiques, Blackburn, Lancs.

Chard Coins, Blackpool, Lancs.

Brittons - Watches and Antiques, Clitheroe, Lancs.

Leigh Jewellery, Leigh, Lancs.

Cathedral Jewellers, Manchester, Lancs.

St. James Antiques, Manchester, Lancs.

Charles Howell Jeweller, Oldham, Lancs.

H.C. Simpson and Sons Jewellers (Oldham)Ltd, Oldham, Lancs.

Priory Collectables, Preston, Lancs.

Keystone Antiques, Coalville, Leics.

Corry's, Leicester, Leics.

Letty's Antiques, Leicester, Leics.

Stanley Hunt Jewellers, Gainsborough, Lincs.

MarcusWilkinson, Grantham, Lincs.

Rowletts of Lincoln, Lincoln, Lincs.

James Usher and Son Ltd, Lincoln, Lincs.

MarcusWilkinson, Sleaford, Lincs.

Dawson of Stamford Ltd, Stamford, Lincs.

C. Rosenberg, Heswall, Merseyside.

Kevin Whay's Clocks & Antiques, Hoylake, Merseyside.

Boodle and Dunthorne Ltd, Liverpool, Merseyside.

Edward's Jewellers, Liverpool, Merseyside.

Stefani Antiques, Liverpool, Merseyside.

Weldons Jewellery and Antiques, Southport, Merseyside.

Bond Street Antiques, Cromer, Norfolk.

Barry's Antiques, Gt. Yarmouth, Norfolk.

Folkes Antiques and Jewellers, Gt. Yarmouth, Norfolk.

Wheatleys, Gt. Yarmouth, Norfolk.

Tim Clayton Jewellery & Antiques, King's Lynn, Norfolk.

Albrow and Sons Family Jewellers, Norwich, Norfolk.

Clive Dennett Coins, Norwich, Norfolk.

Leona Levine Silver Specialist, Norwich, Norfolk.

Maddermarket Antiques, Norwich, Norfolk.

Oswald Sebley, Norwich, Norfolk.

Tombland Jewellers & Silversmiths, Norwich, Norfolk.

Parriss, Sheringham, Norfolk.

Michael Jones Jeweller, Northampton, Northants.

Boadens Antiques, Hexham, Northumbs.

Melville Kemp Ltd, Nottingham, Notts.

Stanley Hunt Jewellers, Retford, Notts.

Barclay Antiques, Headington, Oxon.

Reginald Davis Ltd, Oxford, Oxon.

Payne and Son (Goldsmiths) Ltd, Oxford, Oxon.

MGJ Jewellers Ltd., Wallingford, Oxon.

Churchgate Antiques, Empingham, Rutland.

English Heritage, Bridgnorth, Shrops.

Teme Valley Antiques, Ludlow, Shrops.

Hutton Antiques, Shrewsbury, Shrops.

The Little Gem, Shrewsbury, Shrops.

Abbey Galleries, Bath, Somerset.

D. and B. Dickinson, Bath, Somerset.

E.P. Mallory and Son Ltd, Bath, Somerset.

Castle Antiques, Burnham-on-Sea, Somerset.

Beach Antiques, Clevedon, Somerset.

M.G. Welch Jeweller, Taunton, Somerset.

Winston Mac (Silversmith), Bury St. Edmunds, Suffolk.

A. Abbott Antiques, Ipswich, Suffolk.

Temptations, Ashtead, Surrey.

Scotts of Dorking, Dorking, Surrey.

Temptations, Antique Jewellery &Silver, Dorking, Surrey.

Cry for the Moon, Guildford, Surrey.

Glydon and Guess Ltd, Kingston-upon-Thames, Surrey.

Horton, Richmond, Surrey.

Lionel Jacobs, Richmond, Surrey.

S. Warrender and Co, Sutton, Surrey.

Church House Antiques, Weybridge, Surrey.

Not Just Silver, Weybridge, Surrey.

Harry Diamond and Son, Brighton, Sussex East.

James Doyle Antiques, Brighton, Sussex East.

Paul Goble Jewellers, Brighton, Sussex East.

Douglas Hall Ltd, Brighton, Sussex East.

Hallmark Jewellers, Brighton, Sussex East.

Harry Mason, Brighton, Sussex East.

S.L. Simmons, Brighton, Sussex East.

W. Bruford, Eastbourne, Sussex East.

Trade Wind, Rottingdean, Sussex East.

Aarquebus Antiques, St. Leonards-on-Sea, Sussex East.

Nicholas Shaw Antiques, Billingshurst, Sussex West.

Peter Hancock Antiques, Chichester, Sussex West.

Rathbone Law, Chichester, Sussex West.

Sovereign Antiques, Gateshead, Tyne and Wear.

Davidson's The Jewellers Ltd, Newcastle-upon-Tyne, Tyne and Wear.

Intercoin, Newcastle-upon-Tyne, Tyne and Wear.

Coleshill Antiques and Interiors Ltd, Coleshill, Warks.

Howards Jewellers, Stratford-upon-Avon, Warks.

Russell Lane Antiques, Warwick, Warks.

Peter Clark Antiques, Birmingham, West Mids.

Maurice Fellows, Birmingham, West Mids.

Rex Johnson and Sons, Birmingham, West Mids.

Piccadilly Jewellers, Birmingham, West Mids.

H. and R.L. Parry Ltd, Sutton Coldfield, West Mids.

Hardwick Antiques, Walsall, West Mids.

Cross Keys Jewellers, Devizes, Wilts.

Howards of Broadway, Broadway, Worcs.

Magpie Jewellers and Antiques and Magpie Arms & Armour, Evesham, Worcs.

B.B.M. Jewellery and Antiques, Kidderminster, Worcs.

Lower House Fine Antiques, Redditch, Worcs.

Bygones by the Cathedral, Worcester, Worcs.

Karen Guest Antiques, Beverley, Yorks. East.

Karen Guest Antiques, Driffield, Yorks. East.

Lesley Berry Antiques, Flamborough, Yorks. East.

Ogden of Harrogate Ltd, Harrogate, Yorks. North.

Mary Milnthorpe and Daughters Antique Shop, Settle, Yorks. North.

Barbara Cattle, York, Yorks. North.

Golden Memories of York, York, Yorks. North.

Geoff Neary (incorporating Fillans Antiques Ltd), Huddersfield, Yorks. West.

Jack Shaw and Co, Ilkley, Yorks. West.

Aladdin's Cave, Leeds, Yorks. West.

N. St. JPaint & Sons Ltd, St Peter Port, Guernsey, C.I.

A. & R. Ritchie, St. Helier, Jersey, C.I.

Roberts Antiques, St Helier, Jersey, C.I.

The Country Antiques, Antrim, Co. Antrim, N. Ireland.

Dunluce Antiques, Bushmills, Co. Antrim, N. Ireland.

Brian R. Bolt Antiques, Portballintrae, Co. Antrim, N. Ireland.

Cookstown Antiques, Cookstown, Co. Tyrone, N. Ireland.

McCalls (Aberdeen), Aberdeen, Scotland.

McCalls Limited, Aberdeen, Scotland.

Joseph Bonnar, Jewellers, Edinburgh, Scotland.

Goodwin's Antiques Ltd, Edinburgh, Scotland.

Montresor, Edinburgh, Scotland.

Royal Mile Curios, Edinburgh, Scotland.

John Whyte, Edinburgh, Scotland.

West End Antiques, Elgin, Scotland.

A.D. Hamilton and Co, Glasgow, Scotland.

Jeremy Sniders Antiques, Glasgow, Scotland.

Tim Wright Antiques, Glasgow, Scotland.

Michael Young Antiques at Glencarse, Glencarse, Scotland.

Kilmacolm Antiques Ltd, Kilmacolm, Scotland.

Mir Russki, Linlithgow, Scotland.

Harper-James, Montrose, Scotland.

Moray Antiques, Nairn, Scotland.

Hardie Antiques, Perth, Scotland.

Old St. Andrews Gallery, St. Andrews, Scotland.

Abbey Antiques, Stirling, Scotland.

Hazel of Brecon, Brecon, Wales.

Silvertime, Brecon, Wales.

Audrey Bull, Carmarthen, Wales.

Gold and Silver Shop, Gorseinon, Wales.

Cartrefle Antiques, Mathry, Wales.

James Allan, Swansea, Wales.

Audrey Bull, Tenby, Wales.

Sporting Items & Memorabilia

Holland & Holland, London W1.

Sean Arnold Sporting Antiques, London W2.

Below Stairs of Hungerford, Hungerford, Berks.

Sir William Bentley Billiards (Antique Billiard Table Specialist Company), Hungerford, Berks.

Beer Collectables, Beer, Devon.

Yesterday Tackle and Books, Bournemouth, Dorset.

John Burton Natural Craft Taxidermy, Ebrington, Glos.

Hamilton Billiards & Games Co., Knebworth, Herts.

The Spinning Wheel Antiques, Southport, Merseyside.

Manfred Schotten Antiques, Burford, Oxon.

Billiard Room Antiques, Chilcompton, Somerset.

Academy Billiard Company, West Byfleet, Surrey.

Burman Antiques, Stratford-upon-Avon, Warks.

Grant Books, Droitwich, Worcs.

Dunkeld Antiques, Dunkeld, Scotland.

Old St. Andrews Gallery, St. Andrews, Scotland.

Old Troon Sporting Antiques, Troon, Scotland.

Sporting Paintings & Prints

Swan Fine Art, London N1.

Ackermann & Johnson, London SW1.

Frost and Reed Ltd (Est. 1808), London SW1.

Paul Mason Gallery, London SW1.

Tryon Gallery (incorporating Malcolm Innes), London SW1.

Old Church Galleries, London SW3.

Richard Green, London W1.

Holland & Holland, London W1.

The O'Shea Gallery, London W1.

Frank T. Sabin Ltd, London W1.

Connaught Galleries, London W2.

Iona Antiques, London W8.

Grosvenor Prints, London WC2.
Coltsfoot Gallery, Leominster, Herefs.
G. and D.I. Marrin and Sons, Folkestone, Kent.
Leicestershire Sporting Gallery and Brown Jack Bookshop, Lubenham, Leics.
Paul Hopwell Antiques, West Haddon, Northants.
Sally Mitchell's Gallery, Tuxford, Notts.
H.C. Dickins, Bloxham, Oxon.
Julian Armytage, Crewkerne, Somerset.
Vandeleur Antiquarian Books, Epsom, Surrey.
Julia Holmes Antique Maps and Prints, South Harting, Sussex West.
Burman Antiques, Stratford-upon-Avon, Warks.
Anthony Woodd Gallery, Edinburgh, Scotland.

Stamps

Argyll Etkin Gallery, London W1.
Michael Coins, London W8.
Stanley Gibbons, London WC2.
Avalon Post Card and Stamp Shop, Chester, Cheshire.
Penrith Coin and Stamp Centre, Penrith, Cumbria.
Jeremy's (Oxford Stamp Centre), Oxford, Oxon.
Bath Stamp and Coin Shop, Bath, Somerset.
J. Smith, York, Yorks. North.
Edinburgh Coin Shop, Edinburgh, Scotland.
Glance Back Bookshop, Chepstow, Wales.

Tapestries, Textiles & Needlework

The Textile Company, London N1.
Alexander Juran and Co, London N4.
Joseph Lavian, London N4.
Robert Franses and Sons, London NW8.
Gallery of Antique Costume and Textiles, London NW8.
Coats Oriental Carpets, London SE5.
S. Franses Ltd, London SW1.
Joss Graham, London SW1.
Keshishian, London SW1.
Peta Smyth - Antique Textiles, London SW1.
Iftikhar Bokhari, London SW10.
The Kilim Warehouse Ltd, London SW12.
The Dining Room Shop, London SW13.
Tobias and The Angel, London SW13.
Joanna Booth, London SW3.
Classic Fabrics with Robin Haydock, London SW3.
Orientalist, London SW3.
Robert Stephenson, London SW3.
Antiques and Things, London SW4.
Perez Antique Carpets Gallery, London SW6.
Atlantic Bay Carpets Gallery, London SW7.
Heskia, London SW8.
John Eskenazi Ltd, London W1.
C. John (Rare Rugs) Ltd, London W1.

Pelham Galleries Ltd, London W1.
Linda Wrigglesworth Ltd, London W1.
A. Zadah, London W1.
Sheila Cook, London W11.
Jonathan Horne, London W8.
Storm Fine Arts Ltd, Great Shelford, Cambs.
Martin and Dorothy Harper Antiques, Bakewell, Derbys.
The House that Moved, Exeter, Devon.
The Honiton Lace Shop, Honiton, Devon.
Georgina Ryder, Frampton, Dorset.
Robson's Antiques, Barnard Castle, Durham.
Maureen Morris, Saffron Walden, Essex.
Catherine Shinn Decorative Textiles, Cheltenham, Glos.
Anthony Hazledine, Fairford, Glos.
Huntington Antiques Ltd, Stow-on-the-Wold, Glos.
Meg Andrews, Harpenden, Herts.
Farmhouse Antiques, Bolton-by-Bowland, Lancs.
Rebecca Calvert Antiques, Lincoln, Lincs.
Country and Eastern Ltd., Norwich, Norfolk.
Witney Antiques, Witney, Oxon.
Clutter, Uppingham, Rutland.
Antique Linens and Lace, Bath, Somerset.
Antique Textiles & Lighting, Bath, Somerset.
Ann King, Bath, Somerset.
Susannah, Bath, Somerset.
Winder's Fine Art and Antiques, Newcastle-under-Lyme, Staffs.
Sarah Meysey-Thompson Antiques, Woodbridge, Suffolk.
Patrick and Gillian Morley Antiques, Warwick, Warks.
Avon Antiques, Bradford-on-Avon, Wilts.
Penny Farthing Antiques, North Cave, Yorks. East.
London House Oriental Rugs and Carpets, Boston Spa, Yorks. West.
Clock House Antiques, Keighley, Yorks. West.
Echoes, Todmorden, Yorks. West.
Hand in Hand, Coldstream, Scotland.
Gladrags, Edinburgh, Scotland.
Hart Antiques and Interiors, Bridgend, Wales.

Taxidermy

Get Stuffed, London N1.
Below Stairs of Hungerford, Hungerford, Berks.
Yesterday Tackle and Books, Bournemouth, Dorset.
John Burton Natural Craft Taxidermy, Ebrington, Glos.
Heads 'n' Tails, Wiveliscombe, Somerset.
The Enchanted Aviary, Bury St. Edmunds, Suffolk.
Hawkins & Hawkins, Edinburgh, Scotland.

Tools - including Needlework & Sewing

Norton Antiques, Twyford, Norfolk.
Ark Antiques, Bishop's Castle, Shrops.
Peppers Period Pieces, Bury St. Edmunds, Suffolk.
Trinders' Fine Tools, Clare, Suffolk.
Roy Arnold, Needham Market, Suffolk.
The Tool Shop, Needham Market, Suffolk.

Toys - see Dolls

Trade Dealers - see Shipping Goods

Treen

Eldridge London, London EC1.
Halcyon Days, London EC3.
Robert Young Antiques, London SW11.
Halcyon Days, London W1.
Phoenix Antiques, Fordham, Cambs.
A.P. and M.A. Haylett, Outwell, Cambs.
Baggott Church Street Ltd, Stow-on-the-Wold,
    Glos.
Huntington Antiques Ltd, Stow-on-the-Wold,
    Glos.
Peter Norden Antiques, Tetbury, Glos.
Prichard Antiques, Winchcombe, Glos.
Millers of Chelsea Antiques Ltd, Ringwood,
    Hants.
Mark Seabrook Antiques, West Haddon,
    Northants.
Brian and Caroline Craik Ltd, Bath, Somerset.
Peppers Period Pieces, Bury St. Edmunds, Suffolk.
J. Du Cros Antiques, Petworth, Sussex West.
Moxhams Antiques, Bradford-on-Avon, Wilts.
Annmarie Turner Antiques, Marlborough, Wilts.
Fenwick and Fenwick Antiques, Broadway, Worcs.
Michael Green Pine & Country Antiques,
    Harrogate, Yorks. North.
Brian R. Bolt Antiques, Portballintrae, Co. Antrim,
    N. Ireland.
Islwyn Watkins, Knighton, Wales.

Vintage Cars - see Cars and Carriages

Watercolours

Gladwell and Company, London EC4.
Finchley Fine Art Galleries, London N12.
Lauri Stewart - Fine Art, London N2.
The Totteridge Gallery, London N20.
Barkes and Barkes, London NW1.
Angela Hone Watercolours, London NW1.
Newhart (Pictures) Ltd, London NW3.
Gallery Kaleidoscope incorporating Scope,
    London NW6.
The Greenwich Gallery, London SE10.
Ackermann & Johnson, London SW1.

Chris Beetles Ltd, London SW1.
Miles Wynn Cato, London SW1.
Douwes Fine Art Ltd, London SW1.
Frost and Reed Ltd (Est. 1808), London SW1.
Martyn Gregory Gallery, London SW1.
Messums, London SW1.
Moreton Street Gallery, London SW1.
Old Maps and Prints, London SW1.
Paisnel Gallery, London SW1.
Michael Parkin Fine Art Ltd, London SW1.
Bill Thomson - Albany Gallery, London SW1.
Waterman Fine Art Ltd, London SW1.
Langton Street Gallery, London SW10.
Park Walk Gallery, London SW10.
Regent House Gallery, London SW11.
John Spink, London SW13.
The David Curzon Gallery, London SW19.
Campbell's of Walton Street, London SW3.
Gallery Lingard, London SW3.
Stephanie Hoppen Ltd, London SW3.
20th Century Gallery, London SW6.
Julie Collino, London SW7.
Agnew's, London W1.
Victor Arwas Gallery - Editions Graphiques
    Gallery Ltd, London W1.
Andrew Clayton-Payne Ltd, London W1.
Connaught Brown plc, London W1.
Dover Street Gallery, London W1.
The Fine Art Society plc, London W1.
Maas Gallery, London W1.
Mallett and Son (Antiques) Ltd, London W1.
Mallett Gallery, London W1.
John Mitchell and Son, London W1.
Piccadilly Gallery, London W1.
Royal Exchange Art Gallery at Cork St., London
    W1.
Stephen Somerville (W.A.) Ltd, London W1.
Spink Leger Pictures, London W1.
Waterhouse and Dodd, London W1.
Crawley and Asquith Ltd, London W10.
Charles Daggett Gallery, London W11.
Milne and Moller, London W11.
Justin F. Skrebowski Prints, London W11.
Ealing Gallery, London W5.
Pawsey and Payne, London W8.
Simon Spero, London W8.
Beryl Kendall, The English Watercolour Gallery,
    London W9.
Abbott and Holder, London WC1.
Sebastian D'Orsai Ltd, London WC1.
Michael Finney Antique Prints and Books, London
    WC1.
Baroq & David Ball Antiques, Leighton Buzzard,
    Beds.
Foye Gallery, Luton, Beds.

SPECIALIST DEALERS

Graham Gallery, Burghfield Common, Berks.
J. Manley, Windsor and Eton, Berks.
Grosvenor House Interiors, Beaconsfield, Bucks.
Windmill Fine Art, High Wycombe, Bucks.
Penn Barn, Penn, Bucks.
Cambridge Fine Art Ltd, Cambridge, Cambs.
Sebastian Pearson Paintings Prints and Works of
    Art, Cambridge, Cambs.
Storm Fine Arts Ltd, Great Shelford, Cambs.
Baron Fine Art, Chester, Cheshire.
Harper Fine Paintings, Poynton, Cheshire.
Copperhouse Gallery - W. Dyer & Sons, Hayle,
    Cornwall.
Tony Sanders Penzance Gallery and Antiques,
    Penzance, Cornwall.
St. Breock Gallery, Wadebridge, Cornwall.
Peter Haworth, Beetham, Cumbria.
The Gallery, Penrith, Cumbria.
Kenneth Upchurch, Ashbourne, Derbys.
J. Collins and Son, Bideford, Devon.
Cooper Gallery, Bideford, Devon.
Medina Gallery, Bideford, Devon.
Godolphin Antiques, Chagford, Devon.
Chantry Bookshop and Gallery, Dartmouth,
    Devon.
Mill Gallery, Ermington, Devon.
Honiton Fine Art, Honiton, Devon.
Skeaping Gallery, Lydford, Devon.
Michael Wood Fine Art, Plymouth, Devon.
Hampshire Gallery, Bournemouth, Dorset.
The Swan Gallery, Sherborne, Dorset.
Margaret Bedi Antiques & Fine Art, Billingham,
    Durham.
T.B. and R. Jordan (Fine Paintings), Stockton-on-
    Tees, Durham.
Brandler Galleries, Brentwood, Essex.
Neil Graham Gallery, Brentwood, Essex.
S. Bond and Son, Colchester, Essex.
Newport Gallery, Newport, Essex.
Barling Fine Porcelain Ltd, Wickham Bishops,
    Essex.
Galerie Lev, Woodford Green, Essex.
Cleeve Picture Framing, Bishops Cleeve, Glos.
The Priory Gallery, Bishops Cleeve, Glos.
Alexander Gallery, Bristol, Glos.
The Loquens Gallery, Cheltenham, Glos.
Manor House Gallery, Cheltenham, Glos.
School House Antiques, Chipping Campden, Glos.
The Titian Gallery, Chipping Campden, Glos.
Astley House - Fine Art, Moreton-in-Marsh, Glos.
Nina Zborowska, Painswick, Glos.
The Fosse Gallery, Stow-on-the-Wold, Glos.
Kenulf Fine Arts, Stow-on-the-Wold, Glos.
Roger Lamb Antiques & Works of Art, Stow-on-
    the-Wold, Glos.

Styles of Stow, Stow-on-the-Wold, Glos.
Tetbury Gallery, Tetbury, Glos.
Laurence Oxley, Alresford, Hants.
Antique House, Hartley Wintney, Hants.
J. Morton Lee, Hayling Island, Hants.
Century Fine Arts, Lymington, Hants.
The Petersfield Bookshop, Petersfield, Hants.
The Wykeham Gallery, Stockbridge, Hants.
Bell Fine Art, Winchester, Hants.
Lacewing Fine Art Gallery, Winchester, Hants.
Coltsfoot Gallery, Leominster, Herefs.
Linden House Antiques, Leominster, Herefs.
The Shanklin Gallery, Shanklin, Isle of Wight.
FCooper Fine Arts Ltd, Brasted, Kent.
Cranbrook Gallery, Cranbrook, Kent.
Francis Iles, Rochester, Kent.
Langley Galleries, Rochester, Kent.
Judith Peppitt, Snargate, Kent.
Sundridge Gallery, Sundridge, Kent.
Nicholas Bowlby, Tunbridge Wells, Kent.
Redleaf Gallery, Tunbridge Wells, Kent.
Apollo Antique Galleries, Westerham, Kent.
Old Corner House Antiques, Wittersham, Kent.
Fulda Gallery Ltd, Manchester, Lancs.
Hammond Smith (Fine Art), Leicester, Leics.
P. Stanworth (Fine Arts), Market Bosworth, Leics.
Graftons of Market Harborough, Market
    Harborough, Leics.
The Boydell Galleries, Liverpool, Merseyside.
Crome Gallery and Frame Shop, Norwich,
    Norfolk.
The Fairhurst Gallery, Norwich, Norfolk.
Mandell's Gallery, Norwich, Norfolk.
The Westcliffe Gallery, Sheringham, Norfolk.
Staithe Lodge Gallery, Swafield, Norfolk.
Norton Antiques, Twyford, Norfolk.
Coughton Galleries Ltd, Arthingworth, Northants.
Right Angle, Brackley, Northants.
Dragon Antiques, Kettering, Northants.
Anthony Mitchell Fine Paintings, Nottingham,
    Notts.
John Harrison Fine Art, Aston Tirrold, Oxon.
H.C. Dickins, Bloxham, Oxon.
The Burford Gallery, Burford, Oxon.
Horseshoe Antiques and Gallery, Burford, Oxon.
The Stone Gallery, Burford, Oxon.
Wren Gallery, Burford, Oxon.
The Barry Keene Gallery, Henley-on-Thames,
    Oxon.
Fine Art of Oakham, Oakham, Rutland.
The Old House Gallery, Oakham, Rutland.
Marc Oxley Fine Art, Uppingham, Rutland.
John Boulton Fine Art, Broseley, Shrops.
Teme Valley Antiques, Ludlow, Shrops.
The Mount, Woore, Shrops.

Adam Gallery, Bath, Somerset.
Trimbridge Galleries, Bath, Somerset.
The Court Gallery, Nether Stowey, Somerset.
Sadler Street Gallery, Wells, Somerset.
England's Gallery, Leek, Staffs.
Thompson's Gallery, Aldeburgh, Suffolk.
J. and J. Baker, Lavenham, Suffolk.
Peasenhall Art and Antiques Gallery, Peasenhall, Suffolk.
The Falcon Gallery, Wortham, Suffolk.
Cobham Galleries, Cobham, Surrey.
Hampton Court Palace Antiques, East Molesey, Surrey.
Glencorse Antiques, Kingston-upon-Thames, Surrey.
Limpsfield Watercolours, Limpsfield, Surrey.
Bourne Gallery Ltd, Reigate, Surrey.
The Gallery, Reigate, Surrey.
Roland Goslett Gallery, Richmond, Surrey.
Marryat, Richmond, Surrey.
Palmer Galleries, Richmond, Surrey.
Cedar House Gallery, Ripley, Surrey.
Sage Antiques and Interiors, Ripley, Surrey.
John Day of Eastbourne Fine Art, Eastbourne, Sussex East.
Faringdon Gallery, Arundel, Sussex West.
Lannards Gallery, Billingshurst, Sussex West.
Chichester Gallery, Chichester, Sussex West.
The Canon Gallery, Petworth, Sussex West.
Wilsons Antiques, Worthing, Sussex West.
Anna Harrison Fine Antiques, Gosforth, Tyne and Wear.
MacDonald Fine Art, Gosforth, Tyne and Wear.
Osborne Fine Art Gallery, Jesmond, Tyne and Wear.
Arden Gallery, Henley-in-Arden, Warks.
Colmore Galleries Ltd, Henley-in-Arden, Warks.
Fine-Lines (Fine Art), Shipston-on-Stour, Warks.
The Loquens Gallery, Stratford-upon-Avon, Warks.
The Windmill Gallery, Birmingham, West Mids.
Oldswinford Gallery, Stourbridge, West Mids.
Driffold Gallery, Sutton Coldfield, West Mids.
Audley House Antiques, Bradford-on-Avon, Wilts.
Richard Hagen, Broadway, Worcs.
Haynes Fine Art of Broadway, Broadway, Worcs.
John Noott Galleries, Broadway, Worcs.
The Highway Gallery, Upton-upon-Severn, Worcs.
James H. Starkey Galleries, Beverley, Yorks. East.

W. Greenwood (Fine Art), Burneston, Yorks. North.
Garth Antiques, Harrogate, Yorks. North.
McTague of Harrogate, Harrogate, Yorks. North.
Walker Galleries Ltd, Harrogate, Yorks. North.
E. Stacy-Marks Limited, Helmsley, Yorks. North.
Talents Fine Arts Ltd, Malton, Yorks. North.
Rose Fine Art and Antiques, Stillington, Yorks. North.
Kirkgate Fine Art & Conservation, Thirsk, Yorks. North.
Garth Antiques, Whixley, Yorks. North.
Coulter Galleries, York, Yorks. North.
Huddersfield Picture Framing Co., Huddersfield, Yorks. West.
Robin Taylor Fine Arts, Wakefield, Yorks. West.
Beverley J. Pyke - Fine British Watercolours, Alderney, C.I.
C.I Galleries Ltd, St. Peter Port, Guernsey, C.I.
alle Fine Art Limited, St Helier, Jersey, C.I.
The Bell Gallery, Belfast, N. Ireland.
Phyllis Arnold Gallery Antiques, Greyabbey, Co. Down, N. Ireland.
The Rendezvous Gallery, Aberdeen, Scotland.
Nigel Stacy-Marks Ltd, Auchterarder, Scotland.
The McEwan Gallery, Ballater, Scotland.
Calton Gallery, Edinburgh, Scotland.
John Mathieson and Co, Edinburgh, Scotland.
Anthony Woodd Gallery, Edinburgh, Scotland.
Young Antiques, Edinburgh, Scotland.
The Roger Billcliffe Fine Art, Glasgow, Scotland.
Ewan Mundy Fine Art Ltd, Glasgow, Scotland.
Glendoick Antiques, Glendoick, Scotland.
Inchmartine Fine Art, Inchture, Scotland.
Mainhill Gallery, Jedburgh, Scotland.
Newburgh Antiques, Newburgh, Scotland.
Kirk Ports Gallery, North Berwick, Scotland.
Nigel Stacy-Marks Ltd, Perth, Scotland.
St. Andrews Fine Art, St. Andrews, Scotland.
David Windsor Gallery, Bangor, Wales.
Michael Webb Fine Art, Llangristiolus (Anglesey), Wales.

Wholesale Dealers - see Shipping Goods

Wine Related Items
Christopher Sykes Antiques, Woburn, Beds.
Neil Willcox & Mark Nightingale, Penryn, Cornwall.
Robin Butler, Clare, Suffolk.
Bacchus Gallery, Petworth, Sussex West.

Dealers' Index

In order to facilitate reference both the names of individuals and their business name are indexed separately. Thus A E Jones and C Smith of High Street Antiques will be indexed under:

Jones, A E, Town, County.
Smith, C, Town, County.
High Street Antiques, Town, County.

A

& Barrington, Castle Gate Antiques Centre, Newark, Notts.
(55) For Decorative Living, London SW6.
20th Century Gallery, London SW6.
20th Century, Cambridge, Cambs.
225 Jewellery Exchange, Antiquarius, London SW3.
275 Antiques, London SW6.
291 Antiques, London SW6.
313 Antiques, London SW6.
A & T, Grays Antique Markets, London W1.
A Barn Full of Brass Beds, Conisholme, Lincs.
A J Antiques, Bath, Somerset.
A. & H. Antiques, Welshpool, Wales.
A. M. W. Silverware, London Silver Vaults, London WC2.
A.D.C. Heritage Ltd, London SW1.
A.S. Antique Galleries, Manchester, Lancs.
A1A Antiques, Ulverston, Cumbria.
Aagaard & Co, Robert, Knaresborough, Yorks. North.
Aaron (London)Ltd, Didier, London SW1.
Aaron Ancient Arts & Rare Carpets, David, London W1.
Aaron Antiques, Tunbridge Wells, Kent.
Aaron Gallery, London W1.
Aarquebus Antiques, St. Leonards-on-Sea, Sussex East.
Abacus, Grays Antique Markets, London W1.
Abbas Antiques, Sherborne, Dorset.
Abbey Antiques - Fine Jewellery & Silver, Hemel Hempstead, Herts.
Abbey Antiques, Ramsey, Cambs.
Abbey Antiques, Stirling, Scotland.
Abbey Galleries, Bath, Somerset.
Abbey House, Derby, Derbys.
Abbeygate Gallery & Antiques Centre, Grimsby, Lincs.
Abbot, Deborah, The Swan at Tetsworth, Oxon.
Abbot, Jason, The Swan at Tetsworth, Oxon.
Abbott and Holder, London WC1.
Abbott Antiques and Country Pine, London SE26.
Abbott Antiques, A., Ipswich, Suffolk.
Abbott, C.N., Hartley Wintney, Hants.
Abbott, Dominic Antiquarius, London SW3.
Abbott, Jaki, Antiquarius, London SW3.
Abbott, Nicholas, Hartley Wintney, Hants.
Abbott, S. and R., Needham Market, Suffolk.
Abe, Emmy, Bond Street Antiques Centre, London W1.
Aberdeen House Antiques, London W5.
Aberford Antiques Ltd t/a Aberford Country Furniture, Aberford, Yorks. West.
Abinger Bazaar, Abinger Hammer, Surrey.
Abington Books, Finningham, Suffolk.
Aboudara, M., Antiquarius, London SW3.
Abraham, Gillian, Lubenham, Leics.

Abrahams Books, Mike, Lichfield, Staffs.
Abstract, Kensington Church Street Antiques Centre, London W8.
Academy Billiard Company, West Byfleet, Surrey.
Academy Books, Portsmouth, Hants.
Acanthus Antiques & Collectables, Nottingham, Notts.
Acanthus Design, The Swan at Tetsworth, Oxon.
Accurate Trading Co, Bond Street Antiques Centre, London W1.
Accurate Trading Co. Ltd., Alfies, London NW8
Ackermann & Johnson, London SW1.
Ackroyd, J.L., Guildford, Surrey.
Acorn Antiques, Deganwy, Wales.
Acorn Antiques, Dulverton, Somerset.
Acorn Antiques, Durham House Antiques Centre, Stow-on-the-Wold, Glos.
Acorn Antiques, London SE21.
Acorn Antiques, Sheffield, Yorks. South.
Acorn Antiques, Worthing, Sussex West.
Acquisitions (Fireplaces) Ltd, London NW5.
AD Antiques, Woodseaves, Staffs.
Adam Gallery, Bath, Somerset.
Adam, D. and A., Edenbridge, Kent.
Adam, Philip, Harrogate, Yorks. North.
Adams Antiques, Chester, Cheshire.
Adams Antiques, Grays Antique Markets, London W1.
Adams Antiques, Nantwich, Cheshire.
Adams Antiques, Rodney, Pwllheli, Wales.
Adams Arts & Antiques Ltd, Farningham, Kent.
Adams Furniture Centre, Huntingdon, Cambs.
Adams Ltd, Norman, London SW3.
Adams Room Antiques, London SW19.
Adams Wireless & Bygones Shop, Tony, Ipswich, Suffolk.
Adams, B. and T., Chester, Cheshire.
Adams, Beth, Alfies, London NW8
Adams, M. J., Farningham, Kent.
Adamson Armoury, Skipton, Yorks. North.
Adamson, J.K., Skipton, Yorks. North.
Adamson, N.J.G., Harrogate, Yorks. North.
Adamson, Nigel, Harrogate, Yorks. North.
Adcock, Julie, Melton Mowbray, Leics.
Addison, Mrs Barbara, Colchester, Essex.
Addrison, B. and T., Downham Market, Norfolk.
ADEC, London SW1.
Admiral Vernon Antiques Market, London W11.
Aesthetics, Antiquarius, London SW3.
Afantiques, Wolverhampton, West Mids.
Affordable Antiques, Ashby-de-la-Zouch, Leics.
Affordable Antiques, Hale, Cheshire.
After Noah, London N1.
After Noah, London SW3.

Agar Antiques, Saintfield, Co. Down, N. Ireland.
Agar, Rosie, Saintfield, Co. Down, N. Ireland.
Age of Elegance, Whitchurch, Shrops.
Age of Jazz, Whitby, Yorks. North.
Ager, Adrian, Ashburton, Devon.
Agnew's, London W1.
Agnew, A., London W8.
Ahmed, A.H., Brighton, Sussex East.
Ahmed, A.H., Brighton, Sussex East.
Ailsa Gallery, Twickenham, Middx.
Aindow, R., Kendal, Cumbria.
Ainscough, John, Haslingden, Lancs.
Ainslie's Antique Warehouse, Perth, Scotland.
Ainslie, T.S. and A., Perth, Scotland.
Aitken Dott Ltd, Edinburgh, Scotland.
Aker, Mrs J E, South Molton, Devon.
Aker, Mrs J. E., South Molton, Devon.
Aladdin's Cave, Freshwater, Isle of Wight.
Aladdin's Cave, Leeds, Yorks. West.
Alan Ltd, Adrian, London W1.
Alan's Antiques, Leatherhead, Surrey.
Alba, Mr. and Mrs Jose, North Petherton, Somerset.
Albany Antiques Ltd, Hindhead, Surrey.
Albrow and Sons Family Jewellers, Norwich, Norfolk.
Albrow, R., Norwich, Norfolk.
Alcazar, Maria, Grays Antique Markets, London W1.
Aldbrook, M., London W6.
Alder, T.A., Codford, Wilts.
Aldermaston Antiques, Aldermaston, Berks.
Aldersey Hall Ltd, Chester, Cheshire.
Alderson, Bath, Somerset.
Alderson, C.J.R., Bath, Somerset.
Alexander Antiques & Kate Thurlow, David, London W14.
Alexander Antiques, Henfield, Sussex West.
Alexander Antiques, Portrush, Co. Antrim, N. Ireland.
Alexander Gallery, Bristol, Glos.
Alexander, Mrs M. and D., Portrush, Co. Antrim, N. Ireland.
Alexander, Peter, London W8.
Alexanders, Titchfield, Hants.
Alexandria Antiques, Brighton, Sussex East.
Alexandria Antiques, Brighton, Sussex East.
Alfandary, Alexandra, The Mall Antiques Arcade, London N1.
Alfies Antique Market, London NW8.
Alfred's "Old Curiosity Shop" and The Morris and Shirley Galleries, Mr., Southampton, Hants.
Alfreton Antiques Centre, Alfreton, Derbys.
Alfriston Antiques, Alfriston, Sussex East.
Algar Antiques, Red House Antiques Centre, York, Yorks. North
Alice's, London W11.

Astley House - Fine Art, Stretton-on-Fosse, Warks.
Aston Antiques, Durham House Antiques Centre, Stow-on-the-Wold, Glos.
Aston Pine Antiques, Faringdon, Oxon.
Aston, C.D. and Mrs I., Fordingbridge, Hants.
Aston, Fiona, Ginnel Antiques Centre, The, Harrogate, Yorks North
Aston, Fiona, Red House Antiques Centre, York, Yorks. North
Aston, S., Alnwick, Northumbs.
Astra House Antiques Centre, Hemswell Cliff, Lincs.
Asylum House Antiques, Bradford-on-Avon, Wilts.
At the Sign of the Chest of Drawers, London N6.
Athey, G.M., Alnwick, Northumbs.
Athill, Philip, London WC1.
Atholl Antiques, Aberdeen, Scotland.
Atkin, Miss D.J., Nantwich, Cheshire.
Atkin, Miss S.E., Trevor, Wales.
Atkins, Garry and Julie, London W8.
Atkins, Garry, London W8.
Atkins, T J, Taunton, Somerset.
Atkinson, David, Leeds, Yorks. West.
Atlantic Antique Centres Ltd, London W1.
Atlantic Antiques Centres Ltd, London N1.
Atlantic Antiques Centres Ltd, London SW3.
Atlantic Bay Carpets Gallery, London SW7.
Atlantis Bookshop, London WC1.
Attfield, David, Holt, Norfolk.
Attic Antiques, Saintfield, Co. Down, N. Ireland.
Attic, The, Baldock, Herts.
Attic, The, Newton Abbot, Devon.
Atticus Books, Grays, Essex.
Audley Art Ltd, The Mall Antiques Arcade, London N1.
Audley House Antiques, Bradford-on-Avon, Wilts.
August Antiques and Interiors, Moreton-in-Marsh, Glos.
Auldearn Antiques, Auldearn, Scotland.
Aura Antiques, Masham, Yorks. North.
Aurum Antiques, Grays Antique Markets, London W1.
Aust, Jake and Guy, London SE20.
Austen, S.T. and R.J., Leigh-on-Sea, Essex.
Austin, Barbara, Chappells Antiques Centre, Bakewell, Derbys.
Austin, G., Winchester, Hants.
Austin, J., London WC1.
Austin, S., Swindon, Wilts.
Austin-Fell, A.J. and C.R., Holt, Norfolk.
Austin-Kaye, A.M., Chester, Cheshire.
Austin/Desmond Fine Art, London WC1.
Austwick, Paul, Sowerby Bridge, Yorks. West.
Autodrome, Almshouses Arcade, Chichester, Sussex West
Avalon Post Card and Stamp Shop, Chester, Cheshire.
Avon Antiques, Bradford-on-Avon, Wilts.
Avon House Antiques/Hayward's Antiques, Kingsbridge, Devon.
Avoncroft Antiques, Durham House Antiques Centre, Stow-on-the-Wold, Glos.
Axia Art Consultants Ltd, London W11.
Ayres, Lynne, Wansford, Cambs.
Aytac, Osman, Grays Antique Markets, London W1.
Ayuka Ltd, Stotfold, Beds.

B

B and B Antiques, Stickney, Lincs.
B. and T. Antiques, London W11.
B.B.M. Jewellery and Antiques, Kidderminster, Worcs.
B.C. Metalcrafts, London NW9.
B.R.M. Coins, Knutsford, Cheshire.
Bacchus Gallery, Petworth, Sussex West.
Back 2 Wood, Richard, Appledore, Kent.
Bacou, Guillaume and Louise, London E1.
Baddiel, Colin, Grays Antique Markets, London W1.
Baddow Antique Centre, Great Baddow, Essex.
Badland, Miss, Bradford, Yorks. West.
Bagatelle Antiques, Barton, Cambs.
Baggins Book Bazaar - The Largest Secondhand Bookshop in England, Rochester, Kent.
Baggott Church Street Ltd, Stow-on-the-Wold, Glos.
Baggott, D.J. and C.M., Stow-on-the-Wold, Glos.
Baggott, Duncan J., Stow-on-the-Wold, Glos.
Bagley, B., Brighton, Sussex East.
Bail, A., Ash Vale, Surrey.
Baildon Furniture Co., The, Baildon, Yorks. West.
Baile de Laperriere, H., Calne, Wilts.
Bailey, Avril, Warminster, Wilts.
Bailey, E., Milford, Surrey.
Bailey, Eric, Milford, Surrey.
Bailey, M. and S., Ross-on-Wye, Herefs.
Baileys Home & Garden, Ross-on-Wye, Herefs.
Bailiffgate Antique Pine, Alnwick, Northumbs.
Bain, Cdr. Harry and Mrs. Jean, Wolverhampton, West Mids.
Baines, Henry, Southborough, Kent.
Baird, Pauline, Kincardine O'Neil, Scotland.
Baird, R. and V., Langholm, Scotland.
Bairsto, Peter, Tetbury, Glos.
Baker Antiques, G., Horncastle, Lincs.
Baker Asian Art, Gregg, London W8.
Baker, C.J. and Mrs B.A.J., Lavenham, Suffolk.
Baker, David, Grays Antique Markets, London W1.
Baker, J. and J., Lavenham, Suffolk.
Baker, K.R., Woking, Surrey.
Baker, Keith, Woking, Surrey.
Baker, Manfred, Penzance, Cornwall.
Baker, Martin, London SE9.
Baker, Mrs J., Whitstable, Kent.
Baker, P.B., Midhurst, Sussex West.
Baker, Peter and Pam, Oban, Scotland.
Baker, R. J., Canterbury, Kent.
Baker, S., Crawley, Hants.
Baker, Sandie and Chris, Sandwich, Kent.
Baker, T., Langford, Notts.
Baker, T.R., Stockbridge, Hants.
Bakhtiyar Carpet Gallery, The, Stockbridge, Hants.
Bakhtiyar Gallery, The, Stockbridge, Hants.
Baldfaced Stag, The, Ashurst, Kent.
Baldry, Mrs J., Gt. Yarmouth, Norfolk.
Baldwick, S., Ravenstonedale, Cumbria.
Baldwin and Sons Ltd, A.H., London WC2.
Baldwin, M. and M., Cleobury Mortimer, Shrops.
Baldwin, M.P., Hurst Green, Sussex East.
Baldwin, R.J.S., London SW3.
Baldwin, V.F.S. and J.F., Alcester, Warks.
Baldwin., R.E. and P.J., Scarborough, Yorks. North.

Bale, Craig, Bath, Somerset.
Bale, Vicki, Ditton Priors, Shrops.
Ball and Claw Antiques, Tetbury, Glos.
Ball, Ann and John, Porthcawl, Wales.
Ball, David, Leighton Buzzard, Beds.
Ball, G., Tattershall, Lincs.
Ball, John M., Marlesford, Suffolk.
Ballard, Mrs E.H. and S.R., Thirsk, Yorks. North.
Ballingall, H., Woodbury, Devon.
Balmuir House Antiques, Tetbury, Glos.
Bampton Gallery, Bampton, Devon.
Banana Dance Ltd., The Mall Antiques Arcade, London N1.
Banbury Fayre, London N1.
Bangs, Christopher, London SW6.
Bank House Gallery, The, Norwich, Norfolk.
Banks Antiques, Simon, Finedon, Northants.
Bannister FRGS, David, Cheltenham, Glos.
Barazi, Mario, The Mall Antiques Arcade, London N1.
Barbagallo, Sebastiano, London SW6.
Barbagallo, Sebastiano, London W11.
Barber Antiques, West Haddon, Northants.
Barber's Clock, The, Worcester, Worcs.
Barber, Miss Alison, West Haddon, Northants.
Barber, Sara, Long Melford, Suffolk.
Barbican Antiques Centre, Plymouth, Devon.
Barbican Bookshop, York, Yorks. North.
Barclay Antiques, Headington, Oxon.
Barclay Samson Ltd, London SW6.
Barclay, C., Headington, Oxon.
Barclay, M.J. and D., Friockheim, Scotland.
Barclay, Mrs K., London NW8.
Barclay, Richard, London SW6.
Bardawil, E.S., London W8.
Bardawil, Eddy, London W8.
Barden House Antiques, Tonbridge, Kent.
Bardwell Antiques, Dronfield, Derbys.
Bardwell, S., Dronfield, Derbys.
Bardy, Steve, Jesmond, Tyne and Wear.
Barfoot, Craig, East Hagbourne, Oxon.
Barfoot, I.C., East Hagbourne, Oxon.
Bargain Box, Luton, Beds.
Barham Antiques, London W11.
Barker, Brian, Swanage, Dorset.
Barker, Lynn, Ampthill, Beds.
Barker, Mrs J., Huntly, Scotland.
Barker, Paul, Newcastle-under-Lyme, Staffs.
Barker, Peter, Dunsfold, Surrey.
Barkes and Barkes, London NW1.
Barkes, J. N. and P. R., London NW1.
Barkham Antique Centre, Barkham, Berks.
Barley Antiques, Robert, London SW6.
Barley, R.A., London SW6.
Barling Fine Porcelain Ltd, Wickham Bishops, Essex.
Barn Antiques Centre, Long Marston, Warks.
Barn Antiques, Barnstaple, Devon.
Barn Antiques, Nantwich, Cheshire.
Barn at Bislington, The, Bilsington, Kent.
Barn Book Supply, The, Salisbury, Wilts.
Barn Court Antiques, Crafts & Tearoom, Templeton, Wales.
Barn, The, Petersfield, Hants.
Barnard, Miss Nikki, Horncastle, Lincs.
Barnard, Mrs J.P., Ilminster, Somerset.
Barnes Antiques & Interiors, Jane, Honiton, Devon.
Barnes Jewellers, Bond Street Silver Galleries, London W1
Barnes, H., Stafford, Staffs.
Barnes, J.A.C. and S.J., Honiton, Devon.
Barnes, Mandy, Jubilee Hall Antiques Centre, Lechlade, Glos.

Berktay, Y., Somerton, Somerset.
Berland's of Edinburgh, Edinburgh, Scotland.
Bermondsey Antiques Market, London SE1.
Bernadette's Antiques & Collectables &
  Auctioneers, Luton, Beds.
Berney, G. and M., Pickering, Yorks. North.
Berriman, Peter and Denise, Great Dunmow,
  Essex.
Berry Antiques, Lesley, Flamborough, Yorks.
  East.
Berry Antiques, Moreton-in-Marsh, Glos.
Berry, Chris, Moreton-in-Marsh, Glos.
Berry, F.E., Disley, Cheshire.
Berry, Mrs L., Flamborough, Yorks. East.
Berthoud, N., Bridgnorth, Shrops.
Berwald Oriental Art, London W8.
Berwald, John R., London W8.
Besley, P.A. and P.F., Beccles, Suffolk.
Besleys Books, Beccles, Suffolk.
Best Antiques, Ray, Newton Tony, Wilts.
Bett, H., London W1.
Better Days, Menai Bridge, Wales.
Bettney, Julian, Datchet, Berks.
Betty's, Leicester, Leics.
Bevan, D., Stourbridge, West Mids.
Beverley R, Grays Antique Markets, London
  W1.
Beverley, London NW8.
Bevins, J.R., Ulverston, Cumbria.
Bew, D. and Mrs A., Debenham, Suffolk.
Bewdley Antiques, Bewdley, Worcs.
Bexfield Antiques, Daniel, London W1.
Bexhill Antiques, St. Leonards-on-Sea,
  Sussex East.
Beyer, Jane and Gerd, London N1.
Beyer, Jane and Gerd, London SW6.
Beynon, W.A., Cardiff, Wales.
Bhalla, Mrs A., Lincoln, Lincs.
Bianco, L., Cheltenham, Glos.
Bibby, R., Leigh, Lancs.
Biblion, Grays Antique Markets, London
  W1.
Bibliopola, Alfies, London NW8.
Bichard, R., J. and N., Bradford-on-Avon,
  Wilts.
Bickford, Mr and Mrs D.M., Crediton,
  Devon.
Bicknell, Willow, Nettlebed, Oxon.
Biddulph, Peter, London W1.
Bieganski, Z., Woburn, Beds.
Big Ben Antique Clocks, London SW6.
Bigden Antiques, Edward, Debenham,
  Suffolk.
Bigden, Edward and Christopher, Debenham,
  Suffolk.
Biggs, J. and P., Bideford, Devon.
Biggs, Linda, Tetbury, Glos.
Bigwood Antiques, Brasted, Kent.
Bigwood, C., Tunbridge Wells, Kent.
Bigwood, S., Brasted, Kent.
Bijoux Signes, Grays Antique Markets,
  London W1.
Biles, John, Hartley Wintney, Hants.
Billcliffe Fine Art, The Roger, Glasgow,
  Scotland.
Billiard Room Antiques, Chilcompton,
  Somerset.
Billing, David, Antiquarius, London SW3.
Billington, J.L., Sabden, Lancs.
Binder, D. and A., London NW8.
Bingham, Tony, London NW3.
Bingley Antiques, Haworth, Yorks. West.
Bingley Antiques, Robert, Wing, Rutland.
Binns, David, The Swan at Tetsworth, Oxon.
Birbeck Gallery, Torquay, Devon.
Birbeck, Stephen and Ross, Torquay, Devon.
Birch, C., Gt. Yarmouth, Norfolk.

Birch, T., Cheltenham, Glos.
Birchington Antiques, Birchington, Kent.
Bird, John, Petworth, Sussex west.
Bird, R.J., Cambridge, Cambs.
Bird., M.J. and P.J., Cirencester, Glos.
Birkdale Antiques, Southport, Merseyside.
Birmingham Antique Centre, The,
  Birmingham, West Mids.
Bishop, Jeanette and Norman, Cleethorpes,
  Lincs.
Bishopsgate Antiques, York, Yorks. North.
Bizarre Antiques, Bristol, Glos.
Bizarre Decorative Arts North West,
  Altrincham, Cheshire.
Bizarre, London NW8.
Black Dog Antiques, Bungay, Suffolk.
Black Oriental Carpets, David, London W2.
Black Sheep, The, Tetbury, Glos.
Black, M. J., Alfies, London NW8
Black, Mr and Mrs Victor, Stow-on-the-
  Wold, Glos.
Black, Oonagh, Stow-on-the-Wold, Glos.
Black, Richard, Antiquarius, London SW3.
Black, Robert, Merstham, Surrey.
Blackbrook Antiques Village, Weeford,
  Staffs.
Blackburn, A., Stretton-under-Fosse, Warks.
Blackburn, Joan and David, Clola by
  Mintlaw, Scotland.
Blackburn, Mrs E.M., Tunbridge Wells,
  Kent.
Blackburn, Mrs G., Lancaster, Lancs.
Blackburn, Norman, Stamford, Lincs.
Blackford, M., Calne, Wilts.
Blackhurst, Steven, Crewe, Cheshire.
Blackwater Pine Antiques, Truro, Cornwall.
Blackwell's Rare Books, Oxford, Oxon.
Blackwell's, London WC2.
Bladud House Antiques, Bath, Somerset.
Blair Antiques, Blair Atholl, Scotland.
Blair Antiques, Christopher, Bishop's
  Stortford, Herts.
Blair, J., Guildford, Surrey.
Blair, J., St. Albans, Herts.
Blair, Julian, Oxford, Oxon.
Blair, Julian, Windsor and Eton, Berks.
Blairgowrie Books, Blairgowrie, Scotland.
Blairman and Sons Ltd., H., London W1.
Blake, J., J. and S.T., Puckeridge, Herts.
Blake, Michael, Pembroke, Wales.
Blake, P., London E11.
Blake, Shelley, Alfies, London NW8
Blakey and Sons Ltd (Est. 1905), J.H.,
  Brierfield, Lancs.
Blakey Fireplaces, Colin, Nelson, Lancs.
Blanchard Ltd, London SW1.
Blanchard, Froxfield, Wilts.
Bland Antiques, Judi, Durham House
  Antiques Centre, Stow-on-the-Wold, Glos.
Blant, Martin J., Oxford, Oxon.
Blaxill, Neill Robinson, Sevenoaks, Kent.
Blay Antiques, G. D., Dorking, Surrey.
Blechman, H.L., Bournemouth, Dorset.
Blench & Son, John, St. Helier , Jersey, C.I.
Blench, J. and P., St. Helier , Jersey, C.I.
Blenheim Antiques, Fairford, Glos.
Blewbury Antiques, Blewbury, Oxon.
Bliss, Patsy, Exeter, Devon.
Bloom & Son (1912) Ltd, N., London SW1.
Bloom, A., London Silver Vaults, London
  WC2.
Bloomfield, Mr and Mrs, Rye, Sussex East.
Bloomstein Ltd, A. and B., Bond Street
  Silver Galleries, London W1.
Blower Antiques, Mark, Le Bourg Forest,
  Guernsey, C.I.
Blunderbuss Antiques, London W1.

Bly Valley Antiques, Wrentham, Suffolk.
Bly, J. and V., London SW1.
Bly, John, London SW1.
Bly, John, Tring, Herts.
Blyburgate Antiques, Beccles, Suffolk.
Boaden, Richard, Sandra and Chris, Hexham,
  Northumbs.
Boadens Antiques, Hexham, Northumbs.
Boalch, Mrs J., Cardiff, Wales.
Boam, Clare, Horncastle, Lincs.
Boase Antiques, Exmouth, Devon.
Bobbins Wool, Crafts, Antiques, Whitby,
  Yorks. North.
Bodhouse Antiques, Birkenhead, Merseyside.
Bodmin Antiques Centre, Bodmin, Cornwall.
Bogan House Antiques, Totnes, Devon.
Bokhari, Iftikhar, London SW10.
Bolla, Alexandra, Antiquarius, London SW3.
Bolt Antiques, Brian R., Portballintrae, Co.
  Antrim, N. Ireland.
Bolton Antique Centre, Bolton, Lancs.
Bomzer, Ken, Brighton, Sussex East.
Bon-Accord Books, Aberdeen, Scotland.
Bond & Sons, S., The Swan at Tetsworth,
  Oxon.
Bond and Son, S., Colchester, Essex.
Bond Street Antiques Centre, London W1.
Bond Street Antiques, Cromer, Norfolk.
Bond Street Silver Galleries, London W1.
Bond, Mrs H., London W11.
Bond, Peter, The Swan at Tetsworth, Oxon.
Bond, R., Colchester, Essex.
Bonehill, Lynne and Richard, Truro,
  Cornwall.
Bonino, Paolo, Alfies, London NW8
Bonn, K. and E., Rochdale, Lancs.
Bonnar, Jewellers, Joseph, Edinburgh,
  Scotland.
Bontoft, P.W., Cirencester, Glos.
Bonython Bookshop, Truro, Cornwall.
Boodle and Dunthorne Ltd, Liverpool,
  Merseyside.
Book Art & Architecture & Volume Gallery,
  London WC1.
Book House, The, Ravenstonedale, Cumbria.
Book Jungle, The, St. Leonards-on-Sea,
  Sussex East.
Book Shop, The, Castle Donington, Leics.
Bookends, Emsworth, Hants.
Booker, Poppy and Graham, Birchington,
  Kent.
Books & Bygones, Weymouth, Dorset.
Books Afloat, Weymouth, Dorset.
Books Etc., Cromer, Norfolk.
Books for Collectors Ltd., Toddington, Beds.
Books, Maps and Prints, Brecon, Wales.
Bookshop, The, Cambridge, Cambs.
Bookworm, Holland-on-Sea, Essex.
Bookworms of Evesham, Evesham, Worcs.
Booth & Son, A. E., Ewell, Surrey.
Booth's Bookshop Ltd, Richard, Hay-on-
  Wye, Wales.
Booth, C.M., Rolvenden, Kent.
Booth, David J. and Mrs Ann, Ewell, Surrey.
Booth, Joanna, London SW3.
Booth, Mr and Mrs C.M., Farnham, Surrey.
Booth, Richard and Hope, Hay-on-Wye,
  Wales.
Booth, T.J., Rye, Sussex East.
Bootham Antiques, Red House Antiques
  Centre, York, Yorks. North
Bord (Gold Coin Exchange), M., London
  WC2.
Borne, Francois, London SW1.
Boscombe Militaria, Bournemouth, Dorset.
Boscombe Models and Collectors Shop,
  Bournemouth, Dorset.

Calgie, John, Jubilee Hall Antiques Centre, Lechlade, Glos.
Calleja, L., Ledbury, Herefs.
Callingham Antiques, Northchapel, Sussex West.
Calne Antiques, Calne, Wilts.
Calton Gallery, Edinburgh, Scotland.
Calverley Antiques, Tunbridge Wells, Kent.
Calvert Antiques, Rebecca, Lincoln, Lincs.
Calvert, Anita L., Great Houghton, Yorks. South.
Camberwell Architectural Salvage & Antiques, London SE5.
Cambridge Fine Art Ltd, Cambridge, Cambs.
Cambridge Pine, Bottisham, Cambs.
Camden Art Gallery, London NW8.
Camden Books, Bath, Somerset.
Camden Passage Antiques Market and Pierrepont Arcade Antiques Centre, London N1.
Cameo Antiques, Chester, Cheshire.
Camerer Cuss and Co, London SW1.
Cameron, Jasmine, Antiquarius, London SW3
Cameron, K. and E., Edinburgh, Scotland.
Cameron, Kate, Edinburgh, Scotland.
Cameron, Sheila, Alfies, London NW8
Camilla's Bookshop, Eastbourne, Sussex East.
Campbell Antiques, Peter, Atworth, Wilts.
Campbell Gallery, The Lucy B., London W8.
Campbell Wilson, Brighton, Sussex East.
Campbell's of Walton Street, London SW3.
Campbell, Andrew, Jesmond, Tyne and Wear.
Campbell, David, Hartley Wintney, Hants.
Campbell, F.D., Kelvedon, Essex.
Campbell, Iain, Widnes, Cheshire.
Campbell, Meg, Southampton, Hants.
Campbell, Mrs S., Colchester, Essex.
Campbell, P.R., Atworth, Wilts.
Campbell, R.M., Hartley Wintney, Hants.
Campbell, S., Stirling, Scotland.
Campbell, William, Alfies, London NW8.
Campden Country Pine Antiques, Winchcombe, Glos.
Campion, R.J., London SW6.
Campsie Antiques, Lennoxtown, Scotland.
Candle Lane Books, Shrewsbury, Shrops.
Candlin, Z., London N1.
Candlin, Z., London SW3.
Canetti, A., Antiquarius, London SW3
Cannell Antiques, M.D., Raveningham, Norfolk.
Cannon Antiques, Elizabeth, Colchester, Essex.
Cannonbury, Southwold, Suffolk.
Canon Gallery, The, Petworth, Sussex West.
Canon Gate Bookshop, Chichester, Sussex West.
Canonbury, London W11.
Canterbury Bookshop, The, Canterbury, Kent.
Capel Mawr Collectors Centre, Criccieth, Wales.
Capon, Patric, London N1.
Cardiff Antiques Centre, Cardiff, Wales.
Cardingmill Antiques, Church Stretton, Shrops.
Caris, Gordon, Alnwick, Northumbs.
Caris, Gordon, Hexham, Northumbs.
Carleton Gallery, Birmingham, West Mids.
Carlisle Antiques Centre, Carlisle, Cumbria.
Carlton Antiques, Great Malvern, Worcs.
Carlton Davidson Antiques, London SW10.
Carlton-Smith, John, London SW1.
Carmichael, Wendy, Alfies, London NW8

Carnegie Paintings & Clocks, Yealmpton, Devon.
Carnegie, Chris, Yealmpton, Devon.
Carney, B. and M., Astley Bridge, Lancs.
Carningli Centre, The, Newport, Wales.
Carpenter, John, Llanelli, Wales.
Carpenter, Rosemary, Truro, Cornwall.
Carpenter, Sue, Hartley Wintney, Hants.
Carr Antiques, Harold J., Washington, Tyne and Wear.
Carr, Mrs Dianne M., Coggeshall, Essex.
Carr, R.G., Salisbury, Wilts.
Carr, Ronald, Salisbury, Wilts.
Carrasco, Marylise, London SW1.
Carrick's Antiques and Shipping, S., Gainsborough, Lincs.
Carrington and Co. Ltd, London W1.
Carrington House, Llanrwst, Wales.
Carroll, M. and A., Halifax, Yorks. West.
Carroll, Paul, London SW4.
Carroll, Vivian, Antiquarius, London SW3.
Carruthers, C.J., Carlisle, Cumbria.
Carruthers, J., St. Andrews, Scotland.
Carruthers, L., Buxton, Derbys.
Carshalton Antique Galleries, Carshalton, Surrey.
Carter Antiques, Mark, Fairford, Glos.
Carter, D., London W11.
Carter, Mike, Chichester, Sussex West.
Carter, Neil, Olney, Bucks.
Carter, Nick, Edinburgh, Scotland.
Cartmell, T., Tring, Herts.
Cartrefle Antiques, Mathry, Wales.
Cartwright, Mia, Alfies, London NW8.
Casey Antiques, William J., Warwick, Warks.
Casey, Ann, The Swan at Tetsworth, Oxon.
Casey, William and Pat, Warwick, Warks.
Casimir Ltd, Jack, London W11.
Caslake, J., Sevenoaks, Kent.
Casque and Gauntlet Militaria, Farnham, Surrey.
Cass Interiors, Maria, Nayland, Suffolk.
Cassidy (Books), P.J., Holbeach, Lincs.
Cassidy's Antiques, Warminster, Wilts.
Cassidy, M., Warminster, Wilts.
Castaside, Alfies, London NW8.
Castle Antiques Bookstore, Workington, Cumbria.
Castle Antiques Centre, Middleham, Yorks. North.
Castle Antiques Centre, Westerham, Kent.
Castle Antiques Ltd, Deddington, Oxon.
Castle Antiques, Burnham-on-Sea, Somerset.
Castle Antiques, Lewes, Sussex East.
Castle Antiques, Nottingham, Notts.
Castle Antiques, Orford, Suffolk.
Castle Antiques, Warwick, Warks.
Castle Ashby Gallery, Castle Ashby, Northants.
Castle Bookshop, Colchester, Essex.
Castle Close Antiques, Dornoch, Scotland.
Castle Galleries, Salisbury, Wilts.
Castle Gate Antiques Centre, Newark, Notts.
Castle Hill Books, Kington, Herefs.
Castle Reclamation, Martock, Somerset.
Caswell, Mrs P., Woking, Surrey.
Cat in the Window, Keswick, Cumbria.
Cater, Patricia, Stow-on-the-Wold, Glos.
Cathedral Jewellers, Manchester, Lancs.
Catkins Jewellery, Ginnel Antiques Centre, The, Harrogate, Yorks North
Cato, Lennox and Susan, Edenbridge, Kent.
Cato, Lennox, Edenbridge, Kent.
Cato, Miles Wynn, London SW1.
Cato, Miles Wynn, Tywyn, Wales.
Cattle, Barbara, York, Yorks. North.

Caudwell, Doreen, Span Antiques, Woodstock, Oxon
Causey Antique Shop, Gosforth, Tyne and Wear.
Cavanagh, D., Edinburgh, Scotland.
Cave and Sons Ltd, R.G., Ludlow, Shrops.
Cave, F. and C.H., Northampton, Northants.
Cavendish Antiques & Collectors Centre, York, Yorks. North.
Cavendish Antiques, Rupert, London SW6.
Cavendish Fine Arts, Sonning-on-Thames, Berks.
Cavendish Rose Antiques, Cavendish, Suffolk.
Caversham Antiques, The Swan at Tetsworth, Oxon.
Cavey, Christopher, Grays Antique Markets, London W1.
Cawood Antiques, Cawood, Yorks. North.
Cawson, Peter, St. Leonards-on-Sea, Sussex East.
Cayley, John, London SW15.
Cedar Antiques Centre Ltd, Hartley Wintney, Hants.
Cedar Antiques Limited, Hartley Wintney, Hants.
Cedar House Gallery, Ripley, Surrey.
Cedarstar Ltd., Wantage, Oxon.
Cekay, Grays Antique Markets, London W1.
Central Gallery (Portobello), London W11.
Century Fine Arts, Lymington, Hants.
Ceres Antiques, Ceres, Scotland.
Cerne Antiques, Cerne Abbas, Dorset.
CG's Curiosity Shop, Cockermouth, Cumbria.
Chacewater Antiques, Chacewater, Cornwall.
Chaffer, John, The Swan at Tetsworth, Oxon.
Chair Set - Antiques, The, Woodstock, Oxon.
Chalk, M., Horncastle, Lincs.
Chalon, Jake and Nick, Chard, Somerset.
Chambers Fine Antiques, Ronald G., Petworth, Sussex West.
Chambers, Graham H., Lancaster, Lancs.
Chambers, Ronald G., Petworth, Sussex West.
Champkins, Paul, London W1.
Chan, Linda, Alfies, London NW8
Chancelier, G. Antiquarius, London SW3.
Chancery Antiques, The Mall Antiques Arcade, London N1.
Chantry Bookshop and Gallery, Dartmouth, Devon.
Chantziaras, Panagiotis, London W1.
Chapel Antiques Centre, Barmouth, Wales.
Chapel Antiques Centre, Sheffield, Yorks. South.
Chapel Antiques, Nantwich, Cheshire.
Chapel Emporium Antique Centre, The, Long Sutton, Lincs.
Chapel House Fireplaces, Holmfirth, Yorks. West.
Chapel Place Antiques, Tunbridge Wells, Kent.
Chapel Street Antiques Arcade, Penzance, Cornwall.
Chapman Antiques and Restoration, Peter, London N1.
Chapman, H., London SW6.
Chapman, I., Whixley, Yorks. North.
Chapman, J. and I., Harrogate, Yorks. North.
Chapman, J.W. & A.A., Skenfrith, Wales.
Chapman, M.C., Finedon, Northants.
Chapman, P.J. and Z.A., London N1.
Chappell's Antiques & Fine Art, Chappells Antiques Centre, Bakewell, Derbys.
Chappells Antiques Centre, Bakewell, Derbys.

Clocks in the Peak, Chappells Antiques Centre, Bakewell, Derbys.

Clockwise, Emsworth, Hants.

Cloisters Antique & Collectors Fair, Norwich, Norfolk.

Clola Antiques Centre, Clola by Mintlaw, Scotland.

Close Jewellery Restoration, R., Bond Street Silver Galleries, London W1.

Close, Henry H., Abergavenny, Wales.

Close, Mr and Mrs H., Abergavenny, Wales.

Clubb, A., Twickenham, Middx.

Clutter, Uppingham, Rutland.

Cluzan, M., Framlingham, Suffolk.

Clydach Antiques, Swansea, Wales.

Clyde Antiques, Patrington, Yorks. East.

Coach House Antiques Centre, Canterbury, Kent.

Coach House Antiques Ltd, Stanley, Scotland.

Coach House Antiques, Hastings, Sussex East.

Coach House Antiques, The, Gomshall, Surrey.

Coach House Antiques, Whitby, Yorks. North.

Coach House, The, London W11.

Coakley-Webb, P., London N1.

Coats Oriental Carpets, London SE5.

Coats, A., London SE5.

Cobham Galleries, Cobham, Surrey.

Coblands Farm Antiques, Depden, Suffolk.

Cobra and Bellamy, London SW1.

Cobweb Antiques, Cullompton, Devon.

Cobwebs, London SE9.

Cobwebs, Southampton, Hants.

Cochrane and Leigh Warren Antiques, Fergus, London SW6.

Cockaday, Dean, Diss, Norfolk.

Cockburn, F.J., Northwich, Cheshire.

Cockermouth Antiques Market, Cockermouth, Cumbria.

Cockermouth Antiques, Cockermouth, Cumbria.

Cocking, D., Ginnel Antiques Centre, The, Harrogate, Yorks North

Cockman, N., Ross-on-Wye, Herefs.

Cockram, Mrs A., Lincoln, Lincs.

Cockram, T.A.M., Cowes, Isle of Wight.

Cockrell Antiques, Surbiton, Surrey.

Cockrell, Sheila and Peter, Surbiton, Surrey.

Cockton, Mrs L., London SE26.

Cocoa, Cheltenham, Glos.

Coffey, Norman and Margaret, Louth, Lincs.

Coggins Antiques, Ray, Westbury, Wilts.

Cohen & Cohen, London W8.

Cohen Numismatics, Philip, London WC2.

Cohen, A., Antiquarius, London SW3.

Cohen, Bond Street Antiques Centre, London W1.

Cohen, Jeffrey S., Reigate, Surrey.

Cohn, George and Peter, London WC1.

Cohu Antiques, Stephen, St Ouen, Jersey, C.I.

Coin and Jewellery Shop, The, Accrington, Lancs.

Coinage Hall Antiques Centre, The, Truro, Cornwall.

Coke, P., Sharrington, Norfolk.

Colbrook Antiques, Fakenham, Norfolk.

Coldstream Antiques, Coldstream, Scotland.

Cole, J., London N1.

Colefax & John Fowler, Sibyl, London W1.

Coleman Antiques, Robin, Piccadilly Antiques, Batheaston, Somerset.

Coleman Antiques, Simon, London SW13.

Coleman, G.D. and G.E., London W8.

Coleman, Garrick D., London W11.

Coleman, Garrick D., London W8.

Coles, D.A., Clevedon, Somerset.

Coles, Gail and Zachary, Blackburn, Lancs.

Coles, Graham, Newport, Wales.

Coles, Lorna, Tetbury, Glos.

Coleshill Antiques and Interiors Ltd, Coleshill, Warks.

Coll, Mrs P., Long Melford, Suffolk.

Collard, B., Totnes, Devon.

Collards Books, Totnes, Devon.

Collectables, C.W., Red House Antiques Centre, York, Yorks. North

Collectables, Kingston-on-Spey, Scotland.

Collection Antiques, Grays Antique Markets, London W1.

Collector Limited, The, London N11.

Collector's Corner, Truro, Cornwall.

Collector, The, Barnard Castle, Durham.

Collector, The, Clevedon, Somerset.

Collectors Centre - Antique City, London E17.

Collectors Centre, The, St Peter Port, Guernsey, C.I.

Collectors Choice, Modbury, Devon.

Collectors Corner, Almshouses Arcade, Chichester, Sussex West.

Collectors Corner, Carshalton, Surrey.

Collectors Corner, Northallerton, Yorks. North.

Collectors Old Toy Shop and Antiques, Halifax, Yorks. West.

Collectors Shop, The, Edinburgh, Scotland.

Collectors World, Alfies, London NW8.

Collectors World, Cromer, Norfolk.

Collectors World, Nottingham, Notts.

Collectors' Corner, Faversham, Kent.

Collectors' Paradise, Leigh-on-Sea, Essex.

Collectors' Place, Shrewsbury, Shrops.

Colledge, John and Margaret, Hatton, Warks.

Collet, David, Brampton, Cambs.

Collett, J., Chipping Campden, Glos.

Collicott, R., Honiton, Devon.

Collie, Mr. and Mrs James, Uppingham, Rutland.

Collier, Mark, Fordingbridge, Hants.

Collier, Mrs D.E., Sheringham, Norfolk.

Collinge Antiques, Llandudno Junction, Wales.

Collinge, Nicky, Llandudno Junction, Wales.

Collingridge, Jeremy, Tudor House, Stow-on-the-Wold, Glos

Collingridge, P., The Mall Antiques Arcade, London N1.

Collingridge, Peter, Stow-on-the-Wold, Glos.

Collingridge, Peter, Tudor House, Stow-on-the-Wold, Glos

Collino, Julie, London SW7.

Collins and Hastie Ltd, London SW10.

Collins and Son, J., Bideford, Devon.

Collins Antiques (F.G. and C. Collins Ltd.), Wheathampstead, Herts.

Collins Antiques, Frank, Mendlesham Green, Suffolk.

Collins, A., Lamb Arcade, Wallingford, Oxon

Collins, B.L., London Silver Vaults, London WC2.

Collins, Barry, London Silver Vaults, London WC2.

Collins, Diana, London SW10.

Collins, Edwin, Leominster, Herefs.

Collins, J., Llanrwst, Wales.

Collins, J., London W1.

Collins, Jackie, Ascot, Berks.

Collins, Len and Mary, Barkham, Berks.

Collins, S.J. and M.C., Wheathampstead, Herts.

Collins, Tracey, Horncastle, Lincs.

Colliton Antique Centre, Dorchester, Dorset.

Collyer Antiques, Jean, Boughton, Kent.

Collyer, Bryan, Durham House Antiques Centre, Stow-on-the-Wold, Glos.

Collyer, Mrs J.B., Boughton, Kent.

Collyer, R., Birmingham, West Mids.

Colmore Galleries Ltd, Henley-in-Arden, Warks.

Colnaghi & Co Ltd, P. and D., London W1.

Colonial Times, Cross in Hand, Sussex East.

Colt, R., Farnham, Surrey.

Coltishall Antiques Centre, Coltishall, Norfolk.

Colton Antiques, Kelvedon, Essex.

Colton, Gary, Kelvedon, Essex.

Coltsfoot Gallery, Leominster, Herefs.

Colyer, J.M., Wallasey, Merseyside.

Colystock Antiques, Stockland, Devon.

Comben, Chris, Rait Village Antiques Centre, Scotland

Comberton Antiques, Comberton, Cambs.

Complete Automobilist, The, Bourne, Lincs.

Compton House, Chappells Antiques Centre, Bakewell, Derbys.

Conboy, P.J., Sheffield, Yorks. South.

Conder, R., Grantham, Lincs.

Connaught Brown plc, London W1.

Connaught Galleries, London W2.

Connell - Wargrave Antiques, John, Wargrave, Berks.

Connolly, J., Leominster, Herefs.

Conquest House Antiques, Canterbury, Kent.

Conquest, Rosemary, London N1.

Constable, John, London SW15.

Constantinidi, P.S., London W1.

Conti, V., London NW8.

Continum, Grays Antique Markets, London W1.

Conway, J., London W1.

Cook of Marlborough Fine Art Ltd, Marlborough, Wilts.

Cook, Diana, Henley-on-Thames, Oxon.

Cook, J.A., Almshouses Arcade, Chichester, Sussex West

Cook, K.J., Rochester, Kent.

Cook, R.L., Sheringham, Norfolk.

Cook, Sheila, London W11.

Cook, W., East Budleigh, Devon.

Cook, W.J., Marlborough, Wilts.

Cooke Antiques Ltd, Mary, London SW14.

Cooke Antiques, Sandy, Long Melford, Suffolk.

Cookes Cottage Antiques, Red House Antiques Centre, York, Yorks. North

Cookham Antiques, Cookham Rise, Berks.

Cookson, R., Leominster, Herefs.

Cookstown Antiques, Cookstown, Co. Tyrone, N. Ireland.

Coombes, J. and M., Dorking, Surrey.

Cooney, V., Darwen, Lancs.

Cooper Antiques, John, St. Helier, Jersey, C.I.

Cooper Fine Arts Ltd, Brasted, Kent.

Cooper Gallery, Bideford, Devon.

Cooper, Audrey, The Swan at Tetsworth, Oxon.

Cooper, J., London SW10.

Cooper, Mary, Ginnel Antiques Centre, The, Harrogate, Yorks North

Cooper, Sonia, Aberfeldy, Scotland.

Coopers of Ilkley, Ilkley, Yorks. West.

Copnal Books, Crewe, Cheshire.

Coppelia Antiques, Plumley, Cheshire.

Copperhouse Gallery - W. Dyer & Sons, Hayle, Cornwall.
Coppock, Mrs Jill A., Stockport, Cheshire.
Coppock, P.J., Oxford, Oxon.
Copsey, Stephen, Huntingdon, Cambs.
Cordelia and Perdy's Antique Junk Shop, Lichfield, Staffs.
Corfield Potashnick, London SW19.
Cork Brick Antiques, Bungay, Suffolk.
Corkhill-Callin, Jenny, The Swan at Tetsworth, Oxon.
Corn Exchange Antiques Centre, Tunbridge Wells, Kent.
Corn Mill Antiques, Skipton, Yorks. North.
Corner Antiques, Worthing, Sussex West.
Corner Cottage Antiques, Market Bosworth, Leics.
Corner Cupboard Curios, Cirencester, Glos.
Corner Farm Antiques, Shifnal, Shrops.
Corner Portobello Antiques Supermarket, The, London W11.
Corner Shop Antiques, Camelford, Cornwall.
Corner Shop, The, Bradford, Yorks. West.
Corner Shop, The, Oxford, Oxon.
Cornforth, T.W., Southend- on- Sea, Essex.
Cornforth, Trevor, Westcliff-on-Sea, Essex.
Cornmill Antiques, Ginnel Antiques Centre, The, Harrogate, Yorks North
Cornucopia Antiques, Hebden Bridge, Yorks. West.
Cornucopia, London SW1.
Coromandel, London SW19.
Coronel, H.S., London W11.
Corrall, L. and A.R., Paignton, Devon.
Corrigan Antiques, Paisley, Scotland.
Corrin Antiques, John, Douglas, Isle of Man.
Corry's, Leicester, Leics.
Corry, Mrs E.I., Leicester, Leics.
Corry, P. John, Staveley, Cumbria.
Cossa Antiques, Gabor, Cambridge, Cambs.
Costantini Art & Antiques, Marc, London SW6.
Coster, Sam and Trudie, Hingham, Norfolk.
Cotgrove, R.A.J., London W1.
Cotham Antiques, Bristol, Glos.
Cotham Galleries, Bristol, Glos.
Cotham Hill Bookshop, Bristol, Glos.
Cotswold Antiques. com, Winchcombe, Glos.
Cotswold Galleries, Stow-on-the-Wold, Glos.
Cotswold Pine & Associates, Middle Aston, Oxon.
Cottage Antiques (1984) Ltd, Walsden, Yorks. West.
Cottage Antiques and Curios, Thirsk, Yorks. North.
Cottage Antiques, Chappells Antiques Centre, Bakewell, Derbys.
Cottage Antiques, Leeds, Yorks. West.
Cottage Antiques, Pontefract, Yorks. West.
Cottage Antiques, Ringway, Cheshire.
Cottage Collectables, Holt, Norfolk.
Cottage Curios, Allonby, Cumbria.
Cottage Farm Antiques, Chipping Campden, Glos.
Cottage Style Antiques, Rochester, Kent.
Cotterill, P., Much Wenlock, Shrops.
Cottingley Antiques, Bradford, Yorks. West.
Cotton (Antiques), Joan, West Bridgford, Notts.
Cotton Fine Art, Nick, Watchet, Somerset.
Cotton, Nick and Lynda, Watchet, Somerset.
Couchman, Steve, Canterbury, Kent.
Coughton Galleries Ltd, Arthingworth, Northants.
Coulbon and Sons, Thomas, Sutton Coldfield, West Mids.
Coulborn, P., Sutton Coldfield, West Mids.

Coulter Galleries, York, Yorks. North.
Country and Eastern Ltd., Norwich, Norfolk.
Country Antiques (Wales) Ltd, Kidwelly, Wales.
Country Antiques, Bagshot, Surrey.
Country Antiques, Killearn, Scotland.
Country Antiques, Long Melford, Suffolk.
Country Antiques, The, Antrim, Co. Antrim, N. Ireland.
Country Bedroom, The, Keswick, Cumbria.
Country Clocks, Tring, Herts.
Country Collectables, Fochabers, Scotland.
Country Collector, Pickering, Yorks. North.
Country Cottage Interiors, Kingsley, Staffs.
Country Furniture Shop, Penn, Bucks.
Country House and Cottage Antiques, St Mary, Jersey, C.I.
Country House Antiques, Seething, Norfolk.
Country House Furniture, Easingwold, Yorks. North.
Country Life Antiques, Stow-on-the-Wold, Glos.
Country Life Interiors, Bushey, Herts.
Country Living Antiques, Callington, Cornwall.
Country Markets Antiques and Collectables, Chilton, Oxon.
Country Pine Antiques, Market Bosworth, Leics.
Country Pine Shop, The, West Haddon, Northants.
Country Seat Antiques, Newby East, Cumbria.
Country Seat, The, Huntercombe, Oxon.
Country Seat, The, Llandudno Junction, Wales.
County Antiques, Ashford, Kent.
County Antiques, Ilminster, Somerset.
Court Gallery, The, Nether Stowey, Somerset.
Court House Antique Centre, Sheffield, Yorks. South.
Courtney Ltd, Richard, London SW3.
Courts Miscellany, Leominster, Herefs.
Courtyard Antiques Market, The, Seaford, Sussex East.
Courtyard Antiques, Brackley, Northants.
Courtyard Antiques, Brasted, Kent.
Courtyard Antiques, Coxley, Somerset.
Courtyard Antiques, Williton, Somerset.
Courtyard Collectables, St. Ives, Cornwall.
Cousins and Son, E.W., Ixworth, Suffolk.
Cousins, E.J.A., J.E. and R.W., Ixworth, Suffolk.
Cove Curios, Cove, Scotland.
Cove, Anthony, Windsor and Eton, Berks.
Cove, T. and Mrs K., Swindon, Wilts.
Covent Garden Flea Market, London WC2.
Coward Fine Silver, Timothy, Braunton, Devon.
Cowbridge Antique Centre, Cowbridge, Wales.
Cowderoy Antiques, John, Eastbourne, Sussex East.
Cowderoy, D.J. and R.A., Eastbourne, Sussex East.
Cowen, Christopher, London W8.
Coworth Gallery, The, Sunningdale, Berks.
Cowpland, J.A., Tunbridge Wells, Kent.
Cox and Company, London SW1.
Cox at College Gateway Bookshop, Claude, Ipswich, Suffolk.
Cox's Architectural Reclamation Yard, Moreton-in-Marsh, Glos.
Cox, Anthony, Ipswich, Suffolk.
Cox, John, Craven Arms, Shrops.
Cox, Mr and Mrs R., London SW1.

Cox, Nigel, Wimborne Minster, Dorset.
Crabbe Antiques, Peter , Cambridge, Cambs.
Crabtree, A., Sleaford, Lincs.
Crackston, I., Honiton, Devon.
Cradlewell Antiques, Jesmond, Tyne and Wear.
Craiglea Clocks, Edinburgh, Scotland.
Craik Ltd, Brian and Caroline, Bath, Somerset.
Craik, Angie, Haywards Heath, Sussex West.
Cranbrook Gallery, Cranbrook, Kent.
Cranford Galleries, Knutsford, Cheshire.
Cranglegate Antiques, Swaffham, Norfolk.
Cranston, Enid, Melrose, Scotland.
Craven Gallery, London W2.
Crawford, Alastair, London SW1.
Crawford, M., London N1.
Crawford, M., London SW3.
Crawforth, Andrew, Jubilee Hall Antiques Centre, Lechlade, Glos.
Crawley and Asquith Ltd, London W10.
Crawley, Mrs M., Chislehurst, Kent.
Crawley, R.A. and I.D., Watlington, Oxon.
Crawshaw, H. and E., Lichfield, Staffs.
Creasey, A.A. and S.J., Ipswich, Suffolk.
Creaton, I., St. Helier, Jersey, C.I.
Cree, G.W., Market Deeping, Lincs.
Creek Antiques, London SE10.
Creeke, Miss J.M., Sidmouth, Devon.
Creese-Parsons, S.H., Bath, Somerset.
Cremer-Price, T., Plymouth, Devon.
Cremyll Antiques, Cremyll, Cornwall.
Crest Collectables, Eastbourne, Sussex East.
Crested China Co, The, Driffield, Yorks. East.
Crewe-Read, D., London SW6.
Crewkerne Antique Centre, Crewkerne, Somerset.
Crick Chandeliers, Mrs. M.E., London W8.
Cringle, M. and A., Burnham Market, Norfolk.
Cripps, Lilian, Penrith, Cumbria.
Crispin Antiques, Madeline, London NW1.
Critchlow, Nigel, Shardlow, Derbys.
Crocket, Sue, Brockenhurst, Hants.
Crockwell Antiques, Durham House Antiques Centre, Stow-on-the-Wold, Glos.
Croft Comforts Antiques, Portree, Scotland.
Crofts, Peter A., Wisbech, Cambs.
Cromarty Antiques, Cromarty, Scotland.
Crome Gallery and Frame Shop, Norwich, Norfolk.
Cromwell House Antique Centre, Battlesbridge Antique Centre, Essex
Cronan Ltd, Sandra, London W1.
Crook, Sandra, Stockport, Cheshire.
Crook, W.V. and A., Kidderminster, Worcs.
Crooked Window, The, Dunster, Somerset.
Cross - Fine Paintings, Edward, Weybridge, Surrey.
Cross Antiques, Watlington, Oxon.
Cross Hayes Antiques, Chippenham, Wilts.
Cross Keys Jewellers, Devizes, Wilts.
Cross's Curios, Birmingham, West Mids.
Cross, B. J., Kendal, Cumbria.
Cross, F., Ryde, Isle of Wight.
Cross, John and Valerie, Birmingham, West Mids.
Cross, M. and R., Swaffham, Norfolk.
Crossley, Peter and Mary, Haslingden, Lancs.
Crossroads Antiques, Prestwick, Scotland.
Crouchman, C.C., Shenfield, Essex.
Crown Arcade, London W11.
Crown Silver, London Silver Vaults, London WC2.
Crows Nest, The, Weymouth, Dorset.

Crowson, Colin and Julie, Wainfleet, Lincs.
Crowston, M., Earl Shilton, Leics.
Crowther of Syon Lodge Ltd, London SW1.
Crowther, D.J., Hartlepool, Durham.
Crowther, Mrs V., London SW4.
Crozier, G.R., Bishop's Stortford, Herts.
Crozier, Richard J., Beccles, Suffolk.
Cruck House Antiques, Much Wenlock, Shrops.
Cruz, Mary, Bath, Somerset.
Cry for the Moon, Guildford, Surrey.
Csaky's Antiques, Hook, Hants.
Cudlipp, Jane, Bungay, Suffolk.
Cufflink Shop, The, Antiquarius, London SW3.
Cullen, A. and R.S., Hemel Hempstead, Herts.
Cullen, James, Ripley, Derbys.
Cullompton Antiques Ltd, Cullompton, Devon.
Cullompton Old Tannery Antiques, Cullompton, Devon.
Cullup, S. and K., The Swan at Tetsworth, Oxon.
Cumbley, G.R., King's Lynn, Norfolk.
Cumbria Architectural Salvage, Raughton Head, Cumbria.
Cumbrian Antiques Centre, The, Brampton, Cumbria.
Cumming, A. & Y., Lewes, Sussex East.
Cumming, R.L., Grimsby, Lincs.
Cummins, Cornelius, Bristol, Glos.
Cunnell, Barbara, London SW11.
Cunningham, J.R., Kilmarnock, Scotland.
Cupboard Antiques, The, Amersham, Bucks.
Curá Antiques, London W11.
Curio City, Southend- on- Sea, Essex.
Curios of Chale, Chale, Isle of Wight.
Curiosity Shop, The, South Shields, Tyne and Wear.
Curry, Peter, Finchingfield, Essex.
Curtis, P., London SW3.
Curzon Gallery, The David, London SW19.
Cusack, T., Barnstaple, Devon.
Cutting, Mrs T., Bury St. Edmunds, Suffolk.
Cwmgwili Mill, Carmarthen, Wales.
Cyjer Jewellery Ltd, Grays Antique Markets, London W1.
Cyrlin, Philip, Bond Street Antiques Centre, London W1.
Czerek, John, Dundee, Scotland.

D

D & J Lines Antiques, Wychbold, Worcs.
D & T Architectural Salvage, Birkenhead, Merseyside.
D'Ardenne, D.L and P.J., Branksome, Dorset.
D'Eyncourt, Chertsey, Surrey.
D'Orsai Ltd, Sebastian, London WC1.
D'Oyly, N.H., Saffron Walden, Essex.
D.M. Restorations, Weston-Super-Mare, Somerset.
Da Capo Antiques, Edinburgh, Scotland.
Da Silva, V., Alfies, London NW8.
Dadajan, Grays Antique Markets, London W1.
Dade, Clifford and Roger, Thames Ditton, Surrey.
Dagger, R. K., Farningham, Kent.
Daggett Gallery, Charles, London W11.
Daggett Gallery, London W11.
Daggett, Caroline, London W11.
Daggett, Charles and Caroline, London W11.
Dahling Antiques, Oscar, Croydon, Surrey.
Dahling, Oscar, Croydon, Surrey.
Dairy House Antiques, Semley, Wilts.

Daisycrest Ltd, Grays Antique Markets, London W1.
Dale House Antiques, Moreton-in-Marsh, Glos.
Dale Ltd, Peter, London SW1.
Dale, G.M. and S.M., Wilmslow, Cheshire.
Dale, Joan, Ilchester, Somerset.
Dale, John, London W11.
Daleside Antiques, Markington, Yorks. North.
Dallas, Mrs Wendy, Saintfield, Co. Down, N. Ireland.
Daltrey, Jonathan, The Mall Antiques Arcade, London N1.
Daly, M. and S., Wadebridge, Cornwall.
Daly, Peter M., Winchester, Hants.
Dam Mill Antiques, Codsall, Staffs.
Dams, Tim, Shifnal, Shrops.
Danbury Antiques, Danbury, Essex.
Dance, T.A.B., Martock, Somerset.
Dando, A.P. and J.M., Bath, Somerset.
Dando, Andrew, Bath, Somerset.
Daniel Charles Antiques, Ashbourne, Derbys.
Daniel, Anjula, Brighton, Sussex East.
Daniel, Francoise, Jubilee Hall Antiques Centre, Lechlade, Glos.
Daniel, Francoise, Span Antiques, Woodstock, Oxon.
Daniell, J., Upton-upon-Severn, Worcs.
Daniels, Mrs Gina, Brighton, Sussex East.
Daniels, P., London Silver Vaults, London WC2.
Dann Antiques Ltd, Melksham, Wilts.
Dann, M., Hatherleigh, Devon.
Danz, Gill, Alfies, London NW8.
Daphne's Antiques, Penzance, Cornwall.
Darley, Mike, Coltishall, Norfolk.
Dartmoor Bookshop, Ashburton, Devon.
Daszewski, A.A.W., East Grinstead, Sussex West.
Davenham Antiques Centre, Davenham, Cheshire.
Davey, Alison, Woodseaves, Staffs.
Davey, Mrs P., Blandford Forum, Dorset.
David's, Brampton, Cambs.
David, G., Cambridge, Cambs.
David, P., Aberystwyth, Wales.
Davidson Antiques, Carlton, London N1.
Davidson Antiques, Robert, Todmorden, Yorks. West.
Davidson's The Jewellers Ltd, Newcastle-upon-Tyne, Tyne and Wear.
Davidson, Anthony and Helen, Newcastle-upon-Tyne, Tyne and Wear.
Davidson, Michael, London W11.
Davie, Janet, Pershore, Worcs.
Davies & Son Antiques, Edmund, Whalley, Lancs.
Davies Antiques, London W8.
Davies Gallery, The John, Stow-on-the-Wold, Glos.
Davies Oriental Art, Barry, London W1.
Davies, E. and P., Whalley, Lancs.
Davies, Elinor, Penzance, Cornwall.
Davies, G., Cockermouth, Cumbria.
Davies, H., Coxley, Somerset.
Davies, H.Q.V., London W8.
Davies, John, Piccadilly Antiques, Batheaston, Somerset.
Davies, L., Botley, Hants.
Davies, Mr and Mrs, Chertsey, Surrey.
Davies, P.A., Tunbridge Wells, Kent.
Davies, R.E., Fishguard, Wales.
Davies, W.H., Murton, Wales.
Davies., G.D., South Shields, Tyne and Wear.
Davis (Works of Art) Ltd, Kenneth, London SW1.

Davis Antiquarian Horologist, Roger A., Great Bookham, Surrey.
Davis Ltd, A. B., London W1.
Davis Ltd, Reginald, Oxford, Oxon.
Davis, Amanda, Brighton, Sussex East.
Davis, Andrew, Kew Green, Surrey.
Davis, Jesse, Antiquarius, London SW3.
Davis, Mrs J., Bletchingley, Surrey.
Davison Antiques, Stephanie, Chappells Antiques Centre, Bakewell, Derbys.
Dawes Antiques, Philip, Royston, Herts.
Dawes, Christopher J.L., Huddersfield, Yorks. West.
Dawes, Philip, Durham House Antiques Centre, Stow-on-the-Wold, Glos.
Dawkins, Mrs Lynn, Cranbrook, Kent.
Dawson Furniture Restorers, P., Bentley, Suffolk.
Dawson of Stamford Ltd, Stamford, Lincs.
Dawson, Brian, Leighton Buzzard, Beds.
Dawson, J., Stamford, Lincs.
Day Antiques, Alan, Edinburgh, Scotland.
Day Antiques, Tetbury, Glos.
Day Ltd, Richard, London W1.
Day of Eastbourne Fine Art, John, Eastbourne, Sussex East.
Day, Gillian and Geoff, Enfield, Middx.
Day, Gillian, Rowlands Castle, Hants.
Day, M., London W1.
Day, Vic, Ascot, Berks.
Days of Grace, Budleigh Salterton, Devon.
De Cacqueray, A., London SW1.
De Fresne, Pierre, Edinburgh, Scotland.
De Giles, Gabrielle, Bilsington, Kent.
De Martini, Massimo, London W1.
de Albuquerque Antiques, Wallingford, Oxon.
de Beaumont, Dominic, London NW8.
de Havilland, Adele, Bond Street Antiques Centre, London W1.
de Kort, E.J., Bembridge, Isle of Wight.
de Lotz, P.G., London NW3.
de Rin, V., London SW3.
de Rouffignac, Colin, Wigan, Lancs.
de Ville, Roger, Chappells Antiques Centre, Bakewell, Derbys.
De'Ath, Mrs D. J. A., Huntingdon, Cambs.
Deacon Antiques, Grays Antique Markets, London W1.
Dean Antiques, Colchester, Essex.
Dean's Antiques, Spalding, Lincs.
Dean, Barry, Weybridge, Surrey.
Dean, Mrs B., Spalding, Lincs.
Dearden, Joe, Rye, Sussex East.
Dearden, Martin, East Pennard, Somerset.
Debden Antiques, Debden, Essex.
Debenham Antiques, Debenham, Suffolk.
Decade Antiques & Interiors, Wallasey, Merseyside.
Deco by Design, Fenton Barns, Scotland.
Decodream, Coulsdon, Surrey.
Decographic, Almshouses Arcade, Chichester, Sussex West
Decorative Antiques, Bishop's Castle, Shrops.
Decorative Antiques, London SW6.
Decorator Source, The, Tetbury, Glos.
Decors II Ltd, Deal, Kent.
Deddington Antiques Centre, Deddington, Oxon.
Dee's Antique Pine, Windsor and Eton, Berks.
Dee's Antiques, Hastings Antique Centre, St. Leonards-on-Sea, E. Sussex
Deerstalker Antiques, Whitchurch, Bucks.
Deja Vu Antiques, Leigh-on-Sea, Essex.
Deja Vu Antiques, Shrewsbury, Shrops.

Del-Grosso, Jo, Alfies, London NW8.
Delaforge, Mrs Rita, London W11.
Delawood Antiques, Hunstanton, Norfolk.
Delehar, London W11.
Delehar, Peter, London W11.
Delf, J., London N1.
Delightful Muddle, The, Chichester, Sussex West.
Dellar, P., Potter Heigham, Norfolk.
Delmar Antiques, Hurst Green, Sussex East.
Delomosne and Son Ltd, North Wraxall, Wilts.
Demetzy Books, London W11.
Dench, John, Castle Gate Antiques Centre, Newark, Notts.
Denham Gallery, John, London NW6.
Denham, H., Ripley, Surrey.
Denise, Janet, Dorking, Surrey.
Dennett Coins, Clive, Norwich, Norfolk.
Dennett, C.E., North Cave, Yorks. East.
Denning Antiques, Guildford, Surrey.
Denning, Mrs Sally, Wincanton, Somerset.
Dennis, Mr and Mrs J., Leicester, Leics.
Dennis, P.S., Tewkesbury, Glos.
Dennler Antiques, Guy, Dulverton, Somerset.
Dennys, Nicholas, London SW7.
Denton Antiques, London W8.
Denton, M.T., London W8.
Denton, M.T., London W8.
Denton-Ford, S.J., Long Melford, Suffolk.
Denvir, John, London W11.
Deppner Antiques, Market Drayton, Shrops.
Deppner, J., Market Drayton, Shrops.
Derbyshire Antiques Ltd, Harrogate, Yorks. North.
Derbyshire Clocks, Glossop, Derbys.
Derbyshire, R.C., Harrogate, Yorks. North.
Derham, R., Earsham, Norfolk.
Derventio Books, Derby, Derbys.
Derwentside Antiques, Belper, Derbys.
Deuchar and Son, A.S., Perth, Scotland.
Deuchar, A.S. and A.W.N., Perth, Scotland.
Deutsch Antiques, H. and W., London W8.
Deuxieme, London NW8.
Deva Antiques, Hartley Wintney, Hants.
Dew, Roderick, Eastbourne, Sussex East.
Dewart, Glen, Antiquarius, London SW3
Dewdney, R., Dorking, Surrey.
di Robilant, Edmondo, London W1.
Diamond and Son, Harry, Brighton, Sussex East.
Diamond, R. and H., Brighton, Sussex East.
Dickens Bookshop, Charles, Cowes, Isle of Wight.
Dickens Curios, Frinton-on-Sea, Essex.
Dickens, Colin, Oldbury, West Mids.
Dickenson Fine Silver Ltd, Alastair, London SW1.
Dickins, H.C., Bloxham, Oxon.
Dickins, P. and H.R., Bloxham, Oxon.
Dickinson Ltd, Simon C., London SW1.
Dickinson, Anne-Marie, Nutley, Sussex East.
Dickinson, Bernard, Gargrave, Yorks. North.
Dickinson, D. and B., Bath, Somerset.
Dickinson, J., Chappells Antiques Centre, Bakewell, Derbys.
Dickinson, S.G., D. and N.W., Bath, Somerset.
Dickinson, Simon, London SW1.
Dickson and Lesley Rendall Antiques, Robert, London SW3.
Dickson, J., Lechlade, Glos.
Dickson, R., Bath, Somerset.
Didier Antiques, Kensington Church Street Antiques Centre, London W8.
Didsbury Antiques, Manchester, Lancs.
Dike, L., Bristol, Glos.

Dimmer, I.M. and N.C.S., Cheltenham, Glos.
Dinari, K., London SW6.
Ding, Jacqueline, The Swan at Tetsworth, Oxon.
Dingle, M.R. and M.R., Llanrwst, Wales.
Dining Room Shop, The, London SW13.
Diss Antiques & Interiors, Diss, Norfolk.
Ditchburn-Bosch, Dr. Ursula, Pittenweem, Scotland.
Ditondo, J. and J., Manchester, Lancs.
Dix, S., Hastings, Sussex East.
Dix-Sept, Framlingham, Suffolk.
Dixon Ltd, C.J. and A.J., Bridlington, Yorks. East.
Dixon, Charles, London SW18.
Dixon, Helen, Alfreton, Derbys.
Dixon, Mr and Mrs N., London SW1.
Dixon, Mr. and Mrs N., Blakeney, Glos.
Dobbie, Bob, Fenton Barns, Scotland.
Dobbing, Pete and Elaine, West Burton, Yorks. North.
Dobbyn, David and Alba, Bournemouth, Dorset.
Doble, I., Exeter, Devon.
Dobson's Antiques, Abbots Langley, Herts.
Dobson, G.C and F.W., Abbots Langley, Herts.
Dodd, J., London W1.
Dodd, Robert, London SE10.
Dodd, West Haddon, Northants.
Dodge and Son, Sherborne, Dorset.
Dodge, S., Sherborne, Dorset.
Dodington Antiques, Whitchurch, Shrops.
Dodo, Alfies, London NW8.
Dodson, Gerald, Stockbridge, Hants.
Dodsworth, N.J. and C.S., Spennithorne, Yorks. North.
Dodsworth, Ross, Dorking, Surrey.
Dog Leap Antiques, Newcastle-upon-Tyne, Tyne and Wear.
Doggett, F.C., Somerton, Somerset.
Doghouse (Antiques), The, Walsall, West Mids.
Dolby, D., Shenton, Leics.
Doll's House, The, Northleach, Glos.
Dolleris, A.J., London SW15.
Dolly Land, London N21.
Dolly Mixtures, Birmingham, West Mids.
Dolphin Quay Antique Centre, Emsworth, Hants.
Dolphin Square Antiques, Dorking, Surrey.
Dome Antiques (Exports) Ltd, London N7.
Donaghue, D., Antiquarius, London SW3
Donaldson, Roderick I., Bath, Somerset.
Donay Games & Pastimes, London N1.
Doncaster Sales and Exchange, Doncaster, Yorks. South.
Donn Gallery, Henry, Whitefield, Lancs.
Donn, Henry and Nicholas, Whitefield, Lancs.
Donnachie, R.W., West Byfleet, Surrey.
Donnelly Antique Clocks, Adrian, Shrewsbury, Shrops.
Donnelly, Steven, The Mall Antiques Arcade, London N1.
Donovan, J., The Mall Antiques Arcade, London N1.
Dorchester Antiques, Dorchester-on-Thames, Oxon.
Dorchester Antiques, The Swan at Tetsworth, Oxon.
Dorking Desk Shop, Dorking, Surrey.
Dorking House Antiques, Dorking, Surrey.
Dorothy's Antiques, Sheringham, Norfolk.
Dorridge Antiques & Collectables, Dorridge, West Mids.

Dorset Coin Company, Parkstone, Dorset.
Dorset Reclamation, Bere Regis, Dorset.
Dosanjh, Warren, Great Shelford, Cambs.
Doubleday, S., Colchester, Essex.
Douch & Nicolov, Grays Antique Markets, London W1.
Dougall, Gerald, Alfies, London NW8.
Douglas Antiques, Bobby, Comber, Co. Down, N. Ireland.
Douglas Fine Antiques Ltd, Gavin, London W11.
Douglas, B. and N.R.G., Comber, Co. Down, N. Ireland.
Douglas, Bryan, London Silver Vaults, London WC2.
Douglas, G.A., London W11.
Douwes Fine Art Ltd, London SW1.
Dover Street Gallery, London W1.
Doveridge House Antiques, Wolverhampton, West Mids.
Dower House Antiques, Kendal, Cumbria.
Dowland, C. and V., Whitley Bay, Tyne and Wear.
Dowling and Bray, Looe, Cornwall.
Downes, Shirley Ann, Brighton, Sussex East.
Downey, P., Tetbury, Glos.
Downing, Ralph, Southwell, Notts.
Doyle and Madigan, Lewes, Sussex East.
Doyle Antiques, James, Brighton, Sussex East.
Doyle, Caesar and Reuben, Saintfield, Co. Down, N. Ireland.
Doyle, F.A., Whitby, Yorks. North.
Doyle, J.R., Brighton, Sussex East.
Dragon and the Phoenix, The, South Molton, Devon.
Dragon Antiques, Harrogate, Yorks. North.
Dragon Antiques, Kettering, Northants.
Dragon, The, South Molton, Devon.
Dragons of Walton St. Ltd, London SW3.
Drake, I., Red House Antiques Centre, York, Yorks. North
Drake, Robert, Grays, Essex.
Draper, Andrew, Saltaire, Yorks. West.
Draper, Mr and Mrs, Staplehurst, Kent.
Drawing Room - Interiors & Antiques, The, Pershore, Worcs.
Draysey, Mr and Mrs R., Bournemouth, Dorset.
Draysey, Mr and Mrs R., London SE1.
Drewett, Rosemary, Bradford-on-Avon, Wilts.
Driffold Gallery, Sutton Coldfield, West Mids.
Dring, C. and K.E., Lincoln, Lincs.
Drogin, Marc, Jubilee Hall Antiques Centre, Lechlade, Glos.
Dronfield Antiques, Sheffield, Yorks. South.
Drop Dial Antiques, Bolton, Lancs.
Drummond at Pleasures of Past Times, David, London WC2.
Drummond, J.N., London NW8.
Drummond/Wrawby Moor Art Gallery Ltd, Nicholas, London NW8.
Drummonds Architectural Antiques, Hindhead, Surrey.
Drysdale Ltd, A.F., Edinburgh, Scotland.
Du Cros Antiques, J., Petworth, Sussex West.
Du Cros, J. and P., Petworth, Sussex West.
Dubberley, I.H., Leicester, Leics.
Dubiner, M.J., London W1.
Duc, G.P.A., London W6.
Duck, S., Bristol, Glos.
Duff Antiques, George, Edinburgh, Scotland.
Duff, Sheila, Saintfield, Co. Down, N. Ireland.
Duffy, A.M., Wallasey, Merseyside.

Duggan, David, Bond Street Antiques Centre, London W1.
Duggan, Stuart, The Furniture Cave, London SW10.
Dukeries Antiques, Castle Gate Antiques Centre, Newark, Notts.
Duncan, N., Edinburgh, Scotland.
Dunford, J., Uckfield, Sussex East.
Dunkeld Antiques, Dunkeld, Scotland.
Dunlop, D., Portaferry, Co. Down, N. Ireland.
Dunluce Antiques, Bushmills, Co. Antrim, N. Ireland.
Dunmore Antiques, Kincardine O'Neil, Scotland.
Dunn Antiques, Hamish, Wooler, Northumbs.
Dunn St. James, Chris, The Mall Antiques Arcade, London N1.
Dunn, Mrs J., Freshwater, Isle of Wight.
Dunne, Helen H., Willingham, Cambs.
Dunnett, D., Birmingham, West Mids.
Dunster Antiques, K.W., Staines, Surrey.
Durant, David and Elizabeth, Bristol, Glos.
Durante, Antonio, Alfies, London NW8
Durham House Antiques Centre, Stow-on-the-Wold, Glos.
Durham, M.L. and S.R., Birmingham, West Mids.
Duriez, L., Budleigh Salterton, Devon.
Duriez, L., Exeter, Devon.
Durrant, D. and E., Stockport, Cheshire.
Dusk 'til Dawn, Bristol, Glos.
Dux Antiques, Frank, Bath, Somerset.
Dux, F., Bath, Somerset.
Dycheling Antiques, Ditchling, Sussex East.
Dye, P. and P., Bath, Somerset.
Dyer, A.P., Hayle, Cornwall.
Dyke, Peter, Westerham, Kent.
Dykes, David, Antiquarius, London SW3.
Dylan's Bookstore, Swansea, Wales.
Dynes, Derry Anne, Biggleswade, Beds.
Dyson (Antique Weapons), D.W., Huddersfield, Yorks. West.
Dyson Rooke, Graham and Amanda, Tunbridge Wells, Kent.
Dyson, K., London SW13.
Dytch, D., Dunkeld, Scotland.
Dyte Antiques, John, Burnham-on-Sea, Somerset.
Dyte Antiques, T.M., Highbridge, Somerset.
Dyte, C.W.E., Highbridge, Somerset.
Dzierzek, J. and J., Helmsley, Yorks. North.
Dzierzek, P. and Mrs. T.A., Farningham, Kent.

E

E. R. Antiques Centre, Stockport, Cheshire.
E.K. Antiques, Finedon, Northants.
Ealing Gallery, London W5.
Eames, L., E., S. and C., Hemel Hempstead, Herts.
Earls, Richard and Deby, The Swan at Tetsworth, Oxon.
Earlsfield Bookshop, London SW18.
Earsham Hall Pine, Earsham, Norfolk.
East Side Records, Almshouses Arcade, Chichester, Sussex West
East Street Antiques, Rye, Sussex East.
East-West Antiques, Alfies, London NW8.
Eastbourne Antiques Market, Eastbourne, Sussex East.
Eastgate Antiques, Alfies, London NW8.
Eastgate Antiques, Cowbridge, Wales.
EASY - Edinburgh Architectural Salvage Yard, Edinburgh, Scotland.
Easystrip, Henley-on-Thames, Oxon.
Eaton Gallery, London SW1.

Eccles Road Antiques, London SW11.
Echo Antiques, Reepham, Norfolk.
Echoes, Todmorden, Yorks. West.
Eclectica, London N1.
Ede Ltd, Charles, London W1.
Eden House Antiques, West Auckland, Durham.
Eden, Matthew, Corsham, Wilts.
Eder, V., London N4.
Edgecombe, Sally, Deal, Kent.
Edgeler, John, Winchcombe, Glos.
Edgware Antiques, Edgware, Middx.
Edinburgh Coin Shop, Edinburgh, Scotland.
Edmonds, David, London W4.
Edmonstone, Lady J., Killearn, Scotland.
Edmunds, Andrew, London W1.
Edward's Jewellers, Liverpool, Merseyside.
Edwardian Shop, The, Ipswich, Suffolk.
Edwards, Charles, London SW6.
Edwards, Christopher, London SW11.
Edwards, D. and N., Brereton, Staffs.
Edwards, D., Long Melford, Suffolk.
Edwards, P., Broadstairs, Kent.
Edwards, Vienneta, Tudor House, Stow-on-the-Wold, Glos
Eeles, Adrian , London SW1.
Egerton, Ann and Dale, Alresford, Hants.
Eggleston Antiques, Ben, Long Marton, Cumbria.
Eggleston, Ben and Kay, Long Marton, Cumbria.
Eichler, R.J. and L.L., Whitchurch, Bucks.
Eimer, Christopher, London NW11.
Eisler, Paul, Jubilee Hall Antiques Centre, Lechlade, Glos.
Elden Antiques, Kirk Deighton, Yorks. North.
Eldridge London, London EC1.
Eldridge, B., London EC1.
Electique, Exeter, Devon.
Elias, J.G., Betchworth, Surrey.
Elias, J.G., Dorking, Surrey.
Elisabeth's Antiques, Bond Street Antiques Centre, London W1.
Elizabeth and Son, Ulverston, Cumbria.
Elizabeth Ann Antiques, Chappells Antiques Centre, Bakewell, Derbys.
Elizabeth Antiques, Chappells Antiques Centre, Bakewell, Derbys.
Elizabeth R. Antiques, East Molesey, Surrey.
Elizabethans, Fareham, Hants.
Ellenger, Mrs M., Gomshall, Surrey.
Ellenor Antiques and Tea Shop, Otford, Kent.
Ellenor Hospice Care, Otford, Kent.
Elliott and Scholz Antiques, Eastbourne, Sussex East.
Elliott's, Petworth, Sussex West.
Elliott, C.R., Eastbourne, Sussex East.
Elliott, Lee, Durham House Antiques Centre, Stow-on-the-Wold, Glos.
Elliott, P. D. and A., Totnes, Devon.
Ellis Books, Siri, Bolton, Lancs.
Ellis incorporating Bruntsfield Clocks, Donald, Edinburgh, Scotland.
Ellis, Anne Marie, London W8.
Ellis, D.G. and C.M., Edinburgh, Scotland.
Ellis, G., Moreton-in-Marsh, Glos.
Ellis, G.E., Chester, Cheshire.
Ellis, R., Lincoln, Lincs.
Elm House Antiques, Merstham, Surrey.
Elm Tree Antiques, Flaxton, Yorks. North.
Elsom - Antiques, Pamela, Ashbourne, Derbys.
Elsworth - Beaconsfield Ltd, June, Beaconsfield, Bucks.
Elsworth, Mrs J., Beaconsfield, Bucks.
Elton, S.P., Beckenham, Kent.

Elvins, T. and L., Church Stretton, Shrops.
Elwes and Hanham Ltd, London W1.
Elwes, Ben, London W1.
Emanouel Corporation (UK) Ltd, London W1.
Embden, K.B., London WC2.
Emburey, Mrs G.D., Dorking, Surrey.
Emerald Isle Books, Belfast, N. Ireland.
Emerson, I., Armagh, Co. Armagh, N. Ireland.
Emery, Vicki, Petworth, Sussex West.
Empire Exchange, Manchester, Lancs.
Emporium Antique Centre, The, Lewes, Sussex East.
Emporium Antiques, Collectibles & Craft Centre , The, Welling, Kent.
Emporium, The, Pontarddulais, Wales.
Enchanted Aviary, The, Bury St. Edmunds, Suffolk.
Engine 'n' Tender, London SE25.
England's Gallery, Leek, Staffs.
England, F.J. and S., Leek, Staffs.
English and Continental Antiques, Eye, Suffolk.
English Country Antiques, Uffculme, Devon.
English Heritage, Bridgnorth, Shrops.
English Rose Antiques, Coggeshall, Essex.
English, Toby, Wallingford, Oxon.
Enoch, George, Alfies, London NW8.
Enterprise Collectors Market, Eastbourne, Sussex East.
Eprile, R., Edinburgh, Scotland.
Erbrich, Rosemary, Grays Antique Markets, London W1.
Ernstone, Bernard and Margaret, Hale, Cheshire.
Eskdale Antiques, Sleights, Yorks. North.
Eskenazi Ltd, John, London W1.
Eskenazi Ltd, London W1.
Eskenazi, D.M., London W1.
Eskenazi, J.E., London W1.
Essex Antiques, Richard, Langford, Somerset.
Essex, B.R. and C.L., Langford, Somerset.
Essie Carpets, London W1.
Etcetera Etc Antiques, Seaton, Devon.
Etheridge, B., Burford, Oxon.
Etheridge, John W., Debenham, Suffolk.
Eton Antique Bookshop, Windsor and Eton, Berks.
Eton Antiques Partnership, Windsor and Eton, Berks.
Eton Gallery, Windsor and Eton, Berks.
Europa House Antiques, London SE1.
European Fine Arts and Antiques, Preston, Lancs.
Evans and Evans, Alresford, Hants.
Evans Antiques, Steven, Treorchy, Wales.
Evans, Ann, Valley, Wales.
Evans, B., Burford, Oxon.
Evans, D. and N., Alresford, Hants.
Evans, D., A. and M., Templeton, Wales.
Evans, H.S., Bristol, Glos.
Evans, Mark, London W1.
Evans, Mrs M., Llangollen, Wales.
Evans, Steven, Treorchy, Wales.
Everard, S., Woolhampton, Berks.
Everett Fine Art Ltd, West Buckland, Somerset.
Everett, Tim and Karen, West Buckland, Somerset.
Eversley Antiques, Eversley, Hants.
Eves, Adrian, London SW6.
Evison, Richard, Alfreton, Derbys.
Evonne Antiques, Grays Antique Markets, London W1.
Ewing, J.F., London W11.

Goodman, R.J., Tunbridge Wells, Kent.
Goodson, Christina, Warwick, Warks.
Goodwin and Sons, John, Warwick, Warks.
Goodwin's Antiques Ltd, Edinburgh, Scotland.
Goodwin, Margaret, East Rudham, Norfolk.
Goodwin, Pamela, Tunbridge Wells, Kent.
Goodwin, Peter, London SW6.
Goodwood Antiques, Lamb Arcade, Wallingford, Oxon
Goodyer, Nicholas, London N5.
Gooley, P., London W9.
Gopsill, Graham, Worcester, Worcs.
Gora, A.D., Pateley Bridge, Yorks. North.
Gordon, Brian, Antiquarius, London SW3
Gordon, G., London NW8.
Gordon, Mrs Marilyn, Melton Mowbray, Leics.
Gordons Medals Ltd, Grays Antique Markets, London W1.
Gore, Theresa, Alfies, London NW8.
Gorman, Mrs J.M., Barlow, Derbys.
Goslett Gallery, Roland, Richmond, Surrey.
Gosling Antiques, Alison, Budleigh Salterton, Devon.
Goss and Crested China Centre and Goss Museum, Waterlooville, Hants.
Gottlieb, Marie, Alfies, London NW8.
Gouby, M., London W8.
Gough Books, Simon, Holt, Norfolk.
Gough, B.A., Carshalton, Surrey.
Gough, Maureen, Jubilee Hall Antiques Centre, Lechlade, Glos.
Gould and Co., Herbert, Holywood, Co. Down, N. Ireland.
Gould and Julian Gonnermann Antiques, Betty, London N6.
Gould at Ocean Leisure, Gillian, London WC2.
Gould, Gillian, The Swan at Tetsworth, Oxon.
Gould, James and Stephanie, Exeter, Devon.
Gould, Patricia, Alfies, London NW8.
Goulding, G., Middleton Village, Lancs.
Govan, David, Edinburgh, Scotland.
Government House, Winchcombe, Glos.
Gow Antiques, Forfar, Scotland.
Gow, Jeremy, Forfar, Scotland.
Gowen, M., St. Leonards-on-Sea, Sussex East.
Gower, C., Stow-on-the-Wold, Glos.
Graftons of Market Harborough, Market Harborough, Leics.
Graham and Dianne, Red House Antiques Centre, York, Yorks. North
Graham and Green, London W11.
Graham Gallery, Burghfield Common, Berks.
Graham Gallery, Gavin, London W11.
Graham Gallery, Neil, Brentwood, Essex.
Graham Gallery, The, London W1.
Graham, A., London W11.
Graham, Anthony, Petworth, Sussex West.
Graham, Colin, Cockermouth, Cumbria.
Graham, J., Ross-on-Wye, Herefs.
Graham, Joss, London SW1.
Graham, M.J., Alston, Cumbria.
Grahame, R.G., Grays Antique Markets, London W1.
Grahams of Colchester, Colchester, Essex.
Granary Collectables, Kendal, Cumbria.
Grange Gallery - Fine Arts Ltd, St. Saviour, Jersey, C.I.
Grannie Used To Have One, Longhaven, Scotland.
Grannie's Parlour, Hull, Yorks. East.
Grannie's Treasures, Hull, Yorks. East.
Grannies, Framlingham, Suffolk.

Granny's Attic, Nottingham, Notts.
Granny's Attic, Ramsgate, Kent.
Granny's Cupboard, Wisbech, Cambs.
Grant Antiques, Denzil, Drinkstone, Suffolk.
Grant Books, Droitwich, Worcs.
Grant's Antiques, Barnard Castle, Durham.
Grant, Carl, Barnard Castle, Durham.
Grant, P., Hastings Antique Centre, St. Leonards-on-Sea, E. Sussex.
Grantham Clocks, Grantham, Lincs.
Grantham Furniture Emporium, Grantham, Lincs.
Granville Antiques, London SW10.
Grate Expectations (Fireplaces), Washington, Tyne and Wear.
Grate Expectations, The Swan at Tetsworth, Oxon.
Grater, C., Eye, Suffolk.
Grater, S., Eye, Suffolk.
Gratwick, A., Hartley Wintney, Hants.
Graus Antiques, Bond Street Silver Galleries, London W1.
Graven Image, Kensington Church Street Antiques Centre, London W8.
Gray Antiques, Laila, Kingsthorpe, Northants.
Gray's Antique Centre, Portsmouth, Hants.
Gray's Antiques, Worcester, Worcs.
Gray's Interiors, Worcester, Worcs.
Gray, Alexandra J., Portsmouth, Hants.
Gray, David, Worcester, Worcs.
Gray, G.C.M., Hertford, Herts.
Gray, Lynne, Berwick-upon-Tweed, Northumbs.
Gray, M. and M., Saltaire, Yorks. West.
Gray, M., Aberdeen, Scotland.
Gray, Mr and Mrs A., Penrith, Cumbria.
Graylings Antiques, Andover, Hants.
Grays Antique Markets, London W1.
Great Brampton House Antiques Ltd, Hereford, Herefs.
Great Expectations, Blackburn, Lancs.
Great Expectations, Horncastle, Lincs.
Great Grooms Antique Centre, Billingshurst, Sussex West.
Great Grooms of Hungerford, Hungerford, Berks.
Great Malvern Antiques, Great Malvern, Worcs.
Great Northern Architectural Antique Company Ltd, The, Tattenhall, Cheshire.
Greatrix, J., Hemel Hempstead, Herts.
Greatrix, J., Hursley, Hants.
Greaves, H.J., Sheffield, Yorks. South.
Greco, Linette, Alfies, London NW8.
Green and Son, J., Queniborough, Leics.
Green and Stone, London SW3.
Green Antiques, Anthony, Bond Street Antiques Centre, London W1.
Green Dragon Antiques Centre, Wincanton, Somerset.
Green Lane Antiques, Ormskirk, Lancs.
Green Pine & Country Antiques, Michael, Harrogate, Yorks. North.
Green's Antique Galleries, London W8.
Green, Derek and Sally, Hartley Wintney, Hants.
Green, Jeremy, Petworth, Sussex West.
Green, Laurence, Manchester, Lancs.
Green, M.A., Weston, Herts.
Green, Michael, Nicholas and Christopher, Towcester, Northants.
Green, N. and J., Coventry, West Mids.
Green, O.D., M.E. and W.T.E., North Walsham, Norfolk.
Green, P., Romiley, Cheshire.
Green, R., Queniborough, Leics.

Green, R.J., Colchester, Essex.
Green, Richard, London W1.
Green, Ron, Towcester, Northants.
Green, S., London W8.
Green, T. and A., Lamb Arcade, Wallingford, Oxon
Green, Vivian and Roger, Aldermaston, Berks.
Greenaway, T., London W1.
Greenberg, C.B. and P.R., Honiton, Devon.
Greenfield and Son, Gunmakers (Est. 1805), H.S., Canterbury, Kent.
Greenfield, T.S., Canterbury, Kent.
Greengrass Antiques, Chobham, Surrey.
Greengrass, D., Chobham, Surrey.
Greenman, Sam, London N12.
Greens of Cheltenham Ltd, Cheltenham, Glos.
Greenslade, C. and L., Sherborne, Dorset.
Greenwall Antiques, Jonathan, Sandgate, Kent.
Greenway Antiques, Colin, Witney, Oxon.
Greenwich Antiques Market, London SE10.
Greenwich Gallery, The, London SE10.
Greenwood (Fine Art), W., Burneston, Yorks. North.
Greenwood, Judy, London SW6.
Greer, Robin, London SW6.
Gregg Antiques, Marion, Durham House Antiques Centre, Stow-on-the-Wold, Glos.
Gregory Gallery, Martyn, London SW1.
Gregory, Bottley and Lloyd, London SW6.
Gregory, George, Bath, Somerset.
Gregory, H. and C., London W11.
Gregory, Henry, London W11.
Gregory, M., London SW1.
Gregory, Michael, Chale, Isle of Wight.
Gregory, Mrs G., Churt, Surrey.
Gregory, N., Wendover, Bucks.
Greig, Lindy, London SW15.
Gremner, Bjorn, London W8.
Grenier, Le, The Swan at Tetsworth, Oxon.
Gresham Books, Crewkerne, Somerset.
Grey-Harris and Co, Bristol, Glos.
Greystoke Antiques, Sherborne, Dorset.
Grice Antiques, Alan, Ormskirk, Lancs.
Gridley, Gordon, London N1.
Griffin Antiques Ltd, Simon, London W1.
Griffin Fine Art & Antiques, The Swan at Tetsworth, Oxon.
Griffin, G.E., Croydon, Surrey.
Griffin, Janet and Nick, Leighton Buzzard, Beds.
Griffin, S.J., London W1.
Griffith, J.J., Canterbury, Kent.
Griffiths Antiques, David, London N1.
Griffiths, J., Bath, Somerset.
Griffiths, N.K., Weedon, Northants.
Griffiths, P., Narberth, Wales.
Griffiths, Richard, Tetbury, Glos.
Griffiths, W. and B., Burscough, Lancs.
Grimes House Antiques & Fine Art, Moreton-in-Marsh, Glos.
Grimes Militaria, Chris, Bristol, Glos.
Gripper, Robert, Ascott-under-Wychwood, Oxon.
Grodzinski, W., London SW7.
Groombridge,Sarah, Grays Antique Markets, London W1.
Grosvenor Antiques and Interiors, Chester, Cheshire.
Grosvenor House Interiors, Beaconsfield, Bucks.
Grosvenor Prints, London WC2.
Grote, Ulrich, Penzance, Cornwall.

Grove Antiques Centre, The, Honiton, Devon.
Grove Antiques, Darwen, Lancs.
Grove Bookshop, The, Ilkley, Yorks. West.
Grover, D.R., Chichester, Sussex West.
Groves, Elfyn and Elaine, Woburn, Beds.
Groves, M.A. and A., Doveridge, Derbys.
Groves, Steven and Caroline, Melbury Osmond, Dorset.
Grunfeld, N., Cirencester, Glos.
Guest & Gray, Grays Antique Markets, London W1.
Guest Antiques, Karen, Beverley, Yorks. East.
Guest Antiques, Karen, Driffield, Yorks. East.
Guildhall Fair - Chester, Chester, Cheshire.
Guildhall Street Antiques, Bury St. Edmunds, Suffolk.
Guillesarian, Alice, Grays Antique Markets, London W1.
Guillou-Emary, Alfies, London NW8.
Guinevere Antiques, London SW6.
Guiver, Trevor, Malvern Link, Worcs.
Gullane Antiques, Gullane, Scotland.
Gumb, Linda, Grays Antique Markets, London W1.
Gumbrell, K., Hastings Antique Centre, St. Leonards-on-Sea, E. Sussex
Guthrie, L.W. and R.M., Shipston-on-Stour, Warks.
Gutlin Clocks and Antiques, London SW6.
Gwilliam, D.L., Bruton, Somerset.
Gwilliam, Edred A.F., Cricklade, Wilts.
Gwilliams, Ray, Weybridge, Surrey.
Gwydir Street Antiques Centre, Cambridge, Cambs.
Gwynfair Antiques, Holyhead (Anglesey), Wales.
Gyte, P.S., Ripon, Yorks. North.

H

H.L.B. Antiques, Bournemouth, Dorset.
Haas (A. and M. Rosenthal), Otto, London NW3.
Hacker, Peter F., Harrogate, Yorks. North.
Hackler's Jewellers, Preston, Lancs.
Hackney House Antiques, Barlow, Derbys.
Haddow, P.M., Old Cornmarket Antiques Centre, Warwick, Warks.
Hadfield (Hon. FBHI), G.K. and J.V., Great Salkeld, Cumbria.
Hadfield, G.K., Great Salkeld, Cumbria.
Hadfield-Tilly, D.W. and N.R., Great Salkeld, Cumbria.
Hadi, Abdul, Grays Antique Markets, London W1.
Hadji Baba Ancient Art, London W1.
Hadley Bookseller, Peter J., Norwich, Norfolk.
Hadlow Down Antiques, Hadlow Down, Sussex East.
Hage, Mrs E., Bond Street Antiques Centre, London W1.
Hagen, Richard, Broadway, Worcs.
Hakemi, Farah, Grays Antique Markets, London W1.
Hakeney Antiques, David, Hull, Yorks. East.
Halcyon Antiques, Stockport, Cheshire.
Halcyon Days, London EC3.
Halcyon Days, London W1.
Haldane, J., Finningham, Suffolk.
Hales Antiques, Robert, London W8.
Hales, Roger, Malvern Link, Worcs.
Halewood and Sons, Preston, Lancs.
Halewood, M., Preston, Lancs.
Haley, S., Halifax, Yorks. West.

Haliden Oriental Rug Shop, Bath, Somerset.
Halifax Antiques Centre, Halifax, Yorks. West.
Hall Ltd, Douglas, Brighton, Sussex East.
Hall's Bookshop, Tunbridge Wells, Kent.
Hall, Anthony C., Twickenham, Middx.
Hall, Jacqueline, Tetbury, Glos.
Hall, L.M., Great Malvern, Worcs.
Hall, Liza, Nutley, Sussex East.
Hall, Robert, London W1.
Hall, S., Burford, Oxon.
Hall, Stephen, Alfies, London NW8.
Hall-Bakker, Liz , Span Antiques, Woodstock, Oxon
Hallberg, Mrs Vivien, Horncastle, Lincs.
Haller, Mrs B. J., Deddington, Oxon.
Hallesy, H., Swansea, Wales.
Hallidays (Fine Antiques) Ltd, Dorchester-on-Thames, Oxon.
Hallmark Jewellers, Brighton, Sussex East.
Halsall Hall Antiques, Southport Antiques Centre, Southport, Merseyside
Hamblin, J. and M. A., Yeovil, Somerset.
Hamblin, John, Yeovil, Somerset.
Hamilton and Co, A.D., Glasgow, Scotland.
Hamilton Antiques, Anne, Burnham Market, Norfolk.
Hamilton Antiques, Woodbridge, Suffolk.
Hamilton Billiards & Games Co., Knebworth, Herts.
Hamilton Ltd, Ross, London SW1.
Hamilton, Angela, Birmingham, West Mids.
Hamilton, H., Knebworth, Herts.
Hamilton, K. and J.E., Grantham, Lincs.
Hamilton, M. & J., London Silver Vaults, London WC2.
Hamilton, Nikki, Long Melford, Suffolk.
Hamilton, S., Brockenhurst, Hants.
Hamlyn Lodge, Ollerton, Notts.
Hammond Antiques, Jeffery, Leominster, Herefs.
Hammond, D. and R., Buxton, Derbys.
Hammond, G.and M., Chipping Campden, Glos.
Hammond, J. and E., Leominster, Herefs.
Hampden Trading Company, The, Great Missenden, Bucks.
Hampshire Gallery, Bournemouth, Dorset.
Hampshires of Dorking, Dorking, Surrey.
Hampstead Antique and Craft Emporium, London NW3.
Hampton Court Emporium, East Molesey, Surrey.
Hampton Court Palace Antiques, East Molesey, Surrey.
Hampton Gallery, Tetbury, Glos.
Hampton, G., Christchurch, Dorset.
Hamptons, Christchurch, Dorset.
Hanborough Antiques, Long Hanborough, Oxon.
Hanbury Antiques, Hitchin, Herts.
Hanbury, Mrs M.D., Hitchin, Herts.
Hance, J. and D., Stow-on-the-Wold, Glos.
Hancock Antiques, Peter, Chichester, Sussex West.
Hancock, Mike, Needham Market, Suffolk.
Hancocks and Co, London W1.
Hand in Hand, Coldstream, Scotland.
Hand, Mrs Ruth, Coldstream, Scotland.
Handbury-Madin, Ruth and Greville, Shrewsbury, Shrops.
Hanham, William, London W1.
Hanlon, W. and J., Menston, Yorks. West.
Hannam, Nick, London SW4.
Hannen, L.G., London W1.
Hanover Antiques & Collectables, Scarborough, Yorks. North.

Hansen Chard Antiques, Pershore, Worcs.
Hanshan Tang Books, London SW15.
Hansord & Son, David J., Lincoln, Lincs.
Hansord, David, John and Anne, Lincoln, Lincs.
Harby, Diane, Grays Antique Markets, London W1.
Harcourt Antiques, London W1.
Harcourt, P., London W1.
Hardie Antiques, Perth, Scotland.
Hardie, Ross, Chipping Campden, Glos.
Hardie, T., Edinburgh, Scotland.
Hardie, T.G., Perth, Scotland.
Harding's World of Mechanical Music, Keith, Northleach, Glos.
Harding, A., Gravesend, Kent.
Harding, FBHI, K., Northleach, Glos.
Harding, Hugh, Cambridge, Cambs.
Harding, Mrs J., Duffield, Derbys.
Harding, Mrs Janet, Depden, Suffolk.
Harding, N.J., Tunbridge Wells, Kent.
Harding, R., London W1.
Hardman, Laurens R., Southport, Merseyside.
Hardwick Antiques, Walsall, West Mids.
Hardwick, Trevor and Linda, Rotherham, Yorks. South.
Hardy and Co, James, London SW3.
Hardy Antiques Ltd, James, Barnard Castle, Durham.
Hardy Country, Melbury Osmond, Dorset.
Hardy Pine and Country Furniture, Joyce, Hacheston, Suffolk.
Hardy's Collectables, Bournemouth, Dorset.
Hardy, A., London W1.
Hardy, Alan, Barnard Castle, Durham.
Hardy, J., Bournemouth, Dorset.
Hare, Allan G., Cirencester, Glos.
Hare-Walker, Terry, Old Cornmarket Antiques Centre, Warwick, Warks.
Hares, Cirencester, Glos.
Harkin, D., London NW10.
Harkins Oriental Art, Brian, London SW1.
Harkness, C. S., Edinburgh, Scotland.
Harkness, N. and E., Bournemouth, Dorset.
Harlequin Antiques, Edinburgh, Scotland.
Harlequin Antiques, Grantham, Lincs.
Harlequin Antiques, Nottingham, Notts.
Harlequin Antiques, Porthcawl, Wales.
Harlequin Gallery and Golden Goose Globe Restorers, Lincoln, Lincs.
Harley Antiques, Christian Malford, Wilts.
Harley, Anthony, London SW6.
Harley, G.J., Christian Malford, Wilts.
Harman's Antiques, Dorking, Surrey.
Harman, Paul and Nicholas, Dorking, Surrey.
Harmandian, G., Bath, Somerset.
Harmer, Steve, Eye, Suffolk.
Harms, A., London N6.
Harness Antiques, Jack, Marlow, Bucks.
Harper Antiques, Martin and Dorothy, Bakewell, Derbys.
Harper Fine Paintings, Poynton, Cheshire.
Harper, D. A., Derby, Derbys.
Harper, David, Barnard Castle, Durham.
Harper, P.R., Poynton, Cheshire.
Harper-James, Montrose, Scotland.
Harriet Ann Sleigh Beds, Rolvenden, Kent.
Harrington, Adrian, London W8.
Harrington, Mrs M., London SW3.
Harris & Holt, Chester, Cheshire.
Harris (Jewellery) Ltd, Jonathan, London EC1.
Harris Antiques (Stansted), Stansted, Essex.
Harris Antiques, Colin, Eversley, Hants.
Harris Antiques, Colin, Hartley Wintney, Hants.

Harris Lindsay, London SW1.
Harris, A.R., Stourbridge, West Mids.
Harris, Anita, Jubilee Hall Antiques Centre, Lechlade, Glos.
Harris, C. J., Lewes, Sussex East.
Harris, E.C., D. I. and J., London EC1.
Harris, F.A.D. and B.D.A., Stansted, Essex.
Harris, Ian, London SW1.
Harris, Jonathan, London SW1.
Harris, K., Coventry, West Mids.
Harris, M. S., Swinford, Leics.
Harris, Martin, Grays Antique Markets, London W1.
Harris, S., Stockport, Cheshire.
Harris, Sandra, Chester, Cheshire.
Harris, Steve, Hawarden, Wales.
Harrison Fine Antiques, Anna, Gosforth, Tyne and Wear.
Harrison Fine Art, John, Aston Tirrold, Oxon.
Harrison Steen Ltd, Chorley, Lancs.
Harrison, Beryl and Brian, Durham House Antiques Centre, Stow-on-the-Wold, Glos.
Harrison, J., Newtonmore, Scotland.
Harrison, J.M.C., Aston Tirrold, Oxon.
Harrison, John, Chepstow, Wales.
Harrison, R., London W11.
Harrison, Richard, Grays Antique Markets, London W1.
Harrods Ltd, London SW1.
Harrop Fold Clocks (F. Robinson), Bolton-by-Bowland, Lancs.
Hart and John Giles, Sheila, Aylsham, Norfolk.
Hart Antiques and Interiors, Bridgend, Wales.
Hart, Ann and Bernard, London NW3.
Hart, J.B., Cowfold, Sussex West.
Hart, J.A. and N., Bletchingley, Surrey.
Hart, Mrs Cheryl, Bridgend, Wales.
Hart, Mrs Elizabeth, Ceres, Scotland.
Hart, Rosemary, London N1.
Hart, Sylvia, Bournemouth, Dorset.
Hartley Antiques Ltd, J., Ripley, Surrey.
Hartley, Philip, Deal, Kent.
Hartley, S.N., Wingham, Kent.
Hartnoll, Julian, London SW1.
Hartogs, Goya, Alfies, London NW8.
Harvey & Co (Antiques) Ltd, W.R., Witney, Oxon.
Harvey and Gore, London SW1.
Harvey Antiques and Decoration, Patricia, London NW8.
Harvey, C.S., Ludlow, Shrops.
Harvey, John, The Mall Antiques Arcade, London N1.
Harvey, Kenneth, The Furniture Cave, London SW10
Harvey, Korin, Grays Antique Markets, London W1.
Harvey, Mrs Jacqui, Longhaven, Scotland.
Harvey, Mrs P., Weybridge, Surrey.
Harvey, Victoria, London NW8.
Harvey-Jones, A., Woodbridge, Suffolk.
Harvey-Lee, Elizabeth, North Aston, Oxon.
Harvey-Morgan, R., Stratford-upon-Avon, Warks.
Harwich Antiques Centre, Harwich, Essex.
Haslam and Whiteway, London W8.
Haslam, Katherine, Olney, Bucks.
Haslam-Hopwood, R.G.G., Wadebridge, Cornwall.
Haslemere Antique Market, Haslemere, Surrey.
Hassell, Geoff, Cheltenham, Glos.
Hastie, Caroline, London SW10.
Hastings Antique Centre, The, St. Leonards-on-Sea, Sussex East.
Hastings-Spital, K., Bath, Somerset.

Hatch Rugs, Gideon, London SW11.
Hatchwell Antiques, Simon, The Furniture Cave, London SW10.
Hatherleigh Antiques, Hatherleigh, Devon.
Hatrell, Satoe, Grays Antique Markets, London W1.
Haughey Antiques, Kirkby Stephen, Cumbria.
Haughey, D.M., Kirkby Stephen, Cumbria.
Haughton Antiques, Brian, London W1.
Havard and Havard, Cowbridge, Wales.
Havard, Philip and Christine, Cowbridge, Wales.
Havard, T. and P., Harpole, Northants.
Havelocks, Harrogate, Yorks. North.
Haven Antiques, Wainfleet, Lincs.
Havenplan's Architectural Emporium, Killamarsh, Derbys.
Havlik, Jan, Bond Street Antiques Centre, London W1.
Haw, S., Haslemere, Surrey.
Hawkey, V., Grimsby, Lincs.
Hawkins & Hawkins, Edinburgh, Scotland.
Hawkins The Lanes Armoury, Mark and David, Brighton, Sussex East.
Hawkins, B., London E11.
Hawkins, Emma H., Edinburgh, Scotland.
Hawkins, G. and J., Cambridge, Glos.
Hawkridge, Mrs M., Skipton, Yorks. North.
Hawley Antiques, Beverley, Yorks. East.
Haworth, Mrs Christine, Blackburn, Lancs.
Haworth, Peter, Beetham, Cumbria.
Hawthorn Ltd, Gerard, London W1.
Hay Antique Market, Hay-on-Wye, Wales.
Hay, Henry, Alfies, London NW8.
Haybarn and Bridgebarn Antique Centres, Battlesbridge Antique Centre, Essex
Haydon, Brian, Whitwick, Leics.
Haydon, Mrs Maureen, Chichester, Sussex West.
Hayes, Miss M.L., North Shields, Tyne and Wear.
Haygate Gallery, Telford, Shrops.
Hayhurst Fine Glass, Jeanette, London W8.
Haylett, A.P. and M.A., Outwell, Cambs.
Hayman & Hayman, Antiquarius, London SW3
Haynes - Antiques Finder, Roger, Leek, Staffs.
Haynes Fine Art of Broadway, Broadway, Worcs.
Haynes, A.C., Broadway, Worcs.
Haynes, John, Littlehampton, Sussex West.
Hayward, Andy, Cirencester, Glos.
Hayward, D.H. and M.S., Kingsbridge, Devon.
Hayward, Pat, Lamb Arcade, Wallingford, Oxon
Hayward, Rachel, London N1.
Hazel of Brecon, Brecon, Wales.
Hazel, Guy, Sonning-on-Thames, Berks.
Hazell, S.B. and M.J., London SW8.
Hazell, S.B. and M.J., York, Yorks. North.
Hazledine, Anthony, Fairford, Glos.
Hazlitt, Gooden and Fox Ltd, London SW1.
Head, J. and J., Salisbury, Wilts.
Head, P., St. Peter Port , Guernsey, C.I.
Headrow Antiques Centre, Leeds, Yorks. West.
Heads 'n' Tails, Wiveliscombe, Somerset.
Heanor Antiques Centre, Heanor, Derbys.
Heap, Mrs M.M., Burnham-on-Sea, Somerset.
Heape's Antiques, Burnham-on-Sea, Somerset.
Hearn, K.E., Penzance, Cornwall.

Hearnden, J. and S., Dorchester-on-Thames, Oxon.
Hearne, N.J., Beaconsfield, Bucks.
Hearne, R.E.W., Beaconsfield, Bucks.
Hearth & Home, Penrith, Cumbria.
Heath Antiques, Mike, Newport, Isle of Wight.
Heath, M. and B., Newport, Isle of Wight.
Heath-Bullock, Roger, Mary and Charlotte, Godalming, Surrey.
Heath-Bullocks, Godalming, Surrey.
Heathcote Antiques, Cross Hills, Yorks. North.
Heather, J.C., Woolpit, Suffolk.
Heathfield Antiques & Country Pine, Holt, Norfolk.
Heathfield, J.E., H.B. and S.M., Holt, Norfolk.
Heatley, Paul and Barbara, Ashburton, Devon.
Heaton Antiques, Bradford, Yorks. West.
Hebbard, I., Titchfield, Hants.
Hebbard, P.E., Hay-on-Wye, Wales.
Hebbards of Hay, Hay-on-Wye, Wales.
Hebert, Janice, Hurst Green, Sussex East.
Hedges, J., Salisbury, Wilts.
Hedingham Antiques & Interiors, Sible Hedingham, Essex.
Hedley's of Hexham, Hexham, Northumbs.
Hedley, Mrs E., Maldon, Essex.
Heidarieh, Mo, ,Alfies, London NW8.
Heirloom & Howard Limited, West Yatton, Wilts.
Heirlooms Antique Jewellers and Silversmiths, Wareham, Dorset.
Heirlooms, Worcester, Worcs.
Helena's Collectables, Shere, Surrey.
Helios & Co (Antiques), Weedon, Northants.
Hemswell Antiques Centres, Hemswell Cliff, Lincs.
Hen's Teeth Antiques, The Swan at Tetsworth, Oxon.
Henderson, Elizabeth, London SW11.
Henderson, F.M., Arundel, Sussex West.
Henderson, J.G., Perth, Scotland.
Henderson, Jean and Jenny, Cromarty, Scotland.
Henderson, Perth, Scotland.
Heneage Art Books, Thomas, London SW1.
Henham (Antiques), Martin, London N2.
Henley Antiques Centre, Henley-in-Arden, Warks.
Henley House Antiques, Rumford, Cornwall.
Hennell, Andrew, Woodstock, Oxon.
Hennessy, Carl, Crewkerne, Somerset.
Hennessy, Crewkerne, Somerset.
Henry & Co, Benjamin, Chappells Antiques Centre, Bakewell, Derbys.
Henry's of Ash, Ash, Kent.
Henry, Elizabeth, Lower Stondon, Beds.
Henson, Dennis, Nottingham, Notts.
Henson, E.J., Exeter, Devon.
Henstridge, W.V., Bournemouth, Dorset.
Hepburn, George, Alfies, London NW8.
Hepburn, T. and N., Twyford, Norfolk.
Hepner, R.P., Knutsford, Cheshire.
Heppell, Patricia, The Swan at Tetsworth, Oxon.
Hepworth Fine Art Dealers, Anthony, Bath, Somerset.
Hepworth Fine Art, Gordon, Newton St. Cyres, Devon.
Hepworth, C.G. and I.M., Newton St. Cyres, Devon.
Herald Antiques, Marcelline, Windsor and Eton, Berks.

J.V. Pianos and Cambridge Pianola Company, Landbeach, Cambs.

Jackdaw Antiques Centres, Henley-on-Thames, Oxon.

Jackman, F.T. and J., Jesmond, Tyne and Wear.

Jackson Antiques, Peter, Brackley, Northants.

Jackson, Allan K L, Edinburgh, Scotland.

Jackson, Charles, Westcliff-on-Sea, Essex.

Jackson, G. and A., Leamington Spa, Warks.

Jackson, K., London SW6.

Jackson, Lee, London WC2.

Jackson, Miss A.E., Chesham, Bucks.

Jackson, P. and V.E., London SW3.

Jackson, P., Blackpool, Lancs.

Jackson, P., Windsor and Eton, Berks.

Jackson, R. and J., Flaxton, Yorks. North.

Jackson, S. and Mrs T., Sutton Bridge, Lincs.

Jackson, S. and Mrs T.J., Sutton Bridge, Lincs.

Jackson-Grant Antiques, Teynham, Kent.

Jackson-Grant, D.M., Teynham, Kent.

Jackson-Harris, Valerie, London W11.

Jacob, Robert, London SE13.

Jacobs Antique Centre, Cardiff, Wales.

Jacobs Gallery, Grays Antique Markets, London W1.

Jacobs, Alan, Grays Antique Markets, London W1.

Jacobs, Lionel, Richmond, Surrey.

Jacobs, Peter and Maggie, Bradford-on-Avon, Wilts.

Jadis Ltd, Bath, Somerset.

Jaffray, Alan, Melksham, Wilts.

Jag, Kensington Church Street Antiques Centre, London W8.

Jago, P., Burgess Hill, Sussex West.

Jalna Antiques, Little Haywood, Staffs.

Jamandic Ltd, Chester, Cheshire.

James & Morton Fine Art & Antiques, Ginnel Antiques Centre, The, Harrogate, Yorks North

James - The Clock Shop, R.A., Tutbury, Staffs.

James and Son Ltd, Anthony, London SW3.

James Antiques, Brian, Telford, Shrops.

James Antiques, Joseph, Penrith, Cumbria.

James Antiques, Peter, Sheffield, Yorks. South.

James Antiques, R. A., Sileby, Leics.

James of St Albans, St. Albans, Herts.

James, Allan, Woodstock, Oxon.

James, Allan, Woodstock, Oxon.

James, D.R., Montrose, Scotland.

James, J.A.R. and J.W., East Dereham, Norfolk.

James, Jonathan, London N1.

James, Michael, London SW1.

James, Mr and Mrs N., Dorking, Surrey.

James, N., Winchester, Hants.

James, P.L. & M., London SW6.

James, R.M. and E., Bishops Cleeve, Glos.

James, Rob and Alison, Tutbury, Staffs.

James, S.N. and W., St. Albans, Herts.

James, Stuart, East Molesey, Surrey.

Jameson, Clare, Thirsk, Yorks. North.

Jane, Mrs M., Wallingford, Oxon.

Japanese Gallery, London N1.

Japanese Gallery, London W8.

Jardinique, Beech, Hants.

Jarrett, L.S.A. and C.J., Witney, Oxon.

Jarrett, P., Arundel, Sussex West.

Jarrett-Scott, R.R., Witney, Oxon.

Jarvill, Derek and Joanne, Middleham, Yorks. North.

Jasper Antiques, Span Antiques, Woodstock, Oxon

Javadi-Babreh, B. and Mrs A., Henley-on-Thames, Oxon.

Jay's Antiques and Collectables, North Petherton, Somerset.

Jeacott-Smith, B. and D., Leek, Staffs.

Jean's Military Memories, Great Harwood, Lancs.

Jebb, G., Cookstown, Co. Tyrone, N. Ireland.

Jefferson, Patrick, London W1.

Jefferson, Patrick, London W1.

Jefferson, R. Y., Abridge, Essex.

Jeffery, A. M. and M. H., Barton, Cambs.

Jeffries Antiques, Corrie, Durham House Antiques Centre, Stow-on-the-Wold, Glos.

Jeffs, Peter and Philip, Antiquarius, London SW3.

Jellicoe, Roderick, London W8.

Jellinek Antiques, Tobias, Twickenham, Middx.

Jellinek, Mrs D.L. and T.P., Twickenham, Middx.

Jellings, Bill, Holkham, Norfolk.

Jenkins BA, V. and A., Bradford-on-Avon, Wilts.

Jenkins, Allan, Modbury, Devon.

Jenkins, C.B., Burford, Oxon.

Jenkins, J. and M., London SE26.

Jenner, Sandy, Cheam, Surrey.

Jennings Antiques, Paul, Angarrack, Cornwall.

Jennings, R., Barnstaple, Devon.

Jennings, R., Bideford, Devon.

Jennywell Hall Antiques, Crosby Ravensworth, Cumbria.

Jeremy Ltd, London SW1.

Jeremy's (Oxford Stamp Centre), Oxford, Oxon.

Jeremy, Laura, Pontarddulais, Wales.

Jericho Books, Oxford, Oxon.

Jerram, Mark, Stockbridge, Hants.

Jesse, John, London W8.

Jessop Classic Photographica, London WC1.

Jester Antiques, Tetbury, Glos.

Jethwa, Baba, Grays Antique Markets, London W1.

Jevons, Francis, London SE21.

Jewel Antiques, Leek, Staffs.

Jewell Ltd, S. and H., London WC2.

Jezebel, Brighton, Sussex East.

Jia, Lei, London SW6.

Jillings Antiques - Distinctive Antique Clocks, Newent, Glos.

Jillings, Doro and John, Newent, Glos.

Joan's Antiques, Littlehampton, Sussex West.

Joel, Mrs J., Dorking, Surrey.

Joel, Mrs J., London SW6.

John (Rare Rugs) Ltd, C., London W1.

John Anthony Antiques, Bletchingley, Surrey.

Johns Ltd, Derek, London SW1.

Johns, T., Lytchett Minster, Dorset.

Johnson and Sons, Rex, Birmingham, West Mids.

Johnson Gibbs, Ilona, Chipping Campden, Glos.

Johnson Medals & Militaria, Steve, Newcastle-upon-Tyne, Tyne and Wear.

Johnson Walker & Tolhurst Ltd, London W1.

Johnson's, Leek, Staffs.

Johnson, D., Birmingham, West Mids.

Johnson, D.A., Kilmarnock, Scotland.

Johnson, Lucy, Burford, Oxon.

Johnson, M., Hainault, Essex.

Johnson, Mrs Sarah, St Mary, Jersey, C.I.

Johnson, Peter, London SW1.

Johnson, Peter, Penzance, Cornwall.

Johnson, Quentin, Tenterden, Kent.

Johnson, R. and R., Birmingham, West Mids.

Johnson, Roger and Bridget, Henley-on-Thames, Oxon.

Johnston, Nigel, The Swan at Tetsworth, Oxon.

Johnstone, Patricia, Penzance, Cornwall.

Jones - The Silver Shop, Howard, London W8.

Jones Antique Lighting, London W11.

Jones Antiques, Alan, Okehampton, Devon.

Jones Antiques, Christopher, Flore, Northants.

Jones Antiques, Christopher, London SW6.

Jones at PJ2, Peter, London SW3.

Jones Jeweller, Michael, Northampton, Northants.

Jones, A., Colchester, Essex.

Jones, Ashley, London WC1.

Jones, Danny, Barmouth, Wales.

Jones, E., Chester, Cheshire.

Jones, G. Trefor, Alfies, London NW8.

Jones, G., Godalming, Surrey.

Jones, Gareth, Edinburgh, Scotland.

Jones, Gary, Leamington Spa, Warks.

Jones, I. and Mrs A. S., Shrewsbury, Shrops.

Jones, John and Christine, Sandbach, Cheshire.

Jones, Judy, London W11.

Jones, Keith, Shrewsbury, Shrops.

Jones, L., Ludlow, Shrops.

Jones, M.R.T. and J.A., Cromer, Norfolk.

Jones, Mr and Mrs P., Chepstow, Wales.

Jones, P.W., Oakham, Rutland.

Jones, Rod, Alfies, London NW8.

Jones, Sally and Neil Brent, Sherborne, Dorset.

Jones-Fenleigh, Jennifer, Great Glen, Leics.

Jonkers Rare Books, Henley-on-Thames, Oxon.

Jonkers, Christiaan, Henley-on-Thames, Oxon.

Jordan (Fine Paintings), T.B. and R., Stockton-on-Tees, Durham.

Jordan, James A., Lichfield, Staffs.

Jordan, Robert A., Barnard Castle, Durham.

Jorgen Antiques, London SW15.

Joseph and Pearce Ltd, London EC1.

Joseph, J., Grays Antique Markets, London W1.

Josh Antiques, Debenham, Suffolk.

Journeyman Antiques Centre, East Molesey, Surrey.

Jowitt, C.S., Brasted, Kent.

Joy, F. and E., Grays Antique Markets, London W1.

Jubilee Antiques, Tottenhill, Norfolk.

Jubilee Hall Antiques Centre, Lechlade, Glos.

Jubilee Photographica, London N1.

Judge, D., Emsworth, Hants.

Judge, S., Ginnel Antiques Centre, The, Harrogate, Yorks North

Judson, Grays Antique Markets, London W1.

Jukes, Mr and Mrs G., St. Leonards-on-Sea, Sussex East.

Julian Alexander Antiques, London N20.

Julian Antiques, Hurstpierpoint, Sussex West.

Junk Box, The, London SE10.

Junk Shop, The, London SE10.

Junktion, New Bolingbroke, Lincs.

Juno Antiques, Brackley, Northants.

Juran and Co, Alexander, London N4.

Jury, D., Bristol, Glos.

JUS Watches, Grays Antique Markets, London W1.

Just a Second, London SW18.

Just Desks, London NW8.

Just Glass, Alston, Cumbria.

DEALERS' INDEX

K

K & M Antiques, Grays Antique Markets, London W1.

K D Antiques, Chester, Cheshire.

K. & Y. Oriental Antiques, Grays Antique Markets, London W1.

K.C. Antiques, Darwen, Lancs.

K.L.M. & Co. Antiques, Lepton, Yorks. West.

Kaae, Minoo & Andre, Grays Antique Markets, London W1.

Kaimes Smithy Antiques, Edinburgh, Scotland.

Kaizen International Ltd, Rochester, Kent.

Kalms, Stephen, London Silver Vaults, London WC2.

Kames Antiques & Jewellery, Brodick and Whiting Bay , Scotland.

Kate, Hemswell Cliff, Lincs.

Katharine House Gallery, Marlborough, Wilts.

Katz Ltd, Daniel, London SW1.

Katz, Daniel, London SW1.

Katz, G., Richmond, Surrey.

Kavanagh, Christine, Newark, Notts.

Kay, Barbara, Ashtead, Surrey.

Kay, S., Headley, Hants.

Kaye of Lyndhurst, Lita, Lyndhurst, Hants.

Kaye, N.J., Chester, Cheshire.

Kayes of Chester, Chester, Cheshire.

Kayll, J., London W1.

Kealey, David, Melton Mowbray, Leics.

Kear, P.W., Cranborne, Dorset.

Kearin, J. and J., White Colne, Essex.

Kearney & Sons, T.H., Belfast, N. Ireland.

Keddie, Mrs A.C., East Grinstead, Sussex West.

Keeble Antiques, Sherborne, Dorset.

Keeble, C.P., Sherborne, Dorset.

Keeble, E.J., Fareham, Hants.

Keehan, Michael P., Brighton, Sussex East.

Keene Gallery, The Barry, Henley-on-Thames, Oxon.

Keene, B.M. and J.S., Henley-on-Thames, Oxon.

Keepsakes, Innerleithen, Scotland.

Keil Ltd, H.W., Broadway, Worcs.

Keil Ltd, John, London SW3.

Kellam, Ian, Durham House Antiques Centre, Stow-on-the-Wold, Glos.

Kelleher, Michael, Antiquarius, London SW3.

Keller, Patrica, Saintfield, Co. Down, N. Ireland.

Kelly Antiques, Rodley, Glos.

Kelly Lighting, Sheffield, Yorks. South.

Kelly, Don, Antiquarius, London SW3.

Kelly, Frank R., Sheffield, Yorks. South.

Kelly, G., Rodley, Glos.

Kelsey Antiques, Peter, Chappells Antiques Centre, Bakewell, Derbys.

Kelsey, P., Bramley, Surrey.

Kembery Antique Clocks (inc. K. & D. Antique Clocks), Bath, Somerset.

Kembery, E., Bath, Somerset.

Kemp Ltd, Melville, Nottingham, Notts.

Kemp, Chris and Ann, Bath, Somerset.

Kemp, Martin, London SE10.

Kemp, Peter, London W8.

Kemp, R.J., Broadway, Worcs.

Kemp, Valerie and Tony, Wrentham, Suffolk.

Kemp, W., Newport, Essex.

Kemps, Bristol, Glos.

Kendal Studios Antiques, Kendal, Cumbria.

Kendall, G., Ginnel Antiques Centre, The, Harrogate, Yorks North

Kendall, The English Watercolour Gallery, Beryl, London W9.

Kendons, Ingatestone, Essex.

Kennaugh, P. and C., London SW10.

Kennedy Carpets, London N4.

Kennedy, Frank, Winchcombe, Glos.

Kennedy, Graham and Pippa, Truro, Cornwall.

Kennedy, Jane, Winchcombe, Glos.

Kennedy, K., London NW5.

Kennedy, M., London N4.

Kennedy, Robin, Richmond, Surrey.

Kenny, D. and S., Dorking, Surrey.

Kensington Church Street Antiques Centre, London W8.

Kent & Sussex Gold Refiners, Tunbridge Wells, Kent.

Kent House Antiques, Haverfordwest, Wales.

Kent, G. and P., Marlborough, Wilts.

Kentdale Antiques, Tunbridge Wells, Kent.

Kenulf Fine Arts, Stow-on-the-Wold, Glos.

Kenyon, David S., Burnham Market, Norfolk.

Ker, David, London SW1.

Kern, R.A.B., London SW1.

Kern, Virginia, London SW3.

Kern, Virginia, Stow-on-the-Wold, Glos.

Kerr - Gatehouse Bookshop, Norman, Cartmel, Cumbria.

Kerr Antiques Ltd, Thomas, London SW10.

Kerr, Andrew and Suszanna, Stratford-upon-Avon, Warks.

Kerr, H. and J.M., Cartmel, Cumbria.

Kerr, S., London N12.

Keshishian, London SW1.

Kessler Ford, Ashburton, Devon.

Kessler, Elisabeth, Ashburton, Devon.

Keswick Bookshop, Keswick, Cumbria.

Ketley Antiques, Carol, London N1.

Kettle Ltd, Thomas, London WC2.

Kettle, Michael, Brightlingsea, Essex.

Keverne, Roger, London W1.

Key Antiques, Chipping Norton, Oxon.

Key, Sarah, Cambridge, Cambs.

Keymer Son & Co. Ltd, Brasted, Kent.

Keystone Antiques, Coalville, Leics.

Khachadourian, Simon, London SW1.

Khan, Jo, Alfies, London NW8.

Khawaja, A.H., London SW1.

Kiadah, R.P. ,Grays Antique Markets, London W1.

Kidwelly Antiques, Kidwelly, Wales.

Kikuchi Trading Co Ltd, Grays Antique Markets, London W1.

Kilby, Mrs M., Northfleet, Kent.

Kilgarriff, A ., Biggleswade, Beds.

Kilim Warehouse Ltd, The, London SW12.

Killin Gallery, Killin, Scotland.

Kilmacolm Antiques Ltd, Kilmacolm, Scotland.

Kimber & Son, Malvern Link, Worcs.

Kimber, E.M. and M.E., Malvern Link, Worcs.

Kime Antiques, Robert, Marlborough, Wilts.

King Antiques, Roger, Hungerford, Berks.

King St. Antiques, Southport Antiques Centre, Southport, Merseyside

King Street Curios, Melksham, Wilts.

King Street Curios, Tavistock, Devon.

King's Cottage Antiques, Leamington Spa, Warks.

King's Court Galleries, Dorking, Surrey.

King's Court Galleries, London SW6.

King's Mill Antique Centre, Burnley, Lancs.

King, Amy, Willingham, Cambs.

King, Ann, Bath, Somerset.

King, Cindy, Dorking, Surrey.

King, J.H., St. Leonards-on-Sea, Sussex East.

King, John, London SW1.

King, John, Much Wenlock, Shrops.

King, M., Wymondham, Norfolk.

King, Mr and Mrs R.F., Hungerford, Berks.

King, Wymondham, Norfolk.

King-Smith & Simon W. Nutter, T.M., Stow-on-the-Wold, Glos.

Kingham, Mrs G., London SE21.

Kings Fireplaces, Antiques and Interiors, Cardiff, Wales.

Kingsclere Old Bookshop (Wyseby House Books), Kingsclere, Hants.

Kingsley & Co., Barnard Castle, Durham.

Kingston Antique Market, Kingston-upon-Thames, Surrey.

Kingston, Dennis, Antiquarius, London SW3.

Kingston, Richard J., Henley-on-Thames, Oxon.

Kingswood, T., London WC2.

Kinloch, Clare, Hastings Antique Centre, St. Leonards-on-Sea, E. Sussex

Kinnaird, Jane and John, Keswick, Cumbria.

Kirby Antiques, R., Acrise, Kent.

Kirk Ports Gallery, North Berwick, Scotland.

Kirk, R., Honiton, Devon.

Kirkgate Fine Art & Conservation, Thirsk, Yorks. North.

Kirkland, Chris, Tetbury, Glos.

Kirkland, G., London SW6.

Kirton Antiques, Kirton, Lincs.

Kismet, Ginnel Antiques Centre, The, Harrogate, Yorks North

Kitchen Bygones, Alfies, London NW8.

Klaber and Klaber, London NW3.

Klaber, Miss P., London NW3.

Klaber, Mrs B., London NW3.

Kleanthous Antiques Ltd, Kleanthous Antiques, London W11.

Kleanthous Antiques, London W11.

Kleinman, Patricia, Tudor House, Stow-on-the-Wold, Glos

Kluth, Paula, Alfies, London NW8.

Knicks Knacks Emporium, Sutton-on-Sea, Lincs.

Knight and Sons, B.R., St. Ives, Cambs.

Knight, I.H. and G.M., Hythe, Kent.

Knight, M., St. Ives, Cambs.

Knight, P., Christchurch, Dorset.

Knight-Mudie, George, Aberdeen, Scotland.

Knights, P.H., Norwich, Norfolk.

Knightsbridge Coins, London SW1.

Knowles, Susan and Arnie, Hungerford, Berks.

Knowles, W.A. and M.A., Penkridge, Staffs.

Knutsford Antiques Centre, Knutsford, Cheshire.

Koch, Thomas and Sally, Sidmouth, Devon.

Kojis Antique Jewellery Ltd, London SW1.

Koll, A., London SW1.

Koopman Ltd & Rare Art (London) Ltd, London WC2.

Koopman, Michael, London WC2.

Kowalski, K. S., Macclesfield, Cheshire.

Kreckovic, L. and E., London SW6.

Kubacki, Edward, Finedon, Northants.

Kuhn, Nick, Bath, Somerset.

Kunz, Armin, London SW1.

Kuznierz, Mrs M., Telford, Shrops.

L

La Chaise Antique, Stow-on-the-Wold, Glos.

La Maison, Bourne End, Bucks.

Laburnum Antiques, Poole, Dorset.

Laburnum Cottage Antiques, Eye, Suffolk.
Lace Shop, The, Antiquarius, London SW3
Lacewing Fine Art Gallery, Winchester, Hants.
Lack, Stephen, Grays Antique Markets, London W1.
Lacquer Chest, The, London W8.
Lacy Gallery, London W11.
Lake Antiques, Lake, Isle of Wight.
Lakes Crafts & Antiques Gallery, Grasmere, Cumbria.
Laleham Antiques, Laleham, Surrey.
Lamb Antiques & Works of Art, Roger, Stow-on-the-Wold, Glos.
Lamb Arcade, The, Wallingford, Oxon.
Lambe, Charlotte and John, Belfast, N. Ireland.
Lambert and Son, R.A and S.M., Woodbridge, Suffolk.
Lambert Antiques Centre, Dorrian, Lincoln, Lincs.
Lamberty, The Furniture Cave, London SW10.
Lamont Antiques Ltd, London SE10.
Lamont, N., London SE10.
Lampert, B., London Silver Vaults, London WC2.
Lancaster Leisure Park Antiques Centre, Lancaster, Lancs.
Lancaster, Liz, Croydon, Surrey.
Lancastrian Antiques & Co, Lancaster, Lancs.
Lancefield Antiques, David M., Sandgate, Kent.
Landen Antiques, Rupert, Reading, Berks.
Landen Antiques, Rupert, The Swan at Tetsworth, Oxon.
Landsman, Barry, Alfies, London NW8.
Lane Antiques, Russell, Warwick, Warks.
Lane Antiques, Stockbridge, Hants.
Lane Fine Art Ltd, London SW10.
Lane, Mrs N., London W5.
Lang, P., London SW19.
Langford's Marine Antiques, London SW10.
Langford, Adam and Joel, London Silver Vaults, London WC2.
Langford, J. and R., Llangollen, Wales.
Langford, L.L., London SW10.
Langfords, London Silver Vaults, London WC2.
Langley Galleries, Rochester, Kent.
Langton Street Gallery, London SW10.
Langtons Antiques & Collectables, Sheffield, Yorks. South.
Lankester Antiques and Books, Saffron Walden, Essex.
Lannards Gallery, Billingshurst, Sussex West.
Lansdown Antiques, Bath, Somerset.
Lantern Shop Gallery, The, Sidmouth, Devon.
Lascelles, R., London SW6.
Lassalle, Judith, London N1.
LASSCo, London EC2.
Last Century Antiques and Books, Innerleithen, Scotland.
Latchford Antiques, Cheltenham, Glos.
Latford, Joan, Alfies, London NW8.
Latham Antiques, R.H., Tarleton, Lancs.
Latreville, Claude & Martine, Antiquarius, London SW3
Laurel Bank Antiques, Red House Antiques Centre, York, Yorks. North
Laurence Corner, London NW1.
Laurens Antiques, Whitstable, Kent.
Laurie (Antiques) Ltd, John, London N1.
Laurie Antiques, Peter, London SE10.

Lavender (Antiques) Ltd, D.S., London W1.
Lavian, Joseph, London N4.
Law, Rathbone, Chichester, Sussex West.
Lawrence and Sons, F.G., Redhill, Surrey.
Lawrence Gallery, Bob, London SW1.
Lawson and Co, E.M., East Hagbourne, Oxon.
Lawson Antique Clocks, Keith, Scratby, Norfolk.
Lawson Antiques Limited, Hurst Green, Sussex East.
Lawson Antiques, F. and T., Richmond, Surrey.
Lawson Gallery, The, Cambridge, Cambs.
Laywood, Anthony W., Knipton, Leics.
Lazarell, Grays Antique Markets, London W1.
Lazarus Antiques, David, Hartley Wintney, Hants.
Le Shop, Antiquarius, London SW3
Le Strange Emporium, Horncastle, Lincs.
Le Strange Old Barns Antiques, Arts & Craft Centre, Hunstanton, Norfolk.
Le Vesconte's Collectables, Peter, St Helier, Jersey, C.I.
Leadlay Gallery, The Warwick, London SE10.
Leask Ward, London NW3.
Leatherland Antiques, P.D., Reading, Berks.
Lechlade Arcade, Lechlade, Glos.
Ledger Antiques, Sue, Stockport, Cheshire.
Lee's Antiques, Clitheroe, Lancs.
Lee, Colin and Mary, Jubilee Hall Antiques Centre, Lechlade, Glos.
Lee, James K., King's Lynn, Norfolk.
Lee, Mrs H., Shere, Surrey.
Leek Antiques Centre (Barclay House), The, Leek, Staffs.
Lees and Sons, M., Worcester, Worcs.
Legacy, Alfies, London NW8.
Legard, Ian. P., Ginnel Antiques Centre, The, Harrogate, Yorks North
Legg Antiques, Michael, Dorchester, Dorset.
Legg of Dorchester, Bere Regis, Dorset.
Legg of Dorchester, Dorchester, Dorset.
Legge Oriental Carpets, Christopher, Oxford, Oxon.
Lehane, E. , Antiquarius, London SW3
Lehane, Mr and Mrs, Antiquarius, London SW3.
Leicestershire Sporting Gallery and Brown Jack Bookshop, Lubenham, Leics.
Leigh Antiques, Laurie, Oxford, Oxon.
Leigh Jewellery, Leigh, Lancs.
Leigh, B., London SW19.
Leiston Trading Post, Leiston, Suffolk.
Leith's Brocanterbury, Nan, Canterbury, Kent.
Lemkow Antiques, Sara, Ely, Cambs.
Lennard Antiques, Sible Hedingham, Essex.
Lennox Gallery, Grays Antique Markets, London W1.
Leoframes, Brighton, Sussex East.
Leominster Antiques Market, Leominster, Herefs.
Leon Antiques, London Silver Vaults, London WC2.
Leon's Militaria, The Mall Antiques Arcade, London N1.
Leslie and Leslie, Haddington, Scotland.
Leslie Ltd, Nat, London Silver Vaults, London WC2.
Lethbridge, John, Truro, Cornwall.
Letty's Antiques, Leicester, Leics.
Leuchars and Jefferson, London W1.
Leuchars, Hugh, London W1.

Lev (Antiques) Ltd, London W8.
Lev, Mrs, London W8.
Levene Ltd, M.P., London SW7.
Levine Silver Specialist, Leona, Norwich, Norfolk.
Levy, Lionel, London W1.
Levy, M.P., P.A. and W.Y., London W1.
Lewes Antique Centre, Lewes, Sussex East.
Lewes Flea Market, Lewes, Sussex East.
Lewin, David and Harriett, London SW6.
Lewin, London SW6.
Lewis and Lloyd, London W8.
Lewis Antique and Fine Art Dealers, Ivor and Patricia, Peterborough, Cambs.
Lewis Antiques, Michael, London N1.
Lewis Gallery - Antiquarian Maps & Prints, Michael , Bruton, Somerset.
Lewis Oriental Carpets and Rugs, Michael and Amanda, Wellington, Somerset.
Lewis, Arthur S., Gloucester, Glos.
Lewis, M. and D., London SW1.
Lewis, M. and D., London W11.
Lewis, Mrs B., London W11.
Lewis, Pauline and Robert, Halesworth, Suffolk.
Lewis, R.A., Liverpool, Merseyside.
Lewis, R.G., Bridgnorth, Shrops.
Lewis, Sarah, Alfies, London NW8.
Lewis, Stuart D., Leigh-on-Sea, Essex.
Lexton, Michael, Antiquarius, London SW3.
Leyland, D.J. and C.J, Woodhall Spa, Lincs.
Lhermette, Mrs V.A., Rochester, Kent.
Liberty, London W1.
Libra Antiques, Bournemouth, Dorset.
Libra Antiques, Hurst Green, Sussex East.
Libra Antiques, London W8.
Libson, L.J., London W1.
Licht & Morrison, Grays Antique Markets, London W1.
Lickley, R., Carmarthen, Wales.
Liddell, Jill, The Mall Antiques Arcade, Lower Mall, London N1
Lieber, Ian, London W2.
Light Gallery, The, Leamington Spa, Warks.
Light, P. B., Stamford, Lincs.
Light, Robert, Broadway, Worcs.
Lightbown, Richard and Marion, Manningford Bruce, Wilts.
Lightfoot, Peter, Warwick, Warks.
Lights, Camera, Action UK Ltd., Nottingham, Notts.
Lillistone, C., Ipswich, Suffolk.
Limb Antiques, R.R., Newark, Notts.
Limited Editions, Stockport, Cheshire.
Limpsfield Watercolours, Limpsfield, Surrey.
Linda B, Grays Antique Markets, London W1.
Linden and Co. (Antiques) Ltd, London Silver Vaults, London WC2.
Linden House Antiques, Leominster, Herefs.
Linden House Antiques, Stansted, Essex.
Linden, H, F, H.M. and S. C., London Silver Vaults, London WC2.
Lindfield Galleries - David Adam, Lindfield, Sussex West.
Lindsay, Bruce, London SW1.
Lindsay, Graham, Bushey, Herts.
Lindsey Antiques, North Berwick, Scotland.
Lindsey Court Architectural Antiques, Horncastle, Lincs.
Lindsey, Alan, North Berwick, Scotland.
Lindsey, E.A., Gullane, Scotland.
Lindsey, Stephen, North Berwick, Scotland.
Lineage Antiques, Durham House Antiques Centre, Stow-on-the-Wold, Glos.
Lineham, Andrew, The Mall Antiques Arcade, London N1.

Lines, Derek and Jill, Wychbold, Worcs.
Ling, Susan, The Swan at Tetsworth, Oxon.
Lingard - Rope Walk Antiques, Ann, Rye, Sussex East.
Linsley, Mrs C.M., Gosforth, Cumbria.
Lion Fine Arts, Hay-on-Wye, Wales.
Lion Gallery and Bookshop, Knutsford, Cheshire.
Lion, Witch and Lampshade, Blakeney, Glos.
Lion, Witch and Lampshade, London SW1.
Lipitch Ltd, Michael, Barnet, Herts.
Lipitch Ltd, Peter, London SW3.
Lipka & Son Ltd, B., London W11.
Lipman, Philip and Dorothy, Durham House Antiques Centre, Stow-on-the-Wold, Glos.
Lipson, Paul, Oxford, Oxon.
Lis, J., London SW5.
Lister, H., London W11.
Lister, Mrs Shelagh, Hartley Wintney, Hants.
Lister, Shelagh, The Swan at Tetsworth, Oxon.
Litt Antiques, David, Ampthill, Beds.
Litt, David and Helen, Ampthill, Beds.
Little Gallery, The, Pittenweem, Scotland.
Little Gem, The, Shrewsbury, Shrops.
Little Jem's, Penzance, Cornwall.
Little Nells, Durham House Antiques Centre, Stow-on-the-Wold, Glos.
Little River, Antiquarius, London SW3.
Little Theatre Antiques Centre, Jesmond, Tyne and Wear.
Little Treasures, Dornoch, Scotland.
Little, H., London W11.
Littlebury Antiques - Littlebury Restorations Ltd, Saffron Walden, Essex.
Littles Collectables, Congleton, Cheshire.
Liu, J. and M.C., Otford, Kent.
Livesley, W.H., Macclesfield, Cheshire.
Livingstone, Neil, Dundee, Scotland.
Llanishen Antiques, Cardiff, Wales.
Llewellyn, F., London SE10.
Lloyd Antiques, Michael, Llandysul, Wales.
Lloyd Antiques, Robin, Ross-on-Wye, Herefs.
Lloyd, A., London W1.
Lloyd, Andrew, Bath, Somerset.
Lloyd, J., London W1.
Lloyd, M.R., Sandgate, Kent.
Lloyds of Kew, Kew, Surrey.
Lochhead, Stuart, London SW1.
Lodge, John C., Salisbury, Wilts.
Loftus-Potter, N., Deal, Kent.
Loh, C.Y., London WC1.
Loizou, Maria and Loui, London N12.
Lombard Antiques, Honiton, Devon.
Lombard Antiques, Newark, Notts.
London Antique Gallery, London W8.
London Cigarette Card Co. Ltd, The, Somerton, Somerset.
London House Antiques, Westerham, Kent.
London House Oriental Rugs and Carpets, Boston Spa, Yorks. West.
London House Oriental Rugs and Carpets, Harrogate, Yorks. North.
London Militaria Market, London N1.
London Road Antiques, Edinburgh, Scotland.
London Silver Vaults, The, London WC2.
London, Sue, Stow-on-the-Wold, Glos.
Long Melford Antiques Centre, Long Melford, Suffolk.
Long, D., Tunbridge Wells, Kent.
Long, J.W.H., Aberford, Yorks. West.
Long, Michael D., Nottingham, Notts.
Long, Stephen, London SW10.
Longhi, Janice, Broadway, Worcs.
Longmire Ltd (Three Royal Warrants), London SW1.

Longthorne, K.J., Brighton, Sussex East.
Lonsdale Antiques, Southend-on-Sea, Essex.
Lonsdale Bookseller and Bookbinder, Elaine, Hemswell Cliff, Lincs.
Lonsdale, Elaine, Hemswell Cliff, Lincs.
Looking Glass of Bath, Bath, Somerset.
Loomes, Brian and Joy, Pateley Bridge, Yorks. North.
Loomes, Brian, Ginnel Antiques Centre, The, Harrogate, Yorks North
Loomes, Brian, Pateley Bridge, Yorks. North.
Lopari (Sormeh), Mrs. A., Antiquarius, London SW3.
Lopburi Art & Antiques, Bath, Somerset.
Loquens Gallery, The, Cheltenham, Glos.
Loquens Gallery, The, Stratford-upon-Avon, Warks.
Loquens, S. and J., Stratford-upon-Avon, Warks.
Loraine Antiques, Gordon, Rait Village Antiques Centre, Scotland
Loraine, Liane and Gordon, Rait Village Antiques Centre, Scotland
Lord Antiques, Alan, Folkestone, Kent.
Lord, A.G., J.A. and R.G., Folkestone, Kent.
Lord, J.R. and A.A., Taunton, Somerset.
Lords Antiques, Taunton, Somerset.
Loska, John, Brighton, Sussex East.
Lott, Mr and Mrs G.E., Arundel, Sussex West.
Loudon, W.I., Burnham-on-Sea, Somerset.
Lough, Catherine, Red House Antiques Centre, York, Yorks. North
Lovatt, M., Winchcombe, Glos.
Love Lane Antiques, Nantwich, Cheshire.
Love, David, Harrogate, Yorks. North.
Love, Miss M.A., Worsley, Lancs.
Love, R.M., Worsley, Lancs.
Loveday, David, London N1.
Loveday, David, The Furniture Cave, London SW10
Lovegrove, Candy and Julian, West Malling, Kent.
Lovell, C.A., Watford, Herts.
Lovett, M.J., Northampton, Northants.
Low Antiques, Michael, Forres, Scotland.
Low, G., Melksham, Wilts.
Lowe and Sons, Chester, Cheshire.
Lowe of Loughborough, Loughborough, Leics.
Lowe, D., Mansfield, Notts.
Lower House Fine Antiques, Redditch, Worcs.
Lower, Graham and Penny, Flimwell, Sussex East.
Lower, Graham, Flimwell, Sussex East.
Lower., R.R., London W8.
Lowrie, Mr and Mrs David, Otford, Kent.
Lucas Artmetal, Fay, London SW8.
Lucas, N., Amersham, Bucks.
Luck, R.J., Hastings, Sussex East.
Luck, S., Wallingford, Oxon.
Luck, S.L., West Malling, Kent.
Luckmans Antiques, Coventry, West Mids.
Luczyc-Wyhowska, J., London SW12.
Luffman, J., Haslington, Cheshire.
Lugley Street Antiques, Newport, Isle of Wight.
Lukies, Pearse, Aylsham, Norfolk.
Lumb and Sons Ltd, Charles, Harrogate, Yorks. North.
Lumb, F. and A.R., Harrogate, Yorks. North.
Luna, Nottingham, Notts.
Lunn Antiques Ltd, London SW6.
Lunn, R.J. and Mrs. S.Y., Dorchester, Dorset.
Lunnon, C.M., Haslemere, Surrey.
Lury, R. and J., Cambridge, Cambs.

Lusk, John, London SW1.
Luther Antiques, Michael, London SW6.
Luther, Michael, London SW6.
Luu, Mrs. V., Antiquarius, London SW3.
Lyall Antiques, Alexander, Long Melford, Suffolk.
Lyall, A.J., Long Melford, Suffolk.
Lycurgus Glass, Red House Antiques Centre, York, Yorks. North
Lye Antique Furnishings, Lye, West Mids.
Lymer-Jones., D., Wolverhampton, West Mids.
Lymington Antiques Centre, Lymington, Hants.
Lynas, P., Easingwold, Yorks. North.
Lynch, J., Edinburgh, Scotland.
Lynch, R.C. and I.R., Feniscowles, Lancs.
Lyndhurst Antiques Centre, Lyndhurst, Hants.
Lyon Oliver Antiques, Malmesbury, Wilts.
Lyons, A., Sevenoaks, Kent.
Lyons, David, Birkenhead, Merseyside.
Lyons, H.S., London W8.
Lysaght, J., Old Cornmarket Antiques Centre, Warwick, Warks. L.P. Antiques (Mids) Ltd, Walsall, West Mids.
Lythe Cottage Antiques, Lythe, Yorks. North.

M

M B G Antiques, Fine Art & Jewellery, Newark, Notts.
M'Garry-Durrant, Andrew, Holland-on-Sea, Essex.
M.C.N. Antiques, London W11.
M.G.R. Exports, Bruton, Somerset.
Maas Gallery, London W1.
Maas, R.N., London W1.
Macadie, Mrs M., Crosby Ravensworth, Cumbria.
MacConnal-Mason Gallery, London SW1.
MacDermot, Brian and Gina, London SW1.
MacDonald Fine Art, Gosforth, Tyne and Wear.
MacDonald, Brian, Stow-on-the-Wold, Glos.
MacDonald, G., Inverness, Scotland.
MacDonald, T. and C., Gosforth, Tyne and Wear.
Macdonald, A. and Mrs M., Amersham, Bucks.
MacGillivray, G., Whitchurch, Shrops.
MacGregor, Bill and Nora, Perth, Scotland.
MacHenry Antiques, Newtownabbey, Co. Antrim, N. Ireland.
MacHenry, R. and A., Newtownabbey, Co. Antrim, N. Ireland.
MacInnes Antiques, Kilmarnock, Scotland.
MacInnes, Mrs M., Kilmarnock, Scotland.
Mack Antiques, David, Branksome, Dorset.
Mackay, N.A., Bath, Somerset.
Mackenzie & Smith Furniture Restoration, Ludlow, Shrops.
Maclean, H., Kilmacolm, Scotland.
Maclean, Mrs J., Dornoch, Scotland.
MacNaughton-Smith, J., The Swan at Tetsworth, Oxon.
Macrow, S.K., Solihull, West Mids.
Maddermarket Antiques, Norwich, Norfolk.
Made of Honour, Chester, Cheshire.
Madeira, Mrs C., Flore, Northants.
Madison Gallery, The, Petworth, Sussex West.
Magee, D.A., Canterbury, Kent.
Maggie May's, North Shields, Tyne and Wear.
Maggs Bros Ltd, London W1.
Maggs Shipping Ltd., Liverpool, Merseyside.
Maggs, J.F., B.D. and E.F., London W1.

Mathias, R., Guildford, Surrey.
Mathias, R., St. Albans, Herts.
Mathias, Richard, Oxford, Oxon.
Mathias, Richard, Windsor and Eton, Berks.
Mathieson and Co, John, Edinburgh, Scotland.
Matlock Antiques and Collectables Centre, Matlock, Derbys.
Matsell, Brian, Derby, Derbys.
Matthiesen Fine Art Ltd., London SW1.
Maufe, D.H. and J., Burnham Market, Norfolk.
Maurice and Linda, Red House Antiques Centre, York, Yorks. North
Mautner, Sue, Antiquarius, London SW3.
Mawby, Mrs P., Northampton, Northants.
Maxfield House Antiques, Warminster, Wilts.
Maxtone Graham, Mr and Mrs R.M., Hythe, Kent.
Maxwell, Margaret, Innerleithen, Scotland.
May Antiques & Collectables, Shirley, Chappells Antiques Centre, Bakewell, Derbys.
May, Desmond and Ann, Brambridge, Hants.
May, Greta, Tonbridge, Kent.
Maya Antiques, Honiton, Devon.
Mayes, R.K., Ginnel Antiques Centre, The, Harrogate, Yorks North
Mayfair Antiques, Dorking, Surrey.
Mayfair Antiques, Otley, Yorks. West.
Mayfair Carpet Gallery Ltd, London W1.
Mayfair Gallery, London W1.
Mayflower Antiques, London W11.
Mayhew, Paul, The Mall Antiques Arcade, London N1.
Mayle, Mr. and Mrs., Henley-on-Thames, Oxon.
Maynard Antiques, Mark, London SW6.
Maynard, John, Sawbridgeworth, Herts.
Mayne, J., Newhaven, Sussex East.
Mays, Maggie, Buxton, Derbys.
McAleer, M., London W2.
McAleer, M.J., London W2.
McAskie, Pete, Grays Antique Markets, London W1.
McAuley - The Antique Shop, Marjorie, Greyabbey, Co. Down, N. Ireland.
McBain Antique Exports, McBains Antiques, Exeter, Devon
McBain, I.S., G., R. and M., McBains Antiques, Exeter, Devon
McBains Antiques, Exeter, Devon.
McCall, B., Aberdeen, Scotland.
McCall, Sandra, Chacewater, Cornwall.
McCalls (Aberdeen), Aberdeen, Scotland.
McCalls Limited, Aberdeen, Scotland.
McCann, Mrs A.D., Holyhead (Anglesey), Wales.
McCarthy, Ian, Clutton, Somerset.
McCarthy, Margaret, London SE1.
McCarthy, O., Ross-on-Wye, Herefs.
McClaren, J., Gosport, Hants.
McClenaghan, John, London SW1.
McClenaghan, London SW1.
McClure-Buckie, G., Cambridge, Cambs.
McCollum, D.C., Stockland, Devon.
McConnell, Audrey, Durham House Antiques Centre, Stow-on-the-Wold, Glos.
McConnell, Nick, Sandwich, Kent.
McCourt, Eddie, The Swan at Tetsworth, Oxon.
McCoy, Robert, Alfies, London NW8.
McCreddie, B.S., Ludlow, Shrops.
McCulloch Antiques, John, Felixstowe, Suffolk.
McDonald Antiques, Joy, London SW13.

McDonald-Hobley, Mrs N., Antiquarius, London SW3.
McErlain, Oliver, Tetbury, Glos.
McEvoy, Mrs M., Comberton, Cambs.
McEwan Gallery, The, Ballater, Scotland.
McEwan, D., P. and R., Ballater, Scotland.
McGlynn, Thomas, Long Melford, Suffolk.
McGowan, P., Shenton, Leics.
McGrath, Bernard J., Newark, Notts.
McGregor, Veronica, Halstead, Essex.
McGregor, Veronica, Sudbury, Suffolk.
McHale, Tom, Chichester, Sussex West.
McHugo, M., Lye, West Mids.
McHugo, M., Stourbridge, West Mids.
McKeivor, Mrs J., Chilcompton, Somerset.
McKenna and Co, London SW3.
McKenna, C. and M., London SW3.
McKenzie, J.W., Ewell, Surrey.
McKinley, D., Wiveliscombe, Somerset.
McKinnon, Georgina, Newington, Kent.
McKnight, E.W., Bury St. Edmunds, Suffolk.
McLaughlin, A.J. and Mrs B., Manchester, Lancs.
McLay - Saratoga Trunk, Cathy, Victorian Village, Glasgow, Scotland
McLean, D., Portsoy, Scotland.
McLean, Mrs M., Antiquarius, London SW3.
McLeod, David and Patricia, Knutsford, Cheshire.
McLeod-Brown, William, Antiquarius, London SW3.
McLoughlin, Alan, Truro, Cornwall.
McMullan & Son, D., Manchester, Lancs.
McNaught, Shirley and David, Bury St Edmunds, Suffolk.
McNaughtan's Bookshop, Edinburgh, Scotland.
McNulty Wholesalers, Coleraine, Co. Londonderry, N. Ireland.
McNulty Wholesalers, Market Drayton, Shrops.
McPherson Antiques, R. and G., London W8.
McPherson, I. and H., Coalville, Leics.
McQuade Antiques, Kilbarchan, Scotland.
McQuade, W. G. & W. J., Kilbarchan, Scotland.
McTague of Harrogate, Harrogate, Yorks. North.
McTague, P., Harrogate, Yorks. North.
McVeigh & Charpentier, London SW10.
McWhirter, James, London SW10.
McWhirter, London SW10.
Mead, M.C., Uffculme, Devon.
Mead, T., Launceston, Cornwall.
Meader, Kay, Littlehampton, Sussex West.
Meara, Richard, London N1.
Medd, N.P., Clitheroe, Lancs.
Medina Gallery, Barnstaple, Devon.
Medina Gallery, Bideford, Devon.
Mee, R., London W8.
Meeks & Co, F., Birmingham, West Mids.
Megarry's and Forever Summer, Blackmore, Essex.
Melbourne Antiques & Interiors, London SE22.
Meldrum, D., Chagford, Devon.
Melford Antique Warehouse, Long Melford, Suffolk.
Mellor, C.R.J. and P.J., Lichfield, Staffs.
Mellor, Mrs R., Bath, Somerset.
Melnick House of Ascot, Ascot, Berks.
Melody's Antiques, Chester, Cheshire.
Melody, M. and M., Chester, Cheshire.
Melton Antiques, Woodbridge, Suffolk.
Melton's, London W1.
Meltzer, L., London W11.
Melvin, R., Edinburgh, Scotland.

Memories, Bramley, Surrey.
Memories, Great Dunmow, Essex.
Memories, Rochester, Kent.
Memory Lane Antiques & Collectables, Sidcup, Kent.
Memory Lane Antiques Centre, Ripley, Derbys.
Memory Lane Antiques, Great Bookham, Surrey.
Memory Lane Antiques, Lower Stondon, Beds.
Memory Lane, Sowerby Bridge, Yorks. West.
Mennis, G., Hastings Antique Centre, St. Leonards-on-Sea, E. Sussex
Mercado, Mr and Mrs K., Baythorne End, Essex.
Mercer (Chronometers) Ltd, Thomas, London SW1.
Mercer Antiques, Noel, Long Melford, Suffolk.
Merchant House Antiques, Honiton, Devon.
Merchants House Antiques, Ross-on-Wye, Herefs.
Mercury Antiques, London W11.
Mere Antiques, Topsham, Devon.
Meredith, John, Chagford, Devon.
Mereside Books, Macclesfield, Cheshire.
Merkel, M.P., Dartmouth, Devon.
Merlin Antiques, Tetbury, Glos.
Merlins Antiques, Carmarthen, Wales.
Merrifield, Mr and Mrs B., Paisley, Scotland.
Messums (Contemporary), London W1.
Messums, London SW1.
Metcalfe, C.W. and M., West Auckland, Durham.
Metcalfe, Mrs A., Helsby, Cheshire.
Mews Antique Emporium, Holt, Norfolk.
Meyer, Atalanti, Tudor House, Stow-on-the-Wold, Glos
Meyer, Mr T., London W8.
Meyers, Atalanti, Durham House Antiques Centre, Stow-on-the-Wold, Glos.
Meyler, Olivia, Red House Antiques Centre, York, Yorks. North
Meyler, Rory, Red House Antiques Centre, York, Yorks. North
Meysey-Thompson Antiques, Sarah, Woodbridge, Suffolk.
MGJ Jewellers Ltd., Wallingford, Oxon.
Mibus, Adrian, London SW1.
Micawber Antiques, Bridgnorth, Shrops.
Michael Coins, London W8.
Michael's Boxes, Grays Antique Markets, London W1.
Michael, Judith, Corbridge, Northumbs.
Michelson, E., Bond Street Antiques Centre, London W1.
Michieli, Robert, St Helier, Jersey, C.I.
Middleham Antiques, Middleham, Yorks. North.
Middlemiss, Janet, Sonning-on-Thames, Berks.
Middleton, Arthur, London WC2.
Middleton, Bobbie, Tetbury, Glos.
Middleton, Helen, Durham House Antiques Centre, Stow-on-the-Wold, Glos.
Middleton, Ms Fiona, Portree, Scotland.
Midgley, J.L. and N.M., Settle, Yorks. North.
Midland Goss and Commemoratives, Old Cornmarket Antiques Centre, Warwick, Warks.
Mighell, J., London N5.
Mihok, R.A., Worthing, Sussex West.
Mildenhall Antiques, Mildenhall, Suffolk.
Mileham, Peter, Saffron Walden, Essex.
Miles Antiques, Kinross, Scotland.
Miles Bookshop, Archie, Gosforth, Cumbria.

Nook, The, Sherborne, Dorset.
Nooks & Crannies, Ryde, Isle of Wight.
Noott Galleries, John, Broadway, Worcs.
Norden Antiques, Peter, Tetbury, Glos.
Norden, Peter and Jenny, Tetbury, Glos.
Norfolk Galleries, King's Lynn, Norfolk.
Norfolk House Galleries, Dorking,
 Surrey.
Norfolk Polyphon Centre, Bawdeswell,
 Norfolk.
Norgrove - Antique Clocks, P.W.,
 Haslingden, Lancs.
Norman Antiques and Restorations, Peter,
 Burwell, Cambs.
Norman Antiques Ltd, Michael, Brighton,
 Sussex East.
Norman Antiques, Jennifer and Raymond,
 Needham, Norfolk.
Norman Sue, Antiquarius, London SW3.
Norman, B.E., London SW1.
Norman, Edward, Debden, Essex.
Norman, Geoffrey, Hitchin, Herts.
Norman, P., Burwell, Cambs.
Norman, P., London W1.
Norman, Peter, London EC3.
Norrie, Mrs E., Ceres, Scotland.
Norris, R.F., Hertford, Herts.
Norrish, Paul and John, Torquay, Devon.
North Devon Antiques Centre, Barnstaple,
 Devon.
North Laine Antiques Market, inc. Alan
 Fitchett Antiques, The, Brighton, Sussex
 East.
North London Clock Shop Ltd, London
 SE25.
North Shropshire Reclamation, Burlton,
 Shrops.
North Street Antiques & Interiors,
 Horncastle, Lincs.
North Wales Antiques - Colwyn Bay,
 Colwyn Bay, Wales.
North Wilts Exporters, Brinkworth, Wilts.
North, Desmond and Amanda, East
 Peckham, Kent.
Northcote Road Antiques Market, London
 SW11.
Northern Antiques Company, Norton, Yorks.
 North.
Northern Clocks, Worsley, Lancs.
Northfleet Hill Antiques, Northfleet, Kent.
Northgraves, Jill, Beverley, Yorks. East.
Northumbria Pine, Whitley Bay, Tyne and
 Wear.
Northwich Antiques Centre, Northwich,
 Cheshire.
Northwood, Paul and Elizabeth, Ampthill,
 Beds.
Norton Antiques, Twyford, Norfolk.
Norton, M.S., N.E.L., J.P. and F.E., London
 W1.
Norton-Grant, Kenneth, Alfies, London
 NW8.
Nortonbury Antiques, London WC1.
Norwich City Council, Norwich, Norfolk.
Norwich Collectors Toyshop, Norwich,
 Norfolk.
Nostalgia Architectural Antiques, Stockport,
 Cheshire.
Nostalgia, Blackpool, Lancs.
Nostalgia, Clevedon, Somerset.
Nostradamus Centre, The, East Molesey,
 Surrey.
Nostradamus II, East Molesey, Surrey.
Not Just Silver, Weybridge, Surrey.
Notions Antiques Centre, Grantham,
 Lincs.
Notman, David, Newby East, Cumbria.

Now and Then (Toy Centre), Edinburgh,
 Scotland.
Nowell, Edward A., Wells, Somerset.
NS Watches, Alfies, London NW8.
NSE Medal Dept., Nottingham, Notts.
Number 24 of Frinton, Frinton-on-Sea,
 Essex.
Nunn, C.C., Falmouth, Cornwall.
Nutley Antiques, Nutley, Sussex East.
Nutt, Frank, Hereford, Herefs.
Nutting, Mrs B.H., Brackley, Northants.

O

O'Brien and Son Antiques Ltd, R.J.,
 Manchester, Lancs.
O'Brien, Mrs J., Easingwold, Yorks. North.
O'Connor Brothers, Windsor and Eton,
 Berks.
O'Connor, Bernard, Windsor and Eton,
 Berks.
O'Connor, Mrs Hillary A., Ingatestone,
 Essex.
O'Donnell Antiques, Chris and Lin,
 Wallingford, Oxon.
O'Donnell, Mr and Mrs M., Chester,
 Cheshire.
O'Flynn, F., Red House Antiques Centre,
 York, Yorks. North
O'Flynn, Ginnel Antiques Centre, The,
 Harrogate, Yorks North
O'Gara, M., Faringdon, Oxon.
O'Gara, P., Faringdon, Oxon.
O'Grady, Mrs, London W4.
O'Keefe, B., Hadleigh, Suffolk.
O'Kelly, A. and J., London E8.
O'Shea Gallery, The, London W1.
O'Sullivan Antiques, A.J., Darlton, Notts.
O'Toole, Mrs G., Tarvin, Cheshire.
Oak Antiques, Jubilee Hall Antiques Centre,
 Lechlade, Glos.
Oakes and Son, G., Bolton, Lancs.
Oakley, N., Alfies, London NW8.
Oaktree Antiques, Lubenham, Leics.
Oakwood Gallery, Leeds, Yorks. West.
Oasis Antiques, Brighton, Sussex East.
Oban Antiques, Oban, Scotland.
Obelisk Antiques, Warminster, Wilts.
Objects of Vertu, Huddersfield, Yorks. West.
Occultique, Northampton, Northants.
Octavia Antiques, Ginnel Antiques Centre,
 The, Harrogate, Yorks North
Octavia Antiques, Petworth, Sussex West.
Odd Lot, The, Aberdeen, Scotland.
Odeon Antiques, Leek, Staffs.
Odgers, J.W., London W11.
Odiham Gallery, The, Odiham, Hants.
Odin Antiques, Brighton, Sussex East.
Off the Wall, Hemel Hempstead, Herts.
Offa's Dyke Antique Centre, Knighton,
 Wales.
Offer Waterman and Co. Fine Art, London
 SW10.
Ogden Ltd, Richard, London W1.
Ogden of Harrogate Ltd, Harrogate, Yorks.
 North.
Ogden, G. and D., Alsager, Cheshire.
Ogley, S., Red House Antiques Centre, York,
 Yorks. North
Okeeffe, Timothy, Prestwick, Scotland.
Okker, Nadine, The Mall Antiques Arcade,
 London N1.
Old & Gold , Durham, Durham.
Old Bakehouse Antiques and Gallery,
 Broughton Astley, Leics.
Old Bakery Antiques, The, Wheathampstead,
 Herts.
Old Bakery Antiques, Wymondham, Leics.

Old Bank House Antiques, Petworth, Sussex
 West.
Old Barn Antiques & Furnishings, Sutton
 Bridge, Lincs.
Old Barn Antiques Warehouse, Sutton
 Bridge, Lincs.
Old Brigade, The, Kingsthorpe, Northants.
Old Button Shop Antiques, Lytchett Minster,
 Dorset.
Old Chair Company, The Swan at Tetsworth,
 Oxon.
Old Chapel Antique & Collectables Centre ,
 Tutbury, Staffs.
Old Church Galleries, London SW3.
Old Cinema Antique Department Store, The,
 London W4.
Old Clock Shop, The, West Malling, Kent.
Old Colonial, Tunbridge Wells, Kent.
Old Cop Shop, The, Torquay, Devon.
Old Corner House Antiques, Wittersham,
 Kent.
Old Cottage Antiques, London E11.
Old Country Antiques, Chappells Antiques
 Centre, Bakewell, Derbys.
Old Curiosity Shop, King's Lynn, Norfolk.
Old Curiosity Shop, The, Sidmouth, Devon.
Old Curiosity Shop, The, St. Sampson,
 Guernsey, C.I.
Old Curiosity Shop, The, Stockport,
 Cheshire.
Old Custom House, The, Penzance,
 Cornwall.
Old English Oak, Sandgate, Kent.
Old English Pine, Sandgate, Kent.
Old Father Time Clock Centre, London W11.
Old Flames, Easingwold, Yorks. North.
Old Forge Cottage Antiques, Hartley
 Wintney, Hants.
Old Forge, The, Stretton-under-Fosse, Warks.
Old French Mirror Company Ltd, The,
 Henley-on-Thames, Oxon.
Old Grain Store Antiques, East Rudham,
 Norfolk.
Old Granary Antique and Craft Centre, The,
 Battlesbridge Antique Centre, Essex
Old Granary Antiques and Collectors Centre,
 The, King's Lynn, Norfolk.
Old Hall Antiques, Burton Salmon, Yorks.
 North.
Old Hall Bookshop, The, Brackley,
 Northants.
Old Hall Farm, Long Clawson, Leics.
Old House Antique Centre, Adversane,
 Sussex West.
Old House Gallery, The, Oakham, Rutland.
Old House, The, Seaford, Sussex East.
Old Ironmongers Antiques Centre, The,
 Lechlade, Glos.
Old Malthouse, The, Hungerford, Berks.
Old Maltings Antique Centre, Louth, Lincs.
Old Manor House Antiques, Brasted, Kent.
Old Maps and Prints, London SW1.
Old Mill Antique Centre, Bridgnorth, Shrops.
Old Mint House, The, Pevensey, Sussex East.
Old Mother Hubbard's, Biggleswade, Beds.
Old Palace Antiques, Lostwithiel, Cornwall.
Old Post House, The, Axbridge, Somerset.
Old School (Gardens & Interiors), London
 N19.
Old School Antiques, Penryn, Cornwall.
Old Shoe Box, The, Leominster, Herefs.
Old Smithy, Feniscowles, Lancs.
Old Smithy, The, West Burton, Yorks. North.
Old St. Andrews Gallery, St. Andrews,
 Scotland.
Old Station, The, London SE13.
Old Steam Bakery, The, Redruth, Cornwall.

Q

Q & C Militaria, Cheltenham, Glos.
Q Antiques, Willingham, Cambs.
QS Antiques and Cabinetmakers,
Kilmarnock, Scotland.
Quadrille, London W11.
Quaradeghini, A., London W2.
Quaradeghini, T., London N1.
Quaritch Ltd (Booksellers), Bernard, London
W1.
Quarterjack Antiques, Fontmell Magna,
Dorset.
Quartz and Clay, Durham House Antiques
Centre, Stow-on-the-Wold, Glos.
Quatrefoil, Fordingbridge, Hants.
Quay Gallery Antiques Emporium, The,
Exeter, Devon.
Quayside Antiques, Shrewsbury, Shrops.
Queen Anne House, Chesham, Bucks.
Queen's House Emporium, Teignmouth,
Devon.
Queens Parade Antiques Ltd, Stow-on-the-
Wold, Glos.
Quercus, Debenham, Suffolk.
Quick, C.R., Wolverhampton, West Mids.
Quiet Street Antiques, Bath, Somerset.
Quiet Woman Antiques Centre, The,
Chipping Norton, Oxon.
Quill Antiques, Bletchingley, Surrey.
Quill Antiques, Deal, Kent.
Quillon Antiques of Tetsworth, Tetsworth,
Oxon.
Quilter, Michael and Jackie, Amersham,
Bucks.
Quin, Kevin, Stow-on-the-Wold, Glos.
Quinn, B., Cardiff, Wales.
Quorn Pine and Decoratives, Quorn, Leics.

R

R. G. Antiques, Dunham-on-Trent, Notts.
R.C. Associates, Cullompton, Devon.
Rabi, Abdul, Antiquarius, London SW3.
Rabilizirov, R., London NW2.
Racklyeft, Sharon, London W11.
Radcliffe, J., Hastings, Sussex East.
Radford, Diana and Peter, Alresford, Hants.
Radman, Barbara, Witney, Oxon.
Radnor House, Grampound, Cornwall.
Radosenska, Mrs E., Bath, Somerset.
Rae, William and Helen, Ramsey, Cambs.
Rae-Smith Gallery, The, London WC2.
Rae-Smith, John and Felicity, London
WC2.
Raeymaekers, F., London SW1.
Raffety & Walwyn, London W8.
Rafter, R.J., Edinburgh, Scotland.
Raine Antiques, Harry, Consett, Durham.
Raine, P.W., Red House Antiques Centre,
York, Yorks. North
Raine, Paul, Ginnel Antiques Centre, The,
Harrogate, Yorks North
Rait Antiques, Rait Village Antiques Centre,
Scotland.
Rait Village Antiques Centre, Rait, Scotland.
Raleigh Antiques of Hanwood Hall,
Shrewsbury, Shrops.
Ramm, S., Lewes, Sussex East.
Ramos-de-Deus, Maria Elisabeth, London
SW11.
Ramsell, David A., Pontllyfrii, Wales.
Ramsey Antiques, Alan , Darlington,
Durham.
Ranby Hall, Retford, Notts.
Rand, Vivien and Eddie, Windsor and Eton,
Berks.
Randall, Peter, Marlborough, Wilts.

Rankin and Ian Conn, Daphne, London
SW6.
Rankin Coin Co. Ltd, George, London E2.
Rare Jewellery Collections Limited, Bond
Street Silver Galleries, London W1
Rasoul Gallery,Grays Antique Markets,
London W1.
Ratcliff Ltd, G.T., Kelvedon, Essex.
Ratcliff, J., Todmorden, Yorks. West.
Ratcliffe, A.M., Beccles, Suffolk.
Ratner, R.A., Dorking, Surrey.
Raw Deluxe, Bristol, Glos.
Raw, W.I., Keswick, Cumbria.
Rawlinson, John, Cirencester, Glos.
Ray & Scott Ltd, St Sampson, Guernsey, C.I.
Ray, M. T., Nottingham, Notts.
Rayfield, T., Tunbridge Wells, Kent.
Rayment Antiques, Derek and Tina, Barton,
Cheshire.
Rayment, D.J. and K.M., Barton, Cheshire.
Rayment, D.M., Petworth, Sussex West.
Raymond, Robert, Antiquarius, London
SW3.
Raynalds Mansion, Much Wenlock, Shrops.
Rayner, Barry, Tenterden, Kent.
Rayner, Michael, Cheltenham, Glos.
Rayson, Mrs Gill, Henley-in-Arden, Warks.
RBR Grp, Grays Antique Markets, London
W1.
Rea, C.J., Whitby, Yorks. North.
Read - Period Furniture, Alan, Horncastle,
Lincs.
Read Antique Sciences, Mike, St. Ives,
Cornwall.
Read, Bonnita, Woodford Green, Essex.
Read, Ian and Linda, Reigate, Surrey.
Read, John, Martlesham, Suffolk.
Read., Jane R., Brasted, Kent.
Reason, Mrs C., Limpsfield, Surrey.
Recollect Dolls Hospital, Burgess Hill,
Sussex West.
Recollections, Bournemouth, Dorset.
Recollections, Brighton, Sussex East.
Recollections, Poyton, Cheshire.
Record Detector, London E4.
Red Goblet Ltd, Petersfield, Hants.
Red House Antiques Centre, The, York,
Yorks. North.
Red House Antiques, Yoxford, Suffolk.
Red Lane Antiques, Jubilee Hall Antiques
Centre, Lechlade, Glos.
Red Lion Antiques Arcade, The, London
W11.
Red Lion Antiques, Petworth, Sussex West.
Red Lodge Antiques, Screveton, Notts.
Red Shop, The, Wolverhampton, West Mids.
Redford Antiques & Interiors, Robert,
Altrincham, Cheshire.
Redford, S. and R., Altrincham, Cheshire.
Redleaf Gallery, Tunbridge Wells, Kent.
Redmile, Anthony, The Furniture Cave,
London SW10.
Redroom, London SW6.
Reece Gallery, Gordon, London W1.
Reed Fine Art, Graham, Ginnel Antiques
Centre, The, Harrogate, Yorks North
Reed, Anthony, Bath, Somerset.
Reed, Marilyn, Topsham, Devon.
Rees, Mrs G., Weybridge, Surrey.
Rees, Suzy, Tunbridge Wells, Kent.
Reeve, James, Warwick, Warks.
Reeves, P.W. and L., Gomshall, Surrey.
Reeves, Paul, London W8.
Reeves, V., Canterbury, Kent.
Reference Works Ltd., Swanage, Dorset.
Reffold, London SW6.
Reflections, Lymm, Cheshire.

Regal Antiques, Westerham, Kent.
Regal Watches, Grays Antique Markets,
London W1.
Regan, David M., Southport, Merseyside.
Regency Antique Trading Centre,
Stourbridge, West Mids.
Regent Antiques, London N1.
Regent House Gallery, London SW11.
Reid, D.C., Edinburgh, Scotland.
Reid-Davies, Alison and Graeme,
Berkhamsted, Herts.
Reigate Galleries, Reigate, Surrey.
Reilly, Keiron, Antiquarius, London SW3.
Reindeer Antiques Ltd, London W8.
Reindeer Antiques Ltd, Potterspury,
Northants.
Relf Antiques, Ian, Tunbridge Wells, Kent.
Relic Antiques at Camden Passage, London
N1.
Relic Antiques Trade Warehouse, London
NW1.
Relics - Pine Furniture, Bristol, Glos.
Relics, Ilfracombe, Devon.
Remember When, London W3.
Remington, Reg and Philip, London WC2.
Renaissance Antiques, Chappells Antiques
Centre, Bakewell, Derbys.
Renaissance Antiques, Cowbridge, Wales.
Renaissance Furniture Store, The, Glasgow,
Scotland.
Renaissance, Solihull, West Mids.
Rendezvous Gallery, The, Aberdeen,
Scotland.
Renishaw Antiques, Sheffield, Yorks. South.
Renney Antiques, Hexham, Northumbs.
Rennie, Paul and Karen, London WC1.
Rennies, London WC1.
Restall Brown and Clennell Ltd, London N1.
Retro Antiques, Lye, West Mids.
Retro, Stourbridge, West Mids.
Revell Antiques, Sheila, Hartley Wintney,
Hants.
Revival, Abridge, Essex.
Revival, Colchester, Essex.
Rex Antiques, Chagford, Devon.
Reynold, A., London WC2.
Reynolds Antiques, C., Oakham, Rutland.
Reynolds Antiques, C.H., Pickering, Yorks.
North.
Reynolds Antiques, P., McBains Antiques,
Exeter, Devon.
Reynolds, Julia, Warwick, Warks.
Reynolds, Martyn and Rosemary,
Warminster, Wilts.
Reynolds, Mrs B.A.S., Easingwold, Yorks.
North.
Reynor, Kevin and Christine, Cromer,
Norfolk.
Rezai Persian Carpets, London W11.
Rhodes, G., Ginnel Antiques Centre, The,
Harrogate, Yorks North
Rhodes, G., Red House Antiques Centre,
York, Yorks. North
Rhodes, Isobel, Woodbridge, Suffolk.
Rhodes, Mrs J., London SW6.
Rhudle Mill, Kilmichael Glassary, Scotland.
Rice, Robert J., Great Malvern, Worcs.
Rich & Michael Rich, Steven, London SW1.
Richards and Sons, David, London W1.
Richards, Jane, Heanor, Derbys.
Richards, L., London W11.
Richards, M. and E., London W1.
Richards, P.J. and Mrs. K.M., Shaldon,
Devon.
Richardson and Kailas Icons, London SW6.
Richardson Antiques Ltd, Nantwich,
Cheshire.

Suchar, Victor and Elizabeth, Bath, Somerset.
Suffolk House Antiques, Yoxford, Suffolk.
Suffolk Table Company, The, Debenham, Suffolk.
Sugar Antiques, London N1.
Sugarman, Elayne and Tony, London N1.
Sullivan, N.M., Leek, Staffs.
Sultani Antiques, Grays Antique Markets, London W1.
Summers Davis Antiques Ltd, Wallingford, Oxon.
Summers, Sandy, Nantwich, Cheshire.
Summerson-Wright, S.T., Brampton, Cumbria.
Summersons, Warwick, Warks.
Sumner, Jane, Hungerford, Berks.
Sumner, M.C., Uppingham, Rutland.
Sundial Antiques, Amersham, Bucks.
Sundridge Gallery, Sundridge, Kent.
Sunrising Antiques, The Swan at Tetsworth, Oxon.
Surrey Antiques, Horley, Surrey.
Surrey Clock Centre, Haslemere, Surrey.
Surtees, J., London Silver Vaults, London WC2.
Susands, Margaret and Michael, London SW3.
Susannah, Bath, Somerset.
Sutcliffe Antiques, Tony and Anne, Southport, Merseyside.
Sutcliffe Galleries, Harrogate, Yorks. North.
Sutcliffe, R. and R., Masham, Yorks. North.
Suthburgh Antiques, Long Melford, Suffolk.
Sutherland, A., Bramley, Surrey.
Sutherland, Iain D., Troon, Scotland.
Sutton Valence Antiques, Maidstone, Kent.
Sutton Valence Antiques, Sutton Valence, Kent.
Sutton, Amanda, Newport, Shrops.
Sutton, G. and B., Stow-on-the-Wold, Glos.
Sutton, Leonard, Great Malvern, Worcs.
Swaffer, Spencer, Arundel, Sussex West.
Swaffham Antiques Supplies, Swaffham, Norfolk.
Swainbanks Ltd, Liverpool, Merseyside.
Swale, Jill, Wells, Somerset.
Swan Antiques, Bawtry, Yorks. South.
Swan Antiques, Baythorne End, Essex.
Swan Antiques, Cranbrook, Kent.
Swan at Tetsworth, The, Tetsworth, Oxon.
Swan Fine Art, London N1.
Swan Gallery, Burford, Oxon.
Swan Gallery, The, Sherborne, Dorset.
Swan, J., London SE5.
Swann, Oliver, London SW1.
Swans, Oakham, Rutland.
Swanson, D., Petworth, Sussex West.
Swanson, Nick and Barbara, Petworth, Sussex West.
Sweerts de Landas, A.J.H. and A.C., Ripley, Surrey.
Sweerts de Landas, Ripley, Surrey.
Sweetbriar Gallery, Helsby, Cheshire.
Sweeting, K.J. and J.L., Belper, Derbys.
Sweetings (Antiques 'n' Things), Belper, Derbys.
Swift, J., Ormskirk, Lancs.
Swift., C., Dorridge, West Mids.
Swindells, H. and A., Bath, Somerset.
Swiss Cottage Furniture, Leeds, Yorks. West.
Swonnell (Silverware) Ltd, E., Bond Street Silver Galleries, London W1.
Sydenham Antiques Centre, London SE26.
Sykes Antiques, Christopher, Woburn, Beds.

Sykes, C. and M., Woburn, Beds.
Symes Ltd, Robin, London SW1.
Szolin, A., Grimston, Leics.
Szwarc, John, Antiquarius, London SW3.

T

T'Morrows Antiques, Leominster, Herefs.
Tadema Gallery, London N1.
Tagore Ltd, Grays Antique Markets, London W1.
Tags, Lamb Arcade, Wallingford, Oxon.
Tait, S., North Berwick, Scotland.
Talbot Court Galleries, Stow-on-the-Wold, Glos.
Talbot Walk Antique Centre, Ripley, Surrey.
Talents Fine Arts Ltd, Malton, Yorks. North.
Talish Gallery, The, Edinburgh, Scotland.
Talisman 2, Bury St Edmunds, Suffolk.
Talisman, Gillingham, Dorset.
Talking Machine, London NW4.
Talking Point Antiques, Sowerby Bridge, Yorks. West.
Tallowin, S., Woodbridge, Suffolk.
Talton, J., W. and J.J., Long Sutton, Lincs.
Talton, J.W., Long Sutton, Lincs.
Tamblyn, Alnwick, Northumbs.
Tango Art Deco & Antiques, Warwick, Warks.
Tango Curios, Ginnel Antiques Centre, The, Harrogate, Yorks North.
Tankerton Antiques, Whitstable, Kent.
Tanner, J., Long Melford, Suffolk.
Tanner, J., Long Melford, Suffolk.
Tansu Japanese Antiques, Batley, Yorks. West.
Tanswell, P., Warminster, Wilts.
Tantalus Antiques, Troon, Scotland.
Tantra Art, Grays Antique Markets, London W1.
Tapestry Antiques, Hertford, Herts.
Tapestry, Cheltenham, Glos.
Tapsell, C., London N1.
Tara Antiques, London NW8.
Tara's Hall, Hadleigh, Suffolk.
Taramasco, A., London NW8.
Tarporley Antique Centre, Tarporley, Cheshire.
Tarran, D., Worcester, Worcs.
Tarrant Antiques, Lorraine, Ringwood, Hants.
Tarrant, S.A., Cirencester, Glos.
Tartan Antiques, The Swan at Tetsworth, Oxon.
Tatham-Losh, Julian and Patience, Andoversford, Glos.
Tatham-Losh, Julian, Andoversford, Glos.
Tattersall's, Uppingham, Rutland.
Tattersall, J., Uppingham, Rutland.
Tauber Antiques, Laurence, Surbiton, Surrey.
Taunton Antiques Market - Silver Street, Taunton, Somerset.
Tavistock Antiques, St. Neots, Cambs.
Tavistock Books, Tavistock, Devon.
Tayler, Ron and Sandra, Freshwater, Isle of Wight.
Taylor Antiques and Sarah Taylor Interiors, M. & R., Ludlow, Shrops.
Taylor Antiques, Martin, Wolverhampton, West Mids.
Taylor Antiques, Rankine, Cirencester, Glos.
Taylor Fine Arts, Robin, Wakefield, Yorks. West.
Taylor Gallery Ltd, The, London SW7.
Taylor Robinson Antiques, Alfreton, Derbys.
Taylor, Allison, Dornoch, Scotland.

Taylor, B., Kingston-on-Spey, Scotland.
Taylor, B.R., Kelling, Norfolk.
Taylor, Brian, Plymouth, Devon.
Taylor, C.D., Hampton, Middx.
Taylor, D., Driffield, Yorks. East.
Taylor, D., Halesowen, West Mids.
Taylor, Jeremy, London SW7.
Taylor, John, London SW11.
Taylor, M., London SW12.
Taylor, M., Ludlow, Shrops.
Taylor, M.C., Bournemouth, Dorset.
Taylor, Mark, Bournemouth, Dorset.
Taylor, Seth, London SW11.
Taylor, Stanley, Durham House Antiques Centre, Stow-on-the-Wold, Glos.
Taylor-Robinson, Geoff and Coral, The Swan at Tetsworth, Oxon.
Taylor-Smith Antiques, Westerham, Kent.
Taylor-Smith Books, Westerham, Kent.
Taylor-Smith, Alan, Westerham, Kent.
Teahan, Shelagh, Newcastle-under-Lyme, Staffs.
Teapot World - Museum and Shop, Conwy, Wales.
Tebbs, J.J., Conisholme, Lincs.
Tee, John, Ginnel Antiques Centre, The, Harrogate, Yorks North.
Tee, John, Red House Antiques Centre, York, Yorks. North.
Teger Trading, London N4.
Teignmouth and Son, Pamela, London W8.
Teignmouth, Lady, London W8.
Teme Valley Antiques, Ludlow, Shrops.
Temperley Fine and Antiquarian Books, David, Birmingham, West Mids.
Temperley, D. and R.A., Birmingham, West Mids.
Temple Gallery, London W11.
Temple Lighting (Jeanne Temple Antiques), Milton Keynes, Bucks.
Temple, K., Raughton Head, Cumbria.
Temple, R.C.C., London W11.
Templeman, Lynda, Rait Village Antiques Centre, Scotland.
Templeman, Robert, Doune, Scotland.
Templemans, Abernyte, Scotland.
Templeton, Paul, The Swan at Tetsworth, Oxon.
Temptations, Antique Jewellery &Silver, Dorking, Surrey.
Temptations, Ashtead, Surrey.
Tencati, Sergio, Bond Street Antiques Centre, London W1.
Tendler, A., Grays Antique Markets, London W1.
Tenterden Antiques and Silver Vaults, Tenterden, Kent.
Terrace Antiques, London W5.
Terrett, J.S., Truro, Cornwall.
Tessiers Ltd, London W1.
Tetbury Gallery, Tetbury, Glos.
Tetbury Old Books & Coach House Antiques, Tetbury, Glos.
Tetbury Old Books Ltd, Tetbury, Glos.
Tetlow, Robert, Debden, Essex.
Tew, T., London N2.
Tewkesbury Antiques & Collectables Centre, Tewkesbury, Glos.
Textile Company, The, London N1.
Textilean, Alfies, London NW8.
Thakeham Furniture, Pulborough, Sussex West.
Thames Oriental Rug Co, Henley-on-Thames, Oxon.
Thanet Antiques Trading Centre, Ramsgate, Kent.
The John Lewis Partnership., London SW3.

Watergate Antiques, Chester, Cheshire.
Waterhouse and Dodd, London W1.
Waterhouse, R., London W1.
Waterloo Trading Co., The, London SE10.
Waterman Fine Art Ltd, London SW1.
Waterman, T. and R., London SW1.
Waters, Colin, Dorking, Surrey.
Waters, Geoffrey, Antiquarius, London SW3.
Waterside Antiques Centre, Ely, Cambs.
Waterworth, Mrs F.S., Alderley Edge, Cheshire.
Watkins Books Ltd, London WC2.
Watkins, I., Knighton, Wales.
Watkins, Islwyn, Knighton, Wales.
Watkinson, Lynn, West Burton, Yorks. North.
Watkiss, Elizabeth, Tudor House, Stow-on-the-Wold, Glos.
Watling Antiques, Crayford, Kent.
Watson Ltd, Gordon, London SW3.
Watson, Jean, Shere, Surrey.
Watson, M.E., Market Weighton, Yorks. East.
Watson, P., Moreton-in-Marsh, Glos.
Watson, Pauline, Ashtead, Surrey.
Watts, Captain O.M., London W1.
Watts, Sue and Bruce, Huntly, Scotland.
Waverley Antiques, Upper Largo, Scotland.
Way Bookseller, Richard, Henley-on-Thames, Oxon.
Way, R.E. and G.B., Newmarket, Suffolk.
Way, Richard, Henley-on-Thames, Oxon.
Wayne "The Razor Man", Neil, Belper, Derbys.
Wayside Antiques, Duffield, Derbys.
Wayside Antiques, Tattershall, Lincs.
Weatherell's of Harrogate Antiques and Fine Arts, Harrogate, Yorks. North.
Weaver Antiques, Bernard, Cirencester, Glos.
Weaver, Peter, Aldeburgh, Suffolk.
Weaver, Trude, London W11.
Webb Fine Art, Michael, Llangristiolus (Anglesey), Wales.
Webb Fine Arts, Winchester, Hants.
Webb, Anne and Tony, Brancaster Staithe, Norfolk.
Webb, D.H., Winchester, Hants.
Webb, Graham, Brighton, Sussex East.
Webb, M., London N1.
Webb, Michael, London N13.
Webb, R. and J., Leigh-on-Sea, Essex.
Webb, Roy, Wickham Market, Suffolk.
Webster, A.J., Coleshill, Warks.
Webster, E.T., Blythburgh, Suffolk.
Webster, G., Liverpool, Merseyside.
Webster, M., Cross Hills, Yorks. North.
Webster-Speakman, S. J., Southwold, Suffolk.
Weedon Antiques, Weedon, Northants.
Weedon, Mike and Hisako, London N1.
Weedon, Mike, London N1.
Weeks, Brian, Fakenham, Norfolk.
Weidenbaum, R., Manchester, Lancs.
Weijand Fine Oriental Carpets, Karel, Farnham, Surrey.
Weiner, G.G., Brighton, Sussex East.
Weiner, M., Ipswich, Suffolk.
Weir, Mr and Mrs D., Bottisham, Cambs.
Weiss Gallery, The, London W1.
Weiss, Peter K., London Silver Vaults, London WC2.
Welch Jeweller, M.G., Taunton, Somerset.
Welch, K. and A., Warminster, Wilts.

Welch, Mark and Liz, Taunton, Somerset.
Weldon, H.W. and N.C., Southport, Merseyside.
Weldons Jewellery and Antiques, Southport, Merseyside.
Welier, R.M., Hunstanton, Norfolk.
Well Cottage Antiques Centre, Princes Risborough, Bucks.
Well House Antiques, Tilston, Cheshire.
Wellard, Mary Akin, Grays Antique Markets, London W1.
Wellby Ltd, H.S., Haddenham, Bucks.
Wellby, C.S., Haddenham, Bucks.
Welling Antiques, Anthony, Ripley, Surrey.
Wellington Gallery, London NW8.
Wells Antique Centre, Wells-next-the-Sea, Norfolk.
Wells Reclamation Company, Coxley, Somerset.
Wells, Graham, Wallingford, Oxon.
Wells, Ian and Diane, Bungay, Suffolk.
Welsh Art, Tywyn, Wales.
Welsh Oriental Porcelain & Works of Art, Jorge, London W8.
Wenlock Fine Art, Much Wenlock, Shrops.
Wentworth, Judy, London N1.
Wertheim, Mr and Mrs C.D., London W8.
Wertheim, Mr and Mrs C.D., London W8.
West - Cobb Antiques Ltd, Mark J., London SW19.
West Antiques, Marie, Ely, Cambs.
West Country Jewellery, Antiquarius, London SW3.
West End Antiques, Elgin, Scotland.
West End Antiques, Leicester, Leics.
West End Galleries, Buxton, Derbys.
West Essex Antiques (Stone Hall), Matching Green, Essex.
West Lancs. Antique Exports, Burscough, Lancs.
West Rock Antiques, Warwick, Warks.
West Street Antiques, Dorking, Surrey.
West Wales Antiques, Murton, Wales.
West-Skinn, R., Lincoln, Lincs.
West-Skinn, R., Lincoln, Lincs.
Westcliffe Gallery, The, Sheringham, Norfolk.
Westcott Gallery, The, Dorking, Surrey.
Westenholz Antiques Ltd, London SW1.
Westerham Antiques Warehouse, Westerham, Kent.
Westerham House Antiques, Westerham, Kent.
Westhorpe Antiques, Southwell, Notts.
Westland London, London EC2.
Westland, Geoffrey, London EC2.
Westleigh Antiques, Grays Antique Markets, London W1.
Westminster Group, Grays Antique Markets, London W1.
Weston Antiques, Weston, Herts.
Weston Gallery, William, London W1.
Weston, K.C., Framlingham, Suffolk.
Westport Gallery, Dundee, Scotland.
Westrope, I., Birdbrook, Essex.
Westville House Antiques, Littleton, Somerset.
Westway Pine, Helmsley, Yorks. North.
Westwood Antiquarian Books, Mark, Hay-on-Wye, Wales.
Westwood House Antiques and Beehive Antiques, Tetbury, Glos.
Westwood, F., Petersfield, Hants.
Westwood, J., Great Bookham, Surrey.

Wetherill, J., Northallerton, Yorks. North.
Wetherill, R., York, Yorks. North.
Wetzel, G., Alfies, London NW8.
Weybridge Antiques, Weybridge, Surrey.
Wharton Antiques, Tim, Redbourn, Herts.
Wharton Goldsmiths, Christopher, St. Albans, Herts.
What Now Antiques, Buxton, Derbys.
Whately Ltd, Rollo, London W1.
Whatnots, Strathblane, Scotland.
Whay's Clocks & Antiques, Kevin, Hoylake, Merseyside.
Wheatley, David, Grays Antique Markets, London W1.
Wheatley, R., Empingham, Rutland.
Wheatleys, Gt. Yarmouth, Norfolk.
Wheatsheaf Antiques, Chester, Cheshire.
Wheeler, Bruce, Petworth, Sussex West.
Wheeler, M.J., Crewkerne, Somerset.
Wheeler, Paul, Red House Antiques Centre, York, Yorks. North
Wheeler, Robert, Rye, Sussex East.
Wheels of Steel, Grays Antique Markets, London W1.
Whichcraft Jewellery, Writtle, Essex.
Whiddons Antiques and Tearooms, Chagford, Devon.
Whillock, F., Litton Cheney, Dorset.
Whimsical Wemyss, Rait Village Antiques Centre, Scotland
Whitby, C. and B., Beaconsfield, Bucks.
White Antique & Reproduction Centre, M. & M., Reigate, Surrey.
White Antiques, Joan and David, Barnard Castle, Durham.
White House Antiques & Architectural Reclamation, The, Easingwold, Yorks. North.
White House Antiques, Uttoxeter, Staffs.
White House, The, Waverton, Cheshire.
White Roding Antiques, White Roding, Essex.
White, Charles, Wymondham, Norfolk.
White, Christopher, Uttoxeter, Staffs.
White, Dennis, Ramsbury, Wilts.
White, E. and B., Brighton, Sussex East.
White, Joan and David, Manfield, Yorks. North.
White, Lindsay, Horncastle, Lincs.
White, Mrs K., Shere, Surrey.
White, P., Cranborne, Dorset.
White, R., Cranbrook, Kent.
White, Ray, High Wycombe, Bucks.
White, Shirley, Derby, Derbys.
Whitehead, Joyce & Rod, Oswestry, Shrops.
Whitelaw and Sons Antiques, John, Auchterarder, Scotland.
Whitelaw, Peter, Ironbridge, Shrops.
Whitemoors Antiques and Fine Art, Shenton, Leics.
Whiteside, A.M., Pershore, Worcs.
Whiteway and Waldron Ltd, London SW6.
Whiteway, M., London SW6.
Whiteway, T.M., London W8.
Whiteway-Wilkinson, G.A., Maidencombe, Devon.
Whitfield Antiques, Robert, London SE10.
Whitfield, A.G., Edinburgh, Scotland.
Whitfield, David and Paula, Brewood, Staffs.
Whitford Fine Art, London SW1.
Whitgift Galleries, The, Croydon, Surrey.
Whitmore, Great Malvern, Worcs.
Whitmore, John and Stella, Great Malvern, Worcs.

PLEASE USE THIS FORM FOR A NEW OR SUBSTANTIALLY ALTERED ENTRY

Please complete and return this form; there is no charge

NAME OF SHOP ....

ADDRESS OF SHOP ....

....
full address including actual county (not postal code)

Name (or names) and initials of proprietor(s) ....
(Mr/Mrs/Miss/or title)

Previous trading address (if applicable) ....

State whether 'Trade Only' (Yes or No) ....

BADA (Yes or No) .... LAPADA (Yes or No) ....

Year Established .... Resident on premises (Yes or No) ....

OPENING (One entry, e.g. '9.30-5.30' if open all day or part day
HOURS: Two entries, e.g. '9.30-1.00, 2.00-5.30' if closed for lunch)

Please put 'CLOSED' and 'BY APPT.' where applicable

	Morning	Afternoon
Sunday	....	
Monday	....	
Tuesday	....	
Wednesday	....	
Thursday	....	
Friday	....	
Saturday	....	

SIZE OF SHOWROOM: Small (up to 600 sq. ft.) ....

Medium (600 to 1,500 sq. ft.) ....

Large (over 1,500 sq. ft.) ....

HOW TO GET TO YOUR SHOP (BUSINESS)
Brief helpful details from the nearest well-known road:

....

....

....

....

OF WHAT DOES YOUR STOCK CHIEFLY CONSIST?

(A) Please list in order of importance	(B) Approximate period or date of stock	(C) Indication of price range of stock eg £50-£100 or £5-£25
1. (Principal stock)		
2.		
3.		

IS PARKING *OUTSIDE* YOUR SHOP (BUSINESS) Easy (Yes or No)

TELEPHONE NUMBER Business ....

Home ....
(only if customers can ring for appointments outside business hours)

V.A.T. scheme operated – Standard/Special/Both ....

SERVICES OFFERED:

Valuations (Yes or No) ....

Restorations (Yes or No) ....

Type of work ....

Buying specific items at auction for a commission (Yes or No) ....

Type of item ....

FAIRS:
At which fairs (if any) do you normally exhibit? ....
....
....

CERTIFICATION:
The information given above is accurate and you may publish it in the Guide.
I understand that this entry is entirely free.

Signed .... Date ....

Unmistakably

FRANKLIN

Our door-to-door weekly service throughout Europe is well known and very reliable.

Visit our offices in three prime European locations.

Container and Airfreight Services Worldwide.

Alan Franklin Transport

ALAN FRANKLIN TRANSPORT
Continental Removals to and from the U.K.
SPECIALIST CARRIERS OF ANTIQUES AND FINE ARTS

ENGLAND:
26 BLACK MOOR ROAD,
VERWOOD, DORSET,
ENGLAND BH31 6BB.
TEL: +44 1202 826539
FAX: +44 1202 827337

FRANCE:
2 RUE ETIENNE DOLET,
93400 ST. OUEN, PARIS,
FRANCE.
TEL: +33 1 40 11 50 00
FAX: +33 1 40 11 48 21

FRANCE:
QUARTIER LA TOUR DE SABRAN,
84440 ROBION (VAUCLUSE),
FRANCE.
TEL: +33 4 90 76 49 00
FAX: +33 4 90 76 49 02

BELGIUM:
DE KLERCKSTRAAT 41,
B8300 KNOKKE,
BELGIUM.
TEL: + 32 50 623 579
FAX: + 32 50 623 579